Physics for the Life Sciences

Fourth Edition

COPYRIGHT © 2006 by Nelson, a division of Thomson Limited. Thomson Nelson is a registered trademark used herein under license.

Printed and bound in Canada
  2 3 4 5   07 06

For more information contact
Thomson Nelson
1120 Birchmount Road,
Scarborough, Ontario, M1K 5G4.
Or you can visit our internet site at
http://www.nelson.com

ALL RIGHTS RESERVED. No part of this work covered by the copyright hereon may be reproduced, transcribed, or used in any form or by any means – graphic, electronic, or mechanical, including photocopying, recording, taping, web distribution or information storage and retrieval systems – without the written permission of the publisher.

For permission to use material from this text or product, contact us by
Tel: 1-800-730-2214
Fax: 1-800-730-2215
www.thomsonrights.com

This textbook is a Nelson custom publication. Because your instructor has chosen to produce a custom publication, you pay only for material that you will use in your course.

ISBN 0-17-610138-1

PREFACE

Today's students in the life sciences can benefit greatly from physical methods and concepts if the training in university takes this appropriately into account. It is for this reason that the life sciences students are often required to take an introductory level physics course; but too often they attend lectures intended for physical science and engineering students, primarily due to the lack of a textbook tailored to the life sciences. The present text has been developed to fill this gap.

The comprehensive text contains more than 600 figures and 75 tables. Included are almost 400 problems and examples. The most important feature of the textbook is the integrated approach toward life sciences applications. Each topic is initially motivated by a pivotal application in physiology or other biological sciences. The fundamental physical concepts are then developed rigorously. Frequent references to various life sciences applications maintain the focus on the ultimate purpose of the introduced physics.

While some of the topics are presented in a similar order as in standard physics textbooks, there are significant differences. An example may illustrate this point: electricity, when taught in the traditional way, appears far removed from any physiological applicability. There are no free electrons in vacuum tubes or loosely bound electrons in metallic wires in the human body, but there are ionic solutions of varying concentrations interacting electrically across membranes. Thus, electricity concepts must be combined with the chemical concepts of ionic solutions to illustrate the relevance of the electric concepts in a biological system.

A university level physics course presents to the student a significantly different perspective of nature than introductory biology or chemistry courses. A key component in that distinction is the degree to which a quantitative comprehension of concepts is required, associated with a more intensive use of mathematical tools. The current text represents a compromise between the mathematical rigor traditional physicists expect and a concept–based discussion of the physical content, which is more accommodating to the approach of students in the biological sciences.

The current text is also suitable for self–study and to review the subject for examinations in physics, including the Medical College Admission Test (MCAT). An effort was made to not leave gaps between the current text and standard General Chemistry texts. A minor overlap with material of a General Chemistry course is didactically valuable to illustrate that physics and chemistry together are powerful tools in the life sciences.

This textbook contains more material than can be covered in two terms. This gives lecturers additional flexibility in their choice of topics or allows the development of an additional second–year course.

An ever increasing number of people contribute to the success of this textbook as an integral part of a modern physics curriculum in the life sciences. At this place I acknowledge the support of the following individuals: M. Rasche for her extensive artwork; J. Mansfield, D. Fraser, S. Chadi, and A. Young for numerous text revisions; A. Vandenbogaard for problem set revisions; F. J. Longstaffe (Dean's office, Science), E. Wong, K. Jordan (London Regional Cancer Centre), R. A. Mackenzie (St. Joseph's Hospital, London), B. Chronik, M. Campbell–Brown, M. Singh, S. Mittler, R. J. Sica, S. Basu, S. R. Valluri, K. Kaluarachchi (Physics and Astronomy), J. J. Battista, I. MacDonald, C. Ellis (Medical Biophysics), R. Lipson (Chemistry), M. Bernards, D. Lajoie, T. Haffie (Biology), J. R. Trevithick, T. Lo, S.–C. Li, H. Ling (Biochemistry), D. L. Jones, J. Ciriello (Physiology) and V. Nolte (Kinesiology) for helpful suggestions. At Nelson Thomson Learning, I wish to acknowledge the collaboration with B. Prentice, M. Moman, A. Rezek, H. Winkelmann.

London, Ontario, May 2005

M. Zinke–Allmang

TABLE OF CONTENTS

1	**Physics and Biology**	**1**
	An introduction	
1.1	Case study: the hearing of dolphins	2
1.2	Hierarchy of complexity	6
1.3	Problems	8

2	**Locomotion**	**9**
	The strength of forces	
2.1	The physiological role of components of the locomotive system	10
2.2	Definition of force	16
2.3	Newton's laws of mechanics	17
2.4	Problems	27

3	**Biomechanics**	**31**
	The direction of forces	
3.1	Detection of field forces: the direction of gravity	32
3.2	Detection of contact forces: the weight of an object	34
3.3	Applying Newton's laws with non–collinear forces	36
3.4	Acceleration detection	44
3.5	Physiological applications of Newton's laws	46
3.6	Appendix: momentum and friction	53
3.7	Problems	56

4	**Kinesiology**	**61**
	The action of forces at joints	
4.1	Geometry of the rotation at joints	62
4.2	Mechanic components of an extended rigid body	71
4.3	Mechanical equilibrium for a rigid body	75
4.4	Physiological applications	79
4.5	Case study: since when walk hominids on two legs?	87
4.6	Appendix: center–of–mass position	91
4.7	Problems	94

5	**Bioenergetics**	**101**
5.1	Metabolism at the cellular level: the role of the ATP molecule	102
5.2	Bioenergetics at the organism level: case study of the predatory dinosaurs	104
5.3	Basic concepts	109
5.4	Work	111
5.5	Energy	121
5.6	Conservation of energy	128
5.7	First law of thermodynamics	130
5.8	Appendix: a second look at work and an overview of kinematics	137
5.9	Problems	139

6	**Respiration**	**143**
	The properties of gases	
6.1	Dynamic breathing	144
6.2	The empirical gas laws	151
6.3	Microscopic model of the ideal gas	162
6.4	Internal energy of the ideal gas	165
6.5	Real gases	169
6.6	Basic thermodynamic processes	170
6.7	Cyclic processes	177
6.8	Appendix: point mass collisions	185
6.9	Problems	187

7	**Membranes**	**191**
7.1	Beyond the equilibrium	192
7.2	A new model system	193
7.3	Heat conduction	196
7.4	Diffusion	205
7.5	Problems	214

8	**Order and Evolution**	**219**
	The dynamics of processes	
8.1	Protein synthesis	220
8.2	Reversibility	223
8.3	The second law of thermodynamics	225
8.4	Chemical thermodynamics	231
8.5	Non–equilibrium thermodynamics	238

8.6	Non–linear non–equilibrium processes	243
8.7	Appendix: Fourier's law and the Onsager equation, and interference for finite membrane width	248
8.8	Problems	249

9 Water and Aqueous Solutions
Static electricity
251

9.1	Water in the body fluids	253
9.2	Electric charge and force: fundamental concepts	253
9.3	Electric charge and force: occurrence in physics and biology	259
9.4	Electric field	262
9.5	Electric energy concepts	271
9.6	Electric potential	278
9.7	Conservation of energy	281
9.8	Appendix: electric field of a fixed point charge	283
9.9	Problems	283

10 A second look at Water
Static fluids
287

10.1	Why water?	288
10.2	Model system: the ideal stationary fluid	290
10.3	Basic parameters of the model system: the pressure	290
10.4	Important properties of ideal stationary fluids	295
10.5	Problems	308

11 Cardiovascular System
Fluid flow
311

11.1	Fluids in the human body	312
11.2	Non–viscous flow	317
11.3	Viscous flow	322
11.4	The Newtonian fluid applied in physiology	330
11.5	Transition from laminar to turbulent flow	332
11.6	Problems	337

12 Blood and Air
Mixed phases
339

12.1	Fluid composition in the human body	341
12.2	Mixed phases	343
12.3	Liquid solutions	350
12.4	Osmosis	353
12.5	Physiological and medical applications	354
12.6	Appendix: van't Hoff's law	356
12.7	Problems	357

13 Nerves
The flow of charges
359

13.1	Human nerves	360
13.2	Static properties of a resting nerve	363
13.3	Capacitors	371
13.4	Moving charges in a resting nerve	375
13.5	Stimulated nerve impulses	381
13.6	Problems	395

14 Electrocardiography
Electric phenomena of the heart
397

14.1	Physiology of the heart	398
14.2	The electrocardiogram	403
14.3	Medical use of the ECG	407

15 Elastic Tissue
Elasticity and vibrations
409

15.1	Elasticity	412
15.2	Linear regime of stress–strain curves	420
15.3	Vibrations	424
15.4	Appendix: radians and degrees	436
15.5	Problems	436

16 Ear and Communication
Longitudinal waves
439

16.1	The acoustic environment	441
16.2	Waves in an unconfined medium	442
16.3	Waves in a confined medium	453
16.4	The acoustic systems of humans	463
16.5	Special properties of the auditory system	472
16.6	Problems	477

17 The eye
Ray model of light (Geometric optics)
481

17.1	What is optics?	485
17.2	Reflection	486
17.3	Refraction	492
17.4	Applications in the life sciences	501
17.5	Appendix: single spherical interface, and Lens maker's equation	506
17.6	Problems	509

18	**The microbial world** **Microscopy**	**513**		21.3	Toward a quantum mechanical model	586
				21.4	Molecules	591
				21.5	Problems	597
18.1	From lenses to microscopes	515				
18.2	The magnifying glass	516				
18.3	Optical compound microscope	518	**22**	**Radiation**		**599**
18.4	Electron microscope	520		**X–rays and nuclear physics**		
18.5	Problems	522				
				22.1	Origin of X–rays	600
				22.2	The biological effects of X–rays	603
19	**Color Vision**	**523**		22.3	The stable atomic nucleus	606
	Magnetism and electromagnetic spectrum			22.4	Radioactive decay	609
				22.5	Biological impact of particle radiation	611
19.1	The anatomy of color vision	526		22.6	Applications of radioactivity	612
19.2	Towards a wave model of light: magnetism	528		22.7	Problems	615
19.3	Polarization of light	535				
19.4	The physics and physiology of color	539				
19.5	Problems	546	**23**	**Magnetic Resonance Imaging**		**617**
				Nuclear spin and magnetic resonance		
20	**The Human Body in Space**	**549**		23.1	Spin	618
	Circular motion			23.2	Spins in a magnetic field	621
				23.3	Experiments with the nuclear spin	626
20.1	Outer space: the challenges	550		23.4	The NMR technique in medicine: MRI	629
20.2	The physical concept of weightlessness	553				
20.3	Physiological effect of weightlessness	562				
20.4	Radiation exposure	564	**24**	**General Appendix**		**631**
20.5	Problems	574				
				24.1	Mathematical concepts	632
				24.2	Tables	644
21	**The chemical bond**	**577**		24.3	Problems	645
	Atomic and molecular physics					
				Index		**649**
21.1	Early atomic models	579				
21.2	The hydrogen atom	580				

Title page:

The four images on the cover illustrate the electric fields experienced by a human subject during magnetic resonance imaging (MRI). During MRI a person lies within a very strong magnetic field and the nuclei of the hydrogen atoms in the water molecules (such as those in human tissue) are excited by radio frequency (RF) radiation. The excited protons then rotate at a frequency that is proportional to the strength of the magnet. In order to influence the frequency of the signals received from the body a second magnetic field, called a *gradient* is applied, on top of the main magnetic field. The gradient coil can be switched on and off, and makes the frequency of the received signal dependant on position. In the images the two horizontal lines represent the plates of the gradient coil. The patient is situated with his head and neck inside the magnet. As the gradient coil is switched on and off to obtain the image, the rapidly changing magnetic field induces an electric field. This electric field can cause charges to accumulate on the boundary between tissue and air and results in electric field patterns such as those illustrated.

Fundamental aspects of the medical use of MRI are discussed in Chapter 23. Image and data courtesy of Rebecca Feldman, Department of Physics and Astronomy, The University of Western Ontario. Rebecca is part of an MRI research group working on MRI related issues in the Department. The group is headed by Blaine Chronik. He can be reached at bchronik@uwo.ca.

Backcover:

Three illustrations of optical illusions caused by our color vision (see Volume II, p. 187):
(I) Pudding on a dish: Dim the light in the room. Hold the book at arm's length and move it slowly sideways back and forth. You should see the pudding wobble back and forth on the dish.
(II) Thunderbolt striking a tree: Dim the light in the room. Focus on the blue sky to the left of the thunderbolt. Let your eyes jump back and forth between the blue sky to the right and to the left of the thunderbolt, about once or twice a second. You should see the thunderbolt flashing up brightly every time you move your eyes.
(III) Fish in the fish-bowl: In bright light, focus on the red fish for about a minute (this requires patience). Then, suddenly, look at the black dot in the empty fish–bowl. For a short moment, you should see a red fish and then a greenish–blue background in the bowl. How do these illusions work? You find out in Chapter 19.

Chapter I

Physics and Biology

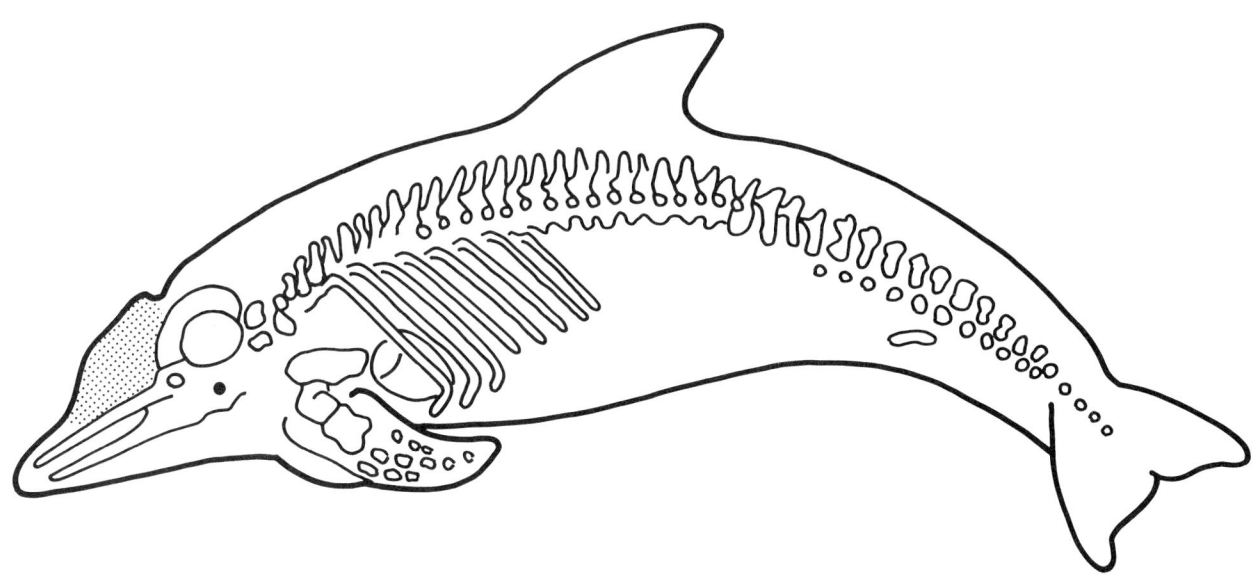

An introduction

PHYSICS AND BIOLOGY
AN INTRODUCTION

Physics and Biology are two different sciences. They differ not only in their respective object of inquiry, but also in their experimental and conceptual methods, in their history, and even in their contributions to culture and philosophy. Physicists explain the properties of the inanimate world on the basis of universal laws – biologists reject the concept of universality and focus on diversity, on singular events, on the individual history of species or the evolution of specific traits. Why, then, should those interested in the life sciences familiarize themselves with the concepts and methods of physics? A trivial answer rests with the fact that physics is a formal requirement for many professional programs and that it is often a subject on admission tests. This, however, only rephrases the question: why is physics a pre–requisite for advanced studies in the life sciences? We provide first a practical answer and then a broader, fundamental answer.

The best way to establish the practical reasons for studying physics as part of the training in the life sciences is to pick a typical example of scientific inquiry in these fields. We choose an example from zoology, one which seems at first sight to be entirely unrelated to physics: the underwater hearing of dolphins.

1.1. Case study: the hearing of dolphins

(I) What do dolphins hear?
The scientific approach begins with a fact–finding stage, i.e., trying to answer the question "do dolphins hear" and if so, "what do dolphins hear?"

We conjecture that dolphins hear from the observation of their vocalizations in the wild or during tests with animals in captivity. To quantify what dolphins hear, however, we require definitions, concepts, and methods from physics. A hydrophone is used to record sounds in the form of frequency spectra, sound intensities and sound amplitudes, all terms which are discussed in Chapter 16. For dolphins, these data allow us to distinguish an almost constantly emitted clicking sound (about 300 sounds per second) and whistle sounds. With a proper combination of acoustic receivers we can also establish that the clicking sounds are focussed in the forward direction, like the headlights of a car.

Further data are obtained from the anatomy of dolphins. The important components are highlighted in Fig. 1.1. The *oily melon* is a unique feature that acts as an acoustic lens. Lenses as physical devices are discussed in Chapter 17. Whales use this device as a powerful weapon, emitting sound shockwaves that stun squids and render them defenceless.

Dolphins share an inner ear and a middle ear with other mammals. However, the outer ear is absent. For the following discussion we keep in mind that the outer ear of humans consists of the external pinna and auditory canal that collect sound waves and channel them to the eardrum. Instead, dolphins have a unique fatty organ which connects the rear end of the lower jaw bone to the middle ear section.

While most of the above information was obtained from extensive studies of *bottle–nosed dolphins*, additional information comes from comparisons with the other 31 known dolphin species and with other closely related species, such as whales and porpoises, all of which form the order *Cetacea*. Such studies show that the two types of sound of the dolphins are shared among all dolphins and porpoises, but that the clicking sound is only observed among the suborder *Odontoceti* (toothed whales, which includes the belugas, narwhals, sperm whales, dolphins and porpoises). The suborder *Mysticeti* (baleen whales, including the blue whales, fin whales, bowheads and minke whales) share only the whistle sounds, though in widely varying form, e.g. including the famous "songs" of the humpback whales.

Studies of animal behavior demonstrate that the sounds of dolphins are not just simple species or mate identification patterns. Particularly the whistle sounds are used to communicate with other dolphins of the same species, to express alarm, sexual excitement, and likely a range of other emotions. The clicking sounds, in turn,

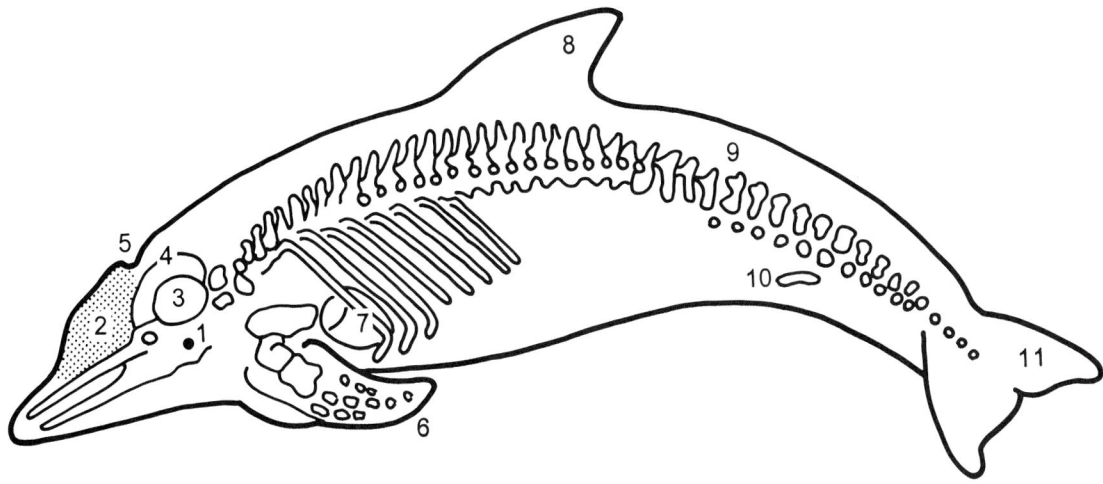

Fig.1.1: Dolphins can vocalize, hear and interpret a wide range of clicking and whistle sounds. The clicking sounds are focussed in the forward direction by the oily melon (2) which is located in the forehead in front of the blowhole (5). The dolphin's ear (1) consists of an inner ear and a middle ear, but lacks the outer ear of land mammals. Arriving sound is transmitted to the middle ear by bone conduction in the skull (4). Dolphins need large brains (3) to interpret the information contained in the sounds from other dolphins and the echos of their own clicking sounds. Other anatomical features highlighted in the figure include: (6) flipper, (7) heart, (8) dorsal fin, (9) spinal column, (10) pelvis, and (11) fluke.

are used to navigate in the physical terrain and relative to other dolphins in the group; and to detect fish, squid and shrimp for food. The clicking sounds of sperm whales allow them to hunt as deep as 450 meters below the sea surface.

As we know from our own species, the ability to communicate requires two attributes besides a variable vocalization: good hearing and a large brain to process the information. Fig. 1.2 demonstrates that dolphins and porpoises have unusually large brains. The figure is a double–logarithmic plot of the brain mass versus the body mass of individuals of various species. The plot illustrates that larger animals have larger brains, with the brain mass of the elephant and the blue whale exceeding our brain mass. This trend is indicated in the figure by a solid straight line. More interestingly, we see from the figure that some species deviate from the general trend in that they possess particularly large brains relative to

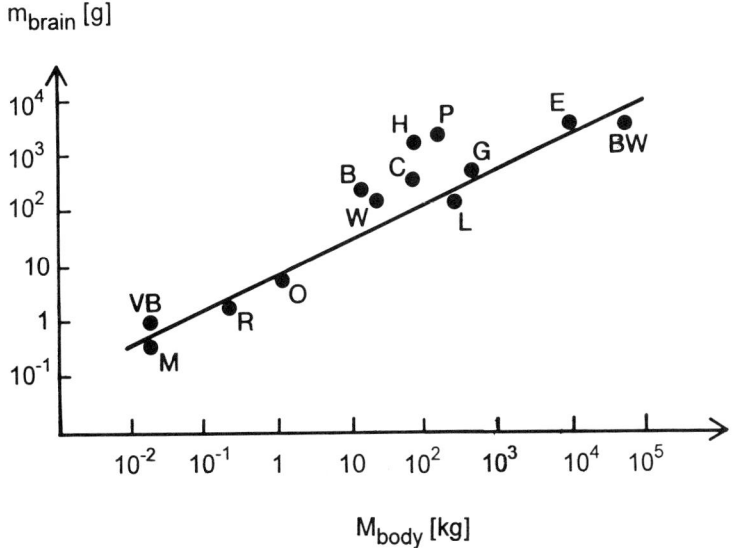

Fig. 1.2: The brain size is not a measure of a mammal's intelligence but is a measure of it's body size. This is illustrated with a double–logarithmic plot which relates the body mass to the brain mass for baboons (B), blue whales (BW), chimpanzees (C), elephants (E), gorillas (G), humans (H), lions (L), moles (M), opossums (O), porpoises (P), rats (R), vampire bats (VB), and wolves (W). The solid line indicates that body mass and brain mass are related by a single power–law. Superior intelligence can be attributed to a species with a brain mass significantly above the solid line. With this definition, only the porpoises qualify besides ourselves.

their body size. These species are found far above the solid line in the figure: humans and porpoises are distinguished in that respect. This reinforces our conjecture that dolphins display a well-developed ability to hear.

(II) How do dolphins hear?

In the second stage of scientific inquiry, these and other observations are used to answer the question "how do dolphins generate these sounds and how do they hear them?" For this we develop a theoretical model. Quantitative tests are then conducted to validate or refute it.

In the current case, the following model is proposed: the whistle sounds originate from a deeper range in the dolphin's larynx, but the clicking sounds are generated by moving air in and out of air sacs near the blowhole. This sound is then focussed forward by the oily melon. The clicking sounds are used for echolocation in the same fashion as used by bats. The whistle sounds of other dolphins and the echo of the clicking sounds are *not* heard like we hear sounds since dolphins lack an outer ear. Instead, the arriving sound is received by the lower jaw bone and then transmitted to the middle ear via the fatty organ found in the anatomical study of the dolphins.

That this model isn't an example of out-of-control science fiction but a reasonable model only becomes clear when we recognize the well-established physical concepts underlying the generation, transmission and reception of sound waves. Focussing the clicking sound with the oily melon allows the dolphin to increase the range of the initial sound energy, which is necessary because sound energy attenuates fast as it travels away from the sound source. Sound waves reflect off an object in water if the object has a different density than the surrounding water. Receiving the reflected sound allows for navigation by echolocation. Echolocation is not only used to locate an object, but also enables the dolphin to determine the object's direction of motion and speed based on the Doppler-effect described in Chapter 16. Even though dolphins have eyesight comparable to that of cats, the echolocation system is necessary at depths greater than 70 meters beyond which sunlight cannot penetrate sea water. Dolphins often dive to such depths; they have been observed as deep as 300 meters below the sea surface. Such dives don't take the dolphin long because they can swim at sustained speeds of 30 km/h. Still, their lungs and cardiovascular systems require modifications to avoid the dangers of diving which are discussed in Chapter 12.

For a mammal to hear, an external sound has to cause an excitation of sound-sensitive cells in the inner ear. There are two ways in which this can occur:

(I) external sounds enter the outer ear through the auditory canal and set the eardrum in vibration. The ossicles of the middle ear amplify this vibration (in humans by a factor 30) and transmit it to the oval window which separates the inner ear from the middle ear. The sound then propagates through the liquid-filled medium of the

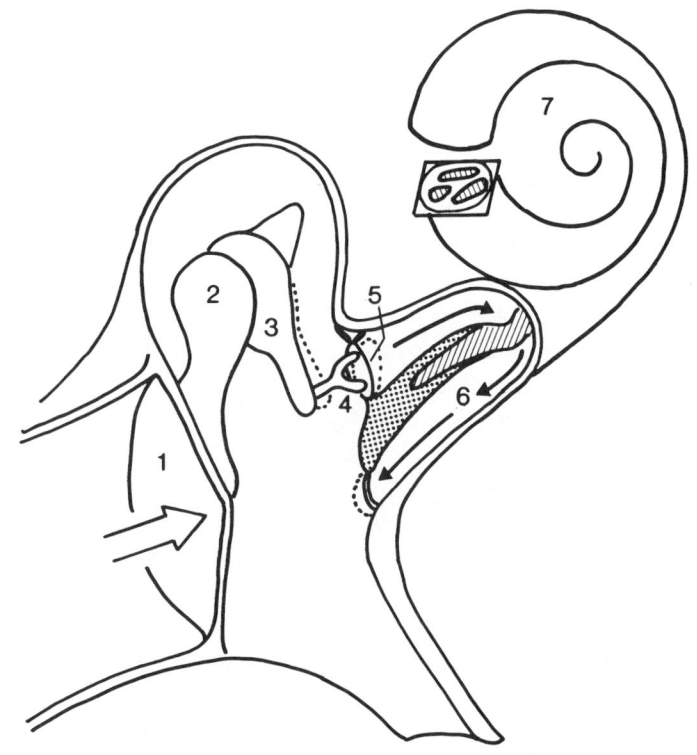

Fig. 1.3: The anatomy of the human middle ear represents 300 million years of evolutionary adaptation to hearing in air. The arriving sound (open arrow) causes the eardrum (1) to vibrate. This vibration is mechanically transmitted to the oval window (5) of the cochlea (7, solid arrows). The sound is amplified by a factor 30 due to the arrangement of the three ossicles, the hammer (2), the anvil (3) and the stirrup (4). The middle ear converts a sound wave in air into a sound wave in the fluid (perilymph, 6) of the inner ear.

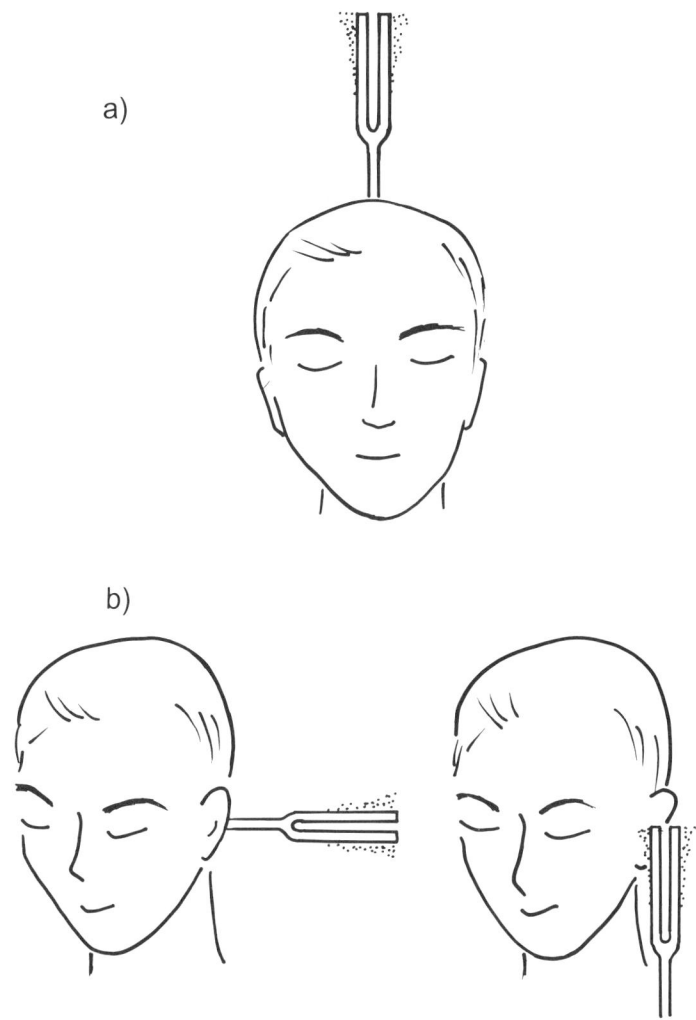

Fig. 1.4: Bone conduction is employed in two audiological tests which allow us to distinguish between middle ear and inner ear diseases. (a) In the Weber–test, a vibrating tuning–fork touches the top of a patient's head. The diagnosis of the health practitioner depends on where the patient perceives the sound source. (b) In the Rinne–test, the vibrating tuning–fork is first brought into contact with the mastoid process behind the auricle until the patient can no longer hear the sound. Then the tuning–fork is moved in front of the auricle. The health practitioner's diagnosis depends on whether the patient hears the sound after the tuning–fork has been moved.

inner ear and excites the sound–sensitive cells of the organ of Corti. This process is described in Chapter 16. (II) Alternatively, external sound waves cause vibrations of the skull bones surrounding the ear. These vibrations stimulate directly the sound–sensitive cells of the inner ear. This process is called *bone conduction*.

Both mechanisms contribute to human hearing, even though we are not consciously aware of bone conduction (which is the main mechanism by which we hear ourselves speak). In audiology, bone conduction is applied by two widely used tests to distinguish hearing impairments caused by diseases of the middle ear versus diseases of the inner ear. The anatomy of the human middle ear is illustrated in Fig. 1.3. Chronic hearing impairments of the middle ear are caused by *otitis media* (bacterial infection of the middle ear) or by *otosclerosis*. Otitis media leads to malformed tissue in the middle ear which negatively affects the mobility of the eardrum and the ossicles. Otosclerosis affects one percent of the adult population and leads to an abnormal amount of spongy bone deposition between stapes and oval window, which immobilizes the stapes. Both diseases lead to a loss of sound transmission from the eardrum to the oval window. Hearing impairments of the inner ear are usually associated with damaged organs of Corti, i.e., sound is not properly processed into signals sent to the brain by the sound–sensitive cells.

The two audiological tests are illustrated in Fig. 1.4. The first test in Fig. 1.4(a) is called *Weber–test*: An A_1–tuning–fork, vibrating at 55 Hz, touches the center top of the patient's head. A healthy patient locates the source of the sound at the proper central position. A patient with a disease of the middle ear will locate the source of the sound near the ailing ear because these patients rely stronger on bone conduction on the ailing side. A patient with a hearing impairment of the inner ear, in turn, locates the source of the sound near the healthy ear since the ailing side does not receive a strong signal either way.

The second test in Fig. 1.4(b) is the *Rinne–test*. In this test, a vibrating A_1–tuning–fork is first brought in contact with the *mastoid process* behind the *auricle*.

When the patient doesn't hear the diminishing sound any longer, the tuning–fork is brought in front of the auricle. A healthy person or a person with a hearing impairment in the inner ear now hears the sound again since bone conduction in humans is less effective than hearing a sound which is transmitted through air to the eardrum. A patient with a hearing impairment in the middle ear, however, does not pick up the sound of the moved tuning–fork. This is due to the ability to circumvent the middle ear mechanism with bone conduction but not with sound arriving at the eardrums.

Bone conduction is more important for hearing under water. Adjustments in the lower jaw of dolphins and the development of the fatty organ to connect the lower jaw to the middle ear are improvements of the ability to hear by bone conduction. Why that is the case is explained by physical concepts, such as resonant coupling of sound waves to vibrations of the rigid bone material, and the amplification of vibrations in elastic materials like the fatty organ. We study these physical concepts in Chapters 15 and 16.

(III) Why do dolphins hear?
The final stage of scientific inquiry deals with the question "why do the dolphins hear by the method described above." In the biological sciences such ultimate questions usually require the study of the evolutionary history.

Whales are an order which developed only in the past 55 million years by radiating from early *ungulates*, which are mammals whose last toe joints are encased in hooves. Emerging from furred carnivores, the early ancestors of the whales spent an increasing fraction of their lives in water, first in river deltas hunting like crocodiles, then along shallow coastlines of the Eocenic oceans. They lost their furs about 47 million years ago and became independent of fresh water supplies about 44 million years ago. Eventually they moved entirely into the sea where their hind–legs disappeared (these did not become the whale's fluke which does not contain any bones). Their front–legs became flippers. This transition was completed about 30 million years ago.

The evolutionary changes to the ear occurred about 45 million years ago, i.e., as an early adaptation to the marine environment. The loss of the outer ear is an example of an evolutionary reversal. Such reversals are evidence against a teleonomic (goal–oriented) interpretation of natural processes; we will discuss in Chapter 4 an example of reverse evolution in homo sapiens, affecting the shape of our pelvis.

Thus, dolphins are descendants of species which had adapted to life on dry land for more than 300 million years. They share with us amphibian ancestors who lived part of their lives in water, then reptile ancestors who developed the egg shell about 300 million years ago to shed the last reason for a waterbound stage in their lives, and finally the early mammalian ancestors which finally flourished when the dinosaurs became extinct 65 million years ago. Thus, comparing the hearing of dolphins to the sound detection of fish is meaningless.

The ear of the dolphin is a device which was initially adapted to use in air, and then got modified for use under water. The adaptation of the mammalian ear to the use on land, but also its ineffectiveness when used under water is described in Chapter 16. Thus, the evolutionary adaptations of the dolphin's hearing are rooted in the physics of acoustics in water and air and must be explained by applying physical reasoning.

The example of the dolphin's ability to hear illustrates therefore the usefulness of physical methods for a specific inquiry in biology. There are numerous examples of this type in the life sciences, many of these discussed in the remainder of this book.

1.2. Hierarchy of complexity

Using the case study of the previous section as a guide, we have only answered the question "what role does physics play in the life sciences", we have yet to answer "how does physics play its role in the life sciences" and "why does physics play such a prominent role in the life sciences". Answering these questions leads us from the numerous facts that it does to the common fundamental reason. This aspect will provide us with a second answer to the question why a life scientist should be familiar with physical methods and concepts.

A widely used approach in textbooks of biology presents the knowledge in that field based on a hierarchy of complexity of the systems studied: an overview of the most frequently occurring biomolecules is followed by a tour of the living cell. This leads to the physiology of tissues and organ systems and from these to the entire organism. At a higher level, species and their evolution are discussed, which finally leads to ecosystems and their ecology. Fig. 1.5 displays this hierarchy and provides an attempt to quantify the progressive complexity of the systems at each level: the numbers shown between the various levels indicate how many of the units of the lower level are needed to assemble a single unit at the upper level. These numbers may vary significantly, but are typical with the human species in mind. Because the implications of Fig. 1.5 rest with the large numerical values shown, the origin of these numbers is briefly discussed.

The major biomolecules at the cellular level are proteins and nucleic acids. An example of a protein is hemoglobin. Hemoglobin is part of red blood cells (ery-

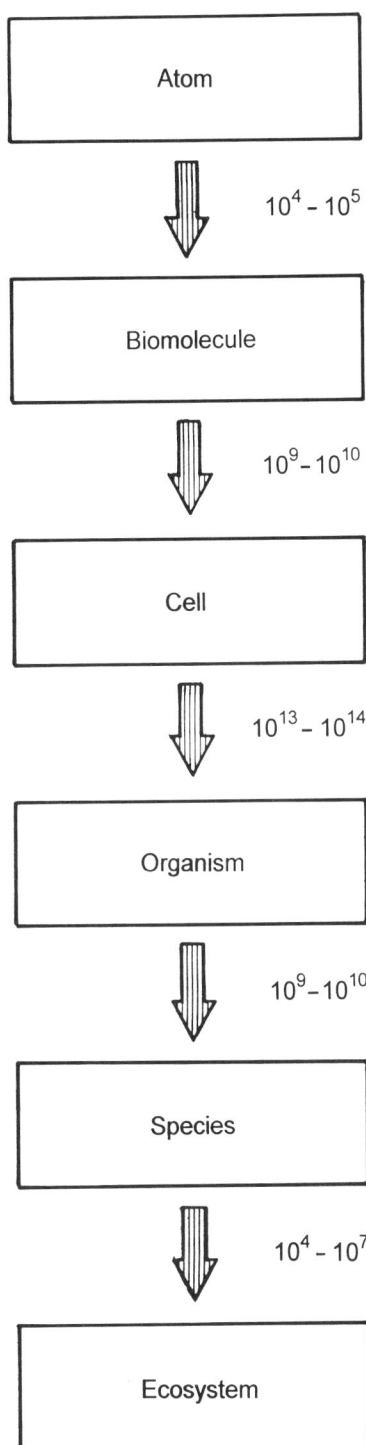

Fig. 1.5: Modern biology textbooks present the scientific knowledge based on a hierarchy of complexity of the various systems, distinguishing an atomic and molecular level, functional biomolecules, living cells, organs, organisms, species and ecosystems. The numbers shown in the figure indicate how many units from the lower level are needed to obtain a single unit at the next higher level. The given numbers are typical for humans. Physical and chemical concepts play a significant role in biology as they enter at the lowest level of the hierarchy.

throcytes) and is responsible for carrying oxygen from the alveolar capillaries in the lungs to the various organs and tissues in the body. This protein has a molecular mass of about 68,000 g/mol which corresponds to over 10,000 atoms forming the biomolecule.

Counting all biomolecules in a human cell is tedious, however we can estimate their number from the size of a cell (with a diameter of about 20 μm) and its density. Accounting for the water content of the cell and assuming an average molecular mass for a biomolecule of 60,000 g/mol, we estimate that there are one to ten billion biomolecules in a human cell.

Cells combine to form organs, tissues or functional organ components. These vary widely in number of cells, e.g. the brain contains about one billion ganglion cells while each kidney contains about one million functional units called nephrons (see Chapter 11) which must, therefore, in turn contain a significantly lesser number of cells. Due to this variability the level of single organs, tissues or functional organ components is skiped in Fig. 1.5. A firm number of cell repetitions is established for the adult human body with 5×10^{13} cells. This number increases for larger mammals: a blue whale has about 1×10^{17} cells.

The species *homo sapiens* currently consists of slightly more than 6 billion individuals. Looking for a more precise number is futile as the human population increases by 100 people every 15 seconds; we will reach 7 billion people by 2015. The total number of individuals of our species ever to live on Earth is estimated to be 106 billion, i.e., 6% of all humans are alive right now.

We define an ecosystem as the sum of all organisms and their abiotic environment in a given area. For studying large–scale processes such as global warming, the entire biosphere must be treated as an ecosystem. The biosphere accommodates million taxonomically classified species, and probably another 10 to 30 million yet unknown species. Still, these represent less than 1 % of species which ever lived on our planet.

So what does Fig. 1.5 imply, what does it contribute to our discussion? In the standard biology textbook two important conclusions are drawn: that it is necessary to develop the knowledge at each level on a solid foundation of the concepts at the lower levels, but that one has also to expect new properties at each level which cannot be predicted from the lower levels. The first conclusion justifies the term "hierarchy" to describe Fig. 1.5, the second observation leads to "emergent properties" at each new level of complexity. Both of these conclusions assign a prominent place to physics and chemistry, the two sister–sciences of biology: the lowest level in the hierarchy of Fig. 1.5 is the level of atoms and molecules, which are the realm of physics and chemistry. Thus, physical concepts and physical reasoning are part of the study of biology right from the lowest level. As emergent properties are observed at higher levels of complexity, these often add further physical concepts to the discussion.

1.3. Problems

P–1.1
Fig. 1.2 shows a double–logarithmic plot of the brain mass in unit [g] versus body mass in unit [kg] for several mammals. The line is a fit to the data. In the formula:

$$m_{brain} = a \cdot M_{body}^{b} \qquad (1)$$

(a) determine the exponent b,
(b) determine the prefactor a.
(c) The statement, "we are smarter than chimpanzees because we have a bigger brain" better be wrong, because otherwise Fig. 1.2 would imply that we are dumber than porpoises, elephants and blue whales. Based on Fig. 1.2, how would you formulate a similar comparative statement about the human brain mass which would address our perception that we are also smarter than the three species with the heavier brains?

Chapter II

Locomotion

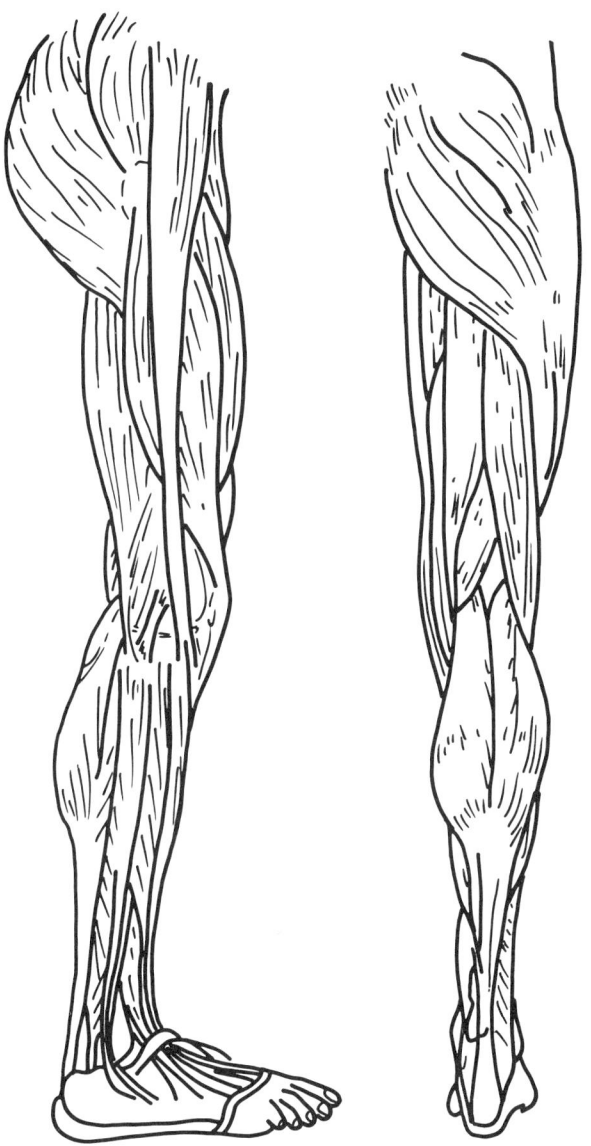

The strength of forces

LOCOMOTION
THE STRENGTH OF FORCES

An interaction of distinguishable objects is defined in physics as a force. If the interaction involves a living organism the resulting change in the state of motion (acceleration) is defined as locomotion. Newton identified three laws governing forces: (I) an object is in mechanical equilibrium if the forces acting on the object are balanced. In this case no acceleration occurs. (II) If instead a set of unbalanced forces acts on the object, it accelerates proportional to the magnitude of the net force. (III) Any two interacting objects exert equal but opposite forces upon each other; such forces are called an action/reaction pair. The laws of mechanics allow us to quantify the locomotion of an organism in its environment, but also provide an insight into forces acting within an organism's body. In animals, these forces are the result of the interplay of muscles (the source of forces) and the skeleton (the frame against which the forces act).

The widely accepted definition of *life* consists of three necessary conditions: (I) metabolism and growth, (II) recognition of external stimuli and the ability to respond, and (III) reproduction. The first two of these conditions are rooted in fundamental physics concepts which we focus on in the early chapters: in Chapters 2 – 4 a range of mechanical receptors are studied which enable an organism to analyse external stimuli. We also introduce the mechanical concepts underlying the ability to respond to these stimuli. In Chapters 5 – 8 we supplement the mechanical concepts with the laws of thermodynamics to describe basic metabolic and growth processes.

The ability to move from place to place (which we call *locomotion*) is one of the basic responses of living organisms to external stimuli. Bacteria and protists use flagellar action to move along chemical gradients in their environment, fungi and plants can adjust to the direction of sunlight, and animals pursue prey or evade predators. In Chapter 2 we develop the physical concepts which enable animal locomotion, particularly in vertebrates.

2.1. The physiological role of the components of the locomotive system

The two major components of the locomotive system are (I) a source of forces and (II) a firm framework against which the forces are applied. In animals the source of forces is provided by *muscles* and the firm framework is called a *skeleton*.

2.1.1. Skeleton

Three types of skeletons evolved in the animal kingdom. The bodies of cnidarians (jelly fish and sea anemones), flatworms, roundworms (nematodes) and segmented worms (annelids) contain a *hydrostatic skeleton* against which the muscles operate to provide for locomotion. A hydrostatic skeleton consists of liquids held under pressure in closed body compartments. The hydrostatic pressure maintains the total volume of the animal. Muscle action causes rhythmic reshaping of the body to propel it forward. The resulting peristaltic locomotion of an earthworm is shown in Fig. 2.1(a). Since we discuss hydrostatics later in Chapter 10, the hydrostatic skeleton is not further considered in the current chapter.

An external rigid or semirigid skeletal structure (*exoskeleton*) provides for protection and static support of soft tissues. Amoeba build such exoskeletons with calcium or silica secretion and sponges use spongin, a tough but elastic substance. A very well known example of an exoskeleton is the stony material deposited by corals. As animal life developed to higher complexity, increased mobility became advantageous for individual creatures. This was achieved by subdividing the exoskeleton into a larger number of connected plates, such as a separated head, thorax and abdomen in insects. The exoskeletal plates are connected by elastic tissue which provides for a good flexibility for motion, particularly along the legs.

The third type of skeleton is the internal skeleton (*endoskeleton*) of vertebrates. The most primitive of

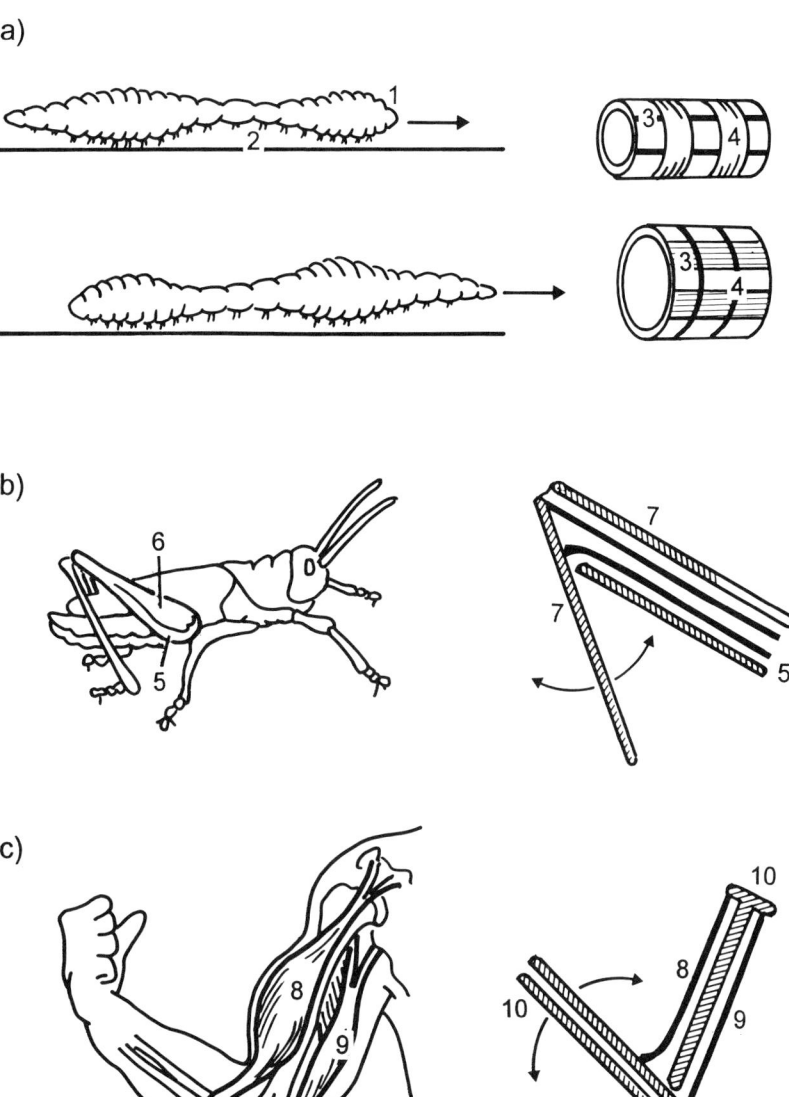

Fig. 2.1: Nature has designed three basic methods of locomotion unique to the animal kingdom: a hydrostatic skeleton illustrated for the earthworm, an exoskeleton shown for the grasshopper, and an endoskeleton illustrated for the human arm.

(a) An earthworm has a head section (1) which defines the forward direction and uses bristles (2) to hold on to the ground. The animal uses two muscle types to move: head–tail oriented longitudinal muscles (3) and circular muscles around the circumference of each segment (4). When the longitudinal muscles contract, the segments shorten (top); when the circular muscles contract, the head section is pushed forward (bottom). We call the system of liquid-filled body cavities a hydrostatic skeleton since the fluid pressure inside prevents a change in the volume, causing a shape change instead.

(b) The leg of a grasshopper illustrates the cooperation of muscles and the exoskeleton (7). Two antagonistic muscles, a flexor (5) and an extensor (6), are contained within the skeleton. When the flexor (flexing muscle) contracts the lower leg is pulled toward the body; when the extensor (extending muscle) contracts the leg stretches backwards. The animal at the left is shown with the flexor muscle contracted.

(c) The lower arm of a human illustrates that the muscles and the endoskeleton (10) cooperate in a similar fashion as in the case of the exoskeleton. The biceps muscle is the flexor (8) and the triceps muscle is the extensor (9).

these endoskeletons is the *notochord*, which is a backbone of cartilage in fish. In more advanced animals, the skeleton formed in the embryo is initially cartilaginous and hardens as the individual creature matures. This process is complete in humans with the ossification of the breastbone at the age of 25.

The mobility of animals with exoskeletons or endoskeletons is based on muscle action for which joints provide leverage, allowing for the rotation of a body part relative to another. Fig. 2.1 illustrates this arrangement for a grasshopper (Fig. 2.1(b) for the exoskeleton) and a human (Fig. 2.1(c) for the endoskeleton). Both types of skeleton need two muscles for each rotation because muscles contract actively but elongate when passively stretched by another muscle (antagonistic action). In vertebrates, muscles are not directly connected to bones but extend as fibrous connective tissue (tendon) which is attached to the bones. Thus, bones, muscles and tendons are the three basic components of the locomotive system of vertebrates. In this and the next chapter we focus on the effects muscles have on bones, in Chapter 4 we then include joints as an element of the skeleton to allow for rotations.

2.1.2. Muscles

Not all muscles are used for locomotion, leading us to distinguish three types of muscles; of these only the *skeletal muscles* are attached to bones and are involved in the motion of the body. The other two types of muscles are the smooth muscles surrounding abdominal organs and blood vessels, and the cardiac muscles of the heart. These muscles also exert forces causing internal motion, for example maintaining the flow of blood through the cardiovascular system. Here we discuss only skeletal muscles.

Skeletal muscles consist of bundles of fibres running the length of the muscle. The diameter of such a bundle lies in the range of 0.1 – 1 mm. Each fibre is a cell. The cells are subdivided into a hierarchy of smaller repetitive units. The muscle cell contains about 100 *myofibrils* which are the functional components of the muscle. Each myofibril has a diameter of about 1 μm. In the elongated direction the myofibril is divided into *sarcomeres*, which are the basic contractile units of the muscle. The sarcomere unit is shown schematically in Fig. 2.2. Each sarcomere has an average length of 2.1 μm. It is confined at both ends by stiff Z discs. These discs hold actin filaments which extend by 1.0 μm to 1.2 μm to both sides. Myosin filaments of 1.65 μm length bridge the gap between the actin filaments of two adjacent Z discs. Actin proteins are present in all eukaryotic cells. They form part of the cytoskeleton of the cell, allowing the cell to bear tension (pulling) forces. The myosin protein acts as a motor molecule by walking along the actin rods. This combined action of both proteins evolved early and is applied by amoeba to move with extruding pseudopodia (false feet).

The microscopic mechanism of muscle contraction is illustrated in Fig. 2.3 (*sliding filament model*). The top sketch shows a resting muscle. A nerve signal triggers the release of Ca^{2+} ions from the sarcoplasmic reticulum. The calcium ions attach to troponin molecules. As a result, the tropomyosin protein strand, which is coiled around the actin filament, loosens. This allows the myosin to bond to the actin filaments. With the 21 nm long myosin head attached to the actin filament, it tilts from an angle of 90° to 45°. This shortens the sarco-

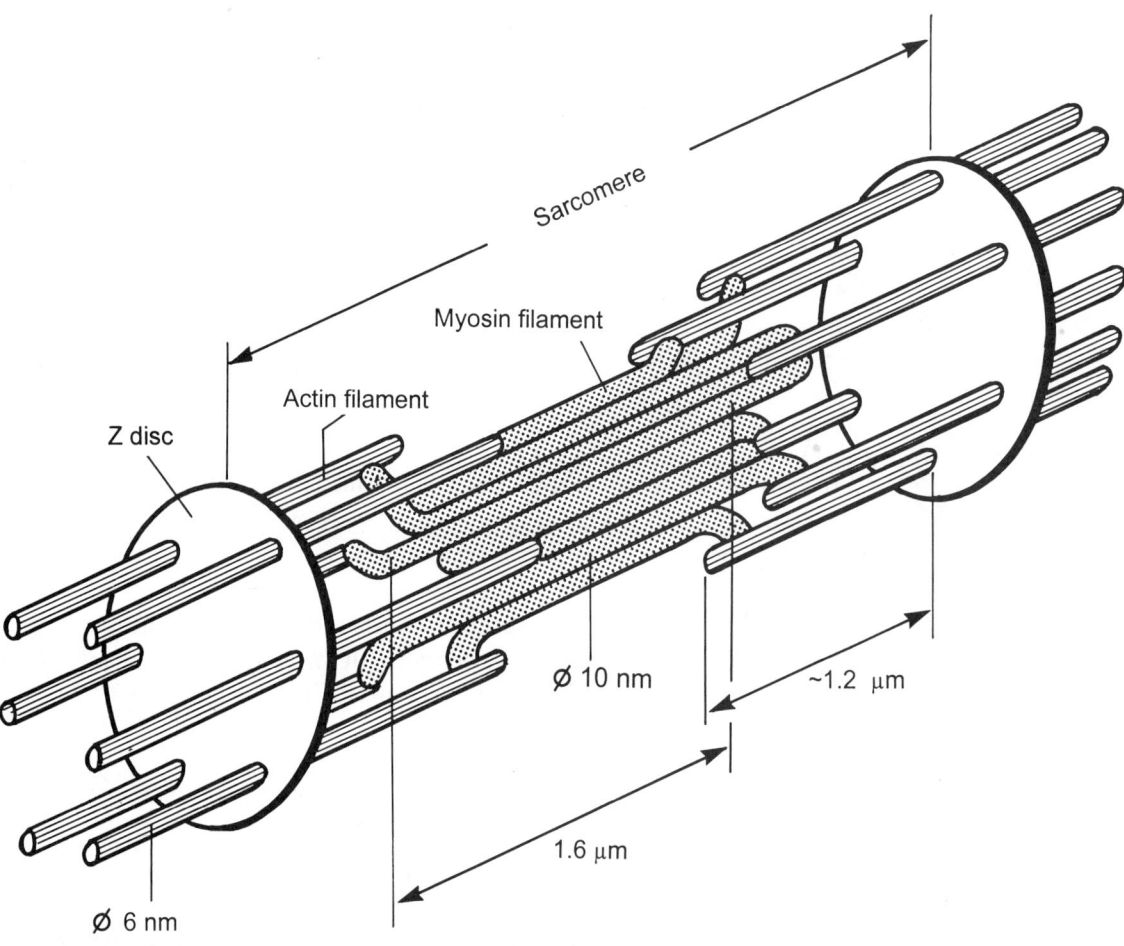

Fig. 2.2: The sarcomere is the contractile unit of the myofibrils in the muscle cell. The length of the sarcomere is defined by the distance between two adjacent Z discs. This length varies during muscle action when the myosin filaments crawl along the actin filaments, which are connected to the Z discs. The actin filaments extend by about 1.2 μm beyond the Z disc at each side. Combined with a 1.65 μm length of the myosin filament, the sarcomere length can typically vary between 1.6 μm and 3.0 μm while maintaining an effective overlap between both filaments. Actin and myosin have a length to cross–section ratio of up to 200.

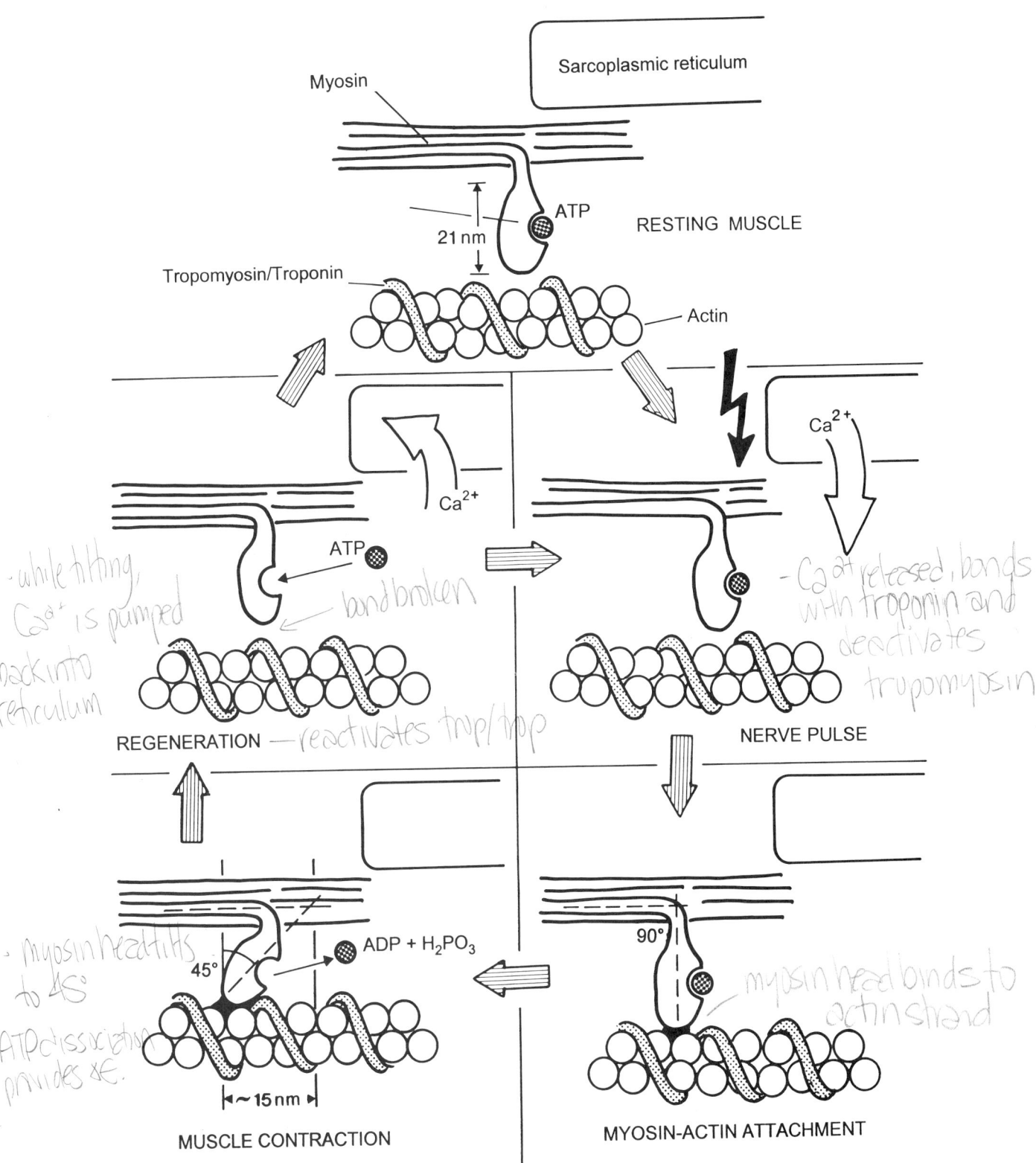

Fig. 2.3: Illustration of the sliding filament model. A resting muscle is shown at the top with its major components: the sarcoplasmic reticulum, the myosin filament with the myosin head charged with an ATP molecule below and the intertwined actin and troponin/tropomyosin filaments at the bottom.

When a nerve pulse arrives a cycle of processes unfolds as shown in the four lower boxes. First, the nerve pulse triggers Ca^{2+} release from the sarcoplasmic reticulum. The calcium ions bond with troponin, deactivating tropomyosin and allowing the myosin head to bond to the actin strand. When the myosin head is firmly attached to the actin it tilts to 45°. An ATP dissociation provides the energy for this step. Concurrent to the tilting, calcium is pumped back into the sarcoplasmic reticulum. This reactivates the troponin/ tropomyosin, and the myosin–actin bond breaks. Further nerve pulses lead to a repetition of this cycle.

mere. At the same time, the sarcoplasmic reticulum pump back the calcium ions, causing the muscle fibre to regenerate, i.e., the actin–myosin bond is severed by the reactivated troponin. This cycle repeats for every new nerve pulse arriving at the muscle. Such pulses arrive at rates between 20 and 100 Hz (Hertz is a unit of frequency: $1\text{ Hz} = 1\text{ s}^{-1}$; thus, 20 Hz means that 20 nerve pulses arrive per second). This leads to an appreciable contraction of the muscle in a short time.

The limit of contraction of sarcomeres can be determined from Fig. 2.2. When the myosin filament hits the Z discs on both sides, a further shortening of the muscle would require a partial crumbling of the myosin filament. This does not occur, and thus the maximum shortening of a sarcomere occurs from an average length of 2.1 μm to a minimum length of 1.65 μm. This means that each sarcomere, and therefore the entire muscle can shorten by slightly more than 20 %. On the other side, muscles do not elongate on their own but are stretched by the action of another contracting muscle. Mechanisms discussed in Chapter 15 protect muscles against overstretching which would occur when the sarcomeres are elongated by more than 35 %.

Example 2.1

We saw in Fig. 2.3 that each myosin head of 21 nm length tilts to an angle of 45° and relaxes to an angle of

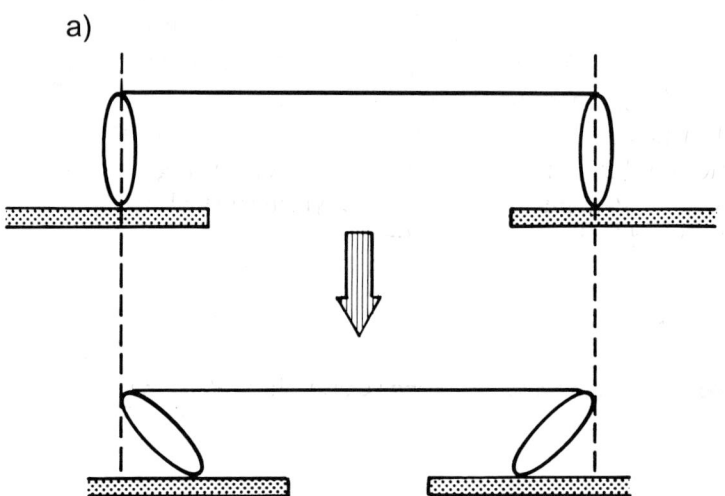

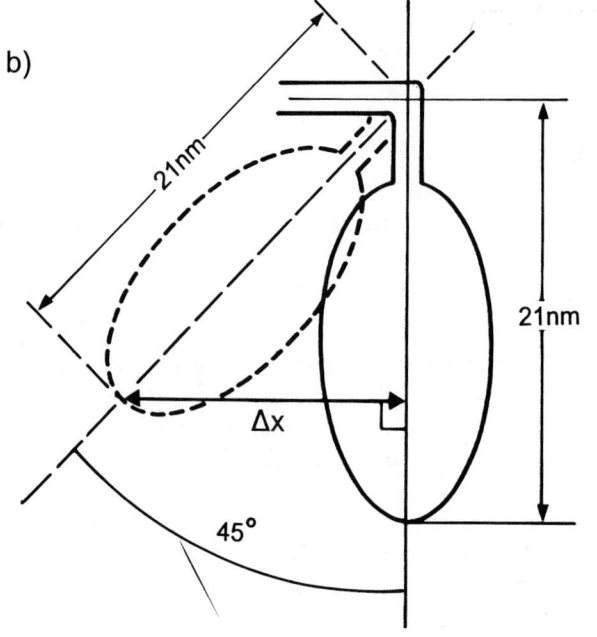

Fig. 2.4: (a) Each cycle of the sliding filament model causes a shortening of the sarcomere. This is achieved by the synchronous tilting of myosin heads at both ends of the myosin molecule.
(b) The tilting of a myosin head is highlighted by comparing the relaxed vertical position (solid ellipse) and the head at maximum 45° tilt (dashed ellipse). The myosin head has a length of 21 nm, measured from the axis of rotation to the tip. The tip is attached to the actin filament. The length Δx represents the distance by which the myosin head pulls the myosin filament along the actin filament per nerve pulse.

90° relative to the rest of the myosin molecule once per nerve pulse.
(a) Calculate the contraction (change in length) of a sarcomere per nerve pulse. Hint: as shown in Fig. 2.4(a), two myosin heads need to tilt simultaneously per myosin molecule, one at each end.
(b) Express the contraction of the muscle per nerve pulse as a fraction of the average length of the sarcomere (use L_{av} = 2.1 μm).
(c) How long does it take to contract a muscle from its average length by 20 % assuming 60 pulses per second?

Solution part (a): The geometry of a tilting myosin head is shown in Fig. 2.4(b). The solid ellipse shows the myosin head in the relaxed position and the dashed ellipse shows the head when tilted to 45°. The figure indicates the displacement Δx of the lower tip of the myosin head in the direction parallel to the myosin filament. This is also the displacement of the actin filament relative to the myosin filament achieved in a single cycle of the sliding filament model. The question in part (a) requires you to calculate 2Δx because a second myosin head undergoes the same tilt at the other end of the myosin molecule, as illustrated in Fig. 2.4(a). We find:

$$2\Delta x = 2 \cdot 21 \, nm \cdot \sin 45^0 = 29.6 \, nm \quad (1)$$

The length of the sarcomere shortens by about 30 nm per nerve pulse. 30 nm can also be written as 3×10^{-8} m.

Solution part (b): The sarcomere has an average length of L_{av} = 2.1 μm = 2100 nm. Thus, the contraction length as a fraction of the average length, $2\Delta x/L_{av}$, is given by:

$$\frac{2\Delta x}{L_{av}} = \frac{29.6 \, nm}{2100 \, nm} = 0.014 = 1.4 \, \% \quad (2)$$

A single nerve pulse shortens each sarcomere and therefore the entire muscle by 1.4 %.

Solution part (c): Using the result from part (b) we conclude that if the sliding filament model operates for one second, a shortening of 84 % would occur. However, the maximum contraction of a sarcomere is 20 %. We use cross multiplication to obtain the time for a shortening by 20 %:

$$\begin{array}{c} 1.0 \, seconds = 84 \, \% \\ \times \\ t \, seconds = 20 \, \% \end{array} \quad (3)$$

This yields t = 0.24 seconds. A 20 % contraction can be achieved in a quarter of a second, which is a reasonable time based on our every–day experience.

2.1.3. Tendons

The force of the muscle is transferred to the bones via tendons. Tendons act like extremely strong strings that

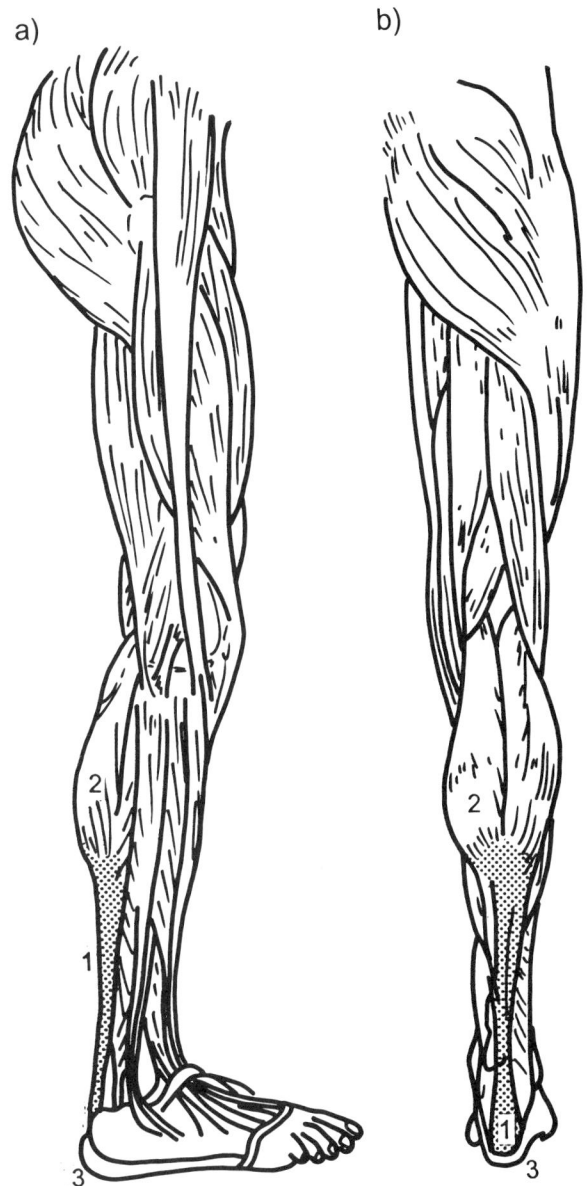

Fig. 2.5: (a) Side view and (b) rear view of the lower leg of a human showing the Achilles tendon (1), connecting the calf muscle (2) to the heel bone (3, calcaneus). The Achilles tendon stretches as a narrow band along the lower one–third of the back of the lower leg. Because the Achilles tendon lies shallow underneath the skin, you can feel for it in your own leg if you bend your leg backwards while seated.

are flexible but do not stretch. They are made of large strands of white, fibrous proteins (collagen). Collagen tissue is different from the muscle tissue but originates within the muscle to provide maximum toughness.

An example of the relative arrangement of muscle, bone and tendon is shown in Fig. 2.5 for the *Achilles tendon*, with part (a) a side view and part (b) a rear view of a human leg. The Achilles tendon is the thickest and strongest tendon in the human body, extending from the calf muscle to the heel bone (calcaneus).

2.2. Definition of force

To quantify the interplay of muscles, bones and tendons, the physical concept of force is introduced. With forces defined, we will develop quantitatively the physical laws governing the locomotive action (mechanics).

Throughout the textbook we often use simplifying models. Our first model is a simplification of what constitutes a body or an object of interest. We define a *point mass* as an object which has a finite mass, which we measure in kilogram [kg], but which has no spatial dimensions. This is a restrictive model as no real object is zero–dimensional. However, it is a useful model as the actual size of an object may be negligible in the context in which we study the properties of the object. The point mass model, like any other physical model, cannot be applied to all objects in every context. For example, it does not allow for the rotation of the object or for internal vibrations. If rotations or vibrations are important, we need to use other models. Such models will be introduced in Chapter 4 to allow the object to rotate and in Chapter 15 to allow the object to vibrate. Because these models are more complicated, we rather use the simple point mass model for now as it proves sufficient to introduce Newton's laws of mechanics.

> *Forces represent the interaction of distinguishable objects.*

Surveying the many ways in which objects affect each other, we group forces into two types: (I) contact forces and (II) field forces. Contact forces act only when physical contact between two distinguishable objects is established while field forces act over a distance. Some of the forces that we distinguish in each group are listed in Table 2.1; most of these forces play a role in the present chapter, others are discussed later in the textbook.

We distinguish four fundamental forces, i.e., forces which are not composite forces of one or several

Table 2.1: The main forces discussed in the textbook.

Force	Example
Field forces	
Gravity	Attraction between Earth and Sun
Weight	Object falling to the surface of Earth
Electric force	Static electricity
Magnetic force	Alignment of a compass needle
Nuclear force	Radioactive decay
Contact forces	
External force	My hand pushing an object
Normal force	Table holding an object up
Tension	Pulling an object with a string
Buoyant force	A fluid supporting a floating object
Friction	Resistance against fluid flow in a tube

other forces: gravity, the electric force, the strong (nuclear) force and the weak force. All but the weak force are discussed in this textbook. Note that all four fundamental forces are field forces. On the other hand, each contact force in Table 2.1 is a synthesis of microscopic electrostatic interactions.

While Table 2.1 indicates that we can observe many different forces acting in our environment, the purpose of a scientific description of these forces is to focus on their common features. Considering a simple experiment with forces, such as throwing a ball or pushing a glass across a table, we note that the quantitative definition of force must allow for a variability in direction and magnitude. A ball drops always toward the Earth, regardless of the position from which it is released. Thus, the force associated with the attraction toward the Earth acts in a well–defined direction. The motion of a glass sliding across a bar table in a Western movie depends on the direction in which it was pushed. Thus, contact forces are also associated with specific directions. We can further push the glass harder or more gently, which leads to different final speeds. Thus, the change in the magnitude of a force leads to different results.

Physical quantities which have a magnitude and a direction in space are mathematically described by vectors. Applying physical laws that include vector quantities requires vector algebra. Vector algebra is not trivial. We separate the initial discussion of the basic laws of mechanics and the first application of vector algebra in physics into two chapters in the current textbook: in the current chapter we focus only on the magnitude of forces, which is a valid approach as long as the forces acting on an object are collinear. The problems in the current chapter can therefore be solved algebraically.

In Chapter 3 we extend the discussion to cases with non–collinear forces; the problems in Chapter 3 will require vector algebra.

We are now ready to discuss specific forces. We start with some of the more obvious forces encountered in our everyday lives. Fig. 2.6 shows a human standing on both legs. The first force we notice in this case is the force of gravity, which pulls us down toward the ground. We call this force *weight* and label it W. Sir Isaac Newton was the first to quantitatively describe gravity as the attractive force between two bodies of masses m and M:

$$F_{gravity} = G^* \frac{m \cdot M}{r^2} \qquad (4)$$

The prefactor G* on the right hand side is the gravitational constant with a value of G* = 6.67 · 10⁻¹¹ Nm²/kg². The right hand side of Eq. (4) further contains r, which is the center–to–center distance of the two objects which attract each other. In the general form given in Eq. (4), the law of gravity is primarily applied in astronomy. We will use it in that form for some discussions of the effect of weightlessness on the human body in Chapter 20. For experiments done on or near the surface of the Earth (as assumed in all other chapters in the textbook) a simplified formula is sufficient to describe the gravitational force:

$$F_{gravity} = m \cdot g \qquad (5)$$

The constant g is the gravitational acceleration with the value g = 9.8 m/s². Note that g is not a force but an acceleration as later defined in Eq. (9). The numerical value of g is obtained from Eq. (4) by substituting for r the radius of the Earth (r = 6,400 km = 6.4 × 10⁶ m), and for M the mass of the Earth (M = 6 × 10²⁴ kg):

$$g \equiv \frac{G^* M_{Earth}}{r_{Earth}^2} = 9.8 \ m/s^2 \qquad (6)$$

Studying Fig. 2.6 further, we identify two more forces acting on the shown human body. Since the weight is the only field force we introduce in the current chapter, all other forces can be identified by a visible contact of the object with something in its vicinity. In the case of Fig. 2.6, the floor pushes the body up through the contact point with each foot. If this were not the case, i.e., if the magnitude of both upward directed forces were zero, then the floor would not have an effect on the body and the body would fall through the floor (think of trying to stand on a cloud). We call these forces *normal forces* because they act in the direction normal (perpendicular) to a surface; in Fig. 2.6 this surface is the floor. N_1 and N_2 are labelled with different subscripts because they may differ in magnitude, e.g. when the person shifts the weight onto the left or the right leg.

Forces can also be identified within our body. This is illustrated in Fig. 2.7 for the main forces acting on the arm of a person intending to do one–arm dumbbell rows in a gym. W_{arm} is the weight of the arm, T is the tension force the trunk exerts on the arm via muscles such as the trapezius and ligaments across the shoulder joint, and F is the force the dumbbell exerts on the fist.

These first examples lead to two important comments about the application of forces:
(I) we are interested in the forces acting on a body, not the forces the body exerts on other objects, and
(II) we must be able to name a source for each force: the trunk causes the tension force, the Earth causes the weight and the dumbbell causes the force F in Fig. 2.7.

2.3. Newton's laws of mechanics

To quantify the action of forces, we introduce three laws of mechanics, originally published by Sir Isaac Newton in 1687 (Principia). The fundamental issue addressed by

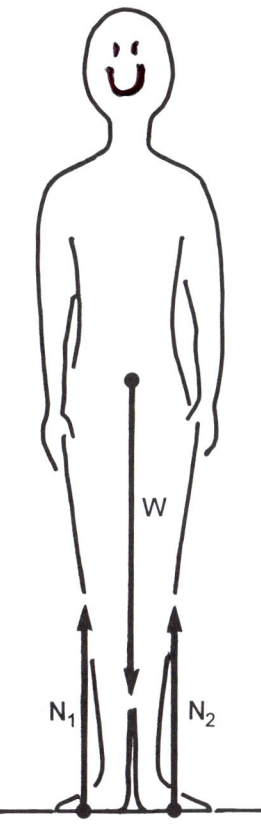

Fig. 2.6: The forces acting on a person standing on both legs. The gravitational force is always present on the surface of the Earth. It is directed straight downwards. We call this force weight and label it W. Upward directed forces act on each foot on the ground. In general, these forces are directed perpendicular to the supporting surface and are therefore called normal forces. The normal force N_1 is identified for the right foot and the normal force N_2 is identified for the left foot. These two forces may differ as the person can shift from one foot to the other.

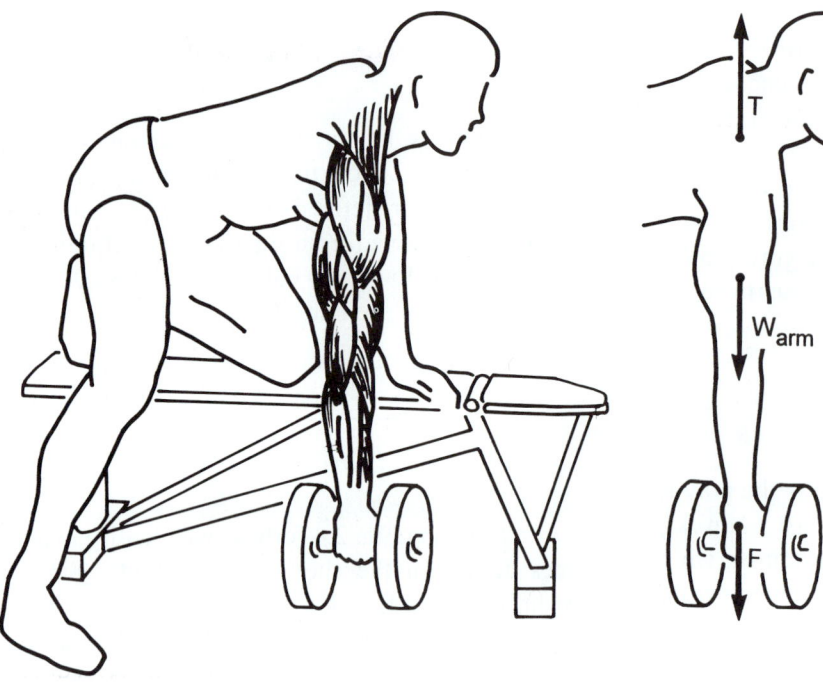

Fig. 2.7: Forces can also be discussed as they act between different parts of an organism. As an example, three major forces are highlighted as they act on the arm of a person intending to do one–arm dumbbell rows in a gym. The forces are F, which is a downward directed force due to the weight of the dumbbell; W_{arm}, which is the weight of the arm; and T, which is a force pulling the arm up due to the tension in muscles and ligaments connecting the trunk and the arm.

these laws is the connection of forces acting on a body and the resulting change of the state of motion. The state of motion of an object is characterized by its position, its velocity and its acceleration, each as a function of time. Position, velocity and acceleration are called kinematic properties. Their mathematical relations are called kinematic equations and are summarized in an Appendix of Chapter 5. While it is historically interesting to study Galileo Galilei's work, for the physiological context it is sufficient to recognize that the acceleration of an object is a consequence of forces and that the speed of an object is linked to its energy. Thus, all we need to know are the definitions of velocity and acceleration. We have to be somewhat careful, however, when trying to define these terms. Our everyday perception of what acceleration or velocity mean is broader than the scientific definitions.

2.3.1. Velocity and acceleration

We confine our discussion to the motion of an object along a straight line. This simplifies the mathematical formulas we have to introduce and allows us again to omit the directional (vector) character of the physical quantities. To define velocity, we measure the time an object needs to pass through a preset distance. We consider a displacement Δx between two positions x_1 and x_2. The corresponding two times, t_1 and t_2, provide the time interval Δt. The slope of the dashed line in Fig. 2.8 then represents the velocity of the object:

$$v_{avg} \equiv \frac{\Delta x}{\Delta t} = \frac{x_2 - x_1}{t_2 - t_1} \quad (7)$$

The unit of velocity is [m/s]. The definition of velocity in Eq. (7) is not satisfactory. For example, assume that we want to determine the speed of a car. Obtaining a certain value from Eq. (7) by timing two different vehicles does not mean that the same motion occurred. The value 25 km/h can mean that the car drove slowly, or it may mean that the car went fast but stopped somewhere along the way. Thus Eq. (7) establishes an *average velocity* between the two points x_1 and x_2; this is the reason the velocity has been given a subscript "avg" in Eq. (7).

For scientific applications of the concept of velocity the definition must be changed. We need the *instantaneous velocity* at point x_1 if an interesting event takes place at that point, e.g. a collision. We start with Eq. (7) and assume that it provides a first estimate for the instantaneous velocity at point x_1. Then we improve that estimate of the velocity by determining the average velocity for a shorter and shorter time interval Δt. The instantaneous velocity at point x_1 is written as v_{inst} and follows when we extrapolate to $\Delta t = 0$ as shown by the slope of the dash–dotted line (tangent) in Fig. 2.8:

$$v_{inst} \equiv \lim_{\Delta t \to 0} \frac{\Delta x}{\Delta t} \quad (8)$$

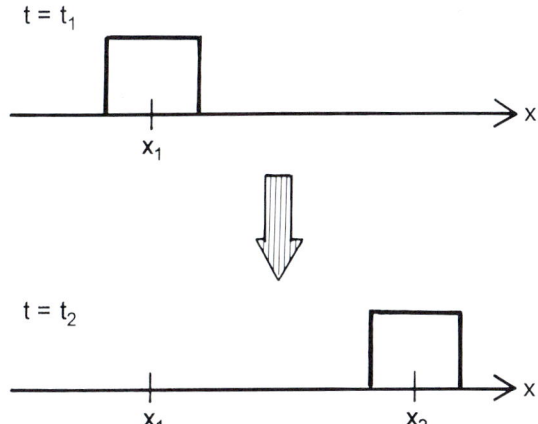

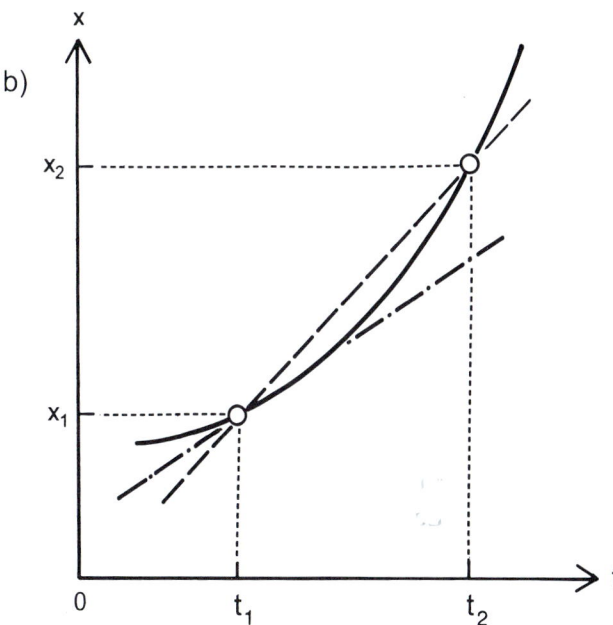

Fig. 2.8: (a) The difference between an average velocity and an instantaneous velocity is illustrated for an object which moves from position x_1 at time t_1 to position x_2 at time t_2.
(b) The solid line in the graph illustrates how the position of the object changes with time. If we measure position and time only twice, at instant 1 and at instant 2 as indicated by two open circles, then we obtain the average velocity as the travelled distance, $\Delta x = x_2 - x_1$, divided by the elapsed time $\Delta t = t_2 - t_1$ (dashed line). To provide a value for the speed at instant 1, we need to record the second position after a shorter period Δt. Mathematically, we can extrapolate a series of such measurements to $\Delta t = 0$, which yields the instantaneous velocity as the tangent to the path, shown as the dash–dotted line.

Note that the limes–notation has an approximative character as we cannot simply set $t_2 = t_1$ because a division 0/0 in Eq. (7) is not defined. Since only the instantaneous velocity is relevant in physical applications, we drop the index "inst" and require that all reported velocities are instantaneous unless stated otherwise.

If the velocity of an object changes with time we say that the object is accelerated. The acceleration is a quantity which may also change with time, and thus a definition in analogy to Eq. (7) is again not useful. We use the definition of the instantaneous acceleration instead. The instantaneous acceleration, which is the acceleration at a specific point along an object's path, is equal to the average acceleration in a time interval Δt when Δt is extrapolated to zero:

$$a \equiv \lim_{\Delta t \to 0} \frac{\Delta v}{\Delta t} \qquad (9)$$

The unit of acceleration is [m/s²]. Eqs. (8) and (9) state:

> *Velocity is the change of position with time and acceleration is the change of velocity with time.*

We now establish the link between acceleration and force experimentally with a set–up that allows us to isolate the action of a single force. To do this we choose the contact force which we apply to push an object on a horizontal surface. Other forces which might act on the object are associated with the object's weight and the contact of the object with any other surface but our hand. The weight of the object plays no role because we confine the object to a horizontal motion. We also neglect the friction between the object and the horizontal support surface by using a very slippery surface, e.g. an air-track system where a car moves on a thin air cushion.

The first observation we make for an object in this case is that it maintains its speed while no force acts on it. When a force is exerted by pushing the object, we find that the acceleration is proportional to the force, i.e., the harder we push the greater the change in the speed of the object. If we push the object with two hands at once, i.e., we exert two different contact forces, we further find that the resulting acceleration is not based on either single force but on the combined force which we call the net force. These observations are summarized:

$$F_{net} = 0 \Rightarrow a = 0 \text{ and } v = const$$
$$F_{net} \neq 0 \Rightarrow a \neq 0 \text{ and } v \neq const \qquad (10)$$

Note that the statement in the second line of Eq. (10) does not contain equations and needs to be examined further. But before doing that in section 2.3.3, we focus on the formulas in the first line of Eq. (10).

2.3.2. Newton's first law

The first line of Eq. (10) is called Newton's first law:

> *A body either at rest or in motion with constant velocity will remain that way unless acted upon by a net force.*

The following comments about this law are useful when we discuss its applications:
(I) All forces can be added. We obtain the net force, F_{net}, when we add all the forces that act on an object. This allows us to write Newton's first law for a body on which n separate forces act:

$$F_{net} = \sum_{i=1}^{n} F_i = 0 \qquad (11)$$

The Σ–symbol used in Eq. (11) means that we add n forces which we distinguish by a running index i. The order in which forces are added does not affect the net force because $F_1 + F_2 = F_2 + F_1$.
(II) The first law does not allow us to identify the unit of force, which is only possible when Newton's second law is introduced in the next section. For calculations we need this unit, however. Since we already know that the gravitational acceleration g has the unit [m/s²] and that the weight of an object is a force, W = mg, we note that [kg m/s²] is the unit of force. A new unit is introduced for force since we deal with forces often. The new unit is called *Newton* [N], with 1 N = 1 kg m/s².
(III) A net force F_{net} equal zero does not imply that any force F_i in Eq. (11) is separately zero! This has to be noted very carefully since in most problems several forces occur.
(IV) A system is said to be in mechanical equilibrium when Eq. (11) applies, i.e., when the various forces acting on the system are balanced. A consequence of Newton's first law is that bodies appear to resist changes to their state of motion. Therefore, the first law of mechanics is also called the law of inertia.

Problem–solving strategy
There is an almost infinite number of ways in which problems in the many sub–disciplines of physics can be phrased. Therefore, there is no simple procedure which we can follow and expect that it succeeds in each case. On the other hand, leaving the approach to a problem to intuition may easily lead to a dead–end calculation. Thus, we follow an intermediate approach in this textbook: the provided approach is structured because it follows three well–defined steps, but it is general enough to be useful in most contexts, not just for the current discussion of Newton's laws.

I Schematic Approach
In the first step you have to comprehend all aspects of the problem, noting what you know and what you do not know. This step often includes a sketch of the problem. If a sketch is given you have to familiarize yourself with it. If it is not given you may want to make your own sketch. Specifically, we identify in the first step the object of interest. In anticipation of discussions in later chapters, we call the body of interest *"the system."* Then we identify all other bodies which interact with the body of interest and call them *"the environment."*

II Physical Model
In the second step you address the physical aspects of the problem, including the physical parameters which play a role and the physical laws you need to solve the problem. A physical model also includes simplifying assumptions. Make sure you are aware of the assumptions you make and test whether they are valid. In this step you may have to draw additional sketches.
 In the current context, you list first all the forces acting on the system. *Do not include any forces which the system exerts on the environment!* Then you draw a dot to represent the system (point mass) and attach to this dot all the forces in your list. The forces are drawn as arrows in the directions in which they act. This graph is called a *free–body–diagram*.

III Quantitative treatment
In the last step the physical model is transformed into mathematical equations and the known parameters are substituted such that an explicit solution is provided.

We follow this problem–solving strategy throughout the textbook. In the early chapters the single steps are clearly identified. Study Example 2.2 not only as an example for the application of Newton's first law, but note also the way in which the problem–solving strategy is applied!

Example 2.2
Fig. 2.9 shows two objects with masses m and M which

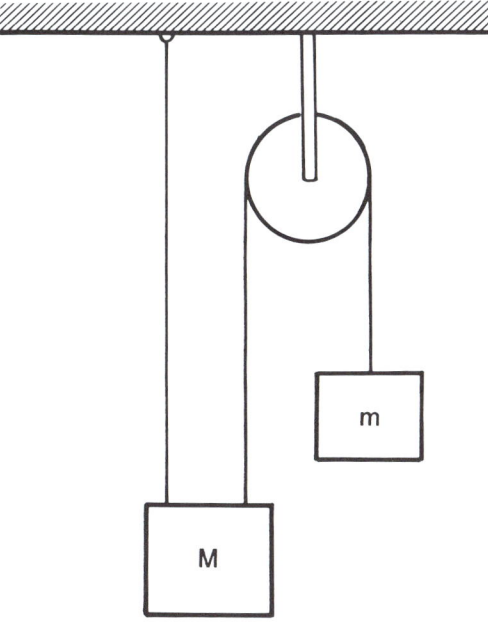

Fig. 2.9: Two objects with masses m and M are connected with a massless string, which runs over a massless pulley. The pulley can rotate without friction. The heavier object with mass M is further connected to the ceiling with a vertical massless string.

are connected with a taut string running over a pulley. The pulley rotates without friction. The two masses are given as M = 5.0 kg and m = 3.0 kg. A second taut sting connects the heavier object vertically to the ceiling. Assuming that both strings and the pulley are massless, calculate
(a) the tension in the string running over the pulley, and
(b) the tension in the string running to the ceiling.

Solution: In this Example problem parts (a) and (b) are considered together until we reach the last step of the problem–solving strategy.

I Schematic Approach

First we identify the object of interest. Likely candidates are the two objects with masses M and m. The way to decide whether just one of these or both have to be taken into account is based on two considerations:
(I) If a variation of the mass of an object alters the outcome of the experiment, the object has to be included. If we were to increase mass m such that m > M, or if we were to decrease mass M such that M < m, we no longer would have a mechanical equilibrium but the object of mass M would accelerate upwards and the string to the ceiling would no longer be taut. Thus, we have to consider both objects.
(II) We check whether the two objects can be combined as a single system. This option has to be ruled out if any of the forces acting between the two objects plays a role in the problem. In the current case, the problem text refers to a tension in the string between objects m and M. Thus we cannot combine the two objects into a single system.

Our last observation studying Fig. 2.9 is that the system is in mechanical equilibrium because neither one of the two objects accelerates at any stage of the experiment.

II Physical Model

We need to get organized with the various labels we want to use to refer to the different forces in the problem. Note that there is no reason to assume that the tensions in the two strings are equal, thus we need distinguishable variables for them. We define the string running to the ceiling as string 1. Tension T_1 is the force acting on the objects attached at the end of string 1. The string running over the pulley is string 2, with tension T_2 the force acting on objects at either end of string 2. Thus, we are asked to calculate T_2 in part (a) and T_1 in part (b). We further have two objects with given masses M and m. We label their weights respectively as W_M for the object of mass M and W_m for the object of mass m.

We group the forces acting on each of the two systems separately. On the object of mass m act its own weight and the tension in the string. On the object of mass M act also its own weight and the tension in two strings. These forces are combined in two free–body–diagrams. They are displayed in Fig. 2.10 with the free–

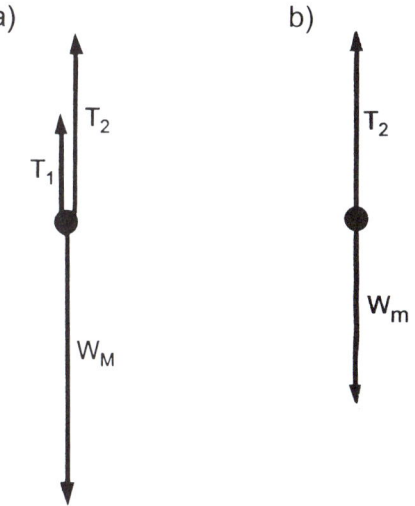

Fig. 2.10: Free–body–diagrams for the two objects shown in Fig. 2.9. Sketch (a) shows three forces acting on the object of mass M. These are its own weight and the tensions in the two strings. Sketch (b) shows the weight and the tension in the string acting on the object of mass m.

21

body–diagram for the object of mass M shown in sketch (a) and the free–body–diagram for the object of mass m shown in sketch (b).

III Quantitative treatment

The forces in a free–body–diagram are distinguished by their magnitudes and by the fact that they are directed parallel or anti–parallel to each other. This directional feature is taken into account by defining an axis such that one of the two directions is positive and the opposite direction is negative. In the current Example, we choose the positive axis upwards for both free–body–diagrams.

Eq. (11) is used next to quantify the mechanical equilibrium. Using Fig. 2.10, one equation is written for each of the two systems. These are:

$$(I) \quad F_{net, M} = T_1 + T_2 - W_M = 0$$
$$(II) \quad F_{net, m} = T_2 - W_m = 0 \quad (12)$$

The first formula applies to the object of mass M. The free–body–diagram contains three forces; two pulling the object upwards and one pulling the object downwards. Based on our choice of axis the first formula in Eq. (12) contains two positive forces and one negative force. The second formula in Eq. (12) applies to the object of mass m. The two forces in the free–body–diagram act in opposite directions, therefore the two forces are entered with opposite signs.

Solution part (a): We use the second formula in Eq. (12) to find the tension T_2. With $W_m = mg$ we get:

$$T_2 = W_m = m\,g = $$
$$= 3\ kg \cdot 9.8\ m/s^2 = 29.4\ N \quad (13)$$

Thus, the tension in the string running over the pulley is $T_2 = 29.4$ N.

Solution part (b): Substituting the result of part (a) into the first formula of Eq. (12) yields:

$$T_1 = W_M - T_2 = W_M - W_m = $$
$$(M - m)\,g = 2.0\ kg \cdot 9.8\ m/s^2 \quad (14)$$

Therefore, the tension in the string running to the ceiling is $T_1 = 19.6$ N.

===

Example 2.3

Let's study a physiological example. In medical physics we are often concerned with the physiology of humans in general, not with the anatomical features of a particular individual. For this purpose, a *standard man* has been defined and the standard man's data, summarized in Table 2.2, are used to calculate typical physiological properties.

The standard man in Fig. 2.11 holds with his left arm vertically a dumbbell of mass M = 4 kg with the in-

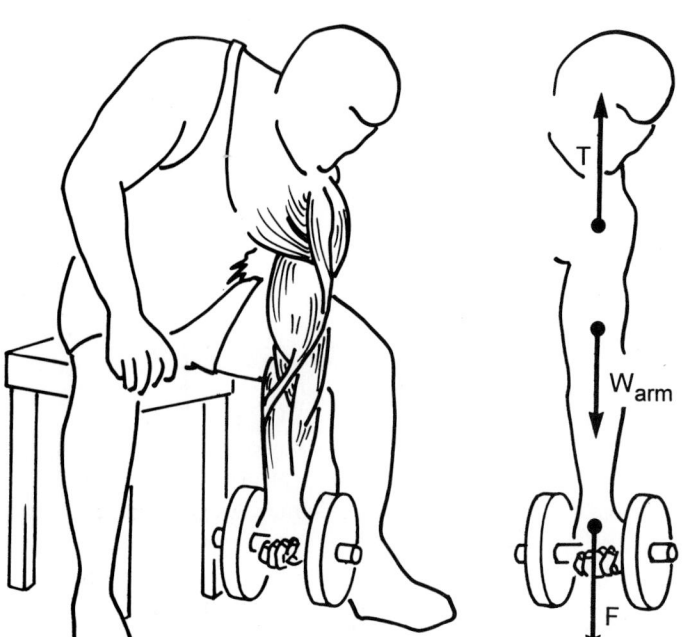
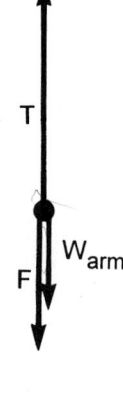

Fig. 2.11: The sketch at the left shows a person in a gym intending to do concentration curls. The sketch at the right indicates which are the major forces acting on the arm of the person: the tension T in the muscles and ligaments connecting the arm to the trunk, the weight of the arm W_{arm}, and the force F acting on the fist due to the weight of the dumbbell.

tention to do concentration curls. For the position shown, we consider the following four major forces: the weight of the dumbbell, the force pulling down the fist, the weight of the arm and the tension in the shoulder. This tension is primarily due to the deltoid muscle and several ligaments which run across the interface between the trunk and the arm. The weight of the dumbbell and the force pulling down the fist are equal in magnitude. Calculate the ratio of the tension in the shoulder to the force which pulls down the fist.

Solution:
I Schematic Approach
We choose the left arm as our system (body of interest) because the problem text refers to several forces acting on that arm. We note, however, that the weight of the dumbbell is not a force acting on the arm but acts on the dumbbell. It is identified because it allows us to quantify the force pulling on the fist. Why the weight of the dumbbell and the force on the fist are related this way is discussed later in the context of Newton's third law.

We know that the mass of the arm is 7 % of the person's body mass since the person is a standard man. We use the mass of the standard man from Table 2.2 to express the mass of the arm as 4.9 kg.

The text indicates that the person holds the dumbbell in the shown position before doing an intended exercise with it. Thus, the dumbbell is at rest and the problem is an application of Newton's first law.

Note also that the question does not ask for a numerical value for one of the unknown parameters, but asks for a ratio. This type of question occurs frequently as such ratios help us to develop an intuitive idea of the magnitude of the effects we study. Note how this type of question leads to a slightly different approach in the quantitative treatment.

II Physical Model
The forces we need to consider are all given in the problem text. You will find this to be typical for physiological or biological problems in this textbook because identifying the major forces acting in our body for a given exercise requires anatomical knowledge you may not have yet. Any one of these problems could be defined as a physiological research project where identifying the major forces would indeed consume most of the time invested in the project.

Finally, we draw the free–body–diagram for the arm. This is shown in Fig. 2.12. We label the tension in the shoulder T and the force pulling down the fist F. The force T acts in the upwards direction and F and W_{arm} act downwards.

III Quantitative treatment
Using the free–body–diagram in Fig. 2.12, we write Newton's first law for the arm in Fig. 2.11 in the form:

Table 2.2: Standard man data. The percentage values indicate the fraction of the total body mass.

Age	30 years
Height	172 cm
Body mass M_{tot}	70 kg
Surface area	1.85 m²
Body core temperature	37.0°C
Skin surface temperature	34.0°C
Specific heat capacity	3.60 kJ/kg K
Oxygen consumption	0.26 liter/min
Carbon dioxide production	0.208 liter/min
Blood volume	5.2 liters
Cardiac output	5.0 liter/min
Systolic blood pressure	16.0 kPa
Diastolic blood pressure	10.7 kPa
Heart rate	70 beats/min
Total lung capacity	6.0 liters
Tidal (breath) volume	0.5 liter
Breathing rate	15 breaths/min
Muscle mass	30.0 kg = 43 %
Fat mass	10.0 kg = 14 %
Bone mass	7.0 kg = 10 %
Blood mass	5.4 kg = 7.7 %
Brain mass	1,500 g = 2.1 %
Mass of both lungs	1,000 g = 1.4 %
Heart mass	300 g
Mass of each eye	15 g
Mass of each leg	15 %
Mass of each arm	7 %
Mass of the head	7 %
Mass of the trunk	49 %

Fig. 2.12: Free–body–diagram for the system (arm) in Fig. 2.11. The three forces act in the vertical direction, with the weight of the arm and the pull of the dumbbell directed downwards, and the tension in the shoulder directed upwards.

$$F_{net} = T - W_{arm} - F = 0 \qquad (15)$$

Substituting $F = W_M$, in which W_M is the weight of the dumbbell, and writing $W_{arm} = 0.07 W_{tot}$, in which W_{tot} is the weight of the standard man, we find:

$$T = 0.07 W_{tot} + W_M \qquad (16)$$

Now we can calculate the ratio we are asked about, T/F:

$$\frac{T}{F} = \frac{0.07 W_{tot}}{W_M} + 1 =$$
$$= \frac{4.9[kg]\, g}{4.0[kg]\, g} + 1 = 2.2 \qquad (17)$$

Thus, the tension in the shoulder is more than twice as large as the force pulling on the fist.

2.3.3. Newton's second law

Next we consider the second experimental finding in Eq.

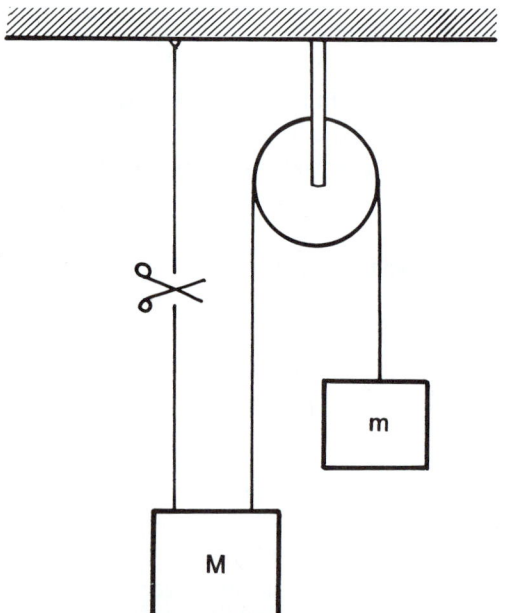

Fig. 2.13: We study once more the arrangement of Fig. 2.9, however, we assume this time that the string between the object of mass M and the ceiling is cut. With this connection eliminated, the two objects accelerate unless M = m.

(10). This is the case in which the net force does not vanish and therefore no mechanical equilibrium exists. To quantify the properties of a system with a non–vanishing net force, we consider once more a glass sliding across a table. We saw that the harder we push the glass the faster it moves after losing contact with the hand. To achieve a faster motion, a larger acceleration was required because acceleration is the change of the velocity with time. This observation leads to the mathematical formulation $F_{net} \propto a$.

Whenever two variables are related linearly we know that the most general equation describing this dependence is $F_{net} = ma + F_0$ with m and F_0 as yet undetermined constants. In the case of the accelerating glass on a table, however, we know from Newton's first law that $a = 0$ for $F_{net} = 0$, yielding $F_0 = 0$. This leads to the second law of mechanics for a system of n forces:

$$F_{net} = \sum_{i=1}^{n} F_i = m\, a \qquad (18)$$

Eq. (18) allows us to put Newton's second law in words:

> *A net force applied to an object of mass m results in that object undergoing an acceleration in the same direction as the net force. The magnitude of the object's acceleration is directly proportional to the magnitude of the net force and inversely proportional to the mass of the object.*

The constant m in Eq. (18) is identified experimentally as the mass of the body. This allows us to establish the units of force as $[N] = [kg\, m/s^2]$. Newton's second law is also called the *equation of motion* because it links the change of the motion (acceleration) with a cause (net force).

Example 2.4:
We consider the same arrangement as in Example 2.2, except that we cut the string connecting the object with the larger mass M to the ceiling, as illustrated in Fig. 2.13. Calculate
(a) the acceleration of the object of mass M,
(b) the acceleration of the object of mass m, and
(c) the tension in the string.

Solution:
I Schematic Approach
Most of our considerations in Example 2.2 still apply. We continue to treat both objects separately as systems.

We use again W_m and W_M as the weight of each object. The tension in the string is labelled T since only one string is left. We note that the two objects are no longer in mechanical equilibrium as the heavier one accelerates downwards, pulling the lighter object upwards. Thus, we need Newton's second law for this problem.

Initially we assign two accelerations to the systems, a_m and a_M. However, we can already at this stage comment on these accelerations further. Note that the string remains taut throughout the experiment while the heavier object falls downwards. This means that the distance between the two objects, measured along the string, never changes. As a consequence, we know that both accelerations must be equal in magnitude. This fact is written in the form $|a_m| = |a_M| = a$. It is very important to understand that this does not necessarily imply that $a_m = a_M = a$; indeed, we will find this to be wrong in the current problem. The reason is linked to our choice of axes, a choice we only make later in the solution. However, you can already see now why both accelerations may differ in sign: when we choose the positive axis for each object upwards $a_m = a_M = a$ would imply that both objects accelerate upwards, which is an impossible outcome of the experiment. Having established these findings about the two accelerations we consider parts (a) and (b) of the problem together in our solution.

II Physical Model

The three forces we need to take into consideration are the tension T, and the weights of the two objects. We draw a free–body–diagram for each of the two objects, shown in Fig. 2.14. Plot (a) applies to the object of mass M and plot (b) at the right side applies to the object of mass m.

III Quantitative treatment

We choose the two positive axes upwards in both free–body–diagrams like in Example 2.2. Eq. (18) is used to quantify the equation of motion for each object. Using Fig. 2.14 we find:

$$(I) \quad F_{net, M} = T - W_M = M a_M$$
$$(II) \quad F_{net, m} = T - W_m = m a_m \quad (19)$$

The first formula applies to the object of mass M and the second formula applies to the object of mass m. Using our chosen axes and the fact that $|a_m| = |a_M| = a$, we can simplify Eq. (19) to:

$$(I) \quad F_{net, M} = T - W_M = - M a$$
$$(II) \quad F_{net, m} = T - W_m = m a \quad (20)$$

Note the negative sign on the right hand side of the first formula in Eq. (20). This sign is caused by the downwards direction of the acceleration of the object of mass M. Eq. (20) contains two unknown variables, T and a. Since we have two independent formulas we can solve for both variables. One way to find a is to multiply the first formula in Eq. (20) with –1, then add formulas (I) and (II). This yields:

$$- T + W_M + T - W_m = M a + m a \quad (21)$$

The two weights are combined on the left hand side of the equation and the acceleration is isolated on the right hand side:

$$Mg - mg = (M - m) g = (M + m) a \quad (22)$$

leading to the following result:

$$a = \frac{M - m}{M + m} g = \frac{5[kg] - 3[kg]}{5[kg] + 3[kg]} 9.8 \left[\frac{m}{s^2}\right]$$
$$\Rightarrow \quad a = 2.45 \left[\frac{m}{s^2}\right] \quad (23)$$

Both objects accelerate with 2.45 m/s² in opposite directions.

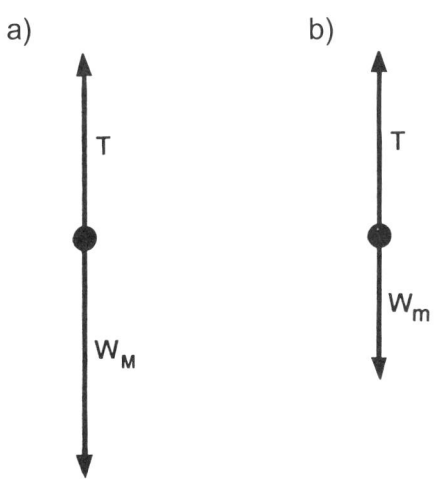

Fig. 2.14: The free–body–diagrams for the two objects shown in Fig. 2.13. On each object act its own weight downwards and the tension in the string upwards. The magnitudes of both tensions are the same because the string is massless.

Solution part (c):
We substitute the result of Eq. (23) into either one of the two formulas in Eq. (20) to find T:

$$T = W_M - Ma = M(g-a) =$$

$$= 5[kg]\left(9.8\left[\frac{m}{s^2}\right] - 2.45\left[\frac{m}{s^2}\right]\right) = 36.75\ N \quad (24)$$

The tension in the string running over the pulley is now T = 36.8 N, which is notably higher than the tension in the same string before the second string in Fig. 2.13 was cut.

2.3.4. Newton's third law

The last law relates specifically to the interaction of the system with other bodies in its environment. Newton stated this law in the form:

> *If an object A exerts a force F on an object B, then object B exerts a force equal in magnitude and opposite in direction back on object A.*

Quantitatively, if we call F_{Ba} the force exerted by object A on object B and call F_{Ab} the force exerted by object B on object A, then:

$$F_{Ab} = -F_{Ba} \quad (25)$$

We call the two forces in Eq. (25) an action/reaction pair of forces. It is very important to distinguish action/reaction pairs from other forces which may be related in a similar fashion coincidentally. *An action force and its reaction force never act on the same body*! Note that we used Newton's third law already in Example 2.3.

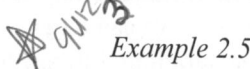

Example 2.5
The calf muscle of a person doing push–ups pulls on the Achilles tendon attached to the heel bone (calcaneus). How are the various forces in the lower leg related?

Additional biological information: Fig. 2.15 shows a simplified sketch of the muscles and bones of a human body during a push–up. Note that the calf muscle connects through the Achilles tendon to the heel. An anatomically correct side–view of the muscles in the lower leg was shown in Fig. 2.5.

Solution:
I Schematic Approach
Study Figs. 2.5 and 2.15 carefully. Note that the heel bone, the Achilles tendon and the calf muscle lie along a horizontal line when the body is in the position shown in Fig. 2.15. This allows us to neglect the weight as a force because we are only interested in the horizontal interactions. A careful labelling must take place since three systems are considered; we label the calf muscle "M", the Achilles tendon "T" and the heel bone "B". Note that we include the tendon since it may not be possible to assume in all applications that it is a massless string. We need only the forces the three parts of the leg exert on each other for the discussion of this problem.

II Physical Model
We develop the (partial) free–body–diagrams for Fig. 2.15. This problem is a typical application of the third law of mechanics since several objects are involved.

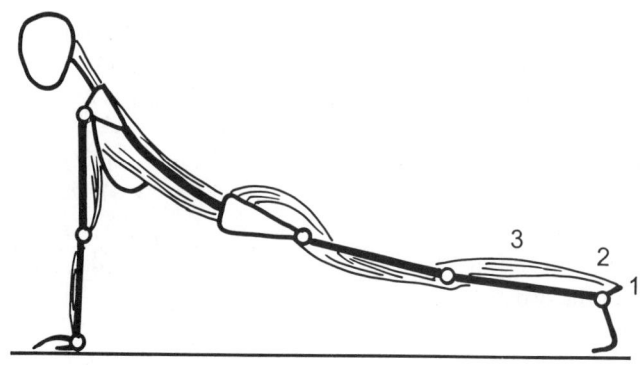

Fig. 2.15: An anatomical sketch for a person doing push–ups. This schematic side–view highlights the relative position of the heel bone (1), the Achilles tendon (2) and the calf muscle (3). Note that the three elements are located along a horizontal line during push–ups.

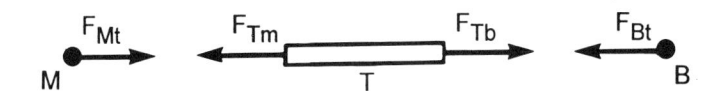

Fig. 2.16 shows the important forces for each system; note that the tendon is drawn as a line. We identify the horizontal interaction forces in each case. The muscle pulls on the tendon towards the right. Labelling the object on which the force acts with a capital letter and the object exerting the force with a lower case letter, this force is F_{Tm}. At the same time, the muscle is pulled in the opposite direction by the tendon. This force is labelled F_{Mt}. At the other end, the tendon pulls on the bone with force F_{Bt}. The bone exerts an equal but opposite force on the tendon, labelled F_{Tb}.

III Quantitative treatment

Among these forces are two action–reaction pairs:

$$F_{Tm} = -F_{Mt} \qquad (26)$$
$$F_{Bt} = -F_{Tb}$$

Note that F_{Tb} and F_{Tm} are not an action–reaction pair as both forces act on the same body! Actually, these two forces need to be different for the muscle to succeed in pulling the foot forward. In that case we write the second law of mechanics for the tendon as the system:

$$\sum_{i=1}^{2} F_{ix} = F_{Tb} - F_{Tm} = m_T a_x \qquad (27)$$

There are two ways in which this equation for a tendon is applied:
(I) For a given mass m_T of the tendon an acceleration can be determined. But we need to identify two different forces, one at each end of the tendon.
(II) If we assume $m_T = 0$, i.e., that the mass of the tendon is negligible, then Eq. (27) simplifies to

$$F_{Tb} = F_{Tm} \equiv T \qquad (28)$$

This equation defines the magnitude of the tension T as introduced before. This case is simpler since only one force magnitude is associated with the tendon, but it requires that the assumption of a taut, massless string is valid for the tendon.

Fig. 2.16: Sketches of the major horizontal forces acting on each of the three systems in Fig. 2.15, the heel bone (B), the Achilles tendon (T) and the calf muscle (M). The tendon is shown as a line for illustration purpose.

2.4. Problems

P–2.1
A standard man rests on a bathroom scale. What are
(a) the standard man's weight, and
(b) the normal force acting on the standard man?
(c) What is the reading on the scale assuming it is calibrated in weight units? Can you suggest a reason why that reading may deviate from the actual value?

P–2.2
Fig. 2.17 shows a standard man intending to do reverse curls in a gym. He holds his arms straight, using an overhand grip to hold the bar. If the mass of the bar is given as 100 kg, what is the tension in each of his shoulders? Consider the weight of the arm (see Table 2.2) and the weight of the bar.

P–2.3
Fig. 2.18 shows a standard man intending to do close-grip lat pulldowns in a gym. In this exercise, the person pulls the weight of the upper body (arms, trunk and head) upwards using a handle while the legs are wedged under a restraint pad. What is the magnitude of the force exerted by the handle on each of the person's hands?

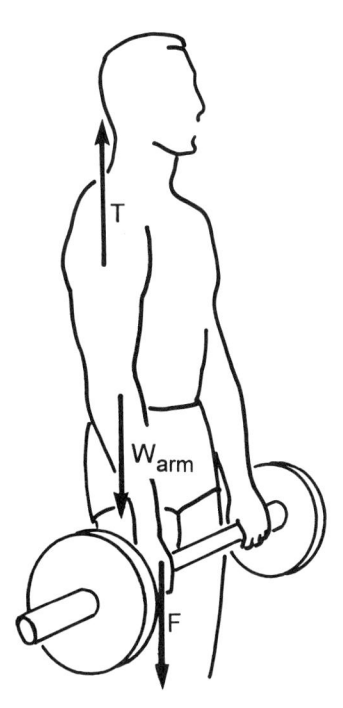

Fig. 2.17 for problem P–2.2.

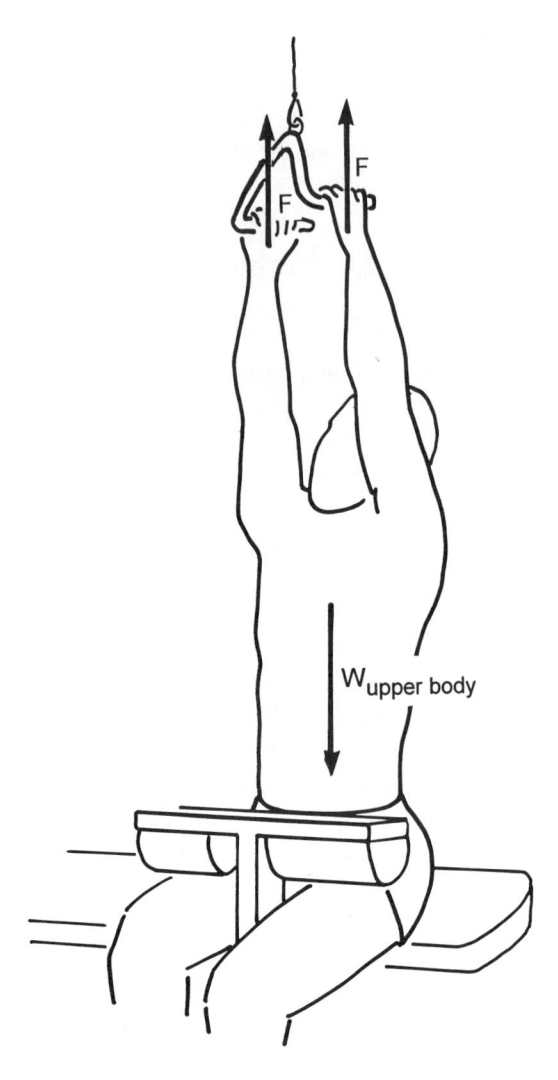

Fig. 2.18 for problem P–2.3.

P–2.4
Large hawks, eagles, vultures, storks, the White Pelican and gulls are Canadian birds sailing on rising columns of warm air. This static soaring requires only 5 % of the energy of flapping flight. The birds are essentially in a level flight, holding their wings steadily stretched. The weight of the bird is balanced by a vertical lift force, which is a force exerted by the air on the bird's wings. How large is the lift force for
(a) a Franklin's Gull (which lives in Alberta, Saskatchewan and Manitoba) with an average mass of 280 g, and
(b) an American White Pelican (which lives in Western Canada) with an average mass of 7.0 kg?

P–2.5
Mantis shrimp (stomatopods) possess some of the most lethal weaponry in the animal kingdom. They either spear or smash their prey to death. Smashers literally pulverize the shells of crabs or lobsters with calcified clubs. The spearers use lance–like appendages to strike soft–bodied prey such as shrimp, fishes and squid. The prey has no chance in these encounters: a spearer can accelerate its weapon from rest to 10 m/s in just 4 milliseconds. Taking into account that an F16 fighter jet has a maximum acceleration of 10 g where g is the gravitational acceleration constant, by what factor beats the mantis shrimp the F16 technology?

P–2.6
There are two horizontal forces acting on an object of mass M = 1.5 kg. In Fig. 2.19 only one of these forces, F_1 = 25 N, is shown. The object moves strictly along the shown axis which we choose as positive to the right. Find the magnitude of the second force for each of the following accelerations observed for the object:
(a) a = 10 m/s²
(b) a = 0 m/s²
(c) a = – 10 m/s²

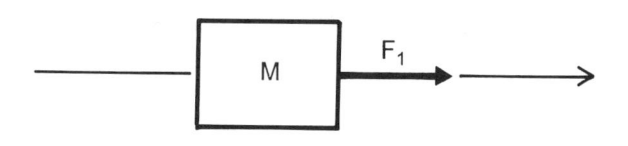

Fig. 2.19 for problem P–2.6.

P–2.7
Two objects are in contact on a frictionless surface. A horizontal force is applied to one object as shown in Fig. 2.20.
(a) Use m_1 = 2.0 kg, m_2 = 1.0 kg and F = 3.0 N to find the force between the two objects.
(b) Find the force between the two objects if the force F is instead applied to the object of mass m_2 but in the opposite direction. Explain the difference between the results in (a) and (b).

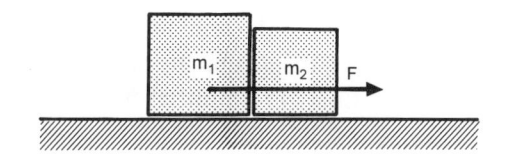

Fig. 2.20 for problem P–2.7.

P–2.8
Fig. 2.21 shows an object of mass M = 3 kg. It is free to move along a horizontal, frictionless surface. This object is further connected to a second object with a mass m = 2 kg by means of a massless string that extends around a massless, frictionless pulley.

(a) What resulting motion of the two objects do you predict?
(b) Find the acceleration of the sliding object,
(c) find the acceleration of the hanging object, and
(d) find the tension in the massless string.

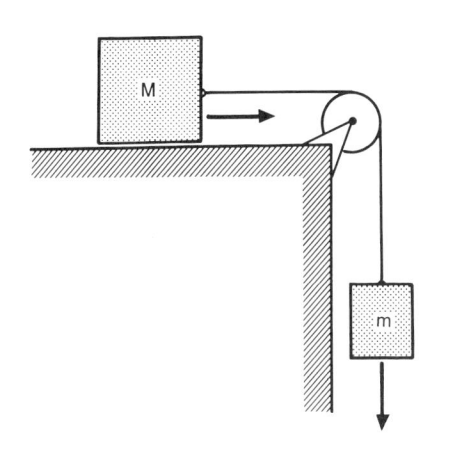

Fig. 2.21 for problem P–2.8.

P–2.9
Three objects are connected as shown in Fig. 2.22. They move along a horizontal, frictionless surface, and are pulled to the right with a force F_{ext} = 50 N. With the three mass values given as m_1 = 10 kg, m_2 = 20 kg and m_3 = 30 kg, calculate
(a) the magnitude of the acceleration of the three objects, and
(b) the magnitude of the tensions T_1 and T_2 in the massless, interconnecting strings.

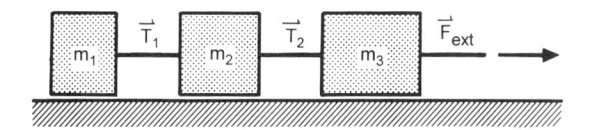

Fig. 2.22 for problem P–2.9.

P–2.10
When patients suffer from a neck injury their cervical vertebrae are kept under tension with a traction device, as shown in Fig. 2.23. The traction device creates tension in the vertebrae by pulling on the head with a force T. This force is in effect applied to the first vertebra at the top of the spine. This vertebra remains in mechanical equilibrium because it is simultaneously pulled in the opposite direction by a force F_{ext} that is supplied by the next vertebra in line. If the physician has prescribed that a force F_{ext} = 40 N should act on the vertebra, what mass m should the object suspended from the rope have?

Summary

Definitions:
Forces represent the interaction of distinguishable objects.
Specific forces:
• The weight W = m g acts near the Earth's surface with g the gravitational acceleration. The force is directed toward the center of the Earth.
• The normal force N is due to contact with a surface. It is directed perpendicular to the surface.
• The tension T is due to a taut, massless string. It is directed along the string.
• The external contact force F_{ext} acts along the direction of the push.

Units:
mass: m [kg]; distance: x [m]; time: t [s]; speed or velocity: v [m/s]; acceleration: a [m/s²]; force: F [N] with [N] equivalent to [kg m/s²]

Laws:
• Newton's first law (law of inertia) for a point mass in mechanical equilibrium:

$$F_{net} = \sum_{i=1}^{n} F_i = 0$$

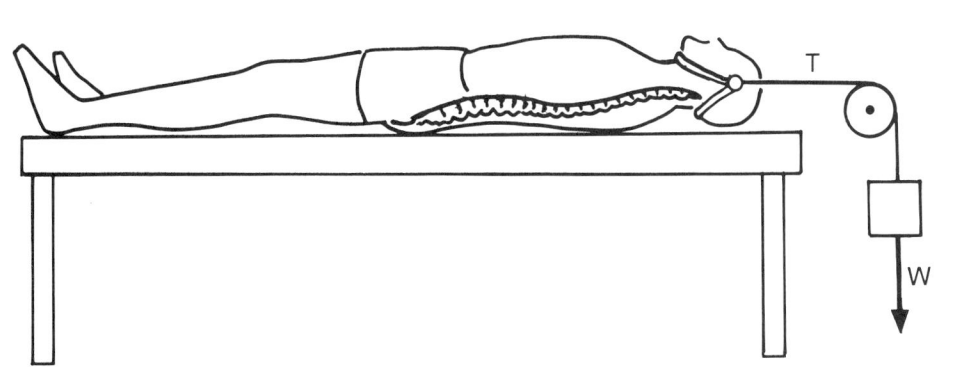

Fig. 2.23 for problem P–2.10.

- Newton's second law (equation of motion) for an accelerating point mass:

$$F_{net} = \sum_{i=1}^{n} F_i = m\, a$$

- Newton's third law:
When an object A acts on an object B with force F_{Ba}, there is a force F_{Ab} exerted by object B on object A with:

$$F_{Ab} = -F_{Ba}$$

Chapter III

Biomechanics

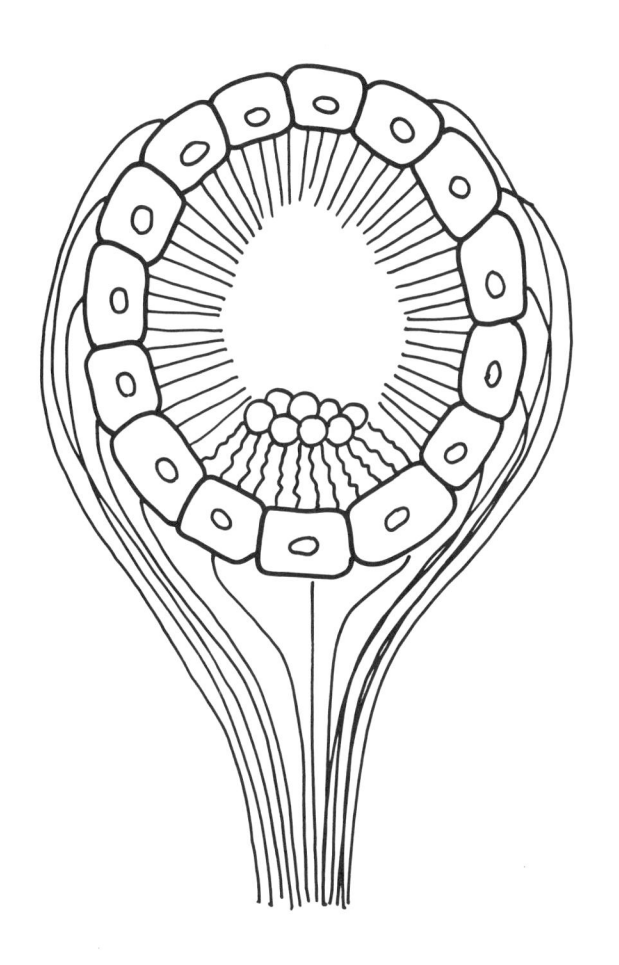

The direction of forces

BIOMECHANICS
THE DIRECTION OF FORCES

A force is characterized by two properties, its magnitude and its direction. A net force resulting from a number of individual forces acting on the same object is either zero (mechanical equilibrium) or leads to an acceleration in the same direction in which the net force acts. Organisms possess a range of receptors which detect external forces directly or measure the acceleration resulting from forces that act on or within the organism. These receptors are called mechanoreceptors. Their mechanisms represent natural applications of Newton's three laws of mechanics.

In the previous chapter we established that forces matter to living organisms. We saw that noticeable forces act on our body when, for example, the floor supports us or our weight pulls us down. We also saw that large forces act within our body, often due to the contraction of a muscle which is connected to two separate bones of the skeleton. We used Table 2.1 to group these forces in field forces and contact forces, with several examples for each occurring in our daily lives.

In the first paragraph of Chapter 2 we defined the term *life* based on three necessary conditions, including the ability to detect and respond to external stimuli. With a force constituting such a stimulus, we want to focus in the current chapter on the methods how a living organism detects such mechanical stimuli. We will find that vertebrates and other organisms are indeed sensitive to environmental forces, including the field force gravity and all contact forces.

The discussion of the detection of forces leads us back to the distinct roles of magnitude and direction of a force. This observation motivates us to supplement our discussion of Chapter 2 with a study of systems with non–collinear forces.

3.1. Detection of field forces: the direction of gravity

We start with the following simple self–tests. Close your eyes, stretch your arms, concentrate on your hands and tilt your upper body to the side. The sensation in your hands has not changed despite the change of orientation.

Fig. 3.1: Overview of the human ear. We can distinguish three main sections of the ear: the outer ear with the auditory canal (1) ending at the ear drum, the middle ear with the three ossicles, hammer, anvil and stirrup (from left, 2), and the inner ear with the vestibular organ. The vestibular organ includes the semicircular canals (3) which we discuss in the context of acceleration detection in the head, and the maculae (4) which we discuss in the context of gravity detection. Other highlighted components of the inner ear are the cochlea (5), the endolymphatic canal (6) and the cerebral artery (7).

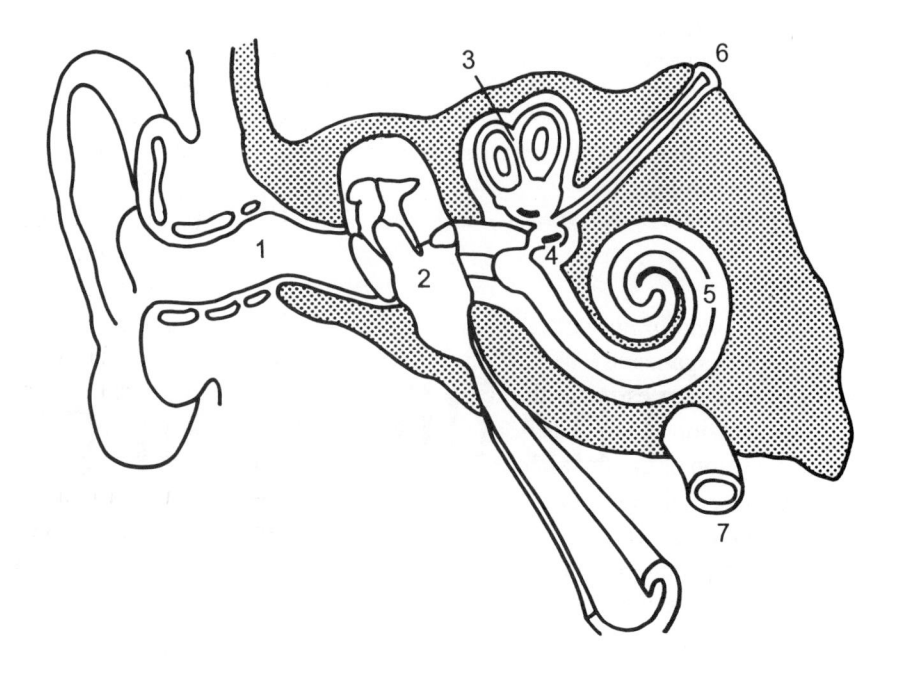

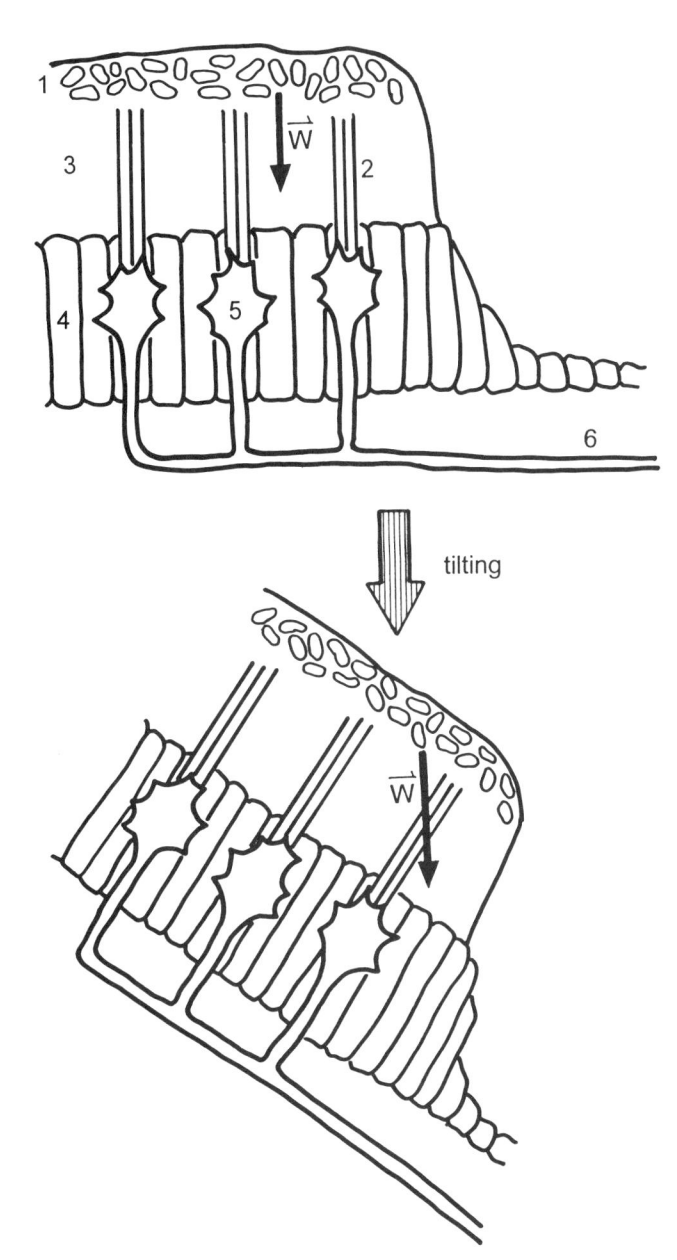

Fig. 3.2: The mechanism of gravity detection in a macula is illustrated for a person tilting the head to one side. At top the macula is shown in an upright position and at bottom the head is tilted. The components highlighted in the upper plot are the otoliths (1), the dendrites (2) which are embedded in the otolithic membrane (3), the supporting cells (4) containing the neurons (5) and the nerve to the brain (6).

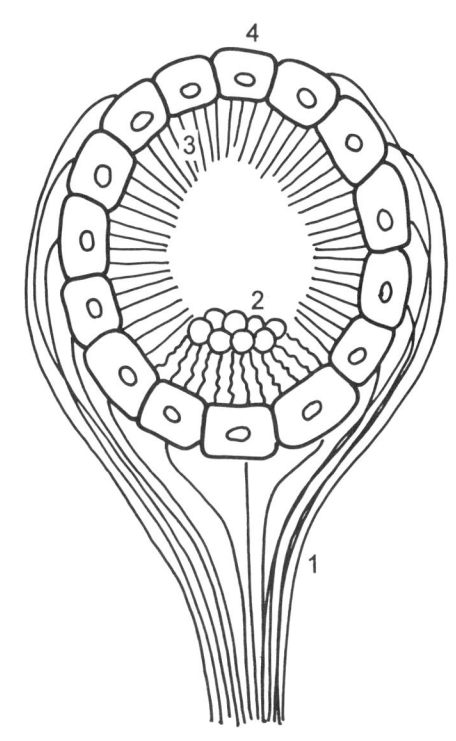

Fig. 3.3: The arrangement of a statocyst found in invertebrates. The statoliths (2) are settled to the lowest point in a space encapsulated by receptor cells (4). The receptor cells have hair–like extensions toward the interior of the capsule (cilia, 3). The cilia bend when the statoliths rest on their interior ends, triggering a nerve signal which is carried to the centre of the nervous system by the sensory nerve fibers (1).

Thus, there is no gravity detector in your hands. Now close the eyes again and lean your head to the side. This time you can even estimate the angle of tilt without a visual impression of your environment. Thus, our sense for the direction of gravity resides in our head. Note that the magnitude of the gravitational force during this self–test did not change; it is $W = mg$ in which m is the mass of the object which our body uses to detect this force. Thus, we detect a change of the direction of a force of constant magnitude.

Our ability to detect the direction of the gravitational force is located in the *vestibular organ* in the inner ear. Fig. 3.1 presents an overview of the ear. The vestibular organ consists of two components:
(I) the orthogonal *semicircular canals* which allow the measurement of accelerations (as discussed later in this chapter), and
(II) the *maculae* (plural of macula) which are located just below the semicircular canals. The maculae are indicated in Fig. 3.1 as elongated bars. The upper one is called the utricular macula, and the lower one is called the saccular macula, because they are located in small chambers called the utricle and the saccule, respectively. Both maculae measure the orientation of the head relative to the direction of gravity.

How we use the utricular macula to determine the vertical direction during a sideways tilt of the head is illustrated in Fig. 3.2. The top sketch shows the macula in the upright position. It is built on supporting cells that house the main body of nerve cells (neurons). From these neurons emerge dendrites, which are the fine ends of nerves. The dendrites reach into a gelatine–like membrane above the supporting cells. This membrane is called the otolithic membrane because it supports small calcite crystals which are called otoliths. The membrane has a density of about 1.0 g/cm³, which is close to the density of water, the CaCO₃ otoliths have a density of 3.0 g/cm³, comparable to the density of rocks. If the head is turned, as shown in the bottom sketch of Fig. 3.2, the heavier otoliths pull the soft membrane in the direction of gravity, thus exerting a force on the dendrites. This force causes the dendrites to fire nerve impulses which travel to the brain (nerve impulse transport is discussed in Chapter 13). We will calculate the forces acting on an otolith in the macula in section 3.5. Then we will also discuss why we have two maculae in each ear.

The concept of gravity detection with otoliths resting on a sensitive cellular surface has been developed in the animal kingdom early. Receptors of this type are called *statocysts* in invertebrates, such as jellyfish. Fig. 3.3 illustrates the statocyst design. In animals, the otoliths are called statoliths. They rest at the low point of a chamber of receptor cells with hair–like extensions (cilia). Due to their weight, the statoliths bend the cilia which act as dendrites. Any change of the direction of gravity causes the statoliths to move. As a result, another group of ciliated receptor cells becomes stimulated. The sensory nerves carry this information to the center of the nervous system of the animal.

3.2. Detection of contact forces: the weight of an object

When you close your eyes and lay an object on your hand with the palm up you notice at what position the object pushes on your skin. Note also that you sense the object continuously even though it does not move. When you hold a different object you can tell which of the two objects is heavier. If you instead push the object against your hand from below, you also sense where the object touches you. This time, however, you do not measure the weight of the object but rather how hard it is pushed against your skin. Thus, contrary to our sense of gravity, the sensitivity for contact forces exists locally in the hand.

To find the sensors for contact forces in the hand we study Fig. 3.4, which shows an overview of the near–surface structure of the palm, including the corpuscles typically contained in the skin. The outmost layer of the skin is called the *epidermis* which varies in thickness between 30 μm and 4 mm. The next deeper layer consists of 0.3 to 4 mm thick connective tissue (corium) with fat cells below (subcutis). Large numbers of various corpuscles are located in the shallower sections of the skin just below the epidermis with other corpuscle types located deeper. We will discuss most of these corpuscles in the textbook because they all measure various physical parameters. The deep corpuscles (Pacinian corpus-

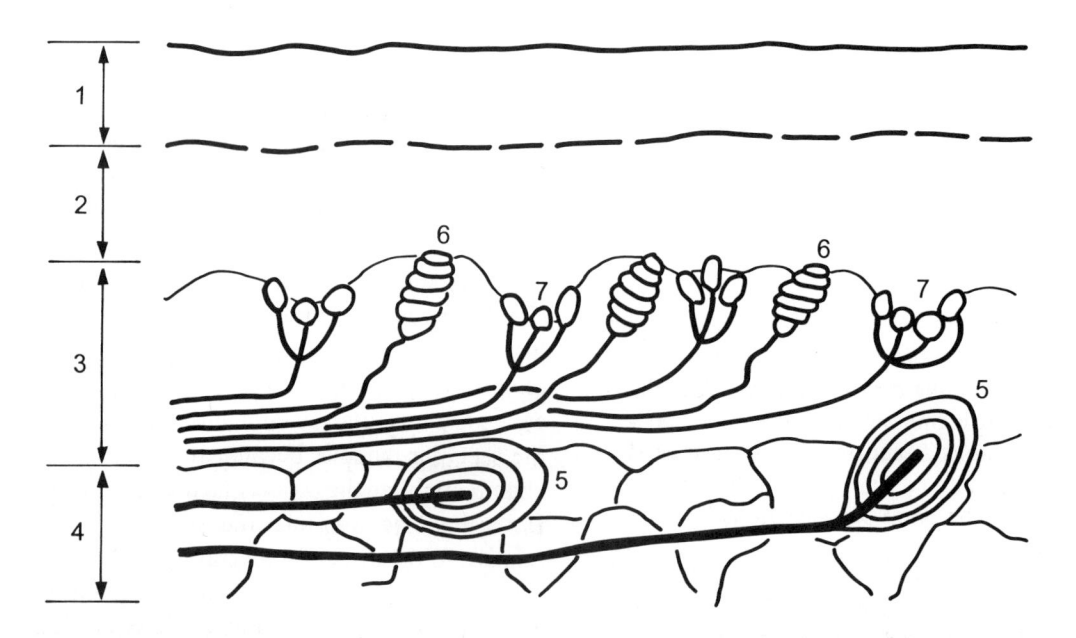

Fig. 3.4: Cross–section through a section of hairless skin. The skin is divided in four distinguishable layers: the epidermis (1 and 2) at the outer surface, the corium (3) and the subcutis (4) forming its inner boundary. The skin contains a large number of receptor systems which measure a wide range of external parameters. Highlighted in the figure are three types of mechanoreceptors, which are corpuscles detecting mechanical stimuli. The Pacinian corpuscles (5) are located in the subcutis and measure accelerations of the body; Meissner's corpuscles (6), measuring the speed of incoming objects, and Merkel's corpuscles (7), measuring the weight of objects resting on the skin, lie in a shallow region below the epidermis.

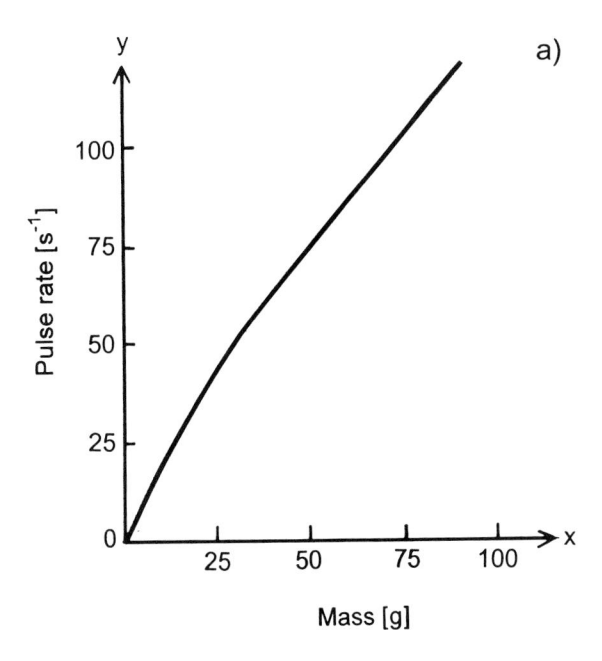

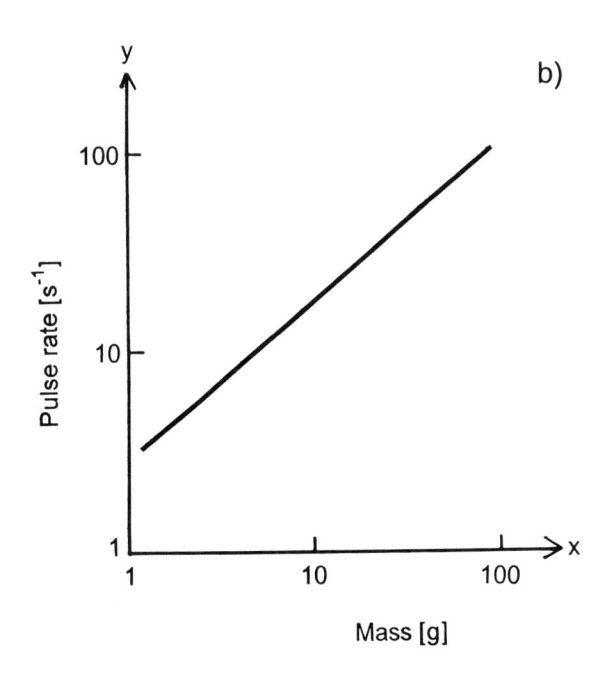

Fig. 3.5: Quantitative analysis of the impulse rate of the dendrites terminating in Merkel's corpuscles, as a function of the mass of an object placed on the open hand with the palm facing up. The impulse rate is the number of impulses sent to the brain per second and carries therefore the unit [s^{-1}].
(a) Linear representation of the data, indicating that the impulse rate is not linearly proportional to the mass because this would have to lead to a straight line in this type of plot.
(b) Double–logarithmic representation of the data, illustrating that the actual dependence of the impulse rate is described by a power–law. Power–law relations occur frequently in nature; analyzing the exponent in the power–law often is the first step toward developing a model for the mechanism of the studied process.

cles) are discussed later in this chapter, the beehive–shaped corpuscles (Meissner's corpuscles) are discussed in Chapter 5. Here we focus on the disc–shaped corpuscles just below the epidermis (Merkel's corpuscles). These are the receptors sensitive to contact forces.

Merkel's corpuscles appear in high density in the palms of our hands and in the soles of our feet. The function of Merkel's corpuscles is easiest illustrated when we repeat our self–test placing various weights on the open hand with the palm up. Fig. 3.5 shows the impulse rate (impulses per second) sent by the dendrites ending in Merkel's corpuscles as a function of the mass placed on your hand. The mass is varied between 1 g and 100 g. Fig. 3.5(a) is a linear representation of these data and shows that the impulse rate does not depend linearly on the weight because the curve is not a straight line. This means two things, (I) that the linear graph is inconvenient for quantitative data analysis, and (II) that the linear graph is not sufficient to judge whether a single or several mechanisms are needed to describe the response of Merkel's corpuscles. The double–logarithmic plot in Fig. 3.5(b) helps to clarify this issue. Because this plot of the data yields a straight line, a single power law describes the response of Merkel's corpuscles; therefore, only one mechanism is needed to describe the response of these corpuscles.

Example 3.1
For Merkel's corpuscles, Fig. 3.5 shows the number of nerve impulses per second (pulse rate) as a function of the mass of an object resting on the skin. Fig. 3.5(a) is a linear plot and Fig. 3.5(b) is a double–logarithmic plot of the same data. Determine the power law relation between the impulse rate (P in [1/s]) and the mass (m in [g]), i.e., find the parameters a and b in $P = a \cdot m^b$.

Solution: A detailed discussion of the approach taken to analyze a double–logarithmic plot is provided in Chapter 24. Following that procedure, the two data sets in Table 3.1 are taken from the plot in Fig. 3.5(b).

We rewrite the power law relation $P = a \cdot m^b$ in logarithmic form as:

Table 3.1: Data sets taken from Fig. 3.5(b) for the nerve impulse response of Merkel's corpuscles.

Data set	ln(P [s^{-1}])	ln(m [g])
#1	2.303	1.50
#2	4.606	4.39

$$\ln P = b \cdot \ln m + \ln a \quad (1)$$

Substituting the two data sets from Table 3.1 we find:

(I)	$2.303 = b \cdot 1.50 + \ln a$
(II)	$4.606 = b \cdot 4.39 + \ln a$
(II) – (I)	$2.303 = b (4.39 - 1.5)$

This yields b = 0.8, and, after substituting b in formula (I), $\ln a = 2.303 - 0.8 \cdot 1.5 = 1.103$ follows. From this we obtain a = 3.0.

Note that the relation between impulse rate and mass is not linear because we found a value for b which is not unity (b ≠ 1): $P \propto m^{0.8}$. This is confirmed by the fact that the curve in Fig. 3.5(a) is not a straight line.

A more detailed physiological description of the mechanism of Merkel's corpuscles has to wait to Chapter 15 when the elastic properties of tissues are discussed.

3.3. Applying Newton's laws with non–collinear forces

The discussion of the macula in section 3.1 shows that we have to include the direction when describing force related phenomena. This is possible by starting from the same basic experiments we discussed in Chapter 2. Newton's key observations are:

> (I) an object maintains its velocity (magnitude and direction) while no net force acts on it, and
> (II) an object accelerates in the direction of a non–zero net force.

Note that these observations remain unchanged when the net force is due to non–collinear forces. Thus, Newton's two statements from Eq. (2.10) are now rewritten:

$$\begin{aligned} F_{net} = 0 &\Rightarrow a = 0 \text{ and } v = const \\ F_{net} \neq 0 &\Rightarrow a \neq 0 \text{ and } v \neq const \end{aligned} \quad (2)$$

In Eq. (2) all parameters, the net force, the acceleration and the velocity are vectors. Typographically, this is indicated by bold–faced print of variables, e.g. **F** for the force vector. In figures, an arrow above the variable is used to label vectors. The definition of a vector and the mathematical vector operations as required for this text-

book are outlined in the General Appendix (Chapter 24).

The vector notation for the (instantaneous) velocity is given in the form:

$$\lim_{\Delta t \to 0} \frac{\Delta \mathbf{r}}{\Delta t} \equiv \mathbf{v} \quad (3)$$

in which the direction of the velocity vector is pointing in the same direction as the displacement, which is the difference of the position vectors, $\Delta \mathbf{r} = \mathbf{r}_2 - \mathbf{r}_1$. The displacement vector replaces the term $\Delta x = x_2 - x_1$ in Eq. (2.7). For the transition $\Delta t \to 0$ this direction becomes the direction of the tangent to the path of the object. Thus, the velocity vector **v** points at every instant in the direction of the current motion of the object. The instantaneous acceleration is defined as a vector representing the change of the velocity of an object with time:

$$\lim_{\Delta t \to 0} \frac{\Delta \mathbf{v}}{\Delta t} \equiv a \quad (4)$$

3.3.1. Newton's first law

Newton's first law in vector form follows from the first line of Eq. (2). If an object does not accelerate, then:

$$F_{net} = \sum_{i=1}^{n} F_i = 0 \quad (5)$$

This vector equation is applied in component form. In general, Eq. (5) has to be written as three component formulas, one for the x–components of the forces, one for their y–components and one for their z–components. However, most applications of Newton's laws are such that all relevant forces are found in a two–dimensional plane. We define this plane as the xy–plane. Choosing the xy–plane in this fashion allows us to omit the z–direction formula in Eq. (5). Thus, we apply Eq. (5) in the form:

$$F_{net, x} = \sum_{i=1}^{n} F_{ix} = 0$$
$$F_{net, y} = \sum_{i=1}^{n} F_{iy} = 0 \quad (6)$$

in which the first formula states that the sum of the x–components of all forces acting on the system is zero, and the second formula states that the sum of the y–components of all forces is also zero. If a problem asks for the magnitude of a force, it is calculated from the components of the force by using the Pythagorean theorem:

$$|F| = \sqrt{F_x^2 + F_y^2} \qquad (7)$$

Example 3.2

An object of mass m = 1.0 kg is attached to a taut string of length L = 20.0 cm. The object is pulled to the position shown in Fig. 3.6 with θ = 30°. At this position the object is held stationary which requires a horizontal external force $\mathbf{F}_{ext}$ as shown.
(a) What is the magnitude of the tension **T** in the string?
(b) What is the magnitude of the force $\mathbf{F}_{ext}$?

Solution: We follow the same problem–solving strategy we introduced in Chapter 2:

I Schematic Approach

The object is the system. The massless string is part of the environment. The sketch indicates that the object, if free to move, would move along a circular path. The axis of that motion is the point at which the string is attached to the ceiling (center of curvature) and the length L of the string is the radius of the path. However, the problem text implies that the object does not move, i.e., that Newton's first law applies.

II Physical Model

Studying the problem text and Fig. 3.6 reveals that three forces act on the object. The first is the gravitational force exerted by the Earth, labelled weight **W**. Its magnitude is given as W = mg, in which g is the gravitational acceleration.

The second force is the contact force exerted on the object by the massless string, labelled tension **T**. The tension is not negligible. This becomes clear when you think about the consequence if this force were not present (for example the string were cut): instead of being stationary the object would fall down.

The third force is the external force, $\mathbf{F}_{ext}$, exerted by the person holding the object in place. This person is not shown in Fig. 3.6 and belongs to the environment for the current problem. The external force is also not negligible because releasing the object causes it to swing downwards. At this point make sure that no force has been overlooked. You will not be able to solve the problem if you have missed a force!

Next we construct the free–body–diagram which is shown in Fig. 3.7. We draw a dot for the system, then

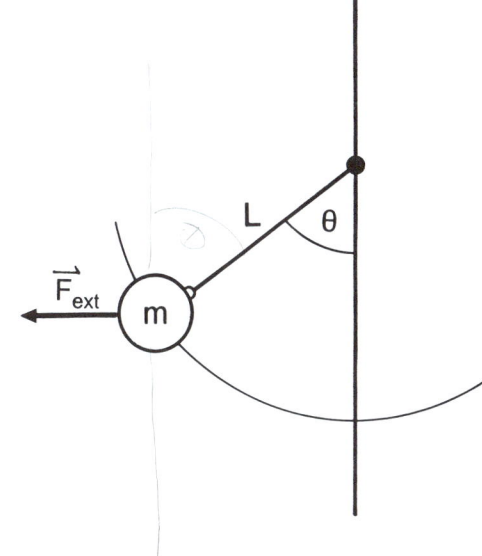

Fig. 3.6: An application of the first law of mechanics. An object of mass m is attached to a string of length L and pulled to the left side. The object is then held stationary by an external force $\mathbf{F}_{ext}$ with the string form-ing an angle θ with the vertical. Compare this set–up with a similar problem shown in Fig. 3.28.

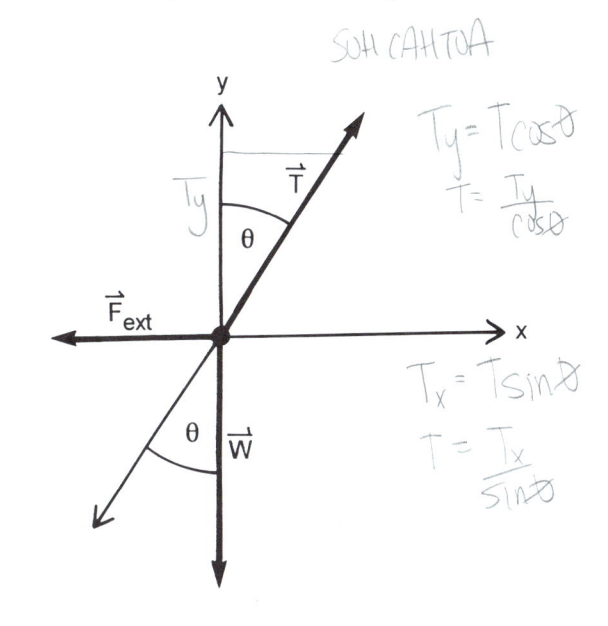

Fig. 3.7: The free–body–diagram for the example shown in Fig. 3.6. The dot represents the object. Note that only forces acting on the object are included; these are the tension **T** in the string, the weight **W** of the object and the external force $\mathbf{F}_{ext}$. In addition to the three forces, the angle θ and a coordinate system are shown. θ is the angle between the tension and the vertical direction. The coordinate systems is chosen such that two of the three forces, **W** and $\mathbf{F}_{ext}$, coincide with the axes.

enter the weight as a vector pointing downwards. The tension is added, drawn in the direction of the string because all contact forces act in the direction along which the contact with the system occurs. The external force $\mathbf{F}_{ext}$ is added in the direction given in the problem text.

III Quantitative treatment

There are only two other things you may add to a free–body–diagram: a coordinate system and the angles between the forces and the axes. Do not combine the free–body–diagram with any other sketch that you make because you need a precise drawing to write the appropriate set of Newton's equations. Two orthogonal directions are added to the free–body–diagram as x– and y–axes. You cannot make a mistake here, but a good choice reduces the extent of later calculations. As a rule of thumb, choose the axes such that the greatest possible number of forces in the free–body–diagram coincide with the axes. In the case of Fig. 3.7, we choose a horizontal x–axis and a vertical y–axis. Thus, the weight is parallel to the y–axis and the external force $\mathbf{F}_{ext}$ is parallel to the x–axis.

Using Fig. 3.7 we write Eq. (6) for the specific forces shown in the free–body–diagram. It is important to not confuse x– and y–components: complete the x–component formula first before you proceed to the y–component formula.

$$\text{(I) } x\text{–dir.:} \quad -F_{ext} + T\sin\theta = 0$$
$$\text{(II) } y\text{–dir.:} \quad -W + T\cos\theta = 0 \quad (8)$$

Solution part (a): From the second formula in Eq. (8) we find:

$$T\cos\theta = W = mg \quad (9)$$

With the given values of θ and m we obtain:

$$T = \frac{mg}{\cos\theta} = \frac{1.0[kg]\ 9.8[m/s^2]}{\cos 30^0} \quad (10)$$
$$\Rightarrow T = 11.3\ N$$

Solution part (b): In the next step the result of part (a) is substituted into the first formula in Eq. (8):

$$F_{ext} = T\sin\theta = \frac{mg}{\cos\theta}\sin\theta = mg\tan\theta \quad (11)$$

which leads to:

$$F_{ext} = 1.0[kg]\ 9.8\left[\frac{m}{s^2}\right]\tan 30^0 = 5.7\ N \quad (12)$$

Thus, for a mechanical equilibrium the external force must have a magnitude of $F_{ext} = 5.7$ N, which is about half of the force found for the tension in the string.

Example 3.3

Two objects with masses m = 2.0 kg and M = 3.0 kg are connected with massless strings, as shown in Fig. 3.8. The string to the vertical wall forms an angle of $\theta = 45^0$ with the horizontal. What is the magnitude of the external force $\mathbf{F}_{ext}$, with which the object of mass m has to be pulled toward the left in order to hold both objects stationary?

Solution:

I Schematic Approach

We choose object m as a system because the problem text asks for $\mathbf{F}_{ext}$, which acts on that object. However, the answer will also depend on the mass of object M. Imagine changing the mass M; the force $\mathbf{F}_{ext}$ would have to be changed in order to maintain a mechanical equili-

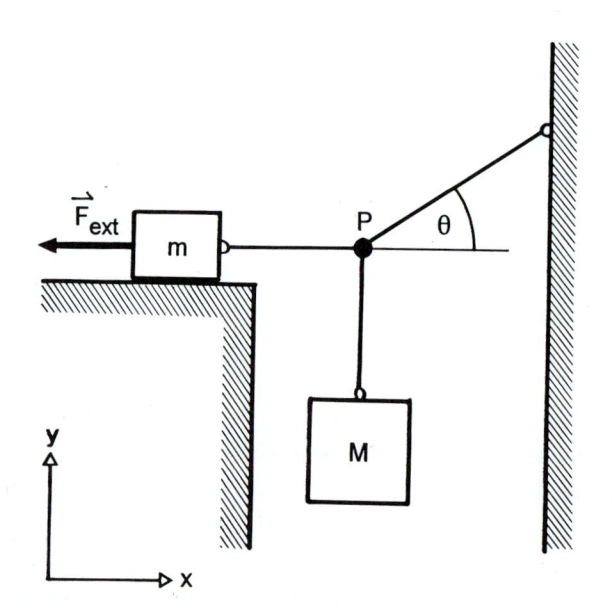

Fig. 3.8: A second application of the first law of mechanics. Two point objects of masses m and M are connected with each other and a vertical wall using three massless strings. The string to the wall forms an angle θ with the horizontal. The two objects are held stationary, i.e., they do not move. To accomplish this, an external force $\mathbf{F}_{ext}$ is required. Note that a choice of coordinate system for this problem is indicated with the figure.

brium. This observation requires that object M is included as a second system.

We further expect the angle θ of the string attached to the vertical wall to influence the result. Again, think about changing this angle. The tension in the string to the wall would change and all other forces with it. This means that the point P, in which the three strings are connected, is a third system. P qualifies as a system even though its mass is zero and it will not be assigned a weight. In turn, the three massless strings, the vertical wall and the horizontal surface remain part of the environment because we cannot change anything about them which alters the outcome of the experiment.

II Physical Model

We find the forces acting on each of the three systems. Four forces act on the object m on the horizontal surface: its weight $\mathbf{W}_m$ and the normal force $\mathbf{N}$ in the vertical direction; the external force $\mathbf{F}_{ext}$ and the tension $\mathbf{T}_m$ in the horizontal direction. The subscript m is added to the tension because the other two strings in Fig. 3.8, the string connected to object M and the string connected to the wall, have different tensions. For the object M, just two forces are identified, both acting in the vertical direction: one is its weight $\mathbf{W}_M$ and the other is the tension in the vertical string, $\mathbf{T}_M$.

The three strings yield three tensions acting on point P. Using the index w for the wall we identify (I) a tension $\mathbf{T}_M$ pulling downwards, (ii) $\mathbf{T}_m$ pulling toward the left and (iii) $\mathbf{T}_w$ pulling under an angle θ toward the wall. With all the forces identified, three separate free–body–diagrams are drawn. These are shown in Fig. 3.9.

III Quantitative treatment

Most forces coincide with the x– and y–axes when the two axes are chosen as indicated in Fig. 3.8 for each of the three systems. Based on the free–body–diagrams in Fig. 3.9 we write five formulas using Eq. (6):

$$\begin{aligned}(I) \ &x\text{–}dir., \ obj. \ m: & T_m - F_{ext} &= 0 \\ (II) \ &y\text{–}dir., \ obj. \ m: & N - W_m &= 0 \\ (III) \ &y\text{–}dir., \ obj. \ M: & T_M - W_M &= 0 \\ (IV) \ &x\text{–}dir. \ P: & T_w \cos\theta - T_m &= 0 \\ (V) \ &y\text{–}dir. \ P: & T_w \sin\theta - T_M &= 0\end{aligned} \quad (13)$$

Unknown in Eq. (13) are the three tensions, the normal force and the external force. Thus, we have five equations and five unknown variables. However, the normal force is not asked for nor required to solve for any other quantity. Thus, the second formula in Eq. (13) can be neglected. From the third formula we find:

$$T_M = W_M = M g = 29.4 \ N \quad (14)$$

We substitute this value in the fifth formula of Eq. (13):

$$T_w = \frac{T_M}{\sin\theta} = \frac{29.4 \ N}{\sin 45^0} = 41.6 \ N \quad (15)$$

We substitute T_w into the fourth formula:

$$\begin{aligned}T_m &= T_w \cos\theta = 41.6[N] \cos 45^0 \\ \Rightarrow \quad T_m &= 29.4 \ N\end{aligned} \quad (16)$$

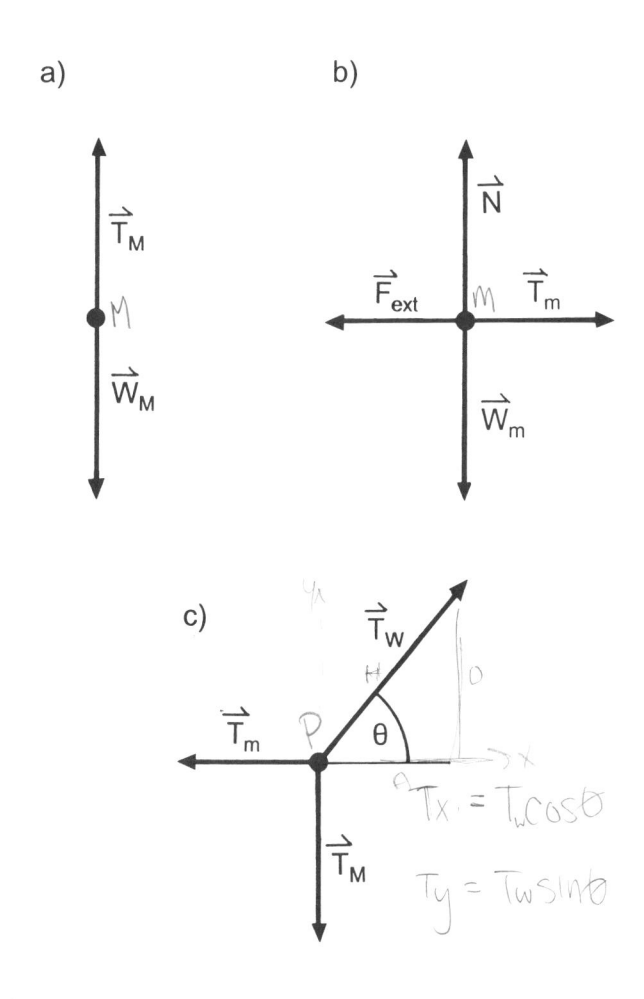

Fig. 3.9: We need three free–body–diagrams for the problem shown in Fig. 3.8, one for each object and one for the massless point P at which the three strings meet. (a) The free–body–diagram for the object of mass M contains its weight and the tension in the vertical string. (b) The free–body–diagram of the object of mass m contains its weight and the normal force due to the table in the vertical direction, and the external force and the tension in the horizontal string in the horizontal direction. (c) The free–body–diagram for point P consists of the tensions in the three strings. No weight acts on point P because it is massless.

Finally, using the first formula we calculate:

$$F_{ext} = T_m = 29.4 \ N \qquad (17)$$

Note that the mass m of the object on the table did not enter into the calculation.

3.3.2. Newton's second law

Now we reevaluate the second experimental finding in Eq. (2) for non–collinear forces. We noted already that the acceleration is a vector. Thus, we write $\mathbf{F}_{net} \propto \mathbf{a}$ or in quantitative form for a system with n forces:

$$F_{net} = \sum_{i=1}^{n} F_i = m \cdot a \qquad (18)$$

in which m is the mass of the object. Applying the second law requires that we use Eq. (18) in component form. We note again that most applications of Eq. (18) are such that all n forces and the resulting motion occur within a two–dimensional plane; we define this plane as the xy–plane. Thus, the following two formulas are used, one for each Cartesian component:

$$F_{net,\,x} = \sum_{i=1}^{n} F_{ix} = m \cdot a_x$$
$$F_{net,\,y} = \sum_{i=1}^{n} F_{iy} = m \cdot a_y \qquad (19)$$

Note that the acceleration in the x–direction depends only on force components in the x–direction. Equally, the accelerations in the y–direction depends only on the force components in the y–direction.

Example 3.4

Two objects with $m_1 = 3$ kg and $m_2 = 2$ kg are connected with a massless, taut string which runs over a massless and frictionless pulley, as shown in Fig. 3.10. The inclined surface, at the left is tilted at an angle of $\theta_1 = 45°$ toward the vertical and the inclined surface at the right is tilted at $\theta_2 = 30°$ toward the vertical. Both surfaces permit the frictionless motion of the objects.
(a) Find the acceleration of the object of mass m_1, and
(b) find the acceleration of the object of mass m_2.

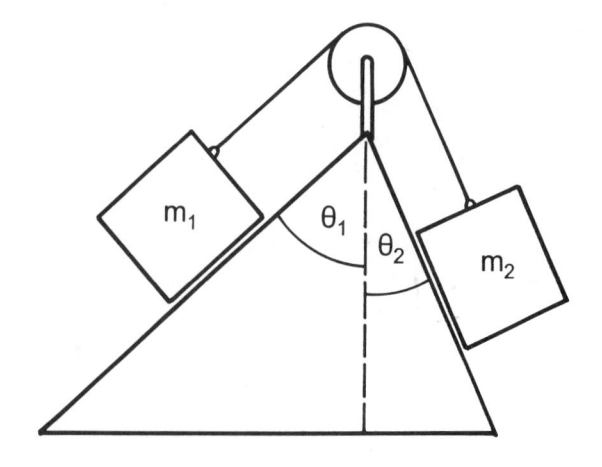

Fig. 3.10: Sketch of two connected objects of masses m_1 and m_2, which are placed on two inclined planes of variable angles θ_1 and θ_2. The connection between the objects is a taut, massless string which runs over a massless and frictionless pulley.

Solution:
I Schematic Approach
In this problem it is more obvious than in the last one that both objects need to be treated as independent systems. The massless string, the massless and frictionless pulley and the frictionless inclined planes are all components of the environment.
    For the purpose of practice you may convince yourself that identifying only one object as a system does not lead to a wrong answer. Instead, you will find that you just do not obtain enough formulas to solve the problem, forcing you back to step I to include the second object as a second system.

II Physical Model
Three forces act on each object: the weight, the normal force exerted by the surface and the tension along the string. Since these forces differ we must identify each with the respective indices for the objects, 1 and 2. The two free–body–diagrams are shown in Fig. 3.11.

III Quantitative treatment
A choice of axes is included in Fig. 3.11. Note that one axis is chosen parallel and one perpendicular to the inclined plane. Note also that the coordinate systems for the two objects do not have to be the same. Choosing the coordinate systems for each system separately is in some cases useful to minimize the amount of algebra in the later calculations.

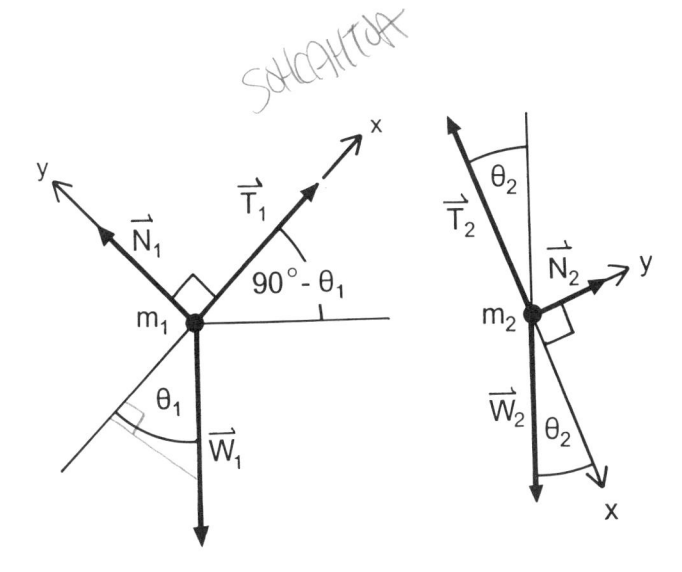

Fig. 3.11: The two free–body–diagrams for the objects shown in Fig. 3.10. Note that we choose two different coordinate systems. The angles taken from Fig. 3.10 are also shown because they are needed to identify the x– and y–components of the weights.

We notice that there is nothing interesting happening in either of the y–directions perpendicular to the inclined plane. Thus, we need not to write all four formulas for the two systems using Newton's laws, but confine the discussion to the two component formulas in the directions along the inclined planes. These formulas are:

System 1: $-m_1 g \cos\theta_1 + T = m_1 a$

System 2: $-T + m_2 g \cos\theta_2 = m_2 a$ **(20)**

in which we used $T_{1,x} \equiv T$ and $T_{2,x} \equiv -T$. This means actually two things. First, we note that the magnitudes of both tension vectors are equal because the string is massless. Secondly, the only non–zero component of the tension is the x–component in each case, and therefore the value of that component is equal to the magnitude of the vector. However, tension **T**$_1$ runs in the positive x–direction and tension **T**$_2$ runs in the negative x–direction, each based on the respective free–body–diagram.

But be careful! Had we chosen, for example, the x–direction in the free–body–diagram at the right in Fig. 3.11 upwards along the inclined plane, then the sign of the respective tension component would be opposite to the sign used in Eq. (20). In this case the sign of the acceleration would also change from – to + in the formula for system 2. This is why we would get the same results if we had chosen a different coordinate system.

The tensions in this problem remind us to distinguish between the magnitude of a vector, which is always a positive value, and the non–zero component of the vector when it is directed parallel to one of the fundamental axes in the problem. Let's look at an example. The vector **p** has a magnitude (or length) +p regardless of the orientation of the vector. If **p** is directed along the x–axis, then the x–component of **p** is either $p_x = +p$ if **p** is directed along the positive x–direction or is $p_x = -p$ if the vector is directed along the negative x–direction.

We also used in Eq. (20) $a_{1,x} = a_{2,x} \equiv a$, i.e. that the x–components of the accelerations of both systems are equal. This follows from the same reasoning as just discussed for the tensions: the magnitudes of both accelerations are the same since the string is and remains taut, i.e., the distance between both systems, as measured along the string, does not change. Further, both x–components of the accelerations are directed in the same direction relative to the respective coordinate systems, i.e., they must both be positive or both be negative, since otherwise the two objects would eventually collide or drift apart.

Solution part (a): The magnitude of the acceleration a is sought first. In Eq. (20) we eliminate the second unknown variable, which is the tension T, by adding the two formulas:

$$\left(-m_1 \cos 45^0 + m_2 \cos 30^0\right) g = \left(m_1 + m_2\right) a \quad \textbf{(21)}$$

This allows us to calculate the acceleration:

$$a = \frac{\left(m_2 \cos 30^0 - m_1 \cos 45^0\right)}{m_1 + m_2} g$$

$$\Rightarrow \quad a = -0.76 \frac{m}{s^2} \quad \textbf{(22)}$$

Note that we found a negative result for the magnitude of the acceleration. Per definition, this must be wrong. However, it is useful to analyze the origin of the mistake in this case, as it is essentially unavoidable and is easy to correct. The result in Eq. (22) is negative because we assumed $a_{1,x} = a_{2,x} \equiv a$ but should have used $a_{1,x} = a_{2,x} \equiv -a$. That means, we made a mistake by assuming that both objects move towards the right because we found in

41

the end that both objects move towards the left, i.e., the object with m₂ = 2 kg moves up the inclined plane and the object with m₁ = 3 kg slides down the inclined plane. Note that the acceleration is quite small in comparison to the gravitational acceleration constant g! For that reason it was next to impossible to guess which way the two objects move. In turn, we can easily correct the mistake by stating the direction of motion correctly, then assigning an acceleration of a = 0.76 m/s².

Solution part (b): We already established $a_{1,x} = a_{2,x}$ before solving part (a). Thus Eq. (22) gives also the answer to this part.

Example 3.5

Fig. 3.12 shows an object of mass m = 10 kg held by a massless string on a frictionless inclined surface.
(a) What is the tension in the string if θ = 35°?
(b) What force does the surface exert on the object?
(c) When the string is cut, with what acceleration does the object move along the inclined surface?

Solution:

I Schematic Approach

The object of mass m is the system. The inclined surface, the massless string and the person cutting the string are part of the environment.

II Physical Model

For parts (a) and (b), three forces act on the object: the tension **T** along the inclined surface, the weight **W** down and the normal force **N** in the direction normal (perpendicular) to the surface. For part (c) the tension is eliminated. The free–body–diagram for parts (a) and (b) is shown in Fig. 3.13.

III Quantitative treatment

The coordinate system in this case is chosen with the x–axis parallel to the inclined surface and the y–axis perpendicular to the surface. Thus, **T** and **N** are parallel to the major axes. The components of the weight are determined from the free–body–diagram: $W_x = -mg\sin\theta$ and $W_y = -mg\cos\theta$. This will be needed below since we will have to apply Newton's laws to each component separately.

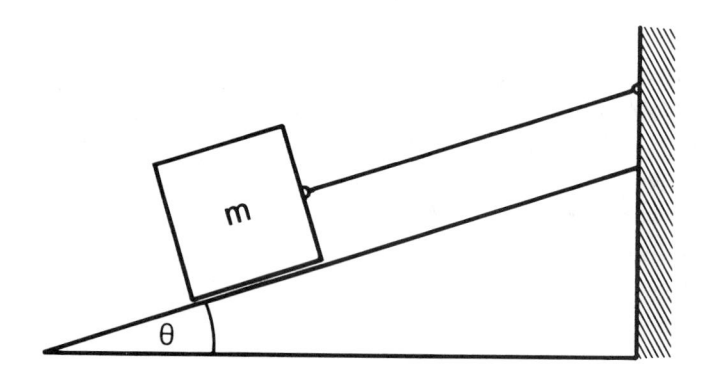

Fig. 3.12: A combined application of the first and second laws of mechanics. An object of mass m on an inclined frictionless surface is connected with a massless string to a vertical wall. We can determine the normal force and the tension by using Newton's first law. When the string is cut, the problem becomes an application of the second law of mechanics because the object accelerates downhill.

Fig. 3.13: We draw the free–body–diagram for the object with the string as shown in Fig. 3.12. Note that the coordinate system is chosen with the x–axis parallel to the inclined plane. The figure also indicates how the two components of the weight are obtained.

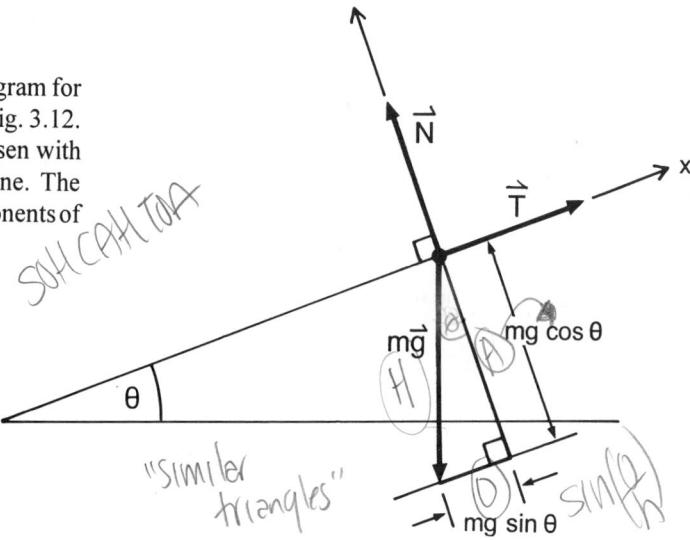

Solutions part (a) and (b): The first two parts of the example are applications of the first law of mechanics as given in Eq. (6), because the object does not move. With Eq. (6) and the free-body-diagram in Fig. 3.13 we find:

$$\text{(I) } x\text{-dir.:} \quad T - mg \sin\theta = 0$$
$$\text{(II) } y\text{-dir.:} \quad N - mg \cos\theta = 0 \quad (23)$$

From the first formula in this equation we find:

$$T = mg \sin\theta = 10[kg] \; 9.8\left[\frac{m}{s^2}\right] \sin 35^0$$
$$\Rightarrow \quad T = 56 \; N \quad (24)$$

From the second formula in Eq. (23) we obtain:

$$N = mg \cos\theta = 80 \; N \quad (25)$$

Note that this example demonstrates that you cannot assume that N = mg in all cases!

Solution part (c): We have to go back to the free-body-diagram in Fig. 3.13. Eliminating the tension by cutting the string reduces the free-body-diagram to just two forces, **N** and **W**. Keeping the coordinate system as chosen before, we have to revise Eq. (23). This time, the problem is an application of the second law of mechanics along the x-direction because the two remaining forces do not balance each other (two non-parallel forces never balance each other). Thus, Eq. (23) is replaced by:

$$\text{(I) } x\text{-dir.:} \quad -mg \sin\theta = -ma$$
$$\text{(II) } y\text{-dir.:} \quad N - mg \cos\theta = 0 \quad (26)$$

in which the acceleration component is $a_x = -a$ because the object accelerates downhill but the x-axis is chosen in the uphill direction. Note that the second formula has not changed and remains an application of the first law of mechanics. This is due to the fact that the object does not move in the y-direction at any time because it remains on the inclined surface. Comparing Eq. (23) and Eq. (26) illustrates why we have chosen the coordinate system with one axis parallel to the inclined plane: the lack of motion perpendicular to the inclined plane allows us to use Newton's first law in formula (II) of Eq. (26), and the acceleration needs not to be written as two components. To answer part (c) we solve formula (I) in Eq. (26):

$$a = g \sin\theta = 9.8\left[\frac{m}{s^2}\right] \sin 35^0 = 5.6 \; \frac{m}{s^2} \quad (27)$$

What we found therefore is a magnitude of the acceleration of $|\mathbf{a}| = 5.6$ m/s². As a vector component along the x-axis this corresponds to $a_x = -5.6$ m/s².

3.3.3. Newton's third law

Newton's third law must be rewritten in vector notation. If we label $\mathbf{F}_{Ba}$ the force exerted by object A on object B, and label $\mathbf{F}_{Ab}$ the force exerted by object B on object A, then we write for this action/reaction pair of forces:

$$\mathbf{F}_{Ab} = -\mathbf{F}_{Ba} \quad (28)$$

Example 3.6
Competitive sprinters reach horizontal accelerations of 15 m/s² out of the starting block. The starting block is tilted such that the vertical component of the force which the starting block exerts on the sprinter compensates for the weight of the sprinter, leading to a zero vertical acceleration. With what force does a 70 kg sprinter push against the starting block?

Solution:
I Schematic Approach
It is advisable to draw a sketch since none is given with the problem. Such a sketch is shown in Fig. 3.14. It indicates why this problem is an application of Newton's third law: we cannot treat the starting block as the system because we know too little about it. However, we are asked about a force acting on the starting block. On the other side, we know everything we need to determine the force exerted by the starting block on the sprinter. Anticipating the use of the third law at the end of the discussion, we therefore treat the sprinter as the system, solve for the magnitude of the force between sprinter and starting block, and then answer the question without further calculations.

II Physical Model
Using Fig. 3.14, we can identify two forces acting on the system: the weight pulling the body of the sprinter downwards and the contact force (normal force) exerted by the starting block on the system. Note that the normal

Fig. 3.14: An application of the third law of mechanics: a sprinter (modelled as a point mass) in the early stage of a sprint. At this stage the sprinter has no contact with the horizontal ground but only with the inclined starting block. The sprinter accelerates in the horizontal direction.

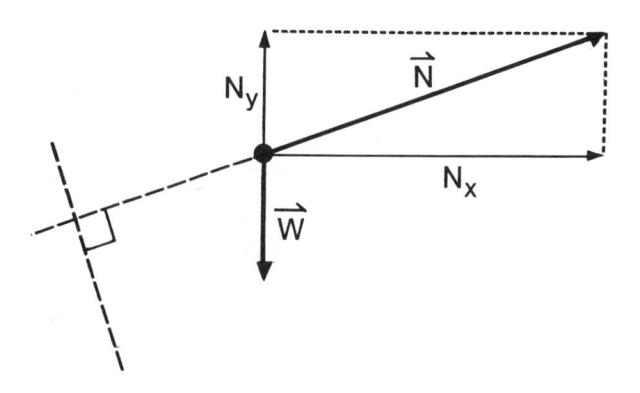

Fig. 3.15: The free–body–diagrams for the sprinter in Fig 3.14. The weight is compensated by the vertical component of the normal force. The horizontal component of the normal force leads to the acceleration. Note that we do not develop a free–body–diagram for the starting block, even though the problem asks for the magnitude of a force acting on it.

force does not act vertically since the starting block is tilted. These two forces yield the free–body–diagram shown in Fig. 3.15.

III Quantitative treatment

The best choice of coordinate system is a horizontal x–axis and a vertical y–axis because the example text refers to the horizontal component of the acceleration. The normal force is split in a vertical and horizontal component in the free–body–diagram.

The free–body–diagram gives two formulas: mechanical equilibrium based on Eq. (6) in the y–direction (the text says that no change of motion occurs in this direction) and an equation of motion based on Eq. (19) in the x–direction in which a net acceleration occurs:

$$(I) \; x\text{–dir.:} \quad N_x = m\,a$$
$$(II) \; y\text{–dir.:} \quad N_y - W = 0 \qquad (29)$$

From the two formula in Eq. (29) we find the two components of the normal force:

$$(I) \; N_x = ma = 70[kg]\,15\left[\frac{m}{s^2}\right] = 1050\,N$$
$$(II) \quad N_y = W = m\,g = 685\,N \qquad (30)$$

The two components yield the magnitude of the normal force:

$$|\mathbf{N}| = \sqrt{N_x^2 + N_y^2} = 1255\,[N] \qquad (31)$$

Note that this does not answer the question, however. We were not asked for the force with which the starting block acts on the sprinter, but the force with which the sprinter pushes against the starting block. As anticipated, at this point the third law of mechanics comes into play. The force exerted by the sprinter on the starting block is equal in magnitude but opposite in direction to the normal force we calculated. Therefore, the sprinter pushes with a force of 1255 N into the starting block.

3.4. Acceleration detection

Since acceleration plays a key role in the laws of mechanics and, consequently, in predicting the motion of objects, it is crucial for organisms to detect and measure accelerations. Vision obviously provides many animals with a high level of alertness for the acceleration of objects in their environment. However, visual control is not always possible. The human body is also capable to sense accelerations in two other ways: accelerations of our own body, particularly the head, and acceleration of objects in contact with our skin, particularly the palms of our hands. The latter is achieved by acceleration sensors located underneath the skin, which are called Pacinian

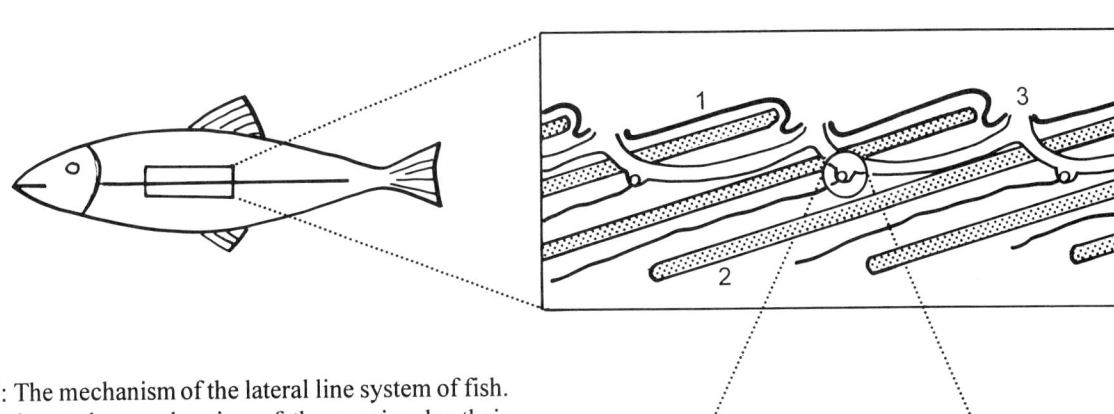

Fig. 3.17: The mechanism of the lateral line system of fish. Fish can detect the acceleration of the passing by their body. The lateral line system consists of a system of canals with external openings (3) which are running below the fish's epidermis (1) between the scales (2). Acceleration receptors are located at various point along these canals. One of these is highlighted in the circle at the bottom. The receptor consists of a very similar arrangement to that of the cupula in the semicircular canals of the vestibular organ: the cupula (4) rests on hair cells (6) with hair–like sensory extensions (5) reaching into the base of the cupula. When these sensory hairs are bent, a nerve signal (7) is sent to the center of the nervous system of the fish.

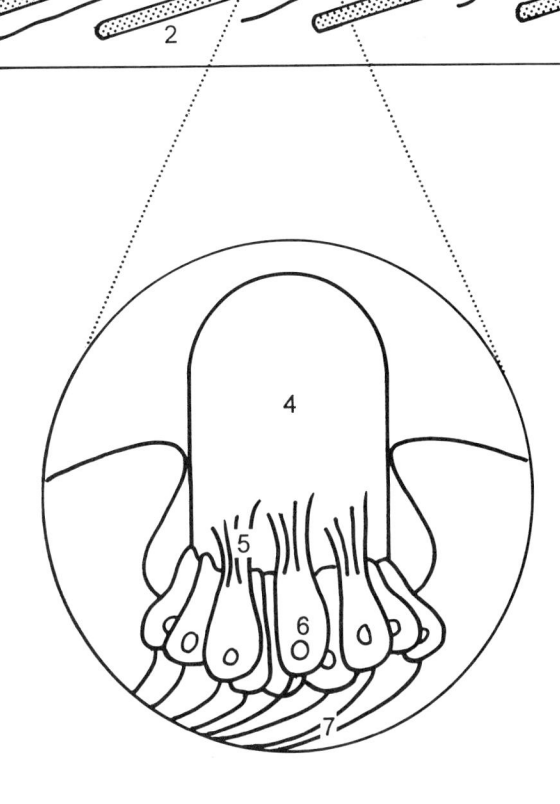

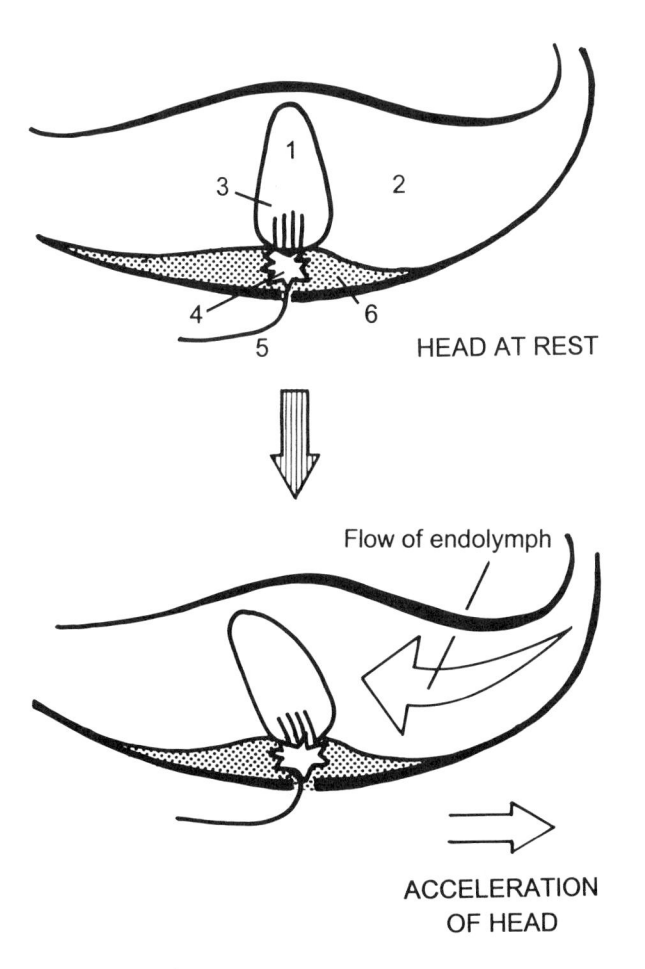

Fig. 3.16: The mechanism of the semicircular canals in the vestibular organ of the inner ear. The top sketch shows the head at rest. When the head accelerates toward the right, as shown in the bottom sketch, the endolymph (2) flows due to its inertia toward the left. The motion of the endolymph pushes the cupula (1), which rests on the crista (6). The cupula tilts, bending the dendrites (3) which reach into the cupula. The dendrites belong to a neuron (4) which is embedded in the crista. This triggers a nerve signal carried by a nerve (5) to the brain.

corpuscles. These will be discussed as an example in section 3.5.

Accelerations of our head are measured by the semicircular canals of the vestibular organ. As shown in Fig. 3.1, the semicircular canals consist of three, orthogonal crescent–shaped tubes which are filled with a fluid (endolymph). The orthogonal orientation of the three tubes provides the brain with a decoupled acceleration analysis along the three Cartesian coordinates, the acceleration component sideways, the component back and forth, and the component up and down.

The mechanism of the semicircular canals is illustrated in Fig. 3.16. Resting on a platform (crista) is the swivel–mounted cupula. Dendrites reach into the cupula with the neuron embedded in the crista. While the head is at rest, the endolymph rests surrounding the cupula. When the head is accelerated parallel to the orientation of a semicircular canal, the inertia of the endolymph (based on Newton's first law) results in a flow of the endolymph in the direction opposite to the direction of the acceleration. This phenomenon can be visualized by holding a half–full glass of water in your hand and suddenly accelerate it. The inertia of the water causes the water to try to stay behind the acceleration of the glass. The flow of the endolymph pushes the cupula to the side. The tilting of the cupula is sensed by the ends of the nerve in the cupula and is communicated to the brain. Note that the semicircular canals cannot sense velocity. There is no net force acting on the endolymph if you move your head with constant speed, therefore the endolymph is at rest and the cupula retains an upright position, in the same fashion as if the head is at rest.

Again, such acceleration detectors have been developed early and are widespread among vertebrates. Fig. 3.17 highlights the lateral line system in fish. A canal system below the scales of the fish allows water to flow past neuromasts, one of which is highlighted in the highest magnification part of the figure. The neuromast is constructed in an analogous fashion to the semicircular canal system of the human ear: a bendable cupula rests on a layer of hair cells with their hair reaching into the cupula. When the cupula is tilted, these hair bend as well and cause a nerve signal to the brain of the animal. The lateral line system allows fish to monitor their own accelerations, but also water pressure changes due to other moving objects (such as predators or prey) and low frequency sounds carried through the water.

3.5. Physiological applications of Newton's laws

We study two examples to highlight how the laws of mechanics are used in specific physiological cases.

3.5.1. Gravity detection in the maculae (Example 3.7)

Determine the force acting perpendicular to the dendrites of each neuron in the utricular macula when (a) the head is upright and (b) when the head is tilted sideways by 30^0.

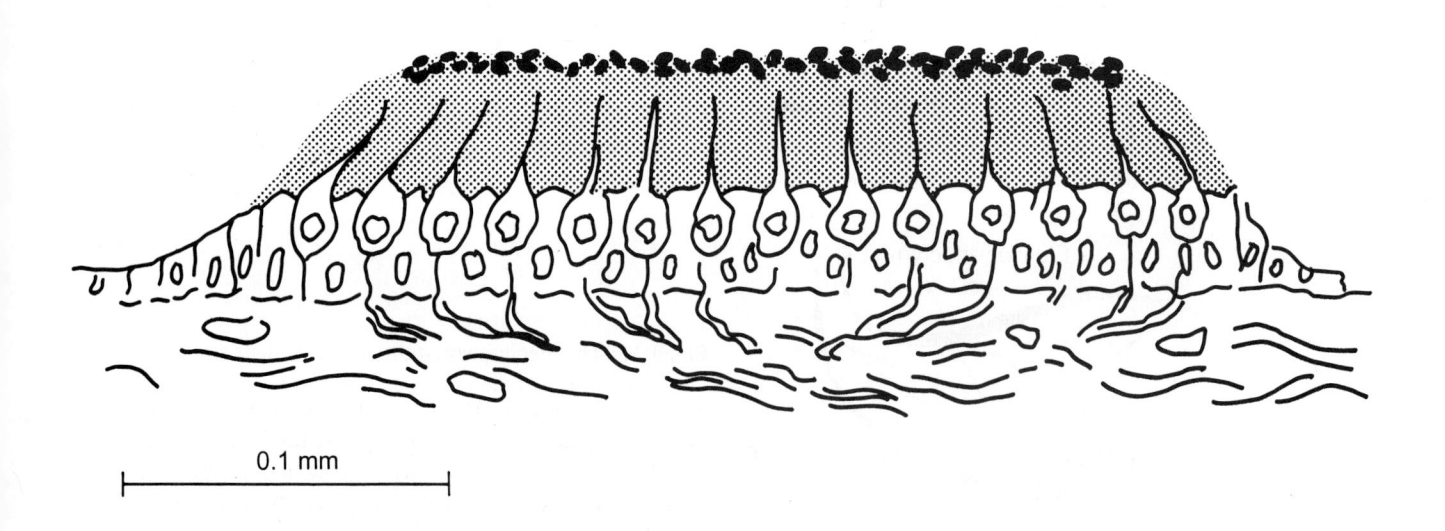

Fig. 3.18: Contrast–enhanced sketch of a vertical cross–sectional micrograph of a complete macula (compare with Fig. 3.2). The larger black dots at the top are the otoliths, which are embedded in the top layer of the otolithic membrane (dotted area). Dendrites are shown as thin lines reaching into this membrane from onion–shaped neurons.

Supplementary biological information: Fig. 3.18 shows a side–view of the macula based on a micrograph and includes a length scale. The mechanism of the macula has been discussed qualitatively earlier in this chapter.

Solution: This is the first example in which we no longer identify the specific steps of the problem–solving strategy we practised in this and the previous chapter. It is a good idea to read through this and later solutions still noting the three components of this procedure.

Solution part (a): We start with the identification of the system and the forces acting on it. We define a single calcite otolith as our system, and consider the otolithic membrane of the macula as the environment. This requires that we later use Newton's third law because the problem text asks for a force acting on the dendrites. We cannot choose the dendrites directly as our system because we know too little about them, but we know that an action/reaction pair of forces exists between the otoliths and the otolithic membrane, and also between the otolithic membrane and the dendrites. Two forces act on the otolith:
(I) The Earth exerts a gravitational force on the otolith, this is the weight **W**.
(II) The otolithic membrane exerts a normal force **N** on the otolith.
Next we develop the free–body–diagram and assign the Cartesian coordinates: the free–body–diagram is shown in Fig. 3.19. The dot at the center represents the otolith (the system). The weight acts downwards and the normal force pushes the otolith upwards. The Cartesian coordinates are chosen such that the x–axis is directed toward the right and the y–axis is directed upwards. The otolith is in mechanical equilibrium in both directions. This is trivial in the x–direction as there are no forces acting on the otolith along the x–axis. In the y–direction we use Newton's first law:

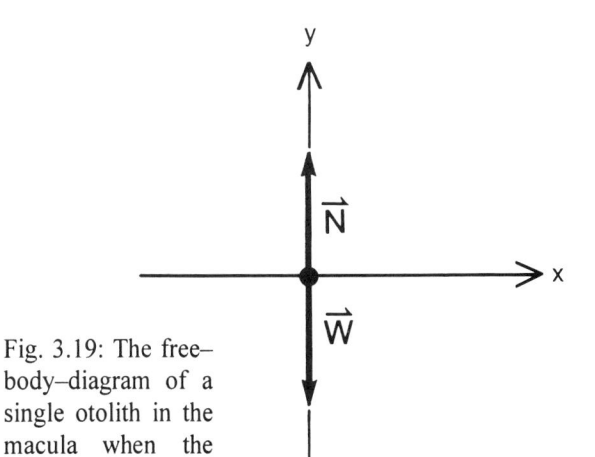

$$y\text{–}dir.: \quad -W + N = 0 \quad (32)$$

i.e., $N = W$. Thus, the solution to part (a) is that there is no force acting perpendicular to the dendrites in the upright position. We can, however, quantify the force the otolithic membrane has to exert on the otolith to keep it in place. This calculation illustrates the use of the density information provided earlier.

Fig. 3.19: The free–body–diagram of a single otolith in the macula when the head is held upright.

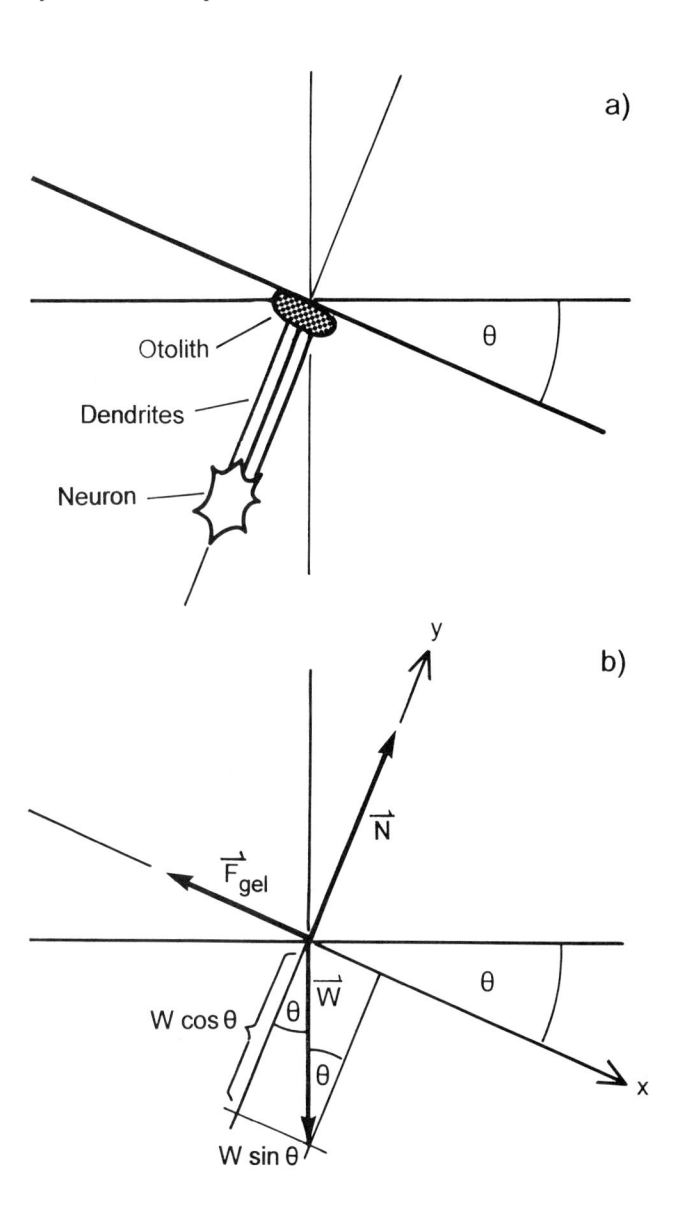

Fig. 3.20: (a) Sketch of an otolith near the membrane surface of the utricular macula with the head tilted sideways by an angle θ. Dendrites near the otolith illustrate the geometry of the otolith–membrane–dendrite interaction. (b) The free–body–diagram of a single otolith as shown in part (a) with three forces acting on the system: its weight **W**, the normal force **N** and a force parallel to the surface layer of the otolithic membrane $\mathbf{F}_{gel}$. The Cartesian coordinates are chosen with the x–axis parallel and the y–axis perpendicular to the membrane surface.

The magnitude of the normal force is $N = W = mg$. Thus, we need the mass of a otolith. Instead, we have information about its size and its density. The density is defined as $\rho = m/V$ [kg/m³] with V the volume. For calcite $\rho = 3.0$ g/cm³ $= 3.0 \times 10^3$ kg/m³. From Fig. 3.18 we find that the length of an average otolith in the macula is near 5 μm. This corresponds to a volume $V = (5\ \mu m)^3$ or $V = 1.25 \times 10^{-16}$ m³. The mass of the otolith is then given by $m = \rho V = 3.75 \times 10^{-13}$ kg. Multiplying with g leads to the magnitude of the normal force which is $N = 3.7 \times 10^{-12}$ [N] for a single otolith.

Solution part (b): The top part of Fig. 3.20 shows a simplified sketch of the otolith and the nearby dendrites when the head is turned sideways by an angle θ. This posture results in the free–body–diagram in the bottom part of the figure. Again, the otolith is the system and is represented as the dot at the center. The weight continues to act on the otolith vertically downwards. The normal force is still directed perpendicular to the otolithic membrane surface. If there were no other forces, then the forces on the otolith would not be balanced along the membrane surface and, according to Newton's second law, the otolith would have to accelerate toward the right. This does not happen because there is one more force to be considered: a contact force along the interface between the otolithic membrane and the otolith. This contact force resists the slipping of the otolith, i.e., the gelatine pushes the otolith upwards along the inclined surface. We call this force $\mathbf{F}_{gel}$. Remember that we are asked to find the force acting perpendicular to the dendrites, thus our answer will be associated with $\mathbf{F}_{gel}$.

After all three forces are entered in the free–body–diagram, directions for the Cartesian coordinates have to be chosen. To have most forces coincide with the main axes, we choose positive y– and positive x–directions perpendicular and parallel to the surface plane of the membrane, respectively. Note that the free–body–diagram contains one force which is not in the direction of a fundamental axis. In the next step, the x– and y–components of this force are found. The components of the weight are shown in Fig. 3.20. They are quantified in the form $W_x = W \sin\theta$ and $W_y = -W \cos\theta$.

Because the otolith is in mechanical equilibrium in both the x– and y–directions, we obtain two formulas applying Newton's first law (Eq. (6)):

$$x\text{–}dir.: \quad -F_{gel} + W \sin\theta = 0$$
$$y\text{–}dir.: \quad -W \cos\theta + N = 0 \quad (33)$$

The first formula in Eq. (33) leads to the force exerted by the otolithic membrane:

Table 3.2: Some typical forces

Force	Magnitude [N]
Gravity	
Gravitational force Sun on Earth	3.5×10^{22}
Weight of a person	7×10^2
Weight of a small insect egg	3×10^{-6}
Weight of a small bacterium	2×10^{-18}
Weight of a hydrogen atom	1.6×10^{-26}
Other forces	
Thrust of a large rocket	5×10^7
Maximum pulling force of a train engine	9×10^5
Electric force proton–electron in H atom	8.2×10^{-8}

$$F_{gel} = W \sin\theta = 3.7 \times 10^{-12}[N]\ \sin 30^0$$
$$\Rightarrow \quad F_{gel} = 1.85 \times 10^{-12}\ N \quad (34)$$

in which W was taken from the solution of part (a). The force calculated in Eq. (34) is the force exerted by the otolithic membrane on a otolith. However, due to the third law of mechanics, a force of same magnitude is exerted by the otolith on the membrane, and thus, in turn on the dendrites embedded in the membrane. To determine the total lateral force on the dendrites of a single neuron, we multiply F_{gel} by the number of otoliths which interact with each neuron. This number is estimated from Fig. 3.18 as about 15 otoliths per neuron. Since forces can be added, we estimate the magnitude of the lateral force on all dendrites of a single neuron to be $|\mathbf{F}_{lateral\ on\ neuron}| = 2.8 \times 10^{-11}$ N. Table 3.2 allows us to compare this force with other typical forces. Note that the calculated force is comparably small due to the small objects involved.

Additional comments: The physical concepts we quantified with Example 3.7 explain why we are equipped with the utricular macula. The ability to detect the vertical direction allows us to judge the alignment of our head with the vertical; this information in turn allows our brain to coordinate our locomotion and correct the information received from other sensory components, such as the eyes. Indeed, due to the importance of our vision, a sideways tilt of the head is not just corrected by adjusting the images received from the eyes, but the alignment of the eyes themselves is adjusted. You can test this simply by leaning with your head to one side while looking in a mirror. The eyes compensate the tilt of the head as shown in Fig. 3.21.

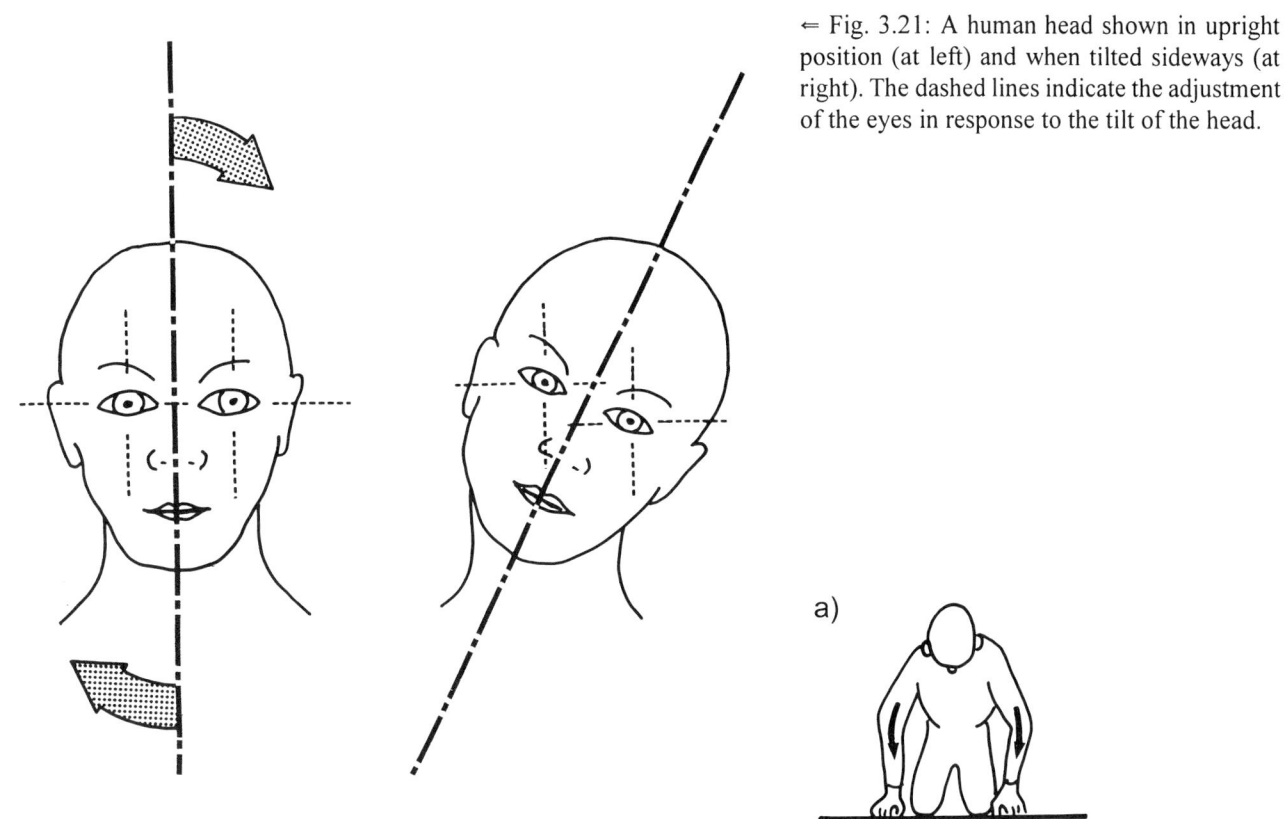

⇐ Fig. 3.21: A human head shown in upright position (at left) and when tilted sideways (at right). The dashed lines indicate the adjustment of the eyes in response to the tilt of the head.

Fig. 3.22: (a) A person knees on a flat surface. ⇒ When the flat surface is tilted, several adjustments are needed for a stable posture. (b) In particular, the forces exerted on the ground in the two arms must differ to maintain mechanical equilibrium. (c) A person not adjusting falls sideways.

⇐ Fig. 3.24: Anatomical sketch of the human head illustrating the orientation of the surface of the otolithic membrane of the utricular (1) and saccular (2) maculae.

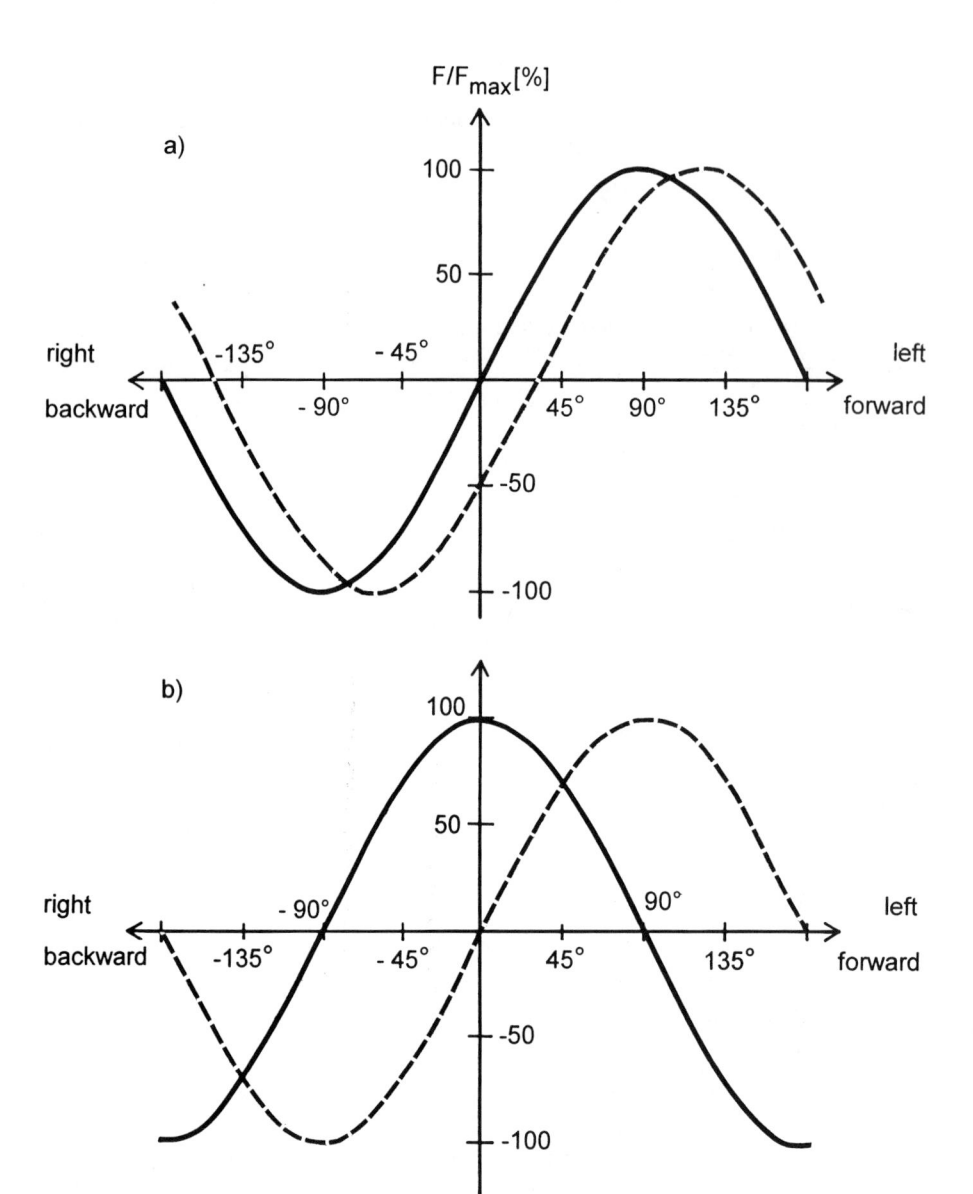

Fig. 3.23: The force on the dendrites in the maculae as a function of the tilt of the head. The force is shown relative to the maximum force. The solid lines apply to sideways tilting, the dashed lines apply to tilting back and forth. (a) The angular dependence of the force in the utricular macula, (b) the angular dependence of the force in the saccular macula.

A second response is a more complex adjustment of our posture. This is illustrated in Fig. 3.22(a) for a person kneeling on a surface. Fig. 3.22(b) shows the appropriate adjustments when the underlying surface is tilted. Would the person instead not react to the tilting of the surface, as shown in Fig. 3.22(c), he/she would lose the balance and fall towards the right.

But why do we have two maculae in each ear? Figs. 3.23 and 3.24 provide the answer: we need a sensitive measure of the angle between the axis of our head and the vertical for every possible orientation of the head. A single macula cannot provide that information. We illustrate this with Fig. 3.23(a) which shows the variation of the force on the dendrites as a fraction of the maximum force for the utricular macula. The solid line applies to tilting the head sideways and the dashed line applies to tilting the head back and forth. These two curves are not identical because you need to tilt your head by 30^0 forward to bring the utricular macula into a levelled position.

The limitations of a single macula are explained by first focussing on the solid line in Fig. 3.23(a). This curve represents the case we discussed in the example above: the head is tilted sideways. When your head is upright, no force acts on the dendrites in the sideways direction. When you tilt your head to an angle θ, then Eq. (34) describes the force acting on the dendrites, i.e. $F/F_{max} = \sin \theta$. Note that the solid curve in Fig. 3.23(a) varies fastest for small angles up to 60^0. However, due to the mathematical form of the sine-function the curve varies much less between 75^0 and 105^0. This means that the signal your brain receives from the utricular macula allows you to judge angles near the vertical position of the head, while the detection of changes of the angle near 90^0 is poor.

However, we often hold our head at angles near 90^0, e.g. when lying down. Our ability ot judge angles relative to vertical in that position, even with closed eyes, is not reduced. This is due to the saccular macula, which is tilted by 90^0 relative to the utricular macula, as illustrated in the anatomical sketch of Fig. 3.24. The dependence of the force on the dendrites in the saccular macula as a function of the angle between the axis of the head and the vertical is shown in Fig. 3.23(b). The solid line applies again to a sideways tilt and the dashed line to tilting back and forth. We use the solid curve in Fig. 3.23(b) to compare with the solid curve in Fig. 3.23(a) for the same sideways tilt of the head. Due to the difference in orientiation of both maculae in Fig. 3.24, the force on the dendrites in Fig. 3.23(b) is shifted by 90^0 relative to the corresponding curve in Fig. 3.23(a). Thus, the saccular macula is most sensitive near tilts of the head of 90^0, the range of least sensitivity of the utricular macula. Therefore, both macula supplement each other for sideways tilts.

We compare both maculae with respect to tilting the head back and forth in the same fashion. In Fig. 3.23, the dashed curves apply to this case. Note that a 30^0 tilt of the utricular macula is important because otherwise both dashed curves in parts (a) and (b) would be identical and we would have limited sensitivity to tilts of 90^0 in this direction, e.g. when lying on the back of our head.

3.5.2. Acceleration detection in the hand with the Pacinian corpuscle (Example 3.8)

What horizontal force acts on the central dendrite in a Pacinian corpuscle when your hand in pronation accelerates with 90 m/s² horizontally? Note that this is a typical acceleration for a discus thrower just before releasing the discus.

Supplementary biological information: The term pronation describes the way the hand is held. Pronation means palm down and supination means palm up. Thus, the acceleration occurs parallel to the palm surface.

Fig. 3.25 shows a cross–sectional side–view and top–view of a Pacinian corpuscle (named after Filipp Pacini). The figure further provides a length scale which shows that the corpuscle is about 0.5 mm long and has a 0.2 mm diameter. It consists of more than 50 lamellar cells (cells that are arranged like the layers of an onion). In the center of the corpuscle is a dendrite. The space between the lamellar cell membranes is filled with extracellular fluid. The entire corpuscle is encapsulated by elastic connective tissue. Fig. 3.4 showed that Pacinian corpuscles are located deep below the epidermis. The central dendrite is either oriented parallel to the skin surface or at about 45^0 to the surface. Pacinian corpuscles are primarily found in the skin of the palm of our hands and the soles of the feet and serve as acceleration or vibration (cyclic acceleration) detectors.

Solution: We first identify the system and the forces to draw a free–body–diagram. The top sketch in Fig. 3.26 shows a schematic sketch of a Pacinian corpuscle with the dendrite at 45^0 relative to the palm surface. The x–axis is defined parallel and the y–axis perpendicular to the palm surface. The bottom sketch in Fig. 3.26 shows the free–body–diagram of the forces acting on the central dendrite when the palm (and therefore the Pacinian corpuscle) is at rest. Four forces act on the dendrite: in the vertical direction the weight **W** pulls the dendrite downwards. The weight arrow in the figure is short to represent the small magnitude of the weight of the dendrite resulting from its small mass. A second force, due to the liquid, pushes the dendrite upwards. We call this force the buoyant force, $\mathbf{F}_{buoy}$. The buoyant force is associated with the weight of the displaced fluid and is the reason that a diver can float horizontally under water. We include the buoyant force as an additional force in the current example; it will be discussed separately in Chapter 10.

There are also two non–vertical contact forces due to the resting fluid pushing perpendicularly on the nerve from both sides: $\mathbf{F}_{fluid,\,left}$ is the force pushing the dendrite from the upper left side and $\mathbf{F}_{fluid,\,right}$ is a force pushing the dendrite from the lower right side.

Next we apply Newton's laws. While the palm and thus the Pacinian corpuscle is at rest, a mechanical equilibrium exists in both directions, i.e., along the x– and the y–axes. According to Newton's first law the respective formulas are:

$$(I) \quad F_{fluid\;left,\,x} - F_{fluid\;right,\,x} = 0$$
$$(II) \quad F_{buoy} - W + F_{fl.right,\,y} - F_{fl.left,\,y} = 0 \tag{35}$$

We must modify Eq. (35) because the question relates to the hand not at rest. However, the acceleration is only in the x–direction, thus a mechanical equilibrium still exists in the y–direction, i.e., the second formula in Eq. (35) remains unchanged. The first formula is changed in accordance with Newton's second law:

$$F_{fluid\;left,\,x} - F_{fluid\;right,\,x} = m\,a_x \tag{36}$$

with $a_x = |\mathbf{a}|$ since the acceleration occurs along the x–axis only. Therefore, the force of the fluid on the den-

Fig. 3.26: (a) Sketch of the dendrite (system) in a Pacinian corpuscle which is tilted $45°$ with respect to the palm surface. The x–coordinate is chosen parallel to the palm because this is the direction of the acceleration of the hand. (b) The corresponding free–body–diagram shows the four forces acting on the dendrite: the weight and the buoyant force in the vertical direction, and two contact forces between the extracellular fluid and the dendrite surface. The indices f, l and r stand for "fluid", "left" and "right." This diagram applies when the hand is not accelerated.

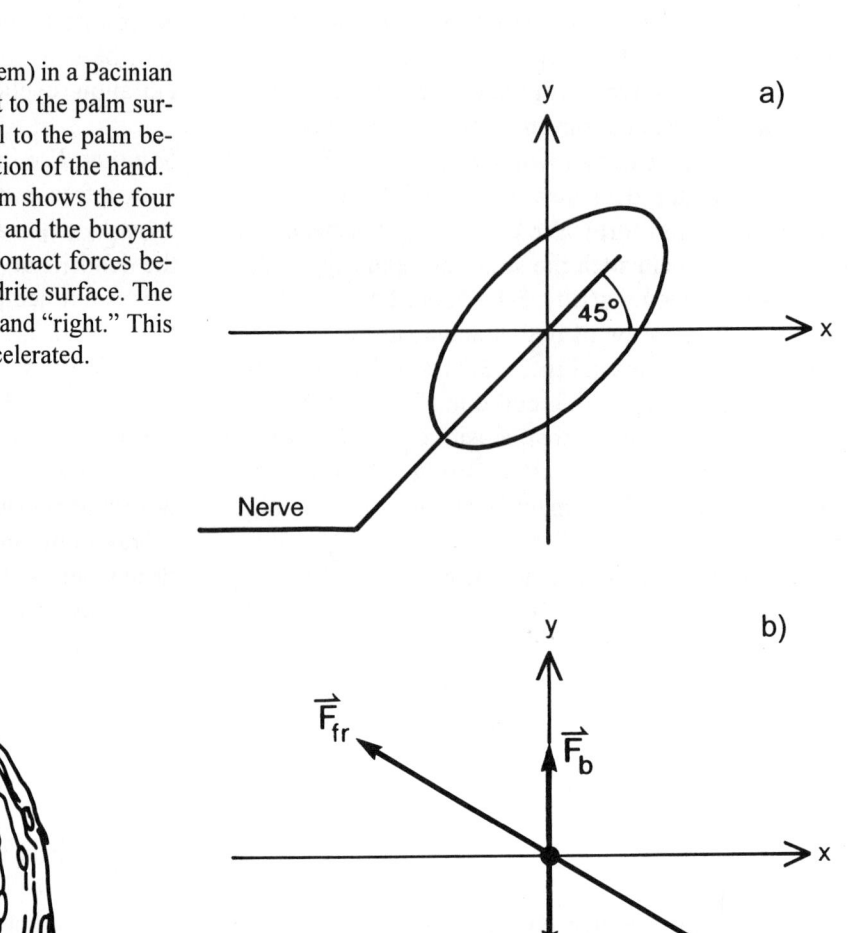

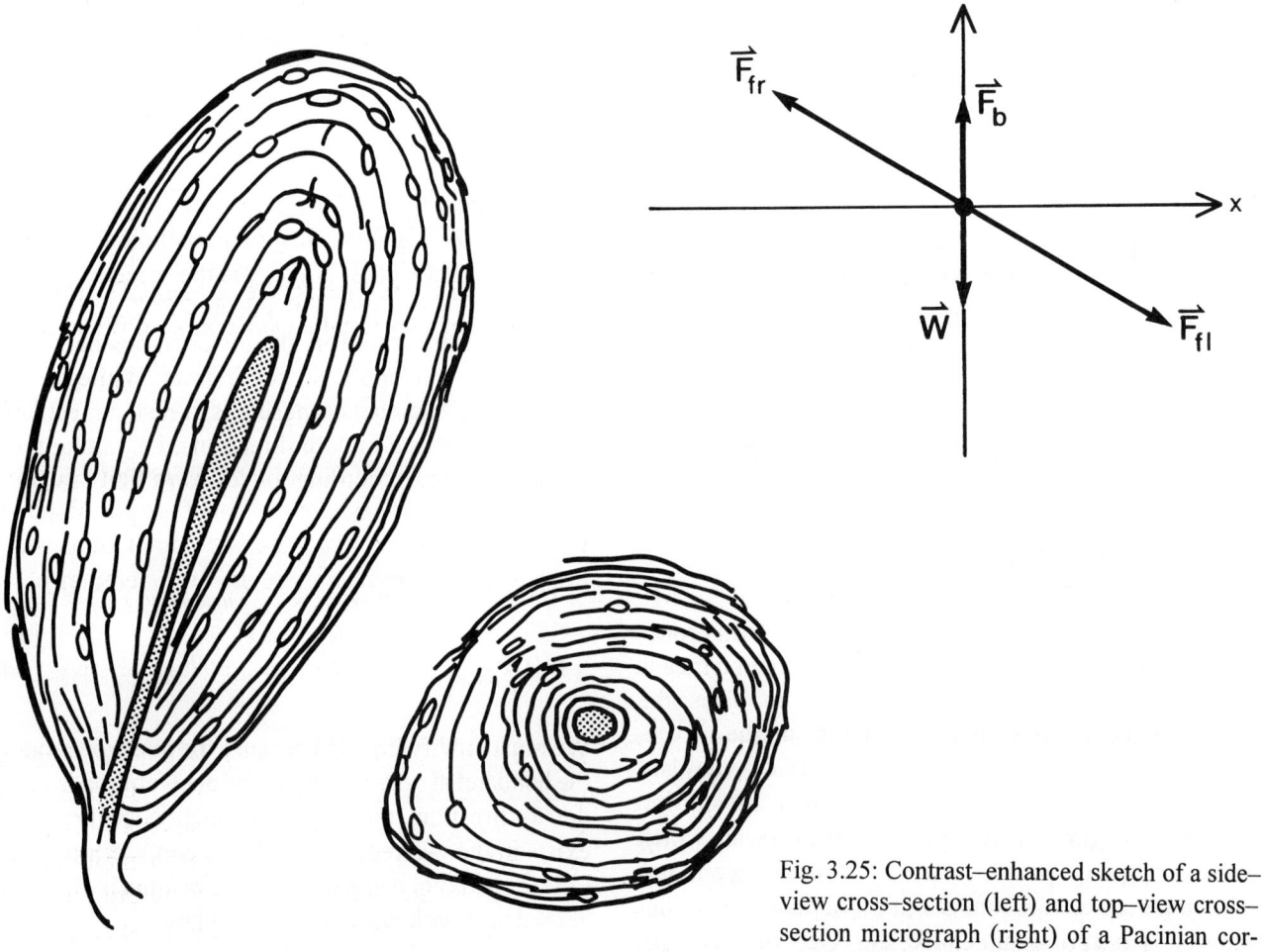

Fig. 3.25: Contrast–enhanced sketch of a side–view cross–section (left) and top–view cross–section micrograph (right) of a Pacinian corpuscle. The scale bar indicates that the size is in the sub–millimeter range. The central dendrite is highlighted with dotted shading. Note the lamellar arrangement of the cells and the extracellular fluid surrounding the dendrite inside the innermost cell membrane.

drite from the left is larger than the force of the fluid from the right because $ma_x \neq 0$.

Using Figs. 3.25 and 3.26, we quantify the difference between the forces in Eq. (36). To do so, we need the mass m of the dendrite. We estimate this mass from the volume and density of the dendrite. The dendrite in a typical Pacinian corpuscle extends slightly more than half the length of the corpuscle, $l \approx 0.33$ mm. The diameter of a myelinated nerve (for a discussion of nerve types see Chapter 13) is 20 μm. We use the density of water ($\rho = 1.0$ g/cm³) as an approximate value for the nerve material (which is a myelin sheath, i.e., a lipid). Modelling the nerve as a cylinder, we determine first its volume V:

$$V = \pi r^2 \, l = \pi (1 \times 10^{-5}[m])^2 \, 3.3 \times 10^{-4}[m] \quad (37)$$
$$\Rightarrow \quad V = 1.0 \times 10^{-13} \, m^3$$

Using this volume we find the mass m of the nerve:

$$m = \rho V = 1 \times 10^{-13}[m^3] \, 1 \times 10^3 \left[\frac{kg}{m^3}\right] \quad (38)$$
$$\Rightarrow \quad m = 1.0 \times 10^{-10} \, kg$$

Thus, the difference in magnitude between both contact forces on the central dendrite ΔF is given as:

$$\Delta F = F_{fluid\ left,\ x} - F_{fluid\ right,\ x} = ma_x \quad (39)$$

which leads to the following numerical value:

$$\Delta F = 1.0 \times 10^{-10} \, [kg] \, 90 \left[\frac{m}{s^2}\right] \quad (40)$$
$$\Rightarrow \quad \Delta F = 9.0 \times 10^{-9} \, N$$

This is the answer to the problem. What does this result mean? In order to accelerate a Pacinian corpuscle, the fluid must push the dendrite faster and faster to the left, in the same way the elastic capsule pushes the liquid, the skin pushes the Pacinian corpuscle and the muscle pushes the whole hand. Due to Newton's third law, the dendrite pushes with the same net force in the opposite direction, i.e., toward the extracellular fluid which encloses it from the left. Since a fluid can flow, this force causes an evasion of the fluid. As this happens, the dendrite bends slightly to the left and this triggers a signal in the nerve.

3.6. Appendix

Momentum
The second law of mechanics also allows us to re-interpret the first law of mechanics for an isolated system. An isolated system does not interact with its environment, which means that it is a system with no external forces. If no external force acts on the system, the net force acting on the system is zero. For such a system, Newton's second law reads:

$$F_{net} = 0 = m \cdot a = m \cdot \lim_{\Delta t \to 0} \frac{\Delta v}{\Delta t} \quad (41)$$

In classical physics, the mass of an isolated system is conserved. Thus, it makes mathematically no difference whether the factor m is outside of the limes–function or pulled inside this function. (This would only lead to a different result if the mass m were a function of time.) Thus, Eq. (41) is equivalent to:

$$\lim_{\Delta t \to 0} \frac{\Delta (m \cdot v)}{\Delta t} = 0 \quad (42)$$

Eq. (42) states that the quantity m**v** for an isolated system is time independent (constant). Such a quantity is called conserved. Since there are very few conserved quantities in nature each is given a name. The product of mass and velocity is called *momentum* **p** [kg m/s]:

$$p = m \cdot v \quad (43)$$

The conservation of momentum also applies to an isolated system containing more than one object. For two or more objects in a system, the total momentum **P** is the vector sum of the individual momentums p_i:

$$P = \sum_i p_i = const \quad (44)$$

in which i is the index identifying the individual objects. Due to Eq. (44), the conservation of momentum is a concept useful in the study of collisions. Collision concepts, however, play only a minor role in biological or physiological applications, and are therefore not discussed in detail. An overview is given in the Appendix of Chapter 6.

Friction
Forces which act against the direction of actual or anticipated motion due to contact between two solid surfaces are called *friction forces*. They originate in a com-

plex fashion from the electrostatic and morphological microstructures of the two surfaces in contact. Electrostatic interactions occur between single atoms or molecules in the two adjacent surfaces; we discuss electrostatic interactions in Chapter 9. The morphological contributions occur at a slightly larger length–scale where the roughness of the two surfaces leads to interlocking. Both processes are too complex to allow us to calculate the macroscopic frictional effect between any two real surfaces.

To circumvent this problem, various simplifying models have been proposed for the frictional force. Due to the wide variations in morphological and electrostatic microstructures of surfaces, such simplifying models are only approximations which may describe a specific case only very poorly.

In some physical literature, particularly in entry–level college textbooks, a very simple model for friction is introduced to allow for a qualitative discussion of sliding processes within the framework of Newton's laws. In this model, friction is not associated with the morphological microstructure of the surface of the object (because that object is modelled as a point mass) nor are the electrostatic features of the surface taken into account. Instead, the frictional force is related to the normal force exerted by the supporting surface. A brief overview of this model for friction is provided here to allow the reader to critically evaluate references to the concept.

For an object placed on a frictionless inclined plane (see Example 3.5) the forces acting on the object parallel to the plane are not balanced. Thus, the object accelerates in the downhill direction. If we replace the point mass with a wooden block with rough surfaces and replace the frictionless inclined plane with a rough, wooden inclined plane, then two other types of motion may result: (I) the wooden block may remain at rest (as if it were glued to the plane) or (II) the wooden block moves down the inclined plane but reaches a *terminal speed* beyond which it does not accelerate.

Studying Example 3.5 more carefully, we recognize the conditions under which either of these two results can occur: an object at rest or moving with a constant speed obeys Newton's first law, i.e., the forces along the inclined plane must be balanced. In Example 3.5 this was initially accomplished by a string which introduced a tension directed upwards along the inclined plane.

We first study the case in which the wooden block remains at rest on the inclined plane. The corresponding free–body–diagram is shown in Fig. 3.27(a). In addition to the forces we discussed in Example 3.5 to act on the object, which are the weight and the normal force, an additional force is introduced in the direction opposed to the direction of the anticipated motion. This direction can be determined by solving the problem for the frictionless case as done in Example 3.5. Note that the additional force $\vec{\mathcal{F}}_{s,\,max}$ is only dashed in the figure. The subscript max indicates that the shown force is the maximum force acting on the object against the direction of motion. The subscript s stands for "static" since the

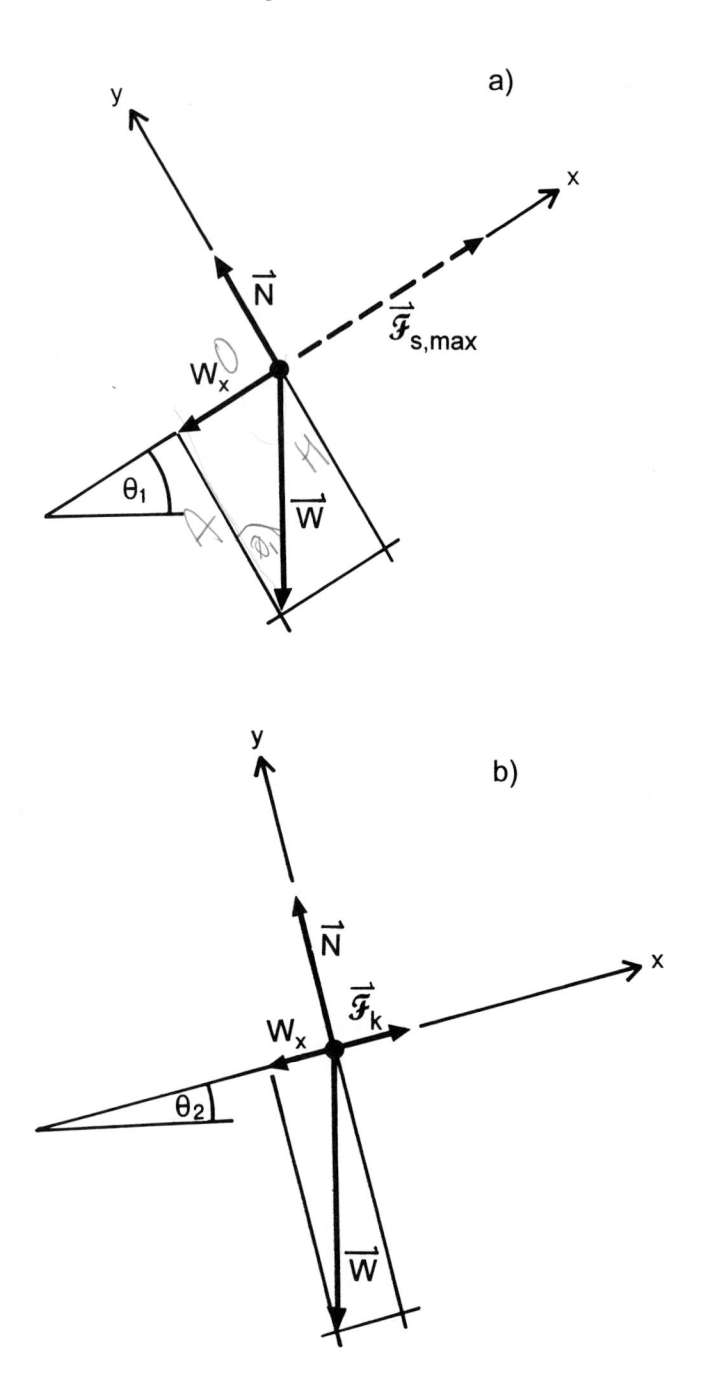

Fig. 3.27: Free–body–diagram for an object on an inclined plane with friction.
(a) The friction force is expressed as a threshold force acting against the direction of anticipated motion while the object is at rest.
(b) When the object is in motion, friction may allow the object to move with a constant terminal speed.

consequence of this force is to allow the object to remain at rest (static case). Based on Newton's first law we know that the actual force acting in the positive x–direction in Fig. 3.27(a) must in magnitude be equal to W_x in order to provide for a mechanical equilibrium along the inclined plane.

Thus, the first type of friction force we introduce is a threshold force $\mathscr{F}_{s,\,max}$; the system remains at rest as long as the force causing the anticipated motion does not exceed this force. We can determine this threshold force experimentally by slowly increasing the angle of the inclined plane until the wooden block starts to move. However, for the friction concept to be considered useful in physics there must be a way to predict the outcome of similar sliding experiments without having to do the experiment every time. This requirement is indeed a weakness of the friction concept since we cannot find a precise method to determine $\mathscr{F}_{s,\,max}$ for all possible combinations of system and inclined surface. What exists is a semi–quantitative estimate of $\mathscr{F}_{s,\,max}$ on the basis of the following equation:

$$|\mathscr{F}_{s,\,max}| = \mu_s \cdot |N| \qquad (45)$$

This equation states that the magnitude of the threshold force is a multiple of the magnitude of the normal force, with the proportionality factor μ_s called the coefficient of static friction. This coefficient depends on the materials of the two objects which are in contact during the sliding (and would further depend on the electrostatic and morphological microstructures of both objects, which are, however, neglected). Values for μ_s lie usually between 0.01 (a synovial joint) and 1.0 (rubber tire on dry concrete). The smaller the coefficient of static friction the easier it is to set the object on the surface in motion.

Next we study the second case in which the wooden object is actually moving along the inclined plane but does so with a constant terminal speed. This case is illustrated in the free–body–diagram shown in Fig. 3.27(b). The object moves with a constant speed, i.e., without acceleration, if the net force along the x–direction is zero (Newton's first law):

$$x\text{–dir.:} \quad \mathscr{F}_k - W_x = 0 \qquad (46)$$

which yields $\mathscr{F}_k = W_x$. A second friction force has been introduced in Eq. (46) which is distinguished with the subscript k for "kinetic." The kinetic friction force is the force which resists the actual motion of an object. Eq. (46) illustrates that this force can be calculated when all other forces in the problem are known and specific conditions have been established such that the object moves with terminal speed. We are faced with the same dilemma as before that the kinetic friction force must be established experimentally for each case and is not predictable for even very similar cases. In analogy to the static friction force, a formula has been developed which allows a rough estimate of the kinetic friction force based on the normal force exerted on the sliding object:

$$|\mathscr{F}_k| = \mu_k \cdot |N| \qquad (47)$$

The coefficient of kinetic friction, μ_k, is usually smaller than the coefficient of static friction. This means that an object needs a larger angle of the inclined plane to overcome the threshold for motion, and that the object then needs a smaller angle of the inclined plane to cease accelerating and reach a terminal speed. Note that this is in general not true. More realistic friction models recognize also a dependence on the velocity of the moving object. A terminal speed can be obtained at any angle of the inclined plane when the velocity dependence is included in the friction model.

Example 3.9
(a) An object is placed on a horizontal surface. Subsequently the surface is tilted. When the surface tilt exceeds an angle of $\theta_1 = 14^0$ with the horizontal, the object starts to slide downhill. What is the coefficient of static friction between the object and the surface?
(b) The object on the same surface moves downhill with a constant speed (terminal speed) if the surface tilt is now changed to a lower angle θ_2. Calculate θ_2 if the coefficient of kinetic friction between the object and the surface is $\mu_K = 0.14$?

Solution part (a): We identify the object on the inclined plane as the system. The forces acting on the object are shown in the free–body–diagram in Fig. 3.27(a). Note that the actual static friction force must be equal to the maximum static friction force at the threshold of motion, which is reached at an angle of $\theta_1 = 14^0$. Thus, we use Fig. 3.27(a) to write Newton's laws for the case just before motion of the objects sets in:

$$\begin{aligned} x\text{–dir.:} &\quad \mathscr{F}_s - W\sin\theta_1 = 0 \\ y\text{–dir.:} &\quad N - W\cos\theta_1 = 0 \end{aligned} \qquad (48)$$

The two formulas in Eq. (48) allow us to substitute the normal force and the static friction force in Eq. (45):

$$\mu_s = \frac{\mathcal{F}_{s,\,max}}{N} = \frac{W \sin\theta_1}{W \cos\theta_1} = \tan\theta_1 \qquad (49)$$

$$\Rightarrow \quad \mu_s = \tan 14^0 = 0.25$$

Solution part (b): Fig. 3.27(b) provides the free–body–diagram when the object slides downwards. Applying Newton's laws, the following formulas are written:

$$\begin{aligned} x\text{--dir.:} &\quad \mathcal{F}_k - W \sin\theta_2 = 0 \\ y\text{--dir.:} &\quad N - W \cos\theta_2 = 0 \end{aligned} \qquad (50)$$

in which both formulas are applications of Newton's first law because the object has reached a terminal speed. The angle θ_2 follows from the ratio of the friction force and the normal force, as shown in Eq. (47):

$$\mu_k = \frac{\mathcal{F}_k}{N} = \frac{W \sin\theta_2}{W \cos\theta_2} = \tan\theta_2 \qquad (51)$$

$$\theta_2 = \tan^{-1}(0.14) = 8^0$$

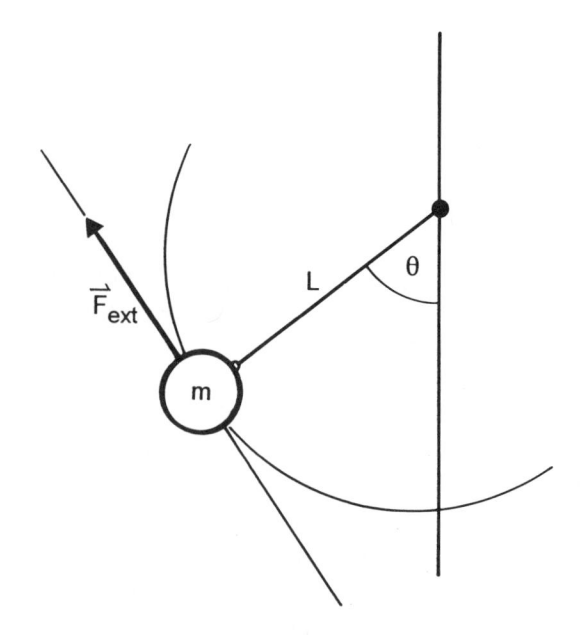

Fig. 3.28 for problem P–3.1.

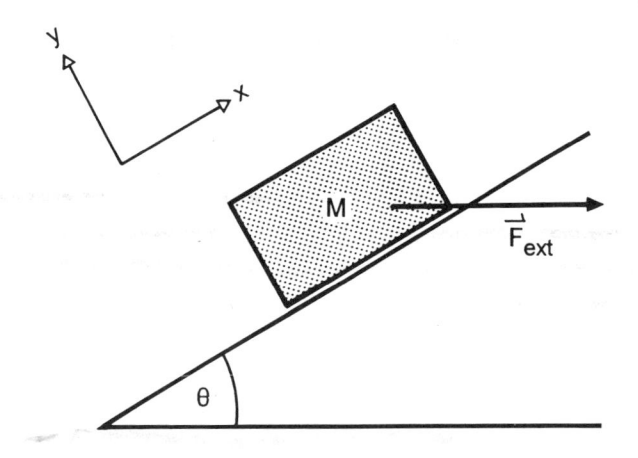

Fig. 3.29 for problem P–3.2.

3.7. Problems

P–3.1
We study once more Example 3.2, except that the direction of the external force is changed to act tangentially to the circular path of the object of mass m = 1.0 kg, as shown in Fig. 3.28. We assume again that the object is held at a position where the string forms an angle of θ = 30⁰ with the vertical.
(a) What is the magnitude of the tension **T** in the string?
(b) What is the magnitude of the force **F**$_{ext}$?
(c) Why is it not possible to repeat the problem with the external force **F**$_{ext}$ acting vertically upwards?

P–3.2
An object of mass M = 75 kg is pushed at a constant speed up a frictionless inclined surface which forms an angle θ = 40⁰ with the horizontal as shown in Fig. 3.29.
(a) What is the magnitude of the horizontal force **F**$_{ext}$?
(b) What force is exerted by the inclined surface on the object?

P–3.3
Fig. 3.30 shows the human leg (a) when it is stretched and (b) when it is bent. Note that the kneecap (3) is embedded in the quadriceps tendon (6) and is needed to protect the quadriceps tendon against wear and tear due to the femur (1) in the bent position.
Assume that the magnitude of the tension in the quadriceps tendon of a bent knee is T = 1500 N. Use an angle of 30⁰ between the horizontal and the direction of the tension above the kneecap, and also use an angle of 70⁰ between the horizontal and the direction of the tension below the kneecap, as shown in Fig. 3.31(a). What are the magnitude and the direction of the resultant force exerted on the femur, as shown in Fig. 3.31(b)?

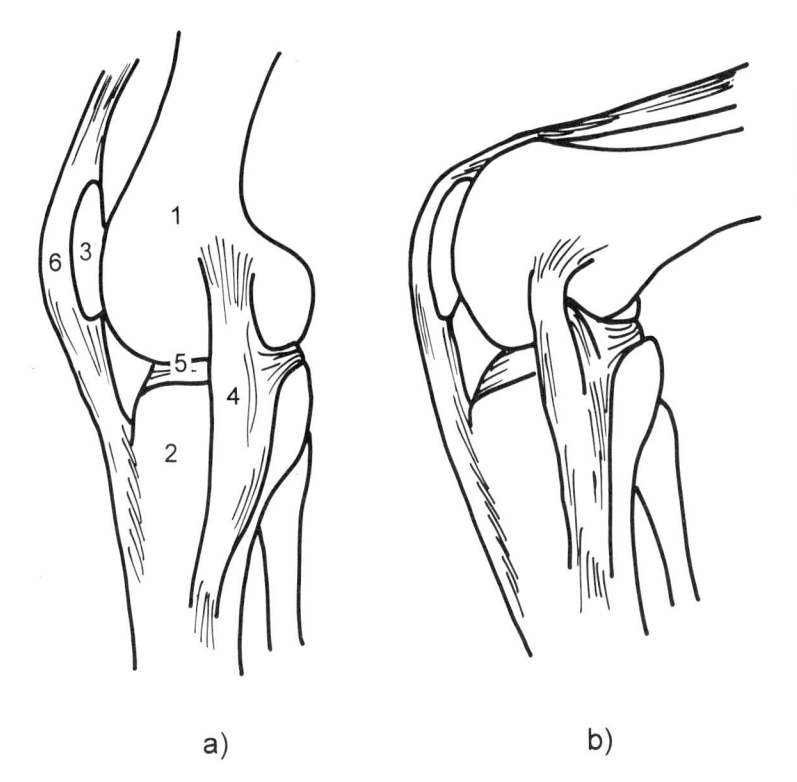

Fig. 3.30 for problem P–3.3. (1) femur, (2) tibia, (3) patella (kneecap), (4) collateral ligaments, (5) meniscus, (6) tendon of quadriceps femoris muscle.

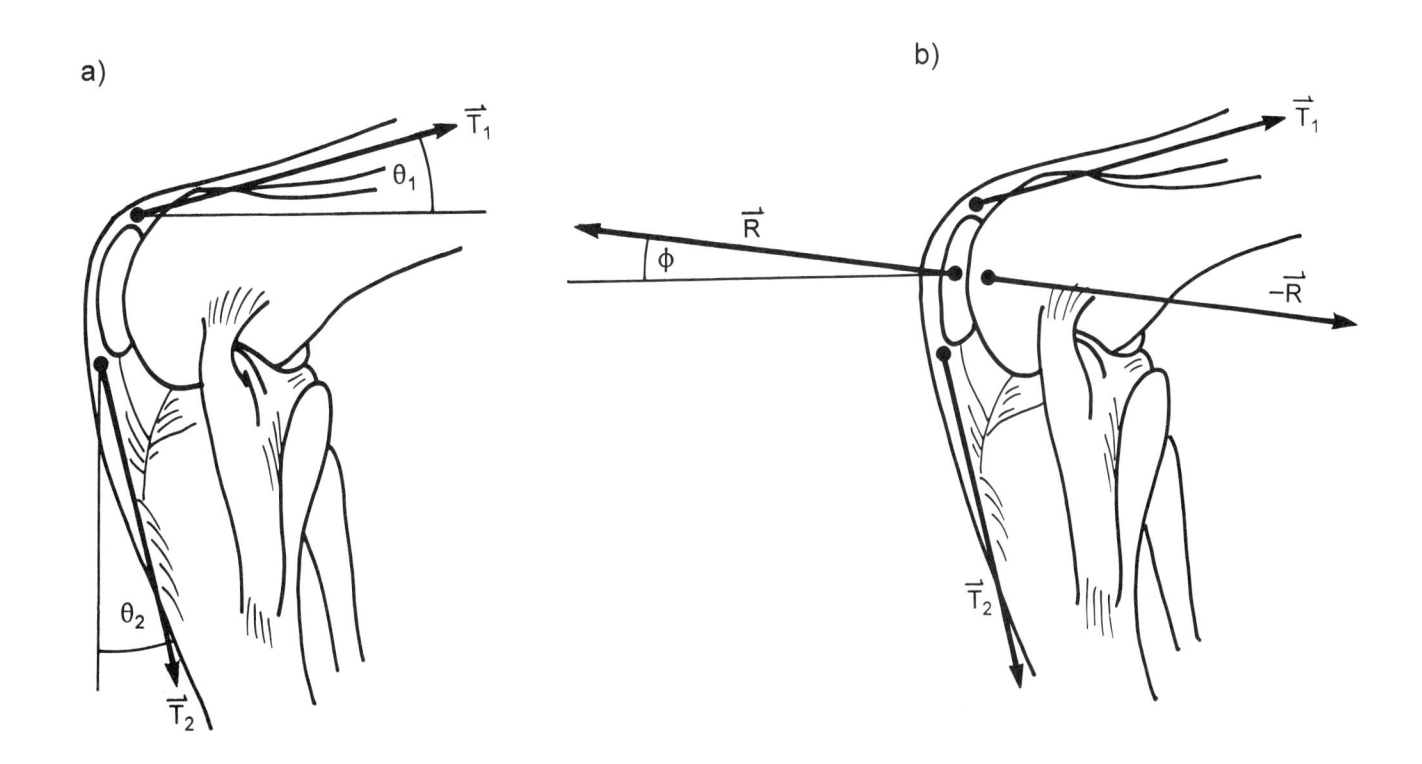

Fig. 3.31 for problem P–3.3.

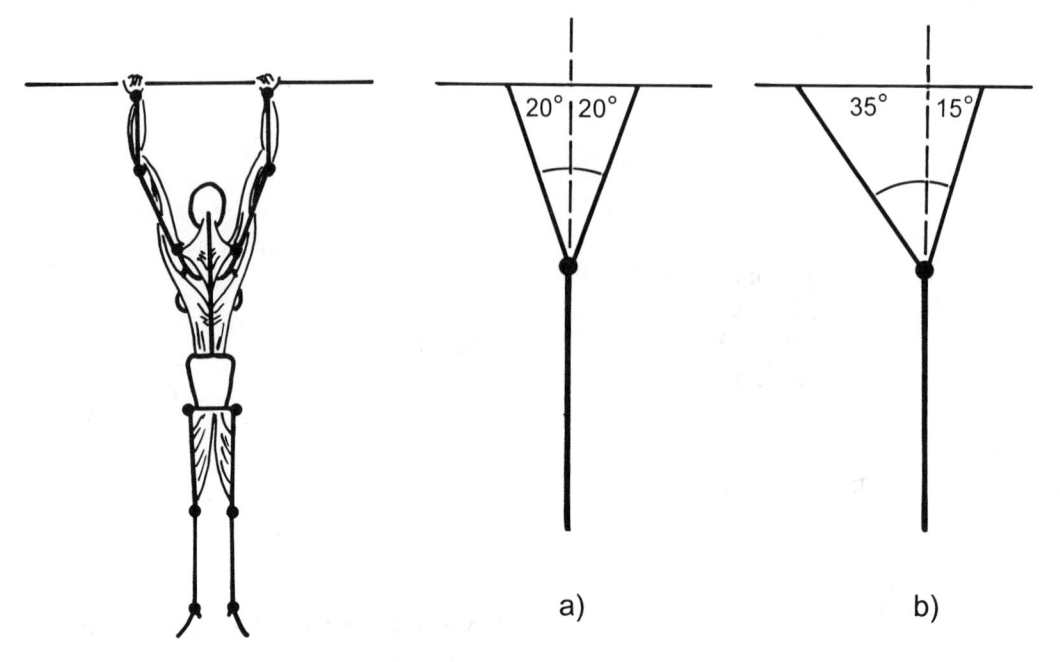

Fig. 3.32 for problem P–3.4.

P–3.4
Fig. 3.32 shows a person of mass m = 70 kg hanging at rest on a horizontal bar.
(a) Assume that the arms are stretched at an angle of 20^0 to the vertical to either side, as shown in the middle sketch. Find the force acting on each arm.
(b) Assume that the arms are held at two different angles as shown in the right sketch. What are the forces acting in each arm in this case?

P–3.5
Leg traction is applied to a patient's leg as shown in Fig. 3.33. If the physician has requested a 50 N force to be applied to the leg and the object hanging from the massless cable has a mass of m = 10 kg, what angle θ must be used?

P–3.6
We consider the standard man shown in Fig. 3.34 using crutches. The crutches each make an angle of $\theta = 22^0$ with the vertical. Half of the person's weight is support-

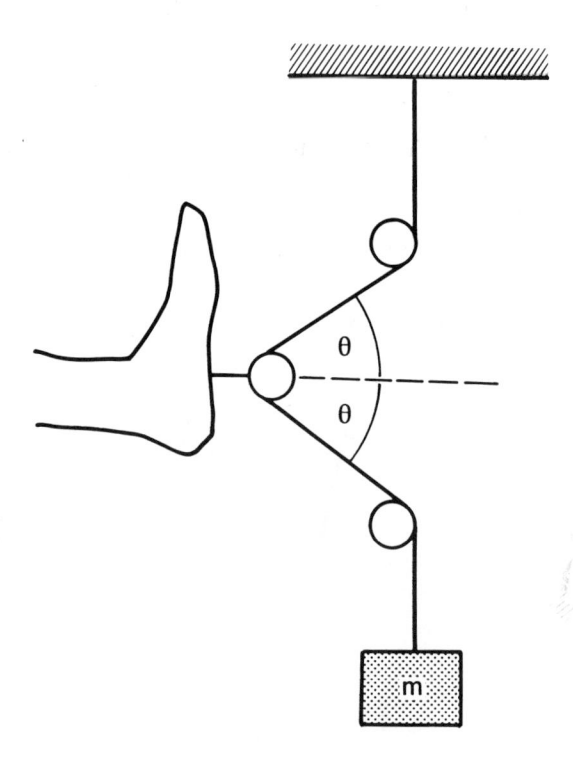

Fig. 3.33 for problem P–3.5.

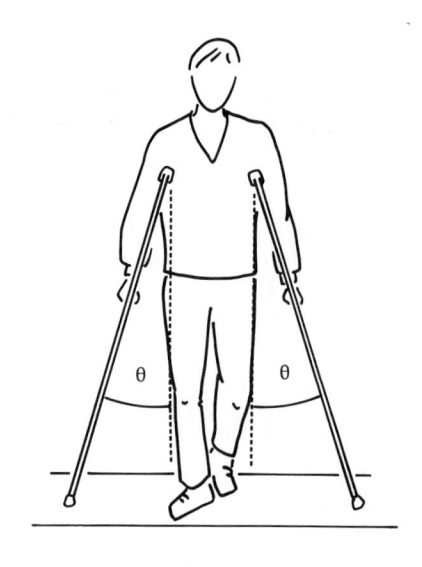

Fig. 3.34 for problem P–3.6.

ed by the crutches, the other half is supported by the normal forces acting on the soles of the feet. Assuming that the person is at rest, find the magnitude of the force supported by each crutch.

P–3.7

There are two forces acting on an object of mass 1.5 kg. Fig. 3.35 shows a top–view of the object. One of the forces is shown and has a magnitude of $|\mathbf{F}_1| = 10$ N. The figure also shows the direction of the acceleration of the object with the magnitude of $|\mathbf{a}| = 10$ m/s² and the angle $\theta = 30°$ with the negative y–axis. Find the missing second force $\mathbf{F}_2$
(a) in component notation, and
(b) as a magnitude and direction.

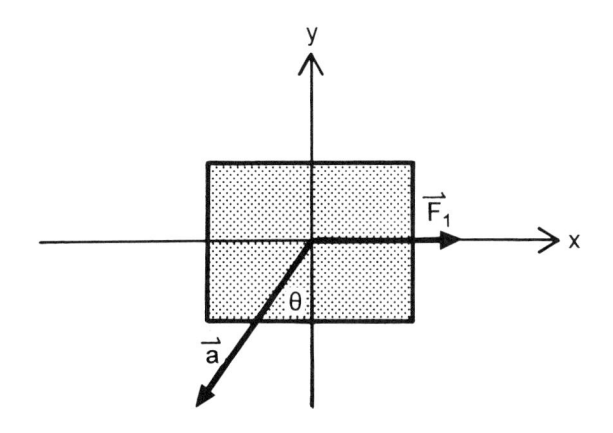

Fig. 3.35 for problem P–3.7.

P–3.8

Fig. 3.36 shows an object of mass $m_1 = 1.0$ kg on an inclined surface. The angle of the inclined surface is $\theta = 30°$ with the horizontal. The object m_1 is connected to a second object of mass $m_2 = 2.5$ kg on the adjacent horizontal surface. Further, an external force of magnitude $|\mathbf{F}_{ext}| = 10$ N is exerted on the object of mass m_1. We observe both objects to accelerate. Assuming that the surfaces and the pulley are frictionless, and the pulley and the connecting string are massless, what is the tension in the string connecting the two objects?

Summary

Laws:

● Newton's first law (law of inertia) for a point mass in mechanical equilibrium:

$$\mathbf{F}_{net} = \sum_{i=1}^{n} \mathbf{F}_i = \mathbf{0}$$

which is equivalent to:

$$F_{net,\, x} = \sum_i F_{ix} = 0$$

$$F_{net,\, y} = \sum_i F_{iy} = 0$$

● Newton's second law (equation of motion) for an accelerating point mass:

$$\mathbf{F}_{net} = \sum_{i=1}^{n} \mathbf{F}_i = m \cdot \mathbf{a}$$

which is equivalent to:

$$F_{net,\, x} = \sum_i F_{ix} = m \cdot a_x$$

$$F_{net,\, y} = \sum_i F_{iy} = m \cdot a_y$$

● Newton's third law:
When an object A acts on an object B with force $\mathbf{F}_{Ba}$, then there is a force $\mathbf{F}_{Ab}$ exerted by object B on object A with:

$$\mathbf{F}_{Ab} = -\mathbf{F}_{Ba}$$

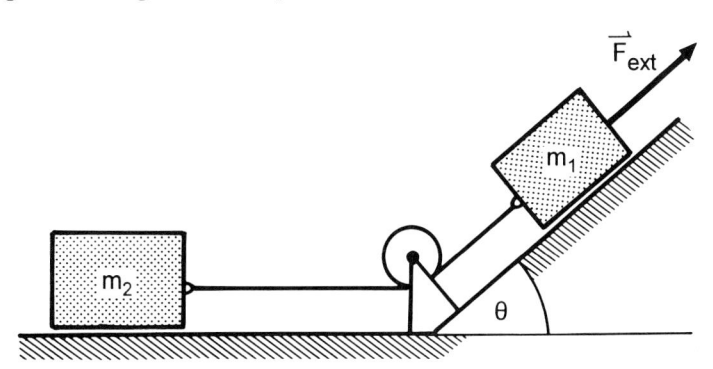

Fig. 3.36 for problem P–3.8.

Chapter IV

Kinesiology

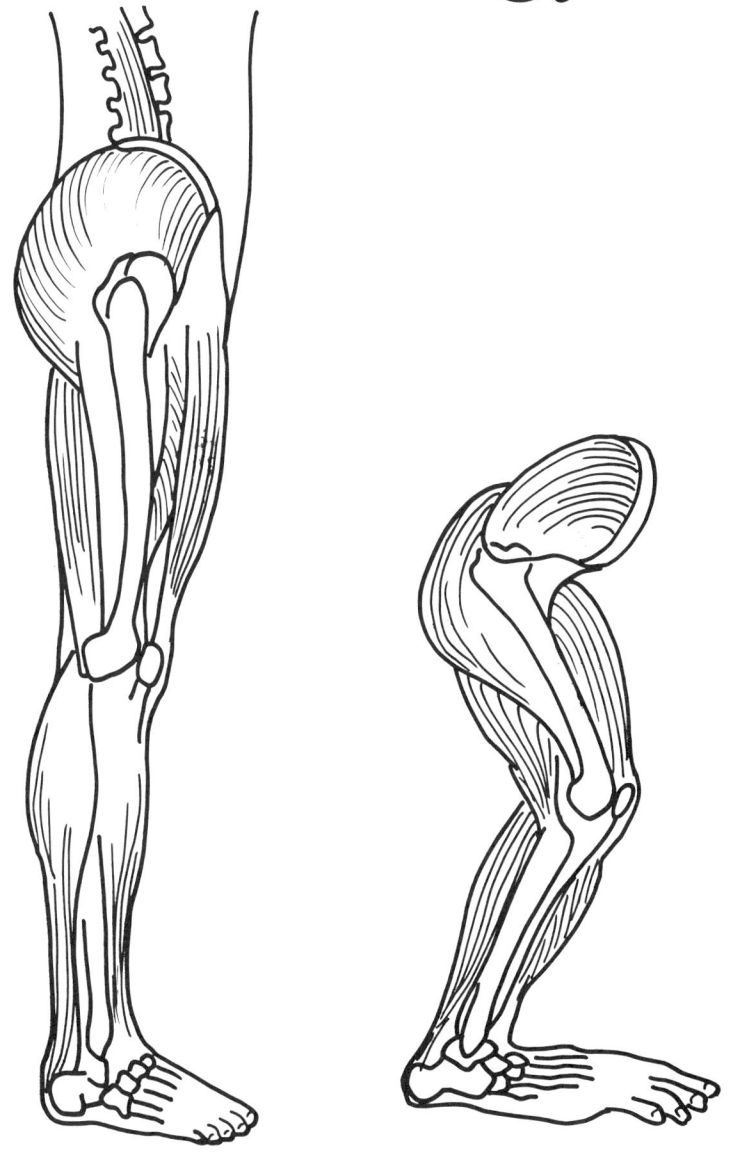

The action of forces at joints

KINESIOLOGY
THE ACTION OF FORCES AT JOINTS

More complex patterns of motion emerge when the size and the shape of objects are no longer negligible. The simplifying assumption of a rigid body excludes vibrations and deformations which we discuss in Chapter 15, leaving us to focus here on rotations. Choosing the rotation of a human lower arm about the elbow joint as a typical example we note that motion in a two–dimensional plane is achieved when the rotation occurs about a fixed axis directed perpendicular to the plane of action.

We distinguish two types of forces acting on a rigid body with a fixed axis: forces which act along a line through the axis of rotation do not lead to a rotation. Forces acting in other directions cause increasingly stronger rotations as the magnitude of the force increases and/or the perpendicular distance from the axis of rotation to the line of action of the force increases. These variables are combined to define the torque as a measure of the effectiveness of a rotation.

The concept of mechanical equilibrium has to be extended to apply to a rigid body; besides Newton's first law (the net force on the object must be zero) the sum of torque contributions due to all forces acting on the object must vanish. If the latter condition is not met, the object begins to spin faster and faster. Applying the mechanical equilibrium for rigid bodies to various joints in the human body reveals the large magnitude of forces acting in tendons during regular locomotion.

In the previous two chapters we discussed the mechanics of objects for which a point mass was a sufficient model. To be a valid assumption, the spatial extension of the body has to be negligible. Often, when for example studying the locomotive system of vertebrates, this assumption is not applicable. This is not only due to the size of bones relative to the size of the body, but has its origin in the rotational rather than translational mobility of the joints. Since rotations cannot be described with the mechanics of point masses, motion at joints requires additional considerations.

In this chapter we study first the various types of joints. They all share a fundamental design principle illustrated in Fig. 4.1: two skeletal muscles are attached to the bones adjacent to the joint, one muscle each for clockwise and counter–clockwise rotation (antagonistic muscles). Since the tendons connecting these muscles to the bones are usually attached close to the joint, large forces are needed to achieve the locomotion. We establish this observation first using geometrical considerations and confirm the occurrence of large forces then by applying a mechanical equilibrium condition to specific cases. The large forces exerted by the skeletal muscles point to a medical relevance of the current chapter: joints have a relatively high likelihood of failure during their life–time, not only as a result of injury (tendon and ligament rupture) but also as a result of degeneration (arthrosis).

4.1. Geometry of the rotation at joints

4.1.1. Fundamental types of movable joints

We distinguish five types of movable joints based on the possible directions of rotation of the adjacent bones. These five types are sketched schematically in Fig. 4.2:
(A) the spheroid or ball–and–socket joint has three orthogonal rotation axes. Note that only the bone farther from the trunk rotates.
(B) The ellipsoid joint has two orthogonal rotation axes. The third rotation along the bone's axis is no longer possible because of the elliptic fit of the head of the bone into the socket of the adjacent bone.
(C) The hinge or ginglymoid joint has one rotation axis perpendicular to both bones.
(D) The pivot joint has one rotation axis parallel to the bones.
(E) The saddle joint has two orthogonal rotation axes.

Fig. 4.2: The five fundamental types of movable joints: (A) the spheroid or ball–and–socket joint with three orthogonal axes of rotation, (B) the ellipsoid joint with two orthogonal axes of rotation perpendicular to the adjacent bones, (C) the hinge or ginglymoid joint with one axis of rotation, (D) the pivot joint with one axis of rotation pointing along the axis of the adjacent bones, and (E) the saddle joint with two axes of rotation, one for each of the two bones adjacent to the joint. The possible directions of rotation are indicated with an icon in each case.

Fig. 4.1: Arrangement of the biceps muscle (1) and the triceps muscle (2) in the upper arm. The biceps is connected to the scapula (6) and the radius (3), which runs parallel to the ulna (4) in the lower arm. The muscle action of the biceps and triceps rotate the lower arm relative to the humerus (5) at the elbow joint. ⇒

63

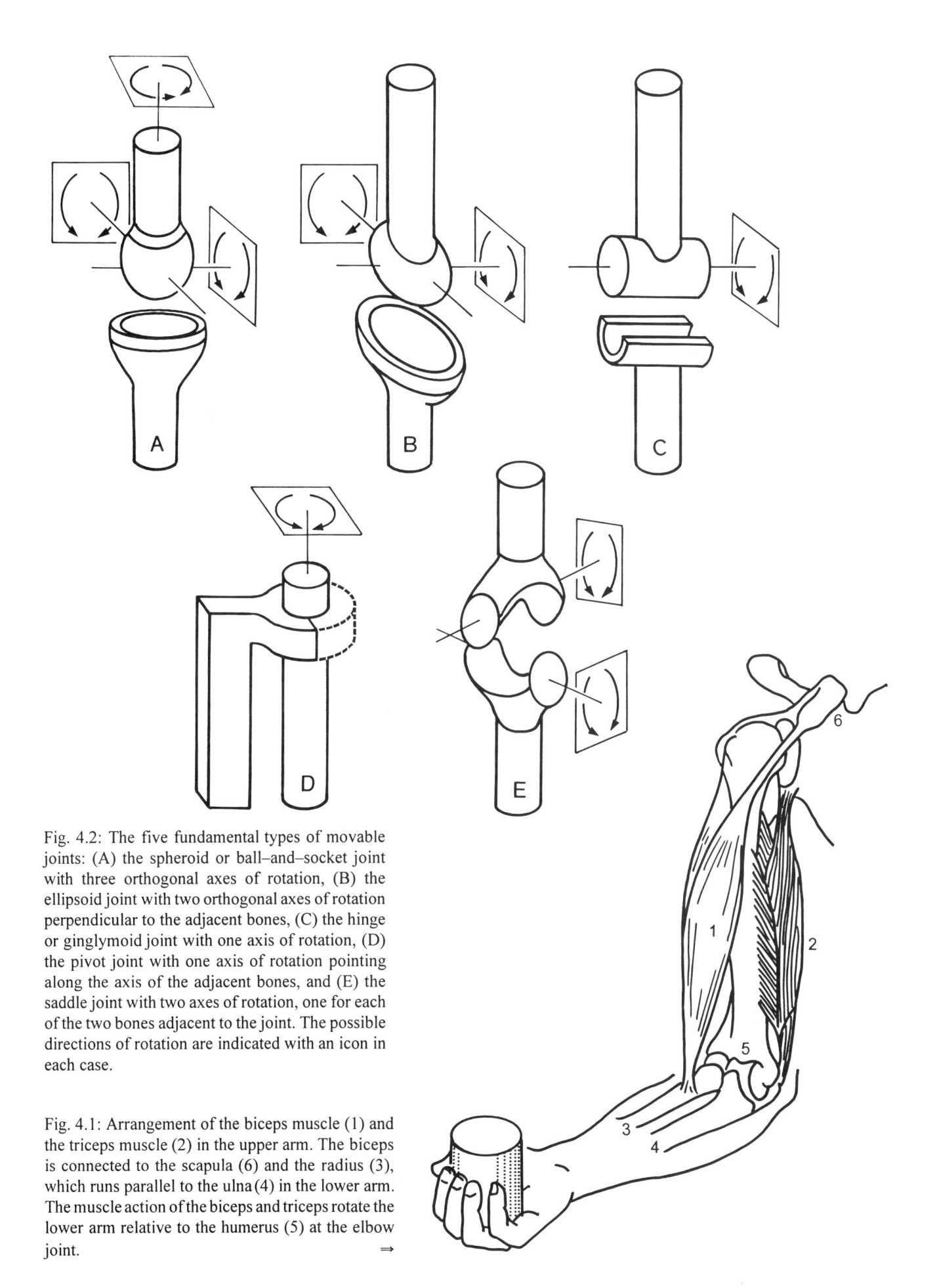

The mobility of the two adjacent bones defines the difference between the ellipsoid joint and the saddle joint: both rotations involve the bone farther from the trunk for the ellipsoid joint while each bone performs one of the rotations for the saddle joint.

Together with the gliding joint, which does not allow for a rotation of bones, these five types of movable joints are called the synovial joints as they contain synovial fluid, a lubricant that prevents wear and tear on the joint. We illustrate the five movable joint types with a few examples each.

Spheroid joint

The spheroid joint has the most degree of freedom of rotation of the five mobile joints, permitting the greatest mobility. For this reason it is most frequently found where limbs are connected to the trunk of an animal. The shoulder and hip joints shown in Fig. 4.3 are examples in the human body.

Due to their versatility, spheroid joints have been developed early in animal life. Each spine of a sea urchin has a ball-and-socket joint to provide for locomotion. The shoulder joint of primates in particular is extremely versatile; we can spin the arm through essentially all points of a hemisphere. Shoulder joints of other vertebrates, such as cats, do not have the same versatility; a similar mobility is only reached by the boneless trunk of an elephant, the boneless arms of an octopus or the multi-boned neck of an ostrich.

Surgical replacement of the highly mobile hip joint requires six steps, as illustrated in Fig. 4.4. The ball-and-socket design required for the replacement parts is clearly evident.

The shoulder and hip joints are studied further in this chapter: the shoulder joint is used to illustrate the concept of rotation of a rigid body; the hip joint is used in Example 4.5 demonstrating the need of a well-developed mutual adaptation of the two adjacent bones to guarantee safe operation of the joint.

Ellipsoid joint

The next most mobile types of joints are the ellipsoid joint and the saddle joint. Of these two joints the ellipsoid joint is much more common because it provides greater mobility for the bone farther away from the trunk. We illustrate this type of joint with the wrist joint in Fig. 4.5. This joint lies between the two arm bones, ulna and radius, on one side and the wrist bones on the other side. You can tilt your hand left/right and back/forth. Because the wrist is an ellipsoid joint, you cannot rotate your hand about the axis defined by your lower arm.

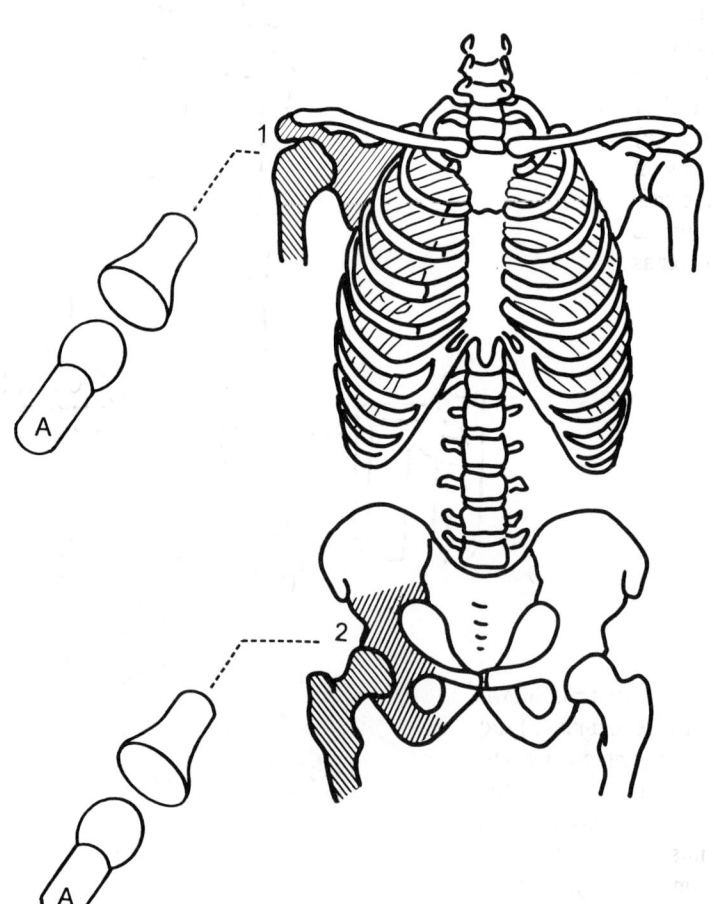

Fig. 4.3: Overview of the human trunk skeleton with shaded highlighting of the shoulder joint (1) and the hip joint (2). The icons illustrate the orientation of the two ball-and-socket joints.

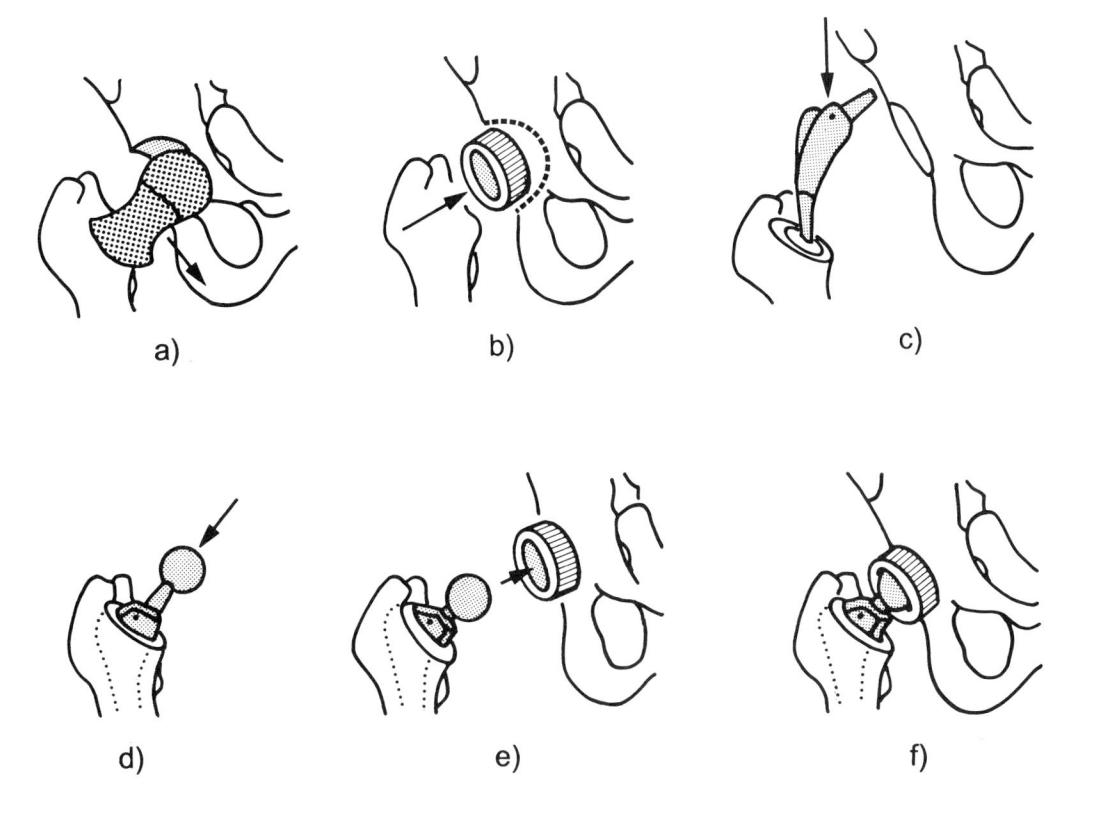

Fig. 4.4: What happens during an artificial hip replacement? (a) The surgeon removes the head of the femur and (b) implants an artificial socket in the acetabulum. In the next step (c) the base of the femur prosthesis is screwed or cemented into the bone and (d) the artificial head of the prosthesis is connected to the base. In the last step (e) the ball is located in the socket and (f) fastened to prevent separation. For elderly patients the cementing of the artifical parts is preferred as the recovery is faster but the longevity is not guaranteed. Screwed parts heal slower as the bone grows into the prosthesis surface.

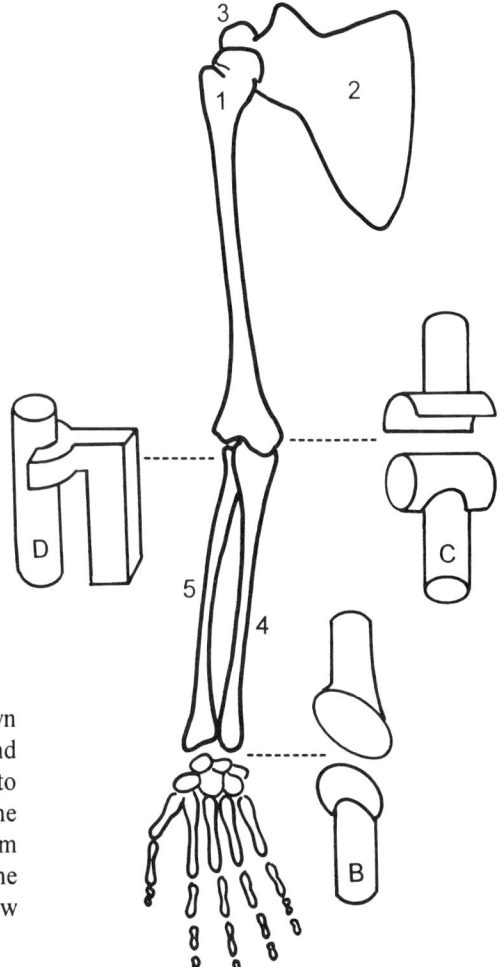

Fig. 4.5: Anatomic overview of the human arm. Shown are the humerus (1) which connects to the scapula (2) and the collarbone (3) at the shoulder joint, and connects to ulna (4) and radius (5) at the elbow joint. Note that the radius is located on the same side as the thumb. The arm includes three different types of joints, a hinge joint at the elbow, a pivot joint between ulna and radius just below the elbow and an ellipsoid joint at the wrist.

65

Hinge joint

Due to the high degree of mobility of the shoulder and hip joints, limb joints further away from the trunk maintain a high flexibility with less mobile types of joints, which in turn are structurally more sturdy. The compromise between versatility and stability favors the hinge joint, making it the most frequently occurring joint of vertebrate skeletons. Examples in the human body include the elbow, the knee and the upper ankle. The elbow is highlighted in Fig. 4.5 for the stretched arm and in Fig. 4.1 for the lower arm lifted. We use the elbow joint below to discuss the implications of the attachment of the biceps and triceps muscles close to the joint. The upper ankle joint is used in Example 4.3 to study the action of the Achilles tendon. This example will illustrate that very large forces act during normal use of our locomotive system.

The knee joint in Fig. 4.6 illustrates the complexity of an actual joint. Several cartilage layers and ligaments protect the joint against wear and tear due to the large forces which frequently act on it. The knee connects the femur of the upper leg to both tibia and fibula in the lower leg. The facing surfaces of the bones are covered by a cartilage layer. In arthrosis, this layer is worn down all the way to the bone. The meniscus lies behind various ligaments which act as shock absorbers. They also distribute the force evenly across the meniscus. Injury to the meniscus often accelerates the deterioration of the joint. Further ligaments, including the cruciate ligaments and the collateral ligaments, stabilize the joint. Rupture or injury of these ligaments loosens the joint and accelerates the wear and tear during regular use. The kneecap (shown in the figure folded down) improves the force transfer from the quadriceps femoris muscle to the lower leg. This force transfer is discussed in one of the problem sets. The kneecap in turn protects the tendon of the quadriceps femoris muscle against wear and tear due to rubbing across the end of the femur when bending the knee; this feature has already been discussed in problem P–3.3.

The complexity of the knee is the result of several design compromises in adopting the joint to an upright posture. These adjustments include a limited ability to rotate, which is not needed in the elbow joint. We would walk like ducks without this feature. At the same time, the knee must be extremely stable because it has to endure forces up to ten times the weight of the person while running. The knees of quadrupeds do not have to meet the same specification.

Pivot joint

The pivot joint and the saddle joint are rare joint types. The pivot joint requires two co–axial bones as the sketch in Fig. 4.2 indicates. Such a connection occurs between

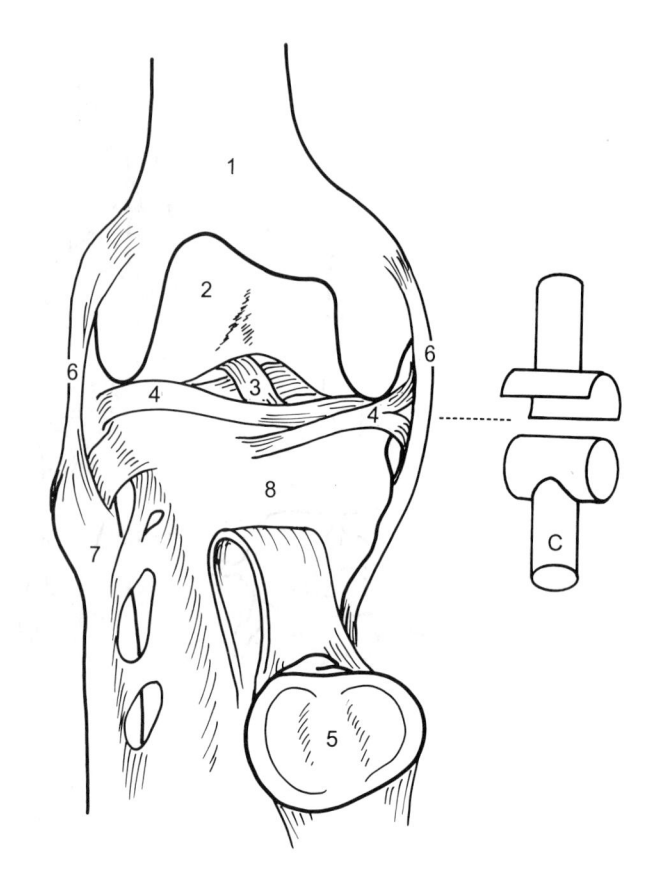

Fig. 4.6: The knee is a hinge joint as indicated by the icon. Its complexity stems from the versatility and robustness required of the knee for a bipedal posture. The main components include: (1) femur, (2) cartilage layer of the bones, (3) cruciate ligaments, (4) meniscus, (5) patella, (6) collateral ligaments, (7) fibula, and (8) tibia.

the first and second cervical vertebra, highlighted in the lateral overview of the head in Fig. 4.7. The second cervical vertebra, which is the lower bone in the close–up in Fig. 4.7, is called the axis and reaches through the center hole in the doughnut–shaped first cervical vertebra, which is called the atlas. Note that the atlas/axis joint of the predatory dinosaurs was a ball–and–socket joint.

The second example of a pivot joint is identified in Fig. 4.5 and allows for limited rotation of the lower arm. This rotation does not occur directly in the elbow joint which is a hinge joint, but is due to the radius rotating about its axis in a groove of the ulna in the lower arm.

Saddle joint

The carpometacarpal joint of the thumb is a saddle joint. As indicated in Fig. 4.8, the corresponding joints for the other fingers are fused, preventing any rotation. To illustrate the saddle motion, note first that your thumb has

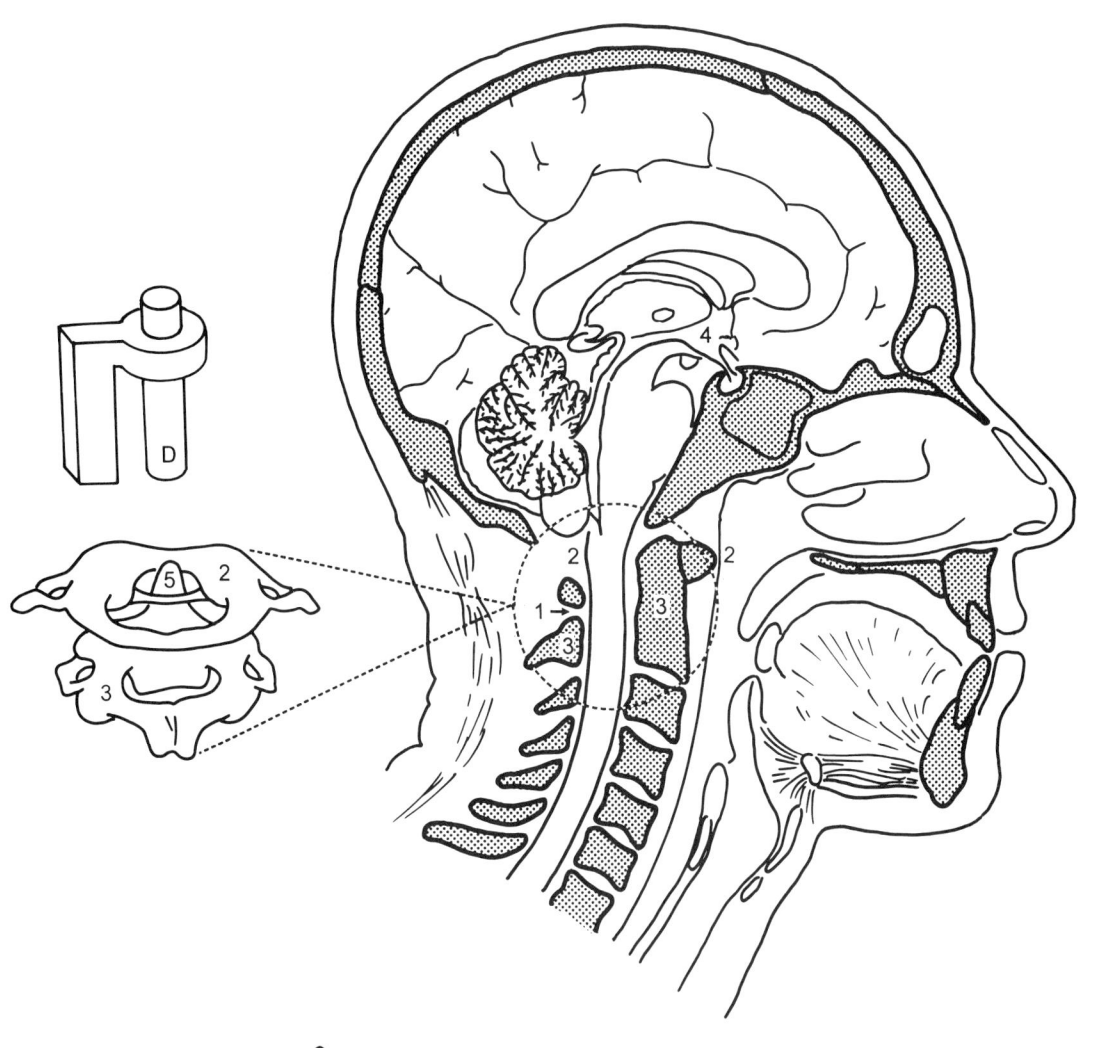

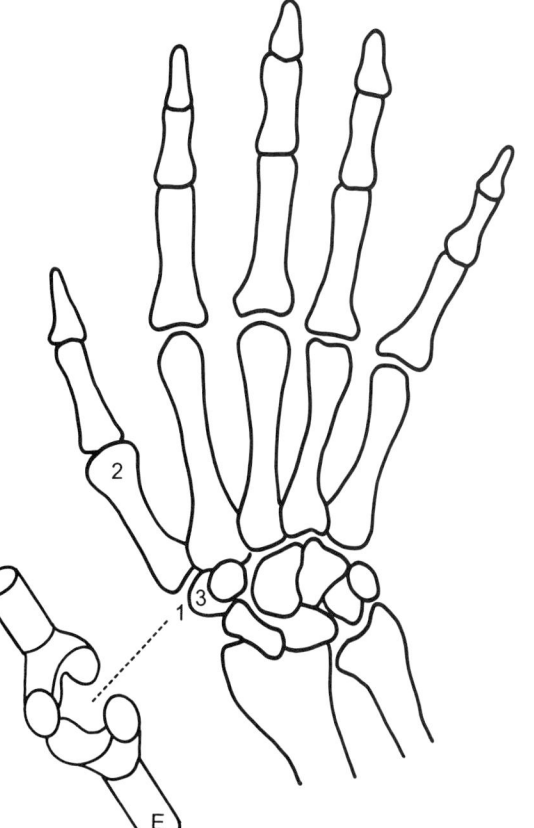

Fig. 4.7: Lateral overview of the head. A pivot joint (1) lies between the first cervical vertebra (atlas, 2) and the second cervical vertebra (axis, 3). This joint allows the head to turn sideways. The arrangement of atlas and axis is highlighted at the left below the icon for the pivot joint. This inset illustrates how a pivot joint is formed between the atlas (2) and the axis (3): the pin–head of the axis (5) reaches between the atlas and the horizontal ligament of the atlas. Note also the hypothalamus region in the main part (4) which we refer to in Chapter 5.

Fig. 4.8: The carpometacarpal joint of the thumb (1) between the first metacarpal (2) and the trapezium (3). The illustration is a simplified sketch of an X–ray image. The icon symbolizes the saddle joint.

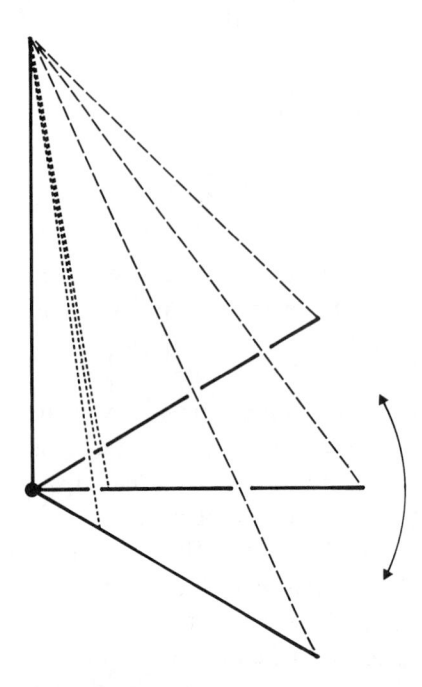

Fig. 4.9: A comparison of the required length of the biceps muscle (and its tendons) for an actual human arm with the muscle attached close to the elbow joint (short dashed line) and a hypothetical biceps muscle attached close to the wrist (long dashed line). Three positions of the lower arm are sketched: horizontal and rotated 45° upwards and downwards.

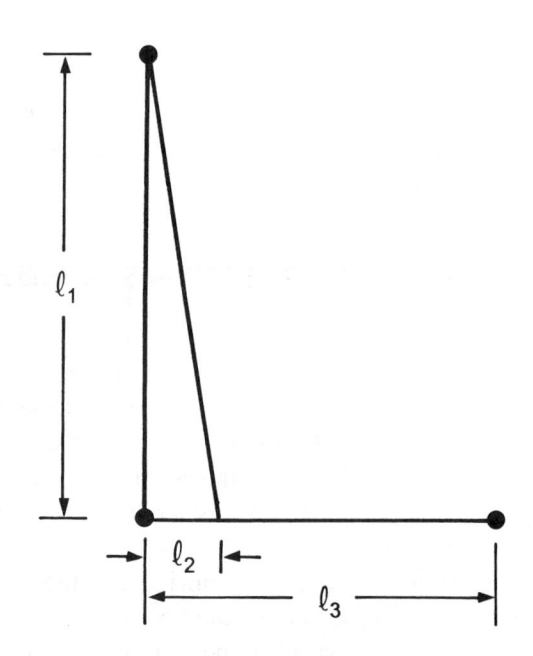

Fig. 4.10: A simplified sketch of the arrangement of the biceps and the upper and lower arm bones. The sketch illustrates l_1, which is the length of the upper arm from shoulder to elbow, l_2, which is the length from the elbow joint to the attachment of the tendon of the biceps muscle, and l_3, which is the length of the lower arm from elbow to wrist.

two directions of rotation, toward and away from the index finger and back and forth relative to the plane of the open palm. The second motion, however, is significantly reduced when you hold the great multangular bone (labelled (3) in Fig. 4.8) with your other hand. This shows that the mobility of this joint is due to rotation of both adjacent bones. To compare with an ellipsoid joint, hold your lower arm tight and observe the mobility of the hand at the wrist joint: neither of the two rotations of the hand is hindered, indicating the different nature of this type of joint in agreement with Fig. 4.2.

4.1.2. Muscular arrangement and the rotation of the elbow joint

Two skeletal muscles are needed for each rotation of a joint; these are called antagonistic muscles. The action of each of the two muscles counter-balances that of the other, i.e., one is stretched because the other contracts. In Fig. 4.1 this is shown for the biceps and triceps muscles which operate the elbow joint. Note that neither of the two muscles is attached to the joint itself. The biceps is attached to the radius a short distance away from the elbow joint. This way, contracting the biceps pulls the lower arm up. The triceps in turn connects to the ulna behind the elbow joint. Thus, contracting the triceps muscle pulls the lower arm down.

We noted for Fig. 2.2 that each single sarcomere in the muscle cell can vary in length between −20 % and +35 % of the average length of 2.1 µm. Assuming that all sarcomeres in a muscle contract or extend in a synchronous fashion, the same relative length variation limits apply to the entire muscle. This finding is important for the evolutionary design of the upper arm in Fig. 4.1: the elbow joint is a hinge joint which works like the hinges on a door. When you try to open a door close to the hinges, you need a much larger force than you need to open the door far from the hinges. This is why the door knob is found far from the hinges. Comparing the lower arm to the door, we conclude that a muscle attached to the radius close to the wrist (i.e., far from the elbow) would significantly reduce the amount of force required to lift the lower arm. Why then is the biceps attached to the radius close to the elbow joint? The reason is illustrated qualitatively in Fig. 4.9, in which the upper arm (humerus) is shown as a stationary, vertical line and the radius is shown in three positions: when horizontal, when tilted up by 45° and when tilted down by 45°. In each case the "actual biceps" (short-dashed line) and an "alternative biceps attached to the wrist" (long–dashed line) are shown. Although a muscle attached to the wrist would indeed require less force, it would in turn have to vary in length much more. With the physiological limitation of −20 % and +35 % of the average length, this would severely reduce the angular range of the motion of the lower arm.

===

Example 4.1
Fig. 4.10 is a simplified sketch of the biceps muscle and bone arrangement shown in Fig. 4.1. Assuming that the three lengths in the figure are given as $l_1 = 38$ cm, $l_2 = 3.5$ cm and $l_3 = 30$ cm, what is the relative contraction (in %) of the biceps (including its tendons) when the lower arm
(a) is raised to $\psi = 45°$ above the horizontal, and
(b) is lowered to $\phi = 45°$ below the horizontal.
(c) If the biceps were instead connected to the end of the radius as shown in Fig. 4.9 (at distance l_3 from the elbow joint), to what angle could the person lift the lower arm when the biceps muscle contracts 20 % (maximum contraction).

Solution parts (a) and (b): Fig. 4.11 illustrates the first two parts of the problem. We label the direction towards the right the x–axis and the direction vertically upwards the y–axis. Starting with the lower arm perpendicular to the upper arm (left sketch), we find with the Pythagorean theorem that the length of the biceps muscle (including its tendons) is:

$$|l_m| = \sqrt{l_1^2 + l_2^2} = \\ = \sqrt{38^2[cm^2] + 3.5^2[cm^2]} = 38.16 \ cm \quad (1)$$

This length is needed to solve the first two parts of the problem because the example asks for changes relative to it.

Solution part (a): We assume that the lower arm is raised to an angle of $\psi = 45°$ with the horizontal as shown in the second sketch of Fig. 4.11. This leads to a shortening of the length of the biceps muscle. We use vector addition to quantify this effect. The vector describing the length and the orientation of the biceps muscle is l_m, it equals the sum of the vector of the stationary upper arm, l_1, and the vector from the joint to the point of the lower arm at which the biceps muscle is attached, l_2:

$$l_m = l_1 + l_2 \quad (2)$$

which is given in component form as:

$$l_m = \begin{pmatrix} 0 \\ -l_1 \end{pmatrix} + \begin{pmatrix} l_2 \cos 45° \\ l_2 \sin 45° \end{pmatrix} \quad (3)$$

In Eq. (3) the brackets represent the components of a two–dimensional vector with the upper entry the x–com-

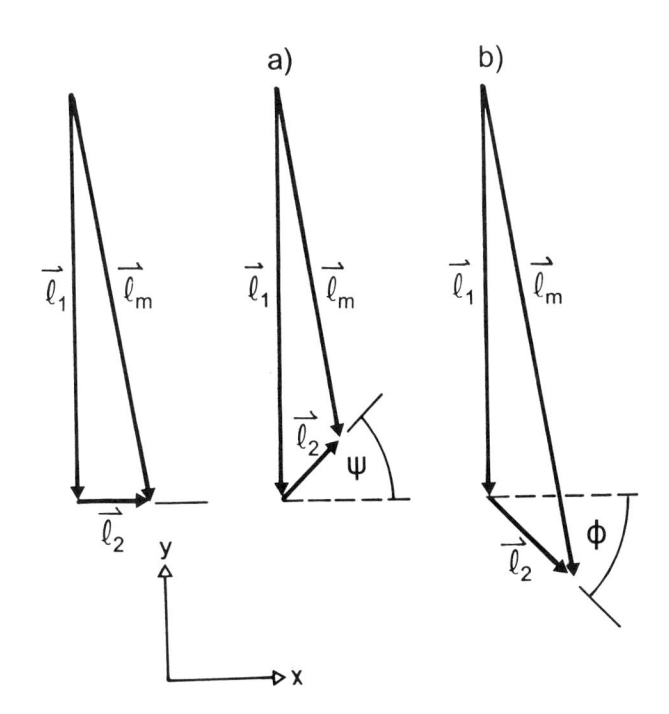

Fig. 4.11: Three geometrical sketches showing the mathematical vector relations for the arrangement in Fig. 4.10: the sum of the vector representing the upper arm l_1, and vector representing the lower arm between the elbow joint and the attachment point of the biceps l_2, equals the vector representing the biceps muscle with its tendons l_m. The sketch at the left shows the lower arm at an angle of 90° with the upper arm. (a) the lower arm lifted by 45°. (b) the lower arm lowered by 45°.

ponent and the lower entry the y–component. Using the Pythagorean theorem we calculate the length of the vector in Eq. (3):

$$|l_m| = \sqrt{l_2^2 \cos^2 45^0 + (l_2 \sin 45^0 - l_1)^2} \quad (4)$$

Eq. (4) yields:

$$l_m = 35.61 \; cm \quad (5)$$

The result in Eq. (5) means that the length of the muscle (with tendon) has changed from 38.16 cm to 35.61 cm.

But this does not answer the question! In the question the relative contraction, in unit of [%], is sought. To get that number an additional step of calculation is needed:

$$\frac{l_{m,\,final} - l_{m,\,initial}}{l_{m,\,initial}} = \frac{\Delta l}{l_{m,\,initial}} =$$

$$= \frac{38.16[cm] - 35.61[cm]}{38.16[cm]} = 0.067 \quad (6)$$

The contraction is 6.7 %, well within the accessible range for the biceps muscle.

Solution part (b): Studying the third sketch in Fig. 4.11, you notice that the muscle is stretched rather than contracted as in part (a). The resulting length change is expected to be similar but not the same as that in part (a). First we determine the length of the biceps (and tendon) in the third sketch of Fig. 4.11:

$$l_m = l_1 + l_2 \quad (7)$$

We rewrite Eq. (7) in component form:

$$l_m = \begin{pmatrix} 0 \\ -l_1 \end{pmatrix} + \begin{pmatrix} l_2 \cos 45^0 \\ -l_2 \sin 45^0 \end{pmatrix} \quad (8)$$

The length of this vector is:

$$|l_m| = \sqrt{l_2^2 \cos^2 45^0 + (-l_2 \sin 45^0 - l_1)^2} \quad (9)$$

Substituting the values for l_1 and l_2 in Eq. (9) yields:

$$l_m = 40.55 \; cm \quad (10)$$

The length increased from 38.16 cm to 40.55 cm and the relative change is:

$$\frac{\Delta l}{l_{m,\,initial}} = \frac{40.55[cm] - 38.16[cm]}{38.16[cm]}$$

$$\frac{\Delta l}{l_{m,\,initial}} = 0.063 \quad (11)$$

The muscle has been stretched by 6.3 %.

Solution part (c): This part of the question is different as the relative contraction is given but not the angle. This complicates the algebraic calculations somewhat and requires a new sketch to guide our approach. The sketch for this part is shown in Fig. 4.12 where we see at the left the now modified arm with the lower arm perpendicular to the upper arm. At the right side of the figure is the same arm shown when the muscle has shortened 20 %, i.e., when it is only 80 % of its original length.

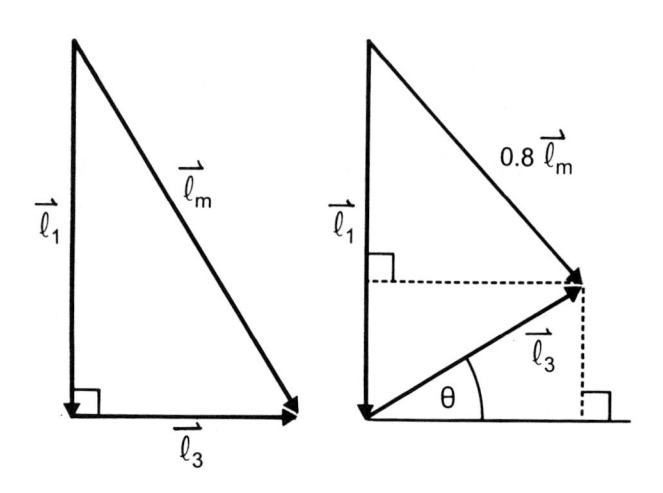

Fig. 4.12: This sketch is an analogous sketch to Fig. 4.11 for the case when a hypothetical biceps muscle were attached to the wrist. The sketch at the left shows the arm with a 90° angle at the elbow joint. The sketch at the right shows the geometrical features of the hypothetical arm raised to the point where the biceps muscle has shortened by 80 % of its original length, which is the maximum possible for the actual biceps in the human arm.

The new average length of the muscle is obtained from the left sketch in Fig. 4.12 by applying the Pythagorean theorem:

$$l_m = \sqrt{l_1^2 + l_3^2} = 48.4 \ cm \qquad (12)$$

80 % of the length l_m is expressed mathematically as $0.8 \, l_m$. If we define the angle θ as the maximum angle to which the lower arm can be raised as shown in the right sketch of Fig. 4.12, then we obtain an equation for $0.8 \, l_m$ using the same approach as in parts (a) and (b):

$$0.8 \, l_m = l_1 + l_3 \qquad (13)$$

which is rewritten in component form:

$$0.8 \, l_m = \begin{pmatrix} 0 \\ -l_1 \end{pmatrix} + \begin{pmatrix} l_3 \cos\theta \\ l_3 \sin\theta \end{pmatrix} \qquad (14)$$

Combining the two vectors on the right side of Eq. (14) yields:

$$0.8 \, l_m = \begin{pmatrix} l_3 \cos\theta \\ l_3 \sin\theta - l_1 \end{pmatrix} \qquad (15)$$

Now we obtain from Eq. (15) the magnitude of the vector $0.8 \, l_m$ by using the Pythagorean theorem:

$$0.8 \, l_m = \sqrt{(0.8 l_m)_x^2 + (0.8 l_m)_y^2} = \\ = \sqrt{l_3^2 \cos^2\theta + (l_3 \sin\theta - l_1)^2} \qquad (16)$$

Eq. (16) is solved by first squaring both sides of the formula:

$$(0.8 l_m)^2 = l_3^2 \cos^2\theta + l_3^2 \sin^2\theta - 2 l_1 l_3 \sin\theta + l_1^2 \qquad (17)$$

We simplify Eq. (17) by using the trigonometric identity $\sin^2\theta + \cos^2\theta = 1$ to combine the first two terms on the right hand side:

$$0.64 l_m^2 - l_3^2 - l_1^2 = -2 l_1 l_3 \sin\theta \qquad (18)$$

Eq. (18) is then solved for $\sin\theta$:

$$\sin\theta = \frac{(1 - 0.64)(l_1^2 + l_3^2)}{2 l_1 l_3} = 0.37$$
$$\Rightarrow \quad \theta = 21.7^0 \qquad (19)$$

This angle is too small for a proper use of the lower arm. You may confirm this by tilting your arm by just 22° in front of a mirror.

4.2. Mechanical components of an extended rigid body

Forces were identified as the cause for motion in the previous two chapters. When acting on a point mass, the only type of motion possible is called translational motion, which is either a motion along a straight line (as discussed in the previous chapters) or along a curved path (for which we will discuss examples in Chapter 20). The rotations considered in the current chapter are a different type of motion. To describe rotations we must find a new way to deal with forces which act on an object.

It turns out that we need two adjustments to the approach taken in the previous chapters: firstly, a point mass model is not sufficient to describe the bones of a skeletal system in locomotion because the position of the rotation axis in the joint and the points at which the various muscles act on the bone do not coincide, as illustrated in Fig. 4.1 for the elbow joint. To be able to take this into account we introduce a new model which allows for an extended object: the rigid body model. Secondly, for rotations we have to distinguish between the effect of forces which act along a line through the joint and the effect of forces which act under an angle to that line. We introduce the concept of torque to make that distinction. With these two concepts introduced we will revisit Newton's first law and extend it such that it allows the definition of a mechanical equilibrium for an extended body.

4.2.1. Rigid body

A rigid body is an extended body for which (I) the distance between any two parts of the body is fixed, and (II) the angle between the lines connecting any three parts of the body is fixed.

We study the humerus (upper arm bone) as an example. Fig. 4.5 gave an overview of the anatomy of the arm. The humerus is the single bone in the upper arm, stretching from the shoulder to the elbow. Because of the various motions of the upper arm a description of the humerus as a point mass is an oversimplification not allowing us to quantify the properties we are interested in.

The rigid body model in turn is suitable for the humerus as long as the bone doesn't change its shape during the processes we study. The rigid body model is still restrictive as a real bone can do several things a rigid body cannot do: the humerus can bend slightly under force or it can break. These two cases are studied in Chapter 15 where we introduce the elastic body as a new model for an extended object. However, the rigid body model is sufficient for the humerus for the studies discussed in this chapter, e.g. when the forces acting on the bone are not too large.

Fig. 4.13 shows a schematic sketch of two forces acting on the humerus. For such forces to lead to a rotation an *axis* is needed about which the rotation occurs. In the case of the humerus, this axis is located at the shoulder joint. In this textbook, we limit the discussion to axes which are fixed in space (fixed axis), i.e., don't change their position or orientation with time. Note that this assumption may oversimplify the anatomy of some joints; Fig. 4.14 shows an example. In Fig. 4.14 the radius of the head of a bone is significantly smaller than the socket of the adjacent bone. In this case the axis is not fixed but moves within the larger socket. Such cases are not considered further.

We also restrict the number of cases we study with a condition for the orientation of the axis of rotation: in all cases in this textbook the axis is oriented perpendicular to the plane in which the motion occurs. We choose the z–axis to point in this direction so that the motion occurs in the xy–plane. Note that the axis of rotation is still not the same thing as the z–axis in a Cartesian coordinate system. While we can choose where to put and how to orient the three Cartesian axes, the location and orientation of the axis of rotation is not arbitrary but is a feature of the physical arrangements.

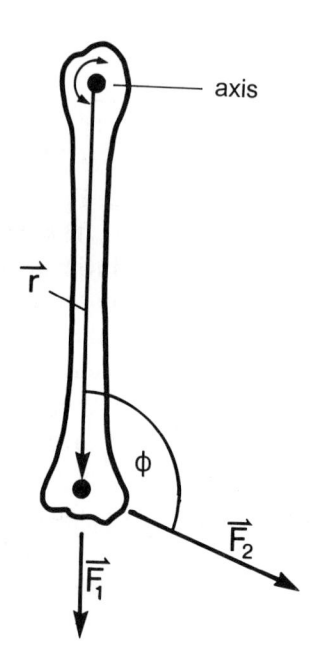

Fig. 4.13: Two forces acting on the humerus. The axis of rotation lies near the top end of the bone at the shoulder joint. Note that both forces lead to quite different types of motion: force $\mathbf{F}_2$ leads to a rotation because it does not act in the direction of the axis of the bone. Force $\mathbf{F}_1$ would lead to a linear acceleration, which is a type of motion we already discussed in the previous two chapters.

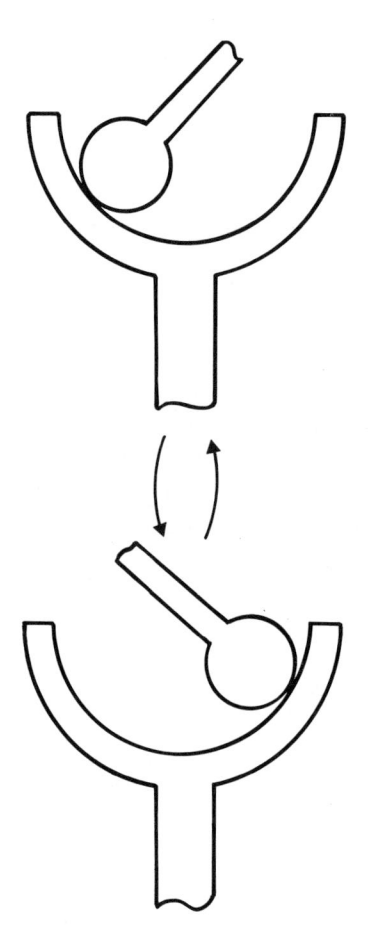

Fig. 4.14: The motion of a joint is not adequately described by the assumption of a fixed axis if the radius of the socket in a ball–and–socket joint exceeds the radius of the ball significantly. We exclude such cases from the discussion in this chapter.

4.2.2. Torque

Starting with a rigid body with a fixed rotation axis, we are now looking for forces acting on the object that do not act in the direction toward the rotation axis. Force F_2 in Fig. 4.13 is such a force, but not force F_1. As we saw in the previous chapter, force F_1 leads to a translational acceleration of the humerus. That motion we have already sufficiently described with the second law of mechanics and need not to consider further.

The resulting motion for force F_2 in Fig. 4.13 is different: a rotation about the fixed axis. The resulting rotational motion depends both on the magnitude of the force F_2 and on the distance between the axis and the point on the object where the force acts, r. It also depends on the angle ϕ between the directions of r and F_2. Varying all three quantities, we find the greatest rotational acceleration of the body when the magnitude of the force and the distance from the axis are large and the angle is 90°. We introduce a new physical quantity, called the torque, which takes the dependence of the rotation on the force, the distance and the angle ϕ into account:

$$\tau \equiv r \cdot F \cdot \sin \phi \qquad (20)$$

The unit of torque is [N m] = [kg m²/s²].

> *Torque is the measure of the effectiveness of a rotation that consists of the product of the force and the perpendicular distance from the line of action of the force to the axis of rotation.*

The following comments on the concept torque are useful:

(I) Torque is a vector because the resulting motion occurs in a well-defined direction. Thus, the complete definition of torque includes Eq. (20) as its magnitude. The directional information is combined with this equation through the vector product notation: $\tau = r \times F$. Note that the mathematical operation of the vector product has not been introduced in this textbook. For all calculations and problems considered here, Eq. (20) is sufficient if the following sign-convention is applied:

> *Sign convention for torque:*
> *If the rotation is counter-clockwise, then $\tau > 0$,*
> *if the rotation is clockwise, then $\tau < 0$.*

Fig. 4.15 illustrates the sign convention for a bar with an axis at its center. If a force acts on the bar like force F_1 or force F_3, the resulting torque leads to a counter-clockwise rotation and the torque is therefore positive; if a force like force F_2 or force F_4 acts on the bar, the resulting torque leads to a clockwise rotation and the torque is negative.

(II) The torque equation confirms that forces which act along a line through the rotation axis do not contribute to the net torque because the angle ϕ is 0° or 180°. This leads to $\tau = 0$ because $\sin 0° = \sin 180° = 0$.

(III) We can read the torque equation in two ways. One way is to interpret it in the form $\tau = r \cdot (F \sin\phi)$, i.e., as the length of the lever arm multiplied by the component of the force that is perpendicular to the lever arm and causes the rotation. This is shown in Fig. 4.16(a) and is the approach usually adopted in the discussions below. It allows us to simplify the formula for the torque if we choose the x-axis perpendicular to the lever arm, as illustrated in Fig. 4.17. Based on Fig. 4.17 we write the torque as $\tau = r \cdot F_x$. The force component F_y can be neglected because force components which act along a line through the axis of rotation do not lead to a torque term.

The second way to think about the torque definition of Eq. (20) is as $\tau = (r \sin\phi) \cdot F$, i.e., as the force multiplied by the component of the lever arm that is perpendicular to the force, as shown in Fig. 4.16(b). This view is taken in the definition of the torque as specified in the highlighted box following Eq. (20). Of course, both ways of thinking give the same value for the torque τ.

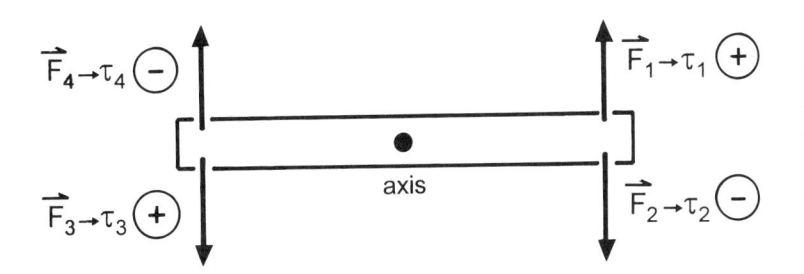

Fig. 4.15: Conceptual sketch for the sign convention of the torque. Shown is a bar with a fixed axis of rotation at its center. Any force acting on the bar and yielding a rotation can be identified as one of the four forces shown in the sketch. For each force the resulting torque is labelled with a sign symbol in a circle that represents the sign of the torque contribution.

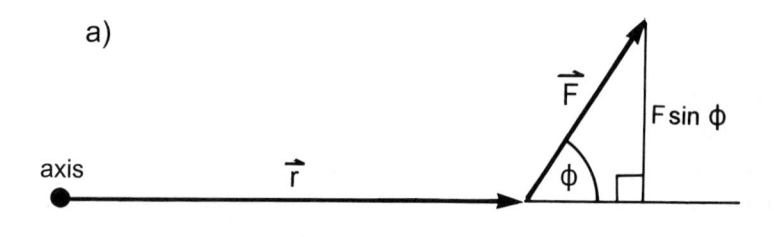

Fig. 4.16: Two alternative graphical interpretations of the torque equation (Eq. (20)) based on the choice of attributing the term sin φ to either (a) the force **F**, or (b) the distance from the axis to the point at which the force is exerted on the rigid body, **r**.

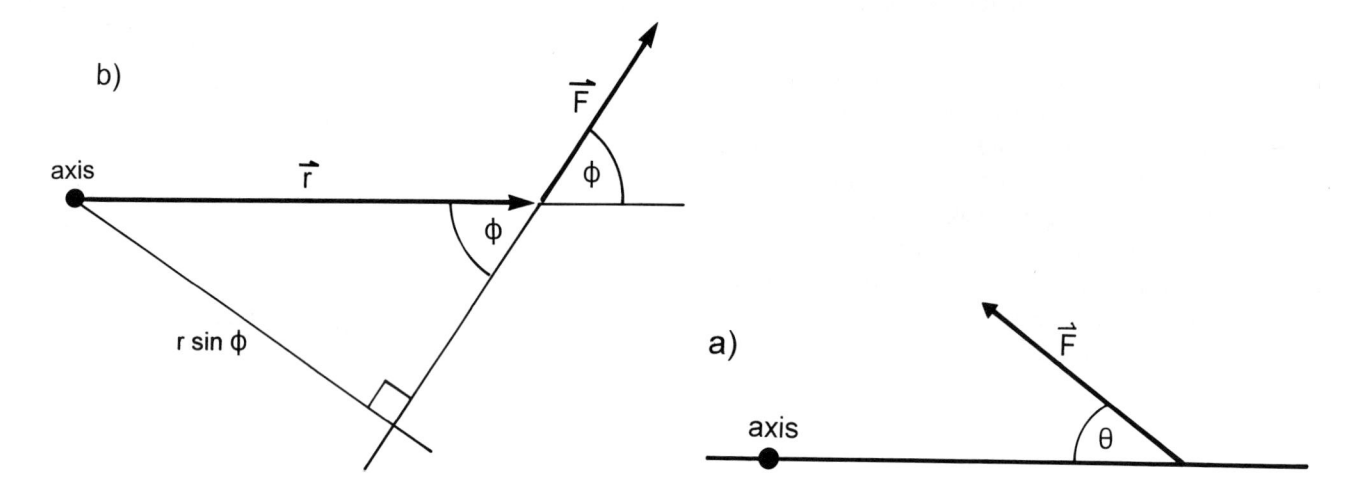

Fig. 4.17: For practical purposes, it is convenient to simplify the application of Eq. (20) for each force acting on the bar by dividing the force in a component parallel and a component perpendicular to the bar as illustrated in (b) for the general force shown in (a). Of the two force components, only the component perpendicular to the bar (shown in (c)) enters the balance of torque equation.

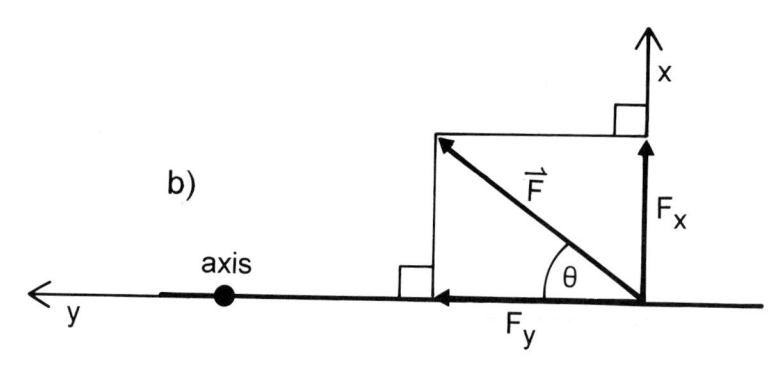

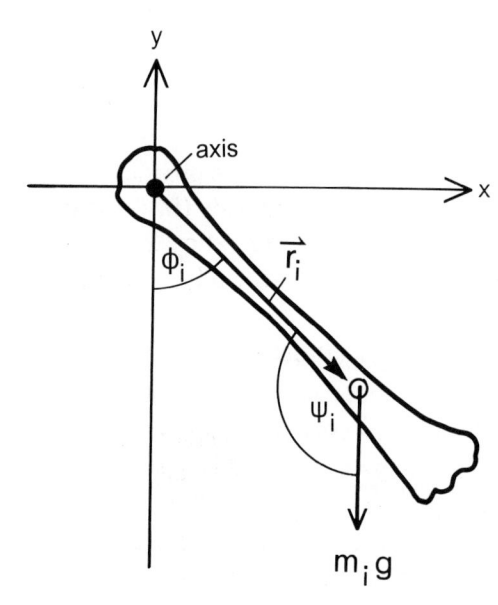

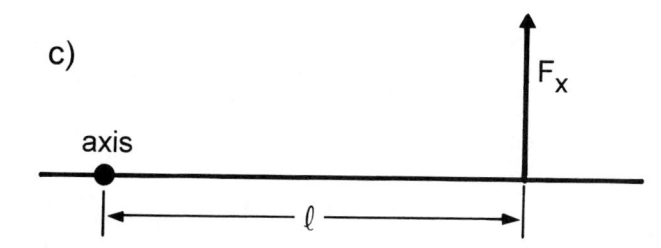

Fig. 4.18: A second illustration of the humerus. This time we focus on the action of its weight. We derive the torque due to the weight of the humerus in several steps. First we place the axis of rotation at the origin for mathematical reasons. Then the humerus is subdivided into a very large number of point masses. We find the torque contribution of the arbitrarily chosen i–th point mass as shown in the sketch (open circle). In the last step the torque contributions due to all point masses are added.

74

4.3. Mechanical equilibrium for a rigid body

We introduce now the concept of mechanical equilibrium for rigid bodies. This equilibrium condition is a combination of the mechanical equilibrium for a point mass as introduced in Chapter 3, and a condition to prevent the rigid body from rotating. Note the similarity between this and the previous chapter in that the possible motion of the object is limited to the xy–plane. Thus, Eq. (3.6) remains part of the mechanical equilibrium condition for the rigid body. To exclude rotational accelerations the sum of all torque contributions acting on the system must be zero as well. In general, this would require three equations, one each for the three Cartesian components of the torque vector. Since we limit our discussion to cases where the axis of rotation is fixed along the z–axis, only one torque component (due to forces in the xy–plane) has to be considered, reducing the number of formulas needed to provide the equilibrium against rotation to just one. Therefore, the equilibrium condition for a rigid body consists of three equations:

$$(I) \quad \sum_i F_{ix} = 0$$

$$(II) \quad \sum_i F_{iy} = 0 \quad (21)$$

$$(III) \quad \sum_i \tau_i = 0$$

With Eq. (21) established you would expect us now to proceed with examples of mechanical equilibria for rigid bodies. Before we can do so, however, we must address one more issue: for contact forces the point of contact of the force on the rigid body is self–evident, but for the weight we still have to determine where the point of contact is located because the weight acts on each part of an extended body.

How we include the weight in the discussion of the rotational equilibrium of a rigid body is illustrated in Fig. 4.18 once again using the humerus. In the figure the bone is shown at an angle with the negative y–axis. The axis of rotation lies at the origin. The torque due to gravity is obtained by subdividing the humerus into a large number of tiny parts which we then treat as point masses. We evaluate the contribution to the torque for each of the tiny parts separately. This is highlighted for one particular such part in Fig. 4.18, which we call the i–th point mass.

The vector pointing from the axis to the i–th point mass has an angle ϕ_i with the negative y–axis. The weight forms an angle ψ_i with the position vector of the i–th point mass. Using Eq. (20) we write the torque contribution for the i–th point mass as:

$$\tau_i = r_i \cdot m_i \, g \cdot \sin\psi_i \quad (22)$$

Using the Z–rule for angles we find from Fig. 4.18 that $\phi_i + \psi_i = 180°$, which leads to $\phi_i = 180° - \psi_i$ and thus to $\sin \phi_i = \sin \psi_i$. We note also from Fig. 4.18 that $\sin \phi_i = x_i/r_i$, where x_i is the x–component of the vector from the axis of rotation to the i–th point mass and r_i is the length of that vector. With this information Eq. (22) is rewritten in the form:

$$\tau_i = r_i \cdot m_i \, g \cdot \frac{x_i}{r_i} = m_i \, g \, x_i \quad (23)$$

For the total torque due to its weight we sum over all point masses into which we divided the rigid body:

$$\tau = \sum_i m_i \, g \, x_i = g \sum_i m_i \, x_i \quad (24)$$

Eq. (24) contains a cumbersome sum and must therefore be addressed further. This is done by defining a new term for the sum on the right hand side of Eq. (24) which then is evaluated separately. We define the horizontal x–component of the center–of–mass position (index *cm*) in the form:

$$x_{cm} \equiv \frac{1}{M} \sum_i m_i \, x_i \quad (25)$$

which allows us to write the torque due to the weight in Eq. (24) in the form:

$$\tau = x_{cm} \, Mg \quad (26)$$

Thus, the torque due to the weight is the product of the magnitude of the weight of the rigid body (Mg) and the horizontal distance from the axis of rotation to the center–of–mass position (x_{cm}). More generally we write:

$$\tau = r_{cm} \, Mg \, \sin\phi \quad (27)$$

in which ϕ is the angle between the position vector of the center–of–mass and the weight vector, and r_{cm} is the length of that vector, $r_{cm} = (x_{cm}, y_{cm}, z_{cm})$. Thus, if we can evaluate Eq. (25) we can proceed with our discussion of the mechanical equilibrium of a rigid body.

For the purpose of this textbook we need not to discuss the mathematical implications of Eq. (25) further because we consider only two types of systems:
(I) simple physical objects to introduce new concepts, and
(II) real biological objects for applications.

Simple physical objects have a symmetric shape and a uniform mass distribution, e.g. a rectangular bar as considered in Example 4.2. In these cases the center–of–mass is located at the geometrical center of the object. Finding the center–of–mass for real biological objects requires extensive calculations or, more often, computer simulations. To circumvent such calculations the center–of–mass will be provided below when needed. We can alternatively guess the center–of–mass position when a rough idea is sufficient, such as in conceptual discussions. All three approaches are discussed in more detail and with a few examples in the Appendix of the current chapter.

Example 4.2
As illustrated in Fig. 4.19, a uniform horizontal bar of mass m = 25 kg and length L = 4 m is attached to a vertical wall in a point about which the bar can rotate. The bar's far end is held by a massless string that makes an angle of 40° with the horizontal. When an object of mass M = 50 kg is placed on the bar l = 1.2 m from the vertical wall,
(a) find the magnitude of the tension in the string, and
(b) find the horizontal and vertical components of the force exerted on the bar by the vertical wall.

Solution: It is best to follow the problem–solving strategy we discussed in Chapter 2. The additional operations you have to include for the rotational equilibrium of a rigid body are highlighted in the solution for the current example.

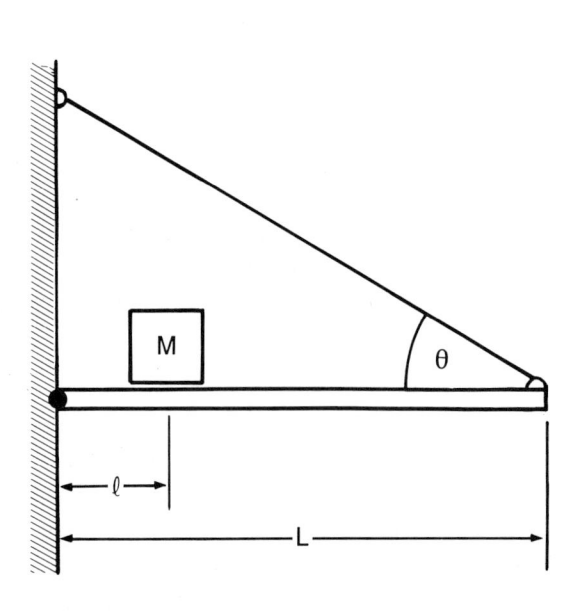

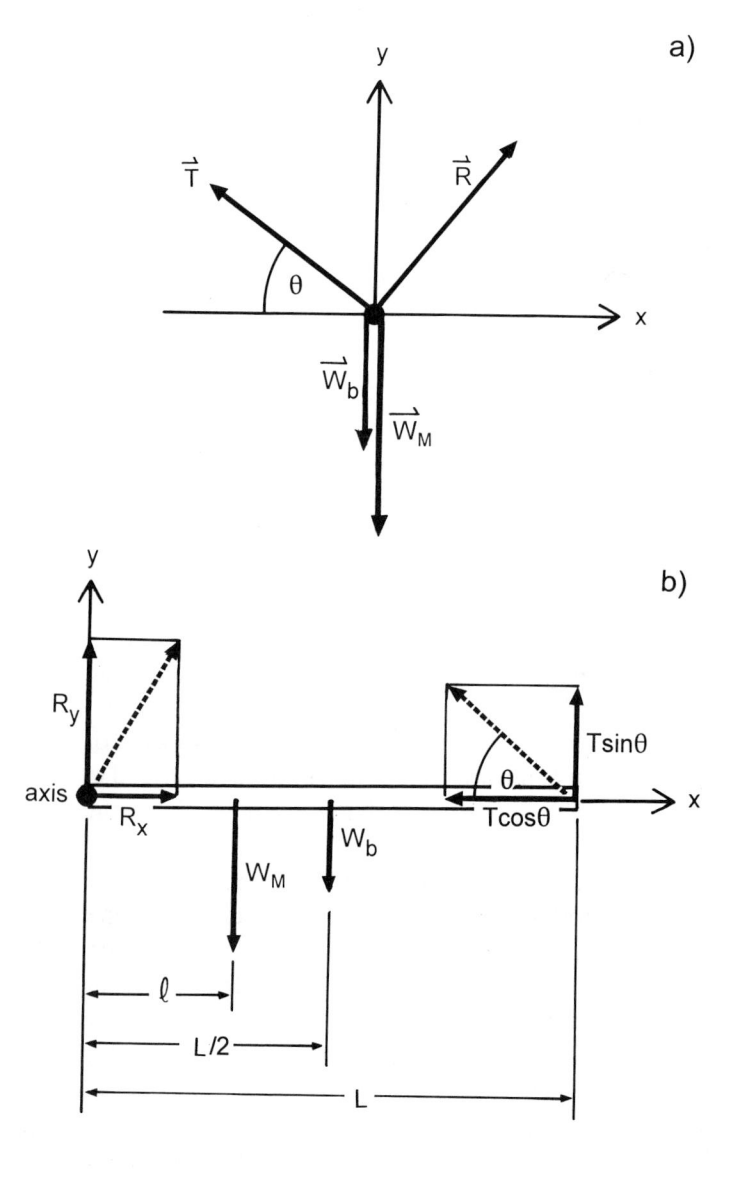

Fig. 4.19: A typical point–and–line set–up for an application of the torque concept: a uniform horizontal bar is attached to a vertical wall in a point about which the bar may rotate. The bar's far end is supported by a massless string. An additional point mass is placed on the bar as shown.

Fig. 4.20: (a) Free–body–diagram for the problem illustrated in Fig. 4.19. Four forces act on the bar, the weight of the bar, the weight of the additional object of mass M, the tension **T** in the string and the force exerted by the vertical wall. (b) The balance of torque plot supplements the free–body–diagram in part (a) of the figure with each force drawn to the actual point of contact.

The bar is the system since both parts of the question refer to forces acting on it. The object of mass M, the wall and the string are part of the environment.

We identify all forces acting on the bar. They are its weight $\mathbf{W}_b$ and the weight of the object of mass M, $\mathbf{W}_M$, both acting downwards; the tension $\mathbf{T}$ in the string, acting along the string; and the force exerted by the wall, $\mathbf{R}$. Note that the direction of $\mathbf{R}$ is not known. When the system is a rigid body, two drawings are required: (I) a free–body–diagram as before, shown for the current problem in Fig. 4.20(a), and a new sketch, called the *balance of torque plot*, as shown in Fig. 4.20(b).

To develop the balance of torque plot, we first draw a line representing the bar. A dot indicates the rotation axis. Next all forces acting on the bar are added at their respective distance from the axis. You may divide each force in two components, one which acts in the direction towards or away from the axis and one which acts perpendicular to the bar. This approach has been illustrated in Fig. 4.17. In the present example the forces for which we include force components are (I) $\mathbf{R}$ with the components R_x and R_y, and (II) $\mathbf{T}$ with $T\cos\theta$ and $T\sin\theta$. Note further that the weight of the bar is drawn at the center–of–mass of the bar. The center–of–mass of the bar lies at its geometrical center since the bar is a symmetric object with a uniform mass distribution.

The coordinate system for the free–body–diagram is chosen in the same fashion as in the previous chapters. For the balance of torque plot the x–axis is chosen along the bar and the y–axis is chosen perpendicular to the bar with the rotation axis at the origin.

From Fig. 4.20, three formulas are derived using Eq. (21). The first two are applications of the first law of mechanics along the x– and the y–axes in the free–body–diagram of Fig. 4.20(a). The third formula is the balance of torque equation resulting from Fig. 4.20(b):

$$(I) \quad -T\cos\theta + R_x = 0$$
$$(II) \quad T\sin\theta + R_y - W_M - W_b = 0$$
$$(III) \quad L\,T\sin\theta - \frac{L}{2} W_b - l\,W_M = 0 \tag{28}$$

The first two formulas in Eq. (28) have been derived in the same way we have done this numerous times in the previous two chapters. We study the derivation of the third formula in more detail. First, note that there are several components of the forces which do not enter the formula. Since torque is associated with forces *not* acting in the direction toward or away from the axis, the force components R_x, R_y and $T\cos\theta$ do not contribute to the balance of torque in this case. Of the remaining three force components, two lead to negative terms and one to a positive term. This is due to the direction of rotation which each of these force components causes if acting alone on the bar. $T\sin\theta$ would lead to a counter–clockwise rotation and the two weights would each cause a clockwise rotation. The signs of the three terms result from the sign–convention for torque defined in Fig. 4.15.

Now we solve Eq. (28). In the present as in most other cases, the torque formula is a good starting point to solve the problem. This is due to the fact that the torque formula does not contain all force components and thus often has the least number of unknown variables.

Solution part (a): Isolating tension T in Eq. (28) yields:

$$T = \frac{\frac{L}{2} mg + l\,Mg}{L\sin\theta}$$
$$= \frac{\left(\frac{L}{2} m + l\,M\right) g}{L\sin\theta} \tag{29}$$

Substituting the given values into Eq. (29) yields:

$$T = \frac{(2[m]\,25[kg] + 1.2[m]\,50[kg])\,g}{4[m]\,\sin 40^0} \tag{30}$$
$$T = 419\,N$$

Solution part (b): The force exerted by the wall has two components, which are found when substituting the result of Eq. (30) in formulas (I) and (II) of Eq. (28).

$$R_x = T\cos\theta = 419[N]\cos 40^0 = 321\,N \tag{31}$$

and

$$R_y = W_M + W_b - T\sin\theta$$
$$= (M + m)\,g - T\sin\theta$$
$$= (25[kg] + 50[kg])\,g - 419[N]\sin 40^0 \tag{32}$$
$$\Rightarrow R_y = 466\,N$$

provide the components of $\mathbf{R}$: $(R_x, R_y) = (321\,N, 466\,N)$.

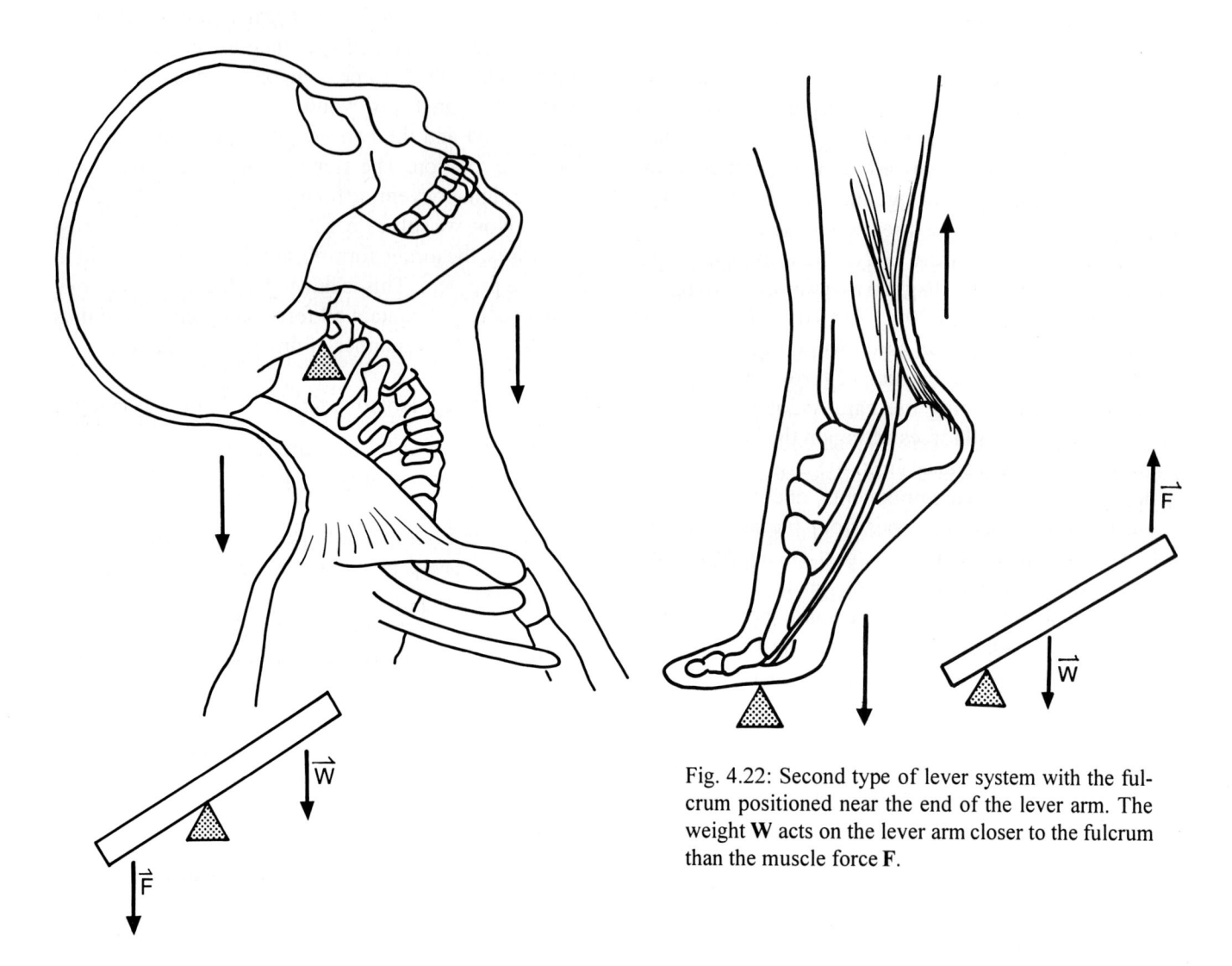

Fig. 4.21: First type of lever system with the fulcrum located between the points at which the weight **W** and the muscle force **F** act on the lever arm.

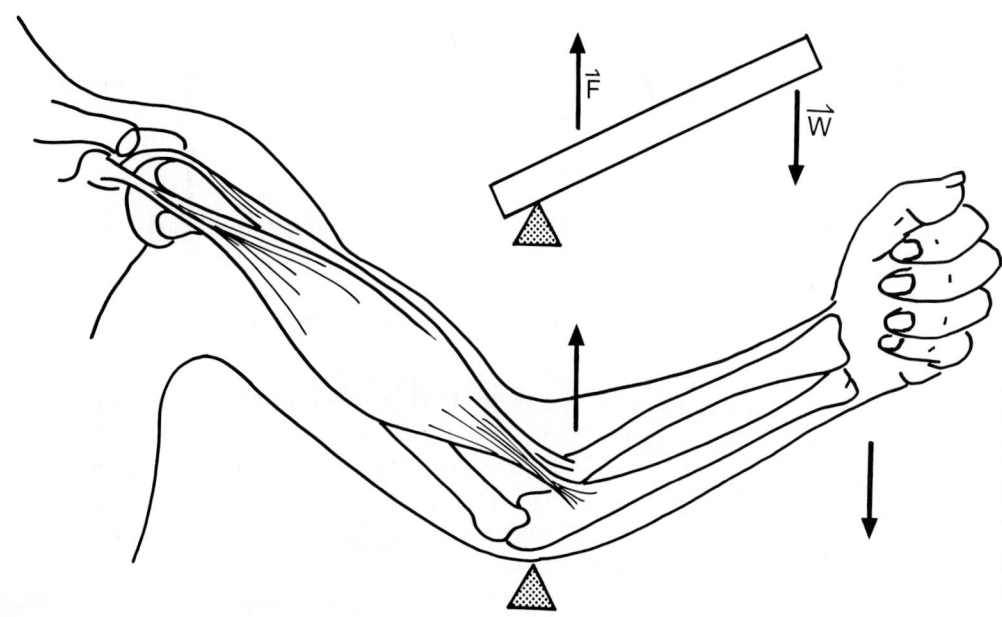

Fig. 4.22: Second type of lever system with the fulcrum positioned near the end of the lever arm. The weight **W** acts on the lever arm closer to the fulcrum than the muscle force **F**.

Fig. 4.23: Third type of lever arm. The fulcrum is near the end of the lever arm. The muscle force **F** acts closer to the fulcrum on the lever arm than the weight **W**.

4.4. Physiological applications

It has become common practice to distinguish three types of lever arm systems in anatomy. The first type is shown in Fig. 4.21 for the human head pivoted on the first cervical vertebra. The pivot point is called the fulcrum and is indicated by a shaded triangle. In this type of lever system, the weight acts on the lever arm on one side of the fulcrum and a muscle force balances the weight by acting on the opposite side of the fulcrum.

The second type of lever arm system is illustrated in Fig. 4.22 for the foot. The fulcrum is at one end of the lever arm. The weight and the muscle force act on the same side of the fulcrum. These forces must act in opposite directions to obtain a mechanical equilibrium. Note that the weight acts at a point closer to the fulcrum than the muscle force.

The last type of lever arm system is shown in Fig. 4.23 for the lower arm. This case is similar to the second type in that the fulcrum is again at one end of the lever arm and the two forces establishing a mechanical equilibrium act on the same side of the fulcrum. This time though the muscle force acts closer to the fulcrum than the weight.

4.4.1. The Achilles tendon (Example 4.3)

In Fig. 4.24 the anatomy of the foot is compared for a person standing on a flat surface (at left) and for an athlete standing backwards on a diving board (at right).
(a) Calculate as a multiple of the weight for the foot on the flat surface the magnitude of the two normal forces supporting the foot, and
(b) the magnitude of the force acting in the tendon.
(c) Calculate as a multiple of the weight the magnitude of the force in the Achilles tendon for the athlete resting on the diving board as shown in Fig. 4.24.
Hint: Neglect the weight of the foot. Use in parts (a) and (c) the values $x_1 = 6.2$ cm and $x_2 = 12.3$ cm (values which correspond roughly to a foot of shoe size 11).

Supplementary anatomical information: Note that the athlete must adjust to standing on the diving board to obtain mechanical equilibrium, because the support forces (normal forces) acting from below the foot have changed. You may convince yourself of this adjustment by trying to balance on the edge of a stair as shown in Fig. 4.24. The angle of the actual forward bending of the athlete is found by solving problem part (b).

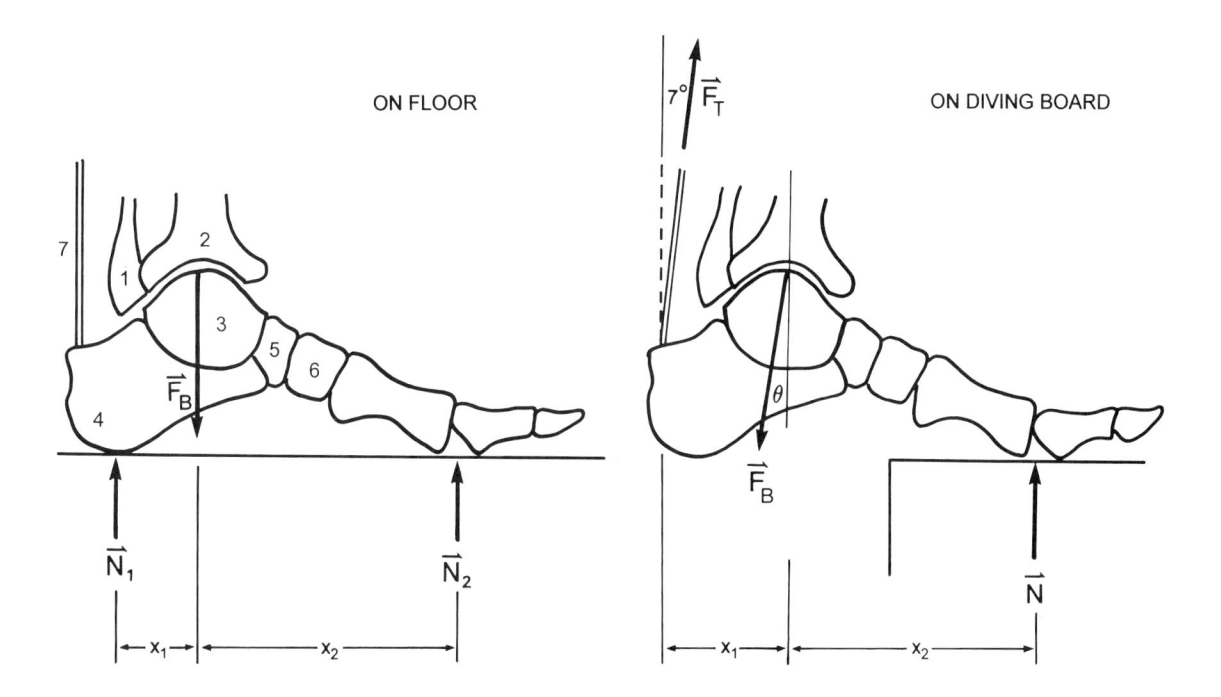

Fig. 4.24: Anatomy of the foot of a person resting on a flat surface (left) and an athlete balancing backwards on a diving board (right). Bones include the fibula (1), the tibia (2), the talus (3), the calcaneus (4), the navicular bone (5) and the medial cuneiform bone (6). Note that the Achilles tendon (7) is not vertical when balancing on the diving board. The calculations demonstrate that the forces F_B due to the upper body pushing into the foot and F_T, which is the force in the Achilles tendon, are very large. Note that F_B is not vertical in the right sketch and is not equal to the weight of the upper body resting on the foot because the force F_T pulls the foot and the leg together beyond the effect of the weight.

The Achilles tendon is shown in Fig. 4.24 as a string connected to the heel bone (calcaneus). We combine all the bones of the foot into a single rigid body, but allow the tibia together with the fibula (the outer bone of the lower leg) to rotate about the talus. Look at your lower leg in a mirror. The Achilles tendon can easily be located and therefore the angle of the Achilles tendon with the vertical can be determined from photographs of athletes on a diving board. We use a value of 7°.

Solution part (a): The system is the foot below the fibula and tibia, excluding the Achilles tendon. The Achilles tendon is treated as a massless string which connects the system to the calf muscle. The calf muscle, fibula and tibia are part of the environment. The fibula and tibia exert a contact force on the system.

The free–body–diagram is shown on the left side in Fig. 4.25. In this plot, the foot is drawn as a point. There are three forces acting on the foot: two normal forces at the support points, $\mathbf{N_1}$ and $\mathbf{N_2}$, and the force of the person's body pushing onto the talus, $\mathbf{F_B}$. We neglect the weight of the foot itself as stated in the hint.

The balance of torque plot is shown on the right side in Fig. 4.25. Note that the system is now drawn as a bar to take its spatial extension into account. The plot shows the same three forces as the free–body–diagram, but each drawn to the appropriate position along the bar: the first normal force to the heel, the second normal force to the ball of the foot, and the force exerted by the person's body at the position of the talus. As the anatomy of the foot in Fig. 4.25 shows, the axis for the rotation is located in the talus. The force $\mathbf{F_B}$ acts therefore toward the axis.

The choice of a coordinate system for the free–body–diagram is straight forward since all three forces act along the vertical direction. For the balance of torque plot the choice of coordinate system is determined by the direction of the bar representing the system.

The conditions of mechanical equilibrium are developed from the two plots in Fig. 4.25: because no force components act in the x–direction, only the two last formulas of Eq. (21) are needed:

$$(II) \quad N_1 + N_2 - F_B = 0$$
$$(III) \quad N_2 x_2 - N_1 x_1 = 0 \qquad (33)$$

Formula (II) is the sum of the force components in the y–direction. For a relaxed body we find the force acting downwards in each leg to be equal to half the weight of the person, $F_B = W/2$. Note that this is a simplifying assumption since the person may distribute the body's weight unequally.

Formula (III) in Eq. (33) is the balance of torque condition about the talus. It allows us to calculate the relative contributions of both normal forces. Using the given values $x_1 = 6.2$ cm and $x_2 = 12.3$ cm, we get approximately $N_1 = W/3$ and $N_2 = W/6$.

Solution part (b): Note that we did so far not identify any force acting in the Achilles tendon. Thus, the tension $\mathbf{F_T}$ is zero.

Solution part (c): Now we consider the athlete on the board. The free–body–diagram and the balance of torque plot for the athlete are shown in Fig. 4.26. Note that the two anatomical sketches in Fig. 4.24 on one side, and the diagrams in Fig. 4.25 and Fig. 4.26 on the other side each appear to display only minor differences. Since one support point is removed from below the foot, the upper body must be tilted slightly forward to maintain balance, i.e., the center–of–mass of the entire body must now be positioned above the ball of the foot. This causes an angle θ between the vertical and the direction along which the upper body pushes into the talus. As a result,

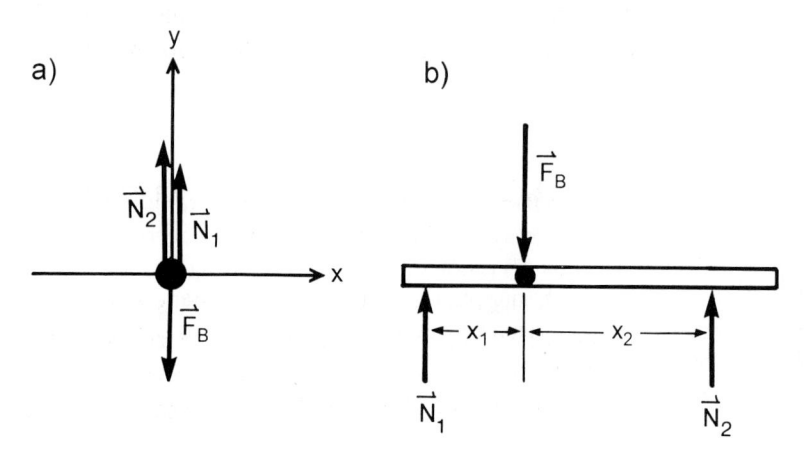

Fig. 4.25: (a) The free–body–diagram and (b) the balance of torque plot for the foot on the flat surface as sketched on the left side in Fig. 4.24. Note that the two normal forces are drawn to different length and are labelled with different indices because we cannot assume that they are equal in magnitude.

Fig. 4.26: The free–body–diagram (left) and the balance of torque plot (right) for the foot on the diving board as sketched on the right side of Fig. 4.24.

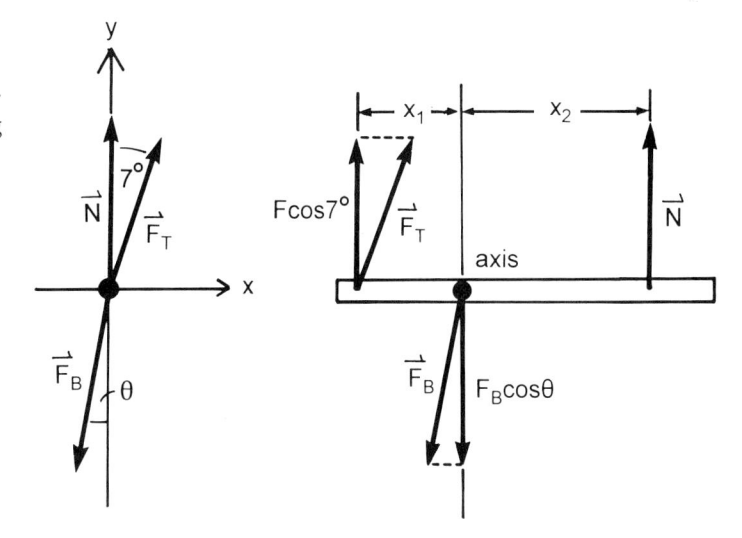

a force acts along the Achilles tendon, $\mathbf{F_T}$, which must provide a balance for the rather small x–component of the force $\mathbf{F_B}$. Despite of these observations we will find surprisingly large forces in comparison to the situation where the foot is on flat ground.

The three equilibrium conditions for the x– and y–directions of the forces and the torque are, respectively:

$$(I) \quad F_T \sin 7^0 - F_B \sin\theta = 0$$

$$(II) \quad F_T \cos 7^0 + N - F_B \cos\theta = 0 \quad \textbf{(34)}$$

$$(III) \quad N x_2 - F_T (\cos 7^0) x_1 = 0$$

As for the foot on the flat surface, we neglect the weight of the foot. We further note that the magnitude of the normal force is equal to W/2, because we assume that the athlete distributes the body weight equal on both legs.

From the third condition in Eq. (34) we determine the magnitude of the force in the tendon $\mathbf{F_T}$:

$$F_T = \frac{W x_2}{2 x_1 \cos 7^0} \approx 1.0 \, W \quad \textbf{(35)}$$

where we used $x_1 = 6.2$ cm and $x_2 = 12.3$ cm once more. Thus, each Achilles tendon supports the equivalent of the entire weight of the athlete! This force is caused by the calf muscle which provides for the mechanical equilibrium in this rather awkward position. You feel this large force when you try to balance on a stair as shown in Fig. 4.24.

We can determine two more variables from Eq. (34) as it contains three independent conditions. The other two variables are the angle θ and the magnitude of the force $\mathbf{F_B}$. Using the result of Eq. (35) we divide the first condition by the second condition in Eq. (34):

$$\frac{\sin\theta}{\cos\theta} = \tan\theta = \frac{W \sin 7^0}{W \left(\cos 7^0 + \frac{1}{2} \right)} \quad \textbf{(36)}$$

which yields:

$$\tan\theta = 0.082 \quad \Rightarrow \quad \theta = 4.7^0 \quad \textbf{(37)}$$

To find $\mathbf{F_B}$, we substitute the result from Eq. (37) into the first or second formula of Eq. (34). Choosing the first formula we find:

$$F_B = \frac{W \sin 7^0}{\sin\theta} \quad \Rightarrow \quad F_B \approx 1.5 \, W \quad \textbf{(38)}$$

Thus, the large force in the tendon we found in Eq. (35) is mostly due to a large force pushing down onto the talus.

4.4.2. The mandible and the masseter (Example 4.4)

Fig. 4.27(a) shows the masseter, which is one of the strongest muscles in the human body. It connects the mandible (lower jaw bone) to the skull. The mandible is pivoted about a socket just in front of the ear. There are

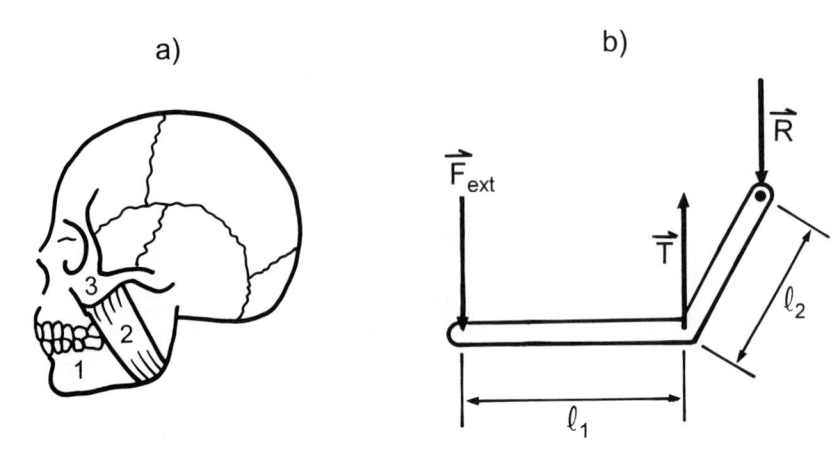

Fig. 4.27: (a) Illustration of the attachment of the masseter (2) to the mandible (1) and the cheek bone (3) for a modern human. (b) Simplified arrangement of the forces acting on the mandible during chewing. The tension **T** is the force exerted by the masseter. The force **R** acts at the joint in the direction towards the axis of rotation. The external force **F**$_{ext}$ is due to the chewing of the person. The mandible consists of two straight parts of lengths l_1 and l_2. The angle between these two parts is 110°.

three forces acting on the jaw bone, as shown in Fig. 4.27(b): **F**$_{ext}$ is the external force exerted by the chewed food, **T** is the tension in the masseter tendon and **R** is the force exerted on the mandible by the socket. We make the simplifying assumption that these three forces act perpendicularly to the lower part of the mandible. Using the two lengths $l_1 = 9$ cm and $l_2 = 5$ cm, and an angle of 110° between the two parts of the mandible,
(a) find the magnitude of the tension **T** when the person bites down with a force of 40 N, and
(b) find the magnitude of the force **R** for the same bite.

Supplementary physical information: This problem is different from the previous examples because the mandible is bent. Therefore the points at which the forces act on the system do not lie along a straight line.

We illustrate the approach to such cases in general terms first. Fig. 4.28 compares two balance of torque plots, for a straight lever arm in Fig. 4.28(a) and for a bent lever arm in Fig. 4.28(b). Two forces, **F**$_1$ and **F**$_2$, act in each case on the lever arm. For the straight lever arm these two forces are each divided into two force components in the same fashion we have discussed and applied several times before. For the bent lever arm in the lower sketch of the figure, the two forces are divided into components in a different fashion: we draw first the

Fig. 4.28: Conceptual sketch illustrating the difference between (a) a straight lever system and (b) a bent lever system. For illustration, two forces are considered acting on each lever arm, **F**$_2$ located in both cases between the axis of rotation and the bent and **F**$_1$ located at the far end of the lever arm. Both forces are divided into components. For force **F**$_1$ in both cases and for force **F**$_2$ in case (a) this is done in the same fashion as described in Fig. 4.17; for force **F**$_1$ in case (b) the components are chosen parallel and perpendicular to the line through the axis.

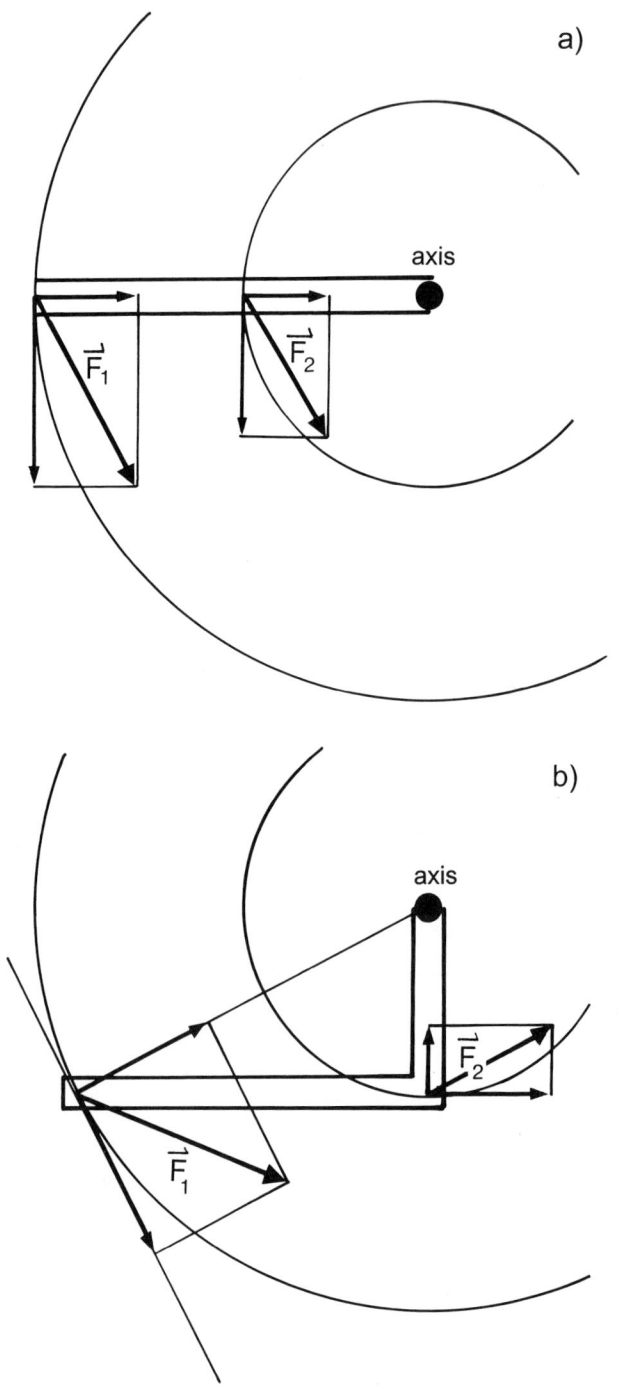

line from the axis to the point along the lever arm at which each force acts. Then the force is divided into components parallel and perpendicular to the direction toward the axis (i.e., along the line we just drew). The perpendicular force component and the distance between the axis and the force along the newly drawn line are used in the equation for the balance of torque.

Solution: The mandible is the system. All the forces acting on the mandible are shown in the right hand sketch of Fig. 4.27.

The free–body–diagram for this case is shown in Fig. 4.29(a) and the balance of torque plot is given in Fig. 4.29(b). Both the tension and the external force are divided into components parallel and perpendicular to the respective line to the axis. Of these components the ones which are perpendicular to the line to the axis are needed for the balance of torque equation. We must develop the balance of torque plot in the fashion shown in Fig. 4.29 because it is not possible to draw a single straight bar through the axis of rotation and the two points at which the tension and the external force act on the mandible.

We choose the horizontal direction as the x–axis and the vertical direction upwards as the y–axis in the free–body–diagram. Thus, all forces are parallel or antiparallel to the y-axis. Since no force components exist in the x-direction, only the y-component of Newton's first law is needed in Eq. (21):

$$(II) \quad -F_{ext} + T - R = 0 \qquad (39)$$

We further apply the torque equilibrium condition, expressed in the last formula of Eq. (21). For this we need the angles between the tension and the external force and their respective bars (θ and ϕ) and the respective distances between **T** and **F**$_{ext}$ and the axis of rotation, i.e., the lengths l_2 and l_3:

$$(III) \quad +F_{ext} l_3 \sin\phi - T l_2 \sin\theta = 0 \qquad (40)$$

The force **R** does not appear in the balance of torque equation because it acts through the axis of rotation. At this point we answer the two parts of the question separately, using Eq. (39) and Eq. (40).

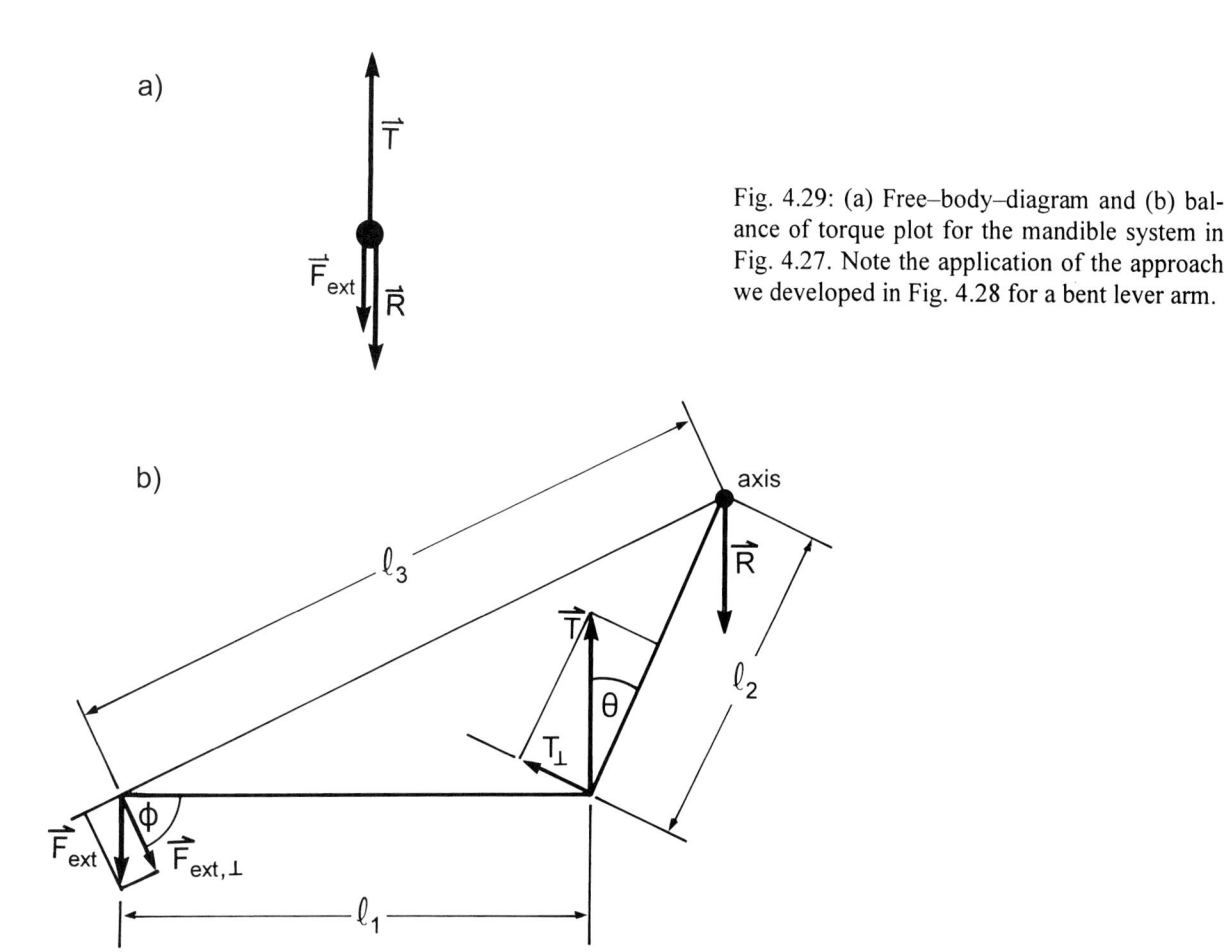

Fig. 4.29: (a) Free–body–diagram and (b) balance of torque plot for the mandible system in Fig. 4.27. Note the application of the approach we developed in Fig. 4.28 for a bent lever arm.

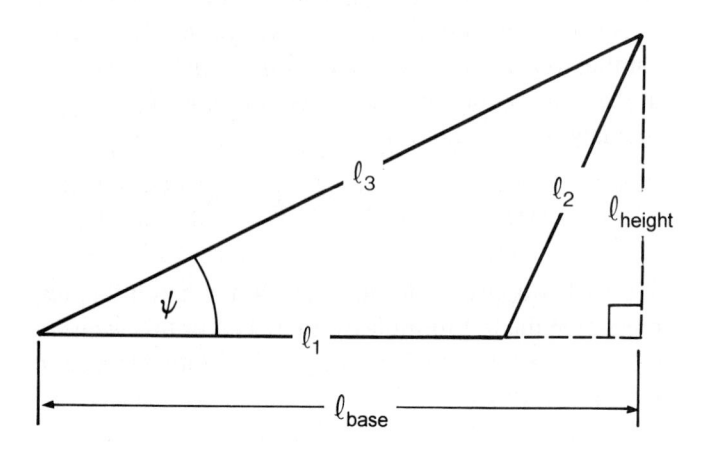

Fig. 4.30: Geometrical sketch illustrating how the angles and side lengths of the triangle in Fig. 4.29 are related to each other.

$l_{height} = l_2 \sin 70° = 4.7$ cm. The two lengths allow us to calculate the angle ψ in Fig. 4.30: $\tan\psi = l_{height}/l_{base} = 4.7/10.7$, which yields $\psi = 23.7°$. The angle ϕ in Fig. 4.29 follows then as $\phi = 90° + \psi = 113.7°$.

Using the Pythagorean theorem on the triangle constructed in Fig. 4.30 further yields:

$$l_3 = \sqrt{l_{base}^2 + l_{height}^2} = \sqrt{(10.7)^2 + (4.7)^2} \quad (42)$$
$$\Rightarrow \quad l_3 = 11.7 \ cm$$

With these results from Fig. 4.30 we return to Eq. (41) to find:

Solution part (a): The magnitude of the tension is obtained from Eq. (40):

$$T = F_{ext} \left(\frac{l_3 \sin\phi}{l_2 \sin\theta} \right) \quad (41)$$

In order to quantify T in Eq. (41) we must determine the values of θ, ϕ and l_3. Because **T** acts perpendicularly to the mandible and the angle between the two parts of the mandible is 110°, we know that $\theta = 110° - 90° = 20°$.

Determining ϕ is trickier. To do this we construct a right angle triangle by extending the lower part of the mandible and drawing another line perpendicular to it running through the axis of rotation. This is shown in Fig. 4.30. We can use trigonometry to evaluate an angle when we have the lengths of two sides of a right triangle. The length of the base of the triangle in Fig. 4.30 is $l_{base} = l_1 + l_2 \cos 70° = 10.7$ cm. The length of the side perpendicular to the base in the figure is given as

$$T = 40[N] \left(\frac{11.7[cm] \ \sin 113.7°}{5.0[cm] \ \sin 20°} \right) \quad (43)$$
$$\Rightarrow \quad T = 250 \ N$$

Note that in this case you can get the correct answer without converting [cm] to [m] because the two quantities with units of [cm] cancel. Of course, you would also get the right answer if you do convert [cm] to [m] and it is a good idea to get used to working with standard units to avoid forgetting to make the conversions when necessary.

Solution part (b): The magnitude of the force **R** acting on the joint is found by substituting Eq. (43) into Eq. (39):

$$R = T - F_{ext} = 250[N] - 40[N] = 210 \ N \quad (44)$$

Calculations like the ones in this Example are useful when we attempt reconstructions of fossil skulls to assess physiological properties of an extinct species.

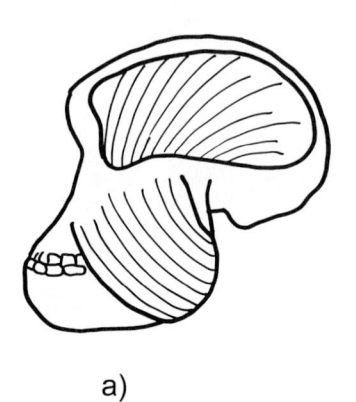

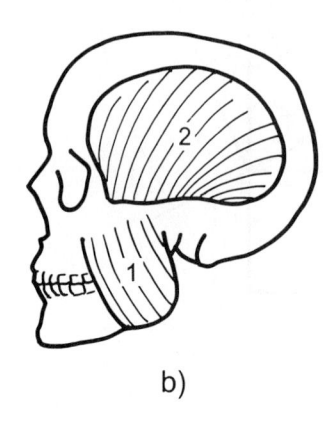

Fig. 4.31: Comparison between the masseter/mandible system of (a) an australopithecus robustus and (b) a modern human. The masseter muscle is labelled (1) and the temporalis muscle is labelled (2). Note the difference in angle in the mandible and the direction at which the masseter exerts a tension force on the mandible. The temporalis muscle connects the temporalis bone to the mandible and allows us to pull the mandible up and backwards. Note that the same australopithecine species is included in Fig. 4.34.

Applying this approach to hominids from the past 5 million years provides a measure of strength of the masseter which in turn is indicative of the diet of an individual. Fig. 4.31 compares a modern human with an australopithecus robustus, a species which lived between 2 and 1 million years ago. Note the variation in angles of the mandible and the angles of the masseter attachment. Calculating the required force for the same strength of bite allows us to judge whether the much more massive masseter of australopithecus robustus represents a lesser adaption due to the earlier stage of evolution or whether it indicates a diet which required a lot of chewing or biting.

4.4.3. The hip joint (Example 4.5)

Fig. 4.32(a) shows the anatomy and the main forces at the human hip joint. The person is a standard man (see data in Table 2.2) and balances on one leg only. Due to the balance the normal force is equal to the weight, $N = W$. The weight of a leg of a standard man is $1/7^{th}$ of the body weight ($W_L = W/7$). Calculate as a multiple of the weight of the standard man

(a) the magnitude of the force due to the abductor muscle **F**,

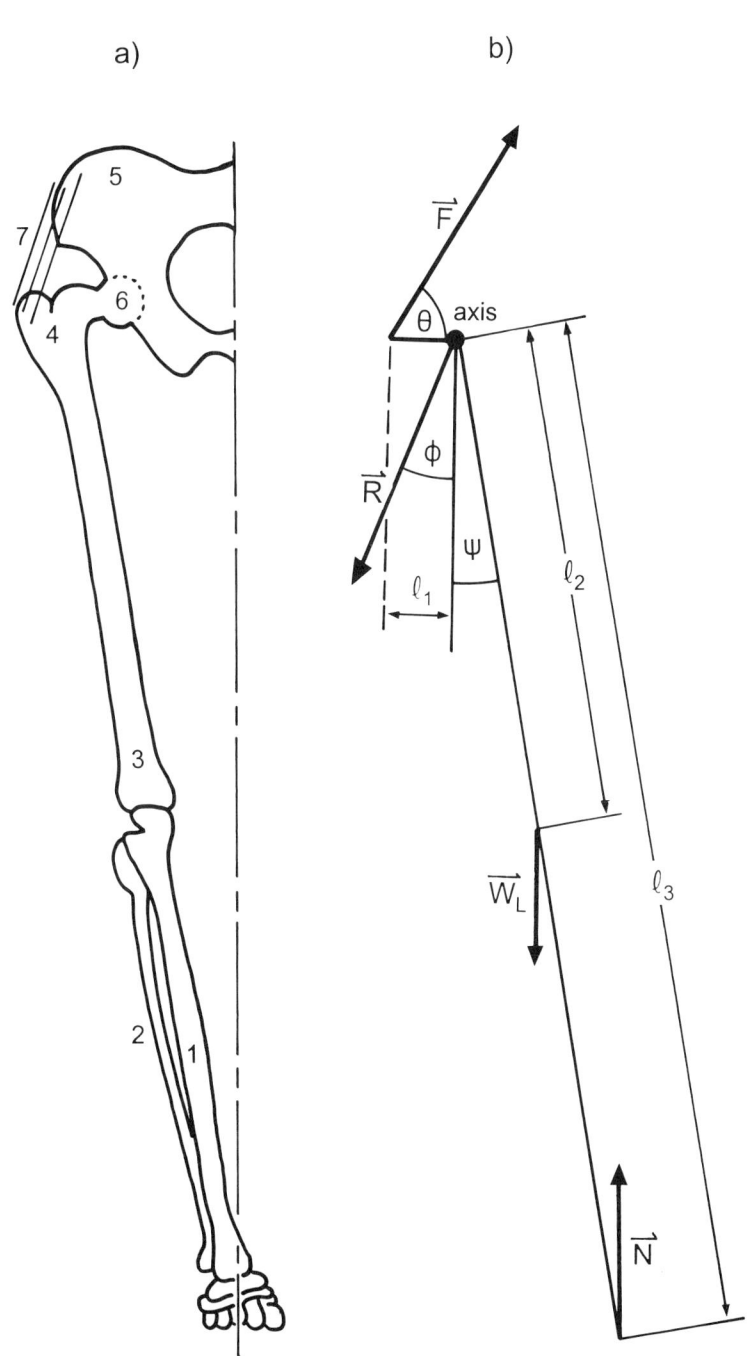

Fig. 4.32: (a) Anatomical sketch for the human hip joint, and (b) arrangement of the various forces considered in the example. Bones of the leg include the tibia (1), the fibula (2), the femur (3) with the great trochanter (4); the hip consists of the pelvis (5) with the acetabulum (6). The abductor muscle (7) connects the great trochanter and the pelvis.

(b) the x–component of the force **R**, R_x, and
(c) the y–component of the force **R**, R_y.

Biological information: Most of the time while walking only one foot is on the ground. Elderly people, who walk slowly, need also to establish a mechanical equilibrium during each step. They achieve this by shifting the center–of–mass of the body over the foot currently on the ground. We thus assume that the center–of–mass of the body lies on the central symmetry line, which is the dashed vertical line in Fig. 4.32(a).

While only one foot is on the ground, the normal force pushing upward through the sole is equal in magnitude to the weight of the person. Due to the arrangement of the bones in the leg and the hip, large forces act on both sides of the head of the femur.

In total fourteen muscles and ligaments connect the pelvis to the femur. To simplify the situation only the major forces are shown in Fig. 4.32(b). The inner head of the femur centers around the rotation axis of the hip joint, fitting into the acetabulum, which is the socket in the pelvis. Also illustrated in Fig. 4.32(a) is the abductor muscle which connects the pelvis to the outer head of the femur, which is called the great trochanter. The force exerted by the abductor muscle forms an angle $\theta = 70°$ with the horizontal and acts on the leg at a distance $l_1 = 7$ cm horizontally left of the axis. The angle ϕ lies between the vertical and the force exerted by the upper body onto the hip joint, **R**.

The leg forms an angle of $\psi = 7°$ with the vertical as shown in Fig. 4.32(b). Since the normal force and the weight of the leg act in the vertical direction, ψ is also the angle between these two forces and the leg. Measuring the distances along the leg, the normal force acts at distance $l_3 = 90$ cm from the axis and the weight of the leg acts at the leg's center–of–mass point, which is $l_2 = 40$ cm from the axis.

Solution: We identify the leg as the system. The environment includes the rest of the human body, in particular the abductor muscle attached to the great trochanter. This leads to two contact forces which act on the leg and are exerted by the rest of the human body:
(I) the force of the abductor muscle **F**, which acts on the greater trochanter at an angle of $\theta = 70°$ with the positive x–axis, where the x–axis is running horizontally to the right.
(II) the force due to the acetabulum **R**, which acts on the head of the femur. This force pushes in the direction of the rotation axis of the hip joint.

There are two further forces we include: (III) **N**, the normal force, exerted by the floor on the sole of the foot, with N = W where W is the weight of the person.
(IV) **W**$_L$, the weight of the leg, acting vertically down-

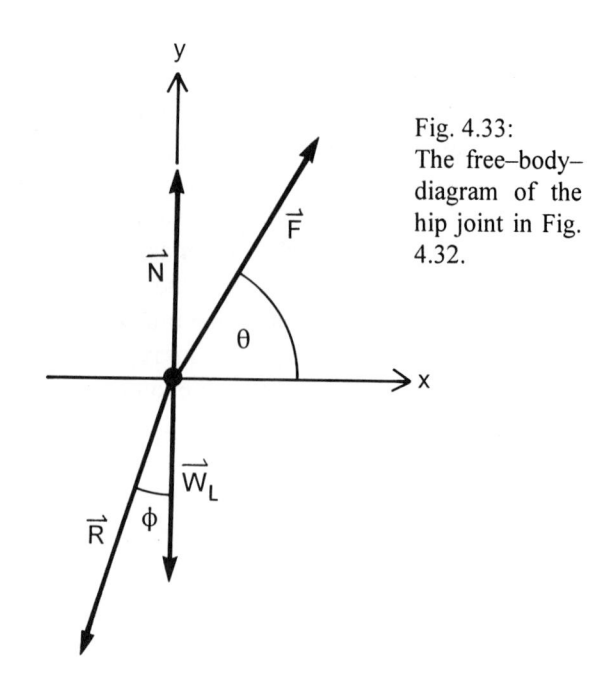

Fig. 4.33: The free–body–diagram of the hip joint in Fig. 4.32.

wards at the center–of–mass of the leg, which is roughly located at the knee.

The free–body–diagram is developed in Fig. 4.33 with the balance of torque plot already given in Fig. 4.32(b). The distances along the leg are given for an average person as: $l_1 = 7$ cm, $l_2 = 40$ cm, $l_3 = 90$ cm. Note that the force **R** and the force components $N\cos\psi$ and $W_l\cos\psi$ are not needed for the balance of torque equation since they all act in the direction of the rotation axis. Based on Fig. 4.32(b) and 4.33 the three conditions of mechanical equilibrium are written as:

$$(I) \quad F\cos\theta - R_x = 0$$

$$(II) \quad F\sin\theta - R_y - \frac{W}{7} + N = 0 \qquad (45)$$

$$(III) \quad -l_1 F\sin\theta - l_2 \frac{W}{7}\sin\psi + l_3 N\sin\psi = 0$$

Solution part (a): We solve for the magnitude of the force **F**. Note that the balance of torque equation, which is formula (III) in Eq. (45), does not contain the components of the force **R** since that force acts in the direction of the axis. Thus, that formula contains the least number of unknown variables in Eq. (45). We substitute N = W in this formula:

$$F = \frac{\sin\psi \left(l_3 - \dfrac{l_2}{7} \right)}{l_1 \sin\theta} W \qquad (46)$$

Eq. (46) yields:

$$F = \frac{\sin 7^0 \left(90[cm] - \frac{40[cm]}{7}\right)}{7[cm]\sin 70^0} W \quad (47)$$

$$\Rightarrow \quad F = 1.56\ W$$

This means that the abductor muscle must provide a force which is about 1.6 times the weight of the person. Such large forces may strain tendons connecting the muscle to the pelvis or the great trochanter. The largest contribution to this force is the torque due to the normal force because the joint is far off the body's symmetry line while the foot must be vertically below the center–of–mass. To circumvent the occurrence of these large forces the person may use a cane on the opposite side. This allows the foot to be further out and greatly reduces the torque contribution due to the normal force.

Solutions part (b) and part (c) : Now we solve for the two components of the force **R**. From formula (I) in Eq. (45) we find the x–component:

$$R_x = F\cos\theta = 0.53\ W \quad (48)$$

and from formula (II) in Eq. (45) we find the y–component:

$$R_y = F\sin\theta + \frac{6}{7}W = 2.32\ W \quad (49)$$

Eqs. (48) and (49) allow us to write the force **R** in polar coordinates. For the magnitude we get:

$$R = \sqrt{R_x^2 + R_y^2} = 2.38\ W \quad (50)$$

and for the angle ϕ we get:

$$\tan\phi = \frac{R_x}{R_y} = 0.23 \quad \Rightarrow \quad \phi = 13^0 \quad (51)$$

The force **R** is very large with a value more than twice the weight of the person. Therefore, the anatomy of our body takes great care to avoid allowing **R** to contribute to the torque on the hip joint. This is done by moving the head of the femur deep into the acetabulum of the pelvis. These forces must also be taken into account when designing hip replacements as shown in Fig. 4.4.

4.5. Case study: Since when walk hominids on two legs?

The two previous examples illustrate the use of mechanical concepts in human physiology. However, the same concepts also contribute to scientific research in other life sciences. As a special example, an interesting issue in human evolution is presented here.

The evolution of the primates began about 45 million years ago when the monkeys of the Americas (platyrrhine) and the monkeys of Africa and Eurasia (catarrhine) split. The African group split again about 32 million years ago into the cercopithecids and the hominoids. The cercopithecids include today's baboons. The hominoids branched four times between 22 and 7 million years ago; with the gibbons, orang–utans, gorillas, chimpanzees and ourselves the contemporary representatives in each group. The chimpanzees are our closest living relatives with a 99.4% DNA match; the separation of their line occurred about half as long ago as the lines of fox and wolf split.

The evolution of the human branch during the past 5 – 7 million years is still not fully understood. The current section illustrates how physical reasoning in comparative anatomy and physiology can contribute to resolving new questions in this field. We want to ask the question whether humans began to walk upright to use tools, and whether walking upright is directly or indirectly linked to the increase in brain volume which did not occur in any of the ape branches.

The study is therefore based on a comparison of three species: (I) the chimpanzee, which still moves on four legs when on flat ground, (II) modern homo sapiens, which is the only living bipedal mammal and (III) *Lucy*, an australopithecus afarensis which lived 3.2 million years ago in what is today Ethiopia. We know the age of Lucy from applying the potassium/argon method which is a method based on radioactive decay processes which are discussed in Chapter 22.

We first establish the major differences between chimpanzees and humans regarding leg and lower body anatomy. Then we use the fossil record of Lucy to demonstrate that she was bipedal and, thus, that walking upright has been a feature of hominids for longer than the past 3 million years. This is an important finding as it excludes the idea that the ability to walk upright was developed to allow humans to use tools with their hands. The use of tools actually emerged only about 2 million years ago, by which time the brain volume of hominids had sufficiently increased! Thus, modern research considers humans to be on an evolutionary track driven by the co–evolution of a complex hand (allowing the use of tools) and a large brain. The development of brain size

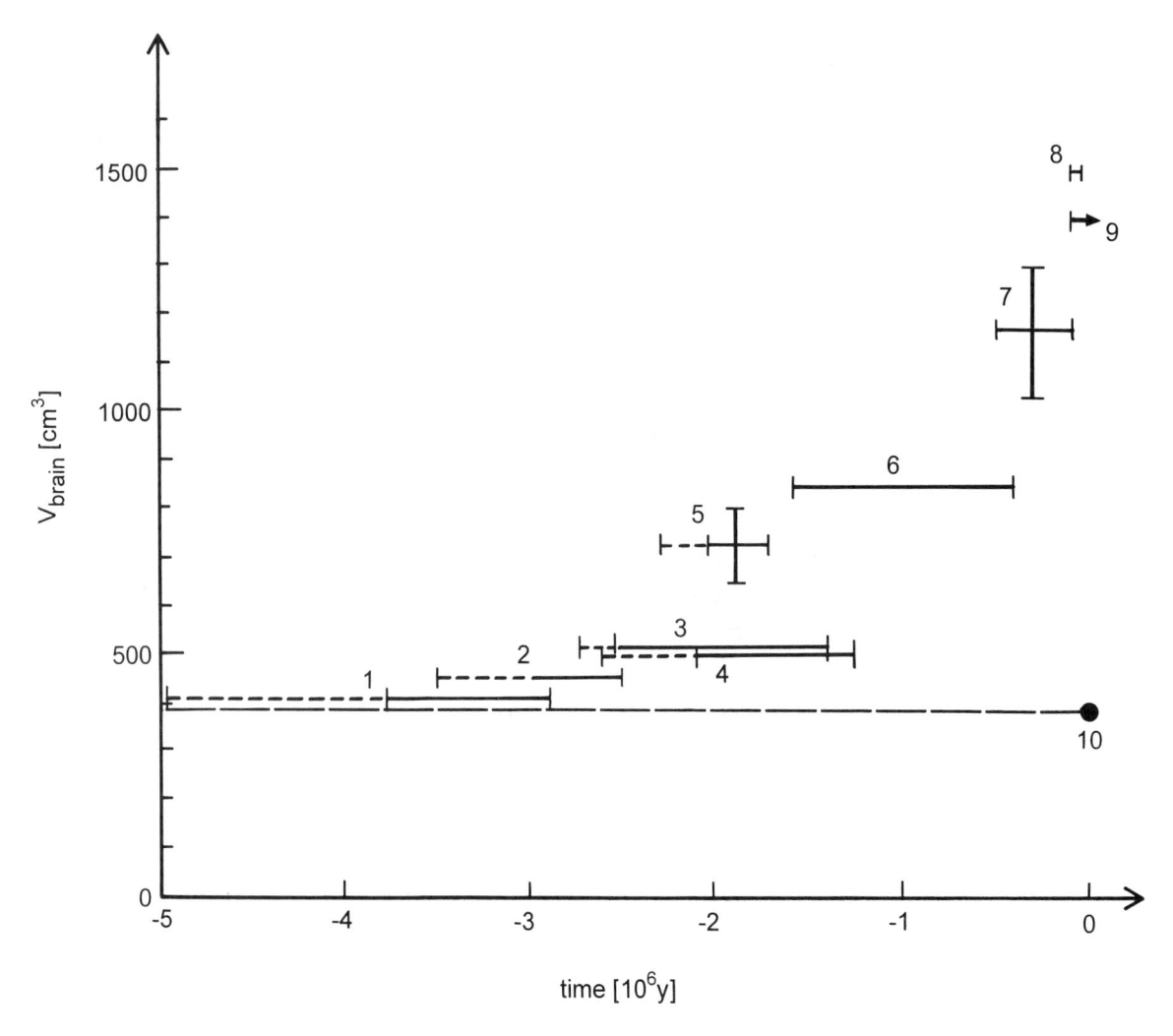

Fig. 4.34: Development of the brain size in [cm³] as a function of time in million years before present for the members of the hominid branch. The first four species were australopithecines, with (1) australopithecus afarensis, (2) australopithecus africanus, (3) australopithecus bosei and (4) australopithecus robustus. The next five species are members of the genus homo, with (5) homo habilis, (6) homo erectus, (7) homo sapiens (archaic), (8) homo sapiens neanderthalensis and (9) homo sapiens sapiens (modern man). For comparison the brain size of a chimpanzee (10) is included. The solid error bars indicate confirmed data, dashed lines indicate possible extensions of the early period of existence of a species.

as a function of time is illustrated in Fig. 4.34. The australopithecines (1 – 4) show a minor brain size increase relative to the modern–day chimpanzees while the first member of the genus homo, homo habilis living about 2 million years ago, displays already a brain size increase of almost 100 % relative to the apes. Homo habilis was the first species known to have used hand–made tools.

Fig. 4.35 compares the major muscles of the leg and pelvis of (a) a chimpanzee and (b) a modern human. Dominating the muscle arrangement of the chimpanzee's upper leg are the small and medium gluteal muscles (called the abductor muscle in humans). These muscles stretch the hip joint of the ape, thus efficiently accelerating its body forward since the center–of–mass of the ape's body is in front of the legs. This means that pushing hard into the floor under a small angle with the horizontal plane accelerates the chimpanzee in a similar fashion as the starting sprinter (see Example 3.6). In this context it is also beneficial that the ape has a comparably long upper body which shifts the center–of–mass far above the pelvis. This is achieved by the shape of the ape's pelvis bones, as shown in Fig. 4.36(a), with the hip bone stretched upwards and a rather narrow sacrum.

The upright posture of humans is associated with significant changes to the shape of the pelvis bones and to the function of the muscles of the legs. Stretching the abductor muscle or the (large) gluteal muscle, which dominates the muscle arrangements of the human upper leg, would only accelerate the upper body upwards (so that you end up standing on your toes) but not forward.

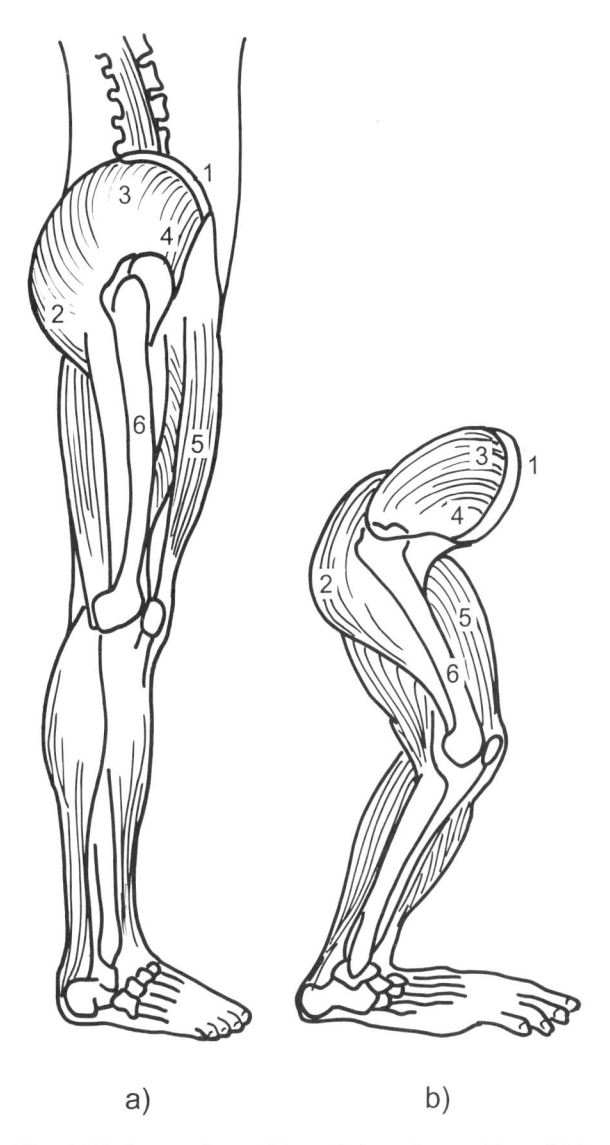

Fig. 4.35: Comparison of the pelvis region and leg of (a) a chimpanzee and (b) a homo sapiens. The figure emphasizes the difference in function of the upper leg muscles and the hip bone. The three gluteal muscles (large gluteal muscle (2), medium gluteal muscle (3) and small gluteal muscle (4)) are the major means of acceleration of a chimpanzee, causing a large, mostly horizontal force on the body when stretched. The gluteal muscle (2) and abductor muscles (3,4) do not contribute to a forward acceleration for humans but are used to balance the upper body upright. This function is supported by a broader and flatter hip bone (1), lowering the center–of–mass for the human body into the pelvis region and thus stabilizing the upright posture. Labelled are also the quadriceps femoris muscle (5) and the femur (6).

Fig. 4.36: Comparison of the top–view of the pelvis of three primates: (a) the chimpanzee with a narrow sacrum (1) and upwards directed wings of the hip bone (2), (b) Lucy, a three million year old australopithecine with a noticeably broader sacrum and forward turned wings of the hip bone, and (c) modern humans where the arrangement of the pelvis bones is similar to those of the australopithecines but resume an overall more rounded shape.

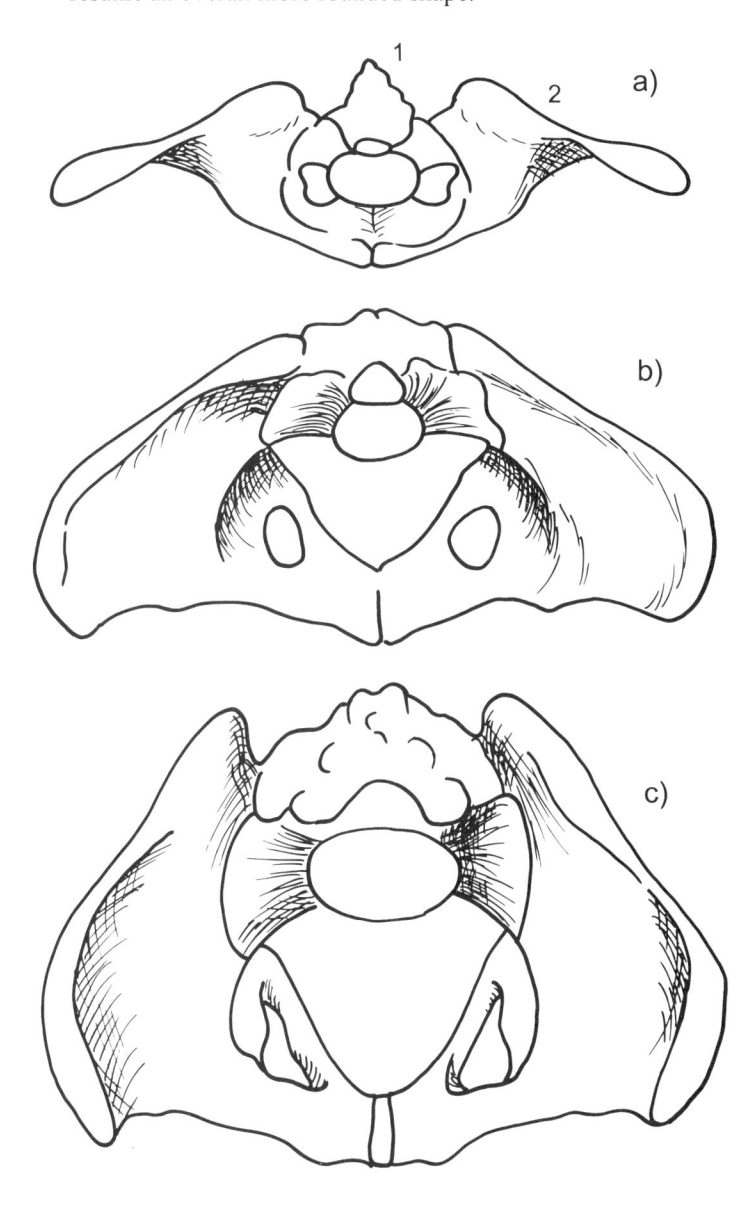

Consequently, an entirely new mechanism for forward motion has been developed and the muscles causing an acceleration in the leg of the chimpanzee serve new purposes in human legs. The abductor muscle stabilizes the upright posture in the sideways direction, as discussed in Example 4.5, and the gluteal muscle keeps our upper body from falling forwards while walking.

This focus on balance rather than rapid acceleration also resulted in evolutionary changes to the pelvis as shown in Fig. 4.36(c): the wings of the hip bone turned and the sacrum widened to accommodate the intestines in order to lower the center–of–mass. This stabilizes the upright posture because the pelvis plane contains the axes about which our body tilts forward and sideways.

These differences between the quadrupedal chimpanzee and the bipedal modern human can now be used to study the fossil record of Lucy. This is possible since the pelvis of this australopithecus was found almost completely intact (Fig. 4.36(b)). The striking similarities between Lucy's hip bone and sacrum and those of humans indicate that Lucy did indeed walk upright. This is further supported by the marks on her pelvis bones indicating where the tendons of the various leg muscles were once attached.

Studying Lucy's pelvis more quantitatively, we surprisingly find her even better adapted to an upright posture than modern humans! This is illustrated in Fig. 4.37, where the front view of Lucy's pelvis and the pelvis of modern humans as well as the respective abductor muscle arrangements are overlapped with a balance of torque plot (dashed line). In both cases, the axis of rotation is located in the head of the femur as discussed in the previous section. When the upper body is balanced on one leg, the abductor muscle must compensate the torque about the axis of rotation. The longer the lever arm of the weight of the upper body, L_{cm}, and the shorter the distance between the abductor muscle and the head of the femur, L_A, the greater is the strain in the tendons of the abductor muscle. We measure these lengths in Fig. 4.37 and find:

$$\left(\frac{L_{cm}}{L_A}\right)_{Lucy} = 2.1 \quad , \quad \left(\frac{L_{cm}}{L_A}\right)_{man} = 2.6 \quad (52)$$

The larger the ratio in Eq. (52) the less favorable is the lever arm arrangement of the pelvis region. Why, then, did the evolution of the genus homo result in more poorly adapted individuals during the last 3 million years? This is due to a competing evolutionary process of modern humans: the development of a large brain. While Lucy was indeed well adapted to an upright posture, her pelvis had an elongated shape with an elliptic, and thus narrow opening for the birth canal. She could never have given birth to the large–headed babies of modern humans. Nature had to compromise by reshaping the pelvis of modern humans to provide a rounder, larger birth canal at the expense of adaptation to the upright posture. Still, the large human brain and the corresponding head size of a baby at birth pose a challenge which required further adjustments. The brain size of a human at birth is 25 % of the brain size of an adult, while a chimpanzee is born with 65 % of the brain size of an adult chimpanzee. A significant fraction of the development of the human brain occurs after birth, requiring a long period of infancy and parental nurturing.

Considering all the problems associated with the

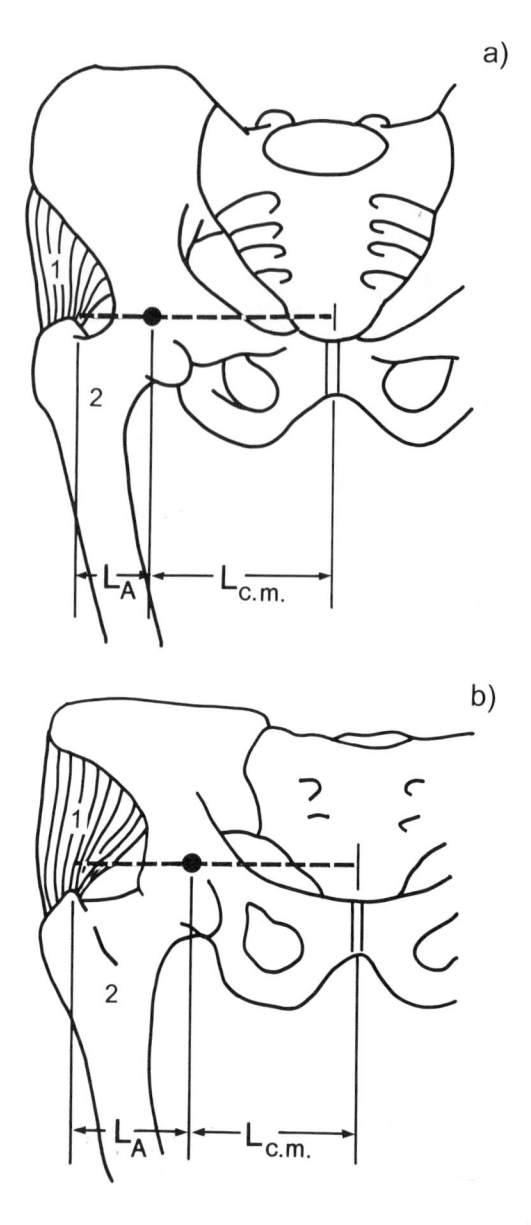

Fig. 4.37: Comparison of the front view of the pelvis region with the abductor muscles (1) for (a) modern humans and (b) the australopithecus Lucy. The australopithecines were better adjusted to upright walking as their head of the femur (2) is longer, providing for a longer lever arm for the abductor muscles.

upright posture, was it worth for the hominid branch to opt for it? The answer is most likely that we had no other choice. About 20 million years ago, the Indian subcontinent collided with Asia, pushing the Himalayan mountains upwards. This caused global climate changes including a significantly drier landscape in Africa and Asia. Forests retreated in favor of open savannahs. While the lines of the great apes remained confined to the dwindling forests, our ancestors adopted to the new environment.

4.6. Appendix: Center–of–mass position

With respect to their weight, rigid bodies respond as if their entire mass is located in a single point which we call the center–of–mass. The center–of–mass is a well–defined position typically located somewhere in the rigid body. For objects of simple geometry and uniform mass distribution (density) Eq. (25) is used to calculate this position; Cases I and II discussed below illustrate how the equation is applied. On the other side, for biological systems the applications of this formula are quite complex and, further, the system may often not be sufficiently characterized to use Eq. (25). In these cases experimental methods are used to determine the center–of–mass or even "educated guesses" are applied. Case III below illustrates how we proceed for biological systems.

Case I: a rigid body of few point masses.
Molecules can often be treated as if they exist of a few atoms (point masses) with well–defined relative positions. The simplest case is obviously a rigid body consisting of just two point masses. You will notice that we are quite familiar with the center–of–mass concept for this case in our everyday life. For $i = 2$ and the x–axis chosen along the axis of the two–body system as indicated in Fig. 4.38, Eq. (25) transforms into:

$$x_{cm} = \frac{x_1 m_1 + x_2 m_2}{m_1 + m_2} \quad (53)$$

because the total mass is $M = m_1 + m_2$.

A frequently used case is a system with two equal masses ($m_1 = m_2$) in which the center–of–mass lies half-way between the two point masses, at the position $x_{cm} = \frac{1}{2}(x_1+x_2)$. An example is the oxygen molecule, O_2, with the center–of–mass half-way between both oxygen atoms. Another frequently used case is a system in which one mass is much greater than the other mass, e.g. $m_1 \gg m_2$, leading to $x_{cm} = x_1$, i.e., the center–of–mass is at the position of the much heavier point mass. An example is the HCl molecule where we often assume that the chlorine atom is much heavier and thus only the hydrogen atom is mobile. This assumption will be used in Chapter 15 when we discuss the molecular vibrations of the HCl molecule.

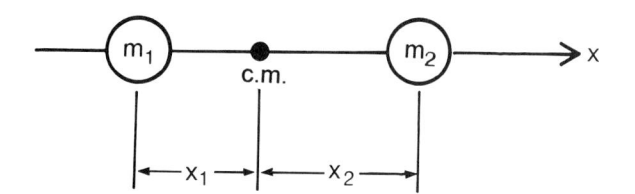

Example 4.6
Why does the Fosbury flop allow athletes to jump higher than the traditional Straddle technique?

Supplementary kinesiological information: In the Straddle technique of high jumping, the athlete ran toward the bar from an angle, then leaped while facing the bar. The jump consisted of swinging first one leg and then the other over the bar in a scissoring motion. At the highest point the athlete's body was oriented parallel to the bar facing downwards.

In 1968, Dick Fosbury introduced a new technique called the Fosbury flop when winning the Olympic gold medal in Mexico City. In this technique, the athletes turn as they leap, flinging their body backward over the bar with the back arched. Throughout the jump the athlete's body is oriented perpendicular to the bar.

Solution: For this example we can simplify the human body as an object of two point masses of about equal mass, connected with a flexible massless string of fixed length. We locate one point mass at the position of the upper chest of the athlete and one point mass in the pelvis area, as illustrated in Fig. 4.39(a). The center–of–mass is always positioned at the half-way point between the two point masses.

Fig. 4.39(b) illustrates the center–of–mass of the athlete at different stages of a high jump using the Straddle technique. The center–of–mass of the athlete is briefly positioned above the bar because both the chest and the pelvis are located above the bar at the same time. The athletes must generate a sufficient force on their body when leaping up to allow the center–of–mass to reach this height.

Figs. 4.39(c) illustrates the athlete's body at various stages of a Fosbury flop. Note that the center–of–mass lies always below the bar, allowing the athlete to pass the bar with a lesser force when leaping.

Example 4.7
The four hydrogen atoms in the methane molecule CH_4 form a regular tetrahedron. Fig. 4.40 illustrates the positions of the hydrogen atoms with respect to a Cartesian

Fig. 4.38: Illustration of the center–of–mass for two point masses positioned along the x–axis. The point masses have masses m_1 and m_2. The center–of–mass is labelled c.m.

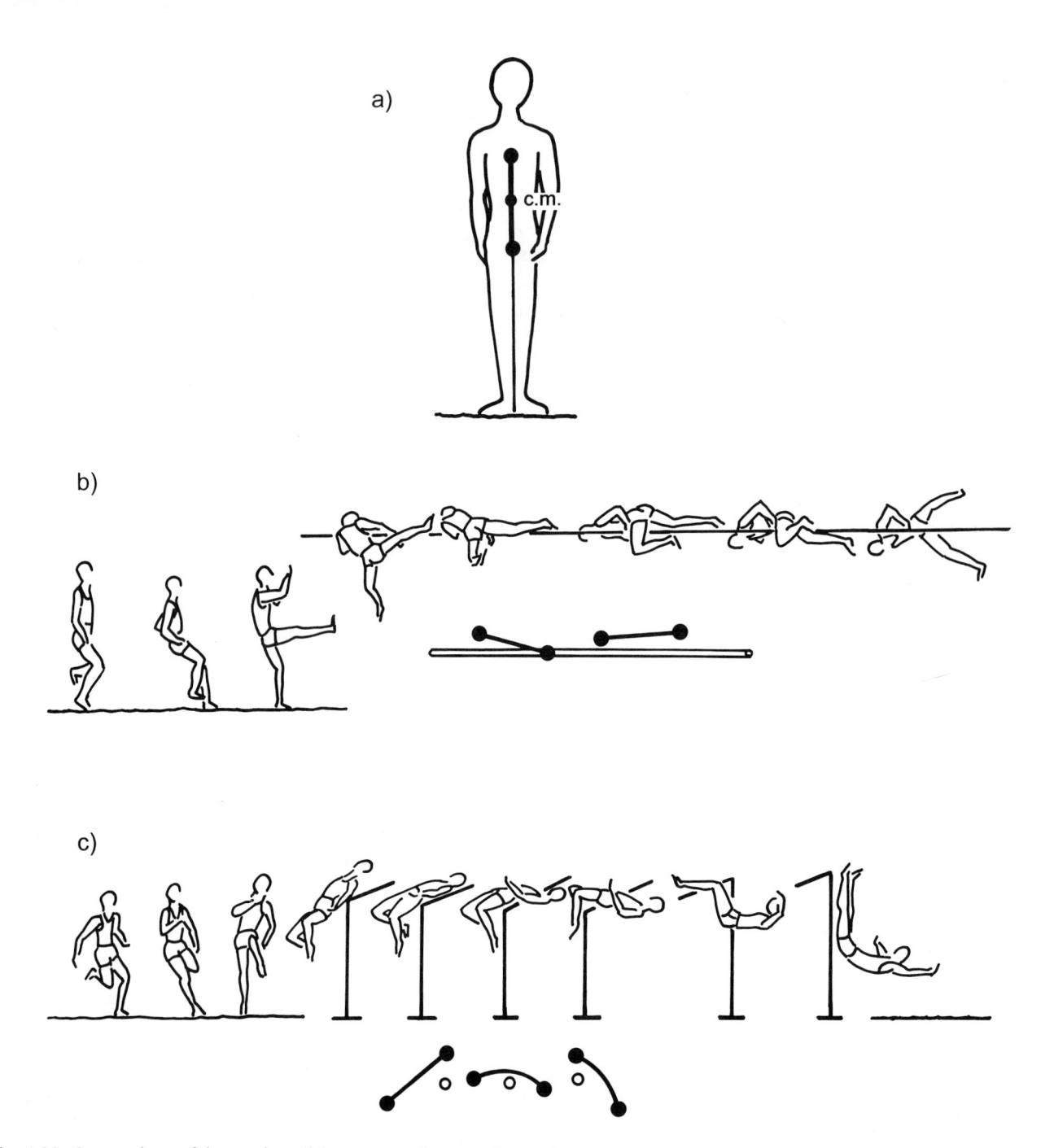

Fig. 4.39: Comparison of the motion of the center–of–mass of an athlete using the two main techniques for high jump. (a) For the comparison of the two techniques it is sufficient to simplify the human body as two equal point masses, located at the chest and at the pelvis. The two point masses are connected with a massless string of fixed length. (b) For the Straddle technique, the critical stage of the jump is highlighted with the two point-mass model, illustrating that both point masses pass over the bar at the same time. (c) For the Fosbury flop, the two point mass model is highlighting three sequential frames of the jump, illustrating that the center–of–mass of the athlete is never above the bar.

coordinate system. Note that there are also two examples in the General Appendix (Chapter 24) dealing with this molecule. The carbon atom is located at the center–of–mass of the four hydrogen atoms. Using Fig. 4.40, calculate the position of the carbon atom.

Solution: We use Eq. (25) and the equivalent formulas for the y–component and the z–component to calculate the three Cartesian components of the position of the carbon atom in Fig. 4.40. In each case, the total mass of the four hydrogen atoms in the denominator is equal to $M = 4\,m_H$ in which m_H is the mass of a single hydrogen atom. For the first formula, i.e., the x–component of the center–of–mass position, the figure shows two hydrogen atoms, H_B and H_D, with $x_i = l$. The other two hydrogen atoms, H_A and H_C, lead to zero–contributions to the sum because their x–components are $x_i = 0$. Proceeding in an analogous fashion for the other components we find:

$$x_{cm} = \frac{l\ m(H_B) + l\ m(H_D)}{4\ m(H)} = 0.5\ l$$

$$y_{cm} = \frac{l\ m(H_B) + l\ m(H_C)}{4\ m(H)} = 0.5\ l \qquad (54)$$

$$z_{cm} = \frac{l\ m(H_C) + l\ m(H_D)}{4\ m(H)} = 0.5\ l$$

Thus the carbon atom is located at the center of the cube shown in Fig. 4.40.

Case II: a uniform, symmetric rigid body
Eq. (25) can also be evaluated when the rigid body is uniform in density and its shape is highly symmetric. Examples of shapes with such symmetry are cylinders, spheres and rectangular prisms. In these cases the symmetry can be used to determine the center–of–mass position without any mathematical calculation. For example, the center–of–mass of a uniform sphere lies at its center, the center–of–mass of a uniform bar lies half–way between the two ends of the bar. The latter case is used in Example 4.2.

Case III: complex and biological bodies.
For an irregularly shaped body, Eq. (25) is evaluated experimentally as illustrated in Fig. 4.41. The figure illustrates the approach for a two–dimensional sheet of irregular shape. We pick two points along the rim of the object, A and B, and suspend the body from each of these points. The two vertical lines, which we draw on the body when it is in mechanical equilibrium in each case, intersect at the center–of–mass of the body.

Sometimes real biological systems can approximately be treated as highly symmetric objects, for example the human leg is sometimes treated as a uniform cylinder. We are using this approach in Chapter 15 when studying the pendulum motion of the leg during walking.

Even when the body has a lesser degree of symmetry, we can often place the center–of–mass intuitively without using Eq. (25). This is illustrated in Fig. 4.42, showing the shape correlation for coniferous trees and

Fig. 4.40: The geometry of the tetrahedral methane molecule CH_4 is best described by placing the molecule in a cube of side length *l* in a Cartesian coordinate system. The four hydrogen atoms form four corners of the cube as shown. They are indistinguishable in a real molecule but have been labelled in the sketch with different indices for calculation purpose.

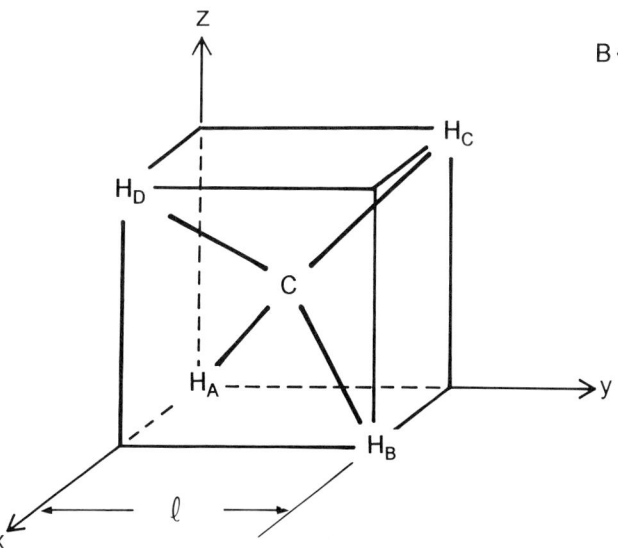

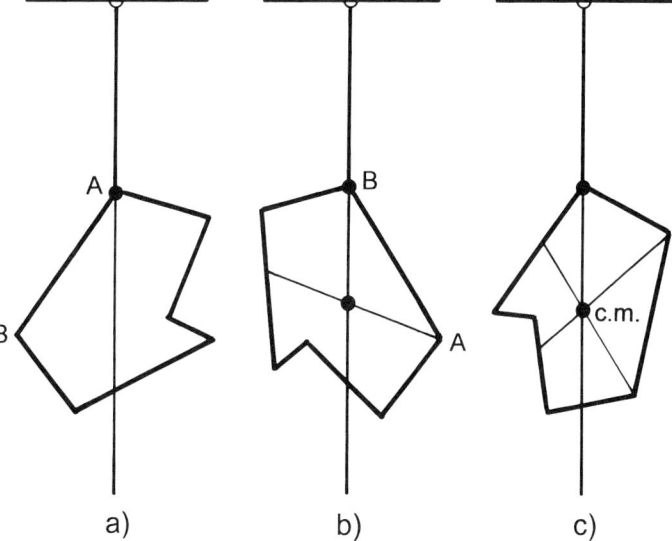

Fig. 4.41: Construction of the center–of–mass position for an irregularly shaped two–dimensional object. (a) An arbitrary point A is chosen along the perimeter of the object. The object is then suspended at point A. When it is in mechanical equilibrium, a vertical line is drawn through point A. (b) A different point B is chosen along the perimeter and the procedure is repeated. (c) The intersection of the two lines drawn in parts (a) and (b) represents the center–of–mass position.

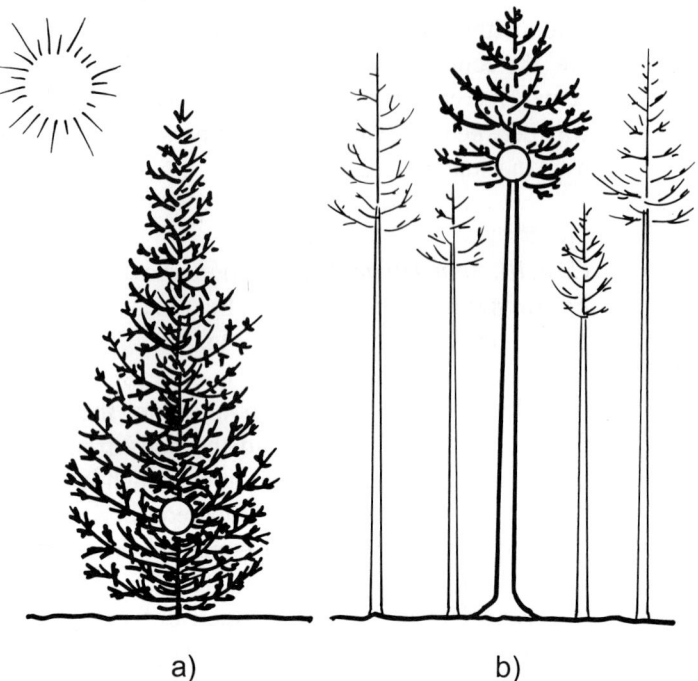

Fig. 4.42: The center-of-mass concept can be applied to the growth of coniferous trees. (a) The shape of isolated trees usually allows for a low center-of-mass. (b) Trees in a forest often have a high-lying center-of-mass. Note that we can guess the position of the center-of-mass in these cases intuitively without requiring a precise calculation.

their usual place of growth. The tree in Fig. 4.42(a) has a low center-of-mass, allowing it to grow at isolated spots. Even gale storms will not topple this tree because the center-of-mass is close to the ground. In turn, the tree shown in Fig. 4.42(b) has a high center-of-mass. Such trees grow in forests where the surrounding trees break the force a storm can apply on any individual tree. In turn, the tree must grow tall with the majority of its needles near the top as this is the only place where sufficient sun light is available for photosynthesis.

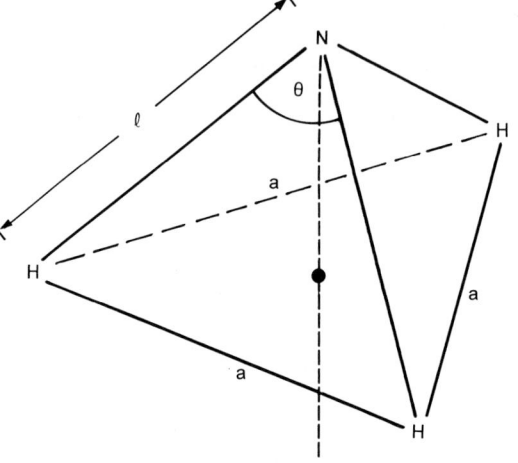

Fig. 4.43 for problem P–4.1.

4.7. Problems

P–4.1
In the ammonia molecule NH_3 the three hydrogen atoms are located in a plane forming an equilateral triangle with side length a as shown in Fig. 4.43. The nitrogen atom oscillates 24 billion times per second up and down along a line which intersects with the plane of the hydrogen atoms at the center-of-mass of the three hydrogen atoms.
(a) Calculate the length a in Fig. 4.43, using for the N–H bond length $l = 0.1014$ nm and for the HNH–bond angle $\theta = 106.8°$.
(b) Calculate the distance between the center-of-mass of the three hydrogen atoms and any one of the hydrogen atoms.

P–4.2
A person of mass m = 70 kg is doing push-ups as shown in Fig. 4.44. The distances are $l_1 = 90$ cm and $l_2 = 55$ cm.
(a) Calculate the vertical component of the normal force exerted by the floor on both hands, and
(b) calculate the normal force exerted by the floor on both feet.

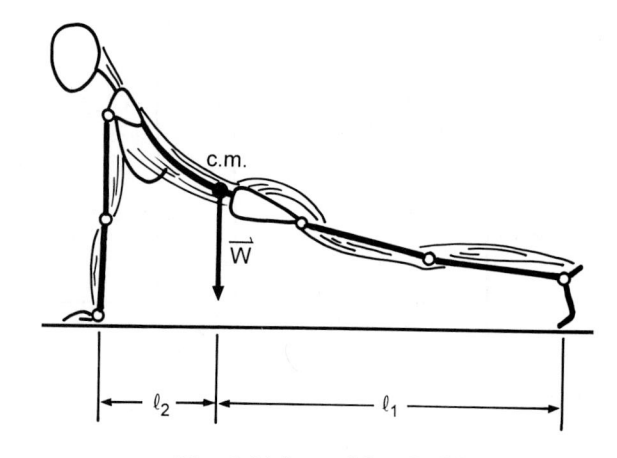

Fig. 4.44 for problem P–4.2.

P–4.3

A person holds the upper arm vertical and the lower arm horizontal with an object of mass M = 6 kg resting on the hand as illustrated in Fig. 4.45. The mass of the lower arm is given as m = 4 kg. We consider four forces acting on the lower arm: (I) the external force $\vec{F}_{ext}$, exerted by the bones and ligaments of the upper arm at the elbow (axis), (II) the tension $\vec{T}$, exerted by the biceps, (III) the weight $\vec{W}_M$ of the object, (IV) the weight $\vec{W}_F$ of the lower arm. The points along the lower arm, at which the forces act, are identified in Fig. 4.45: l_1 = 5 cm, l_2 = 15 cm and l_3 = 25 cm.

(a) Calculate the vertical component of the force $\vec{F}_{ext}$,
(b) calculate the vertical component of the tension $\vec{T}$.

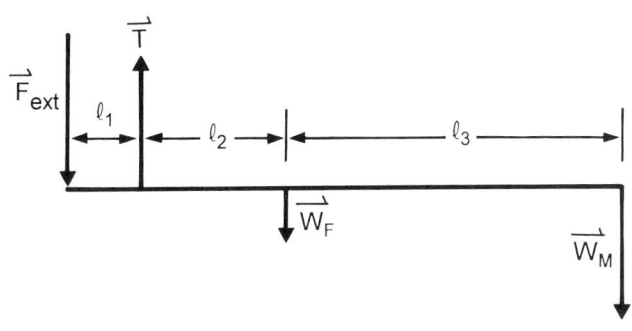

Fig. 4.45 for problem P–4.3.

P–4.4

The deltoid muscle holds the arm when it is stretched out horizontally. The major forces acting on the arm in this case are shown in Fig. 4.46. Use m = 8 kg for the mass of the arm, α = 17° for the angle, l_1 = 11 cm for the distance between the shoulder joint and the attachment point of the tendon of the deltoid muscle, and l_2 = 30 cm for the distance from the shoulder joint to the center-of-mass of the arm.

(a) Calculate the magnitude of the tension $\vec{T}$ in the tendon of the deltoid muscle, and
(b) calculate the magnitude of the external force $\vec{F}$ acting toward the shoulder joint.

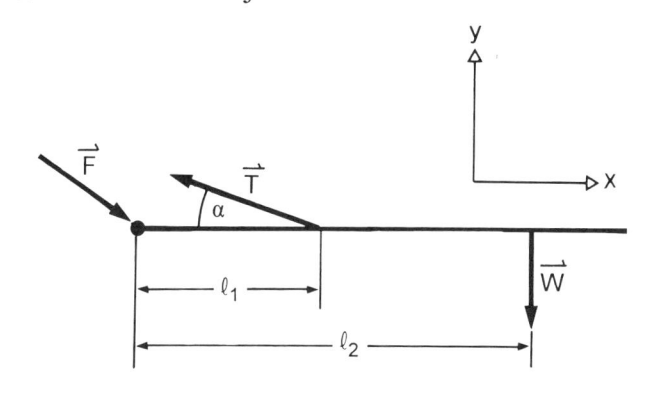

Fig. 4.46 for problem P–4.4.

P–4.5

An object of mass M = 10 kg is lifted with the aid of a pulley as shown in Fig. 4.47. The upper arm is held vertical and the lower arm has an angle of θ = 35° with the horizontal. The label *cm* marks the center-of-mass of the lower arm. Consider the weight of the object M, the weight of the lower arm and hand, the tension due to

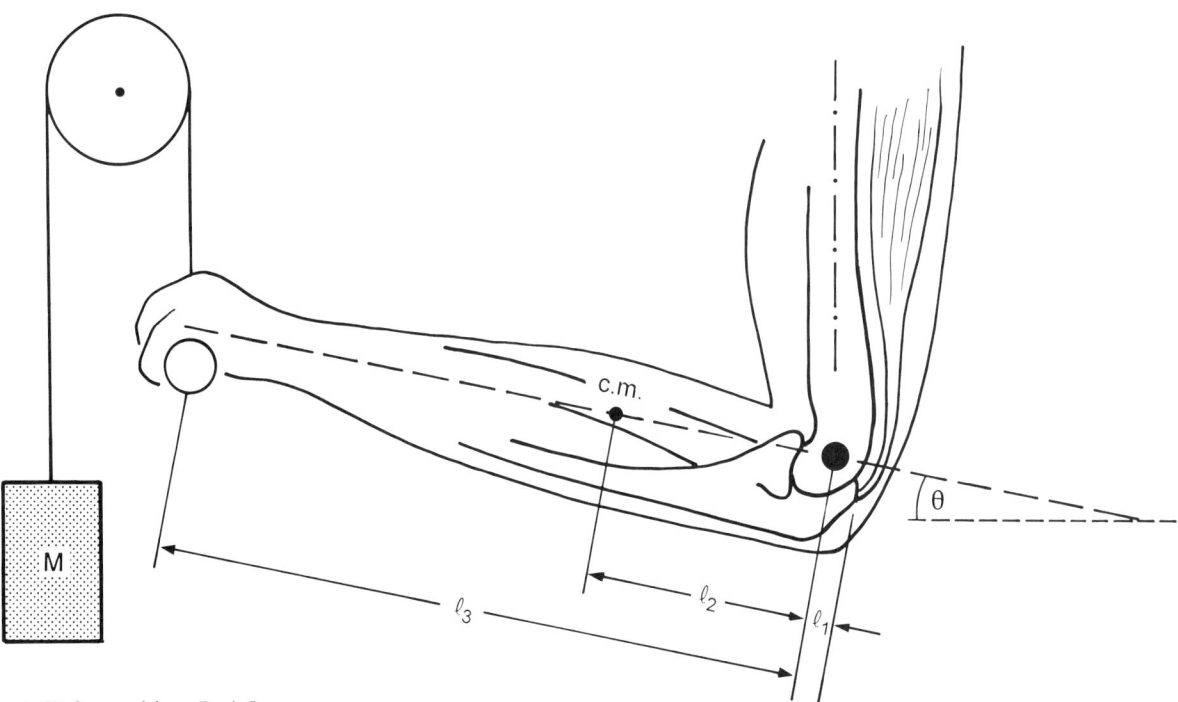

Fig. 4.47 for problem P–4.5.

the triceps muscle and the force due to the humerus. For the lengths we use the following values: $l_1 = 3$ cm, $l_2 = 15$ cm, $l_3 = 40$ cm. The lower arm and the hand have a mass of 2.0 kg.
(a) What is the magnitude of the vertical force exerted on the lower arm by the triceps muscle, and
(b) what is the magnitude of the vertical force exerted on the lower arm by the humerus?
Hint: The triceps muscle pulls vertically upward.

P–4.6
A steel band of a brace exerts an external force of magnitude $F_{ext} = 40$ N on a tooth. The tooth is shown in Fig. 4.48 with point B a distance 1.3 cm above point A, which is the axis of rotation of the tooth. The angle between the tooth and the external force is $\theta = 40°$. What is the torque on the root of the tooth about point A?

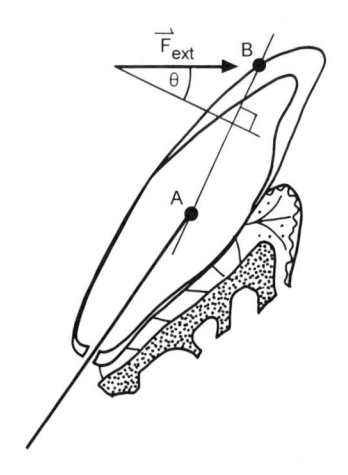

Fig. 4.48 for problem P–4.6.

P–4.7
A person holds an object of mass $m = 2$ kg on the palm of the hand with the arm stretched as shown in Fig. 4.49. Use the torque equilibrium equation to determine the magnitude of the force **F** which is exerted by the biceps muscle, when $a = 30$ cm, $b = 5$ cm and the angle $\theta = 80°$. Neglect the weight of the lower arm.

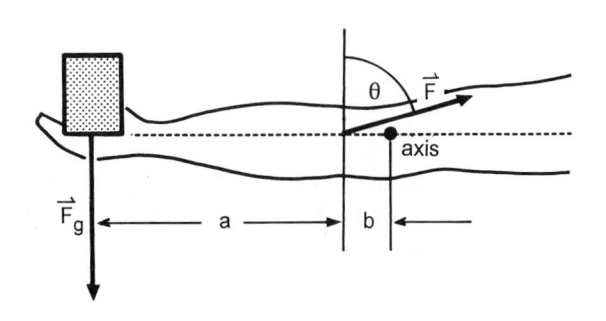

Fig. 4.49 for problem P–4.7.

P–4.8
The quadriceps femoris muscle, shown as (1) in Fig. 4.50(a), is a muscle in the upper leg which serves an analogous purpose to the triceps in the upper arm. Its tendon (2) is attached to the upper end of the tibia (3) as shown in the figure. This muscle exerts the major force of the upper leg on the lower leg when the leg is stretched. Considering also the weight of the lower leg, W_L, and the weight of the foot, **F**, three forces act on the lower leg as shown in Fig. 4.50(b). Find the magnitude of the tension **T** when the tendon is at an angle of $\phi = 30°$ with the tibia using the torque equilibrium. Assume that the lower leg has a mass of 3 kg and the mass of the foot is 1.2 kg. The leg is extended at an angle of $\theta = 35°$ with the vertical and the center–of–mass of the lower leg is at its center. The tendon attaches to the lower leg at a point 1/5 of the way down the lower leg.

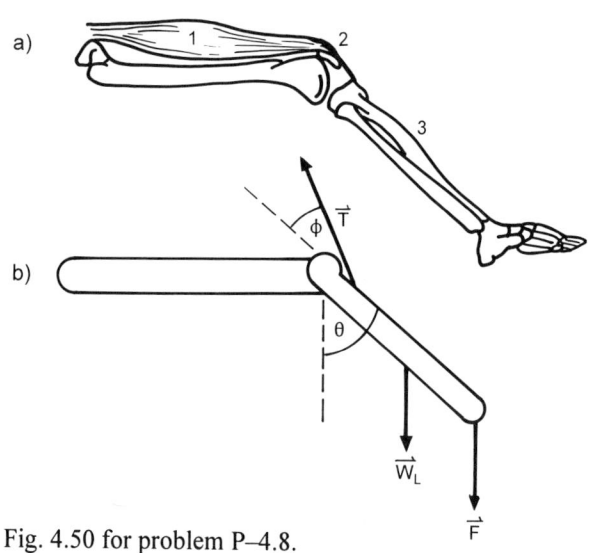

Fig. 4.50 for problem P–4.8.

P–4.9
A person bends over as shown in Fig. 4.51(a) and lifts an object of mass $m = 15$ kg while keeping the back parallel

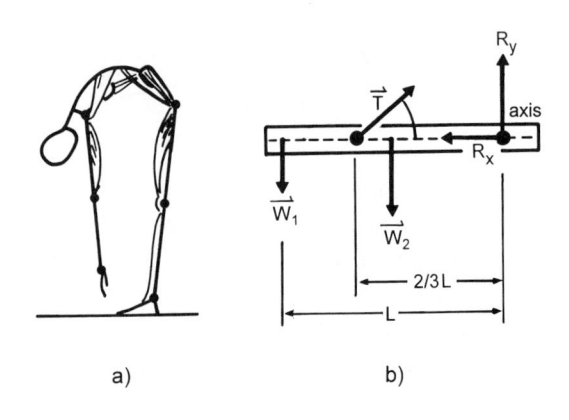

Fig. 4.51 for problem P–4.9.

with the floor. The muscle that attaches 2/3 of the way up the spine maintains the position of the back. This muscle is called the back muscle or latissimus dorsi muscle. The angle between the spine and the force **T** in this muscle is $\theta = 11°$. Use the balance of torque plot in Fig. 4.51(b) and take the mass of the upper body as M = 40 kg.

(a) Find the magnitude of the tension force **T** in the back muscle, and
(b) find the x–component of the compressive force **R** in the spine.

P–4.10
A standard man bends the upper body forward, forming a 30° angle with the horizontal, as shown in Fig. 4.52. Considering the mass of the head to be 7 %, the mass of the arms to be 12 % and the mass of the trunk to be 46 % of the body mass, calculate as a multiple of the person's weight
(a) the magnitude of the force $\mathbf{F_M}$ in the back muscle,
(b) the magnitude of the force $\mathbf{F_B}$ acting on the fifth lumbar vertebra (at which the axis of rotation lies).
Hint: the figure indicates that the force $\mathbf{F_M}$ forms a 12° angle with the spinal column.

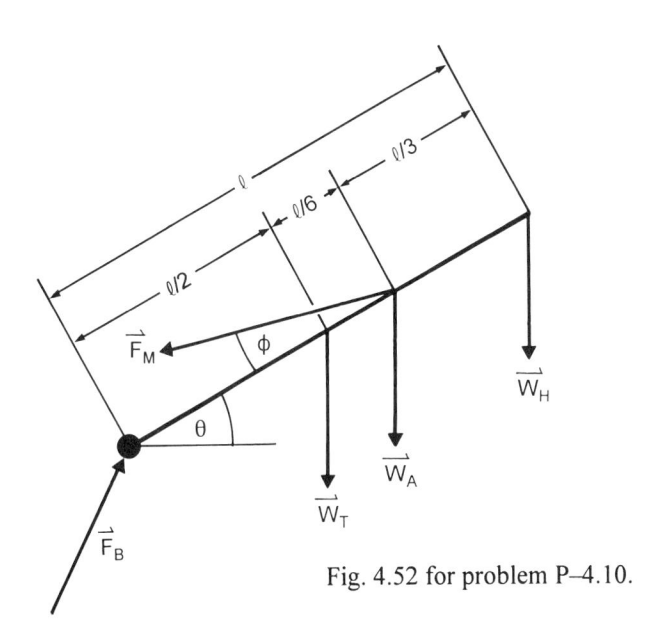

necting points B and C' in the figure). The ribs are pivoted about the points A and A' which mark the joint with the thoracic vertebra. Determine from Fig. 4.54 which muscle contracts during inhalation (volume increase) and which muscle contracts during exhalation (volume decrease).

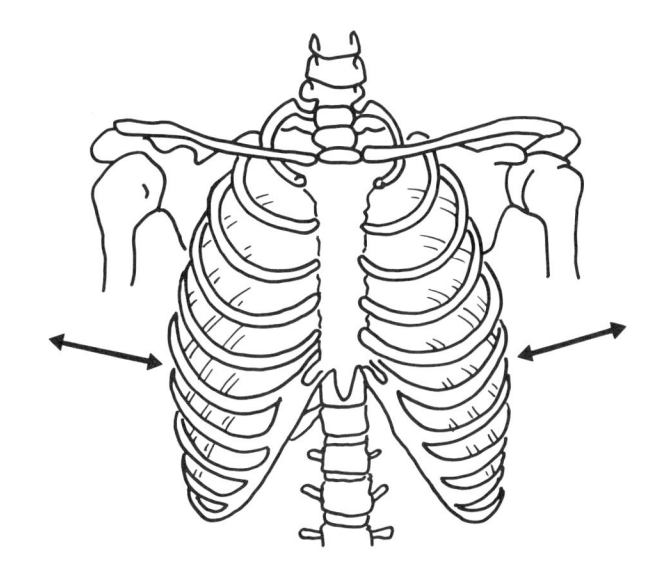

Fig. 4.53 for problem P–4.11.

Fig. 4.52 for problem P–4.10.

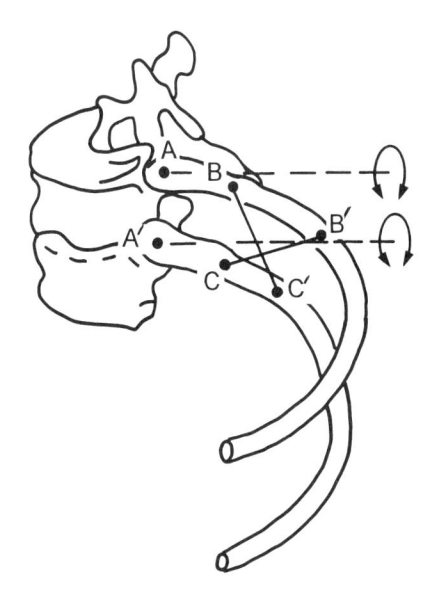

Fig. 4.54 for problem P–4.11.

P–4.11
Fig. 4.53 shows the motion of the thorax during breathing. Air is pulled into the lung and pushed out of the lung by the active change of volume of the lung associated with the change in the volume within the rib cage. Two sets of intercostal muscles allow for the increase and decrease of the volume within the rib cage. These are shown in Fig. 4.54 and include the intercostales interni muscles (connecting points B' and C in the figure) and the intercostales externi muscles (con-

P–4.12
A person is suspended from a high bar as shown on the left side of Fig. 4.55. While at rest, the center–of–mass of the person is directly below the bar. The sketch on the right side in Fig. 4.55 shows the forces acting on the lower arm of the person. Assume that the forces exerted by the bar on the left hand, $\mathbf{F_l}$, and exerted on the right hand, $\mathbf{F_r}$, are equal in magnitude and directed parallel to

each other. Use for the length from the hand to the attachment point of the biceps' tendon $l_1 = 40$ cm and use for the remaining length of the arm to the elbow joint the value $l_2 = 5$ cm. The two angles are $\theta = 10°$ and $\phi = 20°$.
(a) Find the x– and y–components of the force $\mathbf{F}_{ext}$ with $\mathbf{F}_{ext}$ the external force exerted by the bar on each of the two hands.
(b) Calculate the magnitude of the tension force $\mathbf{T}$ in the biceps tendon.
(c) $\mathbf{R}$ is the force exerted by the humerus on the lower arm through the elbow. Calculate the magnitude of the force $\mathbf{R}$ and its angle with the lower arm.
Hint: Neglect the weight of the arm and assume that $\mathbf{T}$ and $\mathbf{R}$ are the only forces exerted on the lower arm by the upper arm.

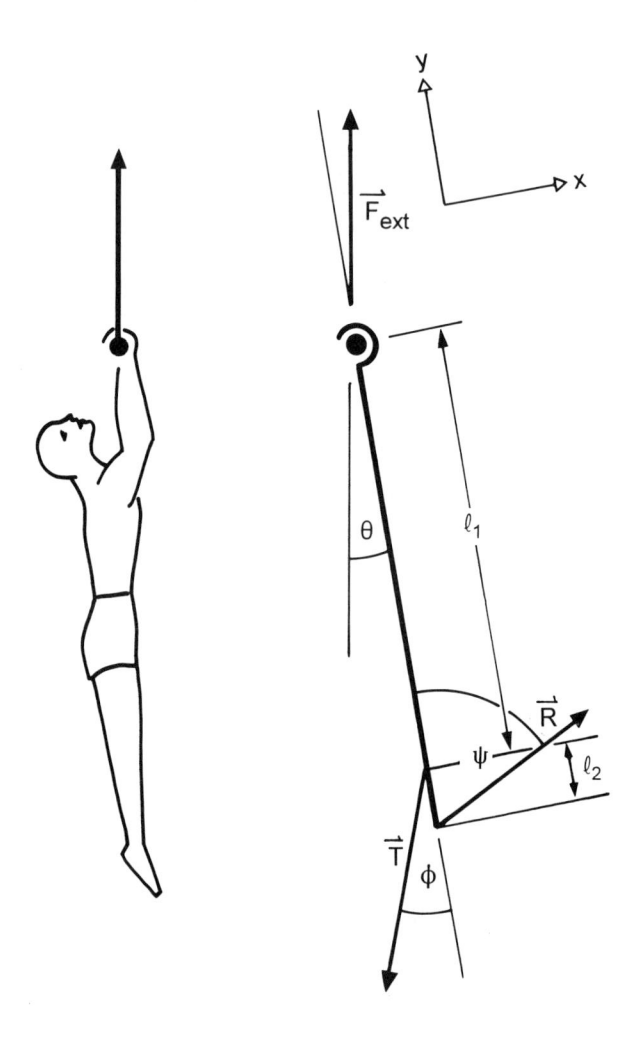

Fig. 4.55 for problem P–4.12.

P–4.13
A disabled arm with the upper arm and elbow in a cast is supported by a sling, which exerts the force $\mathbf{F}$ on the lower arm. The force $\mathbf{F}$ is directed perpendicularly to the lower arm upwards, as indicated in Fig. 4.56. The distance between the shoulder joint and the elbow is $l_1 = 30$ cm, the mass of the upper arm (with cast) is 8 kg. For the distance between the elbow and the supported wrist we use $l_2 = 25$ cm, for the mass of the lower arm we use 2 kg. The angle between the lower arm and the upper arm is $\theta = 75°$. Assuming that the sling supports the lower arm at its center–of–mass, calculate the magnitude of force $\mathbf{F}$.
Hint: There are other forces acting on the arm which we assume to act along a line through the shoulder joint. Thus, equating $\mathbf{F}$ with the weights of the upper and lower arm does not yield the right result. Instead, the problem is solved with the balance of torque equation, into which the unknown forces at the shoulder joint do not enter.

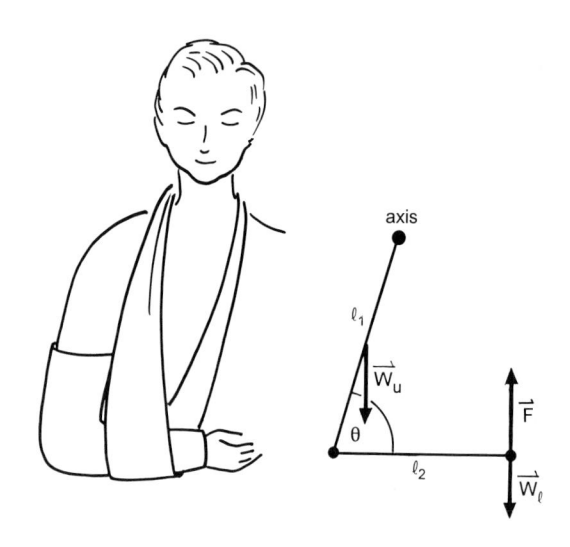

Fig. 4.56 for problem P–4.13.

Summary

Definitions:
• If F is the magnitude of the force acting on a rigid body and r is the distance from the fixed axis of rotation to the contact point of the force, then the magnitude of the torque is defined as:

$$\tau \equiv r \cdot F \cdot \sin \phi$$

where ϕ is the angle between the vectors $\mathbf{F}$ and $\mathbf{r}$.
Sign–convention for the torque:
If the rotation is counter–clockwise then $\tau > 0$
If the rotation is clockwise then $\tau < 0$
• The position of the center–of–mass (index *cm*) of a body of mass M is:

$$r_{cm} \equiv \frac{\sum_i r_i\, m_i}{M}$$

rewritten in component form:

$$x_{cm} \equiv \frac{1}{M} \sum_i x_i\, m_i$$

$$y_{cm} \equiv \frac{1}{M} \sum_i y_i\, m_i$$

$$z_{cm} \equiv \frac{1}{M} \sum_i z_i\, m_i$$

Units:
Torque: τ [N m] = [kg m²/s²]

Laws:
● The mechanical equilibrium for a rigid body with a fixed axis along the z–direction is:

$$(I) \qquad \sum_i F_{ix} = 0$$

$$(II) \qquad \sum_i F_{iy} = 0$$

$$(III) \qquad \sum_i \tau_i = 0$$

Chapter V

Bioenergetics

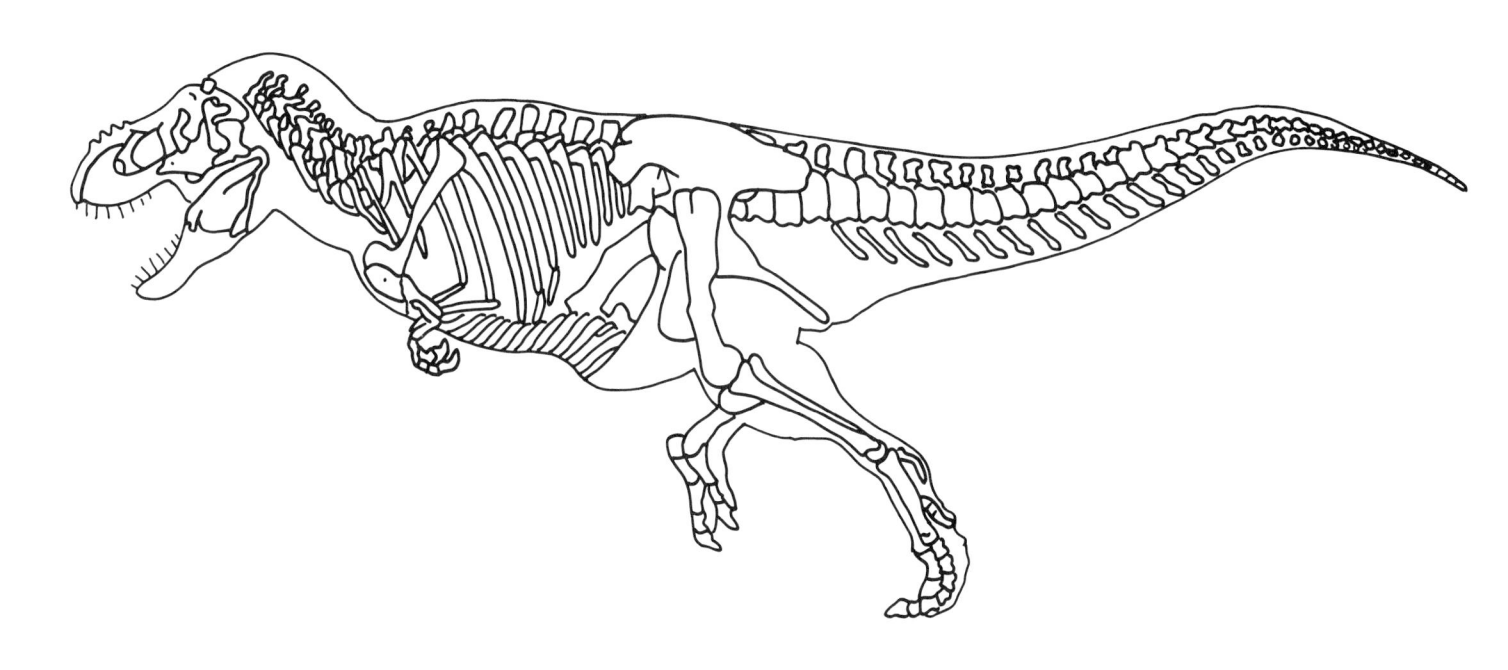

The conservation of energy

BIOENERGETICS
THE CONSERVATION OF ENERGY

Living systems interact in three fundamental ways with their environment: (I) through the exchange of heat, (II) through the performance of work, and (III) through the exchange of matter. The first two interactions are quantified in this chapter.

Two forms of work are introduced using the force concepts we developed in the previous three chapters: for a mechanical object (point mass) work is the product of an applied force and the resulting displacement of the object; for a gas work is the negative product of gas pressure and volume change. The sign convention leads to a positive value of work when work is done on (received by) the system.

Next we define energy to characterize systems and system changes in a more comprehensive fashion. Energy is the capability of a system to do work. It is conserved in an isolated system and therefore better suited than forces actin within the system as these may be applied or removed at will.

The energy of a system interacting with its environment can only vary by the amount of the energy flowing into or from the environment; the transferring amount is called heat or work for a system that does not exchange matter (closed system).

Heat is the transfer of energy resulting in a change of the thermal energy of a system. Thermal energy is the specific form of energy which is stored in the system's temperature.

The term bioenergetics has been coined in 1912 to describe energy transformations and energy exchanges within and between living cells and their environment. It includes in particular the closely related concept of *metabolism* which is the sum of all chemical changes in living cells by which energy is provided for vital processes. These processes can be divided into three types of work done by the cell: (I) mechanical work in the context of locomotion, (II) transport work transferring matter across membranes, and (III) chemical work to facilitate non–spontaneous reactions such as polymerizations. Bioenergetics and metabolism are also studied at the macroscopic level to describe the energy budget of an organism. The current chapter is the first of four chapters in which we address the concepts and principles underlying bioenergetics.

5.1. Metabolism at the cellular level: the role of the ATP molecule

We have discussed in the previous two chapters how the forces generated by muscles allow us to move our body. Fig. 2.3 illustrates that this action of the muscles is based on the repetitive traversing of the sliding filament mechanism which consists of three basic steps: (I) the myosin–actin attachment, (II) the muscle contraction during which the myosin heads tilt, and (III) the regeneration. Every cycle of this process shortens each individual sarcomere by a very short distance; the simultaneous completion of these cycles by all sarcomeres in a muscle allows for a macroscopic motion of a bone attached to the muscle.

We use the term work in our everyday language to describe what the muscle action accomplishes. Work cannot be done for free: we all have experienced the fatigue which results from prolonged use of our muscles, for example in sports. Thus, something must be stored in our body, or specifically in our muscles, which provides us with the capability to do the work. We define this thing as energy.

Fig. 2.3 provides us with a glimpse at how the muscle stores energy. You notice in the sketch of the resting muscle (top frame of the figure) a small circle labelled ATP. This represents a molecule with the chemical name adenosine triphosphate; it is shown in Fig. 5.1. ATP consists of three characteristic components, which are from right to left an adenine group, a pentose sugar group, and three phosphate groups. For the current discussion we focus on the last of the three phosphate groups at the left. If you follow now the ATP molecule

Fig. 5.1: Chemical formula of an adenosine triphosphate (ATP) molecule. The molecule consists of three components frequently found in bio–molecules: A nitrogen–containing double–ring base (adenine, upper right part), a pentose sugar (ribose with an oxygen containing ring at the center) and three phosphate groups.

Fig. 5.2: The mitochondrion is the power plant of the animal cell. The three–dimensional sketch is cut open for illustration of the internal structure. The mitochondrion is about 0.5 μm to 1.0 μm long and has two membranes, a smooth outer membrane and a folded inner membrane, which is called cristae. The folding increases the inner surface to allow for an increased rate of ADP phosphorylation to ATP. Mitochondria replicate independently during cell division. We believe therefore that they were originally bacteria which became incorporated into the eukaryotic cells by way of an intracellular symbiosis. When an egg is fertilized by a sperm, the mitochondria of the sperm do not enter the egg. Therefore only the mother's mitochondria are inherited. This feature is used to trace maternal family trees, including evidence that all humans have descended from a woman who lived as long as 300,000 years ago in Africa. This woman is accordingly called Mitochondrial Eve.

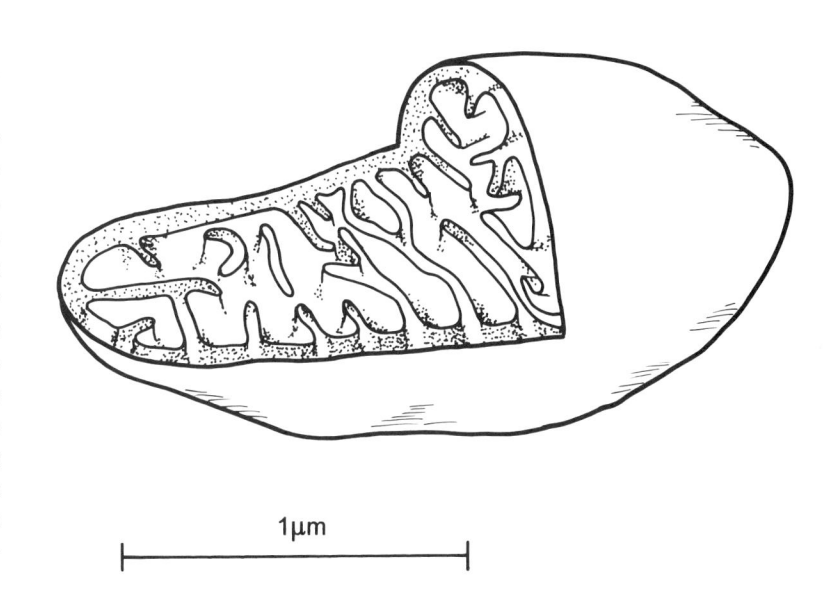

through the sliding filament mechanism of Fig. 2.3 you notice that it splits at the instant when the myosin head tilts from 90° to 45°. This is the instant when the sarcomere contributes to the muscle contraction. The release of the terminal phosphate group of the ATP molecule is a chemical reaction resulting in the formation of an adenosine diphosphate (ADP) molecule:

$$ATP + ROH \rightarrow ADP + R\text{–}OPO(OH)_2 \quad (1)$$

ROH is an alcohol molecule in which R stands for rest molecule. It is the ROH molecule to which the energy in the ATP hydrolysis of Eq. (1) is transferred.

At any given time, the ATP concentration in muscle cells is relatively low and only sufficient for a few contraction cycles shown in Fig. 2.3. This means that the muscle must quickly find energy from somewhere else or it would become disabled before anything is achieved. Since energy cannot be created out of nothing, there are only two options: transport ATP molecules from outside through the cell membrane into the muscle cell or produce new ATP molecules. The first option is not feasible because ATP molecules are too big to pass the cell membrane easily. Thus the cell must recycle its ADP molecules, i.e., it must run the reaction in Eq. (1) backwards. However, there is a problem associated with this: since the reaction in Eq. (1) provides energy when ATP splits to form ADP, the reverse reaction requires energy. Thus the cell needs energy to exert a force (muscle action), but it also needs energy to resynthesize the energy agent it uses.

This is the way the cell deals with this dilemma: the ADP molecule formed in the muscle contraction step of Fig. 2.3 is removed and transported to a mitochondrion in the muscle cell. During the regeneration step of the sarcomere a new ATP molecule is attached to the myosin head. This ATP molecule in turn has been brought from the same or another mitochondrion in the cell. Thus, the ADP molecules are recycled in the mitochondria to provide for a source of ATP molecules. This is indeed the only purpose mitochondria serve in our cells: they produce the energy-carrying agents needed in a living cell.

Fig. 5.2 shows the sketch of a mitochondrion which is cut partially open to reveal its internal structure. A mitochondrion is about 1 to 2 µm long. It is enclosed by two membranes. The outer membrane is a smooth envelope, the inner membrane is heavily folded; this structure is called cristae. The cristae structure increases significantly the inner surface of the mitochondrion and thus increases the surface on which the ATP production takes place. Mitochondria absorb from the cytoplasm of the cell a compound called pyruvic acid, which is a primary product of the chemical break-down of food in the cell. In a series of chemical reactions single hydrogen atoms are isolated from the pyruvic acid. These hydrogen atoms combine with oxygen to form water. The energy released in this reaction is used to produce ATP molecules from ADP at the cristae surface by reversing the chemical reaction shown in Eq. (1). This process is called phosphorylation.

Does the recycling of the ADP molecules in the mitochondria solve the muscle cell's energy problem? Only for a short period: for the first 50 to 100 contraction cycles, which corresponds at most to a few seconds of muscle activity, the mitochondria have stored enough of an energy-rich molecule called keratin-phosphate to recover ATP from ADP molecules. Thereafter, for up to one minute, glycogen is used instead of keratin-phosphate. The chemical reactions of both compounds have short response times because they are anaerobic reactions. Such reactions do not need the supply of oxygen from outside the cell and are called lactic acid fermentations due to the product formed in the process. Fig. 5.3 shows the typical energy output per second for an average healthy adult on a bicycle. The time axis of the figure is a logarithmic scale to highlight short times. As Fig. 5.3 illustrates, the energy output decreases initially fast, but continues after about one minute at a lower rate. This marks the transition from the anaerobic phase to the aerobic phase in which the muscle cells use oxygen acquired through the cell membrane.

The careful budgeting of energy is not limited to the processes occurring in the mitochondria. Most biochemical processes serve the purpose of transforming energy. These chemical processes, which are coordinated with each other throughout the organism, are described by the term *metabolism*. Metabolic processes are divided in two groups based on their energy balance:
(I) *anabolic processes*, which require energy and include the growth of new cells and the maintenance of body tissues, and
(II) *catabolic processes* which involve the release of energy for external and internal physical activities. Catabolism includes the maintenance of the body temperature and the degradation of chemical compounds into smaller substances that can be removed from the body via the skin, the lungs, the kidneys or the intestines.

5.2. Bioenergetics at the organism level: Case study of the predatory dinosaurs

Why do life processes focus so much on energy? This is due to three important properties of energy we will establish in this chapter:

(I) energy cannot be created or destroyed, but
(II) energy can flow from one place to another, and
(III) energy can transfer between its different forms with some restrictions.

Let us highlight these three features with examples of the bioenergetics of bacteria and predatory dinosaurs.

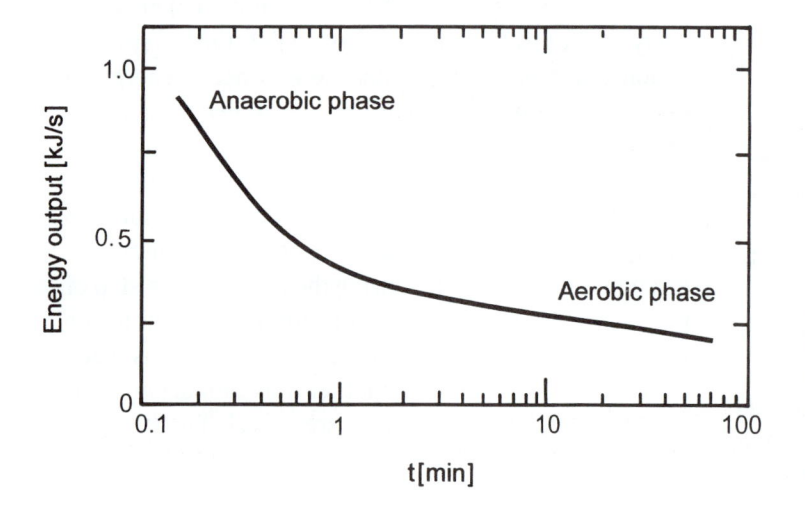

Fig. 5.3: Energy dissipated per second by an average healthy adult on a bicycle. The logarithmic time scale highlights the change at shorter times during the anaerobic phase. The loss of power is slowed in the aerobic phase. The data representation of this figure highlights the transition from the anaerobic to the aerobic phase after about one minute.

Table 5.1: Metabolism of Escherichia coli. The values in the weight fraction column indicate the fraction of the total weight due to each type of compound; the numbers do not add up to 100 % because the DNA contributes another 5 %. The last two columns provide numbers of each molecule synthesized per second and the number of ATP molecules needed for the synthesis per second.

Compound	Weight fraction [%]	Molecules per bacterium	Molecules synthesized	ATP molecules needed
Protein	70	$1.7 \cdot 10^6$	1,400	$2.1 \cdot 10^6$
Fat	10	$1.5 \cdot 10^7$	12,500	$8.8 \cdot 10^4$
Polysaccharides	5	$4.0 \cdot 10^4$	32	$6.5 \cdot 10^4$
RNA	10	$1.5 \cdot 10^4$	12	$7.5 \cdot 10^4$

Escherichia coli (E. coli)

E. coli is a bacterium involved in a wide range of illnesses such as peritonitis, appendicitis, sepsis, sinusitis, otitis, diarrhea and some forms of meningitis. E. coli are very small: their volume is about 2.5×10^{-18} m³ and their mass is about 2.5×10^{-16} kg. Because they divide into two daughter bacteria every 20 minutes, their need for energy from ATP molecules is immense, as illustrated in Table 5.1: excluding the ATP molecules needed to replicate the bacteria's DNA, each E. coli produces more than 14,000 biomolecules per second. To accomplish this it consumes the energy of more than 2.3 million ATP molecules! Since E. coli bacteria do not photosynthesize, this energy must be absorbed as food from the environment.

Predatory dinosaurs

The question whether dinosaurs were cold–blooded or warm–blooded is one of the most contested issues in palaeontology. This has three reasons:
(I) the terms cold–blooded and warm–blooded are ill–chosen for a scientific discussion as the issue raised has nothing to do with the actual blood temperature,
(II) the underlying concepts of bioenergetics are complex even for living species, and
(III) considering the 160 million year reign of the dinosaurs over our mammalian ancestors (from the late Triassic to the end of the Cretaceous) our prejudice stands sometimes in the way of proper analysis of the data.

Dinosaurs are extinct since 65 million years and we have little other than fossilized bones to reconstruct

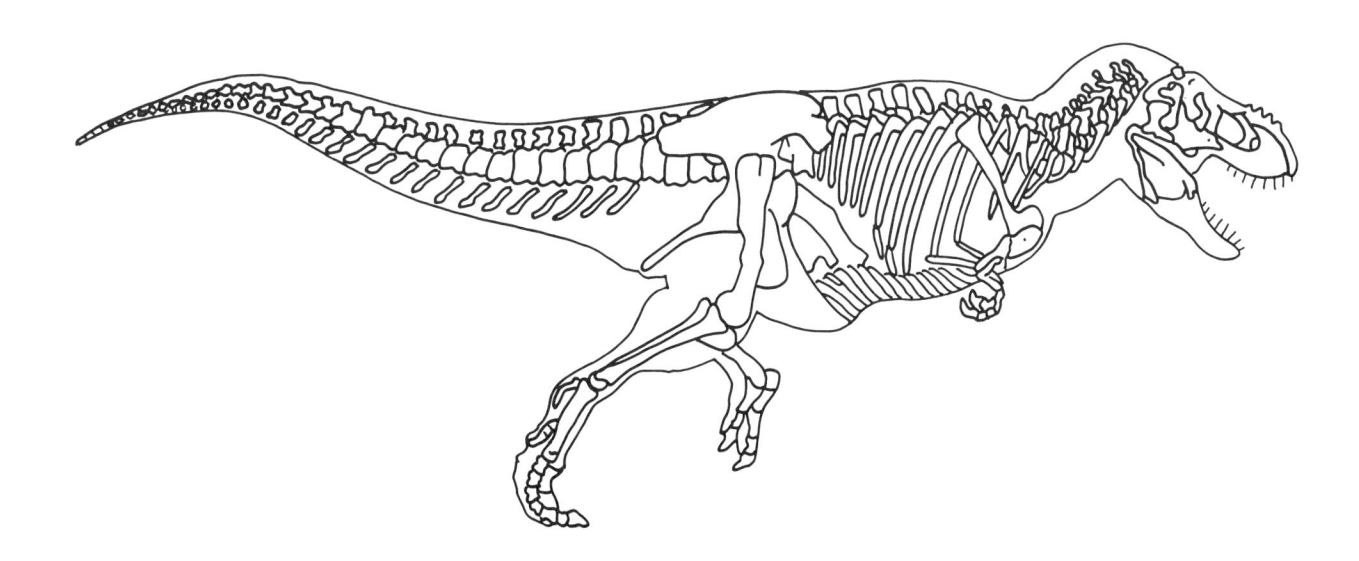

Fig. 5.4: Tyrannosaurus rex was a predatory dinosaur of the late Cretaceous. Individual animals were typically 12 m to 14 m long, up to 5 tonnes heavy and shared a saurischian hip structure with modern birds. With a mouth gape of over 1 meter it removed up to 70 kg of meat in a single bite.

their anatomy and physiology. Fig. 5.4 illustrates some problems for the reconstruction of one of the best-known predatory dinosaurs, the species Tyrannosaurus rex. The way this animal of the late Cretaceous is displayed in Fig. 5.4 is with very high likelihood correct with respect to the anatomical arrangement of the bones. However, the illustration of the five-tonne animal as an aggressive swift hunter can only be correct if a number of physiological assumptions are valid. For example, the elasticity of the leg bones must be such that they withstand bipedal running. This issue is discussed in detail in Chapter 15.

Here we want to test whether the dinosaur in Fig. 5.4 was an endotherm, i.e., an animal with a constant body temperature maintained well above the environmental temperature. Only in that case is the swift hunter assumption feasible. Were T. rex an ectotherm with a body temperature fluctuating with the environmental temperature, it would rather have been a scavenger walking slowly in search of carrion. Dinosaurs are related to both types of animals: they had a common ancestor (archosaurs) with the ectothermic crocodiles until 250 million years ago in the early Triassic, and they are the ancestors of the endothermic birds from which they split about 200 million years ago at the beginning of the Jurassic.

To establish a basis for this discussion we compare modern endotherms (mammals and birds) and modern ectotherms (reptiles). With the differences established we review the dinosaur evidence and judge which group they best fit in. Many features of modern animals can be traced to Fig. 5.5. This figure shows a plot of the resting metabolic rate as a function of body mass. The metabolic rate is defined as the amount of energy an animal uses per unit time. The metabolic rate of a non-growing endotherm at rest (with an empty stomach and experiencing no stress) is called the basal metabolic rate. The corresponding metabolic rate of an ectotherm at rest is called the standard metabolic rate and must be given for a specified environmental temperature. The actual metabolic rate can significantly exceed the basal or standard metabolic rate, for humans by up to a factor of 50 for activities which last a few seconds and by up to a factor of 5 for activities which last about an hour. The metabolic rate is measured in [J/s] which is the unit for energy per time we introduce later in the chapter. Fig. 5.5 indicates an important qualitative difference between ectotherms and endotherms: endotherms need about ten times more energy than ectotherms of the same size. We analyze Fig. 5.5 first quantitatively, draw conclusions from the result and then identify its consequences.

===

Example 5.1
For the three cases in Fig. 5.5, (1) unicellular organisms at 20°C, (2) ectotherms at 20°C, and (3) endotherms at 39°C, find the parameters a and b in the power-law relation $M_r = a\, m^b$, where M_r is the metabolic rate in [J/s] and m is the mass in [kg].

Fig. 5.5: Double-logarithmic plot of the metabolic rate in [J/s] versus mass in [kg] for a wide range of species. Three straight lines represent data representations for (1) unicellular organisms at 20°C, (2) ectotherms at 20 °C, and (3) endotherms at 39°C core body temperature. The three lines are essentially parallel (same power law exponent) but differ in the prefactors.

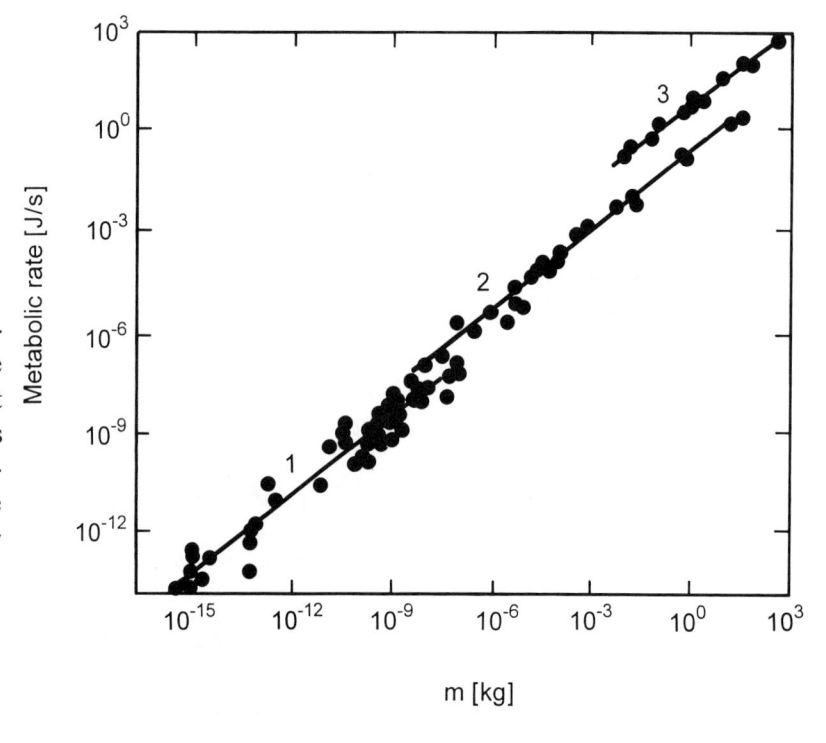

Solution: The mathematical approach is discussed in the General Appendix (Chapter 24). We begin by supplementing the logarithmic axes in the figure with linear axes showing ln(m) and ln(Mr). Then we determine the two parameters a and b based on the linear relation ln(Mr) = b ln(m) + ln(a). This procedure must be repeated three times to solve for each animal group in Fig. 5.5.

We start with the unicellular organisms. From Fig. 5.5 we obtain two data pairs of ln(Mr) and ln(m) based on the straight line labelled 1. These data are listed in Table 5.2.

Using Table 5.2 we substitute into the linear formula ln(Mr) = b ln(m) + ln(a):

(I) −27.63 = b (−31.28) + ln(a)
(II) −20.72 = b (−22.38) + ln(a)

(II) − (I) 6.91 = b 8.90

Thus, b = 0.78. Substituting this value in either one of the two formulas we find ln(a). From this result we obtain a = 0.04.

Next we study ectotherms, for which the straight line labelled 2 applies. Two data points from this line are listed in Table 5.3.

Using Table 5.3 we write two linear formulas:

(I) −13.82 = b (−16.02) + ln(a)
(II)   0 = b 1.93 + ln(a)

(II) − (I) 13.82 = b 17.95

This leads to b = 0.77 and a = 0.22.

In the last case endotherms are studied. Their data are represented by the straight line labelled 3 in Fig. 5.5. Two data points from that line are listed in Table 5.4.

Table 5.2: Data sets from Fig. 5.5 for unicellular organisms (line 1).

Mr [J/s]	ln(Mr)	m [kg]	ln(m)
10^{-12}	−27.63	$2.6 \cdot 10^{-14}$	−31.28
10^{-9}	−20.72	$1.9 \cdot 10^{-10}$	−22.38

Table 5.3: Data sets for ectotherms from Fig. 5.5 based on line 2.

Mr [J/s]	ln(Mr)	m [kg]	ln(m)
10^{-6}	−13.82	$1.1 \cdot 10^{-7}$	−16.02
1	0	6.9	1.93

Using Table 5.4 we write:

(I) −6.908 = b (−11.33) + ln(a)
(II) +6.908 = b (+6.908) + ln(a)

(II) − (I) 13.816 = b 18.238

This leads to b = 0.76 and a = 5.25.

The results of Example 5.1 are summarized for ectotherms and endotherms in the form:

$$\text{ectotherm}: Mr\ [kJ/day] = 20\ (m\ [kg])^{3/4}$$
$$\text{endotherm}: Mr\ [kJ/day] = 450\ (m\ [kg])^{3/4} \quad (2)$$

What do we learn from Eq. (2)?

First, we note that the values for parameter b are the same for the three groups of animals with b = 3/4. This suggests that all living organisms function at the fundamental metabolic level in the same fashion. Two simple models have been proposed to interpret Fig. 5.5:

Model 1: Each kilogram of tissue has the same metabolic requirements. This model is not correct since it predicts that b = 1, i.e., that the metabolic rate is proportional to the mass. Because this model is not correct, you have to be careful when you find metabolic rates in this textbook or in the literature reported per kilogram body mass. Such values apply only to a specific species. We also learn from problem P–5.2 that such values can only be applied to adults.

Model 2: The metabolic requirements are determined by the loss of heat to the environment through the skin. This model is not correct either as it predicts b = 2/3 because the surface is proportional to the square of the size of the animal and its volume is proportional to the cube of the size. Even though the basal or standard metabolic rates are sometimes measured by placing an animal in a calorimeter (which is an instrument to measure the amount of energy released as heat) a careful averaging

Table 5.4: Two data sets for endotherms from Fig. 5.5 (line 3).

Mr [J/s]	ln(Mr)	m [kg]	ln(m)
10^{-3}	−6.908	$1.2 \cdot 10^{-5}$	−11.33
10^{+3}	+6.908	$1.0 \cdot 10^{+3}$	+6.908

Fig. 5.6: Predator/prey ratios in various ecosystems. The ratio in [%] is the predator biomass divided by the prey (herbivore) biomass. The ordinate shows the number of local systems which have been identified in field studies. The six panels represent from top to bottom increasingly older ecosystems. The data for modern mammals are based on contemporary systems which are unfortunately often under stress due to poaching. Fossil endothermic mammal systems are land ecosystems of the cenozoic era during the last 65 million years, the dinosaurs dominated the Jurassic and Cretaceous, thecodonts dominated in the Triassic 240 to 215 million years ago, and therapsids were mammal–like reptiles representing the top predatory group between 280 and 230 million years ago. The ectothermic early reptiles ruled in the Permian until about 270 million years ago.

over a longer time period is needed to not determine wrong values.

Second, the pre–factors on the right side of Eq. (2) differ significantly between endotherms and ectotherms. Maintaining a 5 to 20 times higher energy throughput can only be managed with numerous anatomical, physiological and behavioral adjustments. Of these, some can be tested for extinct species as they enter the fossil record.

The food consumption F of wet meat of predatory endotherms and ectotherms is given by:

$$\text{ectotherm}: \quad F\,[kg/day] = 0.01\,(m\,[kg])^{3/4}$$
$$\text{endotherm}: \quad F\,[kg/day] = 0.11\,(m\,[kg])^{3/4}$$
(3)

in which m is again the mass in [kg]. To maintain a high metabolic rate, endotherms must consume about ten times as much food as ectotherms. Ectothermic predators therefore display a laid–back non–confrontational lifestyle while endothermic predators are always aggressive and compulsive about food. Note that this contrasts with our prejudice: it is much safer to swim to a crocodile than getting within 100 meters of a polar bear.

An intriguing ecological difference caused by Eq. (3) is the predator/prey ratio in a stable ecosystem. This ratio is quantified as the percent of predator biomass relative to the biomass of the herbivores in the same area. Modern ecosystems are dominated by endothermic mammals. Because of the high amount of food these predators require based on Eq. (3), a large number of prey is required to sustain the predator population. Consequently, predators only represent about 2 % of the local biomass. This is illustrated in the top panel of Fig.

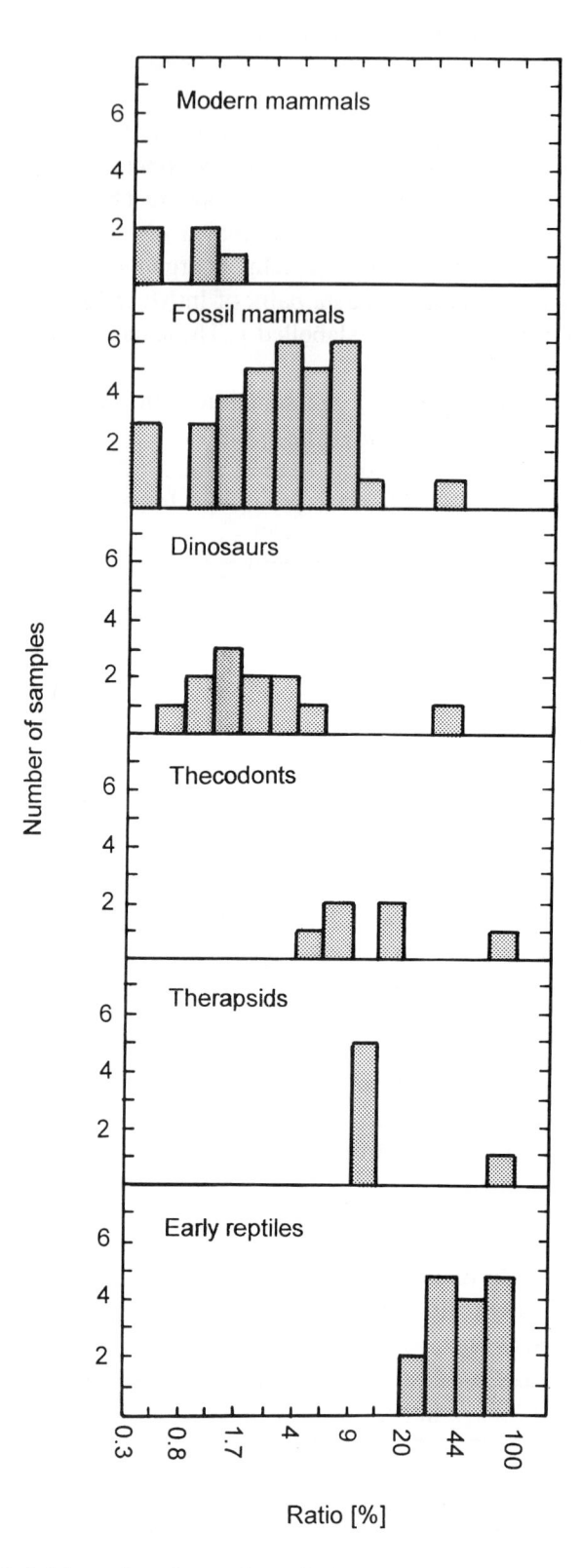

5.6. Note that the ratio axis is not linear. The second panel represents fossilized mammals. They represented up to 9 % of the biomass. We believe that fossil mammals are more representative of a balanced ecosystem and that the modern mammalian predators are under stress in their ecosystems due to poaching. Equivalent data for an ecosystem dominated by modern ectotherms do not exist because they stand no chance in competition with modern endotherms. However, the early reptiles at the transition from the Permian to the Triassic dominated the ecosystem of their time. The predator/prey ratio for the early reptiles is shown in the bottom panel of Fig. 5.6. The biomass of the ectothermic predators was between 20 % and 100 %, i.e., predators and prey shared the ecosystem in roughly equal numbers.

These data indicate that ectotherms and endotherms differ significantly as a result of their tenfold difference in energy consumption. Since energy has to be budgeted at every level, the limited supply of energy ultimately controls the number of individuals of a certain species living in an ecosystem. Endothermic predators need much more food per individual than ectothermic predators and are therefore rarer in their ecosystem and occur more seldom in the fossil record. The predator/prey ratio of dinosaurs is included in Fig. 5.6 as the third panel from top. Their presence in the ecosystem resembled that of fossil mammals.

The data of Fig. 5.6 have been combined with two other distinctions endotherms and dinosaurs shared:
(I) ectotherms grow to adult size much slower than endotherms. Therefore, the endothermic bones must grow faster which is reflected in the fibrolamellar microstructure which differs from the bone histology of the ectotherms.
(II) All animals with erect gait and long limbs are endotherms as this posture allows rapid breathing while running. The erect gait also requires a four–chambered heart because the three–chambered heart of reptiles cannot maintain a high blood pressure needed to supply oxygen to the brain if the head is significantly raised above the heart.

It is these observations related to the energy consumption of animals which opened the discussion about endothermic dinosaurs in the 1970s. To appreciate the details of this discussion in the literature, and, more generally, to understand the limiting conditions in the design of individual creatures, the governing principles of energy conservation, energy flow and energy conversion must be established. This is the purpose of Chapters 5 to 8.

5.3. Basic concepts

One of the challenges of working with thermal physics concepts is the diversity of processes we have to describe in this context. This diversity is the result of the three properties of energy we identified above: the conservation of energy, the ability of energy to flow from place to place, and the ability of energy to convert back and forth between different energy forms. We must stick to a set of definitions and conventions to avoid confusion in the discussion of thermal physics. The following three issues are particularly important and therefore are discussed at the beginning of this chapter:
(I) the distinction between energy flow and energy conversion;
(II) the distinction between equilibrium and non–equilibrium states, and
(III) the distinction between the properties of a system and the properties of the system's environment.

5.3.1. Energy flow and energy conversion

Although energy is conserved, there are two ways in which in a given experiment energy may change: energy can flow from one place to another and/or energy can be converted from one form into another. It is important that we distinguish these two processes because they lead to significantly different consequences in experiments. To support the distinction different terms are used:
(I) we use the two terms *heat* and *work* for energy which flows, and
(II) we use the term *energy* with a descriptive adjective, e.g. kinetic energy or thermal energy, when energy converts from one form to another at the same place. We label specific energy forms in this textbook E and add a subscript to specify the particular form of energy. For example, E_{kin} will be defined in section 5.5.1 to mean the kinetic energy.

5.3.2. Equilibrium

We defined the mechanical equilibrium in Chapter 2. At that time you may have noticed that the distinction between Newton's first and second laws on the basis of a mechanical equilibrium appeared artificial as the second law includes the first when we extend it to zero acceleration $a = 0$. Why then did we keep these two laws separate? We did it because both laws are at the root of entirely different branches of the natural sciences:
(I) Newton's first law focuses on the equilibrium state of a system, which leads to thermodynamics and later to stationary fluids and electrostatics, and
(II) Newton's second law deals with dynamic changes of the state of a system, which leads to kinetics and non–equilibrium processes, as well as fluid dynamics and issues of electric currents.

The mechanical equilibrium is distinguished as a special state for an object in which all relevant mechanical properties of the object do not change with time: the net force on the object and its acceleration are zero, and its velocity is time independent. This observation characterizes equilibria in general:

> *A system is in equilibrium when all essential physical parameters which describe the system do not change with time.*

Note that this does not mean that all physical parameters are constant. For example, the position of an object in mechanical equilibrium changes continuously if the object is not at rest. However, for an isolated object the position is not an essential parameter since no possible physical observations such as those discussed in the previous three chapters depend on the position.

The physical parameters which we consider to be essential vary with the physical concepts we study. For that reason, we must specify the context in which we refer to an equilibrium. This is done by using a descriptive adjective with the term "equilibrium." Examples of equilibria used in this textbook are:
(I) the thermal equilibrium, which we introduce together with the concept of temperature in section 5.7,
(II) the chemical equilibrium, which is associated with chemical reactions as discussed in Chapter 8,
(III) the electric equilibrium, which we introduce after defining electric charges in Chapter 9,
and, as a case of combining such equilibria,
(IV) the electrochemical equilibrium, which is used in Chapter 13 to study the microscopic processes of nerve membranes.

5.3.3. Systems and their environment

In the discussion of the muscle action, we chose as our system of interest a single myosin head, a single sarcomere or an entire muscle cell. At each level we noted the exchange of matter with the system's environment: the myosin head releases an ADP molecule and receives an ATP molecule in turn; the sarcomere releases ADP molecules to the mitochondria for new ATP molecules; and the muscle cell acquires food from outside the cell to allow the mitochondria to run as cellular power plants. Thus, the environment is always involved with the processes we want to study. To deal with the system/environment interface properly, we distinguish three types of systems based on their interactions:

(1) Isolated systems are systems which do not exchange energy or matter with their environment. Perfectly isolated systems are hard to establish experimentally but are conceptually of great relevance. Technical examples include the calorimeter, which is an instrument to measure the energy content of chemical compounds, and closed Dewar containers, which are used to store liquid nitrogen.

For isolated systems the conservation of energy law is introduced in the current chapter: once all forms of energy of a system are identified, we calculate the total energy of the system by adding all individual contributions. The total energy is called the internal energy of the system and is labelled U. Conservation of energy then means that the change of the internal energy, ΔU, between an initial and a final state of the system is zero:

$$\Delta U = U_{final} - U_{initial} = 0 \quad (4)$$

> *The internal energy of an isolated system is conserved.*

We distinguish two types of isolated systems: isolated systems in equilibrium and isolated systems which are not in equilibrium.

(1a) Isolated system in equilibrium: Above we noted that the important parameters of a system are constant (time independent) if the system is in equilibrium. Thus, for an isolated system in equilibrium each type of energy is separately constant. This represents the simplest situation we can study. We will therefore define new system parameters such as temperature for isolated systems in equilibrium first.

(1b) Isolated system which is not in equilibrium: A system which is not in equilibrium is characterized by changes of the essential parameters. Thus, each specific form of energy may vary with time in the system. However, Eq. (4) remains true as it states that the sum of all forms of energy remains unchanged. We will use Eq. (4) in this chapter also to describe mechanical systems outside of the equilibrium; however, when we move on to more general systems the fact that the system is not in equilibrium will greatly limit the use of Eq. (4). Biological systems often display complex temperature, pressure and energy profiles which are hard to describe with basic physics concepts. We can circumvent this problem by confining the boundaries of the system more narrowly such that the system has uniform parameters. In turn, all other components of the original biological system are now components of the environment. Instead of an isolated system in non–equilibrium we now have a local system which we can treat as if it is in equilibrium but exchanges heat and matter with the newly defined environment. This leads to the definition of closed and open systems.

(2) Closed systems are systems that interact with their environment in a limited fashion, exchanging energy but not transferring matter. A typical example is an organic chemistry experiment where the reaction takes place in some glassware with external oil bath heating. Such a system is closed as long as no gas exchange with the external atmosphere occurs. A biological example is a dormant virus which is separated from the environment by a rigid membrane.

For closed systems we introduce the first law of thermodynamics, which states that the change of the internal energy of the system between an initial and a final state is due to two contributions:
(i) work W released to or received from the environment, and
(ii) heat Q that is exchanged with the environment. These two forms of energy flow across the boundary of the system. This leads to the following equation:

$$\Delta U = U_{final} - U_{initial} = W + Q \quad (5)$$

> *The internal energy of a closed system increases or decreases when*
> *(I) heat is exchanged with the environment, and/or*
> *(II) the system receives/releases work.*

We note the importance of the distinction between a closed and an isolated system by comparing Eq. (4) and Eq. (5): the same quantity, ΔU, is calculated in different ways for both types of system.

In general, the initial and final states of the system need not to be equilibrium states. We are using Eq. (5) only for systems with an initial and a final equilibrium state. This will allow us to neglect the transfer of energy within the system. It also enables us to connect the change of a specific type of energy in the system to the heat and/or work exchanged with the environment:

$$\Delta E_{thermal} = E_{thermal, final} - E_{thermal, initial} = Q$$
$$\Delta E_{other} = E_{other, final} - E_{other, initial} = W \quad (6)$$

Eq. (6) states that thermal energy changes in the system are associated with heat flow and that changes of all other types of energy are associated with work released or acquired by the system.

(3) Open systems are systems that exchange matter and energy with their environment. Note that exclusive exchange of matter without an exchange of energy is not possible as matter always carries energy. Biological systems from cells to organisms are open.

We do not introduce equations equivalent to Eqs. (4) or (5) for open systems in this textbook. Open systems are only considered when we discuss non–equilibrium processes such as diffusion in Chapter 7, then using a different, phenomenological approach.

Isolated systems are easiest to describe but are usually not sufficient as models for real biological systems. Closed and open systems are, on the other hand, complex because we have little control over the environment. To make processes in open or closed systems manageable, an additional, artificial boundary must be drawn around the system and its environment such that both together are isolated. This is then called an *isolated superstructure*, as illustrated in Fig. 5.7. Whenever we quantify processes for closed or open systems, we have to not only carefully identify the boundary between the system and the environment, but also ensure that the superstructure is defined in such a way that it is isolated.

5.4. Work

Eqs. (4) to (6) connect three concepts: heat, work and energy. The remainder of this chapter focusses on defining these terms quantitatively. We begin with work as Eq. (6) indicates that it will give us access to all but one form of energy. After we have used the second formula in Eq. (6) to establish several energy forms and are fa-

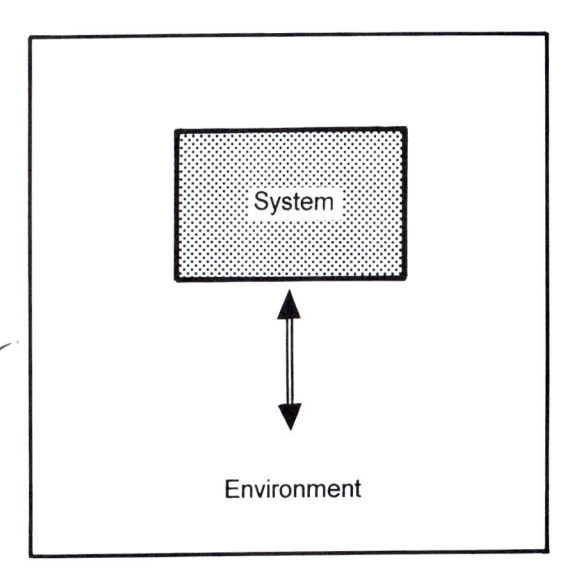

Isolated superstructure

Fig. 5.7: An isolated superstructure is subdivided into an open or closed system and a well–confined environment which interacts with the system.

111

miliar with the approach, we proceed in the later part of the chapter to define heat and, related to it through the first formula in Eq. (6), thermal energy.

5.4.1. Work for a point mass

We base the definition of work on our everyday experience. Consider pushing a heavy crate across a room. We associate work with both, the amount of force needed to move the crate and the distance that the object is moved. Note that we do not think of all the forces acting on the crate but are only concerned with the specific force we exert on it. This distinguishes the discussion in this chapter from the previous three chapters where we needed to consider the net force. We also do not consider the force the crate exerts on our hands but think of the force we exert on the crate when defining the work we do. This in turn is consistent with the approach we took in the previous three chapters where we also used only forces which act on the object of interest. Thus, in the most general form we write for the work done by a force $\mathbf{F}$ to achieve the displacement $\Delta \mathbf{s} = \mathbf{s}_f - \mathbf{s}_i$ from an initial position $\mathbf{s}_i$ to a final position $\mathbf{s}_f$:

$$W = f(\mathbf{F}, \Delta \mathbf{s}) \qquad (7)$$

The notation $f(...)$ indicates that work is a function of the two vectors in the bracket. Note that the parameter W is not printed bold-face, indicating that work is a scalar, i.e., a non-directional quantity.

As a simplification we limit our discussion from here onwards to cases where the force and displacement vectors are collinear. Then we need no longer to include the vector character of the parameters in Eq. (7). Note that a discussion of cases with non-collinear force and displacement vectors is provided in the Appendix of this chapter. For collinear force and displacement Eq. (7) becomes Eq. (8):

$$W = \pm F \cdot \Delta s \qquad (8)$$

F is the magnitude of the force acting on the system and Δs is the length of the displacement vector. Writing the work in this form goes significantly beyond Eq. (7): First, Eq. (8) specifies that work depends linearly on both, the force and the displacement. Pulling with twice the force for the same distance or pulling with the same force for twice the distance doubles the work. This correlates with our everyday expectation what work is. Second, Eq. (8) does not contain a constant offset term, e.g. a term W_0 added on the right hand side. Such an offset term is not present because either F = 0 or $\Delta s = 0$ must result in W = 0. This means, if we do not exert a force or do not accomplish a displacement then no work has been done.

The ± symbol in Eq. (8) indicates that the work can be positive or negative, depending on whether the force and the displacement point in the same direction (positive sign) or point in opposite directions (negative sign). We illustrate this with the example of Fig. 5.8 in which we study the interaction of a piston-like level and an object (shaded box). The piston exerts a force $\mathbf{F}_{ext}$ on the shaded box.

We start with Fig. 5.8(a) where the displacement occurs in the same direction $\mathbf{F}_{ext}$ acts. We may choose either the shaded box or the piston as the system. If the system is the shaded box in Fig. 5.8(a), then the work is positive because $\mathbf{F}_{ext}$ and the displacement $\Delta \mathbf{s}$ point in the same direction regardless of our choice of coordinate system. Work is done on the system by the environment (here the piston).

If we choose the piston in Fig. 5.8(a) to be our system, we must calculate the work using a force exerted on the piston. The force we need to study is the force that the shaded box exerts on the piston, i.e., the reaction force to $\mathbf{F}_{ext}$. Newton's third law states that this force is $-\mathbf{F}_{ext}$, i.e., that it has the same magnitude but acts in the opposite direction of $\mathbf{F}_{ext}$. Consequently, the work is negative because $-\mathbf{F}_{ext}$ and $\Delta \mathbf{s}$ point in opposite directions. The piston does work on its environment (here the shaded box).

We now turn our attention to Fig. 5.8(b) where the displacement occurs in the opposite direction of $\mathbf{F}_{ext}$. The piston still pushes against the shaded box, and the box still exerts a force on the piston due to Newton's third law. In Fig. 5.8(b), however, the box succeeds to push the piston to the left, causing a displacement to the left. This has an impact on the sign of the work. If we choose the shaded box as the system the work is now negative because $\mathbf{F}_{ext}$ and $-\Delta \mathbf{s}$ have opposite directions. If we choose in turn the piston to be the system the work is positive because $-\mathbf{F}_{ext}$ and $-\Delta \mathbf{s}$ have the same direction. In Fig. 5.8(b) the box does work on the piston. In summary:

$$\begin{aligned} W > 0 &\Leftrightarrow \text{ system receives work} \\ W < 0 &\Leftrightarrow \text{ system releases work} \end{aligned} \qquad (9)$$

> *The quantity work is positive when the system receives work, i.e., work is done on the system; work is negative when the system releases work, i.e., work is done by the system.*

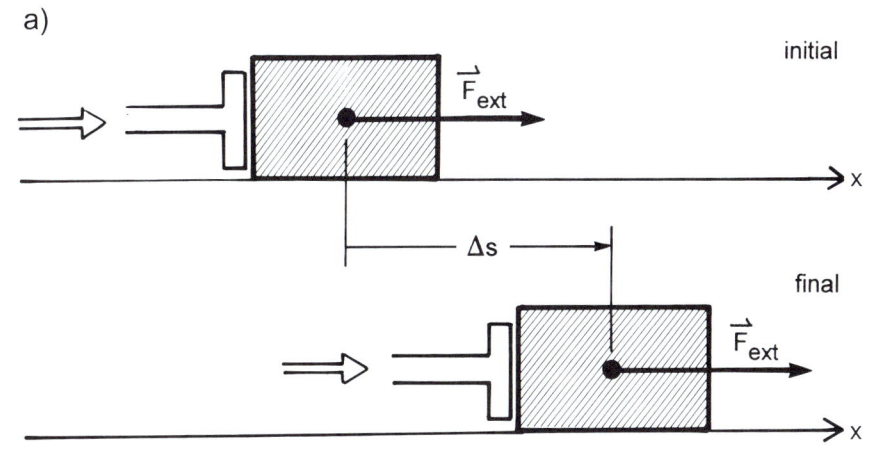

Fig. 5.8: (a) A piston is used to displace an object by a distance Δs along the x–axis. The experiment is conducted between an initial time (shown at top) and a final time (shown at bottom). To achieve the displacement an external force $\vec{F}_{ext}$ is needed. We assume that the external force acts collinear to the displacement.
(b) For the same arrangement a displacement of the object in the negative x–direction is possible, for example if the object had an initial negative velocity $v_{initial}$, and is slowed down to v_{final} while moving toward the left. In this case the displacement and the external force act in anti–parallel directions.

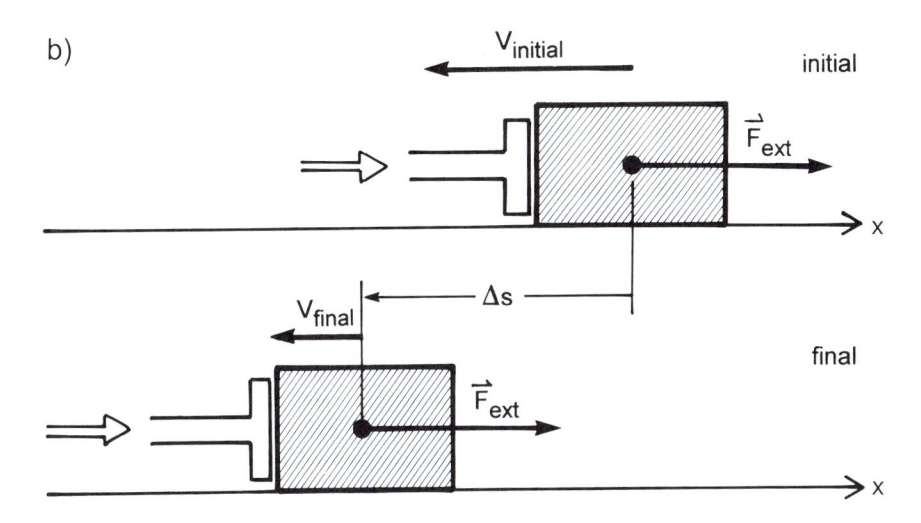

This sign convention can be memorized by identifying yourself with the system: whatever you receive (here work) is positive since you have more afterwards; whatever you release is negative since you have less afterwards.

Recall that the unit of force is [N]; thus, based on Eq. (8) the unit of work is [N m] = [kg m²/s²]. We define a derived SI unit for work: the *Joule*, [J]. 1 J is the work done when a force of 1 N moves an object a distance of 1 m.

Example 5.2
Determine the work done by a person when lowering an object of mass 1.0 kg by a distance of 1.0 m. The person applies a force $\mathbf{F}_{ext}$ such that the object moves with constant speed, i.e., without acceleration, as shown in Fig. 5.9.

Solution: It is worthwhile to re–emphasize the shift of focus in this chapter: while we combined all forces acting on a system as a net force when using Newton's laws, we are now focussing on a specific interaction between the system and its environment. In Fig. 5.9, the object (a rectangular box of mass m) is the system and the person (not shown) is one interacting component of the environment. Another component of the environment interacting with the system is the Earth as it exerts a gravitational pull on the object. Therefore, the person, the Earth and the object together form an isolated super-structure with all interactions still identified as forces for this problem.

Two free–body–diagrams are included in Fig. 5.9, each applied to the system in one of the two states which we are interested in: the initial state at height y_i and the final state at height y_f. We apply the mechanical equilibrium condition for a non–accelerating object to determine the external force:

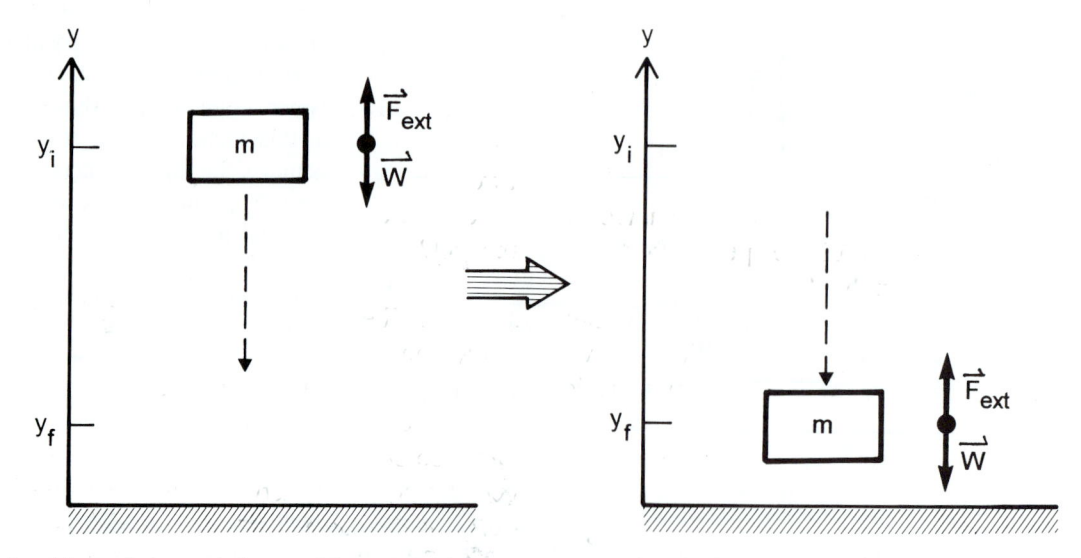

Fig. 5.9: An object of mass m is lowered from an initial height y_i (shown at left) to a final height y_f (shown at right). The object moves from the initial to the final state with a constant speed if the external force is equal in magnitude to the weight of the object.

$$F_{ext} - W = 0$$
$$\Rightarrow F_{ext} = W = m g \quad (10)$$

W is the weight. From point of view of Newton's laws, there is no difference between the system at the initial and the final height. However, based on our discussion in the current chapter, we can quantify as work the effort involved in the displacement of the system. We start with Eq. (8). Instead of the ± sign, we allow the force and/or the displacement to resume negative values when they point in the direction of the negative y–axis. Then the work is given by W = F Δs with:

$$W = F_{ext}(y_f - y_i) = mg(y_f - y_i) \quad (11)$$

In Eq. (11) the force is positive as it points in the positive y–direction and the displacement $\Delta s = y_f - y_i$ is negative as it points in the negative y–direction. Substituting the values given in the problem text we find:

$$W = 1.0[kg]\ 9.8\left[\frac{m}{s^2}\right](-1.0[m]) \quad (12)$$
$$\Rightarrow W = -9.8\ [J]$$

The negative result is interpreted with the sign convention in Eq. (9): the system has released work.

Power is the rate at which work is done: P = W/Δt, in which Δt is the time interval during which the work W is obtained or released. The SI unit of power is Watt [W] (named for James Watt). Thus, 1 W = 1 J/s. To reduce confusion the unit Watt is not further used in this textbook.

5.4.2. Work for a gas

Next we want to define work done on or by a gas in an analogous fashion. Fig. 5.10 shows a gas sealed off with a mobile piston in a container. We assume that the piston is an ideal piston, which means that it can move without friction back and forth in the cylindrical container. When the piston moves in the positive x–direction the gas is compressed and when the piston moves in the negative x–direction the gas expands. The source of the external force pushing the piston is not included in the figure. Studying Fig. 5.10 more carefully we notice that it is now more difficult to imagine the force acting on the gas. When the piston moves toward the right, some gas

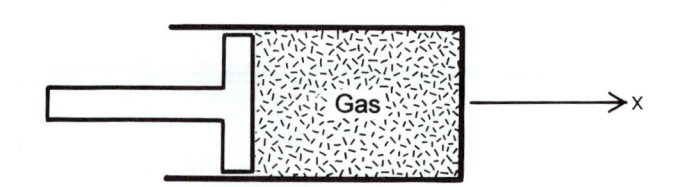

Fig. 5.10: A piston seals a gas in a closed container. The piston is mobile along the x–axis. The motion of the piston is considered to be without friction.

particles are pushed away, others are not. Also the concept of displacement of the gas is less obvious. Some gas particles get displaced when the piston moves, other particles not. Thus, we want to exchange force and displacement with the more appropriate parameters volume and pressure.

Pressure is defined as a force acting per unit area on a surface. If the force is not oriented perpendicular to the surface, only the perpendicular component of the force, $F_\perp$, is considered because the component parallel to the surface cannot move the surface. Calling the area on which the force acts A in unit [m²], the pressure is written as:

$$p = \frac{F_\perp}{A} \quad \left[\frac{N}{m^2}\right] \quad (13)$$

Because we will use pressure often, a derived unit is established, replacing the unit [N/m²] with the unit Pascal ([Pa], named for Blaise Pascal). Note that you find pressures often reported in [kPa], e.g. the standard atmospheric pressure is 101.3 kPa.

Example 5.3
In 1650, Otto von Guericke invented the vacuum pump. To secure continuous research funding he demonstrated his new device at the Imperial Diet at Regensburg, Germany, in 1654. Historical sources report that he used two hollow bronze hemispheres of 42 cm diameter sealed together with a rubber gasket as sketched in Fig. 5.11(a). Two teams of eight horses on each side could not pull the evacuated cavity apart. Do you believe the historic account?

Solution: The cavity is the system. Three forces act on the system, (i) a tension caused by the team of horses on the right side, (ii) a tension caused by the horses on the left side, and (iii) a force due to the air pressure acting on the outer surface of the cavity. This force is not compensated by a force acting on the inner surface since the cavity is evacuated. The arrows pointing toward the cavity in Fig. 5.11(a) illustrate the varying directions of the force $\mathbf{F}_{air}$. These arrows are all directed toward the center of the sphere as this is the direction perpendicular to the cavity's surface, as needed in Eq. (13).

First we simplify the problem, using the symmetry of the experimental set–up in Fig. 5.11(a). Of the two teams of horses, one is needed to keep the cavity in its place; were only one team present, the cavity would accelerate like a carriage. We can, however, replace one team, the attached string and one half of the cavity by a wall as shown in Fig. 5.11(b), because such a wall can provide for mechanical equilibrium. To solve this sim-

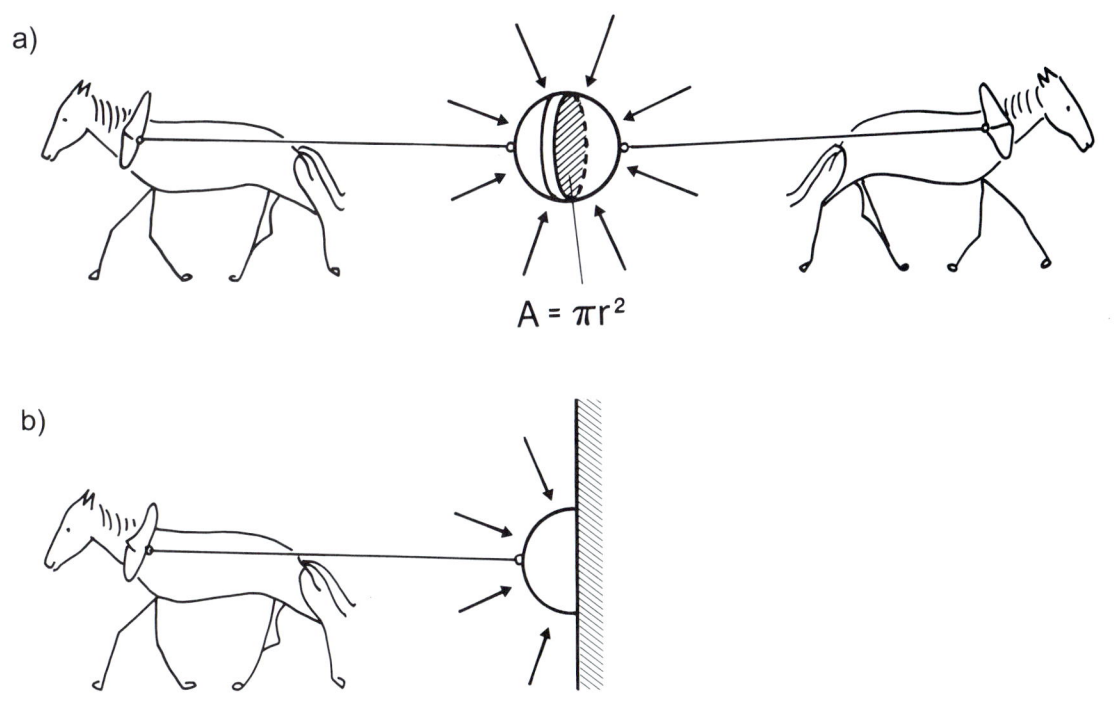

Fig. 5.11: (a) Sketch of the experimental set–up by Otto von Guericke. Two teams of horses on both sides of an evacuated cavity try to pull the cavity apart. The cross–sectional area of the cavity is A = πr² (dashed area). The arrows indicate the direction of the force exerted by the atmosphere on the surface of the cavity. (b) Equivalent approach with one half of the set–up (team of horses, half cavity) replaced by a wall to which the cavity is sealed.

plified version of the problem, we have to identify the force the horses have to overcome to pull the half–cavity away from the wall.

The problem is not a simple application of the concepts of Chapter 2 since the force $\mathbf{F}_{air}$ acts from variable directions across an extended surface. How can we quantify the force against which the horses try to pull the half–cavity away from the wall? The proper approach is to find the horizontal component of the net force caused by the air pressure on the hemisphere. This is mathematically difficult. Luckily, we can circumvent this approach with some reasoning: note that the wall in Fig. 5.11(b) forms the circular base of a hemisphere which is equivalent to the shaded area in Fig. 5.11(a). All forces on the outer surface of the hemisphere must be equal to the force exerted by the wall because the cavity stays stationary after evacuation and before the horses pull. The net force acting on the flat circular area is much easier to calculate. If we label the radius of the sphere r, then $A = \pi r^2$ is the wall area covered by the cavity. Using for the atmospheric pressure $p_{atm} = 1.01 \times 10^5$ Pa we find from Eq. (13) for the horizontal component of the net force due to the air pressure:

$$F_{air} = p_{atm} \cdot \pi r^2 = \qquad (14)$$
$$1.01 \times 10^5 [Pa] \cdot \pi (0.21[m])^2 = 14\ kN$$

Eight horses can overcome that force. To see this, note that a force of 14 kN is equivalent to lifting an object with a mass of 14 kN / 9.8 m/s² ≈ 1400 kg, i.e., 175 kg per horse. Von Guericke surely used fewer horses than the historic record claims.

With the definition of pressure established in Eq. (13), we evaluate the work done when the piston in Fig. 5.12(a) is pushed by an external force resulting in a displacement Δs. Note that for all piston arrangements the external force acts parallel to the displacement of the piston. Thus, vector notation is unnecessary and the work done on the system reads:

$$W = F_{ext}\ \Delta s = \frac{F_{ext}}{A}(A\ \Delta s) \qquad (15)$$

which is rewritten with the definitions of pressure and volume in the form:

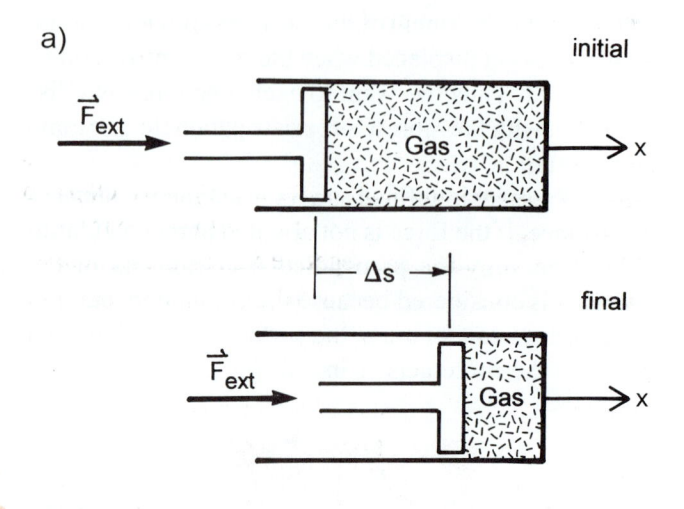

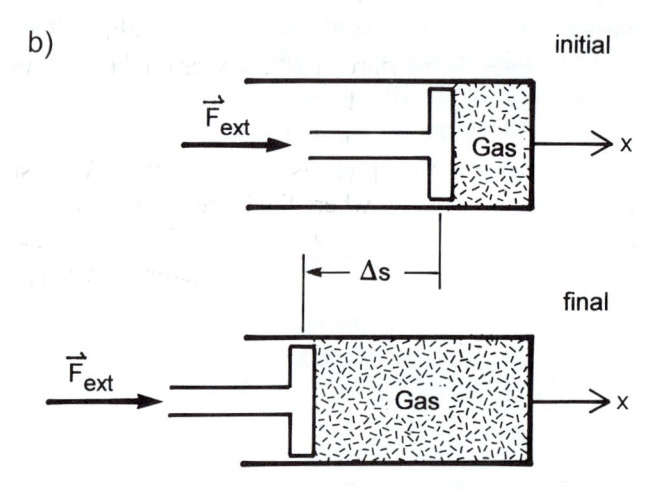

$$W = -p \cdot \Delta V \qquad (16)$$

Fig. 5.12: (a) A piston is pushed along the x–axis from an initial to a final state by an external force $\mathbf{F}_{ext}$. This causes the piston to move a distance Δs toward the right which leads to a compression of the gas. (b) Alternatively, the gas may expand and push the piston against an external force in the direction of the negative x–axis toward the left.

It is important to note the origin of the negative sign in Eq. (16). Using the first step in Eq. (15) the work done on the system gas is positive because the force F_{ext} acting on the gas and the displacement of the gas point in the same direction. You may think of the displacement of the gas to be its shift of center–of–mass to the right. The subsequent multiplication with A/A = 1 in the last step of Eq. (15) has no effect on the sign. Proceeding from Eq. (15) to Eq. (16), we replace $F_{ext}/A = p$ which is the gas pressure when the system is in mechanical equilibrium. All absolute pressure values are positive. We also replace $A\Delta s = -\Delta V$ which is the volume change. The volume change introduces an additional negative sign because $A\Delta s$ in Fig. 5.12(a) is positive but ΔV is negative as the gas is compressed. The work for a compression of a gas is positive because work is done on the gas.

In Fig. 5.12(b) an expansion of a gas is studied. The external force and the displacement of the gas point in this case in opposite directions and the work is negative. This is consistent with Eq. (16) in which p and ΔV are positive for Fig. 5.12(b). The work then is negative due to the additional negative sign on the right hand side of Eq. (16).

5.4.3. Work for systems with variable force or pressure

The work definitions for a point mass in Eq. (8) and for a gas in Eq. (16) have to be revised when the force varies during the displacement or the pressure varies during a compression or expansion. We need to include such cases because gas pressure often depends on the volume and the force on an object attached to a spring depends on the expansion of the spring (see Chapter 15).

To see how Eq. (8) is modified, we take first another look at the case where the force is constant during displacement. This is shown in Fig. 5.13 with $F = F_0$, a constant value for all positions x, including the range from the initial position x_i to the final position x_f of the displacement Δs. The equation for the work in this case is $W = F_0 \Delta s$. This formula implies that the dashed area is mathematically equal to the work, because the area of a rectangle is given by the product of its length and its width. This observation holds generally: work is the area under a curve of the force as a function of position. The area must always be taken from the initial to the final position of the displacement. If the area is determined from a graph it is also important to note that the lower end of the area must be taken at $F = 0$.

With this observation we can quantify the work for a position–dependent force, e.g. the case shown in Fig. 5.14. Again, a displacement Δs is shown from an initial position x_1 to a final position x_2. We do not obtain a simple rectangular area under the curve because the force varies with the position x. Various methods are available to determine the shaded area in the figure. If the mathematical function describing the position–dependence of the force, $F = f(x)$ is known, analytical or numerical methods can be used. The mathematical technique we apply in this case is called integration which is a subfield of calculus.

However, for most biological or physiological applications, including respiration which we discuss at the beginning of the next chapter, the dependence of the force on the position is not known as an explicit mathematical formula because too many parameters play a role in how the two parameters are related to each other. In

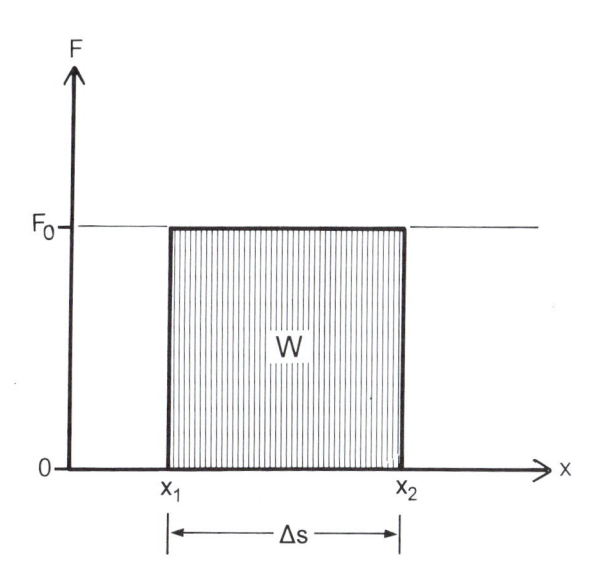

Fig. 5.13: A graphical interpretation of the work for a system with collinear force and displacement, such as shown in Fig. 5.8, is based on a plot of the force F as a function of position x. As a first case we study a constant force F_0, and a displacement from an initial position x_1 to a final position x_2 with $\Delta s = x_2 - x_1$. From Eq. (8) we find $W = F_0 \Delta s$ which corresponds to the shaded area in the figure. Thus, the work is quantified by the area under the curve of the force as a function of position between the initial and final states of the system.

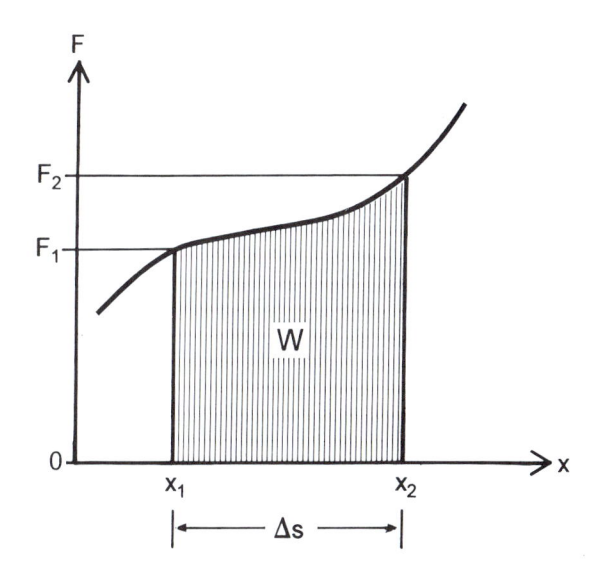

Fig. 5.14: Equivalent plot to Fig. 5.13 for the case in which the force varies with position during a displacement. We consider a displacement from position x_1 to position x_2. In this interval the force varies from F_1 to F_2. The amount of work done on/by the object corresponds again to the area under the curve $F = f(x)$, but cannot be obtained from Eq. (8).

such cases, the scientific approach to determine the work is based on experimentally measuring the force as a function of the position and then using graphical methods to determine the area under the curve. The approach most often used is computer–based: the measured curve is entered into a computer with an algorithm to determine the area. It is still useful to practice this approach on a piece of paper since the computer–based method does not allow us to see how it is done.

Example 5.4

Determine the work done on an object which is brought from an initial position $x_1 = 1$ m to a final position $x_2 = 4$ m, requiring at each position the external force shown in Fig. 5.15.

Solution: We superimpose on Fig. 5.15 a narrow–spaced

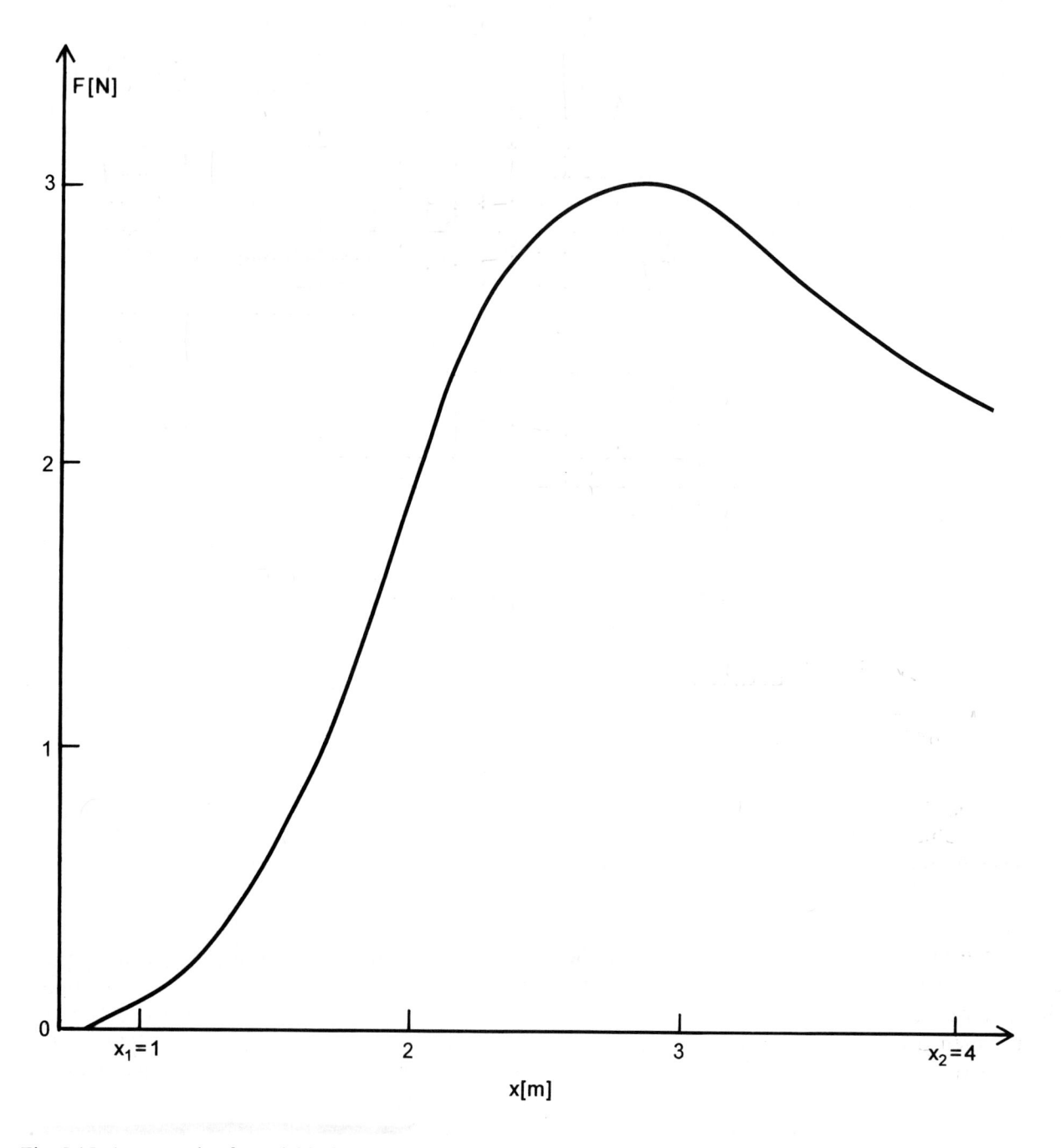

Fig. 5.15: An example of a variable force acting on an object. The force varies between 0 N and 3 N between positions x_1 and x_2. The work done on/by the object can be determined from measuring the area under the curve of this plot between the initial and final positions.

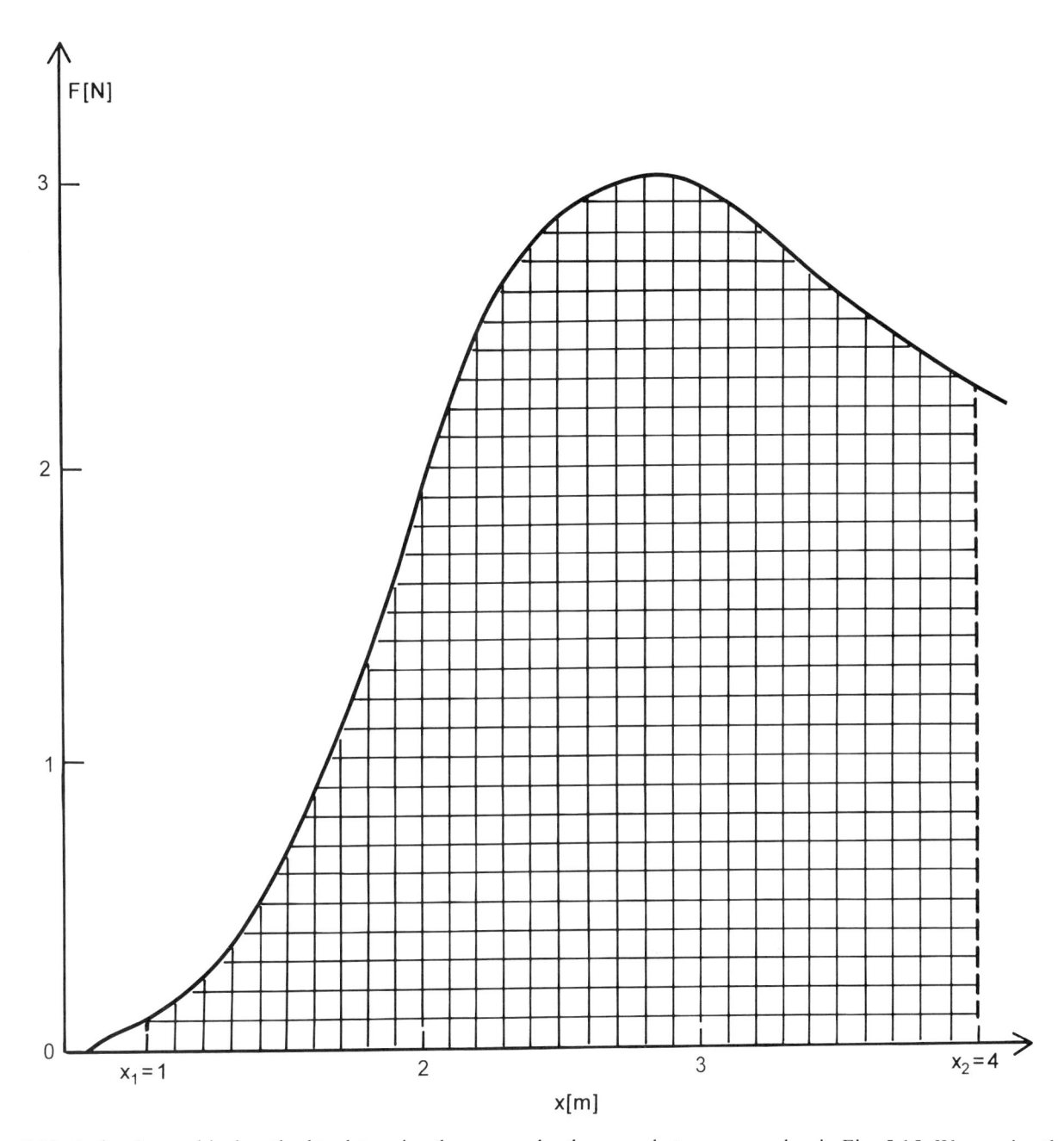

Fig. 5.16: A simple graphical method to determine the area under the curve between x_1 and x_2 in Fig. 5.15. We overlap the figure with a sufficiently fine grid of lines which are spaced by 0.1 m horizontally and by 0.1 N vertically. Each square corresponds to a work contribution of 0.01 J; the total area is determined by counting the number of such squares.

grid as shown in Fig. 5.16. In the particular case, the distance between any two horizontal lines is 0.1 N and the distance between any two vertical lines is 0.1 m. From the chosen grid we determine that the area of each small square is:

$$W_{grid} = \Delta F \cdot \Delta x = \tag{17}$$
$$= 0.1 \, [N] \cdot 0.1 \, [m] = 0.01 \, J$$

This is a work term since it is associated with an area in a force versus position plot. Now we count the small rectangles below the curve in Fig. 5.16. This number is $N = 610$. The work in Fig. 5.15 equals therefore the work due to each small rectangle, multiplied with the number of rectangles under the curve. In the present case this leads to:

$$W = N \cdot W_{grid} = 610 \cdot 0.01 \, [J] \tag{18}$$
$$\Rightarrow \quad W = 6.1 \, J$$

Note that this is an absolute value. We must apply Eq. (9) to determine the sign of work in this case. Since the work is done on the object in the example we find as the answer that W = + 6.1 J.

The same considerations apply to the case of a gas sealed by a piston. In this case the work is the area under the function p(V) as illustrated in Fig. 5.17. If the pressure does not depend on the volume the area in the figure becomes a rectangle which is represented by the product of the pressure and the change in volume, as written in Eq. (16).

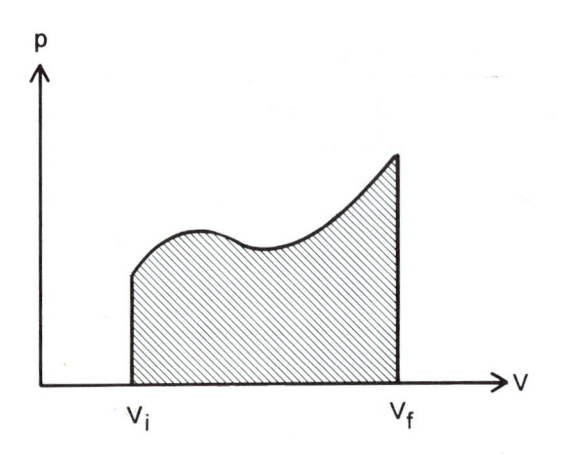

Fig. 5.17: Sketch of the area under a curve for a process where the pressure varies with volume between an initial volume V_i and a final volume V_f of the system. The figure indicates that Eq. (16) can be quantified in the same fashion as Eq. (8).

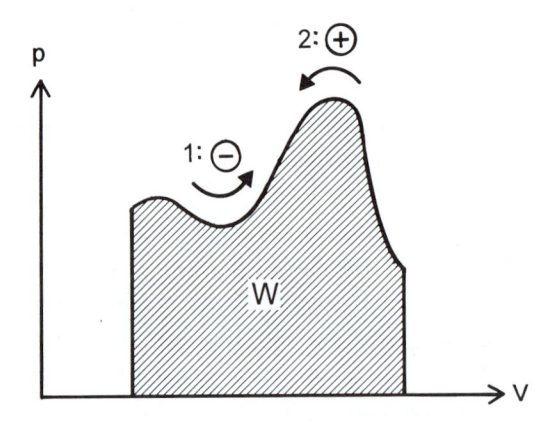

Fig. 5.18: Sketch illustrating the two possible directions in which a process in a pressure versus volume diagram may occur. Path 1 is an expansion with a positive value for ΔV. Because pressure values are always positive, the signs in Eq. (19) leads to a negative value of work W. Path 2 is a compression with a negative value for ΔV. Combined with a positive pressure this leads to a positive value of W.

The only difference between analysing Fig. 5.17 and Fig. 5.14 is that we have to take into account an additional negative sign for the gas illustrated in Fig. 5.18. We anticipate one of two opposite cases, an expansion (volume increase indicated by arrow 1 to the right) and a compression (volume decrease indicated by arrow 2 to the left). The shaded area represents the absolute value of the work for both processes. Based on the definition of work we find:

$$\text{path } 1: \quad V_i < V_f \Rightarrow W < 0$$
$$\text{path } 2: \quad V_i > V_f \Rightarrow W > 0 \quad (19)$$

As an example, Fig. 5.17 shows a volume expansion since the initial volume V_i is smaller than the final volume V_f. Therefore the work for the case in Fig. 5.17 is negative.

Example 5.5
Fig. 5.19 shows four curves for the pressure of a gas varying with the volume in different ways. The gas expands in each case from the initial volume (labelled i) to the final volume (labelled f). Rank the work in each of the four cases, starting with the highest value.
Hint: − 5 J < − 2 J but + 5 J > + 2 J.

Solution: The work is measured by the area under the curve as indicated in Fig. 5.18. Note that path 1 of Fig.

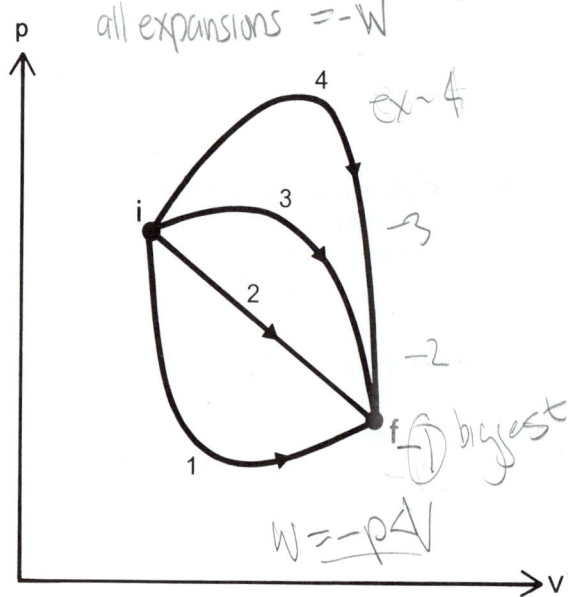

Fig. 5.19: Four possible paths for a process operating between an initial state (i) and a final state (f) of a system shown in a pressure versus volume diagram.

5.18 corresponds qualitatively to each of the four processes shown in Fig. 5.19, because all four processes are expansions. Thus, the work terms are negative in all four cases and, based on the area under each curve, we find:

$$0 > W_1 > W_2 > W_3 > W_4 \qquad (20)$$

Example 5.6

A gas is compressed from an initial volume of 8 m³ to a final volume of 2 m³. If the pressure depends on the volume as shown in Fig. 5.20, what is the work required to complete the compression?

Solution: We first determine the absolute value of the work. This value is obtained from the area under the curve in Fig. 5.20. Analysing the area is straight forward because of the linear pressure increase. We add the area of the lower rectangle and the area of the top triangle:

$$W = 10[kPa]\,(8[m^3]-2[m^3]) + \ldots$$
$$\ldots + \frac{1}{2}(30[kPa]-10[kPa])\,(8[m^3]-2[m^3]) \qquad (21)$$

which yields:

$$W = 1.2 \times 10^5\ J \qquad (22)$$

Fig. 5.20: pV–diagram for a gas which is compressed from an initial volume of 8 m³ to a final volume of 2 m³. The pressure increases linearly during the compression from 10 kPa to 30 kPa. This is an example of a system with varying pressure for which Eq. (16) cannot be applied.

Note that the area of the lower rectangle must be included because the area under the curve includes every part down to the line p = 0.

In the second step we determine the sign of the work. In a compression the volume change is negative. Eq. (19) leads to a positive work W > 0. This means the gas receives W = + 1.2 × 10⁵ J, or in other words, this amount of work is done on the gas.

5.5. Energy

When a system is capable of doing work, that work needs not to be done instantaneously. A system can store work; stored work is called energy.

> *Energy is the capability of a system to do work.*

When the system interacts with its environment, the exchange of work is linked to a change of the amount of energy in the system as defined in Eq. (6). Energy can be stored in systems in several different ways. The following list includes the major forms of energy we discuss in this textbook:

(I) Kinetic energy is work stored in the speed of an object. This form of energy must be dissipated when blood shoots from the heart into the arch of the aorta, to slow it down in the cardiovascular system.

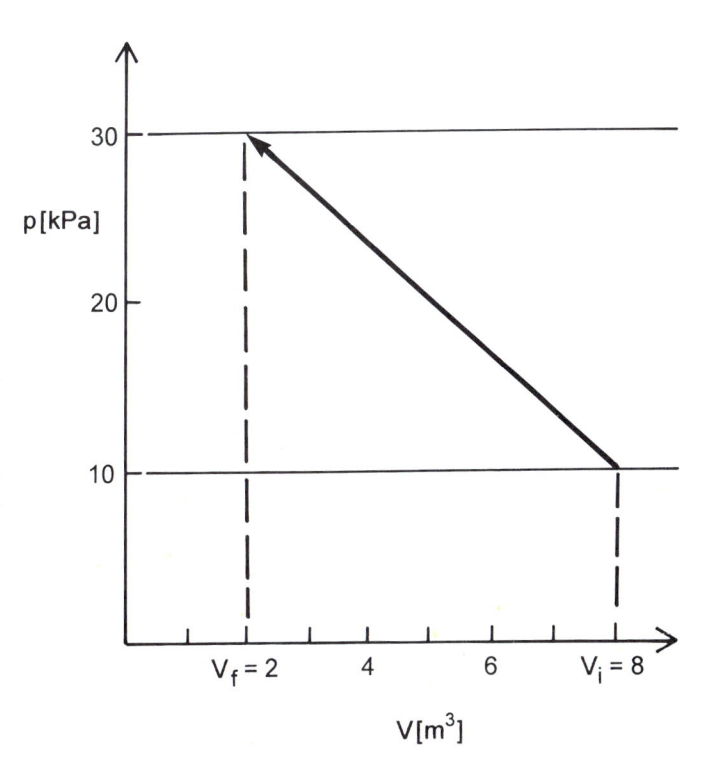

(II) Potential energy is work stored in the position of an object relative to other objects. We discuss:
(IIa) Gravitational potential energy, which is the energy of an object due to its position relative to the surface of the Earth. This form of energy matters when we discuss the blood pressure in the brain in comparison to the blood pressure in the heart for a species with erect gait. This form of energy is discussed in the current chapter.
(IIb) Electric potential energy, which is the energy of a charged object due to its position relative to other electric charges. This form of energy is important for the transport of nerve signals. We introduce this form of energy in Chapter 9.
(IIc) Elastic potential energy, which is the energy due to the relative position of two bodies connected with a spring. This form of energy allows us to characterize the vibrations of molecules. It is introduced in Chapter 15.
(III) Thermal energy is stored in the temperature of a system (irregular motion of particles). This form of energy is generated and released as heat when endotherms maintain a constant core body temperature.
(IV) Chemical energy is work stored in chemical bonds of molecules. This form of energy is transferred in the process shown in Eq. (1).
(V) Latent heat is work stored in the phase of matter, i.e., the liquid, gas or solid state. This form of energy is dissipated during perspiration.

One consequence of the relation between work and the various forms of energy is that each form of energy has the same unit [J] as work. Only the kinetic, gravitational potential and elastic potential energies can be defined for a single point mass. They are therefore called mechanical energies. Since the point mass concept simplifies the discussion, we introduce some of the mechanical energy forms first.

5.5.1. Kinetic energy

To define kinetic energy, we study a system for which only its speed changes, but no other parameters vary. Such a system is shown in Fig. 5.21: an isolated point mass is allowed to interact for a well-defined time interval Δt with its environment. The interaction leads to an acceleration of the system. For simplicity we choose the external force which causes the acceleration to be constant. Newton's second law, $F_{net} = ma$, then leads to $a = $ const during Δt. The acceleration changes the speed of the system from $v_{initial}$ to v_{final}.

We use the acceleration step to quantify the difference between the initial and final kinetic energy by applying Eq. (6). The work done on the object during the acceleration step is determined by using the definition of work, $W = F \Delta s$.

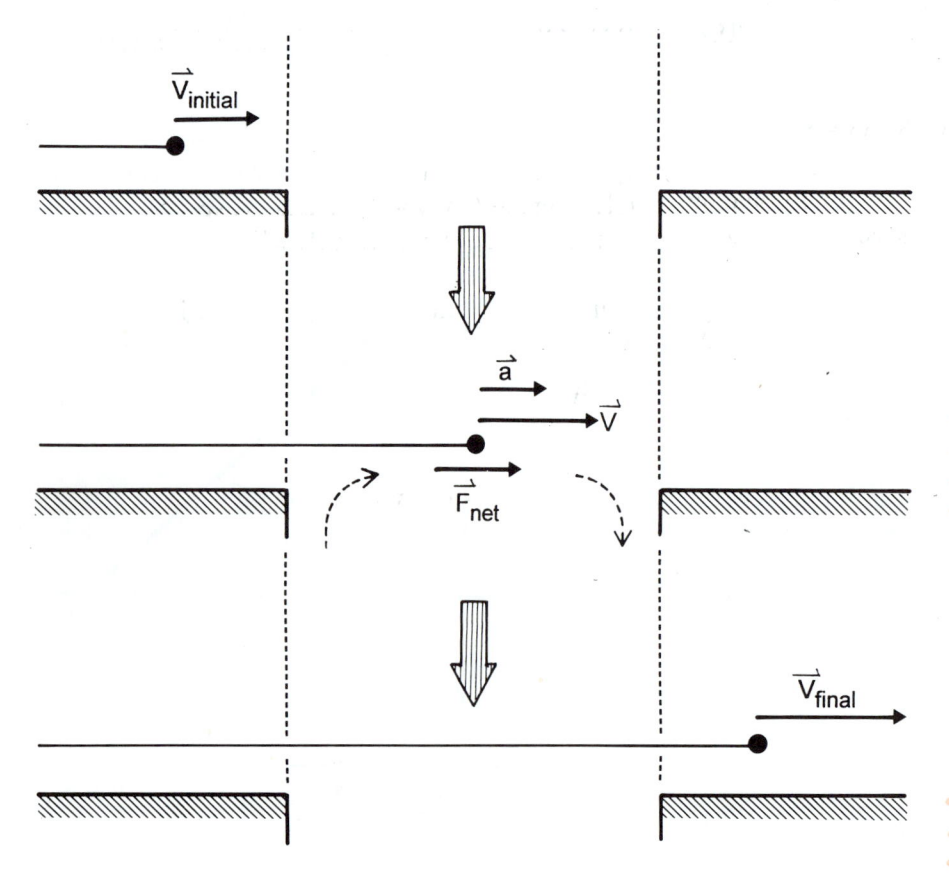

Fig. 5.21: To define kinetic energy we need to compare two states of a system in mechanical equilibrium which differ only in the speed of an object. The initial state is shown at top with speed v_{init} and the final state is shown at the bottom with $v_{final} > v_{init}$. To quantify the correlation between the equilibrium states a well defined (non-equilibrium) change of the state of the system is applied as shown in the middle panel: the object is accelerated with a constant force acting from the left end to the right end of an interaction zone.

In order to express the change in kinetic energy as a function of the speed of the object, a relation between the acceleration and the resulting change in speed of the object is needed. Such a relation is called a kinematic equation. Kinematic relations are derived from the definitions of velocity and acceleration, given in Chapter 2. For the special case of a constant acceleration the kinematic relations are derived in the Appendix of the current chapter. The kinematic equation relating acceleration and speed is given in the form:

$$a = \frac{v_{final}^2 - v_{initial}^2}{2 \Delta s} \quad (23)$$

Eq. (23) states that a constant acceleration can be expressed as a function of the square of the initial and final speeds and the displacement Δs. Substituting the acceleration from Eq. (23) into Newton's equation of motion, $F = ma$, yields:

$$F = ma = \frac{m}{2 \Delta s}\left(v_{final}^2 - v_{initial}^2\right) \quad (24)$$

The work is obtained by multiplying both sides of this equation with the displacement Δs:

$$W = F \Delta s = \frac{m}{2}\left(v_{final}^2 - v_{initial}^2\right) \quad (25)$$

Eq. (25) defines the work done on the object during the time interval Δt when the external force acts on the system. The terms relating to the initial conditions and the terms relating to the final conditions can be separated:

$$W = \frac{m}{2} v_{final}^2 - \frac{m}{2} v_{initial}^2 \quad (26)$$

Comparing Eq. (26) with Eq. (6) we find

$$E_{kin,\ initial} = \frac{1}{2} m\, v_{initial}^2$$
$$E_{kin,\ final} = \frac{1}{2} m\, v_{final}^2 \quad (27)$$

or, generally

$$E_{kin} = \frac{1}{2} m v^2 \quad (28)$$

Note that this equation has been derived by using the work associated with the transfer of a system from an initial to a final equilibrium state since $v_{initial}$ = const before the interaction and v_{final} = const after the interaction. Thus, we have defined the kinetic energy strictly for a system in mechanical equilibrium. The intermediate acceleration altered the system temporarily from an isolated to a closed system for which we were able to use the second formula in Eq. (6) to quantify the change in the parameter kinetic energy.

When the object does work on the environment, it becomes slower and the kinetic energy decreases, reflecting the amount of energy needed to do the work. If work is done on the object, it accelerates and then stores a larger amount of kinetic energy. There is a maximum amount of work a moving object can do, which is equal to the kinetic energy it loses by slowing down to rest. When $v_{final} = 0$ is reached, all the energy of the system has been released. In summary:

$$\begin{array}{c} W > 0 \quad \Leftrightarrow \quad E_{kin,\ final} > E_{kin,\ initial} \\ \text{System receives work} \\ \\ W < 0 \quad \Leftrightarrow \quad E_{kin,\ final} < E_{kin,\ initial} \\ \text{System releases work} \end{array} \quad (29)$$

Example 5.7
An object of mass m = 0.5 kg moves with initial speed $v_{initial}$ = 5.0 m/s, then interacts with its environment, releasing 5.0 J of work. What is the speed of the object after the interaction is completed?

Solution: We combine Eqs. (26) and (27):

$$W = E_{final} - E_{initial} = \frac{1}{2}mv_f^2 - \frac{1}{2}mv_i^2 \quad (30)$$

Next we isolate the final speed of the object:

$$\frac{1}{2}mv_f^2 = W + \frac{1}{2}mv_i^2 \quad (31)$$

which leads to:

$$v_f = \sqrt{\frac{2W}{m} + v_i^2} \quad (32)$$

Applying the convention of Eq. (9) we note that work released by the system has to be entered into Eq. (32) negative, W = –5.0 J. This leads to:

$$v_f = \sqrt{\frac{2\,(-5.0[J])}{0.5[kg]} + \left(5.0\left[\frac{m}{s}\right]\right)^2} \quad (33)$$

$$\Rightarrow \quad v_f = 2.23\ [m/s]$$

It is obviously important to understand whether work is released or received by the system to determine the sign of W. Using W = +5.0 J instead of W = –5.0 J in Eq. (33) leads to a different, wrong result.

5.5.2. Meissner's corpuscles and hair

In Chapter 3 we discussed acceleration detectors in the human body: the Pacinian corpuscles and the semi-circular canals in the vestibular organ. The argument for their existence is that acceleration is an important parameter in nature as it occurs explicitly in some fundamental natural laws (Newton's laws). Our body must measure it to be in a position to properly respond to its natural environment. Now we found that the concept of speed is also relevant to physical phenomena as it is connected to kinetic energy. Does our body therefore also have speed detectors? The answer is yes, we possess two independent detection systems in the form of Meissner's corpuscles below the skin (about half a million corpuscles with the highest concentration in the skin of the finger tips) and hair.

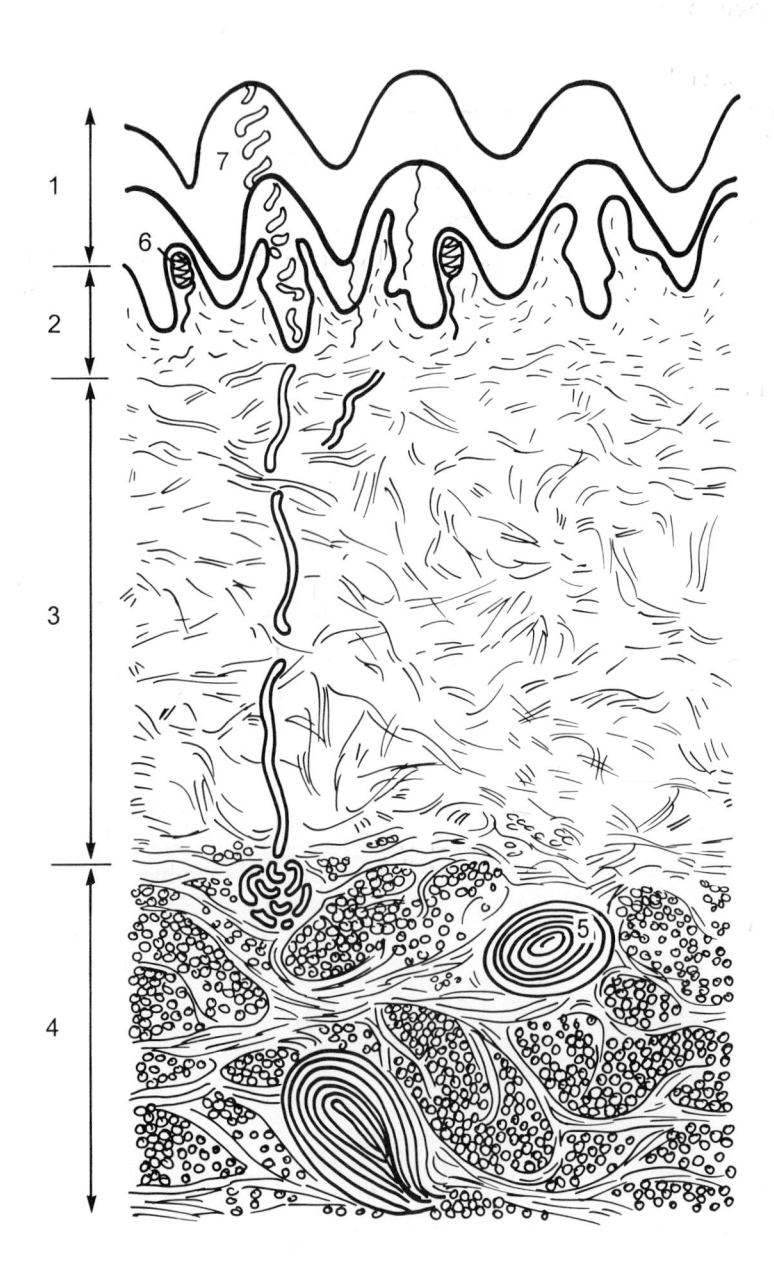

Fig. 5.22: Sketch of a cut through the skin of a finger tip. The skin is composed of four layers, including the epidermis (1), the outer ridge-shaped layer of the corium (stratum papillare, 2), the inner mesh-like layer of the corium (stratum reticulare, 3) and the subcutis (4). Other features shown in the micrograph are two Pacinian corpuscles (5), two Meissner's corpuscles (6) and a sweat gland (7).

Meissner's corpuscles

Fig. 3.4 shows a sketch of the cross–section of the outer layers of our palm, including Meissner's corpuscles just below the epidermis. Fig. 5.22 is an equivalent sketch based on a micrograph. Notice how much closer to the surface Meissner's corpuscles are located than the Pacinian corpuscles we discussed earlier. This is an important feature for the functional role of Meissner's corpuscles as velocity detectors. Fig. 5.22 also identifies their position with respect to the ridge–valley pattern of the finger tips, showing that the corpuscles are near the steepest slope.

Meissner's corpuscles measure the speed of objects which come into contact with the skin and consequently increase the tension on the skin. The microscopic structure of a Meissner's corpuscle is shown in Fig. 5.23(a). Each corpuscle consists of a stack of cells in the shape of an ellipsoid, with the more rigid cell nuclei located on alternating sides from cell to cell. The dendrites of a nerve are intertwined between these cells as shown in Fig. 5.23(b). This sketch is based on a methylene blue coloring of the corpuscle which highlights the position of nerve tissue.

The mechanism of the velocity detection of a Meissner's corpuscle is illustrated in Fig. 5.24. Shown is a piston–like device just before and while pressing the skin of the finger. The corpuscle gets squeezed together, which leads to a change in the stacking structure of the cells. As a consequence, the intertwined dendrite is bent

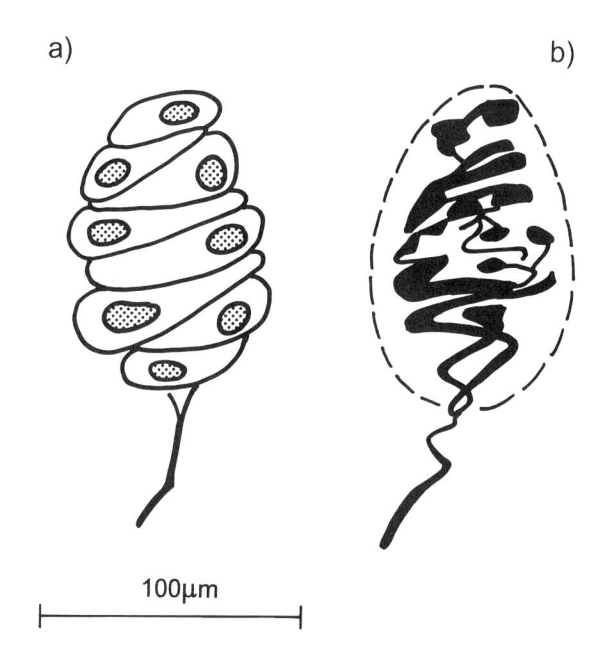

Fig. 5.23: (a) Morphological micrograph of Meissner's corpuscle. Shown are eight cells with an alternating arrangement of the cell nuclei. (b) The intertwined dendrite structure is highlighted for the same corpuscle by applying the methylene blue tissue coloring technique.

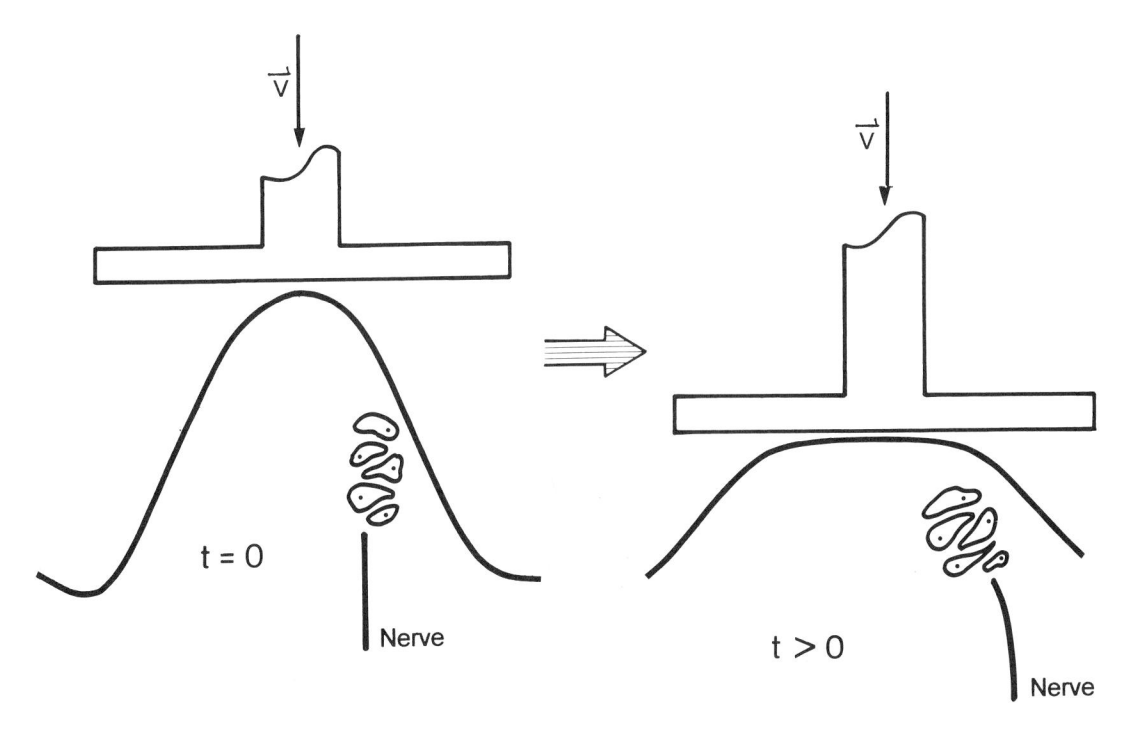

Fig. 5.24: Mechanism of Meissner's corpuscles. At left a piston is shown at time zero approaching the skin surface with speed **v**. At right the same area is shown after the piston has pushed the skin a certain distance down. The piston is assumed to move with constant speed. Meissner's corpuscles get deformed in the process.

causing nerve pulses to the brain. The pulse rate, which is the number of pulses sent per second, is higher when the dendrite is bent faster.

We use graphs to establish this relationship between the velocity and the pulse rate. In Fig. 5.25, the pulse rate is plotted as a function of the speed of the approaching piston. Fig. 5.25(a) shows a linear plot of the data and Fig. 5.25(b) is a double–logarithmic representation of the same data. The linear plot highlights variations in the steepness of the curve. Thus the linear graph is suitable to pinpoint greatest sensitivity, corresponding to the interval of greatest steepness. The greatest sensitivity of Meissner's corpuscles occurs at very small speeds up to $v \leq 1$ cm/s. They are suitable for gentle touching not to measure the speed of an incoming baseball!

The double–logarithmic plot allows us to distinguish whether one or more mechanisms are involved in the process. It shows straight line segments for each power law. The mathematical aspects of double–logarithmic plots are discussed in the General Appendix (Chapter 24). In the specific case of Fig. 5.25(b) the power law for the nerve pulse rate, P, is written in the form $P = a v^b$ in which v is the speed of the object making contact with the skin. If the prefactor a or the exponent b in this power law are not constant, deviations from a straight line in the double–logarithmic plot occur. Any deviation from a straight line is, therefore, an indication that additional physical explanations are needed. In the present case, however, no such deviations occur, and thus the single mechanism of Fig. 5.24 is sufficient to explain Meissner's corpuscle based on the experimental data.

Hair

Fig. 5.26 shows a sketch of a cross–section of the human skin where it contains hair. In comparison to Fig. 3.4 for the hair–free skin, the epidermis is usually thinner and no Meissner's corpuscles are present. Pacinian corpuscles are still found in the deeper layers and Merkel's corpuscles, which we discussed in Chapter 3, are still present below the epidermis. This selective absence of Meissner's corpuscles is explained by the hair replacing them as velocity detectors.

Unlike Meissner's corpuscles, hair can detect the velocity of objects not yet in contact with the skin. Their mechanism is illustrated in Fig. 5.27. Shown is a piston which moves parallel to the skin in near proximity to the skin surface. When the piston pushes the hair to the side, a force is exerted on the root sheath. This force is sensed by the dendrites coiling around the root of the hair. Like in the case of Meissner's corpuscles, the rate of nerve pulses is a function of the speed of the piston.

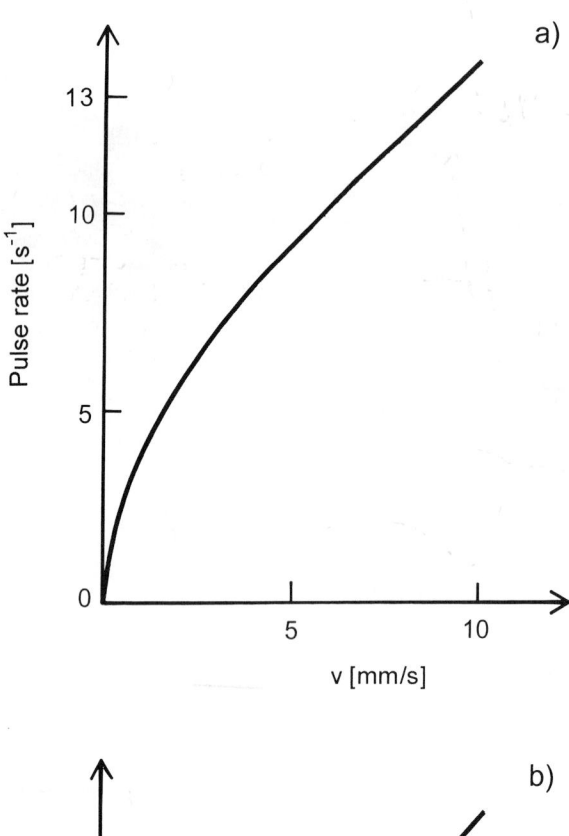

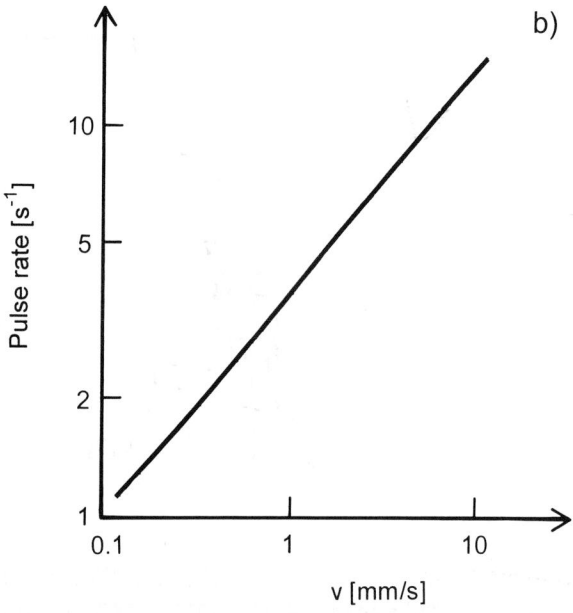

Fig. 5.25: The nerve pulse rate for a Meissner's corpuscle as a function of the speed of an approaching object. The pulse rate is given in unit pulses per second and the speed is given in unit [mm/s]. (a) A linear plot of the data showing the greatest sensitivity to speeds of 5 mm/s. (b) In the double–logarithmic plot the same data follow a straight line segment. This means that a single power law describes the data and, therefore, that a single mechanism explains the operation of the corpuscle.

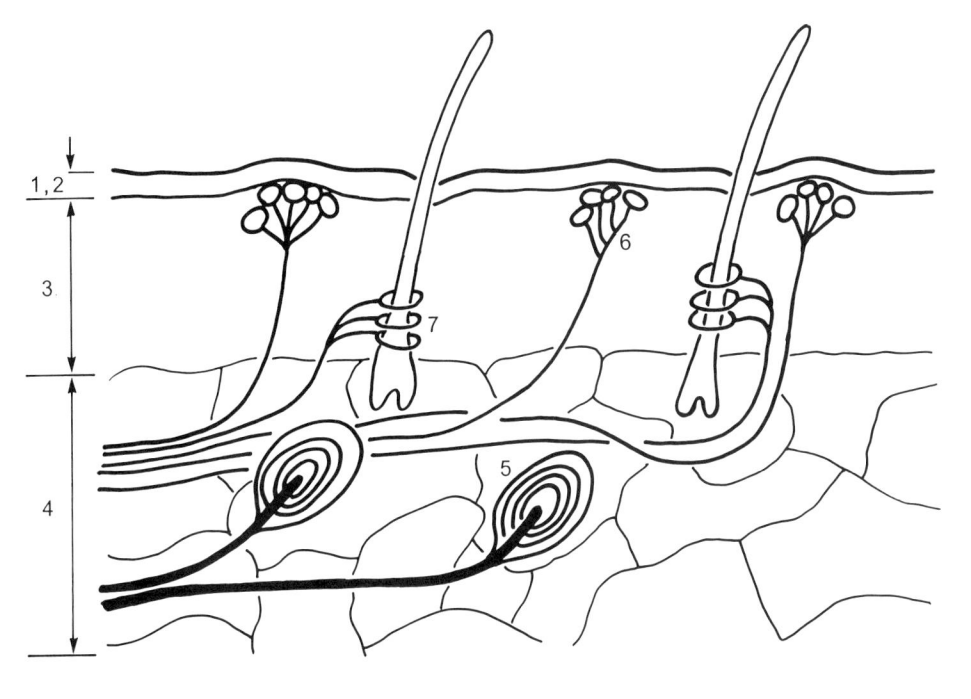

Fig. 5.26: Cross–section of skin with hair. The skin layers are labelled in the same fashion as in Fig. 3.4: (1,2) represent a shallow epidermis, (3) the corium, and (4) the subcutis. Other features shown in the figure include the Pacinian corpuscles (5), Merkel's corpuscles (6) and the dendrites encircling the sheath of the hair (7). Note that this type of skin does not contain Meissner's corpuscles.

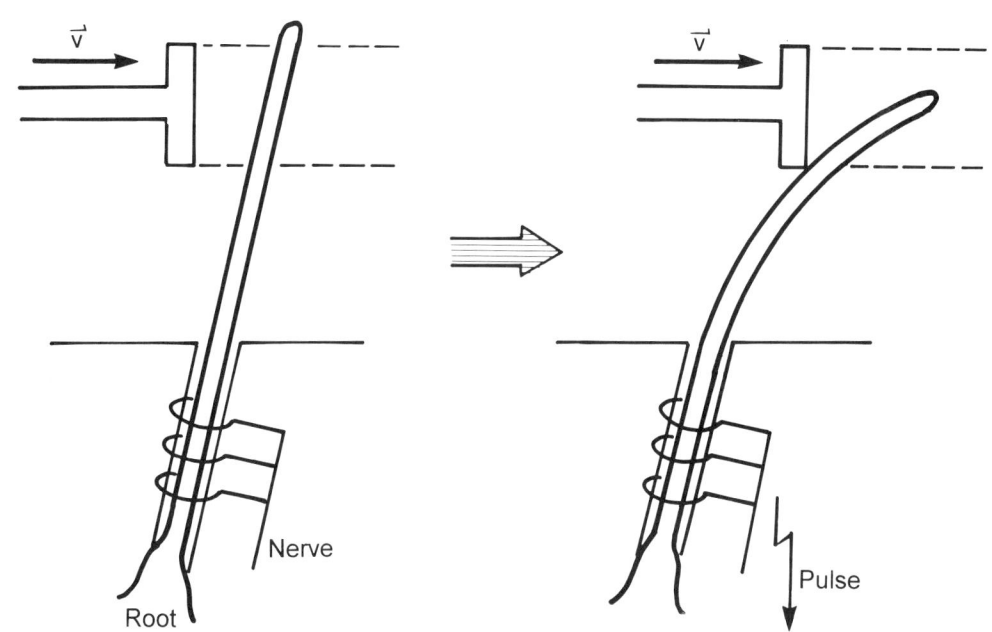

Fig. 5.27: Illustration of a hair as a velocity detector for an object moving with speed **v** parallel to the skin in close proximity. The bending of the hair causes the nerves at the root to send a signal to the brain.

5.5.3. Gravitational potential energy

Next we study cases in which the work is stored in the relative position of objects, particularly the work stored in the position of an object relative to the surface of the Earth, called gravitational potential energy. To quantify this form of energy, we have to carefully develop an experimental set-up. The system cannot be an isolated object like for the definition of kinetic energy in section 5.5.1. For the gravitational interaction the Earth becomes part of the environment. An isolated superstructure consisting of the Earth as the environment and the object as the system is still insufficient because there is only one force acting on the object (gravity). This does not allow us to establish a mechanical equilibrium for the system. We need to add a second force with its source in the environment such that the system is in mechanical equilibrium. This source is a person holding the system as shown in Fig. 5.9. The two different equilibrium states of the system, which we need to define gravitational potential energy, are shown in Fig. 5.9:

(I) the system of mass m held at rest at height y_i at an initial time, and

(II) the system again held at rest at height y_f at a later, final time. We choose y_f to be lower than y_i.

The transfer between these two equilibrium states of the system can be accomplished in several ways. Dropping the system and catching it at the lower height is one possibility. This represents a more complicated transfer as non–equilibrium processes are involved such as the slowing of the object near the final equilibrium state. The simplest transfer in Fig. 5.9 is to lower the system very slowly from the initial to the final height, moving with a constant speed. In this case, the system is always in mechanical equilibrium and we know that $F_{ext} - W = 0$, i.e., $F_{ext} = mg$ during the transfer. Thus, the work due to the external force, which establishes the mechanical equilibrium for the system, is calculated as:

$$W = F_{ext} \Delta s = mg \left(y_f - y_i \right) \quad (34)$$

The work for the process in Fig. 5.9 is negative because the bracket $(y_f - y_i)$ is negative while the external force is positive. Comparing Eq. (34) with the general formula in Eq. (6), we find:

$$E_{pot,\ initial} = m g y_i$$
$$E_{pot,\ final} = m g y_f \quad (35)$$

Therefore, we define the gravitational potential energy in the form:

$$E_{pot} = m g y \quad (36)$$

The gravitational potential energy is the larger the further the system is separated from the surface of the Earth.

This energy is applied in an interesting fashion by several types of birds. In parts of southern Europe, golden eagles live mainly on tortoises although their talons are no match for an animal tucked resolutely inside its shell. The eagle's solution is recorded in Greek mythology: a soothsayer warned the poet Aeschylus that he would die by a house falling on his head. Aeschylus wisely ensured that he was in open country on the day the prediction was to come true, in case an earthquake destroyed his house. It was in vain, a passing eagle fulfilled the soothsayer's prophecy by dropping a tortoise's house on the poet. Similar strategies are applied by Egyptian vultures to open ostrich eggs, and crows feeding on gastropod mollusks along the coast of British Columbia.

In the case of the crows, the birds fly with their prey to a certain height and drop the mollusk onto the rocky beach below. For each attempt, the bird must do work proportional to the height as shown in Eq. (34). Interestingly, crows do not rise to a height from which

Table 5.5: Total work done by a crow to break the shell of a mollusk. Crows at the coast of British Columbia lift mollusks above the rocky beach and drop them to reach the soft tissue inside. The work is given per kilogram mass lifted in the process.

Height of release [m]	Repetitions	Work per kg [J/kg]
2	55	1080
3	13	380
5	6	295
7	5	340
15	4	590

they would be assured that the mollusk cracks on the first attempt, but rather rise to only 5 meters from where they need to drop the mollusk an average six times to reach the soft tissue they intend to eat. This behavior is consistent with minimizing the work done by the crow as illustrated with the experimental data in Table 5.5. The table shows the height of releasing the mollusk, the average number of drops required to break the mollusk's shell and the total work done by the crow to reach its food. The work is given per kilogram mass lifted, which includes the crow itself and its prey. We obtain this value from $W/m = g\Delta y$. The data illustrate that the most efficient way for the crow is indeed to rise to five meters and drop the mollusk from there until it breaks open.

5.6. Conservation of energy

In equilibrium, both the kinetic energy as defined in section 5.5.1 and the gravitational potential energy as defined in section 5.5.3 are independently constant. In this section we want to find out how these energy forms depend on time for a system that is not in mechanical equilibrium but interacts with its environment.

The experiment we study is shown in Fig. 5.28: an object is released at an initial height and drops. The final observation is taken at a height where the object is still above the point of impact on the ground. During the time which elapses while the object moves from its initial to its final height, $\Delta t = t_2 - t_1$, only the speed and the height above the ground change. This means that we take a sufficient approach when considering only the kinetic energy and the gravitational potential energy. The system is the object; the isolated superstructure contains in this case also the Earth. No other object (such as a person) interacts with the system. For the system in this isolated superstructure, we quantify the energy changes

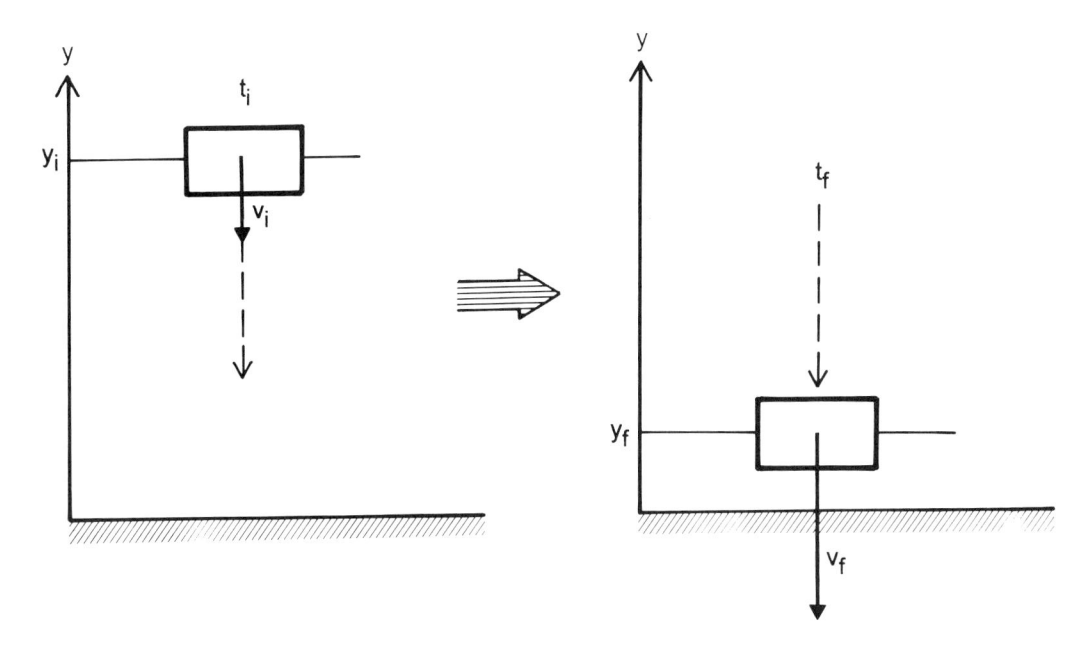

Fig. 5.28: An object is released at time t₁ (at left) and falls toward the surface of the Earth. The final observation of the object is done at time t₂, when the object has not yet hit the ground (at right). Note that this experiment is similar to the experiment shown in Fig. 5.9, but that the person holding the object in the previous case is not part of the isolated superstructure this time because no interaction between a person and the object occurs during the experiment.

during the process of falling. To do so, we start with Eq. (23) which is written for the case of Fig. 5.28 with $\Delta s = y_f - y_i$ since the motion occurs in the y–direction:

$$v_f^2 - v_i^2 = -2g\left(y_f - y_i\right) \quad (37)$$

The negative sign on the right hand side of Eq. (37) is due to the acceleration $a = -g$ because the gravitational acceleration is directed in the negative y–direction. We multiply Eq. (37) on both sides with the mass of the object and divide by 2:

$$\frac{1}{2}mv_f^2 = \frac{1}{2}mv_i^2 - mg\left(y_f - y_i\right)$$
$$\Rightarrow \quad \frac{1}{2}mv_f^2 + mgy_f = \frac{1}{2}mv_i^2 + mgy_i \quad (38)$$

The second line in Eq. (38) shows that the sum of the potential and kinetic energy is the same at the final and at the initial positions for the object in Fig. 5.28. We generalize this result for any initial and final positions in two ways:

$$(I) \quad E_{kin} + E_{pot} = const$$
$$(II) \quad \Delta E_{kin} + \Delta E_{pot} = 0 \quad (39)$$

The first formula in Eq. (39) states that the sum of the kinetic and gravitational potential energies remains unchanged at any time instant, and the second formula states that the change of the kinetic energy and the change of the gravitational potential energy offset each other during any process.

Example 5.8
An object of 0.2 kg is thrown at a speed of 30.0 m/s vertically upwards.
(a) What is the kinetic energy of the object at the highest point of its trajectory?
(b) What is the gravitational potential energy of the object at the highest point?
(c) How far is the highest point above the release point of the object?

Solution: Fig. 5.29 shows the rather simple free–body–diagram for this problem: the weight of the object is the

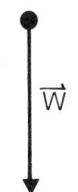

Fig. 5.29: Free–body–diagram of an object released from an initial position above ground. Until the object hits the ground its weight is the only force acting on the object.

only force acting on the system. We know from Chapter 2 that we need to apply Newton's second law (equation of motion) in the vertical y–direction:

$$\sum_i F_{iy} = -mg = ma_y \quad (40)$$

$$\Rightarrow a_y = -g$$

Solution part (a): At the highest point, the downwards directed gravitational acceleration has eliminated the initially upwards directed speed component in the y–direction ($v_y = 0$). Thus:

$$v_{at\,top} = 0$$

$$\Rightarrow E_{kin,\,at\,top} = \frac{1}{2}mv_{at\,top}^2 = 0\,J \quad (41)$$

Solution part (b): We first calculate the total mechanical energy of the system. Since energy is conserved, we can do this for any instant of the experiment. For convenience, we choose the instant of release of the object as we know all the data of the system at that time. We further choose arbitrarily the height at which the object is released as the reference height $y_{initial} = 0$. This means the same as assigning a potential energy $E_{pot,\,initial} = 0$ to that point. This is done without loss of generality and does not affect the result! As a consequence, the total energy of the object has at the instant of release only a kinetic energy component which is equal to the value $E_{kin,\,initial} = \frac{1}{2}mv^2 = 90\,J$. This is also the total energy of the system, as well as the gravitational potential energy at the highest point, $mgy_{at\,top} = 90\,J$, as the kinetic energy is zero at that point.

Solution part (c): Using Eq. (36) and the result from part (b), we obtain as the maximum height $y_{at\,top} = 45.9$ m.

═══════════════════════════════════════

The energy of the system is conserved for the particular experiment shown in Fig. 5.28. This is only of interest if the same result is consistently found for other mechanical experiments. Since this is the case, we predict that the mechanical energy is conserved for all mechanical experiments, including those which have not been tried yet. When we make such as statement we generalize a particular result to the level of a scientific law: an energy conservation law is formulated. Before we formulate that law, however, we test whether we can overcome the limitation posted by the term "mechanical". To do so we first check whether energy is also conserved when other forms of energy are involved.

5.7. First law of thermodynamics

The most important form of energy missing in the discussion so far is the thermal energy. Thermal energy is unavoidably set free in the form of heat even in the most careful attempt of a mechanical experiment. For example, a falling rain drop reaches fast a terminal speed. As it continues to fall its potential energy is steadily decreased but its kinetic energy remains unchanged. The loss of energy occurs in the form of frictional heating of the air through which the rain drop moves.

To include thermal energy we leave mechanics and enter a new subfield of physics: the study of heat and thermal energy related phenomena is called *thermodynamics*. We won't need a new model system for this discussion because we have already introduced the gas system. However, we need to establish the temperature as a new parameter for a gas before we can proceed with the definition of thermal energy.

5.7.1. Temperature

At Newton's time, experimental inclusion of thermal energy was impossible since temperature had not been defined. There was a qualitative understanding that the temperature is high when something feels warm and that the temperature is low when something feels cold, but no instrument was available to quantify temperatures.

This changed sixty years later when Anders Celsius observed that the height of a liquid in a hollow glass cylinder varies with temperature. He postulated in 1742 that the expansion of common liquids, such as water, alcohol and mercury (Hg, the only elementary metal which is liquid at room temperature), is linear with temperature. Choosing Hg we define the temperature therefore in the form:

$$T = T_0 + \frac{1}{\alpha_{Hg}} \cdot \left(\frac{(h-h_0)}{h_0}\right)_{Hg} \quad (42)$$

in which T_0 is an arbitrary reference temperature, usually $T_0 = 0°C$ or the temperature at which the thermometer is filled with mercury. The term in the bracket on the right hand side of Eq. (42) is the fraction of the height change of the mercury column during a temperature change. α_{Hg} with $\alpha_{Hg} = 1.82 \times 10^{-4}$ [1/°C] is the *coefficient of linear expansion* of mercury, i.e., the coefficient which quantifies the proportionality between height and temperature changes. Both the values for T_0 and α_{Hg} are needed to allow us to use Eq. (42) to measure temperatures. These two parameters are determined by choosing two reference points. Celsius chose the melting point of ice, which he designated as zero degrees, and the boiling point of water, which he designated as 100 degrees. In Celsius' honor, we call the resulting temperature scale the Celsius scale with the temperature unit [°C].

The two reference points Celsius has chosen are easily reproducible in experiments because the thermometer reading for a slowly heated ice block stops at these two temperatures. This is illustrated in Fig. 5.30. We start by heating an ice block which is initially at −25°C. The temperature increases steadily except at the phase transition temperatures when heat supplied to the system is used to complete the phase transition of the material. This heat is called the latent heat. At 0°C we add the latent heat of melting and at 100°C we add the latent heat of evaporation.

Note that the definition of temperature implies practically and conceptually the existence of a thermal equilibrium.

> *In a thermal equilibrium every part of the system has the same temperature.*

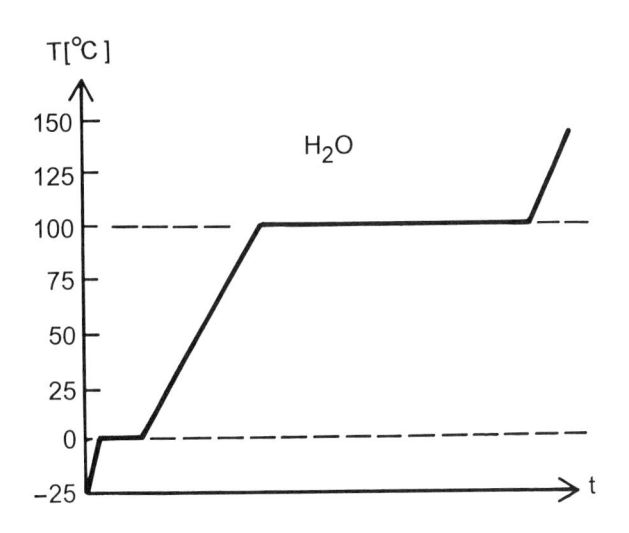

Fig. 5.30: Graph of the temperature versus time for a continuously heated beaker of water, starting with ice of −25°C. The temperature rises to 0°C, then remains unchanged while the ice melts. After this phase transition the temperature rises steadily to 100°C. The water begins to boil and the temperature remains constant until the entire amount of water has turned into water vapor. After the second phase transition the water vapor temperature rises steadily, shown up to about 140°C.

When we bring a thermometer in contact with an object we can only read a proper temperature off the thermometer if the object and the thermometer have the same temperature. If various parts of an object are at different temperatures we cannot define a meaningful single temperature for the object; this object is also not in a thermal equilibrium. If two systems in contact are not in thermal equilibrium, then heat flows from the hot body to the cold body until the temperatures are equal. We discuss such non–equilibrium cases in Chapter 7.

Due to the complex nature of the liquid state of matter, Celsius' thermometer is scientifically unsatisfactory. However, it was sufficient to get studies of thermal physics started. Due to the simple design of Celsius' thermometer it also continues to be used to measure moderate temperature changes, e.g. for fever thermometers. We have to return to the definition of temperature in the next chapters for two reasons, (I) to obtain a more precise definition and (II) to develop a better idea what temperature really means.

5.7.2. Temperature detection in the human body

Temperature is also an important physiological parameter. Mammals and birds are endotherms with a core body temperature for birds in the range of 39°C to 42°C and for mammals in the range of 36°C to 38°C. Individuals of a given species maintain their core body temperature within a very narrow window, in the case of humans 37.0 ± 0.5°C. To exercise this control, continuous temperature measurements in the core part of the body and at the interface to the environment (at the skin) are required. All temperature information gathered by the body is centrally analysed in the hypothalamus, which is located at the lower end of the brain (see Fig. 4.7). Our body then employs complex regulation mechanisms to maintain the core temperature. We discuss homeostasis and some of the major regulation mechanisms it requires in Chapter 7. Here we focus only on the temperature detection.

Animal testing suggests that temperature is measured in all core body parts. However, the anatomical structure of these sensors is still unknown. Temperature sensors in the skin detect the peripheral temperature of the body, which is also a measure of the temperature of the environment. These thermoreceptors are not associated with distinguishable corpuscles but consist of a locally confined network of dendrites which terminate at the lower end of the epidermis (see Fig. 3.4).

The temperature dependence of the number of nerve pulses sent to the brain allows us to distinguish

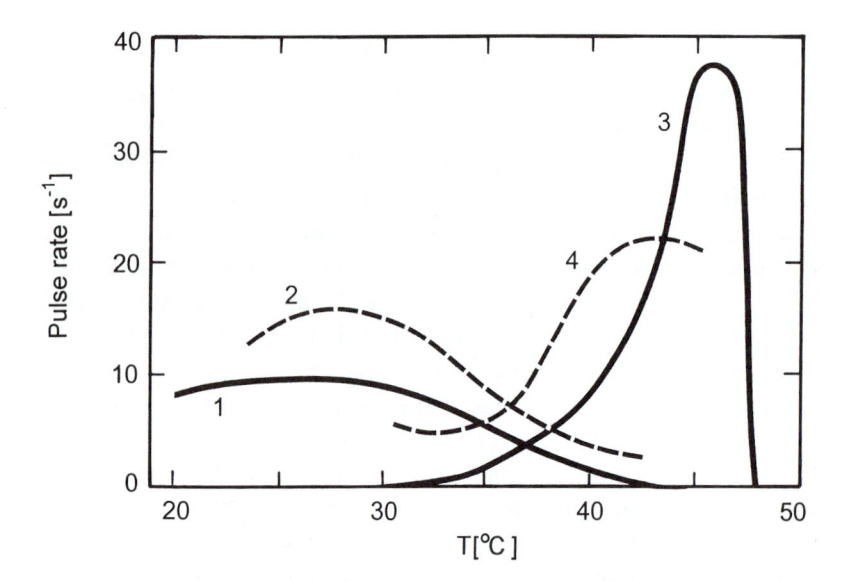

Fig. 5.31: The nerve pulse rate of cold spots and warm spots as a function of the temperature in the human skin (solid lines), and in the spinal cord (dashed lines). The curves are numbered, with (1) the cold spot response in the skin, (2) the cold spot response in the spinal cord, (3) the warm spot response in the skin, and (4) the warm spot response in the spinal cord. The sensitivity interval is defined as the temperature interval in which the pulse rate varies significantly, e.g. from 25°C to about 40°C for the cold spots and from 35°C to about 45°C for the warm spots.

two types of thermoreceptors in Fig. 5.31. Cold spots are most sensitive to temperatures between 25°C and 40°C. In comparison to about 250,000 cold spots, only about 30,000 warm spots are scattered across our skin. The warm spots are primarily sensitive to temperatures in the range of 35°C to 45°C. Fig. 5.31 also provides a comparison between cold and warm spots in the skin and in the spinal cord. We note that each pair of spots, curves 1 and 2 for the cold spots, and curves 3 and 4 for the warm spots, follow a similar sensitivity pattern.

Neither cold spots nor warm spots measure absolute temperatures, they measure temperature changes. As a consequence, the nerve pulse transmission to the hypothalamus ceases when the temperature remains constant (receptor adaptation). You can test this by immersing your hand in water of 25°C. The water is only initially perceived as cold. Extreme temperatures are, however, continuously sensed as too hot or too cold. This is associated with separate pain receptors, called nocireceptors, which respond similar to other sensors, but become sensitized by repeated stimulation.

5.7.3. Joule's experiments

Anders Celsius' definition of temperature made a proper definition of thermal energy possible. In 1798, Benjamin Thompson Count Rumford concluded from cannon drilling experiments that mechanical work leads to heating which represents an increase in the thermal energy of the system. In 1842, Julius Robert von Mayer studied human blood in a tropical environment and found that a change in the thermal energy of the blood was connected to work obtained from chemical energy. In 1843, James Prescott Joule defined both terms, thermal energy and heat, and connected them quantitatively to the concepts of work and potential energy. His arguments are based on two experiments shown in Fig. 5.32: the first experiment in Fig. 5.32(a) is used to define heat and the second experiment in Fig. 5.32(b) relates thermal and potential energy.

Joule concluded from the first experiment in Fig. 5.32 that the heat Q, that is added to the system, which consists of a beaker with water and a thermometer, is directly proportional to the change of temperature of the system, i.e., $Q \propto \Delta T$. He used the amount of burned propane gas as a measure of heat added to the beaker. Joule further discovered that the amount of heat needed in the experiment to achieve a particular temperature increase is directly proportional to the amount of the water in the beaker, $Q \propto m(H_2O)$. Finally, the amount of heat needed to increase the temperature of a given amount of liquid by a given number of degrees varies from liquid to liquid. This means that a materials specific constant is needed. These observations led Joule to the following formula for the heat flowing into the beaker:

$$Q = c \cdot m \cdot \Delta T \qquad (43)$$

with the material constant c called the *specific heat capacity*. The heat flowing into the beaker is then identified as the change in the thermal energy in the system as stated in the first formula of Eq. (6): $Q = \Delta E_{thermal} = E_{thermal, final} - E_{thermal, initial}$. Historically the unit calorie [cal] was introduced for heat. You should always convert this unit into the SI unit of Joule [J] using 1 cal = 4.184 J. We note further that [J/(kg °C)] is the unit of the specific heat capacity. The term heat capacity is proper since a large heat capacity means that the material can absorb more heat than a material with a small specific heat capacity before the temperature rises by a given amount.

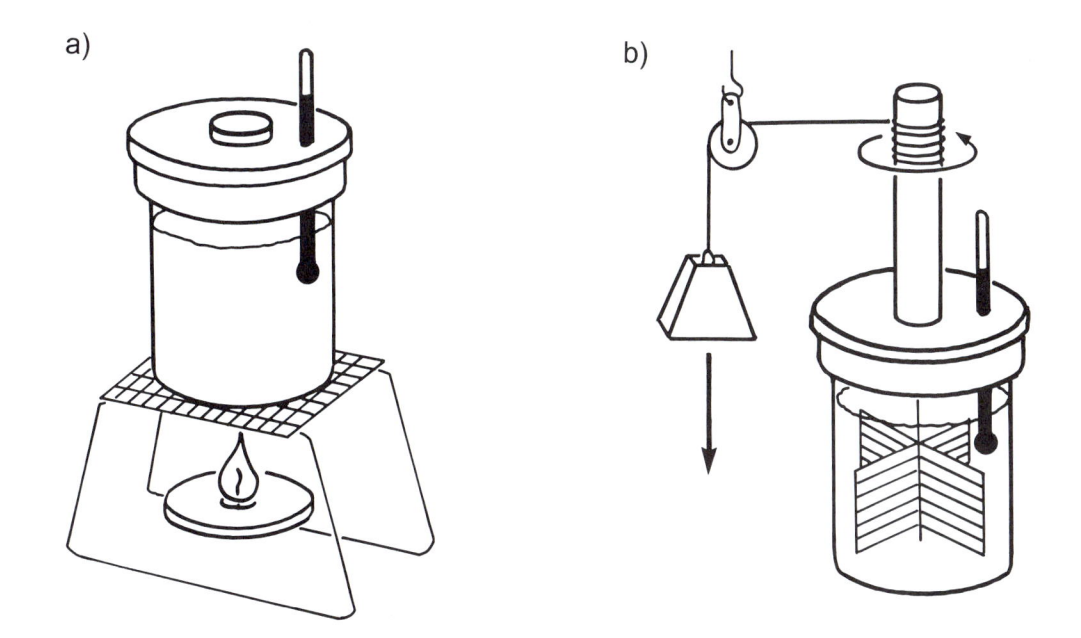

Fig. 5.32: Conceptual sketches of the two experiments done by Joule. (a) In the first experiment heat is quantified by measuring the amount of burned gas. (b) The second experiment illustrates conceptually the equivalence of mechanical and thermal energy. The mechanical energy, released by the falling object at the left, is used to heat the water by operating a stirrer.

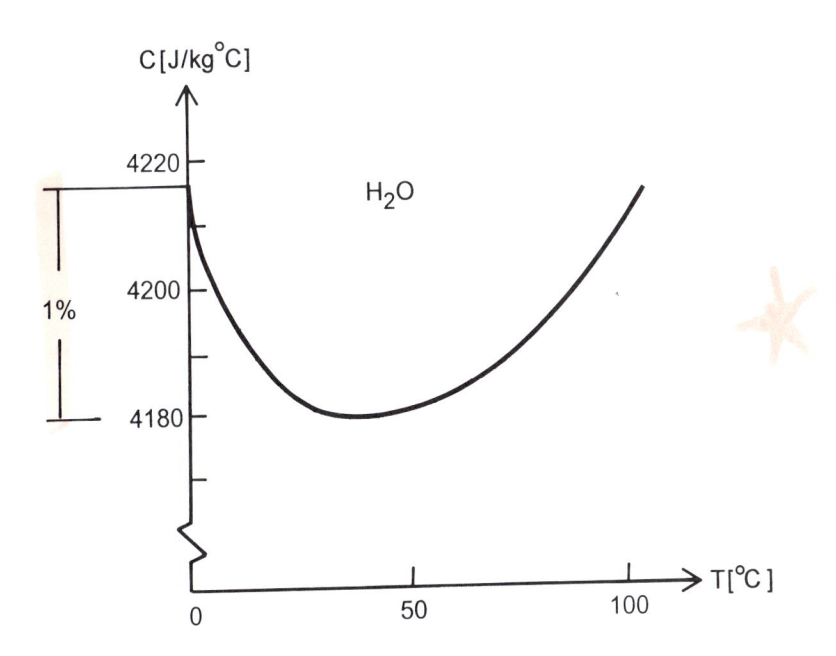

Fig. 5.33: The specific heat capacity for water between 0°C and 100°C. The variation in this temperature interval corresponds to about 1 % of the absolute amount.

However, treating c as dependent only on the material is a simplification as illustrated in Fig. 5.33. The figure shows that the heat capacity for water is not strictly constant but varies by about 1% between the melting point and the boiling point. We neglect this minor variation in the further discussion.

For many applications, Eq. (43) is rewritten to replace the mass of the liquid by the amount of material in unit [mol]. For this step we define the number of moles as $n = m/M$, where m is the mass of the material and M is its molar mass. This leads to:

$$Q = C \cdot n \cdot \Delta T \qquad (44)$$

with C the *molar heat capacity*, which is a material constant with unit [J/(mol °C)].

According to Eqs. (43) and (44) the exchange of energy can occur in both directions: heat can flow into or out of a system, in the same fashion as a system can do work on a piston or the piston can do work on the system. Thus we need to adhere to a strict sign convention for both work and heat. Any amount of heat flowing into the system or any work done on the system are positive as they increase the internal energy. The opposite processes are negative as they lead to a reduction of the internal energy. When checking a calculation, always identify yourself with the system; whatever you receive is positive, whatever you give away is negative.

We emphasize once more the difference between heat and thermal energy. Temperature detectors are not needed by ectotherms as their body temperature adjusts to the environmental temperature. While ectotherms usually not measure the thermal energy in their body, some ectotherms are able to measure heat arriving from the environment. They do this for a different purpose: vipers, such as the rattlesnake, possess a heat detector between their eyes and nostrils to allow these night hunters to find their endothermic prey without visual contact.

5.7.4. Equivalence of mechanical and thermal energy

Now we examine Joule's second experiment in Fig. 5.32(b). The idea of the experiment is that the object on the left falls, moving the stirrer through the water. The water resists the motion of the stirrer. As the stirrer is forced through the water the water is heated. The experiment, however, cannot be done as shown since we want to study the conversion of the potential energy into thermal energy, not into kinetic energy. Thus we must ensure that the object falls with a constant speed, which does not alter its kinetic energy. This would require large stirrer blades in a large beaker of water because the force with which the water resists the spinning of the blades is proportional to the stirrer blade surface area. A large beaker, however, means a large amount of water and consequently a too small temperature increase of the water due to the mass dependence in Eq. (43). Thus, Joule did the experiment differently, using his brewery horses to move the stirrer steadily for a longer time, and calibrating the work of the horses independently. Fig. 5.32(b) is, therefore, not a real experiment but a conceptual sketch to illustrate the principle.

Experiments such as the one sketched in Fig. 5.32(b) show that thermal energy and mechanical energy are equivalent. In Joule's case, the lost gravitational potential energy ΔE_{pot} is quantitatively converted into thermal energy $\Delta E_{thermal}$:

$$-m_{block}\, g \Delta y = c_{H_2O}\, m_{H_2O}\, \Delta T$$
$$\Rightarrow \quad \Delta E_{pot} + \Delta E_{thermal} = 0 \quad (45)$$

Example 5.9

(a) Calculate the work that an object with m = 400 g can do as a result of falling a distance of 3 m.
(b) Assume that the object falls into 10 liters of water in an isolated beaker. If the entire kinetic energy of the object is converted into thermal energy at impact, by how much does the water temperature rise?
Hint: For the specific heat of water use the value at 0°C from Fig. 5.33.

Solution part (a): By dropping the object 3 m the potential energy of the object has been reduced by:

$$\Delta E_{pot} = mg\left(h_{final} - h_{initial}\right) =$$
$$= 0.4[kg]\, 9.8[m/s^2]\, (-3.0[m]) = -11.8\ J \quad (46)$$

Solution part (b): When the object is released and falls toward the Earth, it is converting potential energy into kinetic energy. When the object is then stopped at a certain height it must convert the kinetic energy into another form of energy. If the entire kinetic energy is converted into thermal energy, then Eq. (45) predicts $\Delta E_{thermal} = +11.8$ J. This value is positive since the released potential energy is added as thermal energy to the system water. We use Eq. (43) to determine the associated change in the water temperature, ΔT:

$$\Delta E_{thermal} = c_{H_2O}\, m_{H_2O}\, \Delta T$$
$$\Rightarrow \quad \Delta T = \frac{\Delta E_{thermal}}{\rho_{H_2O}\, V_{H_2O}\, c_{H_2O}} \quad (47)$$

in which ρ_{H2O} is the density of water: $\rho_{H2O} = 1.0$ g/cm³. The value $c_{H2O} = 4.22$ kJ/(°C kg) in the denominator is taken from Fig. 5.33. This leads to:

$$\Delta T = \frac{11.8\ [J]}{1.0\left[\frac{kg}{l}\right]\, 10[l]\, 4.22\left[\frac{kJ}{°C\ kg}\right]} \quad (48)$$

$$\Rightarrow \quad \Delta T = 2.8 \times 10^{-4}\ °C$$

We find only a negligible temperature change of the temperature!

Joule's experiment in Fig. 5.32(b) can be interpreted in two ways: (I) we consider the falling object, the stirrer, the beaker and the water together as an isolated system, or (II) we consider the water in the beaker as the system and the stirrer and the falling object as the environment. We use the above discussion of Fig. 5.32(b) in each case to confirm the earlier observation that the total energy of an isolated superstructure is conserved, and that energy can only be converted between different energy forms or flow between the system and the environment.

A first view of Fig. 5.32(b)
We first consider all components in the figure as the system. In this case Eq. (45) states that energy conservation applies also when non–mechanical energies, such as thermal energy, are involved. In 1874, Hermann von Helmholtz generalized this finding and formulated the first law of thermodynamics for an isolated system:

> *Conservation of energy:*
> *The sum of all energy forms*
> *in an isolated system is constant*

The sum of all energy forms in the system is called the internal energy of the system. It is usually labelled U. Thus, the energy conservation is written in equation form:

$$\Delta U_{isolated\ system} = 0 \qquad (49)$$

This is a law since it predicts the outcome of future experiments. It even correctly predicts the outcome of experiments that Helmholtz could not have imagined in 1874, such as Enrico Fermi's 1942 nuclear fission experiment which led to the development of the nuclear power technology. The first law of thermodynamics is not limited to mechanical systems and therefore surpasses the range of applicability of Newton's laws.

A second view of Fig. 5.32(b)
Now we consider only the water as the system. That means that the term on the left hand side of the first formula in Eq. (45) is read as a work term because it represents energy which flows into the system. We combine this observation with Fig. 5.32(a) in which heat is flowing into the system. In both cases the energy flowing into the system leads to the same change in internal energy. This allows us to formulate the first law of thermodynamics for a closed system:

> *The sum of all energy forms in a closed system*
> *changes by the amount of heat and work which*
> *flow between the system and the environment.*

This is written in equation form:

$$\Delta U_{closed\ system} = Q + W \qquad (50)$$

In Eq. (50) neither the order in which the exchange of energy with the environment occurs nor the form (heat or work) of the exchange matter for the change of the internal energy as the system goes from an initial to a final state. A system property that does not depend on the detailed history of the system, but only on the current state of the system is called a *variable of the state*. Thus, the internal energy is a variable of the state of the system, like temperature, pressure and volume. The change of a variable of state is zero for any sequence of processes which return the system to its original state. Such processes are called cyclic processes and will be discussed in detail in the next chapter.

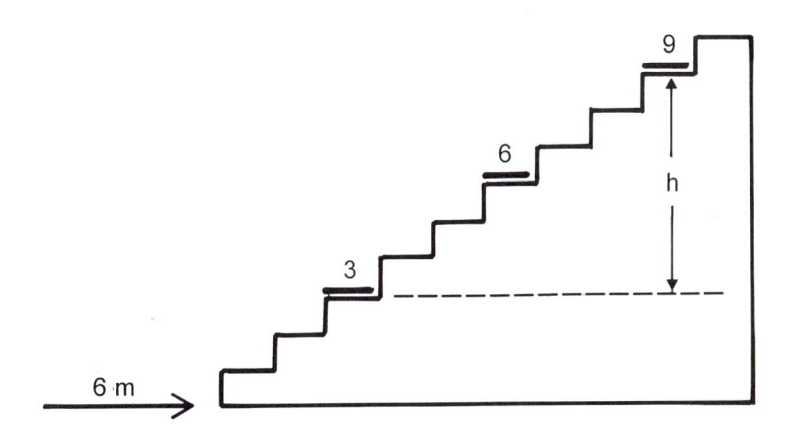

Fig. 5.34: Standard ergometer test as discussed in Example 5.10. The person must run 6 meters towards a staircase and then move upwards at least 10 stairs. Contact mats on the third, sixth and ninth stair record the motion. The height difference between the 3rd and the 9th step is h = 1.05 m.

Fig. 5.35: Bicycle ergometer used in sport physiology and for Exercise ECGs. The set–up allows for continuous stationary recording of the person's vital parameters. The attending physician can vary the resistance R of the frictional belt slowing the front flywheel.

Example 5.10

A 60 kg person performs the standard ergometric test illustrated in Fig. 5.34. The test consists of a 6 meter horizontal run followed by running upwards the staircase by at least nine steps. For our calculations we focus only on the second part of the test in which the person moves upwards by h = 1.05 meters from the third to the ninth step. For this part of the test the person requires an amount of 0.72 kcal of stored (food) energy. How much heat must the body of the person dissipate due to this part of the ergometric test?

Supplementary physiological information. The step–test in Fig. 5.34 is usually supplemented by contact mats on every third step to allow a measure of the time the patient needs to complete the test. It was considered the standard ergometric test until stationary devices such as bicycle ergometers or the treadmill came into use. A stationary bicycle ergometer is shown in Fig. 5.35. It is for example applied for *Exercise ECGs* as several vital parameters are measured on the patient during the test. To test athletes for fitness, the front wheel of the bicycle is slowed with a belt at variable resistance (R). Coaches use measurements of oxygen consumption, pulse frequency and lactose levels in the blood of the athlete to predict performance in track and field events.

Solution: The problem is solved using the conservation of energy for the person moving between the initial position on the third step and the final position on the ninth step. Treating the person as an isolated system in this experiment, the formula for the conservation of energy (Eq. (49)) can be written in the form:

$$\sum_i E_i = const = \qquad (51)$$
$$= E_{pot} + E_{kin} + E_{therm} + E_{chem}$$

The food energy is labelled E_{chem} in Eq. (51). The kinetic energy in the equation can be neglected when assuming that the person's speed between the third and ninth step does not change. For the other three forms of energy we use Eq. (51) in the form:

$$E_{pot,\,init} + E_{therm,\,init} + E_{chem,\,init} = \qquad (52)$$
$$= E_{pot,\,fin} + E_{therm,\,fin} + E_{chem,\,fin}$$

which can be rewritten as:

$$\Delta E_{pot} + \Delta E_{therm} + \Delta E_{chem} = 0 \qquad (53)$$

In Eq. (53) each term represents the difference between the final and initial amount of energy in the system. The thermal energy difference, ΔE_{therm}, is sought in the problem, the other two terms in Eq. (53) are:

$$\Delta E_{pot} = mg(h_{fin} - h_{init}) =$$
$$= 60[kg]\,9.8\left[\frac{m}{s^2}\right]1.05[m] = +620\ J \qquad (54)$$

$$\Delta E_{chem} = -720\ cal = -3010\ J$$

× 4.18 (conversion to J)

136

The potential energy difference is positive because the final potential energy is higher than the initial potential energy of the body. The food energy is negative because the body stores this amount less at the end of the test. Substituting these values in Eq. (53) yields:

$$\Delta E_{therm} = 3010[J] - 620[J] = +2390\ J \quad (55)$$

(handwritten: $\Delta E_{pot} + \Delta E_{therm} + \Delta E_{chem} = 0$; $620 + x + (-3010) = 2390\ J$)

The thermal energy released in the process is almost equal to 2.4 kJ. This thermal energy must be dissipated by the body in the form of heat as it would otherwise contribute to a permanent temperature increase of the body which cannot be tolerated.

5.8. Appendix: a second look at work and an overview of kinematics

Work in cases where the force and the displacement are not collinear

We start once more with Eq. (7). From vector algebra we know that the simplest mathematical way to obtain a scalar from two vectors is the dot product:

$$W \equiv \mathbf{F} \cdot \Delta\mathbf{s} \quad (56)$$

This formula therefore replaces Eq. (8) when we want to treat the force and the displacement as vectors, which we must do in cases when the displacement occurs in another direction than the force acting on the object.

Mathematically, Eq. (56) simplifies to Eq. (8) if the force and the displacement are parallel. The positive sign in Eq. (8) applies if **F** and Δ**s** are parallel and the negative sign applies if the force and the displacement are anti–parallel. When there is an angle other than 0° or 180° between the direction of the force and the direction of the displacement the angle θ between the force and the displacement has to be included. Based on the definition of the dot product in the General Appendix we find:

$$W = |\mathbf{F}|\ |\Delta\mathbf{s}|\ \cos\theta \quad (57)$$

Note that this equation states that W = 0 when the force and the displacement are perpendicular to each other. As an example, you do no work on an object when you carry it across the room at a constant velocity. In this case your external force on the object acts upwards and the displacement is perpendicular to that direction. Note that no force is exerted in the direction of the displacement because there is no acceleration.

For applications it is also useful to note the component–wise representation of Eq. (56). For a two dimensional problem in the xy–plane Eq. (56) is written in the form:

$$W = F_x\ \Delta s_x + F_y\ \Delta s_y \quad (58)$$

Example 5.11

Fig. 5.36 shows an object on an inclined plane which forms a 20° angle with the horizontal. An external force **F** of magnitude 10 N is applied to the object. The force **F** acts in a direction which forms a 60° angle with the horizontal. As a result of the force **F** the object moves a distance of 1 m along the inclined plane. What work was done by the source of force **F**?

Solution: We must first determine the angle between the displacement and the force as this angle enters Eq. (57). This angle θ is obtained from the data given in the problem text: θ = 60° − 20° = 40°. Now the given data can be entered in Eq. (57):

$$W = F\ \Delta s\ \cos\theta = 10[N]\ 1[m]\ \cos 40°$$
$$W = +7.7\ J \quad (59)$$

The result in Eq. (59) is consistent with the sign convention as the source of the external force is doing work on the object shown in Fig. 5.36.

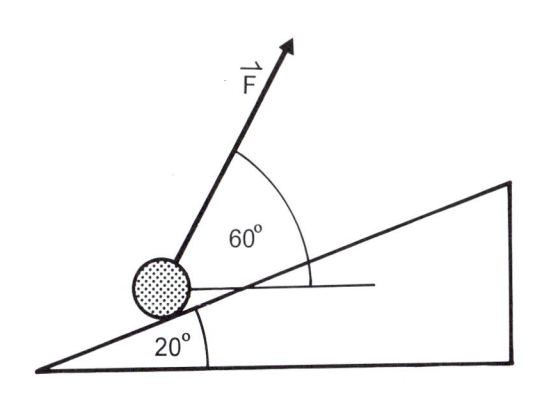

Fig. 5.36: An object is pulled with a force **F** of given magnitude in a direction forming a 60° angle with the horizontal. As a result, the object is pulled a given distance along the underlying surface which forms a 20° angle with the horizontal.

Kinematic relations

In kinematics we describe the motion of objects using the variables position, x (or in three dimensions **r**), the velocity, **v**, the acceleration, **a**, and the time, t. These kinematic relations are useful in the derivation of two equations used in the text: Eq. (23) for the definition of kinetic energy and Eq. (37) for the derivation of the conservation of energy. This appendix is provided to illustrate how the kinematic relations are obtained.

We limit our discussion to the kinematic relations which can be derived for systems with a constant acceleration. Although this is a restrictive assumption, it does include the most important cases such as the acceleration due to gravity where the acceleration is a = g, with g the gravitational acceleration constant of 9.8 m/s². We also limit the discussion to one–dimensional motion along the x–axis to avoid vector algebra.

We start with the equation for the average acceleration. This equation is obtained from Eqs. (2.7) and (2.9):

$$a_{avg} = \frac{v_f - v_i}{t_f - t_i} \quad (60)$$

For $t_i = 0$ this leads to:

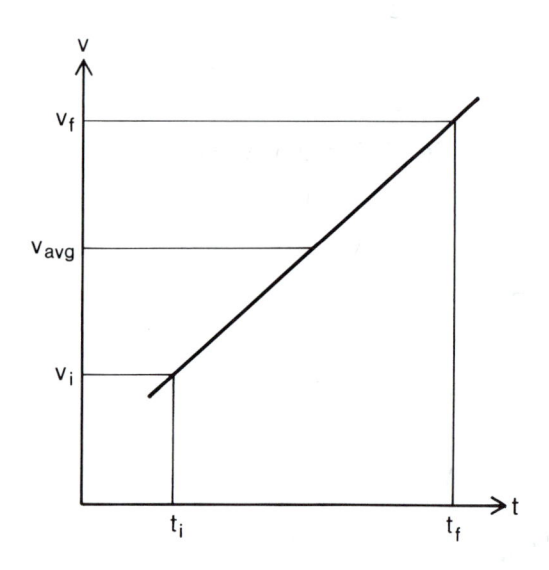

$$v = v_i + a \cdot t \quad (61)$$

Fig. 5.37: An object moves with constant acceleration. The acceleration is defined as the rate of change of the velocity with time. Therefore, the velocity changes linearly with time from an initial value v_i to a final value v_f. v_{avg} is the average speed for the time interval from initial time t_i to final time t_f.

in which we dropped the index "avg" for the acceleration because the average acceleration and the instantaneous acceleration are the same when the acceleration is constant. To obtain Eq. (61) we used $t_i = 0$ for the initial time and allow the final time and velocity to vary. For this we dropped the index f in Eq. (60). Eq. (61) is the first of three fundamental kinematic equations; it connects the speed, the acceleration and the time.

We note that the velocity depends linearly on the time in Eq. (61) as shown in Fig. 5.37. Thus, we write the average velocity in two ways: (I) as the geometric average velocity of the moving object between the initial and final time instant in Fig. 5.37:

$$v_{avg} = \frac{v_i + v_f}{2} \quad (62)$$

and (II) using Eq. (2.2) for the average velocity:

$$v_{avg} = \frac{x_f - x_i}{t_f - t_i} \quad (63)$$

Eqs. (62) and (63) are combined and the initial time is again set zero, $t_i = 0$:

$$x_f - x_i = \frac{t_f}{2}(v_f + v_i) \quad (64)$$

Now the index *f* for "final" is dropped as Eq. (64) applies for any final instant. Eq. (61) is combined with Eq. (64) to obtain the position as a function of time and acceleration:

$$x - x_i = \frac{t}{2}(2v_i + at) \quad (65)$$

which leads to:

$$x = x_i + v_i t + \frac{1}{2}at^2 \quad (66)$$

Eq. (66) is the second kinematic equation frequently used; it connects the position, the acceleration and the time.

The first kinematic equation (Eq. (61)) and the second kinematic equation (Eq. (66)) can be combined to eliminate the variable time. This is useful when we are interested in the path of an object as opposed to the timing of the motion. To obtain this third kinematic equation, first the time variable *t* is isolated in Eq. (61):

$$t = \frac{v - v_i}{a} \quad (67)$$

Next Eq. (67) is substituted into Eq. (66):

$$x = x_i + v_i \frac{v - v_i}{a} + \frac{1}{2} a \left(\frac{v - v_i}{a} \right)^2 \quad (68)$$

which leads to the third kinematic equation:

$$v^2 = v_i^2 + 2a(x - x_i) \quad (69)$$

The term $x - x_i$ represents the displacement between the initial position (index i) and a variable final position of the object, $x - x_i = \Delta s$. Eq. (56) can be written with the acceleration as the independent variable, which is the form of this third kinetic equation we used twice in the text (in Eq. (23) and Eq. (37)):

$$a = \frac{v_{final}^2 - v_{initial}^2}{2 \Delta s} \quad (70)$$

5.9. Problems

P–5.1
Fig. 5.25(b) shows in double–logarithmic representation the nerve pulse rate (we use the variable P for the pulse rate) as a function of the speed of an approaching object for a Meissner's corpuscle. Using the power law relation $P = a v^b$, determine the constants a and b.

P–5.2
Fig. 5.38 shows the height h [mm] versus mass m [kg] (solid lines) and the active metabolic rate E [kcal/day] versus height (dashed line) for growing children. Determine the three exponents b in
(a) $h = a_1 m^{b1}$ for m < 25 kg (curve I),
(b) $h = a_2 m^{b2}$ for m > 25 kg (curve II), and
(c) $E = a_3 m^{b3}$ for m < 40 kg (curve III).
The energy conversion is 1 cal = 4.19 J.
For those interested:
(d) Find pictures of children and adults and compare the body proportions to see what causes the differences in the exponents.

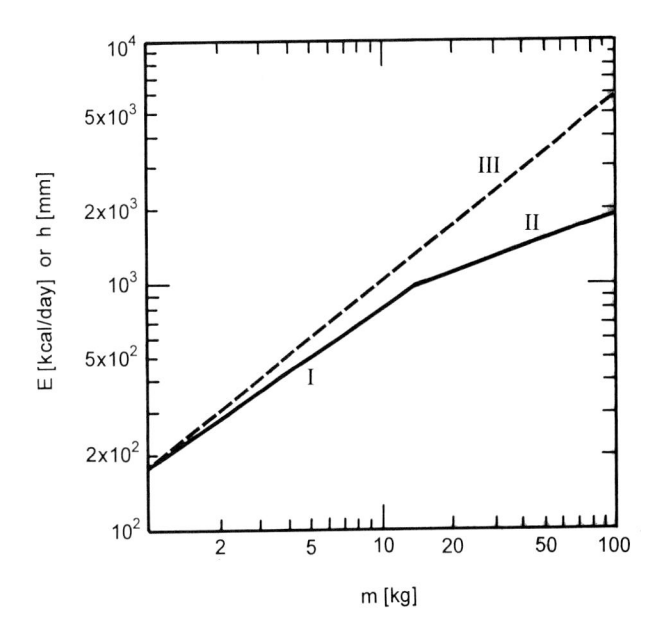

Fig. 5.38 for problem P–5.2.

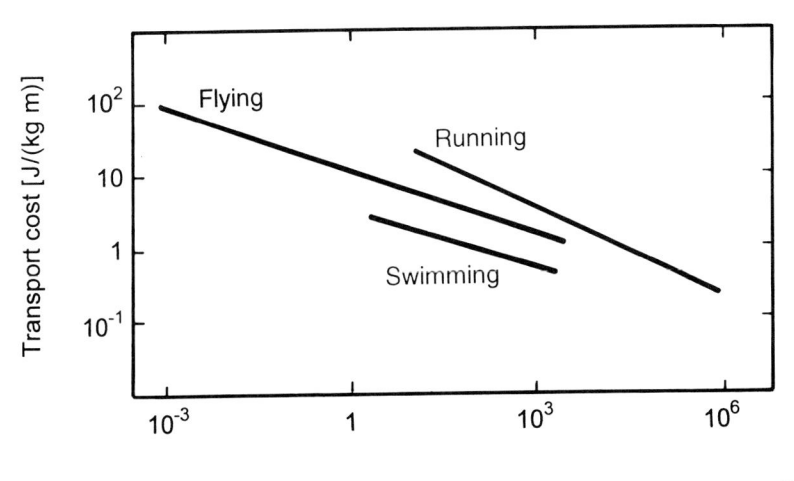

Fig. 5.39 for problem P–5.3.

P–5.3

In the mid–Cretaceous (110 to 100 million years ago) dinosaurs lived near the poles, e.g. at 80°N with fossils in North Alaska and the Yukon and at 80°S with fossils near Melbourne, Australia. The polar regions of the Cretaceous were densely forested with only occasional light freezes in the winter, but non–hibernating ectotherms cannot tolerate prolonged periods without sunlight. Indeed, the most northern fossil find of a large ectotherm is a giant crocodile (phobosuchids) at 55°N. Fig. 5.39 illustrates the energy consumption in [J/(kg m)] for animals specialized for swimming, flying and running as their normal mode of locomotion. The energy cost for long–distance migration across land is given as:

$$E_{mig}\left[\frac{J}{m}\right] = 14\,(m\,[kg])^{3/4} \qquad (71)$$

(a) Using Eqs. (2) and (71) evaluate the hypothesis that ectothermic southern polar dinosaurs migrated annually between 80°S and 55°S latitudes for
(I) Leaellynasaura, which was a 10 kg herbivore,
(II) Dwarf Allosaur, which was a 500 kg carnivore, and
(III) Muttaburrasaurus, which was a 4 tonne herbivore.
(b) Using the energy consumption for running in Fig. 5.39 and Eq. (36) for the potential energy, compare the benefits of living in plains versus mountainous terrain for small and large endotherms.

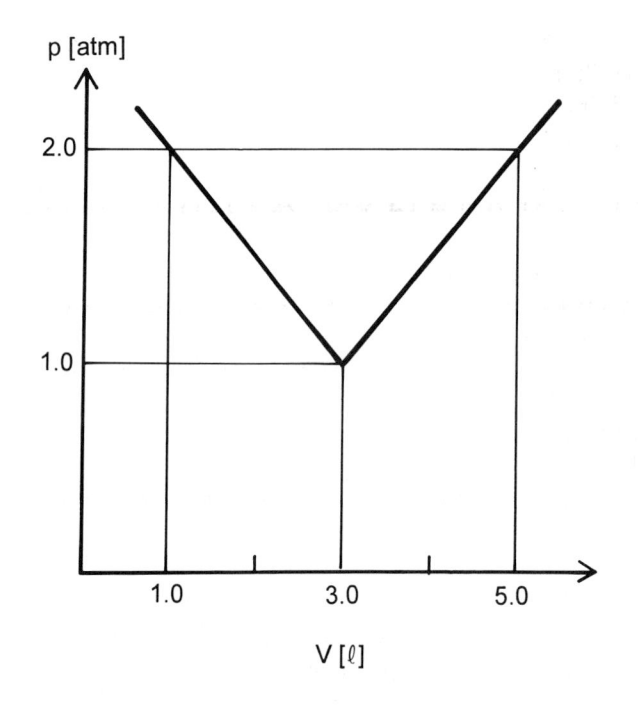

Fig. 5.40 for problem P–5.4.

P–5.4

A gas expands from a volume of 1.0 liter to a volume of 5.0 liters as shown in the pV–diagram of Fig. 5.40. How much work does the gas on the piston?

P–5.5

A massless string runs around two massless, frictionless pulleys, as shown in Fig. 5.41. An object with mass m = 15 kg hangs from one pulley. A force **F** is exerted on the free end of the string.
(a) What is the magnitude of the force **F** if the object is lifted at a constant speed?
(b) To lift the object by 2.5 m, how far must the free end of the string be pulled?
(c) During the lift in part (b), what is the work done on the object by the force **F** via the string?
Hint: Use the lower pulley and the attached object as the system.

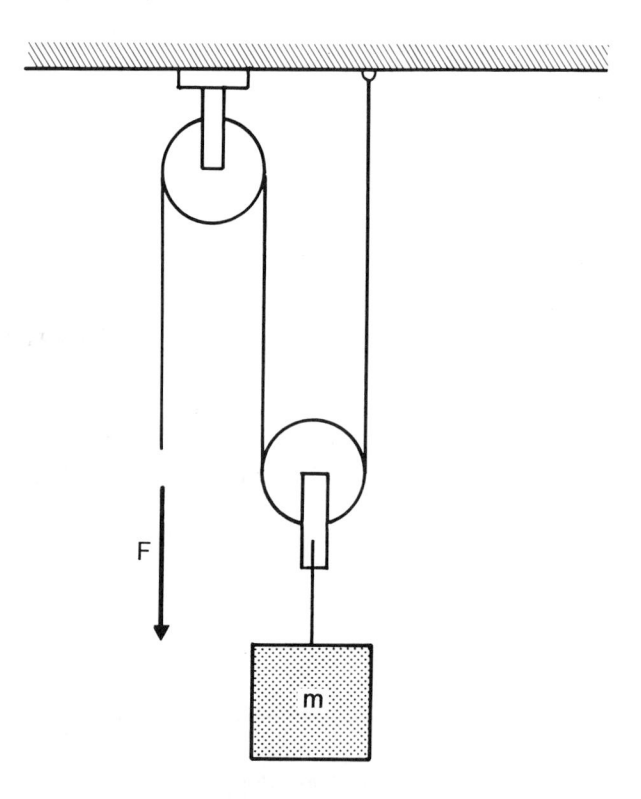

Fig. 5.41 for problem P–5.5.

P–5.6

When people run, they dissipate about 0.6 J of mechanical energy per step and per kilogram of body mass. If a certain person of 70 kg body mass dissipates 80 J of energy per second while running, how fast is the person running? Assume that the steps taken are 1.6 m long.

P–5.7

Two objects are connected by a massless string as shown in Fig. 5.42. The pulley is massless and rotates without friction. The object of smaller mass m = 1.2 kg slides without friction on an inclined plane which makes an angle of θ = 35° with the horizontal. The mass of the larger object is M = 2.5 kg and hangs on the string. If the two objects are released from rest with the string taut, what is their total kinetic energy when the object of mass M has fallen 30 cm?

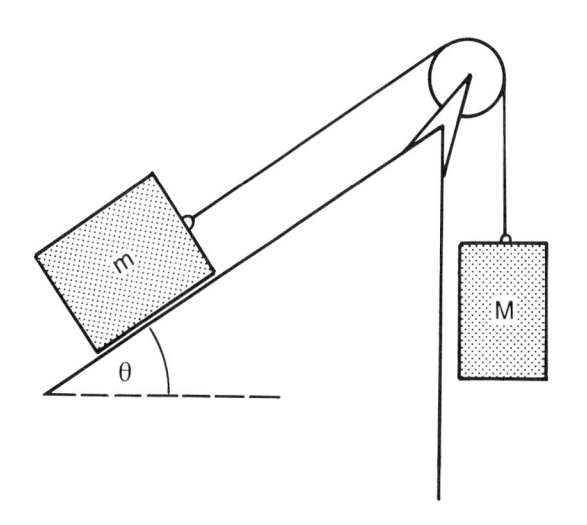

Fig. 5.42 for problem P–5.7.

P–5.8
Three objects with masses $m_1 = 5.0$ kg, $m_2 = 10.0$ kg and $m_3 = 15.0$ kg, are attached by massless strings over two frictionless pulleys, as shown in Fig. 5.43. The horizontal surface is frictionless and the system is released from rest. Using energy concepts, find the speed of m_3 after it has moved down 0.4 m.

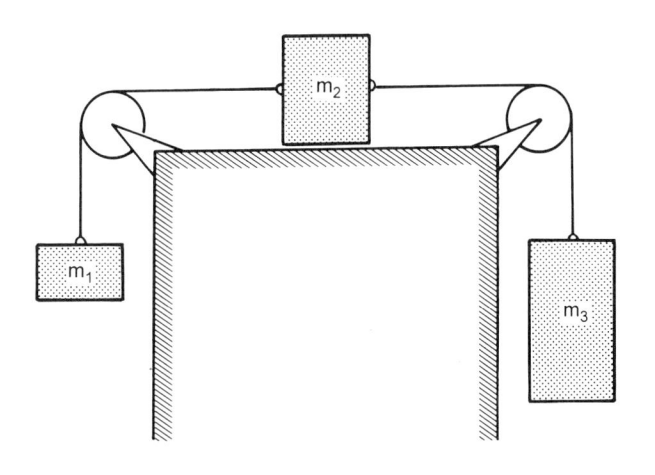

Fig. 5.43 for problem P–5.8.

P–5.9
A pendulum consists of an object of mass m = 1.5 kg swinging on a massless string of length l = 3.0 m. The object has a speed of 2.0 m/s when it passes through its lowest point.
(a) If the gravitational potential energy is taken to be zero at the lowest point of the trajectory of the object, what is the total mechanical energy of the system?
(b) What is the speed of the object when the string is at 75° below the horizontal?
(c) What is the greatest angle with the vertical that the string reaches during the motion of the object?

P–5.10
Table 5.6 shows the metabolic rate for given activities of the adult human body and Table 5.7 gives the energy content of the three most important components of food. Answer the following two questions using the two tables:
(a) how much energy is expended by a person of mass of 75 kg who walks for one hour every morning?
(b) If the body of the person consumes body fat reserves to produce this energy, how much mass will be lost per day? Use 1 cal = 4.19 J.

Table 5.6 for problem P–5.10

Activity	Metabolic rate [cal/s kg]
Sleeping	0.263
Sitting	0.358
Standing	0.621
Walking	1.0
Biking	1.81
Swimming	2.63
Running	4.3

Table 5.7 for problem P–5.10

Food	Energy content [cal/g]
Carbohydrate	4100
Protein	4200
Fat	9300

P–5.11
A person of body mass 50 kg climbs 10 m up a vertical rope. How much energy in calories is dissipated as heat in a single climb if 20 % of the total energy required is used to do the work?

P–5.12
Assume that Joule's brewery horses did each 750 J of work per second (this corresponds roughly to the definition of horse power). If he had 4 horses moving in a circle for one hour to operate a stirrer in a well isolated container filled with 1 m³ water at initial temperature of 25°C, to what final value did the water temperature rise? Use Fig. 5.33 for the specific heat of water at 25°C.

Summary

Definitions:
- Isolated system: no exchange between system and environment.
- Closed system: no exchange of matter between system and environment, only exchange of work and/or heat.
- Open system: exchange of matter included.
- Pressure:

$$p = \frac{F_\perp}{A} \quad \left[\frac{N}{m^2}\right]$$

where $F_\perp$ is the force acting perpendicular to the area A.
- Work W
(i) for point mass with the displacement Δs:

$$W = \pm F \Delta s$$

(ii) for a gas in a container:

$$W = -p \Delta V$$

- Heat Q
(i) for a liquid or solid system of m [kg]:

$$Q = c \, m \, \Delta T$$

in which c [J/(kg K)] is the specific heat capacity.

(ii) for a liquid or solid system of n [mol]:

$$Q = C \, n \, \Delta T$$

in which C [J/(mol K)] is the molar heat capacity.
- Energy E of a system in equilibrium:
For any type of energy except thermal energy:

$$\Delta E = E_{final} - E_{initial} = W$$

For thermal energy:

$$\Delta E_{thermal} = E_{therm,\, fin} - E_{therm,\, init} = Q$$

Examples of various forms of energy:
- Kinetic energy: $E_{kin} = \frac{1}{2}mv^2$
- Gravitational potential energy: $E_{pot} = mgh$
in which h is the height of the object relative to a pre-chosen height $h = 0$.

Units:
Work W, heat Q, energy E: [J] = [N m] = [kg m²/s²]
Temperature: T [K]
Pressure: p [Pa] = [N/m²]

Laws:
- Conservation of energy in a mechanical system:

$$E_{kin} + E_{pot} = const$$

- The internal energy U is the total energy of a system. First law of thermodynamics for an isolated system (conservation of energy):

$$\Delta U_{isolated} = U_{final} - U_{initial} = 0$$

- First law of thermodynamics for a closed system:

$$\Delta U_{closed} = U_{final} - U_{initial} = W + Q$$

Chapter VI

Respiration

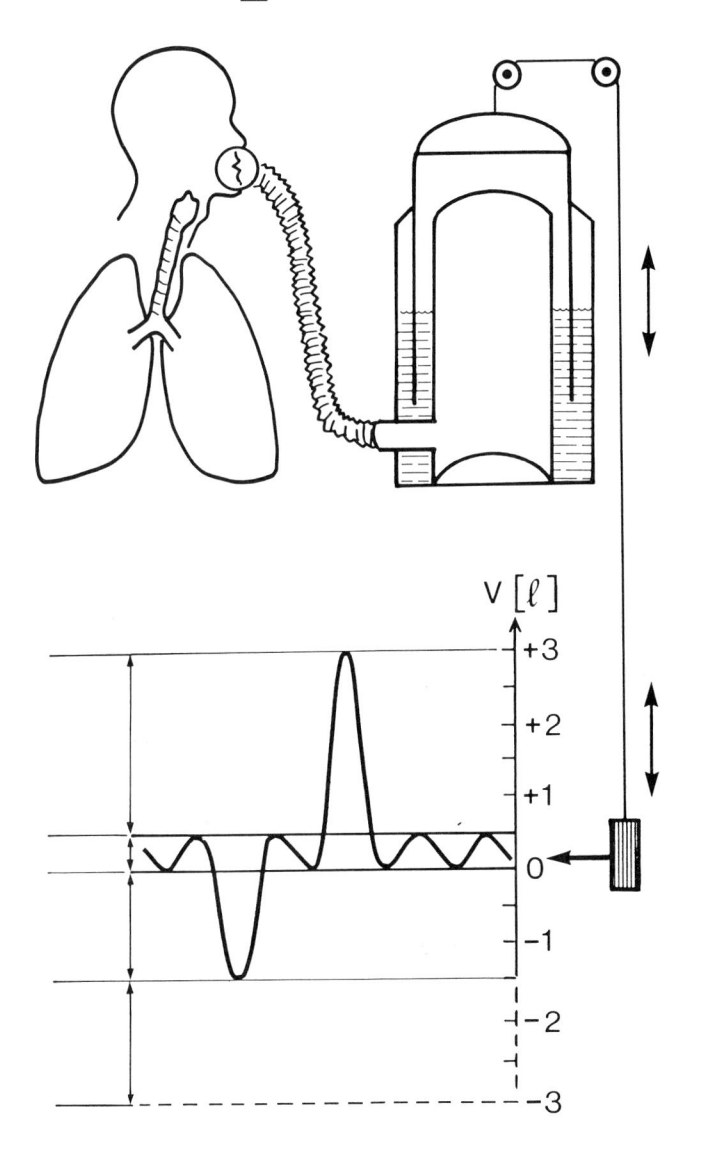

The properties of gases

RESPIRATION
THE PROPERTIES OF GASES

A systematic study of thermodynamics requires a model system with well-defined but simple relations between its basic parameters. The ideal gas is introduced as such a model system. Experimental observations by Boyle and Charles reveal that its pressure is inversely proportional to its volume at constant temperature ($p \propto 1/V$), and that its volume is directly proportional to its temperature at constant pressure ($V \propto T$). The combination of these observations yields the relation pV/T = constant for the possible states of the gas. In this formula the constant term on the right hand side depends only on the number of moles of the ideal gas.

The ideal gas is further characterized microscopically by a mechanical model, called the kinetic gas theory. In this model the gas is represented by a large number of point masses which collide elastically with the container walls and each other. The combination of the experimental and microscopic models leads to the internal energy of the ideal gas: it depends linearly on temperature, but is independent of the volume and pressure of the gas. The ideal gas law allows us to identify four fundamental thermodynamic processes: the isochoric process (processes at constant volume), the isothermal process (processes at constant temperature), the isobaric process (processes at constant pressure) and the adiabatic process (processes which do not allow for exchange of heat between the system and the environment). From these four processes all practical processes of interest can be derived, including the important cyclic processes in respiration and blood circulation. The cyclic Carnot process is introduced because it leads in Chapter 8 to the definition of entropy and the formulation of the second law of thermodynamics.

The discussion in the previous chapter allowed us to relate work, heat and internal energy to each other for an isolated or a closed system. However, our formulations of the conservation of energy and the first law of thermodynamics in Eqs. (5.4) and (5.5) remained very general because we did not identify a specific system for our studies. In the current chapter we introduce the ideal gas as such a system. Using the ideal gas we then develop the basic thermodynamics concepts of interest.

6.1. Dynamic breathing

All cells in the human body obtain most of their energy from internal chemical processes requiring oxygen. Sufficient amounts of oxygen for these metabolic processes must be provided to the cell from the ambient atmosphere in a timely fashion. Passive diffusive transport from the skin surface would only suffice to a depth of about 100 µm, i.e., for the outmost layers of cells. This supply problem has been solved in animals with a four-step respiratory system: oxygen reaches the lungs within 1 – 2 seconds as part of the inhaled air. From the lungs it passes in less than a second to the red blood cells in the blood stream. The cardiovascular system carries the oxygen in 30 seconds or less to the various organs. In each organ, O_2 is distributed in the capillary bed to the cell tissue. It diffuses out of the capillary to its final destination in the cells in again less than one second.

To understand this four-step process quantitatively requires a large number of physical concepts. We divide its discussion into several chapters: in the current chapter the air exchange between the ambient atmosphere and the lungs is described. The various chemical components are not distinguished in that discussion. We focus on the oxygen component in the air in the next chapter when we discuss diffusion processes, which describe the transfer of molecules e.g. across the membrane between lungs and blood capillaries. The role of the physiologically active components of air, oxygen, nitrogen and carbon-dioxide, is presented in Chapter 12. The concepts of blood flow in the cardiovascular system are developed in Chapter 11.

6.1.1 Volume of the lungs

The *spirometer* is the instrument allowing us to measure the gas volume in the lungs. This instrument is shown schematically in Fig. 6.1. The person breathes through a mouthpiece and a pipe into the instrument, which measures volume changes in the lungs in the form of an elevation of a sealed inverted jar.

The spirometer allows us to identify several breathing patterns. During regular breathing a person inhales and exhales about 0.5 liter. This volume is called the *tidal volume*. Based on 15 inhalations per minute a typical person exchanges 7.5 liter air per minute. We can breathe deeper, with an inspiratory reserve volume of 2.5 liter and an expiratory reserve volume of 1.5 liter. The two reserve volumes allow for a short–term, additional air exchange when a larger oxygen intake is required. Even after a deep exhalation the lungs are not empty. The remaining gas volume is called the residual volume and is about 1.5 liter. The residual volume cannot be measured with a spirometer, but must be determined indirectly by other methods. The most precise measurement is based on using an inert tracer gas, e.g. an air/helium mixture of known ratio of the gases. This method is illustrated in Example 6.1.

Combining the various volumes from Fig. 6.1 leads to a volume of 3.5 liters after inhalation and to 3.0 liters after exhalation for a standard man.

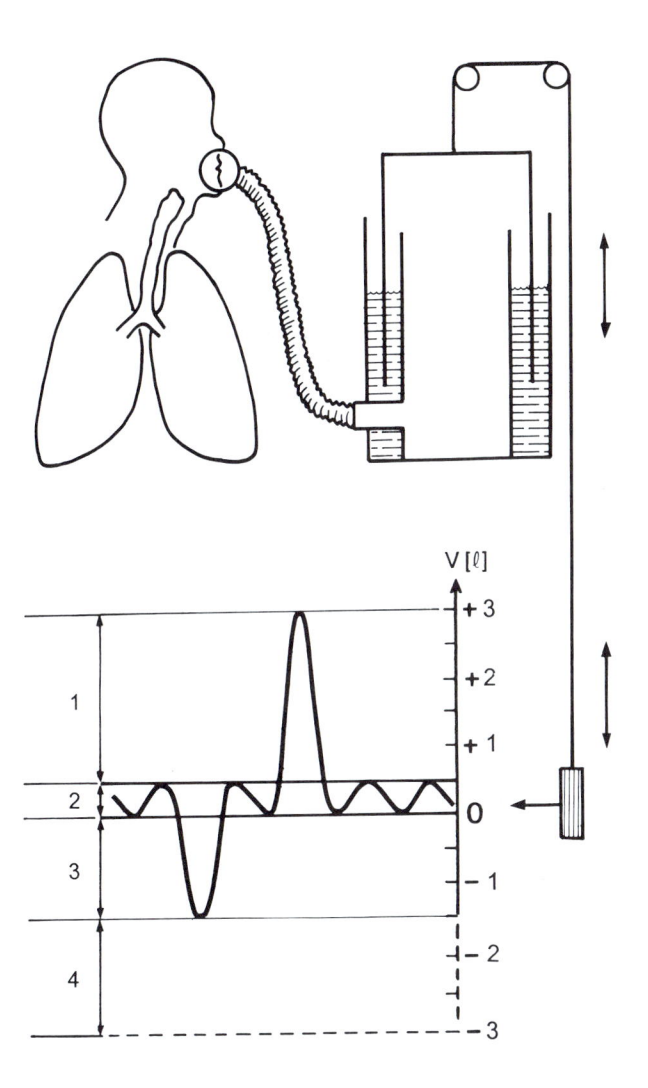

Fig. 6.1: Conceptual sketch of a spirometer and its typical data output. In the top part of the figure the instrument is illustrated. A spirometer consists of a fixed air volume into which the patient breathes through a mouthpiece. The top part of the container is a freely moving inverted cylinder jar. The open end of the jar is immersed in water to seal off the air in the instrument. The changing amount of air in the sealed volume causes the jar to move up and down. This vertical motion is recorded on a plotter. The measured data identify various contributions to the human lung volume: (1) the inspiratory reserve volume, (2) the tidal volume (regular breath volume) and (3) the expiratory reserve volume. These three volumes combined are called the vital capacity of the person. The instrument cannot measure the residual volume (4).

Example 6.1
A spirometer of volume $V_{spiro} = 5.0$ liter is filled with air at atmospheric pressure and room temperature. A fraction of $F_{initial} = 10$ vol% of that air has been replaced by helium gas. A standard man is connected to the spirometer via a mouthpiece. After a single inhalation and exhalation, a valve in the mouthpiece is closed and the gas mixture in the spirometer is analysed. The fraction of helium is found to be $F_{final} = 6.25$ vol%. Calculate V_{pulm} (the index *pulm* is an abbreviation for pulmonary, which means in the lungs).

Additional information: When reporting fractions of matter, we use either volume–percent (vol%) or weight–percent (wt%) values. Gas and liquid mixtures are usually given in vol%. A given component with 5 vol% represents 5 % of the total volume occupied by the system. Solid mixtures are often given in wt%, with 5 wt% referring to 5 % of the total mass of the system.

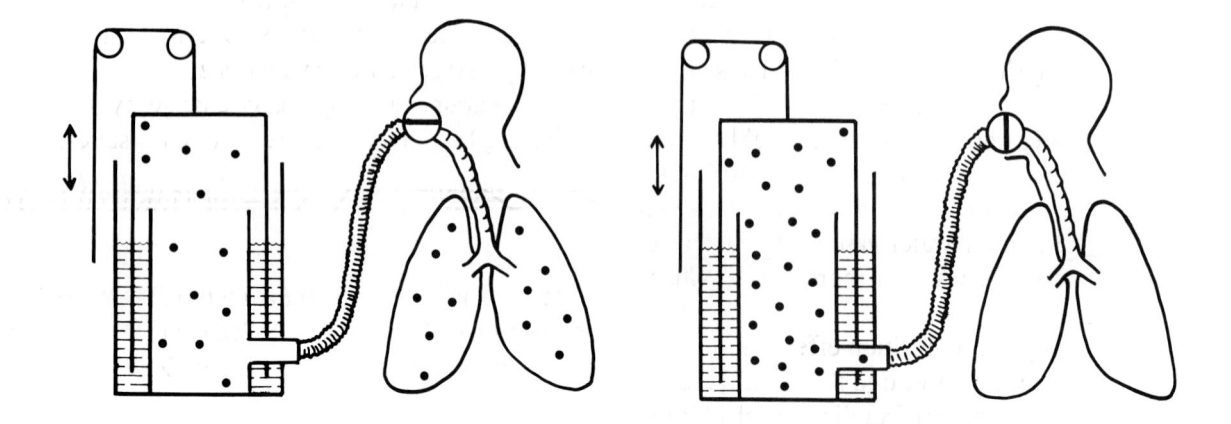

Fig. 6.2: Experimental procedure to determine the lung volume: a known air/helium mixture is filled into a spirometer at atmospheric pressure. The helium component is illustrated by dots in the gas space. The test person is asked to inhale and exhale once (step from left to right in the figure). This leads to a uniform distribution of helium in the combined space of lungs and spirometer. The fraction of helium in the spirometer after the respiratory cycle is a measure of the lung volume.

Solution: A homogeneous mixture of the gas in the spirometer and the air in the lungs is established after a completed breath, i.e., the helium gas is then diluted across the entire volume of the lungs and the spirometer. This is illustrated in Fig. 6.2. To quantify the lung volume, we calculate the total volume of helium gas contained in the combined volume before and after the breathing cycle. Before the standard man breathed, the helium is exclusively in the spirometer:

$$V_{He} = F_{init} V_{spiro} = 0.10 \cdot 0.5 \ [l] = 0.5 \ l \quad (1)$$

i.e., the part of the spirometer volume occupied by helium gas is 0.5 liters. After completing the breathing cycle, the same amount of helium is distributed in the combined volume with a uniform fraction F_{final}, i.e.,

$$V_{He} = F_{final}(V_{spiro} + V_{pulm}) \quad (2)$$

Since the total amount of helium has not changed during the experiment, we know that the right hand sides of Eqs. (1) and (2) must be equal:

$$F_{init} V_{spiro} = F_{final}(V_{spiro} + V_{pulm}) \quad (3)$$

which leads to:

$$V_{pulm} = V_{spiro}\left(\frac{F_{init}}{F_{final}} - 1\right) \quad (4)$$

Substituting the numerical values from the example text yields:

$$V_{pulm} = 5.0 \ [l]\left(\frac{0.10}{0.0625} - 1\right) = 3.0 \ l \quad (5)$$

The volume in the lungs is therefore 3.0 liters before inhalation.

Is it indeed that simple? Not quite. Before we accept the result, the assumptions we made must be evaluated. There are two issues in particular to be addressed: the unknown initial pressure and temperature of the gas in the lungs, and the changes in chemical composition of the exhaled air.

We discuss the unknown pressure and temperature in the lungs first. If either one of these parameters initially differs between the lungs and the spirometer, then we can expect that their final values lie somewhere between the initial values. If that is the case and the volume of a gas is related to its pressure and temperature, i.e., V = f(p,T), then we need to apply correction factors for an accurate value of V_{pulm}. The relation V = f(p, T) for a gas is developed in the current chapter for this reason.

In the particular case of Example 6.1, the pressure values initially in the lungs and in the spirometer turn out to be the same; however, the temperature is different (core body temperature in the lungs, room temperature in the spirometer). Thus, a correction of the result has indeed to take place. We introduce this type of correction in Example 6.3(a).

Second, we consider the compositional changes to the inhaled air during the breathing cycle. The two major changes taking place are the exchange of some oxygen for carbon–dioxide and a water vapor saturation of the incoming air in the nasal cavity and the trachea. The O_2/CO_2 exchange has only negligible effects on the pressure of the gas as shown in Example 6.3(b), but the saturation with water vapor adds more notably to the absolute pressure of the gas, with a pressure contribution of 2.3 kPa for water vapor saturated air at 20 °C, and a contribution of 6.3 kPa for water vapor saturated air at 37°C. These effects are discussed in more detail in Chapter 12.

We neglect gas composition effects in the current chapter; however, it is useful to note that there are three different reference states of air distinguished in the physiological literature:
(1) BTPS = body temperature pressure saturated. For this reference state the gas temperature is 37°C, the absolute pressure of the gas is 1.013×10^5 Pa (= 1.0 atm), and the partial pressure of water vapor is 6.3 kPa,
(2) ATPS = ambient temperature pressure saturated. This means that the gas temperature is the temperature in the spirometer, the absolute pressure of the gas is 1.013×10^5 Pa (= 1 atm), and the partial pressure of water vapor is the saturation pressure of water vapor at the temperature of the spirometer; and
(3) STPD = standard temperature pressure dry. In this reference state the gas temperature is 0°C, the absolute pressure of the gas is 1.013×10^5 Pa (= 1 atm), and the partial pressure of water vapor is zero.

Parameters may easily change by 10 % when switching between these three reference states.

A second, more cumbersome method to determine the total volume of the lungs is called the plethysmographic technique and is discussed in Example 6.4.

6.1.2 Pressure in the lungs

The discussion in section 6.1.1 indicates that the gas pressure is an important parameter that must be measured in physiological studies of the respiratory system. A more detailed look at the anatomy of the human chest indicates that we need indeed two pressure measurements. As illustrated in Fig. 6.3, each lung (1) is surrounded by a double–layered membrane called the *pleura* (2). The layer in contact with the lungs is called the

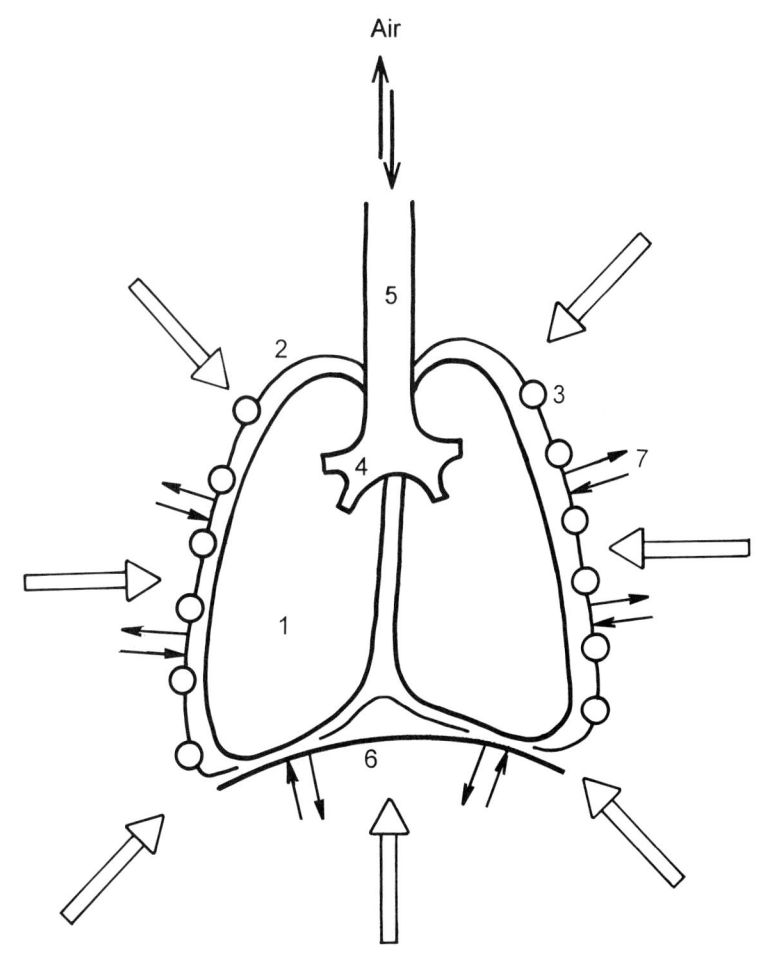

Fig. 6.3: Sketch of the human thorax/lung system, showing the two lungs (1), the double–layered membrane enclosing the lungs (pleura, (2)), the rib cage (3), the trachea (5) which branches into the primary bronchi (4), the diaphragm and the abdominal muscle (6) and the intercostal muscles (arrows indicate their action, 7).

visceral layer, and the outer layer is the *parietal layer*, which is attached to the inside of the rib cage (3). A small amount of fluid in the pleura allows frictionless movements of the lungs against the rib cage and prevents the harder ribs from puncturing the soft lung tissue. The pleura completely envelopes the lungs, except for the entrance of blood vessels and the bronchus (primary bronchial branches (4) of the trachea (5)).

Active breathing is achieved by several sets of muscles acting on the parietal layer: the *diaphragm* (6) is a muscular layer which separates the chest cavity from the abdominal cavity. It is attached at the back to the spine, to the lower ribs along the side of the chest, and to the sternum at the front. The diapragm pulls the lungs downwards during inhalation and pushes them upwards during exhalation. Muscles located between neighboring ribs open the chest upwards and sideways during inhalation and contract the rib cage during exhalation. These muscles are called *intercostal muscles* (7); their antagonistic action is described in Problem P–4.11.

Thus, we need to record the following two pressures during respiration:

(i) The pressure inside the lungs, p_L. It is obtained from a pressure gauge in the spirometer tube on the mouth-side of a valve which allows to disconnect the test person from the spirometer.

(ii) The pressure in the pleura, i.e., specifically the pressure in the gap between the visceral and parietal layers of the pleura, p_G (subscript G for gap). This pressure can be estimated with a non-intrusive pressure gauge lowered into the lower one-third of the esophagus, which is the muscular passage from the pharynx to the stomach.

With volume and pressure measured and applying the gas laws we will develop in the current chapter, the respiratory processes in the lungs can be understood. A brief overview of the key observations will guide us through the development of the basic physics concepts.

We saw in the previous chapter that work and energy are key parameters in characterizing a physical or a biological system. When gases are involved, the work is determined from a p–V diagram of the process. Thus, representing respiration in a p–V diagram is the first step toward a quantitative description. Since the respiratory

Fig. 6.4: p–V diagram of the respiratory system at rest with relaxed breathing muscles. The three curves show the alveolar pressure p_a (the dashed curve), the pleural pressure p_{pl} (dash-dotted curve), and the transmural pressure difference between the lungs and the thorax (labelled $p_a - p_{pl}$, solid line). The transmural pressure difference is positive for all lung volumes V, holding the lungs open. The pressure in the lungs exceeds atmospheric pressure for all volumes above 3.0 liters (large open dot, lung volume at rest). The pressure in the pleural gap exceeds atmospheric pressure for lung volumes above 4.5 liters. The horizontal short-dashed line indicates the consequences of a punctured lung: the lungs and the pleural gap collapse toward the small open dots: the lungs shrink to a volume of about 0.5 liters (at which the transmural pressure becomes zero) and the pleural gap widens toward the thorax (to a volume corresponding to a lung volume of 4.5 liters).

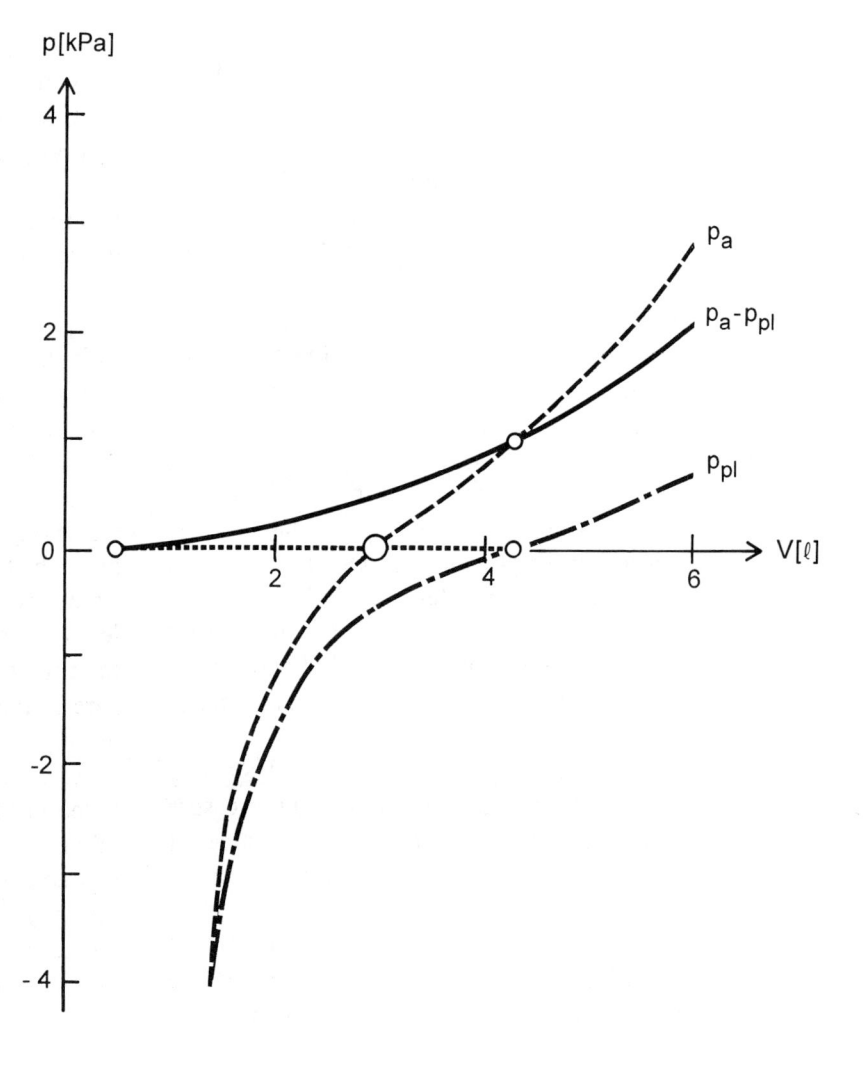

system is more complex than a simple piston–sealed container, this is not quite as straight forward as it sounds. We noted above already that there are two relevant pressure measurements. Also, there are several different ways in which the experiment can be conducted. This leads to a number of possible p–V diagrams for respiration. Of these, the most important p–V diagrams are shown in Figs. 6.4, 6.5 and 6.6. Each of these diagrams shows three pressure measurements:
(I) The curve labelled p_a represents the gauge pressure inside the lungs (index a for alveolar),
(II) the curve labelled p_{pl} represents the gauge pressure in the pleura (index pl for pleural), and
(III) the curve labelled $p_a - p_{pl}$ represents the pressure difference between lungs and pleura, called the transmural pressure.

Note that both pressures p_a and p_{pl} are given as gauge pressures, i.e., as pressure values relative to the atmospheric pressure. When labelling the absolute pressure in the lungs p_L and the absolute pressure in the gap between the visceral and the parietal layers of the pleura p_G, we write:

$$p_{pl} = p_G - p_{atm}$$
$$p_a = p_L - p_{atm}$$
(6)

While absolute pressures are always positive, gauge pressure values can be positive or negative. For example, the alveolar pressure is negative for lung volumes smaller than 3.0 liters in Fig. 6.4. This means that the pressure inside the lungs is less than the atmospheric pressure for small lung volumes under the conditions under which the data in Fig. 6.4 were recorded.

The p–V diagram in Fig. 6.4
This diagram represents the respiratory system at rest. The three curves were obtained as follows: the test person inhales a certain amount of air from the spirometer. Then the valve to the spirometer is closed and the test person relaxes his/her respiratory muscles. The pressure gauge on the mouthpiece allows us to record the alveolar pressure p_a because the test person's epiglottis remains open.

The respiratory equilibrium is defined at a lung volume of 3.0 liters because the alveolar gauge pressure is zero at that lung capacity. Nothing would happen if the test person removed the mouthpiece of the spirometer at this stage.

When the test person inhales a large amount of air (to a lung volume larger than 4.5 liters) then both the alveolar pressure and the pleural pressure become positive, the latter because the lungs press the pleura against the rib cage from inside. In turn, both the alveolar and the pleural pressures are negative when the test person exhales to a lung volume below three liters. The transmural pressure difference between the lungs and the pleura remains positive under all conditions because otherwise the lungs would collapse like a balloon from which the air escapes. The curves in Fig. 6.4 are drawn between lung capacities of 1.5 liters and 6.0 liters, representing the maximum range of volume values accessible in breathing (compare with Fig. 6.1).

The p–V diagram in Fig. 6.5
This diagram represents the respiratory system with infinitesimally slow breathing, i.e., a case where the flow resistance in the air passage ways is negligible. Note that this diagram covers only the volume range from 3.0 to 4.0 liters as the assumption of such slow breathing does not allow a test person to reach larger or smaller lung volumes. We note that this p–V diagram looks distinctively different from the one in Fig. 6.4: the alveolar pressure is given at all lung volumes as zero. This is true because the test person breathes with open air passage ways, i.e., with the lungs open to the external air pressure. The curve for the transmural pressure difference, labelled $p_a - p_{pl}$, is the same as in Fig. 6.4, indicating that the volume of the lungs and this pressure difference are independent of the type of breathing. Consequently, the pleural pressure varies in Fig. 6.5 in the opposite way than in Fig. 6.4: p_{pl} decreases with lung volume for slow breathing, while it increases with lung volume when the thorax is at rest and the respiratory muscles are relaxed.

The p–V diagram in Fig. 6.6
This diagram represents the dynamic breathing we do continuously. The three pressure curves are based on Fig. 6.5, except that the alveolar and pleural pressures are modified between 3.0 liters (exhaled) and 3.5 liters (inhaled). In regular breathing, air is inhaled and exhaled fast enough that a flow resistance in the air passage ways has to be taken into account. This viscous flow of air in a tube is discussed in Chapter 11. In that chapter we will learn that a pressure difference along the tube is needed to achieve gas flow through the trachea. Thus, the pressure in the lungs is smaller than atmospheric pressure during inhalation ($p_a < 0$), and it is larger than atmospheric pressure during exhalation ($p_a > 0$). This is illustrated in Fig. 6.7 for the alveolar pressure as a function of time for a complete breathing cycle. Dynamic breathing requires excess pressures of up to 100 Pa. Note that the dynamic part does again not affect the transmural pressure difference in Fig. 6.6 as both, alveolar and pleural pressure are modified in the same fashion.

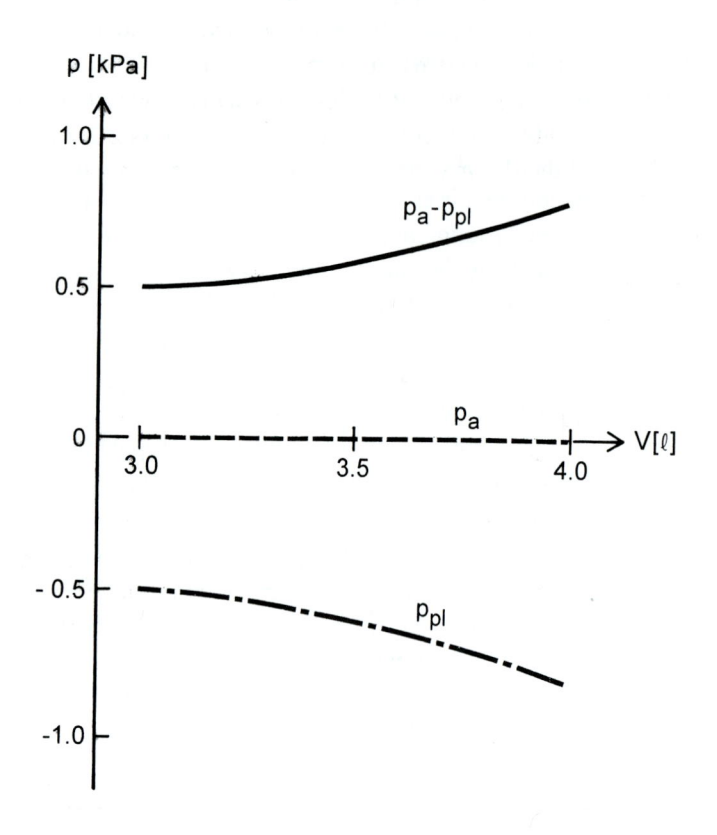

Fig. 6.5: p–V diagram for a person breathing very slowly, i.e., without air flow resistance in the airways. The figure shows the same three pressure curves as Fig. 6.4 for the volume range from 3.0 to 4.0 liters. The pressure in the lungs (dashed curve) remains at atmospheric pressure because the test person's mouth is open and provides an open passage between the lungs and the outside air throughout the breathing cycle. The transmural pressure difference (solid curve) has the same values as in Fig. 6.4 because it is only a function of the lung volume and does not depend on the details of the breathing process. Thus, the pleural pressure is negative across the regular breathing range (dash–dotted curve).

Fig. 6.6: p–V diagram for a person breathing regularly. Two of the pressure curves in Fig. 6.5 are modified between 3.0 and 3.5 liters (tidal volume) in this case: the pressure in the lungs is larger than atmospheric pressure during exhalation (upper dashed curve with arrow to the left) and it is smaller than atmospheric pressure during inhalation (lower dashed curve with arrow to the right). These pressure variations are needed to push or pull the air through the airways. The same changes occur for the pleural pressure (dash–dotted lines). The transmural pressure difference (thin solid line at the top, labelled in the figure as $p_a - p_{pl}$, is not affected because the transmural pressure difference depends only on the lung volume.

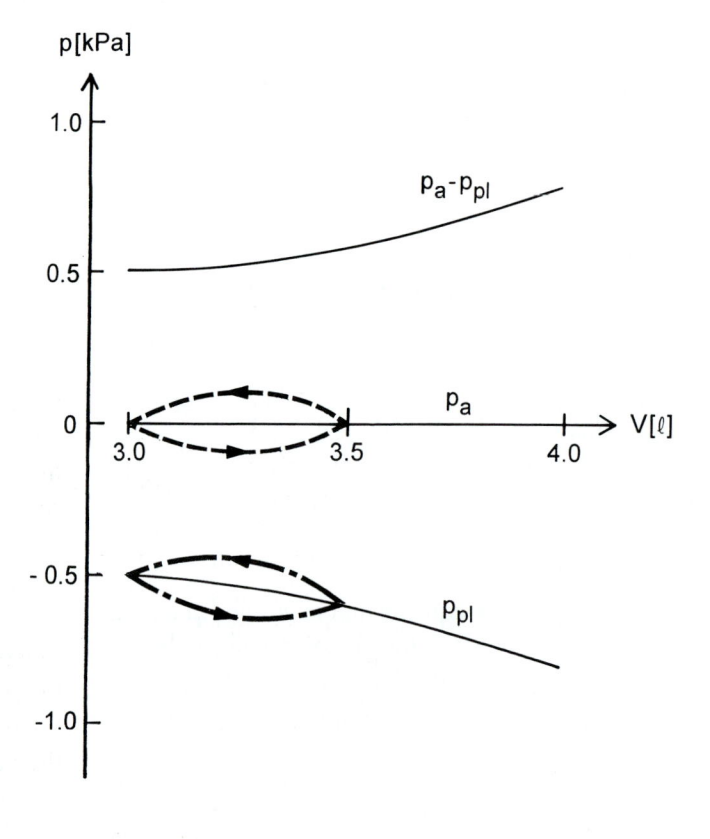

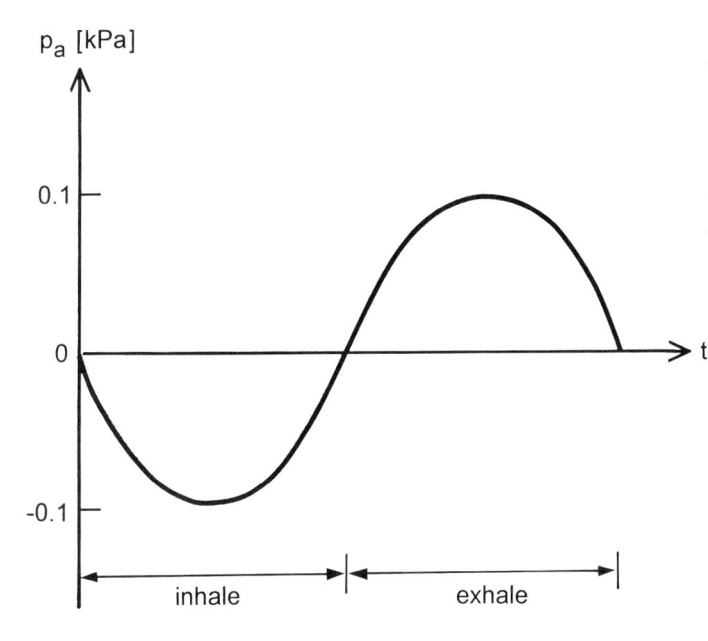

Fig. 6.7: The alveolar pressure p_a as a function of time. The pressure in the lungs drops to 100 Pa below atmospheric pressure during inhalation, and exceeds the atmospheric pressure by up to 100 Pa during exhalation. These pressure variation allow the air to flow through the airways against the flow resistance.

How do we interpret Figs. 6.4, 6.5 and 6.6? Can we determine the work required for respiration from these figures? What role does the gas in the lungs play, or, more precisely, how do the physical parameters of the inhaled air influence the physiological processes? To answer these questions the system *gas* is introduced first.

6.2. The empirical gas laws

We introduce the ideal gas as the model system of thermal physics since it will turn out to be simple, but still sufficient to describe all the important features. We will see that the versatility of this model stems from the fact that both a macroscopic and a microscopic approach to the ideal gas exist. The macroscopic model is empirical because it is based on experimental observations; it is discussed first. The microscopic model is an extension of the mechanical concepts we developed in Chapter 2 and will be introduced in section 6.3.

We base the empirical gas model on two key experiments, the first one done by Robert Boyle in 1664 and the second one done by Jacques Alexandre Charles in 1787. The interpretation of the results of these two experiments leads to a quantitative formulation of the ideal gas law in section 6.2.3. Studying Boyle's and Charles' experiments in detail illustrates how the properties of gases are developed from an analogy to mechanical systems, but also how the experimental findings reach beyond mechanics. This will allow us to move beyond the concepts developed in Chapters 2 to 4 and link to the thermal physics concepts from Chapter 5.

6.2.1. Boyle's law

Boyle's experiment is illustrated in Fig. 6.8. In the top frame, a U–shaped glass tube is filled with mercury. The liquid metal reaches a mechanical equilibrium when its surfaces no longer move up or down. This mechanical equilibrium is indicated by a free–body–diagram for the mercury surface in the left column: the normal force due to the mercury beneath the surface pushes the surface up and the weight of the air column above the metal pushes the surface down. In equilibrium, the mercury surfaces in both glass tubes are at the same height because the same air pressure, p_{atm}, acts on both surfaces.

In the next step, shown in the middle frame of Fig. 6.8, the left glass tube is sealed. Since this step as such does not change the air pressure in the sealed volume, no other changes occur. Note that the sealed volume is now identified by the height of the air column above the mercury, $h_{init}(air)$.

Boyle then added mercury through the open column, as illustrated in the bottom frame of Fig. 6.8. He measured the excess height of mercury between the two columns, $h(Hg)$, and the height of the air in the sealed volume, $h_{final}(air)$. When mercury was added repeatedly, he noticed that these measurements are related as:

$$h_{final}(air) \propto \frac{1}{h(Hg)} \qquad (7)$$

In the analysis of Eq. (7) we want to replace $h_{final}(air)$ with the volume and $h(Hg)$ with the pressure of the sealed air. $h_{final}(air)$ is related to the volume of air in the sealed space, $V(air)$, by multiplying with the cross–sectional area A of the glass tube:

$$V(air) = h_{final}(air) \cdot A \qquad (8)$$

The excess height of the mercury in the bottom frame of the figure is related to the pressure of the sealed air. This relation is established by applying Newton's first law to the mercury surface in the left column. Newton's first law must apply because we observe no accelerations in the system. We identify three forces acting on this mercury surface:

(I) the weight of the excess mercury in the right column, W_{Hg}, pushes the mercury below in the right column downwards. Correspondingly, this force pushes the mercury in the horizontal part of the tube to the left, and pushes the mercury in the left column upwards. Thus, W_{Hg} is a force pushing the left mercury surface toward the sealed air at the top of the left column.

(II) The open air column above the right mercury surface pushes in the same fashion downwards as the excess mercury. It therefore contributes a second force pushing the left mercury surface upwards, $p_{atm}A$.

(III) Acting in the opposite direction on the mercury surface is the gas pressure in the sealed air volume. It exerts a force $p_{air}A$ downwards.

The relation of these three forces is written in the form:

$$p_{atm} A + |W_{Hg}| = p_{air} A \qquad (9)$$

The weight of the excess mercury is rewritten by replacing its mass with volume and density:

$$|W_{Hg}| = m_{Hg} g = \rho_{Hg} V_{Hg} g \qquad (10)$$

in which the mercury volume is $V_{Hg} = Ah(Hg)$. Thus, Eq. (9) yields:

$$p_{atm} A + \rho_{Hg} A h_{Hg} g = p_{air} A \qquad (11)$$

Dividing both sides of Eq. (11) by A leads to:

$$\rho_{Hg} h_{Hg} g + p_{atm} = p_{air} \qquad (12)$$

Eq. (12) shows that the pressure in the sealed air volume, p_{air}, is proportional to the height of the excess mercury column, $h(Hg)$. Note that $p_{air} \propto h(Hg)$ is correct because p_{atm} in Eq. (12) is constant. Thus, Boyle's experimental result leads to:

$$h_{final}(air) \propto \frac{1}{h(Hg)} \quad \Rightarrow \quad V(air) \propto \frac{1}{p_{air}} \qquad (13)$$

in which we drop the index *air* to write the general form of Boyle's law:

$$V \propto \frac{1}{p} \quad \Rightarrow \quad pV = const \qquad (14)$$

Eq. (14) states that the product of the pressure and the volume of a gas is constant. The product pV has a stan-

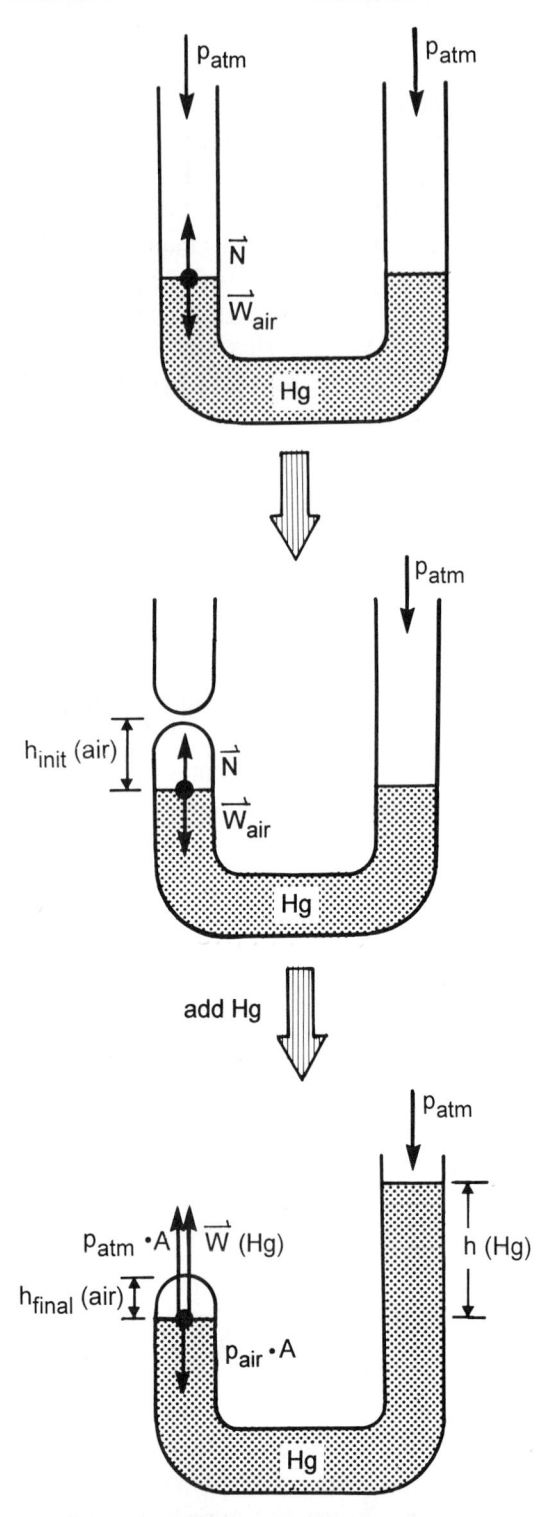

Fig. 6.8: Boyle's experiment. A U–shaped, hollow glass cylinder is filled with mercury and the left glass column is sealed. Adding mercury to the open column compresses the air in the sealed column. The free–body–diagram included at the left mercury surface of in the middle panel indicates a mechanical equilibrium. This free–body–diagram changes in the lower panel due to the addition of mercury through the right column. Three forces acting on the mercury surface are balanced: the weight of the excess mercury and the air pressure above the open column push the mercury surface upwards and the pressure of the sealed gas pushes the mercury surface downwards.

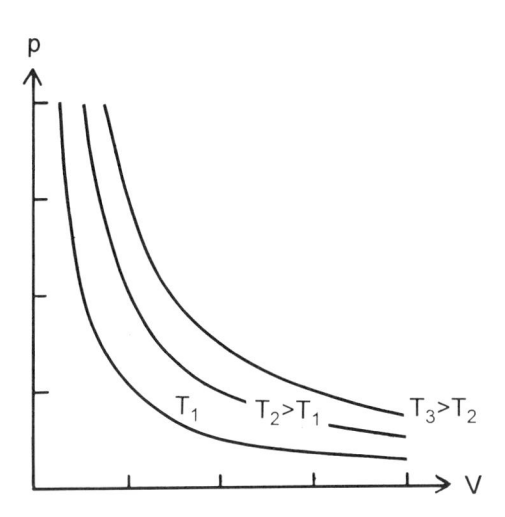

Fig. 6.9: Boyle's pressure versus volume data for three different temperatures. Note that Boyle's law does not lead to a linear relation between pressure and volume but to an inverse relation in the form p ∝ 1/V.

dard unit of [Pa m³]. In the physicochemical literature the equivalent unit of [kPa l] is often used for the product pV, in which [l] stands for liter. Boyle's law is often applied in a second form when we compare an initial and a final state of the gas:

$$p_{initial} \, V_{initial} = p_{final} \, V_{final} \qquad (15)$$

The dependence of the gas pressure on the gas volume in Boyle's law is shown in Fig. 6.9: Mathematically, Eq. (14) represents an inverse proportionality between pressure p and volume V. Note that the constant term on the right hand side of Eq. (14) is not a universal constant; it is only independent of the parameters p and V. In particular, a strong dependence on the temperature is observed. Thus, Boyle's law applies only to isothermal processes, i.e., processes during which the temperature does not change. This is illustrated in Fig. 6.9 by displaying three separate curves for temperatures T_1, T_2 and T_3, with the temperature increasing from T_1 to T_3.

6.2.2. Charles' law

We want to overcome the restriction to isothermal processes in Boyle's law to obtain a generally applicable law. Boyle could not do this, however, since Celsius invented the thermometer only 78 years after his studies. Charles was the first scientist to use a thermometer for studies of gases when he revisited Boyle's experiments in 1787. To investigate the temperature dependence of a gas, he modified the experiment as shown in Fig. 6.10.

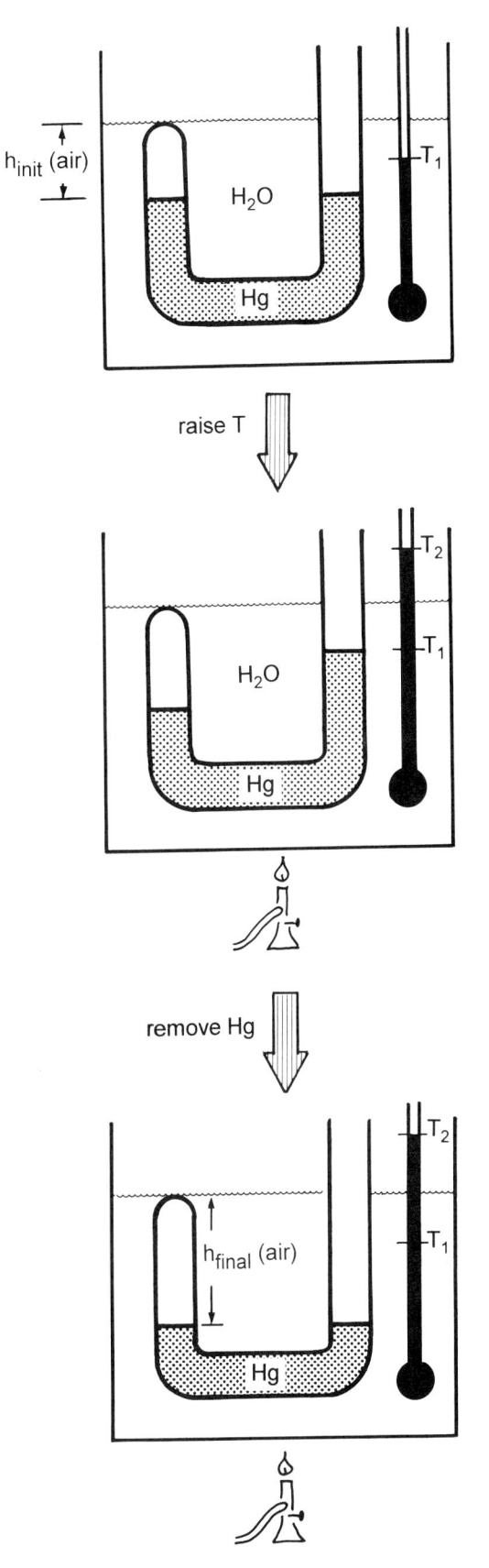

Fig. 6.10: Charles' experiment. A U–shaped, hollow glass cylinder is filled with mercury. The left column is sealed and the set–up is immersed in a bath at fixed temperature T_1. Heating the bath to a higher temperature T_2 causes the sealed air volume to increase. Mercury is then removed with a syringe to level out the two mercury columns.

After sealing an air volume of height h_{init}(air) in the same fashion Boyle had done, the glass tube with the mercury was immersed in water at an initial temperature T_1 (room temperature) as shown in the top frame of Fig. 6.10. Then the temperature of the entire set-up is raised to a temperature T_2 with $T_2 > T_1$ and held at that temperature as indicated in the middle frame of Fig. 6.10. It is observed that the volume of the sealed air increases, pushing some of the mercury to the right side column. In the last step, shown in the bottom frame of the figure, mercury is removed with a syringe until both mercury columns are levelled again. This means that the pressure of the confined air column at the left returns to its initial value since no excess mercury any longer causes a compression of the air at the left side. The final height of the air on the sealed side, h_{final}(air), is recorded. Charles found that h_{final}(air) $\propto$ T(air), in which T(air) is equal to the temperature of the water bath and everything in it: T(air) = T_2.

To interpret his results, Charles used Eq. (8) to convert the height h_{final}(air) in the bottom frame of Fig. 6.10 to the volume of air, V(air). Dropping again the index *air* we formulate his experimental results in the form:

$$h_{final}(air) \propto T(air) \quad \Rightarrow \quad V \propto T \quad (16)$$

That a gas expands as a result of a temperature increase can easily be demonstrated: use an empty plastic bottle and rinse it thoroughly from outside with boiling water. Then close the lid so that the bottle is airtight. Place the bottle in the refrigerator and let it cool down. It will crumble under the external air pressure as the cooling air inside requires less and less volume at air pressure.

Next we study a graphical representation of Charles' data in Fig. 6.11. In the experiment, Charles was able to vary the temperature between 0°C and 300°C by using an oil bath. Thus, we draw the results as solid lines between these two temperatures. The graph shows two experimental curves, one at atmospheric pressure, p_1 = 1 atm, and one at elevated pressure, using a fixed excess height of mercury in the right glass tube of Fig. 6.10. When we extrapolate the two curves in Fig. 6.11 towards lower temperatures (shown as the dashed lines in the figure) we find that the curves meet at a common point: T = -273.15°C and V = 0. In 1848, William Thomson Baron Kelvin of Largs (Lord Kelvin) concluded that there is a real physical meaning to this observation, which will be discussed further in section 6.3 when we study the microscopic approach to the ideal gas. Lord Kelvin also concluded that the temperature -273.15°C is the lowest possible temperature we can achieve in any experiment. This allows us to eliminate negative temperature values by introducing the Kelvin temperature scale. For this temperature scale we recalibrate the zero point from -273.15°C to 0 K:

$$T[K] = T[^0C] + 273.15 \quad (17)$$

The Kelvin scale is closely related to the Celsius scale since the difference between the melting and boiling temperatures of water is 100 degrees for both scales. The Kelvin scale has, however, a great advantage over the Celsius scale: all scientific laws which depend on the temperature can be written much more simply. This is illustrated here with Charles' law. If we quantify the experimental data of Fig. 6.11 for one of the given pressure values and with the temperature measured in degrees Celsius, we have to write:

$$V = V_0 + const \cdot T$$
$$\frac{V}{T + 273.15} = const \quad (18)$$

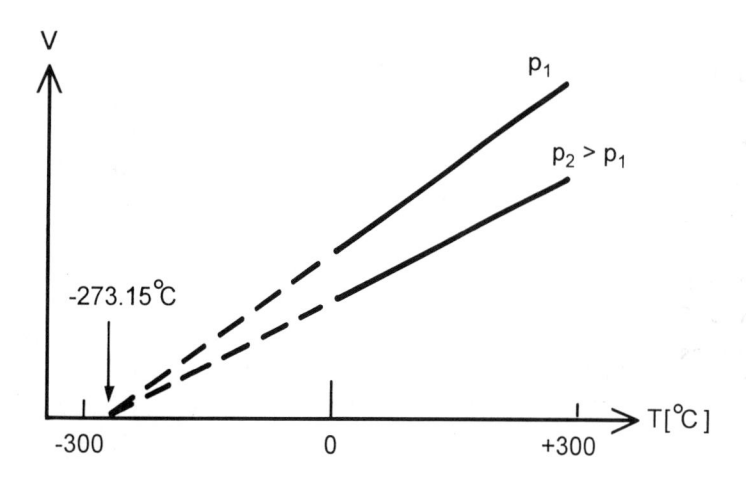

Fig. 6.11: Charles' volume versus temperature data for two different pressures (combination of air pressure and excess mercury pressure). The solid part of the lines indicates the temperature range experimentally accessible at Charles' time. The dashed part of the lines is a linear extrapolation of the experimental data.

in which the constant term V_0 requires an additional volume measurement at 0^0C. For the temperature measured in degree Kelvin, we find instead:

$$V = const \cdot T$$
$$\frac{V}{T} = const \quad (19)$$

Comparing Eqs. (18) and (19), it is obvious that the formulation in Eq. (19) is simpler and thus preferable. Eq. (19) states that the quotient of the volume and the temperature of a gas at a given pressure is constant. Charles' law is often applied in a second form to compare an initial and a final state of a gas:

$$\frac{V_{initial}}{T_{initial}} = \frac{V_{final}}{T_{final}} \quad (20)$$

From the existence of two curves with different slopes in Fig. 6.11 we conclude that the proportionality factor in Eq. (19) is not a universal constant, but varies with pressure. Thus, Charles' law applies only to experiments done at constant pressure. Such experiments are called isobaric experiments.

6.2.3. Formulation of the ideal gas law

In the next step, Charles' and Boyle's laws are combined to formulate the ideal gas law. We want to follow this step carefully for two reasons. First, we learn how two earlier, but more restricted laws are combined to yield a law which is much wider applicable. This is a common way in which new results emerge in the natural sciences. Secondly, the mathematical steps involved in the transition from Boyle's and Charles' laws to the ideal gas law illustrate nicely how we can deal with multivariable functions.

The derivation of the ideal gas law is illustrated in Fig. 6.12. We discuss this figure frame after frame. Fig. 6.12(a) shows the complete parameter space for a fixed amount of a gas: from Charles' and Boyle's experiments we know that the three parameters pressure p, volume V and temperature T are variable. If these three parameters were independent of each other, we would not need any further discussion: any value in a p–V–T diagram would describe an independent state of the gas. However, Boyle's and Charles' experiments showed already that p, V and T are not gas parameters we can choose independently. What we rather expect is a relation in the form

$$V = f(p, T) \quad or \quad p = f(V, T)$$
$$or \quad T = f(p, V) \quad (21)$$

Recall that the notation f(...) means "function of". Which of the three forms in Eq. (21) applies depends on the specific purpose for which a given system is studied; in the remained of this section we use V = f(p, T), i.e., the pressure and the temperature are independent variables and the volume is the dependent variable.

Mathematically, a function of two variables like V = f(p, T) represents a two–dimensional surface in a three–dimensional p–V–T diagram. To illustrate this point, we consider Figs. 6.12(a) and 6.12(b). In Fig. 6.12(a) we find a particular volume, V_i, after choosing the pressure and temperature parameters as p_i and T_i. This volume can for example be found experimentally by measuring for a given amount of a gas the volume once the desired pressure and temperature values are reached. Note that the subscript i indicates a particular state of the gas, which is characterized by the three parameters V_i, p_i, T_i. We choose this state later as the initial state for a process in which the state of the gas is changed. That change is then discussed with the later frames of Fig. 6.12.

The steps which led to identifying the state of the gas shown in Fig. 6.12(a) can be repeated for other combinations of pressure and temperature. In each case a point in the p–V–T diagram is found which shows the corresponding volume. Instead of showing all these systems as independent dots, we illustrate all these states in Fig. 6.12(b) as a two–dimensional surface. The points on this surface represent possible states for the gas; points which are not on the surface cannot be states of the gas. This surface is useful later when discussing a change of the gas: a process the gas undergoes must start at a possible state of the gas and reach a final possible state of the gas; it must further move through a sequence of possible intermediate states. Thus, a possible process must be represented by a line which lies fully in the surface we found in Fig. 6.12(b).

We do not necessarily expect a simple mathematical formula to describe the surface in Fig. 6.12(b). However, we already know two mathematical statements which must hold: Boyle's law in Eq. (14) for constant temperature, and Charles' law in Eq. (19) for constant pressure. Requiring a constant temperature means that we allow only states of the gas which lie on a vertical plane as illustrated in Fig. 6.12(c); requiring a constant pressure leads to the second plane shown in Fig. 6.12(c). Note that these two planes are perpendicular to each other in the p–V–T diagram.

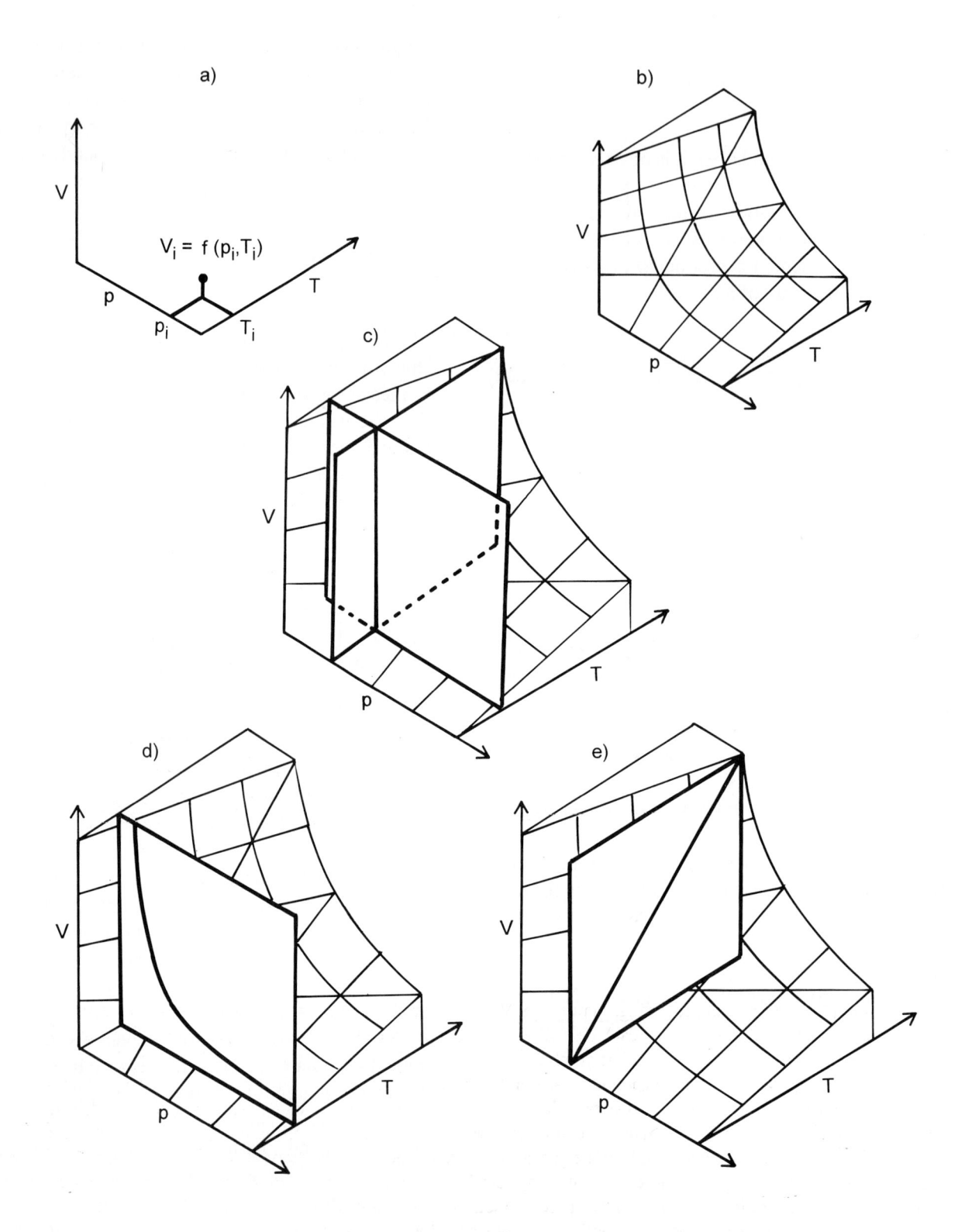

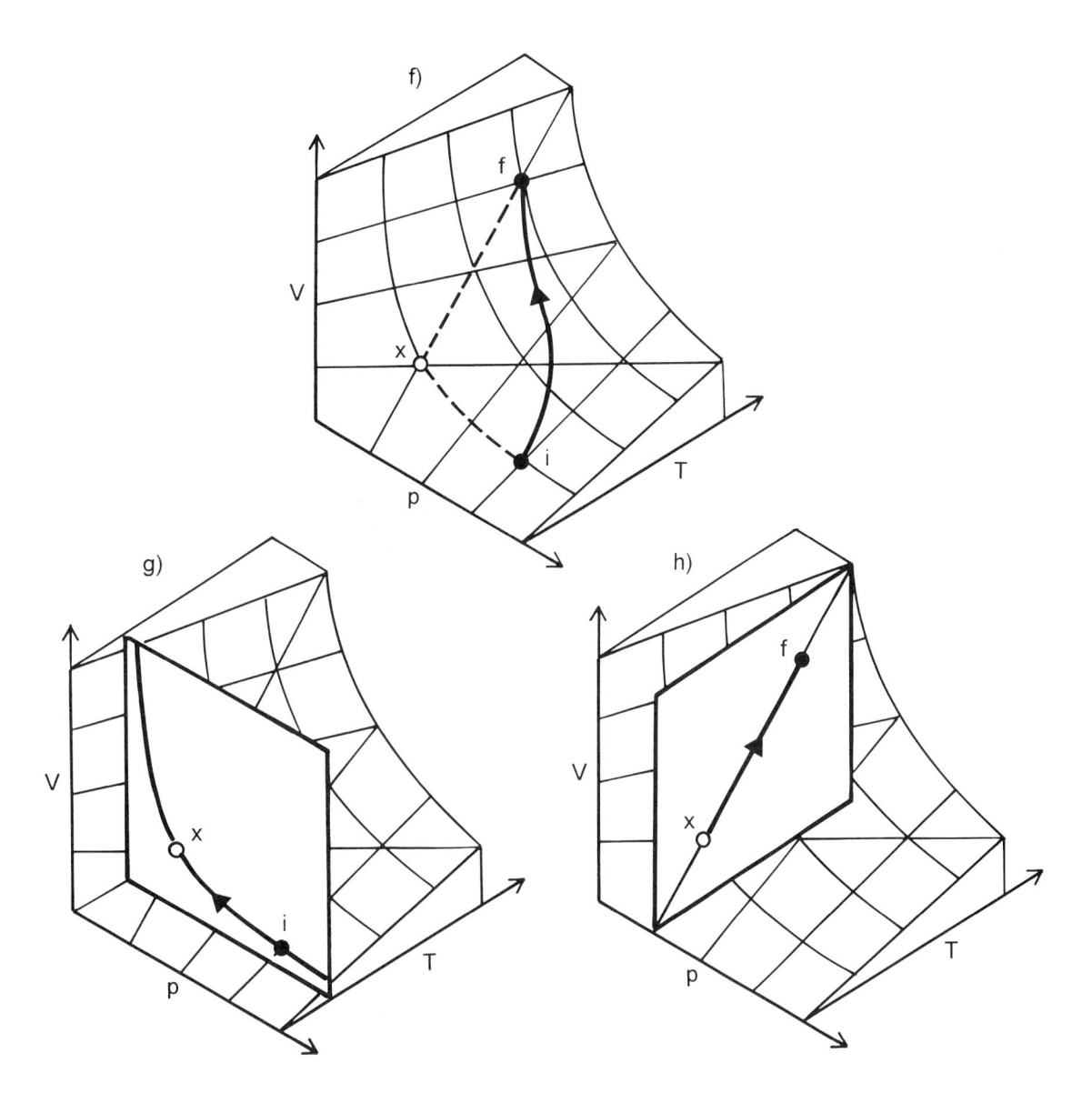

Fig. 6.12: Graphical display of the ideal gas law in a p–V–T diagram. (a) The diagram is constructed by measuring the volume for a given amount of an ideal gas for each pair of independent parameters: p_i and T_i. The corresponding state of the system i has the volume V_i, which is entered into the graph. (b) The graph combining the volumes for all pairs (p_i, T_i) shows all possible states of the ideal gas as a two–dimensional surface in the three–dimensional p–V–T diagram. (c) Vertical planes can be positioned in the diagram to represent all states with a given temperature or a given pressure, respectively. These planes are perpendicular to each other. (d) A plane for constant temperature intersects the plane of possible states of the system. The resulting curve shows all possible states of the gas at that fixed temperature (isothermal condition). (e) A plane for constant pressure intersects the plane of possible states of the system. The resulting curve shows all possible states of the gas at that fixed pressure (isobaric condition). (f) an arbitrary process (solid line with arrow) which guides the system from an initial state (labelled i) to a final state (labelled f). The dashed line shows an alternate possible path from the initial to the final state through an intermediate state (labelled x). The alternate path in part (f) consists of two steps which we discussed previously: (g) an isothermal process leads from the initial state to the intermediate state (Boyle's law), and (h) an isobaric process leads from the intermediate to the final state (Charles' law).

We study the plane with T = const first. This plane is shown in Fig. 6.12(d) with the possible states of the gas in this plane highlighted as the intersection with the surface of all possible states of the gas. The curve which results in the vertical plane is equivalent to one of the curves shown in Fig. 6.9. It is a representation of Boyle's law.

Fig. 6.12(e) illustrates in the same fashion the plane with p = const. The intersection of this plane with the surface of all possible gas states leads to a straight line, which is equivalent to one of Charles' data curves in Fig. 6.11.

With these features established in Fig. 6.12, we now turn our attention to an arbitrarily selected process which takes the gas from an initial state (index i) to a final state (index f). This process must follow a line on the surface shown in Fig. 6.12(b) if it is physically possible; such a process is shown in Fig. 6.12(f). We use Fig. 6.12 to establish the form in which the initial gas parameters V_i, p_i, T_i are related to the final gas parameters V_f, p_f, T_f.

We choose a pair of vertical planes such that the initial state lies in the T = const plane and that the final state lies in the p = const plane. This defines an intermediate state of the gas, which lies at the intersection of the two vertical planes and on the surface of allowed gas states. We label this intermediate state with subscript x.

Figs. 6.12(g) and 6.12(h) provide an alternative path from the initial state to the final state of the gas. This path passes through intermediate states which lie on either one of the two vertical planes. The process from the initial state to the intermediate state at the intersection of the two vertical planes (Fig. 6.12(g)) is an isothermal process:

$$p_i, V_i, T_i \Rightarrow p_f, V_x, T_i$$

$$\text{apply Boyle's law:} \quad V_x = V_i \frac{p_i}{p_f} \quad (22)$$

in which the system reaches its final pressure while the temperature is still at the initial value.

The process from the intermediate state to the final state, shown in Fig. 6.12(h) is an isobaric process:

$$p_f, V_x, T_i \Rightarrow p_f, V_f, T_f$$

$$\text{apply Charles' law:} \quad V_f = V_x \frac{T_f}{T_i} \quad (23)$$

We eliminate the intermediate volume V_x by substituting Eq. (22) into Eq. (23):

$$V_f = \left(V_i \frac{p_i}{p_f}\right) \frac{T_f}{T_i} \quad (24)$$

Finally, the variables describing the initial and final states are separated:

$$\frac{p_i V_i}{T_i} = \frac{p_f V_f}{T_f} \quad (25)$$

Note that Eq. (25) no longer contains any parameter of the intermediate state we chose in Fig. 6.12. The equation only contains the initial and final parameters of the gas for the process of interest. Thus, Eq. (25) is valid independent of the path chosen between the initial and final states, i.e., the path is Fig. 6.12(f) must yield the same result.

Eq. (25) can also be written in the form:

$$\frac{pV}{T} = const \quad (26)$$

Thus, Boyle's and Charles' laws represent special processes which are possible for an ideal gas, and Eq. (26) represents all possible processes for the ideal gas.

The constant in Eq. (26) depends only on the amount of the gas and is, thus, a more fundamental constant than the two constants that appear in Eqs. (14) and (19). Amedeo Avogadro showed in 1811 that it is not the best approach to quantify the amount of gas as the mass of the gas, m. If we do this, the result is a new constant that still depends on the identity of the gas, i.e., it would be a materials constant. Instead, Avogadro found an approach which yields a fundamental, materials independent constant by expressing the amount of gas as the number of moles, n. The number of moles is related to the mass of the gas by:

$$n = \frac{m}{M} \quad (27)$$

in which M is the molar mass of the gas. For a given material, the value of the molar mass is obtained from the Periodic Table (see General Appendix) and is given in unit [g/mol]. For example, the molar mass of carbon is M = 12.01 g/mol, and the molar mass of methane (CH_4) is M = 12.01 + 4 × 1.008 = 16.04 g/mol. This convention for the molar mass defines 1 mol as a macroscopic amount of matter. 1.0 mol of ideal gas contains

6.02×10^{23} atoms or molecules; this number is called the Avogadro number.

When the number of moles is separated from the constant in Eq. (26), it is found that the constant can be written as $n \cdot R$ with $R = 8.314$ J/(K mol) a fundamental constant called the universal gas constant. The universal gas constant is independent of any other parameter, including the identity of the gas. Thus, the ideal gas law reads:

$$pV = nRT \qquad (28)$$

We want to confirm that the units in Eq. (28) are correct. In SI units, the left side equals [Pa m³], which is equal to [(kg m³)/(m s²)] = [kg m²/s²] = [J]. The right hand side of Eq. (28) has units [mol K J/(K mol)] = [J], i.e., the units of both sides of the equation match.

The observation that for any gas at 0°C, and at 1.0 atm pressure (STPD conditions, see section 6.1.1), 1.0 mol fills always the same volume of V = 22.414 liter led to Avogadro's hypothesis of the molecular nature of gases. This was one of the earliest hints of an atomic structure of matter, which was not explored systematically until the beginning of the twentieth century.

Example 6.2
(a) Using for the density the definition $\rho = m/V$ and Eq. (27) for the number of moles in a gas, show that the ideal gas equation can be written in the form:

$$M = \frac{\rho}{p} RT \qquad (29)$$

(b) Consider an ideal gas at 25°C and 2.0 atm with a density of 2.76 kg/m³. What is the molar mass of this gas?
(c) Table 6.1 shows density measurements for CO_2 gas at 10°C as a function of pressure. Using the formula derived in part (a) and graphical methods, determine the molar mass of CO_2.

Table 6.1: Density versus pressure data for carbon–dioxide

pressure [atm]	density [kg/m³]
0.68	1.29
2.72	5.25
8.14	16.32

Solution part (a): We start by substituting Eq. (27) into the ideal gas law:

$$pV = \frac{m}{M} RT \qquad (30)$$

Next we isolate the ratio m/V which is the density ρ:

$$M = \frac{m}{V} \frac{RT}{p} = \frac{\rho}{p} RT \qquad (31)$$

This is the formula sought in the problem.

Solution part (b): Using Eq. (31) with T = 25°C = 298 K and the data given in the example text we find:

$$M = \frac{2.76 \left[\frac{kg}{m^3}\right]}{2.026 \times 10^5 [Pa]} 8.31 \left[\frac{J}{K\, mol}\right] 298 [K] \qquad (32)$$

which yields:

$$M = 0.03375 \frac{kg}{mol} = 33.75 \frac{g}{mol} \qquad (33)$$

Solution part (c): The data given in Table 6.1 are plotted in Fig. 6.13 (solid dots). Note that the pressure axis has been converted to the standard unit [Pa]. To analyze this plot to obtain the molar mass of carbon–dioxide, we re-write Eq. (31) in the form:

$$\rho = \frac{M}{RT} p \qquad (34)$$

which describes the straight line in Fig. 6.13. Thus, the slope of the straight line in the figure, written as $\Delta\rho/\Delta p$, is equal to M/RT, which contains the molar mass. Using the data point indicated by the dashed lines in Fig. 6.13 we find:

$$\frac{\Delta\rho}{\Delta p} = \frac{10.0 \left[\frac{kg}{m^3}\right]}{5.2 \times 10^5 [Pa]} \qquad (35)$$

$$\Rightarrow \frac{\Delta\rho}{\Delta p} = 1.92 \times 10^{-5} \frac{s^2}{m^2}$$

ρ [kg/m³]

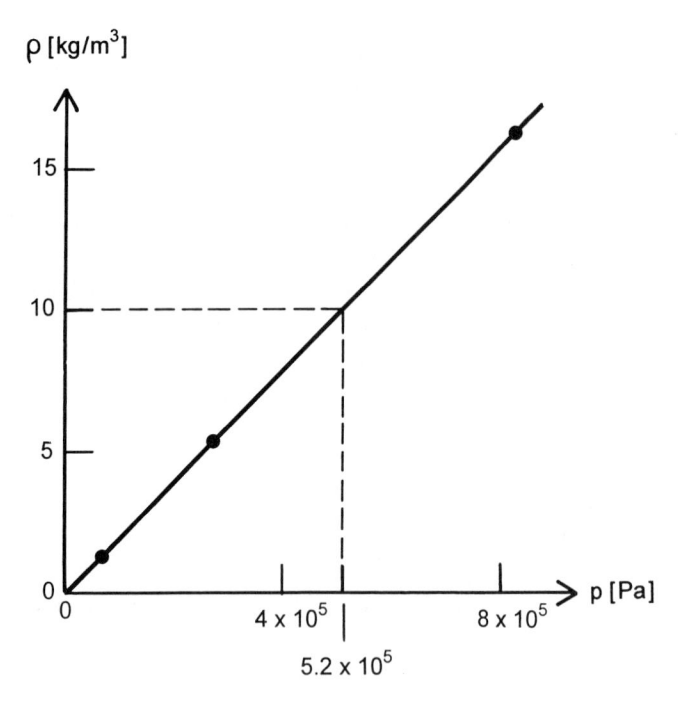

Fig. 6.13: Plot of the density of carbon dioxide (CO_2) as a function of pressure.

A single data point is sufficient to determine the slope since the straight line in Fig. 6.10 passes through the origin of the plot, i.e., in the general equation for a linear function, y = ax + b, the constant b is zero.

Using the value from Eq. (35) we calculate the molar mass:

$$M = RT \frac{\Delta \rho}{\Delta p} =$$

$$8.31 \left[\frac{J}{K\,mol}\right] 283[K]\, 1.92 \times 10^{-5} \left[\frac{s^2}{m^2}\right] \quad (36)$$

which yields:

$$M = 0.0452 \frac{kg}{mol} = 45.2 \frac{g}{mol} \quad (37)$$

Example 6.3
Inhaled air reaches body temperature while travelling through the nasal cavities and the trachea, i.e., before it reaches the lungs. Is this required to prevent thermally expanding air to exert excessive forces on the lungs? Specifically,

(a) express the change in lung volume per inhalation if air at STPD conditions (T_{air} = 0°C and p_{air} = 1.0 atm) reaches the lungs, and
(b) compare the volume change in part (a) to the volume change due to oxygen/carbon–dioxide exchange in the inhaled air.
(c) *If you are interested:* can you think of another reason why air at 0°C should not reach the lungs?
Hint: Assume that the processes in the lungs occur under isobaric conditions.

Additional physiological information:
A resting person inhales 7.5 liters air per minute for which 15 inhalation cycles are required. Of the inhaled air, an amount of 0.26 l/min O_2 is absorbed into the blood system and 0.208 l/min CO_2 is released from the blood (standard man data as given in Table 2.2).

Solution part (a): We calculate first the temperature–related change in the volume for the air inhaled in a single breath. The given physiological information confirms that the resting person inhales 0.5 liters air per breath:

$$\frac{7.5 \left[\frac{l}{min}\right]}{15 \left[\frac{inhal.}{min}\right]} = 0.5 \frac{l}{inhal.} \quad (38)$$

Charles' law is used for the calculation in this example because we assume that the processes in the lungs are isobaric, i.e., done at constant pressure. Charles' law is written in the form:

$$\frac{V_{inhale}}{T_{inhale}} = \frac{V_{body}}{T_{body}} \quad (39)$$

We substitute the given values in Eq. (39):

$$V_{body} = V_{inhale} \frac{T_{body}}{T_{inhale}} =$$

$$= 0.5\,[l]\, \frac{310\,[K]}{273\,[K]} = 0.57\, l \quad (40)$$

Thus, one–half liter of dry air at 0°C becomes 0.57 liters at body temperature. Note that the calculation is only done for the air contained in a single inhalation as the remaining lung volume of 3.0 liters is filled with air which had been inhaled earlier and, therefore, is already at body temperature.

160

The calculated volume difference is now expressed as a fraction of the volume of the lungs after an inhalation, which is $V_{inh} = 3.5$ liters as shown in Fig. 6.1. The volume change $\Delta V = 0.07$ liters calculated in Eq. (40) therefore represents

$$\frac{\Delta V}{V_{inh}} = \frac{0.07 \ [l]}{3.5 \ [l]} = 0.02 \tag{41}$$

i.e., a volume change of 2 %. Accommodating a 2 % volume expansion is not a problem for the lungs; the reason for the warming of air before entering the lungs must be a different one.

Solution part (b): the loss of oxygen from the air volume inhaled in a single breath is calculated from the absorption rate of oxygen (0.26 l/min) and the given breathing rate of 15 inhalations per minute:

$$V_{loss}(O_2) = \frac{0.26 \ [\frac{l}{min}]}{15 \ [\frac{inhal.}{min}]} = 0.017 \ l \tag{42}$$

i.e., an amount of 0.017 liters of oxygen is absorbed into the blood system from each breath.

In turn, CO_2 is released into the gas volume. The gain from release of CO_2 is 80 % of the volume calculated in Eq. (42), because:

$$\frac{V_{gain}(CO_2)}{V_{loss}(O_2)} = \frac{0.208 \ l/min}{0.26 \ l/min} = 0.80 \tag{43}$$

80 % of 0.017 liters is 0.014 liters. An amount of 0.014 liters of CO_2 is added to the inhaled air per breath. Thus, the net loss of gas from the 0.5 liter of air inhaled in a single breath is 0.003 liters, which is the difference between the removed O_2 and the added CO_2. This corresponds to 0.6 % of the inhaled air, or less than 0.1 % of the total volume of the lungs after inhalation. Thus, the gas exchange can be neglected when studying the physical processes in the respiratory system.

Solution part (c): The gas exchange between lungs and blood capillaries requires fast oxygen diffusion through the very thin membranes of the air sacs at the end of the bronchial tree (called alveoli, see Figs. 7.19 and 7.20). The protection of these membranes and a maximum efficiency of the diffusion process require invariable conditions, including a constant temperature ($T = 37^0C$) and a constant humidity (water vapor saturated) of the air in the lungs.

Example 6.4

A plethysmograph is an airtight box that allows us to measure the volume change of a patient's body inside the box by recording the pressure in the box. The residual volume in the human lung is determined with a plethysmograph in the following fashion: at the end of a normal exhalation through a mouth–piece, which is connected to the atmosphere outside of the plethysmograph, the air pressure in the lung equals the atmospheric pressure (see Fig. 6.6). A shutter then closes off the mouth–piece. The patient is requested to continue breathing against the closed shutter. During the next inhalation, the chest of the patient enlarges, creating a new lung volume by decompression, i.e., the original volume of V_{lung} becomes $V_{lung} + \Delta V$. ΔV is determined from the pressure change in the plethysmograph. Also, the final gas pressure in the lungs is measured between the shutter and the patient. Determine for this method a formula for the lung volume V_{lung}.

Solution: We call the state of the patient after the exhalation the initial state and the state after the inhalation against the closed shutter the final state. Thus, the initial gas pressure in the lungs is $p_i = p_{atm}$, and the final gas pressure is p_f with $p_f < p_i$. Both are measured in the experiment. The initial lung volume is $V_i = V_{lung}$, the final lung volume is $V_f = V_{lung} + \Delta V$. ΔV is measured indirectly by recording the change in pressure in the plethysmograph and applying Boyle's law. Thus, we determine the lung volume V_{lung} as:

$$p_i V_i = p_{atm} V_{lung} = p_f V_f = p_f (V_{lung} + \Delta V) \tag{44}$$

which leads to:

$$V_{lung} = \frac{p_f \Delta V}{(p_{atm} - p_f)} \tag{45}$$

6.3. Microscopic model of the ideal gas

The discussion of the ideal gas law in the previous section has raised several new questions: why is there a minimum temperature of –273.15 °C below which matter cannot be cooled? Why is the gas defined in Eq. (28) called an ideal gas? Which gases behave ideally? These questions are answered here, as we obtain a deeper insight into the properties of the ideal gas by introducing a microscopic description. This approach was first proposed by Ludwig Boltzmann, James Clerk Maxwell and Rudolf Clausius in the 1880's as the *kinetic gas theory*. Its most important application is to allow us to quantify the internal energy of the ideal gas in section 6.4.

The kinetic gas theory is based on a mechanical model of the gas. The gas itself is characterized by identical microscopic units called atoms or molecules. Four properties of these gas molecules in a macroscopic container are postulated:
(I) The atoms or molecules act like point masses, i.e., their individual volume is negligible. This is an acceptable assumption as long as the total volume of the gas particles is small compared to the volume of the container.
(II) The gas consists of a very large number of identical atoms or molecules. This adds a further restriction on the applicability: when we combine the first two postulates we conclude that the actual size of the gas particles must also be much smaller than the inter–molecular distance.
(III) The gas particles are in continuous random motion. This means that the motion of any particle is independent of the motion of neighboring particles (irregular motion).
(IV) The only form of interaction between the gas particles or between gas particles and the container walls are elastic collisions.

Example 6.5
Test the validity of the first two postulates of the kinetic gas theory for air at STPD conditions. Specifically, find a lower limit for the ratio of the inter–molecular distance to the molecule radius. Use for the density of air at STPD the value $\rho = 1.2$ kg/m³. Estimate the size of molecules using liquid water of density $\rho = 1.0$ g/cm³.

Solution: We assume that water molecules are spheres and fill the space in liquid water such that neighboring molecules touch each other. The volume per molecule is then calculated from the density and Avogadro's number. In the first step, the density is converted to a molar density:

$$\rho = \frac{m}{V} = \frac{nM}{V}$$
$$\Rightarrow \frac{n}{V} = \frac{\rho}{M} \quad (46)$$

which yields for liquid water with M = 18 g/mol:

$$\frac{n}{V} = \frac{1000\ [kg/m^3]}{0.018\ [kg/mol]} = 5.6 \times 10^4 \frac{mol}{m^3} \quad (47)$$

The inverse of the result in Eq. (47), $(n/V)^{-1}$, is the volume per mol of water. With Avogadro's number, this is converted into the volume per molecule:

$$\frac{1}{N_A}\left(\frac{n}{V}\right)^{-1}_{H_2O} = 3.0 \times 10^{-29}\ m^3 \quad (48)$$

We estimate the diameter of the water molecule, which we label d_{H_2O}, by drawing the third root from the value in Eq. (48): $d_{H_2O} = 3.1 \times 10^{-10}$ m = 0.31 nm.

Repeating the same calculation for air yields the center–to–center distance between the molecules in the gas. We find for the molar density:

$$\frac{n}{V} = \frac{1.2\ [kg/m^3]}{0.029\ [kg/mol]} = 40 \frac{mol}{m^3} \quad (49)$$

in which we used M = 29 g/mol as an average molecular mass for air. This yields for the space occupied by each molecule:

$$\frac{1}{N_A}\left(\frac{n}{V}\right)^{-1}_{air} = 4.2 \times 10^{-26}\ m^3 \quad (50)$$

which yields for the average distance between air molecules $d_{air} = 3.5 \times 10^{-9}$ m = 3.5 nm. Using the result in Eq. (48) as the typical molecular size, we illustrate the implications of Eqs. (48) and (50) in Fig. 6.14. The average distance between air molecules is larger than the diameter or radius of individual molecules. We quantify this with the data calculated above:

$$\frac{d_{air}}{d_{H_2O}} = \frac{3.5\ [nm]}{0.31\ [nm]} = 11 \quad (51)$$

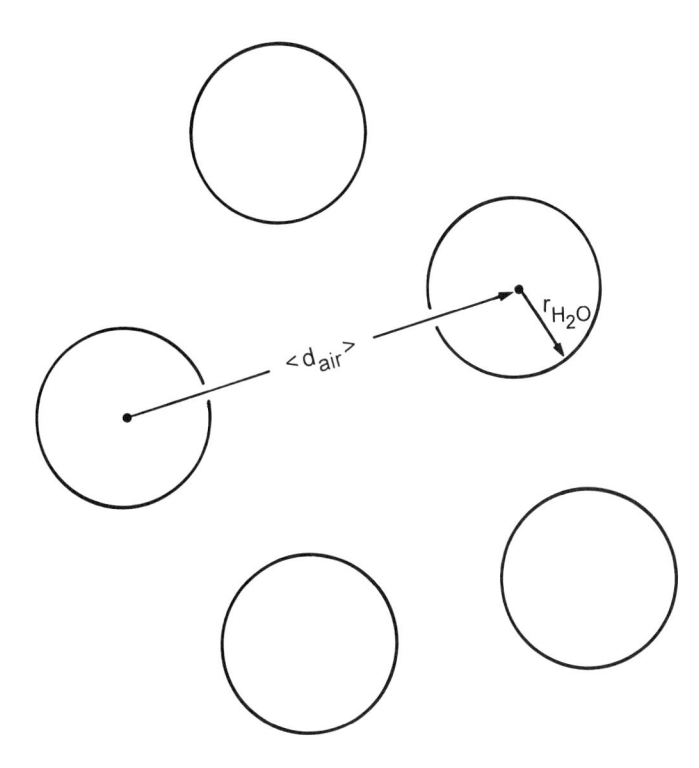

Fig. 6.14: Five randomly chosen gas particles in close proximity. The radius of the particles is estimated from liquid water (r_{H_2O}). The average distance between neighboring gas particles is estimated from the density of air at standard conditions ($<d_{air}>$).

i.e., the inter–molecular distance in a gas at STPD is about 10 times larger than the size of the individual molecules.

This calculation results in a lower limit for the ratio in Eq. (51) because the radius of an actual water molecule is smaller than the value we calculated in Eq. (48).

The fourth postulate of the kinetic gas theory requires a brief discussion. Collisions were not discussed before because the independent motion of macroscopic system parts does not lead to biological applications. At the microscopic level, which we are now interested in, the concept of a collision becomes useful as it allows us to develop a mechanical model of the interaction between atoms and molecules. Collisions between real gas molecules typically lead to a range of effects, from very limited interactions comparable to the hard–sphere collisions of two billiard balls to very strong interactions leading to the formation of stable chemical bonds. Molecular collisions also cause rotations and vibrations, which give rise to various types of spectroscopic analysis methods in chemistry.

Since this multitude of effects is too complex to describe in a single model, a more restrictive approach is required. In the current context, the atoms and molecules are replaced by point masses which excludes rotations, vibrations and other possible excitations from the discussion. For point masses, only two types of collisions are possible: elastic collisions or inelastic collisions. Elastic collisions are relevant to the kinetic gas theory; therefore, they are briefly outlined below and discussed in detail in the Appendix (section 6.8). Inelastic collisions are only presented for comparison in the Appendix.

In the case of an elastic collision the combination of the two colliding point masses form an isolated system. They further do not interact with each other except for a given instant called the collision. This is a simplification as real molecules always exert an attractive force on each other. Since the system of two point masses is isolated, both the energy and the momentum are conserved. The energy conservation is postulated in the first law of thermodynamics; momentum conservation is an equally fundamental law and is briefly discussed in the Appendix of Chapter 3. These two conservation laws allow us to fully quantify the collision process. Some typical cases are outlined in the Appendix, including the only result we need for the discussion of the kinetic gas theory: the collision of a particle of initial velocity $\mathbf{v}_{initial}$ with an object of much larger mass at rest. This is the type of collision that occurs when the particles collide with the wall of a container. In this case we find for the velocity component perpendicular to the wall (x–direction) that $v_{x, final} = -v_{x, initial}$.

We now use the postulates I – IV to develop a microscopic model of a gas. More specifically, we begin with Fig. 6.15 which shows a single particle in a container. The container has sides of length l and the particle has a velocity $\mathbf{v}$. The first quantity we calculate is the pressure this particle exerts on the shaded wall in the container. This wall is oriented perpendicular to the x–axis. We are looking for the pressure so that we can later compare with the ideal gas law. However, we cannot calculate the pressure directly, but have to use the force exerted by the particle on the container wall. This force results from the particle–wall interaction when using Newton's second law:

$$F_x = m\, a_x = m\, \frac{\Delta v_x}{\Delta t} \qquad (52)$$

in which the acceleration along the x–axis is replaced by the change of the speed along this axis, $\Delta v_x/\Delta t$. The total

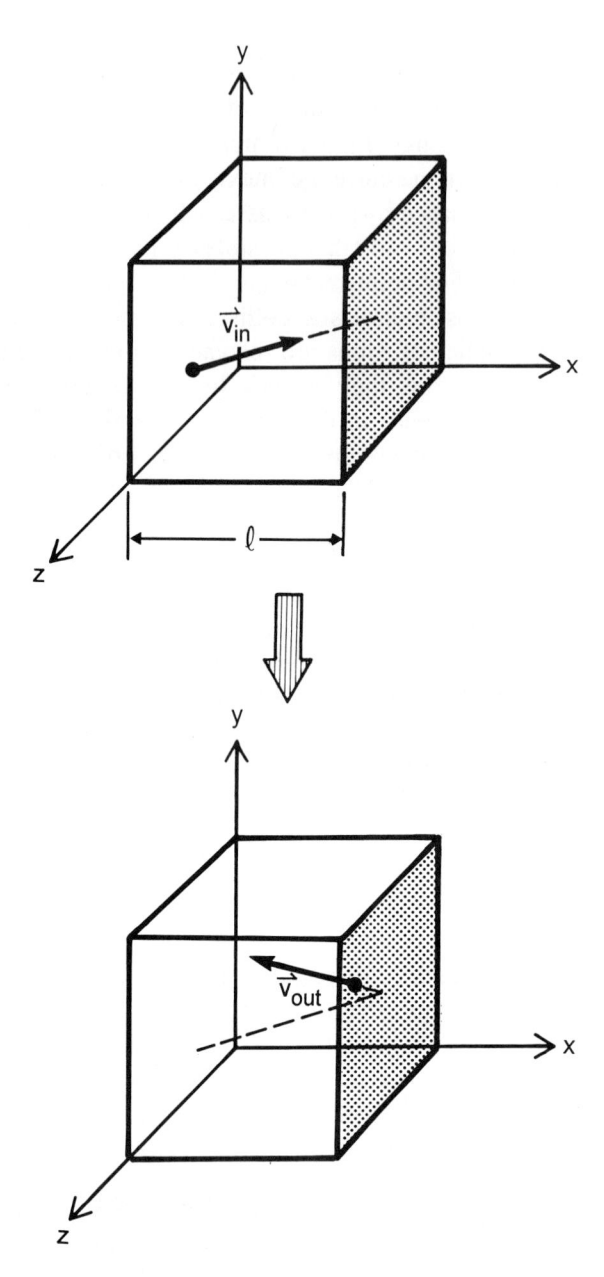

Fig. 6.15: Model system for the kinetic gas theory. The system consists of a single point mass which moves with velocity v in a cubic box of side length l. The interaction of the point mass with the shaded wall is studied to relate pressure and volume of the gas to its microscopic properties. We assume that the particle collides with the wall elastically: the velocity components of the particle perpendicular to the wall before and after collision are related as $v_{x,\text{in}} = -v_{x,\text{out}}$.

change of the velocity component during collisions with the shaded wall in one second is the product of:
(i) The change of the velocity component per collision, which equals to $2v_x$ for an elastic collision. The value is twice the speed component of the particle perpendicular to the wall because the particle approaches with a positive value of $+v_x$ and leaves the wall with a negative value of $-v_x$, and
(ii) the number of collisions with the shaded wall per second, which is the number of $2v_x$ velocity changes at the shaded wall per second. This term is obtained as follows: $v_x = 2l/\tau$ is the x-component of the particle's velocity, expressed as the distance between two collisions with the shaded wall, $2l$, divided by time of flight between these collisions, τ. Therefore, $1/\tau$ is the number of collisions per second with:

$$\frac{1}{\tau} = \frac{v_x}{2l} \qquad (53)$$

Next we combine both contributions to rewrite Eq. (52):

$$F_x = m(2v_x)\left(\frac{v_x}{2l}\right) \qquad (54)$$

in which the first bracket on the right hand side is the contribution per collision from (I). The second bracket is the number of collisions per second from (ii). Thus:

$$F_x = \frac{mv_x^2}{l} \qquad (55)$$

Since we are developing a model for a gas, we want to use the pressure instead of the force. To obtain the pressure, the force must be divided by the area on which the force acts: $A = l^2$, as shaded in Fig. 6.15:

$$p = \frac{F_x}{l^2} = \frac{mv_x^2}{l^3} = \frac{mv_x^2}{V} \qquad (56)$$

in which $l^3 = V$ is the volume of the cubic container in the figure.

To describe a gas we need not one, but a very large number of particles in the box. As we add more and more particles, they start to hit each other. This is of no concern to our calculation as in elastic collisions no kinetic energy is lost, it is just redistributed between the particles. However, both the speed and the x-components of the velocity of the individual particles vary. To avoid following each of the particles individually, we use an average velocity of the molecules instead of the individual velocity. Note that we cannot simply use $\langle v_x \rangle$ (where the notation $\langle ... \rangle$ indicates that an average over a large number of values is taken), since $\langle v_x \rangle = 0$ when particles move with the same probability toward left and right. Looking once more at Eq. (56) we note, however, that it is not the velocity component v_x we are interested in, but the square of this velocity component. Thus we use the average square of the x–component of the velocity $<v_x^2>$. This value is not zero since all particles contribute a positive value of the square of the velocity. For a box containing N particles we rewrite Eq. (56):

$$p = N \frac{m<v_x^2>}{V} \qquad (57)$$

Up to this point, we have focussed on the shaded wall of the container in Fig. 6.15. However, we expect the pressure to be independent of any particular direction such as the x–direction because pressure is a scalar property of matter. The only quantity in Eq. (57) which is direction–dependent is the speed term. From everyday experience we know that there is no distinction between the x–, y– and z–directions in a gas. For the air in the room you are in, for example, you do not sense a higher air pressure from any particular direction onto your skin. Thus the average of the square of the speed components must be equal in all directions:

$$<v_x^2> = <v_y^2> = <v_z^2> \qquad (58)$$

Applying the Pythagorean theorem in three dimensions yields:

$$<v^2> = <v_x^2> + <v_y^2> + <v_z^2> = 3<v_x^2> \qquad (59)$$

Substituting this result in Eq. (57) leads to the main prediction of the kinetic gas theory:

$$pV = \frac{1}{3} Nm<v^2> \qquad (60)$$

i.e., the product of pressure and volume is connected to the microscopic properties of the gas, namely the mass and the average velocity of the molecules, and the total number of molecules in the container.

We recognize the similarity of the term $m<v^2>$ on the right hand side of Eq. (60) with the kinetic energy. Indeed, $\frac{1}{2}m<v^2>$ is the average kinetic energy of a single point mass in the gas and $N \frac{1}{2}m<v^2>$ is the kinetic energy of all N particles in the container. Thus, Eq. (60) relates the pressure and volume of an ideal gas to its kinetic energy:

$$pV = \frac{2}{3}\left(\frac{1}{2}Nm<v^2>\right) = \frac{2}{3} E_{kin} \qquad (61)$$

6.4. Internal energy of the ideal gas

Eq. (60) is now compared with the experimentally derived ideal gas law in Eq. (28), pV = nRT. Because the product pV is the same in both equations, we can state:

$$\frac{2}{3} E_{kin} = nRT \qquad (62)$$

When we identified the particles in the gas as point masses in section 6.3 we restricted their variable forms of energy to only two types of energy: the kinetic and the gravitational potential energy. The gravitational potential energy is negligible; otherwise the particles would have to sink to the bottom of the container (sedimentation). Therefore, the kinetic energy of the particles in the box is equal to their total energy, which we defined in Chapter 5 as the internal energy: $E_{kin} = U$.
Comparison of this formula for the internal energy of the gas with Eq. (62) yields:

$$U = \frac{3}{2} n R T \qquad (63)$$

This is an extremely important result: Eq. (63) states that the internal energy of n moles of an ideal gas depends only on the temperature. In the remainder of this section several key ramifications of Eq. (63) are discussed.

6.4.1. The existence of a smallest possible temperature at 0 K

Eq. (63) explains the existence of a minimum temperature as postulated by Lord Kelvin based on Fig. 6.11. At T = 0 K, the internal energy vanishes, i.e., U = 0 J. Thus, the entire kinetic energy is removed from the system and $<v^2> = 0$ m/s. With no motion left all point masses collapse and fill a zero volume, V = 0 m³. Thus, this prediction by Charles' law makes sense. In reality, however, atoms and molecules have a finite volume and the extrapolation of Charles' law cannot be made as indicated in Fig. 6.11. For that reason, the low–temperature end of the lines in the figure are only dashed as we expect deviations from the ideal behavior to be most notable at low temperatures.

6.4.2. A physiological example: the internal energy of the air in the lungs

Eq. (63) is written with macroscopic amounts of gas in mind. However, the successful introduction of the kinetic gas theory suggests that it is also applicable at the microscopic scale of gas molecules. To rewrite the equation per particle, it is first written for 1 mol (n = 1):

$$U \left[\frac{J}{mol}\right] = \frac{3}{2} RT = \frac{1}{2} M\langle v^2\rangle \quad (64)$$

in which M is the molar mass in unit [kg/mol]. In the next step, Eq. (64) is divided by Avogadro's number N_A, with $M = m N_A$ and m the mass of a single particle (atom or molecule), given in unit [kg/particle]:

$$\epsilon \left[\frac{J}{particle}\right] = \frac{3}{2} \frac{R}{N_A} T = \frac{3}{2} kT \quad (65)$$

in which ε is the internal energy per particle and k is the Boltzmann constant, $k = R/N_A = 1.38 \times 10^{-23}$ J/K. Numerical values for the internal energy at room temperature of 298 K are calculated from Eqs. (64) and (65): for 1.0 mol of an ideal gas we get U = 3.7 kJ/mol, and for the energy per gas molecule $\epsilon = 6.2 \times 10^{-21}$ J.

Example 6.6
Calculate for the air in the lungs after regular exhalation
(a) the number of moles, and
(b) the internal energy.
Treat air as an ideal gas with molar mass M = 29 g/mol.

Solution part (a): We know from the spirometer data of Fig. 6.1 that the gas volume of the lungs after exhalation is 3.0 liters. Fig. 6.4 shows that the gas pressure in the lungs after exhalation matches the atmospheric pressure, for which we use $p_{atm} = 1.013 \times 10^5$ Pa. The temperature of the gas in the lungs after exhalation is 310 K as this corresponds to 37°C which is the human core body temperature. With these data we use the ideal gas law from Eq. (28) to determine the number of moles of air in the lungs:

$$n = \frac{pV}{RT} = \frac{1.013 \times 10^5 [Pa] \, 3 \times 10^{-3} [m^3]}{8.314 \left[\frac{J}{K \, mol}\right] 310 [K]} \quad (66)$$

which yields n = 0.12 mol.

Solution part (b): From Eq. (63) we determine the internal energy of the gas in the lungs. With the data from the problem text and part (a) we find:

$$U = \frac{3}{2} nRT =$$

$$\frac{3}{2} 0.12 [mol] \, 8.314 \left[\frac{J}{K \, mol}\right] 310 [K] \quad (67)$$

$$\Rightarrow \quad U = 464 \, J$$

It is interesting to compare this result to the work values we find at the end of this chapter for the cyclic respiration process. There we find that a single inhalation requires work of about 50 J, which is slightly more than 10% of the total internal energy of the gas in the lungs. It is therefore not possible that the energy for the inhalation is taken from the internal energy of the gas. The following calculation illustrates this point further: if the energy for the inhalation were taken from the gas, Eq. (63) would require a temperature change in our lungs:

$$\Delta U = \frac{3}{2} nR \left(T_{final} - T_{initial}\right)$$

$$T_{final} = T_{initial} + \frac{2}{3 nR} \Delta U \quad (68)$$

which leads to:

$$T_{final} = 310 [K] + \ldots$$

$$\ldots + \frac{2 \, (-50.6 [J])}{3 \cdot 0.12 [mol] \, 8.314 \left[\frac{J}{K \, mol}\right]} \quad (69)$$

$$\Rightarrow \quad T_{final} = 276 \, K$$

Thus, the temperature in our lungs would sink close to the freezing point to accomplish just a single inhalation. Even though energy would flow fast into the lungs to maintain their temperature, during physical activities we are breathing at an accelerated rate and equilibration of the temperature would soon lack behind. In fact, the energy for the respiration work is provided in part by the various active components (muscles and diaphragm) and in part by the elastic action of the thorax.

6.4.3. The root–mean–square speed of gas particles

We calculate the mean speed of the particles in an ideal gas from Eqs. (64) and (65). This speed is called the root–mean–square speed, v_{rms}, and is given as:

$$v_{rms} = \sqrt{\langle v^2 \rangle} = \sqrt{\frac{3RT}{M}} = \sqrt{\frac{3kT}{m}} \quad (70)$$

(Boltzmann.)

The second last term follows from Eq. (64) and expresses the root–mean–square speed as a function of two macroscopic parameters, the gas constant and the molecular mass. The last term in Eq. (70) follows from Eq. (65) expressing the root–mean–square speed as a function of two microscopic parameters, the Boltzmann constant and the mass of a molecule.

$$v_{rms} = \sqrt{\frac{3 \cdot 8.314 \left[\frac{J}{K \cdot mol}\right] \cdot 298\,[K]}{0.02802 \left[\frac{kg}{mol}\right]}} \quad (71)$$

$$\Rightarrow v_{rms} = 515\,\frac{m}{s}$$

At first this may appear to be a very high speed; 1850 km/h far exceeds the speed of most macroscopic objects we observe. It may also seem a high speed when you realize that this is the speed of billions of billions of particles hitting your skin right now. Can we put this result in some perspective? The speed in Eq. (71) can be related to the speed of sound because nitrogen is a major component of air and sound is carried by air. The speed of sound is about 330 m/s; thus, the speed of 515 m/s for the typical nitrogen molecule appears to be of the right order of magnitude. A detailed discussion of the speed of sound in gases is provided in Chapter 16.

===

Example 6.7
(a) What is the speed of a typical nitrogen molecule at room temperature (T = 298 K)?
(b) How much faster does a typical nitrogen molecule get when inhaled?
Hint: Base your answers on the root–mean–square speed of the nitrogen component of the air, which is treated as an ideal gas.

Solution part (a): The molar mass of nitrogen is given as $M(N_2) = 28.02$ g/mol. This quantity has to be converted into standard unit [kg/mol]. We find:

Solution part (b) : To solve this part we could simply substitute the core body temperature into Eq. (71). However, it is more useful to compare both velocities:

$$\frac{v_{rms}(T_2 = 310\,K)}{v_{rms}(T_1 = 298\,K)} = \frac{\sqrt{3RT_2/M}}{\sqrt{3RT_1/M}} \quad (72)$$

$$\sqrt{\frac{T_2}{T_1}} = \sqrt{\frac{310\,[K]}{298\,[K]}} = \sqrt{1.04} = 1.02$$

The nitrogen molecules become 2 % faster, leading to a root–mean–square speed of nitrogen in the lungs $v_{rms} = 525$ m/s.

===

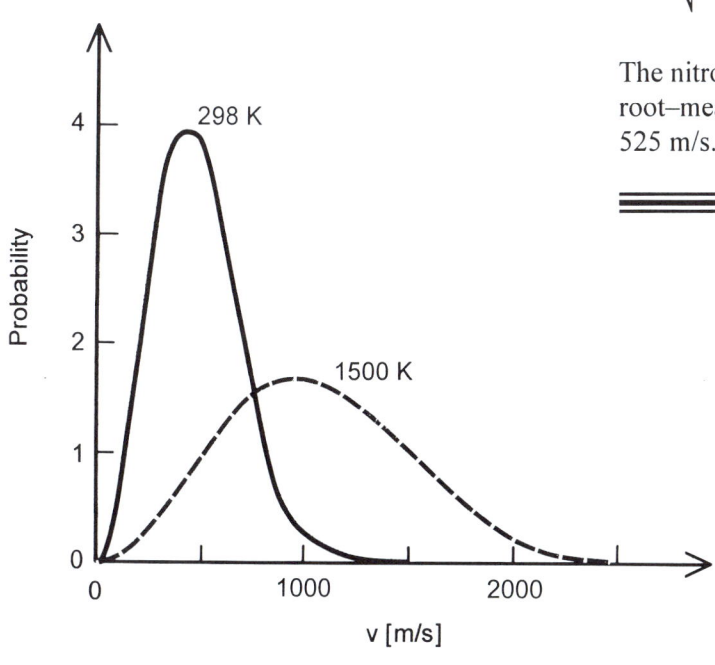

Fig. 6.16: The Maxwell–Boltzmann velocity distribution of nitrogen molecules at room temperature (solid line) and at 1500 K (dashed line). The horizontal axis is the velocity of the gas particles in unit [m/s]. The vertical axis is the probability P to find a particle in a small interval around the given speed. This axis is given in arbitrary units, which means that numbers read off the axis can only be used for relative comparison.

6.4.4. Maxwell–Boltzmann velocity distribution

There is a wide range of individual speeds in a box filled with gas particles. The root–mean–square velocity is only a representative velocity in the actual distribution of speeds. Fig. 6.16 shows the probability distribution of velocities for nitrogen molecules at 298 K and 1500 K. This plot is called the Maxwell–Boltzmann velocity distribution and shows the number of gas particles in each velocity interval for a given temperature. We saw in Example 6.7 that the root–mean–square speed of nitrogen at 298 K is 515 m/s. Finding this speed on the solid curve in Fig. 6.16 we see that the root–mean–square speed lies above the most probable speed at 450 m/s (speed at the peak of the curve). The root–mean–square speed and the most probable speed are different because the curves in Fig. 6.16 are not symmetric. The tail toward high speeds causes a higher root–mean–square speed as larger speeds contribute more effectively to an average when the average is calculated for square values.

6.4.5. A second look at the thermal equilibrium

Both the internal energy and the temperature of a system are defined only when the system is in thermal equilibrium. A thermal equilibrium is established for a gas when the speed distribution of the particles matches the Maxwell–Boltzmann distribution of Fig. 6.16. Note that the bell–shaped curve flattens and shifts to larger speeds as the temperature increases to 1500 K (dashed curve in Fig. 6.16), indicating that at higher temperature more gas particles are moving at higher speeds. This distribution plays a key role in the physical sciences: the definition of temperature, as introduced in the previous chapter, relied on the concept of thermal equilibrium. Note that a thermal equilibrium can only be defined when there are enough particles to generate a speed distribution that can be compared to the Maxwell–Boltzmann distribution. Thus, temperature is a collective property, i.e., it is meaningless to talk about the temperature of a single particle or just a few.

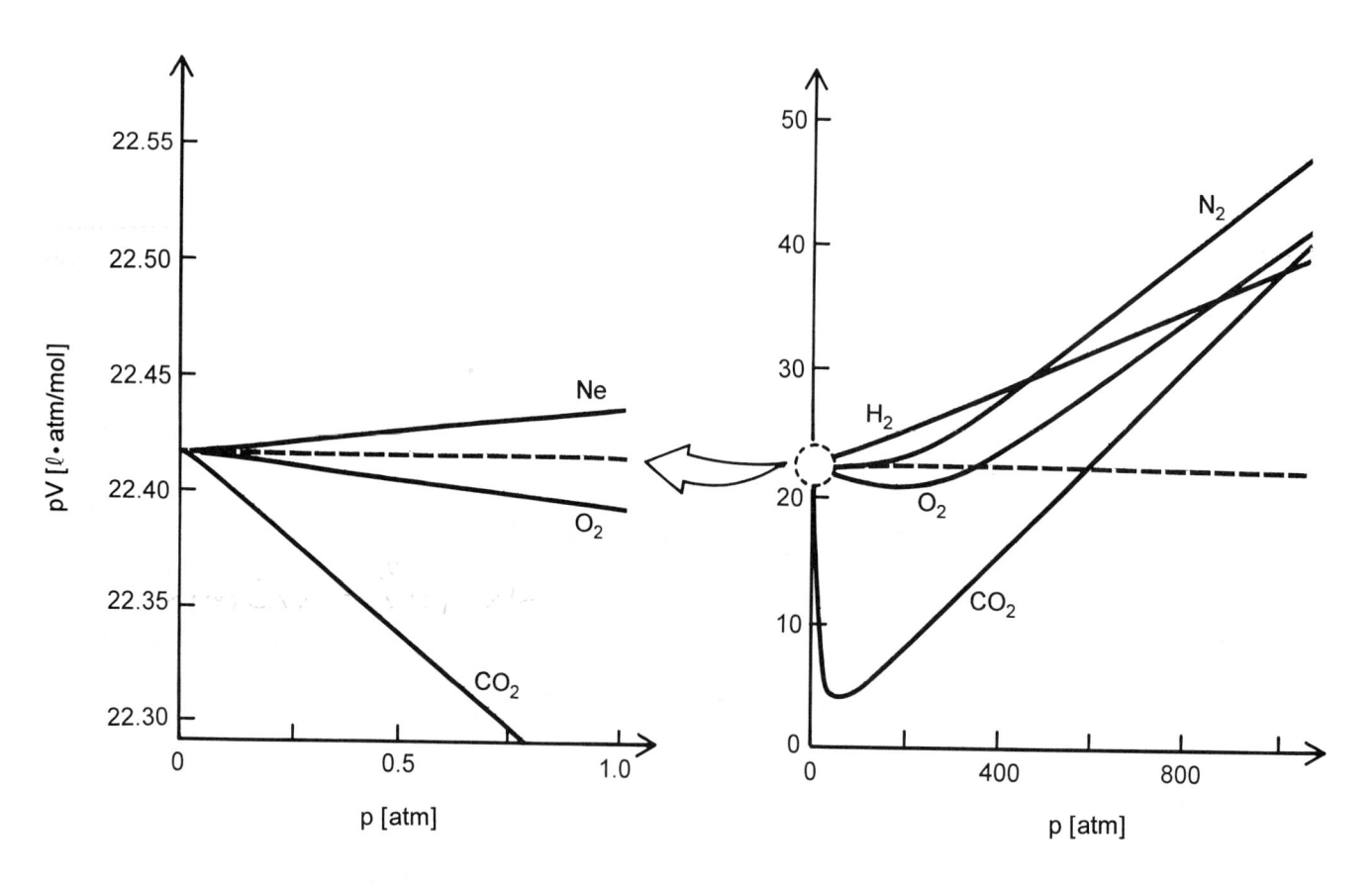

Fig. 6.17: Comparison of real gases with the ideal gas at 0°C, using measurements of the product pV. The figure at the right shows pV data for 1.0 mol of oxygen (O_2), carbon–dioxide (CO_2), hydrogen (H_2) and nitrogen (N_2) in the pressure range from 1.0 atm to 1200 atm. The horizontal dashed line corresponds to the prediction for the ideal gas (Boyle's law). In the figure at the left we focus on the narrower pressure range between 0.0 atm and 1.0 atm for 1.0 mol of the same gases and neon (Ne). Note that the product pV is given in the non–SI units [liter atm/mol].

6.5. Real gases

Simplifying models such as the ideal gas model are utilized throughout the sciences. While we can learn a lot from such models, we need always to be cautious about the limits of their applicability. The use of the ideal gas law to model the air we breathe is a good example for such a test.

The ideal gas law connects three parameters for a closed gas system: pressure, volume and temperature. If the system were open, the amount of gas (number of moles) would have to be included. Due to the number of parameters, there are several ways to compare real gases with the ideal gas law.

A first approach is based on Figs. 6.12(d) and 6.12(e): we test the validity of Boyle's law at constant temperature, or Charles' law at constant pressure.

Fig. 6.17 illustrates an experimental attempt to verify Boyle's law for several gases. Recall that Boyle's law states that the product pV is constant for an isothermal change of the ideal gas. Even though Boyle derived his law from experiments, we need to take a second look with greater precision, evaluating a larger number of gases and a wider range of parameter values than he could more than 300 years ago. Fig. 6.17 shows that the product pV is actually not constant for isothermal variations in the pressure, not even for small pressure intervals (graph at the left), and not either for a noble gas with little interatomic interactions, such as neon.

Example 6.8

Using Fig. 6.17, quantify the deviation from ideal behavior in isothermal experiments at 0^0C for the air components (a) oxygen and (b) carbon–dioxide. Use the gas composition in the lungs.

Supplementary information: Air consists of a mixture of gases, including nitrogen, oxygen, carbon–dioxide and water vapor. The air composition and its role in respiration are discussed in greater detail in Chapter 12. The concept of partial pressure is introduced in that chapter, with partial pressures representing the pressure of each individual gas component. When discussing the properties of a particular component, the partial pressure is used. In the alveoli, the following partial pressures are found: $p(O_2) = 13.3$ kPa $= 0.13$ atm; $p(CO_2) = 5.2$ kPa $= 0.05$ atm (see Table 12.3).

Solution part (a): The ideal gas value in Fig. 6.17 is 22.418 l·atm/mol. For oxygen, we read at p = 0.13 atm a value of 22.415 l·atm/mol off the left figure; this corresponds to a deviation of slightly more than 0.01 %.

Solution part (b): For carbon–dioxide at p = 0.05 atm, we find from Fig. 6.17 a value of 22.411 l·atm/mol; this corresponds to a deviation of slightly more than 0.03 %.

Thus, both gases act essentially like ideal gases at 0^0C. The same applies in the lungs at 37^0C, as gases become more ideal at increased temperatures.

Studying the plot at the right side of Fig. 6.17 indicates significant deviations from ideal behavior when the pressure varies between 0 atm and 1000 atm. These effects have to be studied further.

In 1873, Johannes Diderik van der Waals concluded that two assumptions in the kinetic gas theory are too restrictive: (I) real gas molecules have a finite volume, and (II) real gas molecules interact inelastically. He made two modifications on the ideal gas equation. First, he introduced an effective volume per mole of gas, labelled b, which represents the volume not available to gas particles as they cannot penetrate each other. The modified ideal gas equation therefore reads:

$$p(V - nb) = nRT \qquad (73)$$

Second, van der Waals argued that the attractive interaction between the gas molecules leads to the measurement of an apparent pressure which is smaller than the actual pressure: every time when a gas molecule approaches the container wall, it is pulled back by the other gas molecules and exerts therefore a reduced force on the wall during the collision. The effect on the pressure is proportional to $(n/V)^2$ with n/V the molar density of the gas. One n/V term is contributed by the number of collisions with the container wall per second, the second n/V term is contributed by all other gas particles pulling those back which approach the container wall. Van der Waals introduced a proportionality factor a and implemented the pressure correction into Eq. (73):

$$\left[p + a\left(\frac{n}{V}\right)^2\right](V - nb) = nRT \qquad (74)$$

Eq. (74) is called the van–der–Waals equation. It is a better description of real gases, but represents a mathematically and experimentally more complex formula. Its experimental draw–back is the need to determine two new gas–specific constants, a and b in Eq. (74). Its mathematical draw–back is that all formulas we derived with the ideal gas law become more complicated for the van–der–Waals gas model. In particular, the internal energy can no longer be written in the form of Eq. (63) and one finds that the total energy for a van–der–Waals gas does also depend on the pressure.

When do we use Eq. (74) and when do we retain the simpler ideal gas law from Eq. (28)? Example 6.8 illustrates a case in which the additional effort required with the van–der–Waals equation is usually not justified. When the ideal gas law is consistent with experimental observations to within a percent, no further corrections are needed. Thus, the gases playing a major role in respiration can be treated as ideal gases with one exception: water vapor does not behave ideal. Indeed, water vapor deviates from the ideal gas law so much at BTPS conditions that also van–der–Waals equation is insufficient to describe it – water at BTPS conditions has reached the saturation level, i.e., it is at the transition point between the gaseous and the liquid state.

The two most frequent uses of van der Waals' idea are conceptual. First, his model allows us to understand why for example the internal energy of a real gas depends on the pressure. If you lower the pressure in a gas and therefore increase the average distance between gas molecules in the container, energy is required to separate the molecules because of the inter–molecular attractive forces. Thus, energy is stored in the relative position of the gas particles; this is a form of potential energy contributing to the internal energy. Second, van der Waals' ideas allow us to predict the process of condensation for gases at low temperatures: when the thermal energy in the gas can no longer overcome the attractive inter–molecular forces, the gas collapses and forms a dense liquid state. This occurs more likely at higher pressures because the gas particles are closer to each other in such a gas.

6.6. Basic thermodynamic processes

In this section we introduce the fundamental processes possible based on the first law of thermodynamics. We stated this law for a closed system in the form:

$$\Delta U = U_{final} - U_{initial} = Q + W \quad (75)$$

in which Q is the heat, W the work and ΔU the change in the internal energy of the system. Fig. 6.18 illustrates how the various terms in the first law can be changed for an ideal gas. The ideal gas itself is confined in a container, which guarantees that we deal with a closed and not an open system. A mobile piston allows the gas to exchange work with the environment. We assume an idealized piston that moves frictionless back and forth,

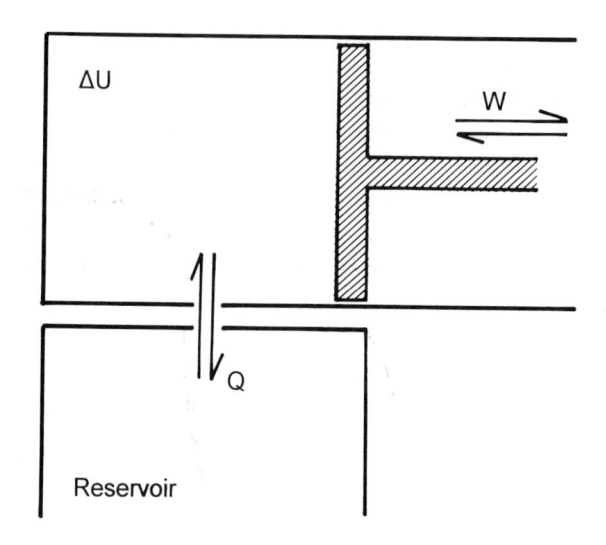

Fig. 6.18: Conceptual sketch illustrating a model system for allowing those processes to act on an ideal gas which are possible due to the first law of thermodynamics. The gas is sealed in a container (closed system with internal energy U). Work W is exchanged with the environment via motion of a frictionless piston. Heat Q is exchanged with a heat reservoir in the environment. The heat reservoir is ideal, i.e., its temperature remains unchanged during heat transfer.

i.e., without generating heat during its motion. A heat reservoir allows the gas to exchange heat with the environment. We assume an ideal heat reservoir, which is characterized by a fixed temperature which remains constant during heat exchange.

For the system in Fig. 6.18, what do we consider to be a *fundamental thermodynamic process* ? In the context of this textbook, fundamental means not only important, but also sufficiently easy to handle mathematically. Thus, we seek processes for which at least one parameter does not change, either in the ideal gas law (Eq. (28)) or in the first law of thermodynamics (Eq. (75)). We will find four processes which satisfy this requirement:

(I) the *isochoric process*, for which the volume in the ideal gas law remains constant and the work term in the first law of thermodynamics is zero,

(II) the *isothermal process*, for which the temperature in the ideal gas law remains constant and the internal energy in the first law of thermodynamics remains unchanged,

(III) the *isobaric process*, for which the pressure in the ideal gas law remains constant, and

(IV) the *adiabatic process*, for which the heat term in the first law of thermodynamics is zero.

6.6.1. Isochoric processes

An isochoric process is a process which takes place at constant volume. Such a process is illustrated in Fig. 6.19. The top part of the figure illustrates the system before and after an isochoric heating. We expect the temperature and the internal energy of the system to increase in this process. The sketch in the large dashed circle at the bottom shows what happens during the isochoric heating: a propane flame provides heat to the gas. Isochoric processes require rigid containers such as steel vessels. Rigid confinement is unusual in biological systems, thus isochoric conditions are usually not applicable. In physics such conditions are typically found in high pressure or high vacuum experiments. High pressure experiments are used to simulate conditions below the Earth's crust (geophysics) and vacuum experiments are often used in surface physics.

Fig. 6.20 shows the p–V diagram for an ideal gas undergoing an isochoric heating process. The two thin lines in the figure represent the p–V relation for an ideal gas for two different temperatures T_1 and T_2 as given in Eq. (28). The upper curve represents the higher temperature T_2. The bold arrow indicates the specific path the system takes in the p–V diagram during an isochoric heating: both pressure and temperature increase during isochoric heating; the pressure increases from p_i to p_f with $p_i < p_f$ and the temperature increases from T_1 to T_2.

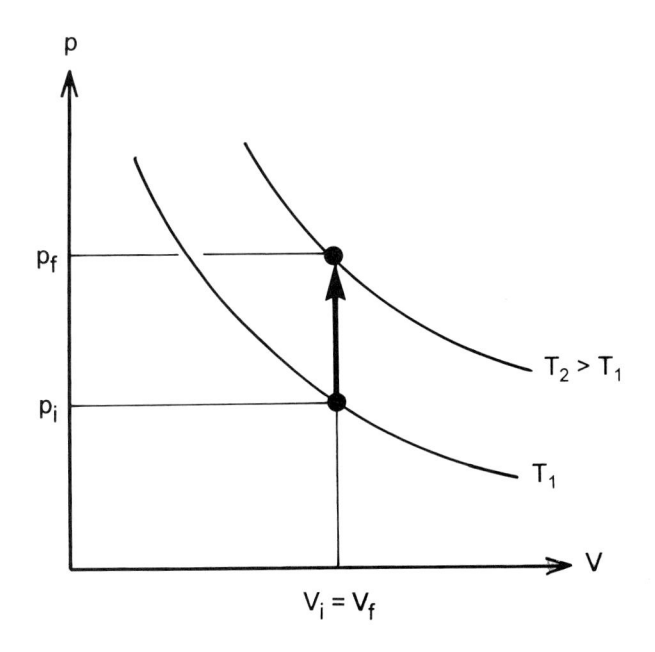

Fig. 6.20: p–V diagram of an isochoric heating of an ideal gas. The bold arrow indicates the change of the temperature from T_1 to the higher temperature T_2 during the process. The arrow is vertical as this corresponds to a constant volume $V_i = V_f$.

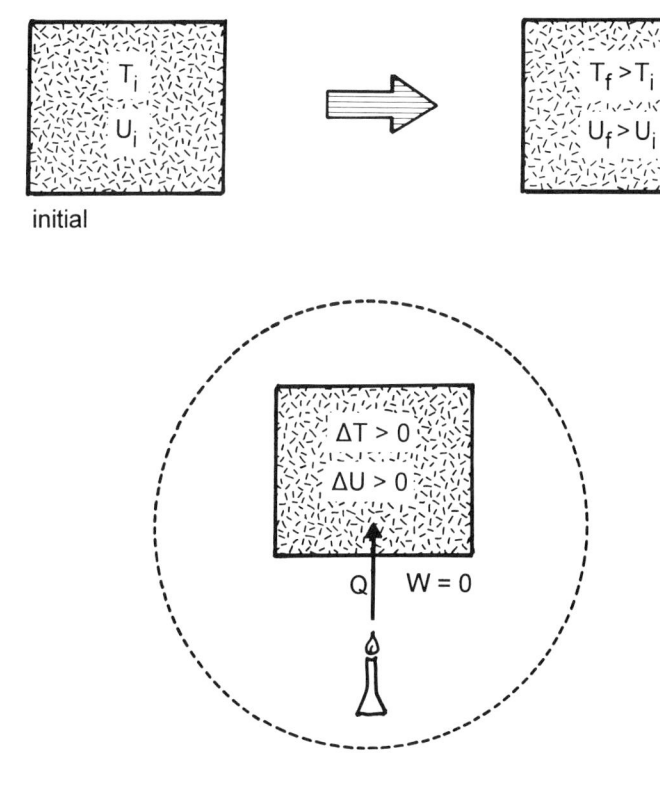

Fig. 6.19: Sketch of an isochoric heating process. Isochoric processes are processes at constant volume. The top two boxes show the system before and after the heating process indicating the temperature and internal energy of the system. The box in the large dashed circle illustrates the heating process itself. The container has fixed walls. Heat is supplied to the system from a hotter source, e.g. a propane burner. The work done in the process is zero and the internal energy increases with the temperature. Note that the heat source must at least have temperature T_f.

The work associated with an isochoric process is W = 0 because the volume does not change and, thus, the area under the curve from V_i to V_f is zero. From the first law of thermodynamics it follows then that $\Delta U = Q$ for an isochoric process. The heat exchange is calculated from Joule's formula, Eq. (5.44): $Q = nC_V\Delta T$, where the index V indicates that C_V is the molar heat capacity of a gas at constant volume. For the ideal gas, we further know from Eq. (63) that $\Delta U = (3/2)nR\Delta T$. This provides us with a value for the molar heat capacity of an ideal gas at constant volume:

$Q = nC_V\Delta T$

$$C_V = \frac{3}{2} R \qquad Q = \frac{3}{2} Rn\Delta T \qquad (76)$$

In summary: for an *isochoric process of an ideal gas*

$$W = 0$$
$$Q = n\, C_V \left(T_f - T_i \right) \qquad (77)$$
$$\Delta U = Q$$

with $C_V = 3R/2$. From $\Delta U = Q$ we conclude that the system absorbs heat from the environment to increase its internal energy during isochoric heating. During isochoric cooling, which is the inverse process, heat is removed from the system, which leads to a lowering of its internal enery.

6.6.2. Isothermal processes

Isothermal processes are processes which take place at constant temperature T. An isothermal process is illustrated in Fig. 6.21. The top part of the figure illustrates the system before and after an isothermal expansion. The sketch in the large dashed circle at the bottom of the figure illustrates what happens during an isothermal expansion: heat flows into the system and work is done by the system on a piston. In section 6.2.1 we discussed Boyle's experiment, which is an example of an isothermal process.

We quantify the isothermal process using a p–V diagram. Fig. 6.22 shows the p–V diagram for an ideal gas undergoing an isothermal expansion, in which the pressure decreases from p_i to p_f with $p_i > p_f$, and the volume increases, from V_i to V_f with $V_i < V_f$.

From Eq. (63) we find for the internal energy change during an isothermal process that $\Delta U = 0$ since $\Delta T = 0$. Thus, the first law of thermodynamics connects for an isothermal process the heat and the work in the form $Q + W = 0$, i.e., $Q = -W$. The work is determined

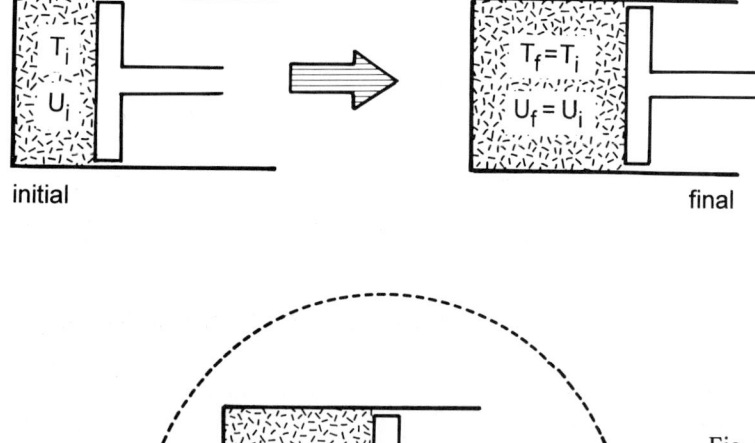

Fig. 6.21: Sketch of an isothermal expansion. Isothermal processes are processes at constant temperature. The top two boxes show the system before and after the expansion indicating the temperature and internal energy of the system. The box in the large dashed circle illustrates the expansion process itself. Heat Q is absorbed by the gas from a heat reservoir, which is at the same temperature as the system. This heat does not change the temperature or the internal energy of the gas, but transfers through the system and is released as work to the piston.

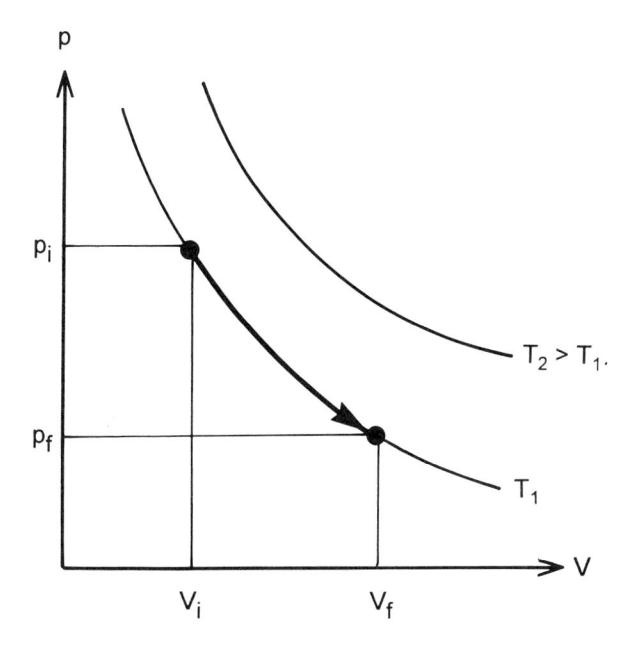

Fig. 6.22: p–V diagram of an isothermal expansion of an ideal gas. The bold arrow shows an isothermal expansion at temperature T_1 from an initial volume V_i to a final volume V_f.

from the area under the curve in Fig. 6.22. Note that Figs. 6.21 and 6.22 represent a case in which the pressure is not constant between the initial and final volume. This means that we need to apply the concepts we discussed for Fig. 5.17 to calculate the work. The resulting work can be expressed in mathematical form:

$$W = -nRT \ln\left(\frac{V_f}{V_i}\right) \quad (78)$$

The work is negative for an isothermal expansion because the final volume is greater than the initial volume (see Fig. 6.21). This means that the system releases work to the piston. The energy to do this work does not come from the internal energy of the gas as the internal energy remains unchanged in an isothermal process. Instead, the energy is passed through the system and originates in a heat reservoir in thermal contact with the system. In summary: for an *isothermal process of an ideal gas*

$$W = -nRT \ln\left(\frac{V_f}{V_i}\right)$$
$$Q = -W \quad (79)$$
$$\Delta U = 0$$

Example 6.9
Find the work for an isothermal expansion of 10 mol of an ideal gas at temperature 0^0C from $p_i = 1.0$ atm to $p_f = 0.1$ atm.

Solution: Because the expansion is done isothermally, we use Eq. (79). Boyle's law in the form $p_i V_i = p_f V_f$ (Eq. (15)) is used to substitute the volume terms for pressure terms as independent variables:

$$W = -nRT \ln\left(\frac{V_f}{V_i}\right) = -nRT \ln\left(\frac{p_i}{p_f}\right) \quad (80)$$

Inserting the given values we find:

$$W = -10[mol]\, 8.314\left[\frac{J}{K\, mol}\right] \times \ldots$$
$$\ldots \times 273[K] \ln\left(\frac{1.0}{0.1}\right) \quad (81)$$
$$\Rightarrow \quad W = -52.3\ kJ$$

This work is negative, which indicates that the gas does work on the environment, e.g. by pushing a piston.

6.6.3. Isobaric processes

Isobaric processes are processes which take place at constant pressure. Fig. 6.23 shows the p–V diagram for an ideal gas undergoing an isobaric process. The specific process shown in the figure is an isobaric expansion in which the volume increases from V_i to V_f, with $V_i < V_f$. The temperature increases from T_1 to T_2, with the initial temperature lower than the final temperature, $T_1 < T_2$. Earlier we discussed Charles' experiment in Fig. 6.10, which is an example of an isobaric process.

The work associated with an isobaric process is calculated from the area under the curve in Fig. 6.23. This area is rectangular since the pressure p is constant:

$$W = -p\left(V_f - V_i\right) \quad (82)$$

The calculation of other quantities for isobaric processes is slightly more complicated, however, since none of the variables in the first law of thermodynamics vanishes in

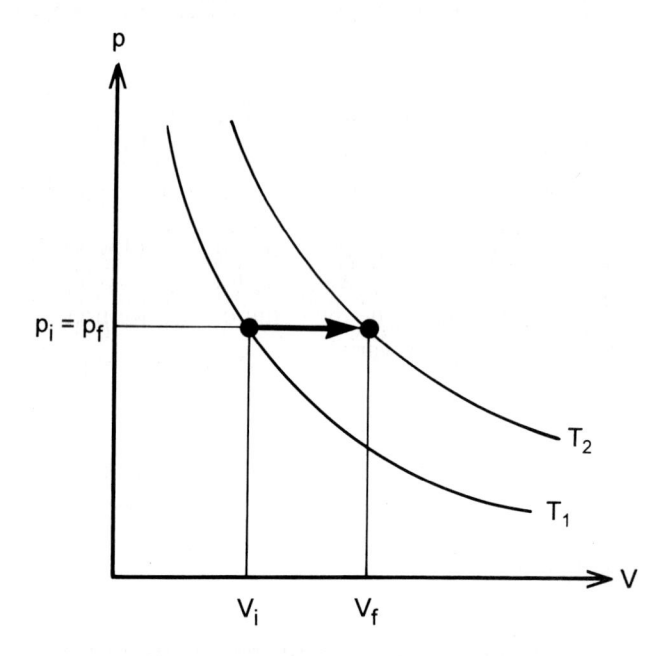

Fig. 6.23: p–V diagram of an isobaric expansion of an ideal gas. Isobaric processes are processes at constant pressure. The bold arrow indicates an expansion from an initial volume V_i to a final volume V_f. Note that the temperature increases during the process from an initial temperature T_1 to a final temperature T_2. The arrow is horizontal because this corresponds to an isobaric process with $p_i = p_f$.

this case: $\Delta U \neq 0$ and $Q \neq 0$ since $\Delta T \neq 0$. Still, isobaric processes are important because any experiment conducted in a set–up that is open to air (e.g. in chemistry) takes place at constant pressure.

One possible way to deal with the isobaric case starts from the change of the internal energy of the ideal gas in Eq. (63):

$$\Delta U = \frac{3}{2} n R \Delta T = n C_V \Delta T \qquad (83)$$

in which $C_V = 3R/2$ is the molar heat capacity. Substituting this result and the work $W = -p \Delta V$ into the first law, $\Delta U = Q + W$, we find:

$$n C_V \Delta T = Q - p \Delta V \qquad (84)$$

which yields for the heat:

$$Q = n C_V \Delta T + p \Delta V \qquad (85)$$

We use the ideal gas equation to replace the last term on the right hand side by $nR\Delta T$. We get as the final result:

$$Q = n \left(C_V + R\right) \Delta T \qquad (86)$$

This is not the approach usually taken in physicochemical studies. Instead, a new variable is defined to replace the internal energy: the *enthalpy* H:

$$H = U + pV \qquad (87)$$

To illustrate the benefit of introducing this new variable, we study small changes of H, which we write as ΔH. If a change is small, it can be expressed from Eq. (87) as three terms, which in turn allow for small changes in each of the parameters on the right hand side:

$$\Delta H = \Delta U + p\Delta V + V\Delta p \qquad (88)$$

Note that this formula is not suitable to describe a larger change in H since then the pressure and the volume may change at the same. For cases where Eq. (88) applies, we can substitute the first law of thermodynamics for the internal energy in the form $\Delta U = \Delta Q + \Delta W$. Also, using $\Delta W = - p\Delta V$ from Eq. (5.16) leads to the form of the internal energy we need: $\Delta U = \Delta Q - p\Delta V$. We find:

$$\Delta H = \Delta Q + V \Delta p \qquad (89)$$

This formula applies generally, but illustrates that the enthalpy is a particularly useful parameter when the pressure is constant (in isobaric processes), because then $\Delta H = \Delta Q$. Therefore, the enthalpy H plays the same role in isobaric processes as the internal energy U plays in isochoric processes. In particular,

$$\Delta H = n C_p \Delta T \qquad (90)$$

with C_p the molar heat capacity at constant pressure. For an ideal gas we note:

$$C_p = C_V + R = \frac{5}{2} R \qquad (91)$$

In summary, we find for an *isobaric process of an ideal gas*:

$$W = - p \left(V_f - V_i\right)$$
$$Q = n C_p \left(T_f - T_i\right) \qquad (92)$$
$$\Delta H = Q$$

174

Note that we distinguish two molar heat capacities, C_V and C_p for the ideal gas, but that we introduced only one molar heat capacity in the previous chapter when we studied Joule's definition of heat (Eq. (5.44)). This is due to the fact that we used liquid water as our system in the discussion in the last chapter. The conditions of constant volume and constant pressure need not to be distinguished when studying solids or liquids.

6.6.4. Adiabatic processes

So far we have found that the first law of thermodynamics is easiest to apply to isothermal and isochoric processes because in each of these cases one variable is zero: for isothermal processes $\Delta U = 0$ and for isochoric processes $W = 0$. This leads us to wonder whether there are also processes with $Q = 0$. The answer is yes; processes with no heat exchange with the environment exist. Such a process is called an *adiabatic process* and is illustrated in Fig. 6.24. The top part of the figure shows an ideal gas before and after adiabatic expansion.

The lower part of Fig. 6.24 illustrates the system changes during the adiabatic expansion. Note that an adiabatic process requires that all heat reservoirs are disconnected from the system as indicated by the dashed line between the heat reservoir and the gas container.

For adiabatic processes, we determine from the first law of thermodynamics that $\Delta U = W$. Thus, the energy for pushing the piston during the adiabatic expansion in the bottom part of Fig. 6.19 ($W < 0$) must be taken out of the internal energy ($\Delta U < 0$). Consequently,

Fig. 6.24: Sketch of an adiabatic expansion. In an adiabatic process the system does not exchange heat with the environment. The top two boxes show the system before and after the expansion indicating the temperature and internal energy of the system. The box in the large dashed circle illustrates the expansion process itself. The dashed line between the reservoir and the system indicates that they are isolated from each other.

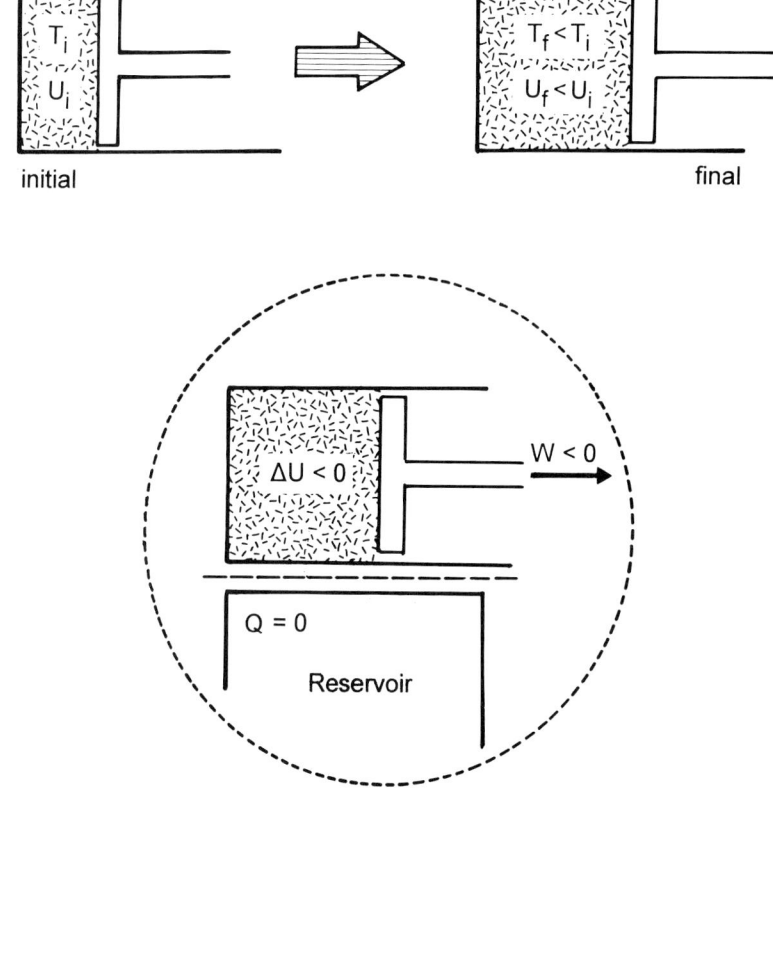

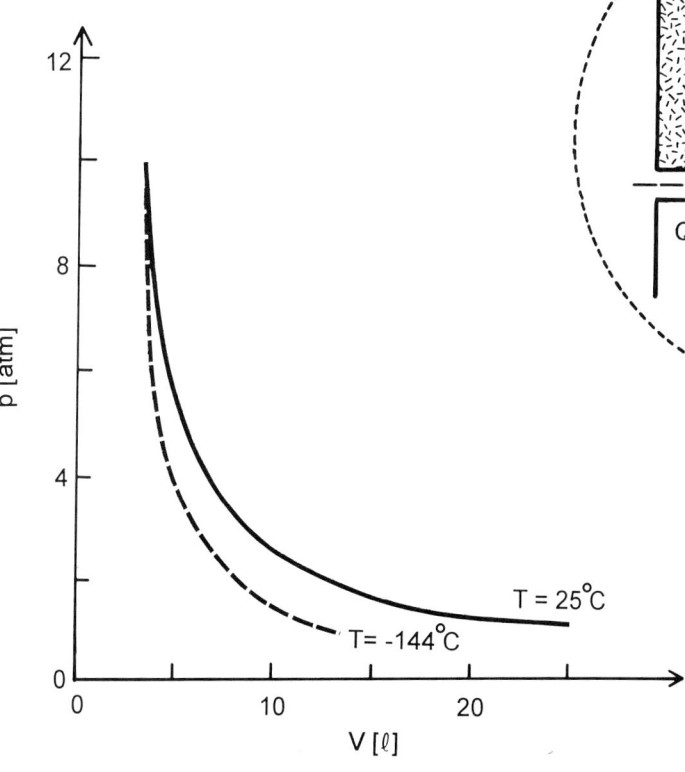

Fig. 6.25: Comparison of an adiabatic expansion (dashed line) and an isothermal expansion (solid line) in a p–V diagram. Both systems are ideal gases and start from the same state with pressure 10 atm. At the final pressure of 1 atm, the adiabatically expanded gas has a significantly lower temperature.

the temperature of the gas decreases. For an ideal gas, the change of the internal energy during an adiabatic process follows from Eq. (63) as:

$$\Delta U = \frac{3}{2} n R \Delta T = n C_V \Delta T \qquad (93)$$

Fig. 6.25 compares an isothermal expansion and an adiabatic expansion from 10 atm to 1.0 atm pressure for an ideal gas initially at 25°C. The comparison shows that the adiabatic expansion in volume is smaller but that a significant drop in temperature to −144°C occurs. The dashed adiabatic curve in Fig. 6.25 follows mathematically the relation:

$$V T^{\frac{C_V}{R}} = const \qquad (94)$$

which can also be written for any particular pair of initial and final states of the gas:

$$V_i T_i^{\frac{C_V}{R}} = V_f T_f^{\frac{C_V}{R}} \qquad (95)$$

This formula is called *Poisson's equation*. Alternatively, we can replace the temperature in Eqs. (94) and (95) by using the ideal gas law in the form T = pV/nR. We further use $C_V = C_p - R$ for the relation between the two molar heat capacities for the ideal gas. This leads to a second formulation for the adiabatic process in the form:

$$p V^\kappa = const \quad \text{with} \quad \kappa = \frac{C_p}{C_V} \qquad (96)$$

which is often used for any particular pair of initial and final states of the gas in the form:

$$p_i V_i^\kappa = p_f V_f^\kappa \qquad (97)$$

κ is called the *adiabatic coefficient* with a value κ = 5/3 for the ideal gas. Since κ > 1, the dashed adiabatic curve in Fig. 6.25 is steeper than the solid isothermal curve which follows pV = const.

When reading physical chemistry texts, you will find a range of values reported for κ, which is a consequence of the behavior of real gases. We do not consider such variations since we continue to use the kinetic gas theory model of the ideal gas, which is based on point masses. Molecules which can rotate or vibrate, which are the properties leading in turn to different values of κ, are therefore excluded. In summary, we find for an *adiabatic process of an ideal gas*:

$$W = \Delta U$$

$$Q = 0 \qquad (98)$$

$$\Delta U = n C_V (T_f - T_i)$$

Example 6.10
1.0 mol of an ideal gas undergoes an adiabatic expansion from an initial volume of $V_i = 1.0$ m³ to twice that volume. The initial temperature is $T_i = 270$ K.
(a) What is the initial pressure, and
(b) what is the final pressure?

Solution part (a): The initial pressure is obtained from the ideal gas law:

$$p_i = \frac{nRT_i}{V_i} = \frac{1[mol]\, 8.31 \left[\frac{J}{Kmol}\right] 270[K]}{1\,[m^3]} \qquad (99)$$

which leads to:

$$p_i = 2245\ Pa \qquad (100)$$

Solution part (b): We use the formula for the adiabatic expansion, Eq. (95), to determine the final temperature of the gas. Using $C_V = 3R/2$ from Eq. (76) we write:

$$V_i T_i^{3/2} = V_f T_f^{3/2} \qquad (101)$$

which leads to:

$$T_f^{3/2} = \left(\frac{V_i}{V_f}\right) T_i^{3/2} \qquad (102)$$

Next we raise both sides of Eq. (102) to the 2/3 power:

$$T_f = \left(\frac{V_i}{V_f}\right)^{2/3} T_i \qquad (103)$$

We substitute the given values in Eq. (103):

$$T_f = \left(\frac{1}{2}\right)^{2/3} 270.0\ [K] = 170.1\ K \quad (104)$$

The final pressure follows from the ideal gas law:

$$p_f = \frac{nRT_f}{V_f} =$$

$$\frac{1.0[mol]\ 8.31\left[\dfrac{J}{K\ mol}\right]\ 170.1[K]}{2[m^3]} \quad (105)$$

which yields:

$$p_f = 707\ Pa \quad (106)$$

6.7. Cyclic processes

The last application of the first law of thermodynamics which we will discuss in this chapter are cyclic processes. These processes begin and end at the same point in a p–V diagram, i.e., they start and end at the same state of the system. A generic cyclic process is shown in Fig. 6.26(a). Such cyclic processes are of broad interest because many biological processes are based on cycles, such as respiration in Fig. 6.26(b), which we discuss below, or blood circulation in Fig. 6.26(c), which is addressed in problem P–6.7.

There is one cyclic process which is of particular importance for the development of thermal physics: the Carnot cycle which opened the path toward the second law of thermodynamics which we introduce in Chapter 8. The Carnot process is discussed first in this section due to its fundamental importance.

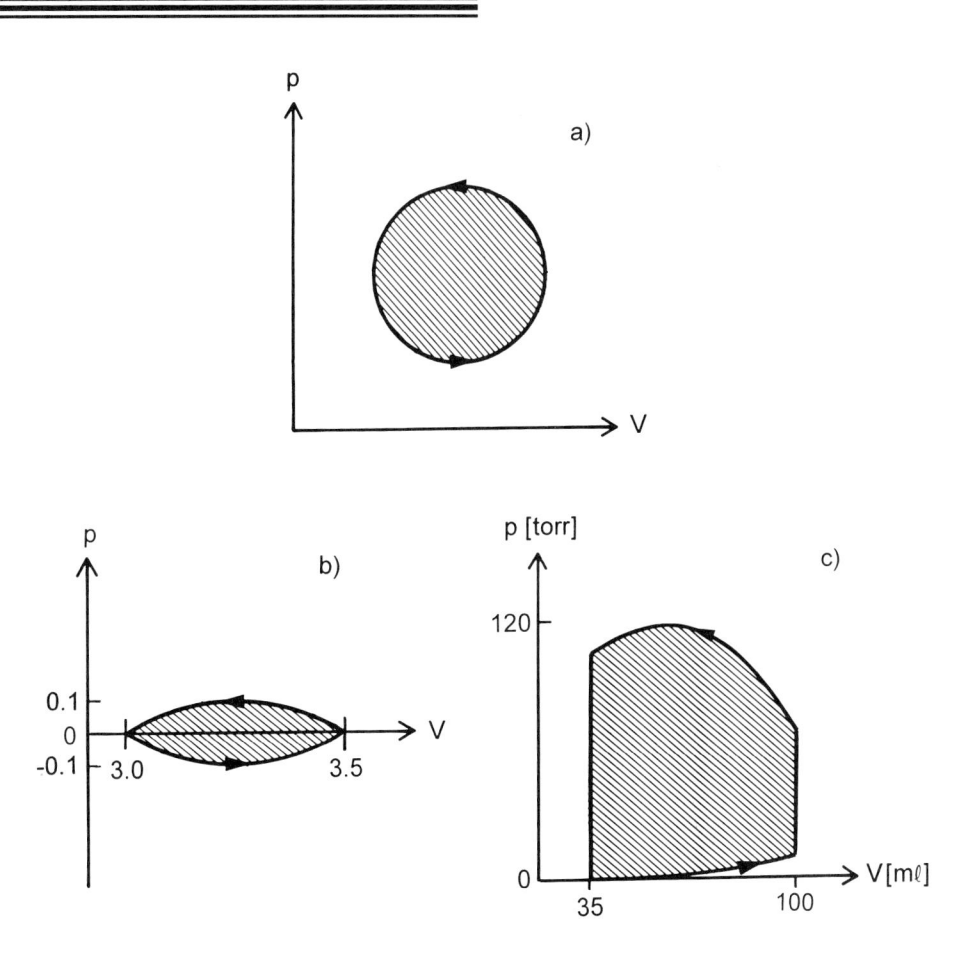

Fig. 6.26: Conceptual sketch and key applications of cyclic processes. (a) A cyclic process is a process that returns to its initial state. Thus, it follows a closed curve in a p–V diagram. The shaded area enclosed by the curve indicates the amount of work required or released per cycle. In the shown case, the work is positive, i.e., the process receives work from the environment. (b) Respiration is a cyclic process discussed in detail in this chapter. The curve shows the alveolar pressure during regular breathing (compare Fig. 6.6). (c) The repetitive action of the heart is another macroscopic cyclic process important in physiology. It is discussed in problem P–6.7 (compare Fig. 6.32).

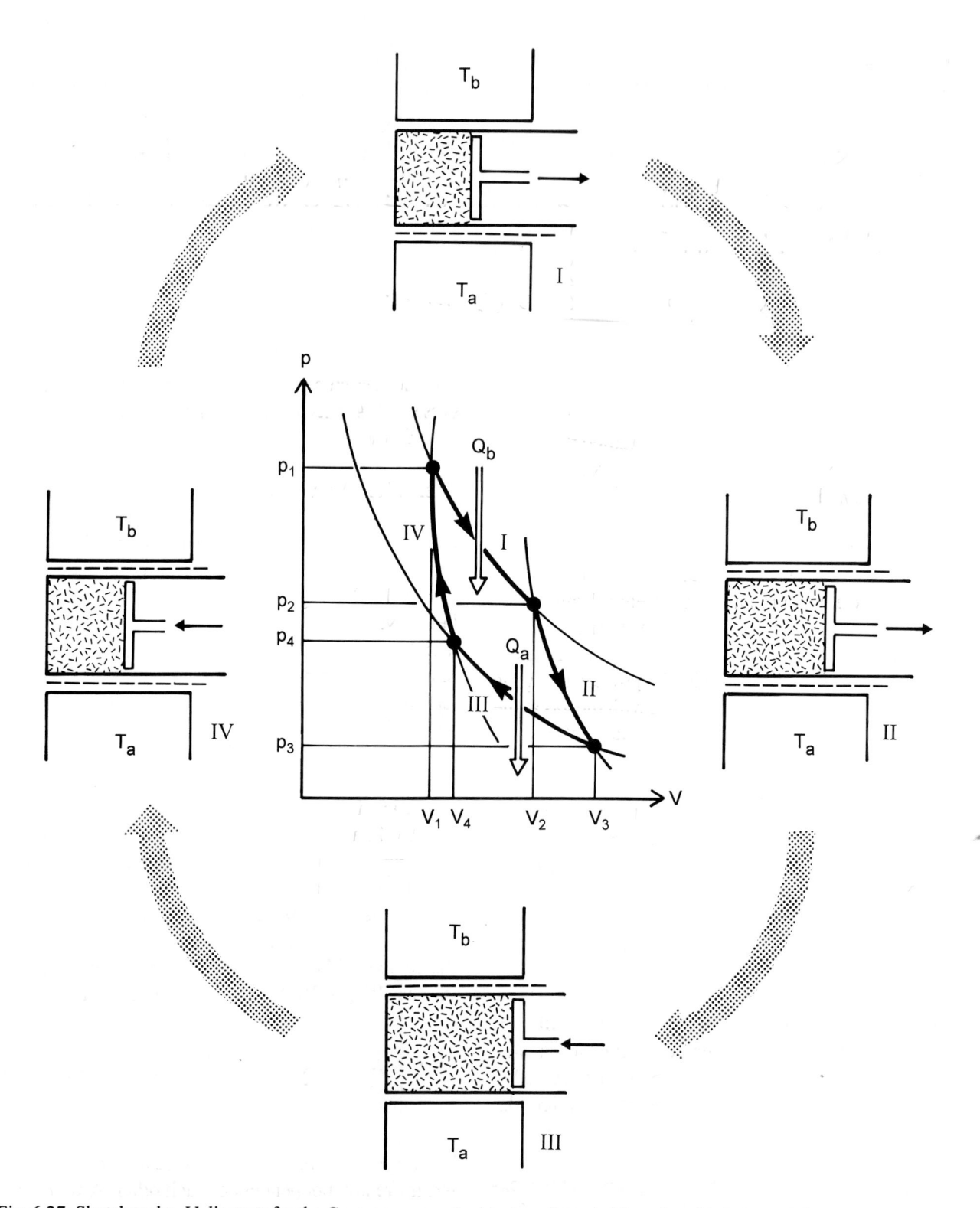

Fig. 6.27: Sketch and p–V diagram for the Carnot process. An ideal gas is sealed in a chamber by a mobile piston. Two heat reservoirs at temperatures T_b and T_a, with $T_b > T_a$ are part of the environment. The Carnot process is divided into four steps: (I) an isothermal expansion, (II) an adiabatic expansion, (III) an isothermal compression, and (IV) an adiabatic compression. The Carnot process is a cyclic process because the four steps return the system to its initial state. The p–V diagram is shown at the center of the figure. The two isothermal curves are extended to both sides as thin lines. The four processes are indicated by the same roman numerals. Heat is taken up from the higher temperature heat reservoir in step I and is released to the lower temperature heat reservoir in step III.

Table 6.2: Summary of work, heat and internal energy change during each step of the Carnot cycle.

Step	I	II	III	IV
Process	isothermal expansion	adiabatic expansion	isothermal compression	adiabatic compression
Work W	$-RT_b \ln(V_2/V_1)$	ΔU_2	$-RT_a \ln(V_4/V_3)$	ΔU_4
Heat Q	$-W_1$	0	$-W_3$	0
Internal Energy Change ΔU	0	$C_V(T_a - T_b)$	0	$C_V(T_b - T_a)$

6.7.1. The Carnot process

In 1824, Nicolas Léonard Sadi Carnot studied the cyclic process shown in Fig. 6.27. The system is an ideal gas, which is contained in a chamber by a frictionless piston. This piston and two heat reservoirs, one at a higher temperature T_b and one at a lower temperature T_a, are part of the environment. The superstructure, consisting of the system and the environment, is not in equilibrium since the two heat reservoirs are at different temperatures. However, Carnot's careful choice of the steps of the cyclic process enables us to describe the process using the first law of thermodynamics. We start with the gas at the temperature T_b, pressure at p_1 and the volume at V_1. The cyclic process consists then of four steps:

(I) First, an isothermal expansion with the system in thermal contact with the heat reservoir at temperature T_b. The dashed line between the heat reservoir at temperature T_a and the system indicates that the lower temperature heat reservoir is currently isolated from the system. The pressure and volume at the end of the first step are p_2 and V_2.

(II) Next the high temperature heat reservoir is disconnected from the system. The gas continues to expand, but now adiabatically, to a pressure p_3 and a volume V_3. During the adiabatic expansion the temperature decreases from T_b to T_a.

(III) After completing the second step the gas has expanded to its largest volume and lowest pressure. The next step is an isothermal compression during which the lower temperature heat reservoir at temperature T_a is in thermal contact with the system. When the pressure reaches p_4 and the volume reaches V_4,

(IV) the heat reservoir is disconnected from the system and the last step, an adiabatic compression, brings the system back to its initial state at temperature T_b, pressure p_1 and volume V_1.

Thereafter, the process repeats, forming a continuous sequence of four-step cycles. The p–V diagram for the Carnot process is shown at the center of Fig. 6.27. The figure is based on two isothermal lines at temperatures T_b and T_a. The four steps of the Carnot process are labelled with roman numerals. In addition, the flow of heat is indicated, with Q_b received by the gas to maintain its temperature during the isothermal expansion, and Q_a released by the system to keep its temperature from rising above T_a during the isothermal compression.

We have already quantified heat, work and internal energy for each of the processes of the Carnot cycle. The isothermal process has been discussed in section 6.6.2, and the adiabatic processes in section 6.6.4. The relevant energy terms are summarized in Table 6.2 for 1.0 mol of an ideal gas as the system.

Using Table 6.2, we determine the work done by the gas, the heat exchange with the heat reservoirs and the change of the internal energy for one full cycle. Noting that $W_2 = -W_4$, the total work is calculated as:

$$\sum_{i=1}^{4} W_i = -RT_b \ln\left(\frac{V_2}{V_1}\right) - RT_a \ln\left(\frac{V_4}{V_3}\right) \quad (107)$$

To simplify this formula, we notice that the four volume terms are not independent of each other. After completing the first two steps, the isothermal compression has to lead to a specific value V_4, which connects back to V_1 in the final adiabatic step. To quantify the relation between the four volume terms we first write Eq. (95) for each of the two adiabatic steps in the Carnot process (step II and step IV):

$$\text{Step II:} \quad T_b^{\frac{C_V}{R}} V_2 = T_a^{\frac{C_V}{R}} V_3$$

$$\text{Step IV:} \quad T_b^{\frac{C_V}{R}} V_1 = T_a^{\frac{C_V}{R}} V_4 \quad (108)$$

The two formulas in Eq. (108) are divided by each other, leading to:

$$\frac{V_2}{V_1} = \frac{V_3}{V_4} \quad (109)$$

Substituting Eq. (109) in Eq. (107) yields for the total work per full cycle of the Carnot process:

$$W_{total} = -R(T_b - T_a) \ln\left(\frac{V_2}{V_1}\right) \quad (110)$$

Next we determine the heat exchange with the heat reservoirs using Table 6.2:

$$\sum_{i=1}^{4} Q_i = Q_b + Q_a = -W_1 - W_3 = -W_{total} \quad (111)$$

From the two results in Eqs. (110) and (111), the total change of internal energy for the Carnot cycle is calculated:

$$\sum_{i=1}^{4} \Delta U_i = 0 \quad (112)$$

This result is not surprising, since the gas returns to its initial state after each cycle of the Carnot process. The internal energy describes that state, and thus must have the same value whenever the gas returns to this state.

In summary, we find for the *Carnot process per cycle with an ideal gas*:

$$W = -R(T_b - T_a)\ln\left(\frac{V_2}{V_1}\right)$$
$$Q = -W$$
$$\Delta U = 0 \quad (113)$$

There is a second, more applied way to characterize cyclic processes by introducing an efficiency coefficient. The motivation stems from an economic interpretation of the Carnot process: the heat input in step I represents an investment while the total work output represents a gain. Thus, we define the efficiency coefficient η for a cyclic process as the ratio of the net work to the heat input per cycle, with the heat input given by the heat which is taken up by the system from the higher temperature heat reservoir:

$$\eta = \frac{|\text{net work}|}{\text{heat input}} = \frac{|W_1 + W_3|}{Q_b} \quad (114)$$

The work and heat terms in Eq. (114) can be substituted by the values given in Table 6.2. This yields:

$$\eta = \frac{T_b - T_a}{T_b} \quad (115)$$

Thus, the efficiency coefficient η is always smaller than unity because it is technically and conceptually impossible to operate a cycle with the lower temperature heat reservoir at $T_a = 0$ K. The work obtained from a Carnot process never matches the energy invested into the system in the form of heat. The work obtained from a Carnot cycle is the maximum work we can extract from any cyclic process. In Chapter 8 we will show that this is due to the fact that the Carnot process is a *reversible process*, meaning that it is a process that can be fully reversed at any instant. Real cyclic processes are never reversible, and the net work is always less than the net work calculated for the Carnot process.

The efficiency coefficient satisfies the interest of engineers to determine the cost efficiency of engines. For example, a 19th century steam engine operated with steam at 120°C and its cooling water at 20°C. Thus, the maximum efficiency coefficient predicted by Eq. (115) is:

$$\eta = \frac{393\,[K] - 293\,[K]}{393\,[K]} = 0.25 \quad (116)$$

i.e., the efficiency coefficient is 25 %. At that time no actual steam engine had an efficiency coefficient exceeding 10 %!

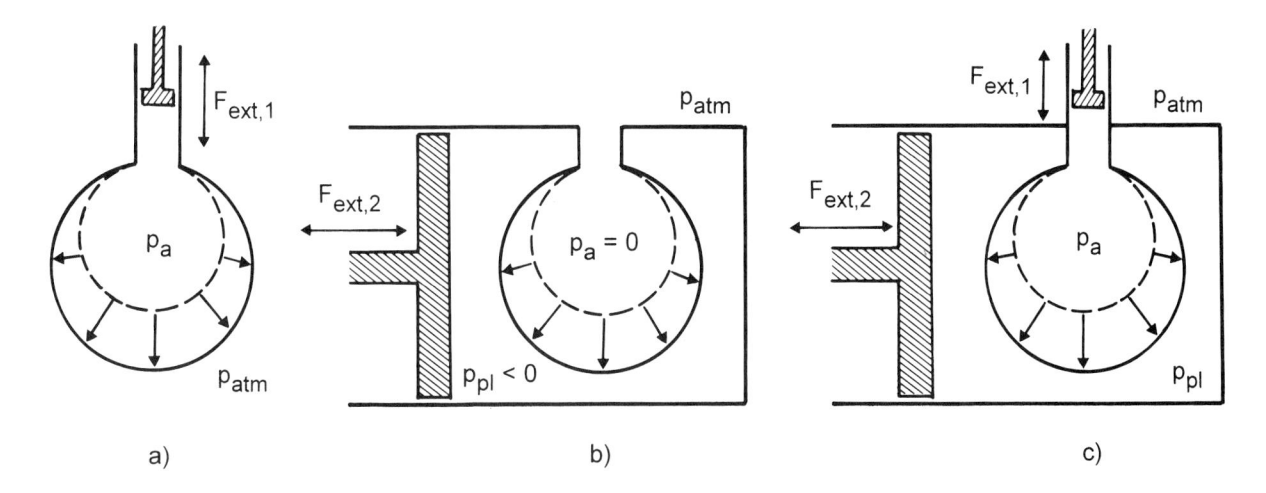

Fig. 6.28: Three models used in the description of the respiratory system. (a) The lungs are represented by a balloon. The gas pressure in the balloon is varied with a piston (subscript 1). We define the gas pressure in the balloon as a gauge pressure (alveolar pressure p_a). A pressure increase in the balloon causes an increase of its volume. Note that the pressure surrounding the balloon is atmospheric pressure. (b) The pleural gap is represented by a container which encloses the balloon. The balloon is open to the external atmospheric pressure. The container allows us to control the pressure surrounding the balloon (using the piston with subscript 2). We define that pressure as a gauge pressure (pleural pressure p_{pl}). (c) In the last step two pistons are included, one to control the alveolar pressure and one to control the pleural pressure.

6.7.2. Respiration cycle

We need a model for the thorax/lung system to study respiration as a cyclic process. This model has to be consistent with the p–V diagrams we introduced at the beginning of the chapter in Figs. 6.4, 6.5 and 6.6.

The best way to introduce this model is to look at Fig. 6.3 and establish the important components in steps. We begin with the lungs. Fig. 6.3 shows that no active muscle forces act directly on the lungs. The only direct interaction occurs with the air inside at pressure p_a and with the pleura at pressure p_{pl}. Recall from our discussion in section 6.1 that p_a and p_{pl} are gauge pressures, i.e., pressure values relative to atmospheric pressure. A suitable model for the lungs is developed in Fig. 6.28.

Fig. 6.28(a): lungs as a balloon with a piston
In the figure, the lungs are modelled by a balloon with a flexible outer membrane. The balloon has an internal pressure p_a and an absolute outside pressure of atmospheric pressure. For such a balloon to remain inflated we require $p_a > 0$. A piston is attached to the balloon to allow us to vary an external force $F_{ext,1}$. This enables us in turn to vary p_a. From our experience in inflating children's balloons we know that the volume of the balloon increases with p_a and that larger and larger pressure increases are needed to achieve a given size increase as the balloon becomes bigger. This observation is consistent with the curve labelled $p_a - p_{pl}$ in Fig. 6.4, which is the transmural pressure difference from lungs to pleura, but it is not consistent with the curve labelled p_a in that figure. Thus, Fig. 6.28(a) is not a useful model for the lungs. Missing in the model is the pleura and the fact that the pleural pressure can differ from atmospheric pressure, i.e., $p_{pl} \neq 0$ is possible.

Fig. 6.28(b): the pleura as a container with piston surrounding the lungs
To improve the proposed model, the pleura is added as a container that encloses the balloon. This container is sealed by a second piston (shown at the left) with which we can exert a second external force, $F_{ext,2}$. Varying the position of the piston allows us to change p_{pl}. In this first extension of our original model the first piston has been removed and the balloon is open to the outside air. This means that $p_a = 0$, and the balloon will only be inflated when $p_{pl} < 0$.

Comparing Figs. 6.28(a) and 6.28(b) illustrates that it is neither one of the absolute pressures nor one of the gauge pressures which ultimately matters for the volume of the balloon: when we increase p_a in Fig. 6.28(a) and decrease p_{pl} in Fig. 6.28(b) such that the balloon has in both cases the same volume, we find $+ p_a$ in part (a) to equal to $- p_{pl}$ in part (b). Thus, the volume of the balloon depends on the pressure difference across the balloon's membrane. Note that this pressure difference is not a gauge pressure as we will see when we discuss the model in Fig. 6.28(c), where both $p_a \neq 0$ and $p_{pl} \neq 0$.

Fig. 6.28(c): Container and enclosed balloon are sealed by a piston

This model for the lung/pleura system is slightly more complex. The additional complexity comes from varying both p_a and p_{pl}, which is possible because the model has two pistons, one attached to the balloon to exert the force $F_{ext,1}$ and one attached to the container surrounding the balloon to exert the force $F_{ext,2}$. It is important to introduce this model because we need both pistons when describing the various curves in Figs. 6.4, 6.5 and 6.6: the model in Fig. 6.28(c) is used to characterize static properties of the respiratory system, i.e., when the test person is asked to inhale or exhale a certain amount of air, then stop (mouthpiece valve closed to spirometer) and relax the breathing muscles. The model in Fig. 6.28(b) in turn is used when studying very slow (air flow resistance free) breathing with an open mouth. The open mouth guarantees in this case that the pressure in the lungs is always equal to atmospheric pressure.

We discuss first in detail how the model in Fig. 6.28(c) explains the data shown in Fig. 6.4. The force $F_{ext,1}$ is required to obtain $p_a \neq 0$. The force $F_{ext,1}$ can be exerted by two sources:
(I) the streaming of air in or out of the lungs, and
(II) the propensity toward elastic collapse of the balloon–like lungs.

When neither one of these sources act on the system, e.g., when we open our mouth and relax, $p_a = 0$ and the respiratory system is in mechanical equilibrium. In a simple self–experiment you can confirm that this state is reached after regular exhalation at a lung volume of 3.0 liters: concentrate on your chest as you breath very slowly. Hold your breath after a regular inhalation and after a regular exhalation. You notice that you are most relaxed after exhalation because the forces on the lungs are balanced and do not need support through muscle action.

The air flow–related force contribution to $F_{ext,1}$ is excluded in Gig. 6.4 because this p–V diagram represents a static view of the respiratory system. Indeed, air flow–related issues enter the discussion only when we discuss Fig. 6.6. This leaves the elastic force of the lungs as the only force contributing to $F_{ext,1}$ in Fig. 6.4. Thus, it is the tendency of the lungs to undergo an elastic collapse which the piston exerting force $F_{ext,1}$ on the gas in the lungs represents.

The force $F_{ext,2}$ is needed to allow variations of the pleural pressure, i.e., $p_{pl} \neq 0$ for the pressure in the container surrounding the balloon. Again, two different sources can provide this force:
(I) the active muscles forces exerted by the diaphragm and the intercostal muscles between the ribs, and
(II) the elastic propensity of the thorax to collapse (outwards toward the rib cage).

The active muscle forces are not included in the force $F_{ext,2}$ in Fig. 6.4 because the curves in that p–V diagram are drawn for a relaxed chest. Thus, the piston exerting the force $F_{ext,2}$ represents in Fig. 6.4 the tendency of the thorax to change toward its elastic equilibrium position. We conclude that both pistons in Fig. 6.28(c) represent elastic forces when interpreting Fig. 6.4, one associated with the propensity toward elastic collapse of the balloon–like lungs and the other associated with the propensity of the thorax to move toward its equilibrium position. For the healthy person, these two forces are not independent because a fixed amount of fluid in the pleural gap provides for a strong adhesion between the visceral layer of the pleura on the lung surface and the parietal layer on the inside of the thorax. We can observe the action of both elastic forces independently for a patient with a punctured pleura. The punctured pleura allows air to enter the gap between lungs and thorax, and each relaxes to its equilibrium shape at zero gauge pressures p_a and p_{pl} (dashed horizontal lines in Fig. 6.4): the lungs collapse to a minimum volume of less than one liter and the thorax widens to a size corresponding to a 4.5 liter capacity of the lungs.

For the healthy person, the curve labelled $p_a - p_{pl}$ in Fig. 6.4 indicates the elastic response of the lungs to the transmural pressure difference; this pressure difference is always positive since otherwise the lungs could not stay inflated. In the range of normal breathing (breathing of the tidal volume between lung capacities of 3.0 and 3.5 liters) the transmural pressure difference varies between 500 Pa and 600 Pa. For lung volumes above 3.0 liters p_a is positive, i.e., upon opening the mouth air will stream out of the lungs. In turn, for lung volumes below 3.0 liters (after a deep exhalation) p_a is negative, i.e., opening the mouth will cause air to stream into the lungs.

The pleural pressure p_{pl} lies always below the alveolar pressure p_a, but crosses from negative to positive values at about 4.5 liter lung capacity. At that point, the direction of stress in the thorax is inverted: for smaller volumes the thorax wants to expand, and for larger volumes it wants to contract. This is the reason why it is particularly hard for a test person to hold more than 4.5 liters air in the lungs.

In the next step toward understanding the actual processes during breathing, we evaluate the p–V diagram in Fig. 6.5, for which the model in Fig. 6.28(b) applies. Note that the piston allowing for the force $F_{ext,1}$ is not present in that figure. Instead, the balloon–like lungs are open to the external air pressure and $p_a = 0$ at all lung volumes. We still neglect effects due to air flow–resistance, for which the second piston would be required. In Fig. 6.28(b) the pressure p_{pl} can still vary; the pleural pressure is changing now due to the action of both possible forces: the active muscle forces and the elastic force of the thorax. The need for an active muscle force is evident from Fig. 6.4: if $p_a = 0$ and p_{pl} were only adjusted by elastic forces in the thorax, then the only possible lung volume would be V = 3.0 liters. However, we cannot breathe at a fixed lung volume. Thus, an active mechanism to vary the lung volume is required.

Breathing is modelled in Fig. 6.28(b) by the back–and–forth motion of the piston. During that motion the pressure p_{pl} changes and with it the pressure difference $p_a - p_{pl} = -p_{pl}$ (because $p_a = 0$). The variation of these pressure values corresponds to different lung volume values in Fig. 6.5. We decrease the pleural pressure during very slow inhalation by expanding the thorax because the lungs expand faster. The effect is reversed during slow exhalation.

Note that the curve of the pulmonary volume versus the pressure difference $p_a - p_{pl}$ is the same in Figs. 6.4 and 6.5: the volume of the lungs depends exclusively on the transmural pressure difference as we already concluded from comparing Figs. 6.28(a) and 6.28(b).

We calculate the work done during very slow breathing in Fig. 6.5 using the following example.

Example 6.11
Calculate the work for very slow breathing from the p–V diagram in Fig. 6.5 for
(a) a single inhalation,
(b) a single exhalation, and
(c) a full breathing cycle.
(d) The work done by muscles during breathing at rest is reported as 0.7 J/s in the physiological literature. How do you explain your results in parts (a) and (c) when compared with this value?

Hint: to simplify the calculations, approximate the pleural pressure curve in Fig. 6.5 as linear. This is shown in Fig. 6.29.

Solution part (a): We calculate the work required from the curve p_{pl} versus lung volume in Fig. 6.5 because the active muscles act on the pleura and therefore most directly affect the pleural pressure.

Fig. 6.29(a) shows the curve p_{pl} versus lung volume for slow inhalation. Recall that the tidal volume is 0.5 liters, i.e., a person at rest inhales from a lung volume of $V_{exh} = 3.0$ liters to $V_{inh} = 3.5$ liters, in which the subscript *inh* stands for inhaled and the subscript *exh* for exhaled. Thus, the work required is the area under the curve between V_{exh} and V_{inh}. This area is shaded in Fig. 6.29(a).

The area under the curve in Fig. 6.29(a) is divided into two parts: a triangle and a rectangle located below the triangle. The rectangle must be included because the work calculation requires the area under the curve down to absolute pressure zero. The area of the triangle is:

$$A_\triangle = \frac{1}{2} 0.5[l] \, 0.1[kPa] = 0.025 \, J \quad (117)$$

The area of the rectangle is:

$$A_\square = 0.5[l] \, 1.007 \times 10^5[Pa] = 50.350 \, J \quad (118)$$

Thus, the work per inhalation is the sum of these two areas with the appropariate sign based on Eq. (5.19): $W_{inh} = -50.375$ J. The value is negative, i.e. work is done by the system on its environment.

The negative sign brings us back to the question of what we identify as the system and what we identify

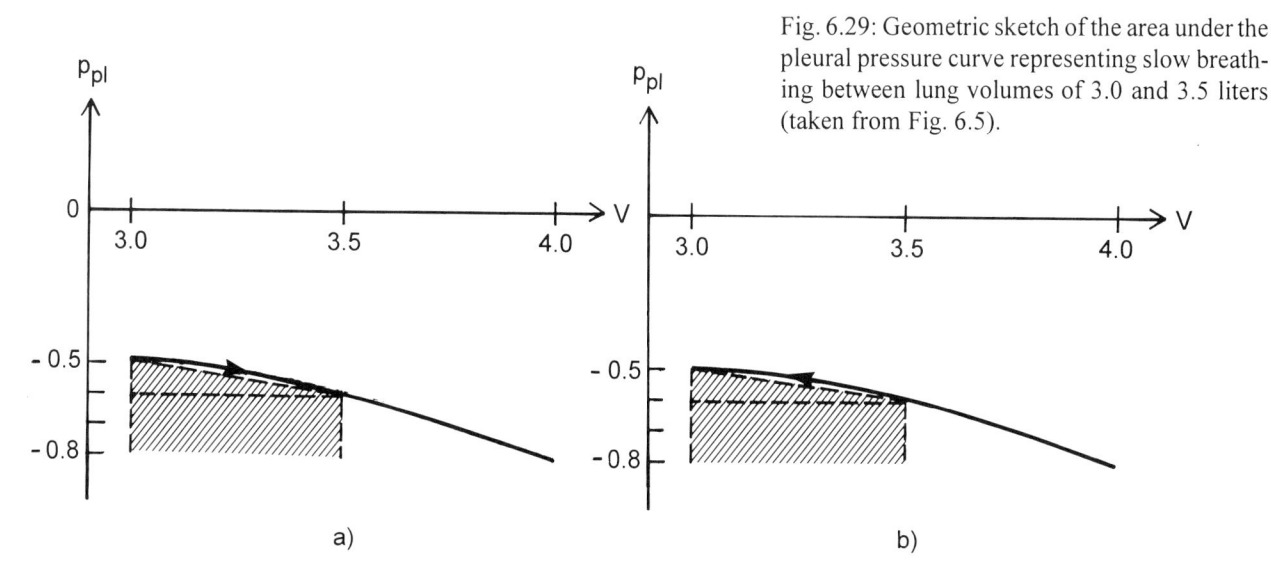

Fig. 6.29: Geometric sketch of the area under the pleural pressure curve representing slow breathing between lung volumes of 3.0 and 3.5 liters (taken from Fig. 6.5).

as the environment. Naively, we would have argued that the gas in the lungs is the system as this gas expands from V_{exh} to V_{inh}. However, the gas in the lungs does not do the work we calculated. The only way the gas could do the work would be at the expense of its internal energy or at the expense of energy the gas absorbs from its environment. But neither of these processes occurs in the lungs as we discussed earlier in this chapter. Instead, as suggested in Fig. 6.28(b), the work originates in the muscles acting on the pleura. Thus, the environment receiving the work consists of the elastic tissues of the pleura and the lungs, the work is done by the active muscles (on behalf of the gas in the lungs). Note that we have to discuss this process in further detail in part (d).

Solution part (b): Next we calculate the work associated with a single exhalation as illustrated in Fig. 6.29(b). This figure shows again the curve p_{pl} versus lung volume, with the work we want to calculate highlighted as the shaded area under the curve between V_{exh} and V_{inh}. The area under the curve in Fig. 6.29(b) is the same as in Fig. 6.29(a): the exhalation work is $W_{exh} = + 50.375$ J due to the sign rules of Eq. (5.19). The value is positive, i.e. work is done on the system by its environment.

Based on the same arguments we used in part (a), this result is interpreted in the following way: the work W_{exh} originates from the elastic tissues of the pleura and the lungs; this work is done on the gas and the active muscles.

Solution part (c): The work for a full breathing cycle is the sum of the work for a single inhalation and the work for a single exhalation. Using the two values we found in parts (a) and (b), we determine that:

$$W_{cycle} = -50.35 \, J + 50.35 \, J = 0 \, J \quad (119)$$

This result implies that no net work has to be done per cycle. From experience we know that this is not true; as the question in part (d) states, work is required during breathing. Thus, the assumptions we made to find the result in Eq. (119) have to be revisited. We will do this by studying Fig. 6.6 in greater detail below. That figure then applies to actual breathing as opposed to very slow breathing, which is an assumption which obviously oversimplifies the issue.

Solution part (d): However, before we turn our attention to the actual breathing process, there is still more we can learn from the current example. In this example we assumed idealized, very slow breathing. For this we found in part (a) that the initial inhalation requires an effort which we quantified as slightly more than -50 J of work. Then we determined that the same amount of work is recovered during the subsequent exhalation, leading to no net effort for the entire cycle. This can only be true if the work done during the inhalation is indeed recovered by the system which did the work in the first step. Otherwise, per breathing cycle, work equivalent of 50 J has to be done and 50 J of energy would then be dissipated during the exhalation, leading to a net total work of -50 J per cycle.

To clarify this issue, we begin with the actual, experimental value of the work done by the breathing muscles. This value is stated in the example text. Using 15 breathing cycles per minute for a resting person, the given value of 0.7 J/s for the work done by the breathing muscles corresponds to:

$$W_{cycle} = \frac{0.7 \frac{J}{s} \, 60 \frac{s}{min}}{15 \frac{cycles}{min}} = 2.8 \frac{J}{cycle} \quad (120)$$

This is only about 5 % of the work we calculated as required for a single inhalation. Thus, in real breathing our muscles need only to do a small fraction of the work which has to be done during an inhalation. Consequently, something else must be doing the lion–share of that work. But what is that? Remember that we already ruled out the gas in the lungs.

The answer for the inhalation is the same as for the exhalation: the work is provided by the elastic action of stretched tissue, the lungs expanding and collapsing inside the pleura leading to an opposite collapsing and expanding of the pleural tissue. Recall that the dashed horizontal line in Fig. 6.4 indicates the response of pleura and lungs when the lungs get punctured: both tissues collapse, the lungs to a small volume and the pleura outwards. Thus, both tissues are stretched in opposite directions. During inhalation the lungs expand and the pleura partially collapses. Then, during the following exhalation, the lungs partially collapse and the pleura expands. Thus, elastic energy is shifting back and forth between the lung tissue and the pleura tissue; only a small fraction of the work has to be done by the breathing muscles accounting for energy losses during the energy transfer between lung tissue and pleural tissue.

Lastly, we study Fig. 6.6 for which we use the model shown in Fig. 6.28(c). The larger piston allows us to vary the pressure in the pleura surrounding the lungs and the smaller piston allows us to vary the pressure inside the lungs. We need both abilities; the processes we just discussed for slow breathing continue to dominate the regular breathing process, including the alternating expansion and collapse of lungs and pleura to conserve the elastic energy. In addition, we need to account for the observation that air has to be pulled actively through the trachea into the lungs during inhalation, and that air has to be pushed actively out of the lungs during exhalation. The small piston in Fig. 6.28(c) allows for this to occur: during inhalation the pressure in the lungs is lowered by up to 100 Pa, and during exhalation the pressure in the lungs is increased by up to 100 Pa. This is illustrated in Fig. 6.7. These pressure differences have to be added on top of the infinitely slow breathing we assumed in Fig. 6.5. Affected are only the pleural pressure and the pressure in the lungs; the transmural pressure remains unchanged because that pressure difference governs exclusively the size (volume) of the lungs. From Fig. 6.6 the fraction of work associated with the flow resistance of air in the trachea can be calculated for a full breathing cycle. This is shown in the example below.

Example 6.12
Calculate the work for a regular breathing cycle due to the air resistance during breathing.
Hint: this work is given as the difference in work calculated for Figs. 6.5 and 6.6. To simplify the calculation, estimate this work from the four shaded triangles illustrated in Fig. 6.30.

Solution: In the first step the combined area of the four triangles in Fig. 6.30 is determined. Note that these triangles are identical, with each displaying a base of 0.25 liters (e.g., the top left triangle has a base stretching from 3.0 liters to 3.25 liters), and a height of 0.1 kPa. Thus, their combined area is four times the area of each triangle:

$$A_{total} = 4 \frac{1}{2} (0.25[l]\, 0.1[kPa]) = 0.05\, J \quad \textbf{(121)}$$

The work in the cyclic process is positive, i.e., $W_{cycle} = +\,0.05$ J. Work has been done on the gas. This work is included in the work we calculated from experimental data in Eq. (120). We note that less than 2 % of the respiratory work is required for forcing the air into and out of the lungs; the flow resistance of the gas is comparably small. A fish requires much more work to obtain the required flow of water through its gills because water is liquid and has therefore a much greater flow resistance than air. Flow resistance is discussed further in Chapter 11.

6.8. Appendix

Collisions
A comprehensive treatment of collisions is a broad task for two reasons: (I) an extensive mathematical formalism results even for simple cases because a combination of a vector formula (conservation of momentum) and a scalar formula (energy redistribution) are involved, and (II) collisions can lead to a wide range of physical processes which need to be treated separately.
   We limit the discussion in this appendix to the most fundamental cases by applying several restrictions: (i) the collision is one–dimensional, i.e., the two objects move along a common straight line before and after col-

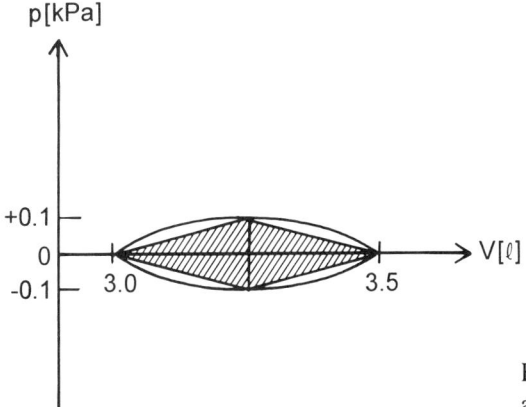

Fig. 6.30: Geometric sketch of the area enclosed by the alveolar pressure during a tidal breathing cycle.

liding,
(ii) the only form of energy exchanged between the two colliding objects is kinetic energy,
(iii) the objects have masses m_1 and m_2, with the object of mass m_1 initially moving at speed v_{1i} and the object of mass m_2 initially at rest.

Two basic types of collisions are introduced with these conditions:

(A) Elastic collisions
For an elastic collision both the conservation of momentum and the conservation of mechanical energy apply. The conservation of momentum reads:

$$m_1 v_{1i} = m_1 v_{1f} + m_2 v_{2f} \quad (122)$$

in which the final speed of the object of mass m_1 is called v_{1f} and the final speed of the object of mass m_2 is v_{2f}. The conservation of energy reads:

$$\frac{1}{2} m_1 v_{1i}^2 = \frac{1}{2} m_1 v_{1f}^2 + \frac{1}{2} m_2 v_{2f}^2 \quad (123)$$

To combine Eqs. (122) and (123), we first isolate v_{2f} in Eq. (122):

$$v_{2f} = \frac{m_1}{m_2} \left(v_{1i} - v_{1f} \right) \quad (124)$$

Then we substitute v_{2f} into Eq. (123):

$$m_1 v_{1i}^2 = m_1 v_{1f}^2 + m_2 \frac{m_1^2}{m_2^2} \left(v_{1i} - v_{1f} \right)^2 \quad (125)$$

Eq. (125) is a quadratic equation which is grouped for the various v_{1f} terms:

$$v_{1f}^2 \left[m_1 \left(1 + \frac{m_1}{m_2} \right) \right] - v_{1f} \left[2 v_{1i} \frac{m_1^2}{m_2} \right] +$$
$$\ldots + v_{1i}^2 m_1 \left(\frac{m_1}{m_2} - 1 \right) = 0 \quad (126)$$

This equation can be solved for v_{1f}. We focus in particular on three specific cases:

(A1) Collision of two objects of equal mass. An example are two identical gas particles colliding in a container. In this case we note that $m_1 = m_2 = m$. The quadratic equation (Eq. (126)) simplifies to:

$$m v_{1f}^2 - 2 m v_{1f} v_{1i} = 0 \quad (127)$$

which yields:

$$v_{1f} = 0 \quad \text{or} \quad v_{1f} = v_{1i} \quad (128)$$

i.e., there are two solutions: either the object of mass m_1 passes through the object of mass m_2 without interaction (physically not possible) or the object of mass m_1 transfers its entire speed to the object of mass m_2 and comes to rest.

(A2) A much heavier object hits a much lighter object at rest. An example is the collision between a fast car and a small, airborne pebble. In this case we use $m_1 \gg m_2$ and Eq. (126) leads to:

$$v_{1f}^2 \frac{m_1^2}{m_2} - 2 v_{1f} v_{1i} \frac{m_1^2}{m_2} + v_{1i}^2 \frac{m_1^2}{m_2} = 0 \quad (129)$$

which simplifies to:

$$\left(v_{1f} - v_{1i} \right)^2 = 0 \quad (130)$$

and yields:

$$v_{1f} = v_{1i} \quad (131)$$

i.e., the heavier object pushes the lighter object away without being affected.

(A3) A much lighter object hits a heavy object at rest. An example is a gas particle hitting a container wall. In this case we use $m_1 \ll m_2$ and Eq. (126) simplifies to:

$$m_1 v_{1f}^2 - m_1 v_{1i}^2 = 0 \quad (132)$$

which yields:

$$v_{1f} = \pm v_{1i} \quad (133)$$

Eq. (133) identifies again two solutions: either the incoming object passes through the heavy object without interaction (physically impossible) or it is reflected with

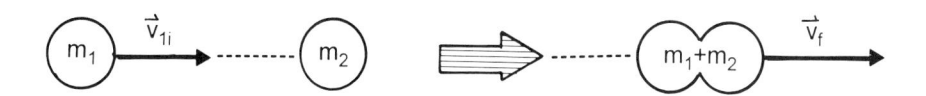

Fig. 6.31: A specific case of an inelastic collision in which the two particles merge. Initially, the object with mass m_1 moves with velocity v_{1i} and the object with mass m_2 is at rest. The merged object moves with velocity v_f after the collision.

the same speed, moving after the collision in the opposite direction than before the collision. This is the case used in section 6.3 to quantify the collision of the particle in the box with the shaded wall, as illustrated in Fig. 6.15.

(B) Inelastic collisions
Inelastic collisions are more complicated because the combined kinetic energy of the two colliding particles is not conserved. Thus, an inelastic collision can only occur in a closed or open system as a fraction of the energy must leave the system. The only case solvable without further assumptions occurs when the two objects merge during the collision, as illustrated in Fig. 6.31. In any other case knowledge of the amount of kinetic energy lost from the system would be required.

We assume again that the object of mass m_1 moves initially with speed v_{1i} and the object of mass m_2 is at rest. We label the final speed of the merged object v_f. This object has a mass of $M = m_1 + m_2$. Since the energy is not conserved in this case, the only condition is the conservation of momentum in the form:

$$m_1 v_{1i} = (m_1 + m_2) v_f \quad (134)$$

This allows us to discuss three special cases analogous to the elastic collision above, namely:
(B1) $m_1 = m_2 = m$ which leads to $v_f = \tfrac{1}{2} v_{1i}$,
(B2) $m_1 \gg m_2$ which leads to $v_f = v_{1i}$, and
(B3) $m_1 \ll m_2$ which results in $v_f = 0$.

6.9. Problems

P–6.1
(a) Draw a graph for the volume of 1.0 mol of an ideal gas as a function of temperature in the range from 0 K to 400 K at constant gas pressures of, first, 0.2 atm and, secondly, 5 atm.
(b) Draw a graph for the pressure of 1.0 mol of an ideal gas as a function of volume between 0 liter and 20 liter at constant temperatures of 150 K and 300 K.

P–6.2
A container of volume 1 mm³ is initially filled with air. The container is then evacuated at 25°C to a pressure of 1.0×10^{-6} torr. How many molecules are in the container after evacuation if we assume that air is an ideal gas?

P–6.3
A container with a volume of V = 500 cm³ has a mass of 38.7340 g when evacuated. When the container is filled with air of pressure p = 1.0 atm at temperature T = 24°C, the mass of the system increases to 39.3135 g. Assuming that air behaves like an ideal gas, calculate from these data the average molar mass of air.

P–6.4
A container of volume V = 10.0 dm³ contains 1.03×10^{23} hydrogen gas molecules (H_2). If the pressure of the gas is 30.0 torr, what is
(a) the temperature, and
(b) the root–mean–square speed of the molecules?
Hint: Treat hydrogen as an ideal gas and use the conversion 1.0 torr = 133.32 Pa. The molecular mass of hydrogen is $M(H_2) = 2.0$ g/mol.

P–6.5
Fig. 5.19 shows a p–V diagram with four paths that a gas can take from an initial state *i* to a final state *f*. Rank the paths in decreasing order according to
(a) the change of internal energy ΔU, and
(b) the amount of heat transfer Q between the system and the environment.

P–6.6
1.0 mol of an ideal gas is expanded from an initial pressure of 10 atm to a final pressure of 0.4 atm in the same fashion as discussed in section 6.6. Calculate separately for two constant temperatures, 0°C and 25°C,
(a) the work done by the gas,
(b) the change of internal energy of the gas, and
(c) the amount of heat taken from the environment.

P–6.7

Fig. 6.32 shows the p–V relationship in the left ventricle of the human heart. The curve is traversed counter-clockwise with increasing time. The stroke volume is 100 ml – 35 ml = 65 ml. The systolic pressure is 118 torr (which is equal to 15.7 kPa) and the diastolic pressure is 70 torr (which is equal to 9.3 kPa). The ventricular pressure drops below the diastolic pressure while the pressure in the arteries remains about 70 torr because the aortic valve has closed and prevents back flow. Determine graphically the amount of work done per cycle.
Hint: Simplify the calculation by using the dashed straight lines in the p–V diagram instead of curved segments.

P–6.8

(a) How much heat is needed to increase the temperature of 3.45 g neon gas (Ne) in a 10 liter container from 0^0C to 100^0C? Treat neon as an ideal gas, and use M(Ne) = 20.18 g/mol.
(b) By how many percent does $<v^2>$ of the neon atoms in the gas increase in this process?
Hint: part (b) does not ask for v_{rms}.

P–6.9

Show that Eq. (94) leads to Eq. (96) when using the operations specified in the text.

P–6.10

1.0 mol of an ideal gas which starts at 1.0 atm and 25^0C does 1.0 kJ of work during an adiabatic expansion.
(a) What is the final temperature of the gas?
(b) What is the final volume of the gas?

P–6.11

Compare the efficiency coefficient for a Carnot machine operating between a low temperature heat reservoir at room temperature (25^0C) and a high temperature heat reservoir at the boiling point of water at two different pressures:
(a) 5 atm with $T_{boil} = 152^0C$, and
(b) 100 atm with $T_{boil} = 312^0C$.

P–6.12

A Carnot process is operated with 1.0 mol of an ideal gas of heat capacity $C_V = 3R/2$. The pressure of the gas is 10.0 atm and the temperature is 600 K in the most compressed state. From there, an isothermal expansion leads to a pressure 1.0 atm. The lower process temperature is 300 K.
(a) Calculate for each step of this Carnot process the work and heat exchange with the environment.
(b) What is the efficiency coefficient of this machine?
(c) Draw this Carnot process as a p–V diagram, then sketch it as a p–T diagram, a V–T diagram, and a U–T diagram.

P–6.13

The cyclic process in Fig. 6.33 consists of (I) an isothermal expansion, (II) an isochoric cooling and (III) an adiabatic compression. If the process is done with n = 2.5 mol of an ideal gas, what are
(a) the total work done by the gas,
(b) the heat exchanged with the environment, and
(c) the change of the internal energy for one cycle.
(d) Sketch the cyclic process of Fig. 6.33 as p–T, V–T and U–T diagrams.

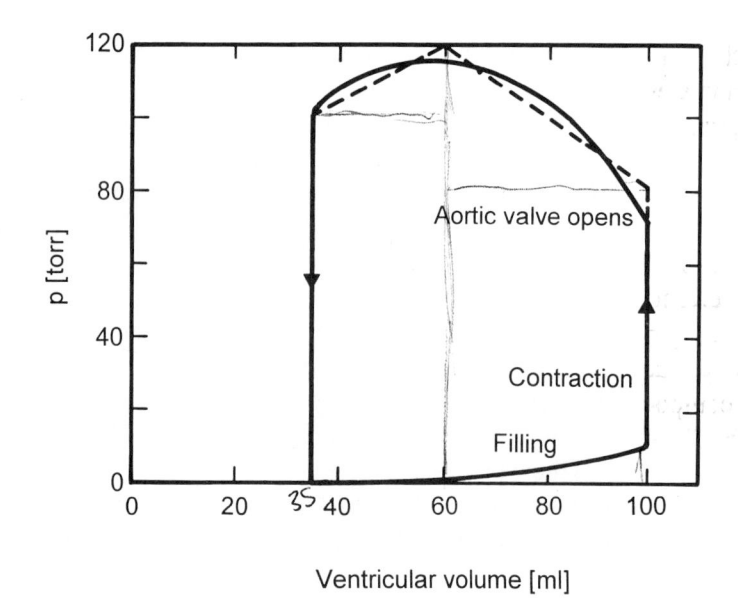

Fig. 6.32 for problem P–6.7. The figure illustrates the p–V diagram for the left ventricle of the human heart. The blood pressure increases initially slowly as blood flows into the ventricle from the left atrium (through the mitral valve), but then jumps to about 75 torr during the contraction of the heart muscle. This pressure causes the aortic valve to open. The blood pressure continues to rise, but the volume of the ventricular chamber decreases concurrently as blood is ejected from the heart. The aortic valve closes when the muscle contraction is complete, leaving the ventricle at a fixed volume of 35 ml until the mitral valve opens again for the next filling step.

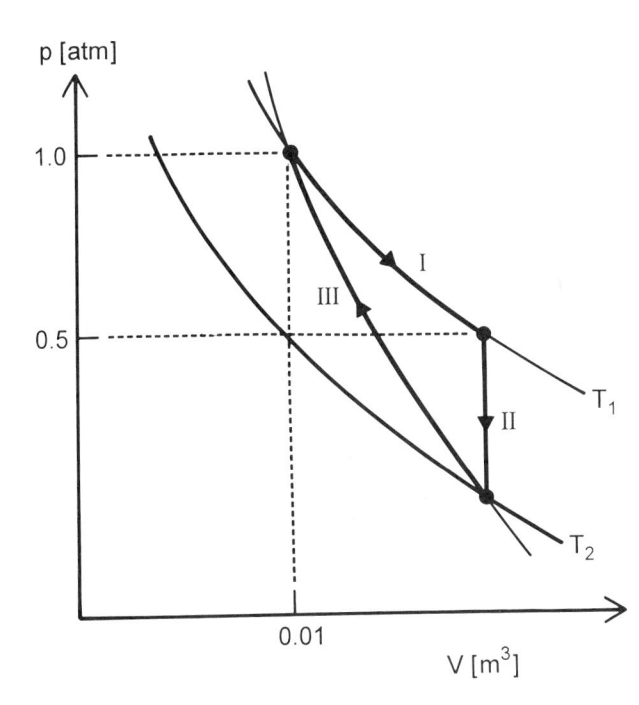

Fig. 6.33 for problem P–6.13.

P–6.14

In section 6.6.3 it is stated that $C_p = C_V + R$ holds for an ideal gas. Derive this result for an isobaric expansion of 1.0 mol of ideal gas without using the enthalpy concept. For this, start with the work in Eq. (82) and the change of internal energy in Eq. (63) for the expansion in Fig. 6.23. Then use the first law of thermodynamics and the definition

$$Q = n C_p \Delta T \qquad (135)$$

which applies for an isobaric process.

P–6.15

A boy wants to pretend that he has a fever. He notices that air he breathes onto his arm feels warmer than the arm itself. Reasoning that breathing on a thermometer should effectively drive up the mercury column, will he succeed to deceive his parents?

P–6.16

We study a tidal volume (0.5 liter) of dry air at two frequently used reference states. With index 1 we refer to the gas at STPD conditions, i.e., $p_1 = 101.3$ kPa, $T_1 = 0°C$, $V_1 = 0.5$ liters; with index 2 we refer to the gas at BTPS conditions, but excluding the water vapor component added during inhalation, i.e., $p_2 = 95.0$ kPa, $T_2 = 37°C$, $V_2 = 0.605$ liters.

(a) Why is V_2 not also given as 0.5 liters?
(b) We transfer the gas from state 1 to state 2. Assuming that we adjust the pressure first in an isothermal step and then the temperature in an isobaric step, what fraction of the total volume change occurs in the isothermal step?
(c) Assuming that we invert the order of the two steps in part (b), i.e., we start with an isobaric step followed by an isothermal step, is the fraction of the total volume change after the first step the same as in part (b)?
(d) Can the process from STPD to BTPS conditions also be achieved with an initial isochoric step followed by an isobaric step?

Summary

Definitions:
- Heat Q for:

(i) isochoric process for an ideal gas:

$$Q = C_V\, n\, \Delta T$$

C_V [J/(mol K)] is the molar heat capacity at constant volume, $C_V = 3R/2$ for the ideal gas.

(ii) isobaric process for an ideal gas:

$$Q = C_p\, n\, \Delta T$$

C_p [J/(mol K)] is the molar heat capacity at constant pressure, $C_p = 5R/2$ for the ideal gas.

Laws:
- Ideal gas law:

$$pV = nRT$$

with R the gas constant.
- Internal energy of an ideal gas:

$$U\left[\frac{J}{mol}\right] = \frac{3}{2} RT = \frac{1}{2} M \langle v^2 \rangle$$

$$\epsilon\left[\frac{J}{particle}\right] = \frac{3}{2} \frac{R}{N_A} T = \frac{3}{2} kT$$

N_A is the Avogadro number, k is the Boltzmann constant and $v_{rms} = (\langle v^2 \rangle)^{1/2}$ is the root–mean–square speed of the gas particles:

$$v_{rms} = \sqrt{\frac{3RT}{M}} = \sqrt{\frac{3kT}{m}}$$

m is the mass of a single particle.
- Work: for an ideal gas with frictionless piston

(i) isochoric process (V = const):

$$W = 0$$

(ii) isothermal process (T = const):

$$W = -nRT \ln\left(\frac{V_f}{V_i}\right)$$

(iii) isobaric process (p = const):

$$W = -p\left(V_f - V_i\right)$$

- Change of the internal energy for a cyclic process:

$$\Delta U_{cycle} = 0$$

Chapter VII

Membranes

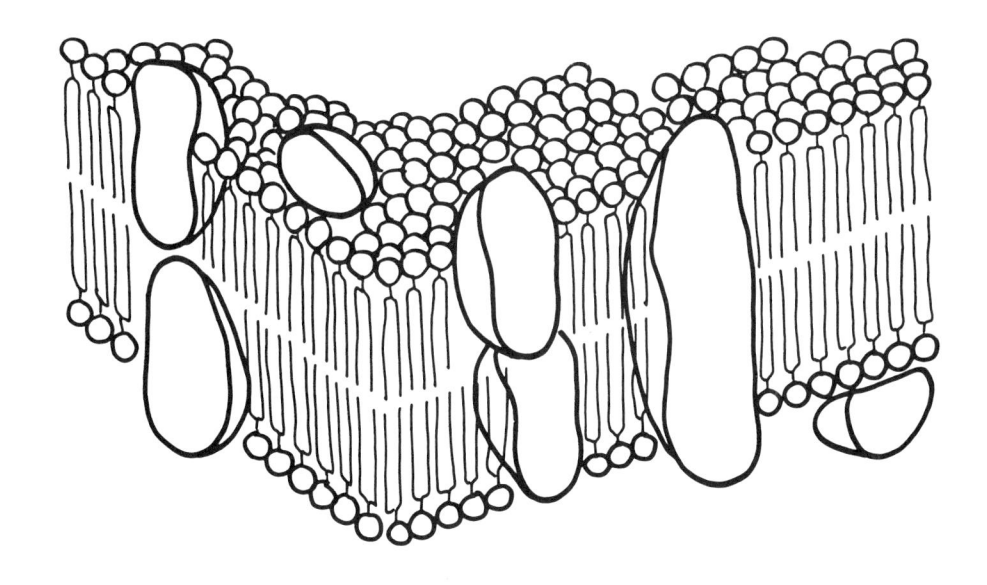

Transport of energy and matter

MEMBRANES
TRANSPORT OF ENERGY AND MATTER

Membranes separate systems. A semipermeable membrane enables two adjacent systems to interact through exchange of heat and/or matter. The exchange occurs if the two systems differ in one or more essential parameters: if they differ in temperature heat flows toward the colder system (heat conduction) and if they differ in the concentration of a chemical component matter flows toward the more dilute system (diffusion). Diffusion and heat conduction are transport phenomena. The transport across the membrane is proportional to the cross–sectional area of the membrane and is inversely proportional to its length. The proportionality constants between heat flow and temperature difference (called the thermal conductivity coefficient) and between matter flow and concentration difference (called the diffusion coefficient) are materials constants.

Diffusion coefficients are strongly temperature dependent. This is explained by a microscopic model of single atoms or molecules hopping between energetically favored adjacent sites in the matrix. In the hopping process an activation energy must be overcome utilizing the thermal energy of the diffusing particle (Arrhenius model). Each particle jumps randomly to any of the available adjacent sites, including the site from which it came in the previous jump. Consequently the particle traverses in N jumps of length a a total distance less than Na. Einstein found that the total distance, defined as the diffusion length, is proportional to $(Dt)^{1/2}$ with D the diffusion coefficient and t the diffusion time.

Heat conduction and diffusion play a key role in many physiological applications such as the protection of whales against hypothermia in the arctic sea or the exchange of oxygen between the gas volume in the lung's alveoli and the adjacent blood capillaries.

Life is about diversity. Life is about incredible complexity down to the microscopic level of the living cell. And life is about continuous change; from change the fossil record documents on a time scale of hundreds of millions of years to change which occurs on a time scale of minutes in which the life cycle of bacteria brings about a new generation. Structural complexity and change with time are key characteristics of life which set it apart from inanimate matter. The distinction between life and inanimate matter on the basis of these characteristics is so profound that many generations of scientists sought a unique ingredient of life: the vis vitalis.

7.1. Beyond the equilibrium

Even though the previous chapters of this textbook contain already many useful applications of physics in the life sciences, you may wonder how the physical sciences can be expected to grasp the essence of life based on the concepts developed so far. Surveying our discussion for assumptions which may have been too restrictive we find that it is indeed the concept we relied most heavily upon throughout the earlier sections which appears to block access to the modelling of real life processes: the equilibrium concept favors uniform, structureless systems in which all essential parameters are time independent, i.e., the equilibrium assumption favors system conditions which are opposite to what we expect from a model of life processes.

But how can we abandon the equilibrium concept as all other parameters we introduced, such as the temperature and the energy, seem so closely linked to the equilibrium state? Do we not risk to lose all what we learned when trying to move beyond the equilibrium? These are indeed non–trivial questions. It took the physical sciences more than 250 years, from the time René Descartes, Sir Isaac Newton and others had opened the door to modern scientific inquiry until we found ways to tackle the concerns caused by the equilibrium assumption in the early part of the twentieth century. This long delay in characterizing non–equilibrium states was due to two prohibitive features:

(i) there are no clues in the material discussed so far in this textbook where to start, and
(ii) many of the equilibrium concepts we have developed need to be altered or abandoned as we proceed beyond the equilibrium state.

The first point is not as bad as it seems. Indeed, there are clues in thermal physics which point in the direction the discussion of non–equilibrium processes must evolve, except that we have not yet completed the discussion of thermal physics to the point where these clues occur. However, following this approach is somewhat more abstract as it requires the introduction of a new physical concept called entropy. The facts that the underlying second law of thermodynamics was only formulated in 1850 and that the ramifications for non–equilibrium processes were only discovered in the 1930s illustrate the more advanced character of these concepts. Nevertheless, the far–reaching importance of non–equilibrium processes in the biological sciences justifies the effort to discuss these concepts. We will do this in the next chapter.

Scientists already wondered about the realm beyond the equilibrium long before these more rigorous concepts were developed. Important observations date back to the beginning of the nineteenth century. Useful phenomenological laws resulted from these early studies including a quantitative description of heat conduction and diffusion. We familiarize ourselves with these non–equilibrium phenomena in the current chapter to then tackle more advanced concepts in Chapter 8.

7.2. A new model system

7.2.1. Physical membranes

Like in previous chapters, we depend on a model system when developing new concepts. Membranes prove to be a simple but powerful model for introducing time dependent, non–mechanical processes. To be able to quantify these processes a simplified membrane is introduced. This model is called the physical membrane. It is a uniform barrier which is characterized by a very limited number of variables, such as its width and a homogeneous chemical composition.

> *A physical membrane is a barrier separating two uniform systems. Each system is in equilibrium. At least one parameter varies between the two systems, establishing a non–equilibrium across the membrane.*

The parameter varying across the membrane is either a physical parameter, such as pressure or temperature, or a chemical parameter, such as the concentration of molecules in solution.

Often more than one parameter varies across real membranes. In Chapter 13, for example, we discuss the case in which the nerve membrane separates different concentrations of positive and negative ions, leading to a combination of electric and chemical effects. Before studying such combinations of effects, however, we need to develop the basic concepts of interactions across a membrane. For that discussion we introduce two important properties of membranes:

Permeability
The major physical property of a membrane is the degree of interaction it allows between the two systems it is separating. This degree of interaction is characterized by the permeability of the membrane.

A membrane can be impermeable, which means that it is blocking the interaction across the membrane completely. This case is of limited interest as it creates two isolated systems on either side, each fully described by the concepts we already discussed in Chapters 5 and 6.

The opposite extreme is a membrane which is fully permeable, i.e., everything transfers freely in both directions across the membrane. Again, such a membrane is not particularly interesting as it does not alter the interactions within the system.

The type of membrane used to develop the concepts of this chapter is, therefore, the semipermeable membrane. In the biological literature, *selective permeability* is often used as an alternate notation. A semipermeable membrane allows some system components to pass but blocks others. Fig. 7.1 illustrates the most important system components in transport processes: energy in the form of heat and matter in the form of atoms, ions or molecules. The simplest type of a semipermeable membrane is a membrane which allows only heat to pass but blocks matter. Such a membrane is used to introduce heat conduction. We later proceed to membranes which block only some chemical components while allowing others to pass. Semipermeable membranes of this type are used to develop the concept of diffusion.

Membrane width
The thickness of a membrane also plays a role in the degree of interaction allowed between the two systems. A semipermeable membrane may be impermeable in practice if it is too thick.

We distinguish conceptually two types of membranes: a zero–width membrane and a finite width membrane. If we want to study the consequences of interac-

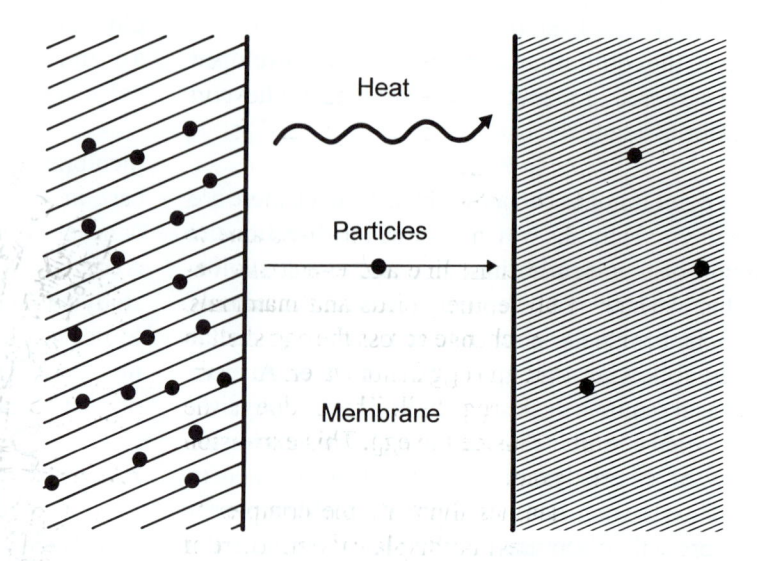

Fig. 7.1: Sketch of the major transport mechanisms operating across a physical membrane (white area at center): particles and/or energy may be transported. When energy flows independently of a material transport it is in the form of heat.

tions across the membrane focussing on the two adjacent systems, a zero–width membrane allows us to neglect the mechanisms of transport through the membrane. In other cases we want to focus on the transport mechanisms in the membrane itself. In these cases a membrane of finite width has to be taken into account. The variation of a system parameter across a finite width membrane requires the introduction of the gradient as a new mathematical concept in this chapter.

The physical membrane is obviously a good description for physical barriers such as windows. Biological membranes are much more complex. In our body, membranes are usually neither uniform in thickness nor chemically homogeneous and they often actively participate in the physiological processes rather than form a passive barrier. The concepts we develop for the physical membrane still apply to biological membranes and illustrate the role of basic transport processes in physiology.

7.2.2. The biological membrane

Membranes shifted into focus of biological studies for most of the 1800s. A heated debate concerned first the presence of membranes encapsulating the cells (the so–called plasma membrane), then the membranes encapsulating the nucleus.

Puzzling to the biologists was in particular that membranes do not only serve as passive envelopes for biological units; they are also actively involved in the dynamic processes occurring in our body, e.g. serving as a filter in the kidneys (this will be described in Chapter 11) or regulating the metabolism of a cell using enzymes embedded in the membrane to gather various chemical molecules from the environment and dispose of them back into the environment.

Biological membranes come in many different forms. One chemically simpler example, but at the same time one of the great success stories of the evolutionary process, is the egg shell. Consisting mainly of calcium

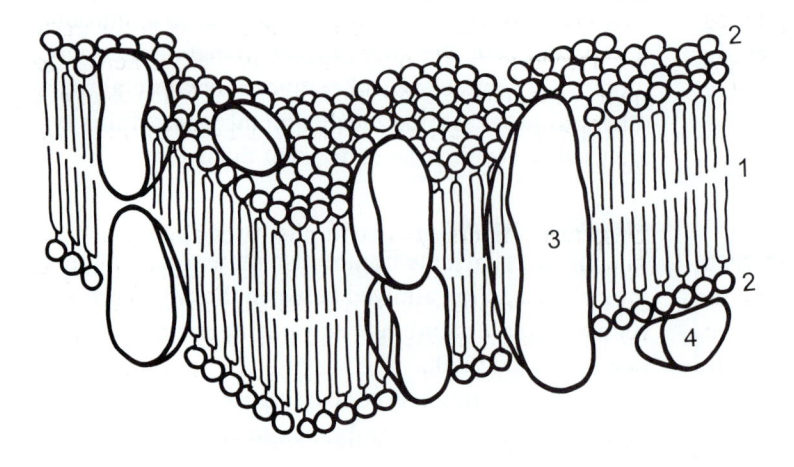

Fig. 7.2: Fluid mosaic model of a human cell membrane. The lipid double–layer consists of chain–like macromolecules with hydrophobic (1) and hydrophilic ends (2). The hydrophilic ends are directed toward the external aqueous milieu. Proteins can be intrinsic to the membrane (3) or extrinsic (4). They are able to diffuse laterally on or within the membrane layer, where the motion of the intrinsic proteins resembles that of floating icebergs. This protein mobility is the reason for the term fluid (versus rigid) used to label this membrane model.

194

carbonate, it allows to maintain a non–equilibrium between the egg inside and the environment outside. The egg shell allows air to get inside but does not allow water to pass through. This feature allowed cotylosaurs about 300 million years ago to move to dry land for its entire life cycle. Its amphibian ancestors had to spend at least part of their life in water since their eggs would desiccate on dry land. Cotylosaurs in turn was able to move far away from the coast line and eventually became the ancestor of all reptiles, birds and mammals. You can confirm the air exchange across the egg shell in a simple experiment. Place an egg in hot water. Air bubbles will form all over the egg shell. This is due to the thermal expansion of air inside the egg. This expansion pushes some of the air out.

Two other examples illustrate the complexity some biological membranes may display: the structure of the outer envelope of bacteria (a prokaryotic cell) and the membrane of a human cell (an eukaryotic cell).

A human cell
Fig. 7.2 shows a schematic sketch of a human cell membrane, which separates the cytoplasm inside from the interstitium outside. Membranes are an example of organic molecules organized into a higher level of order. The aggregation of phospholipids in an aqueous solution is driven by the molecule's amphipathic character: with one end of the molecule hydrophobic (water repelling) and the other end hydrophilic (water attracting), the hydrophilic ends will reach into the aqueous solution while the hydrophobic ends will merge together to exclude water. The result is a bilayer of phospholipids with the hydrophilic ends directed outwards.

These double–layer structures self–assemble into three–dimensional spheric forms called protobionts which can maintain an internal aqueous environment different from the external environment.

The human cell is far more complex than a simple phospholipid bilayer. Various protein molecules are associated with the membrane, some stretching across the membrane layer and some only attached extrinsically. These proteins are involved in specific transport processes across the membrane.

The gonococcus bacterium
Fig. 7.3 shows the cell membrane of a typical bacterium. The membrane consists of three layers needed as it is the outer envelope to protect the bacterium against its environment. The central murein layer is a sturdy, uniform hetero–polymer. Penicillins are deadly for bacteria because they prevent the biosynthesis of the murein membrane. The other two layers of the bacterial membrane

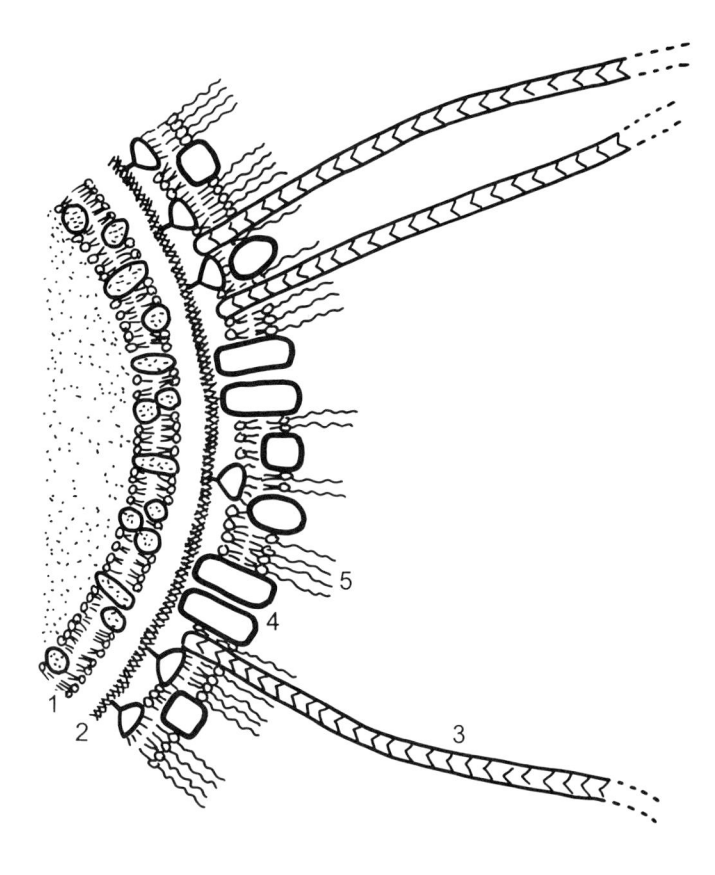

Fig. 7.3: Sketch of the cell membrane of a gonococcus bacterium. The membrane consists of three layers, the cytoplasm membrane (1), the rigid murein layer (2) and an outer layer with fimbria (3), porine–proteins (4) and lipo–polysaccharide chains (5).

are highly structured. The inner layer (plasma membrane) resembles the membrane of human cells as discussed above. The outer membrane contains specialized components for chemical exchange and physical interaction with the bacterium's environment. The long fimbria act as tentacles. Porine–proteins stretch the entire membrane to facilitate diffusion processes across the membrane and the lipo–polysaccharide chains constitute the defense system of the bacterium due to their toxigenic properties.

Despite the diversity and complexity of biological membranes, they all share some common fundamental properties. Developing these properties in the current chapter from experimental observations will allow us to obtain an insight into non–equilibrium processes we need in the next chapter to establish some general laws which apply to systems outside the equilibrium.

7.3. Heat conduction

Using the physical membrane model, we can systematically discuss the time dependent transport of physical or chemical properties of a system. These phenomena are grouped together under the term transport phenomena and include heat conduction, diffusion, viscosity and electric current.

(I) Heat conduction is the flow of energy within a system to eliminate temperature differences. We assume that the initial temperature difference occurs across a membrane which is impermeable for matter but allows the transfer of energy in the form of heat. An example is the continuous heat loss of our body through the skin at moderate temperatures.

(II) Diffusion is the process by which molecules move from a region of higher concentration to one of lower concentration. The initial concentration differences occur across membranes which are semipermeable, permitting some chemical components to pass while others are blocked or significantly slowed down. Two important examples are (a) the transfer of oxygen and carbon-dioxide between blood vessels and the lung, and (b) the resorption of blood plasma components in the renal tubes of the kidney as discussed in detail in Chapter 11. Diffusion is the second transport process discussed in detail in this chapter.

The other two transport processes are discussed elsewhere in the textbook:
(III) Viscosity is introduced in Chapter 11.
(IV) Electric currents are studied in Chapter 13.

7.3.1. Fourier's law

In 1822, Jean Baptiste Fourier developed an experiment suitable for investigating the flow of heat. The experiment is shown in Fig. 7.4. This set–up allowed him to quantify heat conduction in the rod connecting two heat reservoirs at different temperatures. For easy control of the temperatures of both heat reservoirs, one is held at 0°C with an ice–water mixture while the other is held at 100°C by boiling water. The rod is well insulated so that all heat transported through the rod is transferred from the higher temperature heat reservoir to the reservoir of lower temperature. The cylindrical rod has length l and cross–sectional area A. With this experiment, Fourier found an empirical relation for the heat flow by varying every conceivable parameter in Fig. 7.4. Increasing the temperature difference between the two heat reservoirs and increasing the cross–sectional area of the rod increased the amount of heat flowing toward the lower temperature heat reservoir. Decreasing the length of the rod also increased the heat flow, indicating that the length of the rod is inversely proportional to the heat flow. Defining the flow of heat per time interval as Q/t with unit [J/s], Fourier found:

$$\frac{Q}{t} = \lambda A \frac{T_{high} - T_{low}}{l} \quad (1)$$

The proportionality constant λ is a materials constant, which is a constant that depends on the material used for the rod. The constant λ has unit [J/(m s K)]. It is called the thermal conductivity coefficient. Table 7.1 lists thermal conductivity coefficients for a range of materials. All values of λ are positive, i.e., heat always flows from the higher temperature to the lower temperature.

Although Eq. (1) is written as if the thermal conductivity coefficient is temperature independent, the values in Table 7.1 are given specifically at room temperature. It has been found experimentally that the thermal conductivity of most materials indeed varies with the temperature, e.g. for water and air by more than 20 % between 0°C and 100°C. We neglect this temperature dependence in the current section but will address it in the Appendix of Chapter 8.

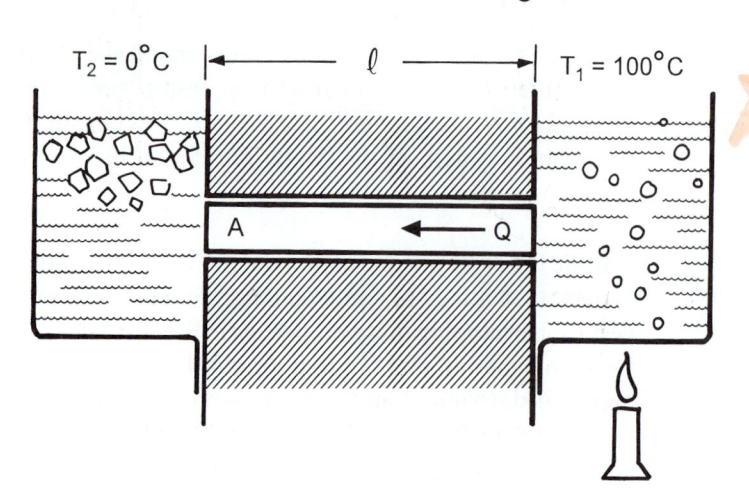

Fig. 7.4: Fourier's experiment of heat conduction. A steady–state heat flow across a rod of length l and cross–sectional area A is achieved by providing for a thermal contact to heat reservoirs at $T_2 = 0$°C (at left) and $T_1 = 100$°C (at right) at the two ends of the rod. The shaded area above and below the rod indicates a thermal insulation of the rod to prevent lateral heat loss.

The term $\Delta T/l$ represents the **temperature step** along the length l of the rod. This term can alternatively be written as the change of the temperature along the rod, $\delta T/\delta x$, in which δx is the change of position along the rod. The term $\delta T/\delta x$ is called a gradient. Different from $\Delta T/l$, which has as single average value, the gradient $\delta T/\delta x$ can be a function of the position coordinate x. Only if the gradient is constant, can we equate the gradient and the value of the step along the entire rod $\Delta T/l = \delta T/\delta x$. Often, however, the gradient is not constant. In these cases more complicated mathematical operations are needed to analyze equations such as Eq. (1). To simplify the current discussion we limit ourselves to cases where the gradient has a constant value.

7.3.2. Physiological role of heat conduction

When we touch an object, it is the **thermal conductivity** and not the actual temperature which affects our impression of warmth or coldness. For example, touching a piece of metal and a piece of wood, which are both at room temperature, the metal feels cold and the wood feels warm. Since our hand in this experiment is warmer than the objects we touch, heat flows from our body into the object. The greater this flow of heat, the colder we perceive the object.

The same heat loss occurs continuously from the skin to the surrounding air. The air is not usually perceived as cold because the heat conductivity of gases is rather low (see Table 7.1) and, thus, the heat loss in room temperature air is not large enough to be felt. Still, the thermal non–equilibrium between the body temperature of 37.0 ± 0.5 °C and the air temperature is reflected in a gradual temperature drop toward the body's surface. This is illustrated in Fig. 7.5 for two environmental temperatures. Fig. 7.5(a) shows a cross–sectional temperature profile in the body for an air temperature of 20°C and Fig. 7.5(b) illustrates the same profile for an air temperature of 35 °C. As the figure shows, the temperature profile is not a single temperature step from 37°C to the environmental temperature. Instead, the temperature decreases by as much as 9 degrees in the limbs in a room temperature environment.

Table 7.1: Thermal conductivity coefficients at room temperature. Note that the coefficients vary only by less than 5 orders of magnitude.

Material	Thermal Conductivity λ [J s^{-1} m^{-1} K^{-1}]
1. Solid metals and alloys	
Silver (Ag)	420
Copper (Cu)	390
Gold (Au)	310
Aluminium (Al)	230
Iron (Fe)	80
Steel	50
2. Nonmetallic solids	
Ice	1.6
Quartz glass (SiO$_2$)	1.4
Window glass	0.8
Fat	0.24
Rubber	0.2
Wood	0.12 – 0.04
Felt, Silk	0.04
3. Liquids	
Mercury (Hg)	8.3
Water (H$_2$O)	0.6
Ethanol (C$_2$H$_5$OH)	0.18
4. Gases	
Air	0.026

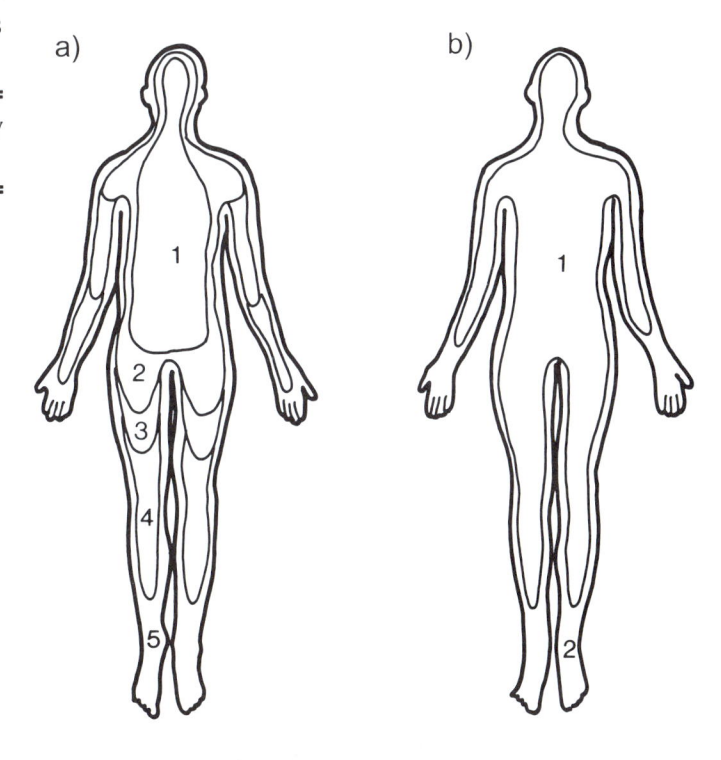

Fig. 7.5: The temperature profile for a human body at environmental temperatures of (a) 20 °C and (b) 35°C. Both sketches show a center–body cross–section. The thin profile lines connect points of same temperature. The various temperature lines are numbered as follows: (1) 37°C, (2) 36°C, (3) 34°C, (4) 31°C, and (5) 28°C.

Table 7.2: Mechanisms of the heat loss in the human body as a function of the environmental temperature. The total loss is given in the second column in unit [J/m²s]. The third, fourth and fifth column show how this amount is distributed between perspiration, convection and radiation.

Temperature of environment	Total heat loss	Fraction of evaporation	Fraction of convection	Fraction of radiation
20°C	63 J/m²s	13 %	26 %	61 %
30°C	38 J/m²s	27 %	27 %	46 %
36°C	43 J/m²s	100 %	—	—

Three primary processes contribute to the continuous loss of heat to the environment: perspiration (evaporation of water from the skin), convection (heat carried away by air passing across the skin) and radiation. Table 7.2 summarizes the relative contributions to the heat loss of the human body at various environmental temperature conditions (dry air). Note that neither convection nor radiation contribute at 36°C and above.

Heat conduction is an effective heat loss process when swimming in water, but contributes little in air. Convection on the other hand, which is caused by the turbulent flow of air across the skin, can significantly enhance the heat loss in air. It is for this reason that beduins in the desert wear black robes below which convection contributes more effectively to the cooling of the skin than below cloth of brighter colors. We discuss convection in more detail in the next chapter.

Heat loss by perspiration is based on the phase transition of water from liquid to vapor on the skin. Sweat glands bring liquid water to the skin. The evaporation of water requires energy. This amount of energy is called the latent heat of evaporation. It is supplied from the body's thermal energy. The vapor leaves the skin, carrying the latent heat into the environment. This heat transfer is very effective, corresponding to a loss of 2428 kJ per liter of water. However, perspiration is only effective in dry air. If the air is humid (saturated with water vapor), temperatures of about 33 °C become unbearable.

Heat loss by radiation is a totally different process. Radiative energy is not carried by the medium air like heat in heat conduction or convection. You notice this when you hold the palm of your hand facing the sun and then turn it 90°. The sun causes the sensation of warmth because heat from the sun reaches the hand. This heat flow must be independent of a medium to transport the heat because most of the distance between the sun and your hand goes through vacuum. The experiment with the hand illustrates also that heat transport by radiation works well when a cooler surface lies in the line of sight of a hotter surface. Thus, a cold wall contributes to loss of heat by radiation even if the air in the room is warm. We discuss heat radiation, which is a form of electromagnetic radiation like radio waves and light, in more detail in Chapter 19.

Example 7.1

(a) Calculate the steady rate at which a person with winter clothing loses body heat if the surface area of the person's body is 1.8 m², the clothing is 1.0 cm thick, the surface temperature of the skin is 33°C and the temperature of the outer surface of the clothing is 1 °C. Use for the thermal conductivity of the clothing 0.04 J/(m s K).
(b) How does the answer to part (a) change if the person's clothes are soaked with water of $\lambda = 0.6$ J/(m s K)?

Solution part (a): We use Fourier's law as given in Eq. (1). Substituting A = 1.8 m², l = 0.01 m, the temperature difference of ΔT = 306 K − 274 K = 32 K and the thermal conductivity λ = 0.04 J/(m s K), we find:

$$\frac{Q}{t} = \frac{\lambda A (T_{high} - T_{low})}{l} = 2.3 \times 10^2 \frac{J}{s} \quad (2)$$

Solution part (b): In this part we are asked to derive an answer relative to the answer in part (a). Instead of repeating the calculation as shown in the first part, we divide the respective left and right hand sides of Fourier's law for the "dry" and the "wet" case:

$$\frac{(Q/t)_{dry}}{(Q/t)_{wet}} = \frac{\dfrac{\lambda_{dry} A (T_{high} - T_{low})}{l}}{\dfrac{\lambda_{wet} A (T_{high} - T_{low})}{l}} = \frac{\lambda_{dry}}{\lambda_{wet}} \quad (3)$$

This leads to:

$$\left(\frac{Q}{t}\right)_{wet} = \left(\frac{Q}{t}\right)_{dry} \frac{\lambda_{wet}}{\lambda_{dry}} = \quad (4)$$

$$230\left[\frac{J}{s}\right] \frac{0.6[J/(m\,s\,K)]}{0.04[J/(m\,s\,K)]} = 3.5 \times 10^3 \frac{J}{s}$$

Thus, the person loses heat 15 times faster when the clothes are wet! An interesting case in this context: Fritjof Nansen, a famous Norwegian polar explorer, tried to reach the North Pole with a second Norwegian in March of 1895. After leaving their ship at 84.4° North, they failed in their quest for the Pole, drifting faster away from the Pole than they could travel. They reached as far north as 86.14°N which was a record at the time. Later they had to struggle through breaking ice on their way back. At one point all their supplies, which were stored in small boats, drifted away and one of them had to swim after them. Before doing so, Nansen stripped off his clothes. Eq. (3) demonstrates that this was an intelligent decision despite the freezing temperatures. It took Nansen only a few minutes to salvage the boats, but his colleague had to warm him up for several hours. Luckily, Nansen survived the incident. Had he jumped into the water with his warm clothes, they would not have protected him from the frigid water but would have dragged him down once soaked.

7.3.3. Whales in the Arctic Ocean (Example 7.2)

Whales are mammals that live in the sea. Their bodies generate heat at the rate given for endotherms in Eq. (5.2) by burning their food. Like humans, they must maintain a core body temperature of about 37°C. Some of these whales spend part or all of the year in the frigid Arctic ocean near the edge of the pack ice (water temperature 0°C). These include large whales such as Bowhead Whales of 100 tonnes body mass and small whales such as the Narwhal with about 1.5 tonnes body mass. Their only protection in the chilly water is a thick fat–layer. Calculate the minimum thickness of that fat layer for any of these whales as a function of body size. Hint: Use a spherical shape for the whale's body.

Solution: Fig. 7.6 shows the model used for the whale in this problem: the spherical animal has an inner body of radius R and a fat layer of uniform thickness l. The minimum thickness of the fat layer is determined by balancing the heat loss and the heat production in the whale's body.

For the heat loss we use Fourier's law (Eq. (1)) with the thermal conductivity coefficient of fat from Table 7.1. The higher temperature in Fourier's law is the core body temperature and the lower temperature is the temperature of the sea water, i.e., $\Delta T = 37$ K. The cross–sectional area across which the heat flows is the surface of the inner body of the whale, $A = 4\pi R^2$ (which is the surface of a sphere of radius R). Thus:

$$\left(\frac{Q}{t}\right)_{loss} = \lambda\, 4\pi R^2 \frac{\Delta T}{l} = 110\left[\frac{J}{m\,s}\right]\frac{R^2}{l} \quad (5)$$

Note that the resulting heat loss is expressed as a function of the radius of the whale and the thickness of the fat layer. We keep these two parameters variable because we want to find their relation for whales of any size. The other parameters, λ and ΔT, and the constant 4π are combined in the prefactor 110 [J/(m s)].

To offset this loss, the whale is assumed to use the heat generated by its metabolism as given in Eq. (5.2). We rewrite Eq. (5.2) in standard units, defining the metabolic rate as the heat gain per time, $(Q/t)_{gain}$:

$$\left(\frac{Q}{t}\right)_{gain}\left[\frac{J}{s}\right] = 5.2\,(m\,[kg])^{3/4} \quad (6)$$

The mass of the whale is rewritten as its density and volume $V = 4\pi R^3/3$ (this is the volume of a sphere of radius R). This leads to the rate of heat gain:

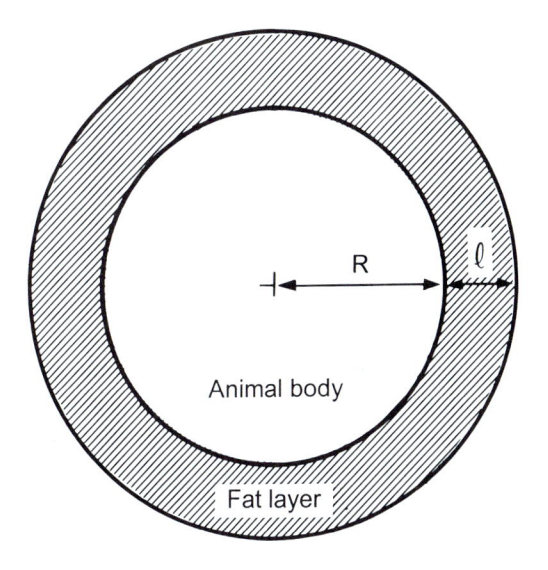

Fig. 7.6: Simplified model of a whale: an inner body of radius R is covered by a fat–layer of uniform thickness l.

$$\left(\frac{Q}{t}\right)_{gain} = 5.2\left(\rho\frac{4}{3}\pi R^3\right)^{3/4} =$$
(7)
$$= 5.2\left(\frac{4}{3}\pi\rho\right)^{3/4} R^{9/4}$$

Since the whale is floating in sea water, the density of its body must be close to that of sea water. We use the value $\rho = 1000$ kg/m³ in Eq. (7) to write:

$$\left(\frac{Q}{t}\right)_{gain}\left[\frac{J}{s}\right] = 2710\,(R\,[m])^{9/4}$$
(8)

The generated heat is again expressed as a function of the radius of the whale to keep this parameter variable.

For calculating the minimum fat layer thickness the balance between the whale's heat loss and heat gain must be found, i.e., Eqs. (5) and (8) are set equal:

$$\left(\frac{Q}{t}\right)_{loss} = \left(\frac{Q}{t}\right)_{gain}$$
$$110\,\frac{R^2}{l} = 2710\,R^{9/4}$$
(9)

which leads to:

$$l\,[m] = \frac{0.0406}{(R\,[m])^{1/4}}$$
(10)

Eq. (7) relates the fat layer thickness to the radius of the whale. The bigger the animal (i.e., the larger R) the thinner a sufficient fat layer (this is called the bulk effect). An animal of radius R = 0.1 m = 10 cm (rat–sized) needs a fat–layer thickness of about l = 7 cm, with radius R = 1 m (sea lion–sized) a fat–layer of 4 cm is needed and with R = 10 m (whale–sized) a fat–layer of 2.5 cm is sufficient. Obviously, a polar rat would be a clumsy creature, and does therefore not exist. Sea lions and whales have no problem to develop a sufficient fat–layer without hindering them in their daily lives.

Real whales indeed have typically fat–layer thicknesses (blubber) of about 0.5 m, which means that the whale's fat–layer is significantly oversized. This is due to the fact that the fat–layer thickness cannot be adjusted on a short time scale, e.g. to accommodate day–night temperature changes or water temperature variations caused by currents. Thus, we require another mechanism of heat regulation. Nature's solution to the problem includes an oversized fat–layer and a secondary mechanism to dissipate excess heat through the fat–layer free tail. Body heat is carried by blood flow to the tail where it is brought close to the skin (perfusion). The efficiency of this mechanism is illustrated in Fig. 7.7 for a dolphin's tail (fluke). The figure shows the temperature profile of the tail from an infrared photograph (thermo-

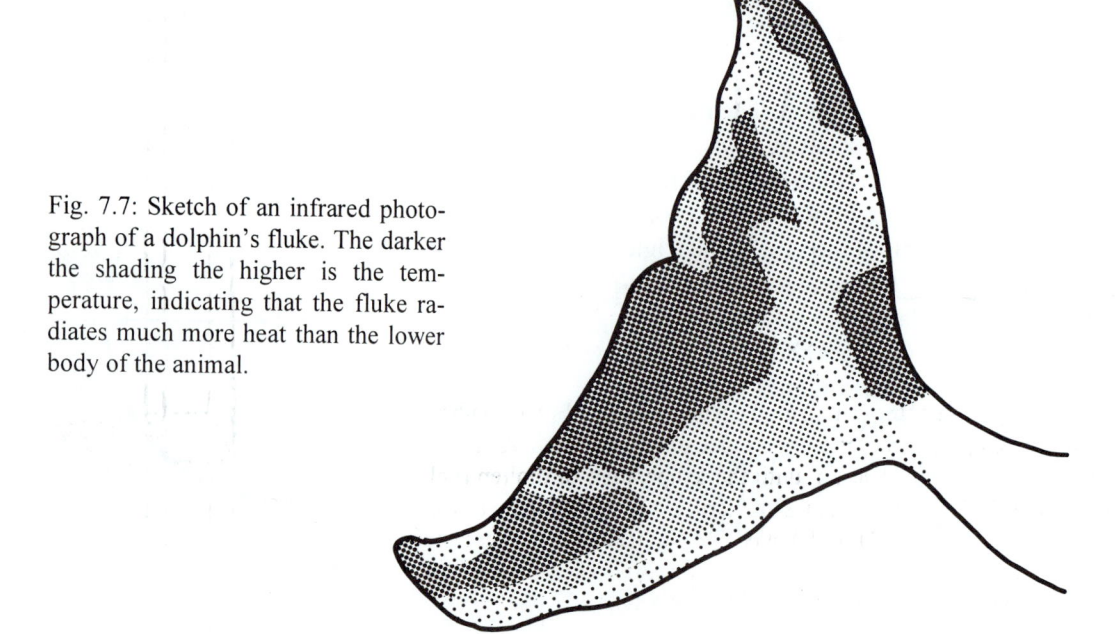

Fig. 7.7: Sketch of an infrared photograph of a dolphin's fluke. The darker the shading the higher is the temperature, indicating that the fluke radiates much more heat than the lower body of the animal.

graphy). The various temperatures are shown in different shades, with the darker the area the hotter. The figure illustrates clearly that the fluke is not only used for motion but also serves as the body's temperature control device.

Whaling was a major branch of the fishing industry in the mid–1800s when Herman Melville wrote the famous adventure story "Moby Dick". At that time whales were little understood creatures, and the described mechanism of heat dissipation was unknown. Thus, whalers often reported their amazement when they found temperatures in whale carcasses to be as high as 60°C and the whale meat half–cooked. This is due to the fact that the heart of a dying whale stops immediately, interrupting the blood flow to the fluke. However, heat generating metabolic processes continue for a short time after death.

7.3.4. Lord Kelvin's age of the Earth (Example 7.3)

After publishing "The Origin of Species by Means of Natural Selection" in 1859, Charles Darwin had to endure some malicious criticism. On the other hand, there were only very few serious objections. The most credible one came from Lord Kelvin, who estimated the age of the Earth to be 400 million years or less and the age of the sun to be 100 million years or less. He later even corrected these numbers downwards to as little as 20 million years.

We consider Lord Kelvin's argument for the age of the Earth. It is based on the following data: from underground mining we know that the temperature below the surface of the Earth increases by 0.03 K per meter. This is called the geothermal effect: the temperature increases by one degree for every additional 30 m of depth. Assuming that the Earth started as molten rock, called the Proto–earth with a uniform temperature of T = 3000°C, how long did it take to reach the current state? Use for the density of rock $\rho = 3$ g/cm³, for the heat capacity of rock c = 1470 J/(kg K) and for the thermal conductivity coefficient of rock $\lambda = 1.7$ J/(m s K).

Solution: Based on the geothermal effect, the current temperature profile of the Earth is shown in Fig. 7.8. At the surface (the radius of the Earth is taken as 6400 km) the temperature is about 0°C. It rises to 3000°C at 100 km depth, i.e., 6300 km from the center of the Earth.

For our quantitative calculations, we consider a rectangular segment of 100 km depth and of surface area $A = 1$ m² as illustrated in Fig. 7.9. The heat loss of this segment is determined using Fourier's law (Eq. (1)):

$$\frac{Q}{t} = \lambda A \frac{\Delta T}{l} \quad \Rightarrow \quad \frac{Q/t}{A} = \lambda \frac{\Delta T}{l} \quad (11)$$

which is quantified as:

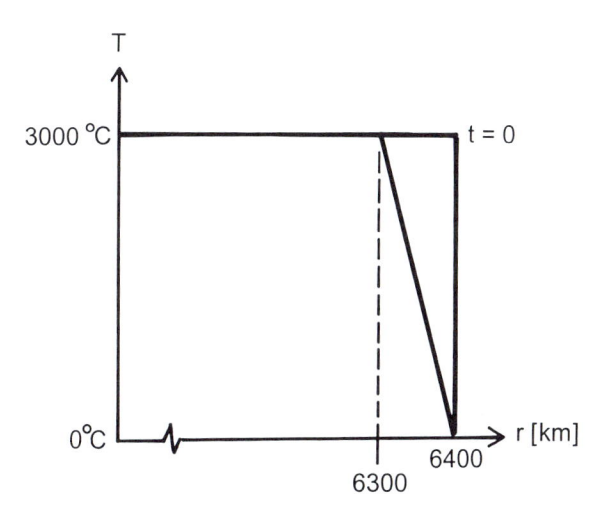

Fig. 7.8: Temperature profile of the Earth based on the well–established geothermal effect. With the temperature increasing by one degree for each 30 m, the temperature increases for about 100 km until the temperature of molten rock (3000°C) is reached. Using for the radius of Earth 6400 km molten rock is reached at r = 6300 km. The second line, labelled t = 0, indicates the temperature profile of the Proto–earth, which was a liquid sphere throughout due to the great bombardment with space debris during the early solar system.

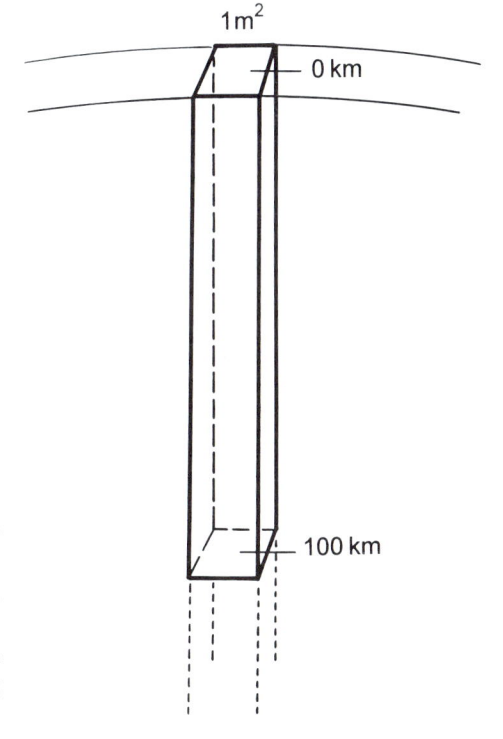

Fig. 7.9: Segment of the Earth's crust used for the calculation of the rate of heat loss of the Earth.

$$\frac{Q/t}{A} = 1.7 \left[\frac{J}{m\,s\,K}\right] 0.03 \left[\frac{K}{m}\right]$$

$$\frac{Q/t}{A} = 0.05 \left[\frac{J}{s\,m^2}\right] \quad (12)$$

The term (Q/t)/A is the rate of loss of heat per time interval through the area A. The term $\Delta T/l$ is the geothermal temperature gradient. It is useful to perform a unit analysis to see that Eq. (12) can be written as shown.

Next we calculate the total heat lost since the times of the liquid Proto–earth using Eq. (5.43):

$$Q = m\,c_{rock}\,\Delta T = \rho\,V\,c_{rock}\,\Delta T \quad (13)$$

in which the mass of the rock slab of Fig. 7.9 has been rewritten as its density and volume. The volume is further written as the surface area times the depth:

$$Q = \rho A l\, c_{rock}\,\Delta T \;\Rightarrow\; \frac{Q}{A} = \rho l\, c_{rock}\,\Delta T \quad (14)$$

in which the term Q/A is the total heat lost through the surface area A. Evaluating Eq. (14) is not simple since the temperature change, ΔT, varies with depth as shown in the lower part of Fig. 7.10. The figure indicates that due to the direct proportionality between heat and temperature in Eq. (14), the total loss of heat corresponds to the triangle enclosed by the dashed lines and the line indicated with vertical arrows. Thus, the total amount of heat lost through the surface area A is found from Fig. 7.10 graphically. The area of the triangle equals ½ of the area of the rectangle with a temperature drop of 3000 degree throughout. This we substitute in Eq. (14) for ΔT:

$$\frac{Q}{A} = \frac{1}{2}\,3000\left[\frac{kg}{m^3}\right]\,10^5\,[m] \times \ldots$$

$$\ldots \times 1470\left[\frac{J}{kg\,K}\right]\,3000\,[K] \quad (15)$$

in which 3000 K is the difference between 0 °C and 3000°C. Eq. (15) yields:

$$\frac{Q}{A} = 6.6 \times 10^{14} \left[\frac{J}{m^2}\right] \quad (16)$$

Next Lord Kelvin divided the total energy lost

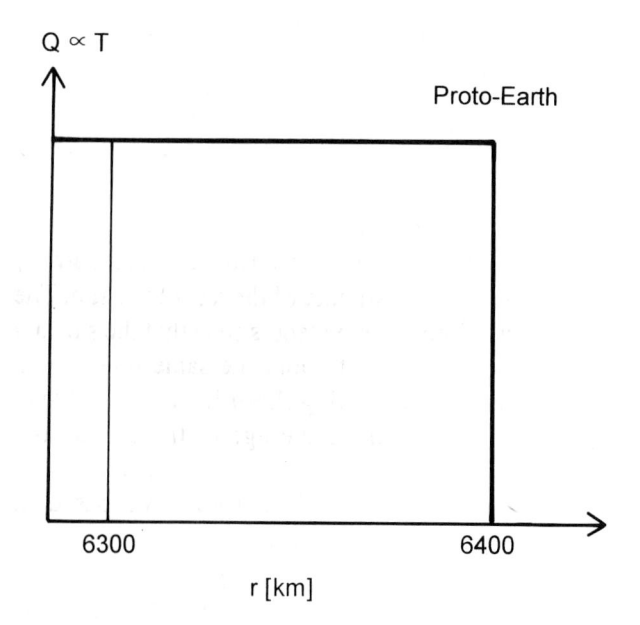

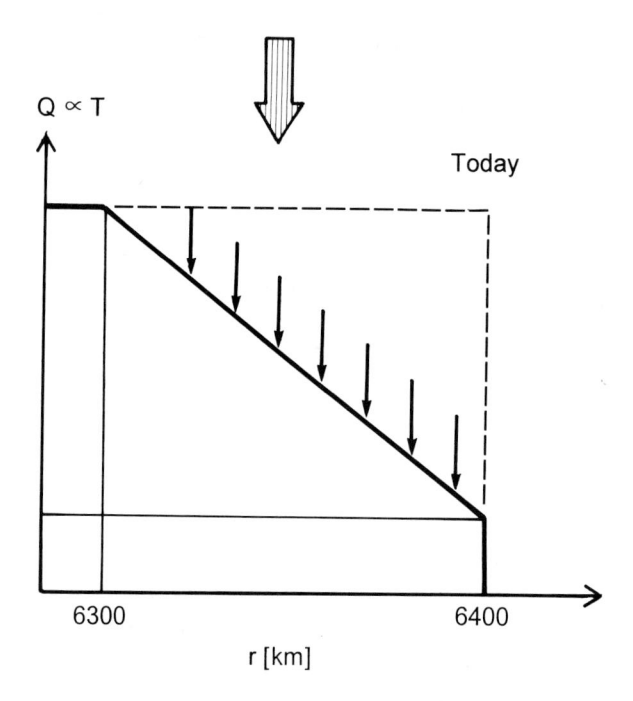

Fig. 7.10: Illustration of the total amount of heat, Q, lost between the times of the Proto–earth (top) and the current state (bottom).

from the 100 km deep segment (Eq. (16)) by the rate of loss through area A from Eq. (12).

$$t_{Earth} = \frac{\frac{Q}{A}}{\frac{(Q/t)}{A}} = \frac{6.6 \times 10^{14}\left[\frac{J}{m^2}\right]}{0.05\left[\frac{J}{s\,m^2}\right]} \quad (17)$$

This leads to the predicted age t_{Earth} of the Earth since cooling began:

$$t_{Earth} = 1.3 \times 10^{16} \, s = 4 \times 10^8 \, yrs \quad (18)$$

which is 400 million years.

Lord Kelvin tried to confirm this estimate by comparing it with an estimate of the age of the sun. The modern view of the solar system is such that the sun and the Proto–earth formed at about the same time. Thus, since the sun is still operating, Lord Kelvin was able to calculate an upper limit to the age of the sun by determining how long the fuel of the sun would last.

His first estimate of the sun's age was based on the assumption that the sun operates with chemical energy, i.e., energy obtained by burning energy rich compounds like coal or hydrogen. This would allow the sun to operate only 1500 to 5000 years, depending on the type of fuel. A better estimate followed when Lord Kelvin added the energy released during a gravitational collapse of the sun. This obviously requires that the sun started with a much larger radius than it has today. Accepting that assumption Lord Kelvin arrived at a value of 2×10^7 years. By taking into consideration the fact that the sun's core is much denser than its outer shell, he was able to push the age of the sun up to 1×10^8 years, which he judged sufficiently close to his estimate of the age of the Earth to confirm the previous result.

Both estimates are much longer than the age predicted on the basis of a literal interpretation of the Bible, which inspired a 17th century vice–chancellor of Cambridge University to claim that "man was created by the Trinity on October 23, 4004 BC, at nine o'clock in the morning". Why, then, was Lord Kelvin's result a problem for Charles Darwin? To answer that question, we take a look at our current knowledge of the history of life on Earth as shown in Table 7.3: given the slow pace of evolution, Lord Kelvin's age of the Earth and the sun would not provide enough time for the emergence of complex organisms such as human beings.

Why were both of Kelvin's estimates wrong by at least a factor of 10? For the estimate of the age of the Earth, his model of a cooling Proto–earth is inadequate. The current geothermal temperature profile is actually a steady state profile, i.e., the temperature profile does not change with time. To offset the heat loss by heat conduction, heat is continuously generated by radioactive processes which occur in the core of the Earth, and the convection in the liquid outer core, which converts gravitational energy into heat. Thus the current temperature profile of the Earth is not the result of the cooling mechanism assumed by Lord Kelvin.

For the sun, Lord Kelvin's model of heat generation is incorrect. Neither chemical energy nor gravitational energy contribute significantly; rather nuclear fusion in the core of the sun generates the heat the sun radiates. In Lord Kelvin's defense, it should be noted that in both cases the underlying physics had not yet been discovered at the time he criticized Charles Darwin's ideas.

Table 7.3: History of life on Earth

Years ago	Event
13×10^9	Age of universe (big bang)
4.7×10^9	Formation of the solar system from an interstellar cloud of gas
4.6×10^9	Proto–Earth (great bombardment)
4.03×10^9	Oldest rock (Yellowknife, NWT)
$3.6–3.8 \times 10^9$	First prokaryote occur (stromatolithic bacteria)
2.5×10^9	First eukaryote occur (algae)
1.7×10^9	Oxygen atmosphere
1.0×10^9	Sexual reproduction
6.7×10^8	Multicelled animal fossils found at many places on the Earth
5.8×10^8	Animals with shells and skeleton
4.8×10^8	Plants expand from sea to land
4.2×10^8	Animals expand from sea to land
2.4×10^8	First mammals
$1 – 4 \times 10^8$	*Kelvin's age of Earth and sun*
65×10^6	End of dinosaurs
4.0×10^6	Early hominids (Australopithecus)
2.5×10^6	Genus homo
0.125×10^6	Modern homo sapiens

7.3.5. Countercurrent flow (Example 7.4)

A circulatory adaptation to thermoregulation in animals is based on an arrangement of blood vessels such that thermal energy is preserved in the body core. Most effective for this purpose is a countercurrent heat–exchange where the arteries transporting blood to the skin are in close contact with the veins transporting blood back from the skin to the heart (body core). This example illustrates a few cases of such heat–exchanger systems.

(a) Heat–exchangers require two adjacent tubes with a good thermal contact. When fluids pass through the two

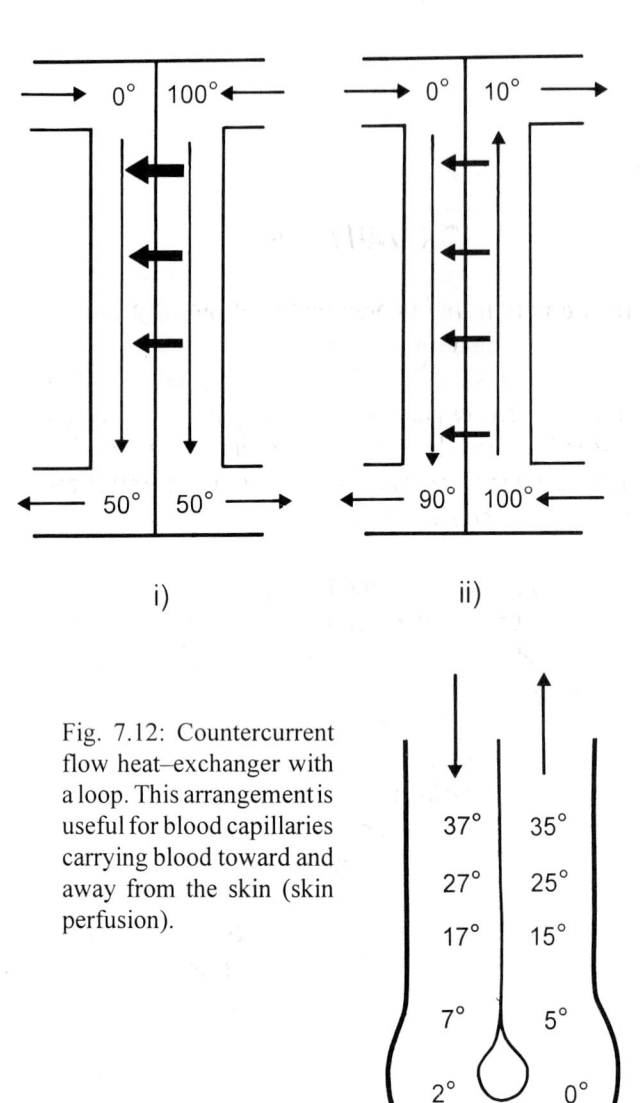

Fig. 7.11: Two tubes with fluid flow in thermal contact. The fluid in the left tube enters at 0°C and in the right tube at 100°C.
(i) Flow in both tubes occurs in the same direction. This leads to significant heat exchange near the top end of the contact zone of the tubes while little exchange occurs at the tail end of the flow.
(ii) A countercurrent flow arrangement allows for the temperature difference between both tubes to be essentially the same along the entire contact length. This provides for a uniform and therefore more effective heat exchange.

Fig. 7.12: Countercurrent flow heat–exchanger with a loop. This arrangement is useful for blood capillaries carrying blood toward and away from the skin (skin perfusion).

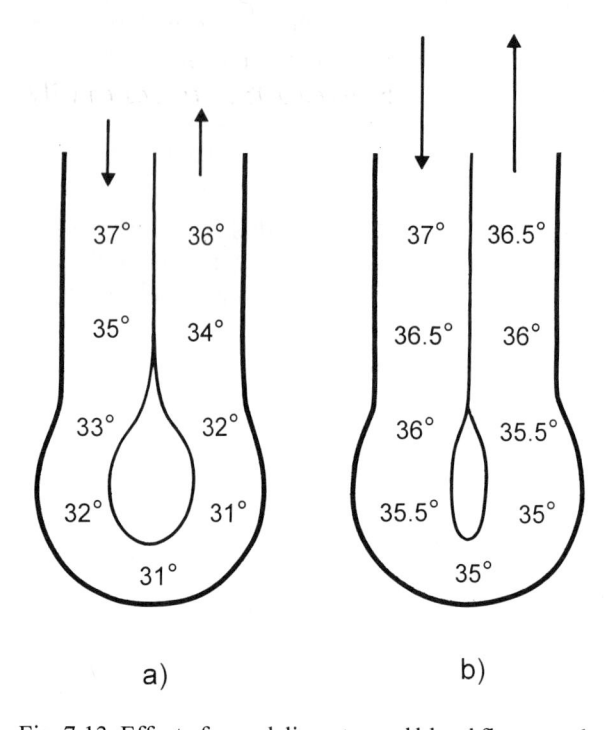

Fig. 7.13: Effect of vessel diameter and blood flow speed on the efficiency of a countercurrent heat–exchange arrangement of capillaries in the human skin.

tubes, heat exchange between the two fluids occurs. Fig. 7.11 distinguishes two types of heat–exchanger designs, (i) a system with parallel flow in the tubes and (ii) a countercurrent flow. In which of the two systems does the heat exchange occur more uniformly?

(b) Fig. 7.12 shows a countercurrent flow heat exchanger with a loop. In a loop the same fluid passes through both tubes sequentially. Why is such an arrangement of blood flow beneficial to a goose or a penguin standing on ice?

(c) Fig. 7.13 shows a similar countercurrent blood flow for a loop in the human skin with the incoming vessel a small artery and the outgoing vessel a small vein. Explain how the increase in the cross–section of the blood capillary from Fig. 7.13(a) to Fig. 7.13(b) leads to a higher dissipation of body heat into the environment.

Supplementary biological information: Even though insects and fish are ectotherms, the application of countercurrent flow allows some species to maintain a core temperature exceeding the environmental temperature. Bluefin tuna can maintain a core temperature of 10 degree above the water temperature despite the high heat conductivity of water compared to air. Winter–active moths use flight muscle action (flapping their wings without take–off) to generate heat which is preserved by a countercurrent heat–exchanger in their thorax. These moths display core body temperatures up to 30°C in sub–freezing environments.

Countercurrent exchangers are also used for diffusive exchange when a concentration gradient exists across a separating, semipermeable membrane. An example is the liver, where bile and arterial blood pass each other in a countercurrent flow to absorb some components back into the blood system. This type of countercurrent exchange in discussed in the next section.

Solution part (a): Fig. 7.14 compares the two heat–exchanger designs of Fig. 7.11 with a detailed listing of the temperatures in both tubes. If the hot and cold fluid enter from the same side at the top (sketch (i)), a high heat flux occurs at the top end of the arrangement since at that point there is a large temperature difference between the two adjacent tubes ($\Delta T = 80$ K). Only a small heat flow occurs at the bottom, where the temperature difference between both tubes is greatly diminished, in the figure to a value of $\Delta T = 10$ K. If the hot and cold fluid enter from opposite sides, as shown in sketch (ii), then a uniform heat flow occurs across the interface since the temperature difference between both tubes is essentially constant along the entire exchange length, $\Delta T = 10$ K from top to bottom in the figure.

Solution part (b): The cold blood flowing upwards from the feet of the penguin warms up quickly without large temperature differences occurring between neighboring blood vessels in the bird's legs.

Solution part (c): Whenever the core temperature in the human body exceeds the homeostatic level of 37°C, an increase in heat dissipation toward the environment is necessary. This is achieved by widening blood capillaries, allowing an increased blood flow to the skin. An increase of the blood volume passing below the skin per time unit corresponds to an increase in the heat transported to the skin surface. The efficiency of heat transport to the skin is further enhanced as the increased blood flow leads to a reduction in the heat exchange between the adjacent arterioles and venules (small blood vessels leading to and from the capillaries. Blood flow rates in various blood vessels are discussed in Chapter 11). Thus, when the blood flow to the skin is increased, blood reaches the body surface at a higher temperature. A larger temperature difference between the blood and the surrounding air causes a larger heat loss per time.

7.4. Diffusion

All membranes have in common the ability to separate and therefore maintain a non–equilibrium among the systems on both sides of the membrane. In addition, biological membranes participate actively in the exchange processes between the two systems they separate. For this role, cell membranes command a range of transport processes as illustrated in Fig. 7.15:

(I) **Passive diffusion**, sketched as an arrow through the uniform membrane material, allows small ions and molecules to penetrate the membrane in the direction of an existing concentration gradient. In the case of diffusion, the flow of material is in the direction from the higher to the lower concentration.

(II) *Facilitated diffusion* is an enhanced diffusion of specific molecules, supported by proteins. This type of diffusion is indicated in the figure by an arrow with the word *protein*. These proteins are embedded in the cell membrane as shown in Fig. 7.2. The diffusion process is the same as in passive diffusion. Proteins which facilitate diffusion are considered to provide gated channels for the motion of the diffusing species.

(III) **Proteins and enzymes** are also capable of transporting (mostly smaller) ions across the membrane against a concentration step. This process is called *active ion transport* and requires energy, typically provided by

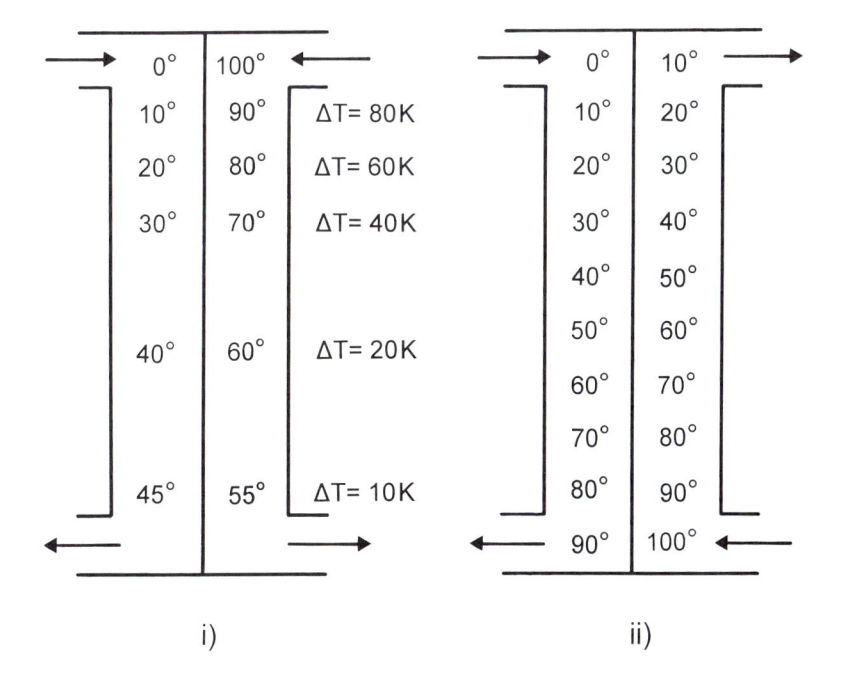

Fig. 7.14: The same two tubes as shown in Fig. 7.11. A larger number of temperature values are provided along the tubes to illustrate the benefit of the countercurrent arrangement.

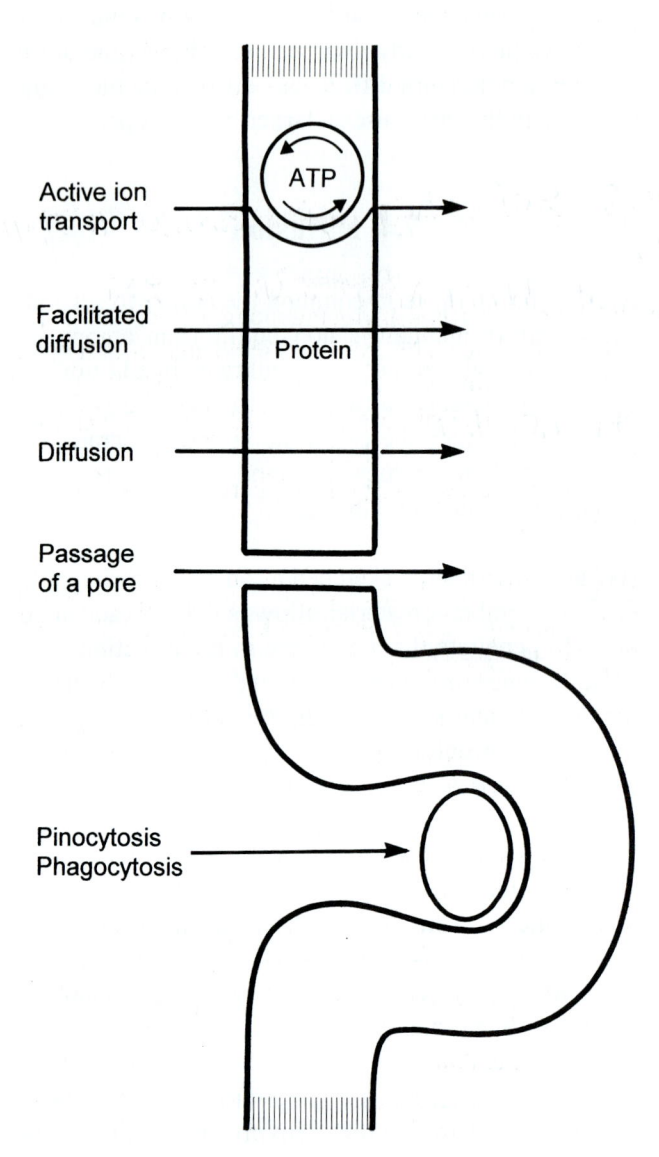

Fig. 7.15: Conceptual sketch illustrating the main mechanisms of material transport across biological membranes: diffusion along a concentration gradient is discussed in this chapter. Facilitated diffusion allows for chemically specific transport and is described by the same formulas we introduce for passive diffusion. Active ion transport against a concentration gradient is discussed in Chapter 13 for the potassium and sodium ion transport across the nerve membrane. Passage of pores in a membrane is discussed in Chapter 11 as a fluid flow phenomenon. Pinocytosis or phagocytosis are more complicated processes which include shape changes of the membrane.

ATP molecules as indicated in Fig. 7.15. Important examples include the transport of potassium and sodium across the membrane of nerve cells, as discussed in Chapter 13, and proton pumps in plants, fungi and bacteria to remove H^+ from the cell.

(IV) Molecules with certain shapes pass through pores in the membrane. An example is the passage of blood plasma components through the basement membrane in the kidneys. This process is not considered a permeation process in the context of this chapter but is treated as a flow process (Chapter 11).

(V) Very large molecules or bacteria are transported across the membrane in processes called pinocytosis (for molecules) or phagocytosis (for bacteria). These processes are more complex and are not included in the current discussion.

7.4.1. Fick's law

In 1855, the physician Adolf Fick described the transport of matter across a membrane in analogy to Fourier's law of heat transport. Fick observed empirically that the amount of a gas passing through a membrane of contact area A and width l is proportional to A and the density difference on both sides of the membrane, $\rho_{high} - \rho_{low}$. The transported amount of a given component i is also inversely proportional to the width of the membrane:

$$\frac{m_i}{t} = D\,A\,\frac{\rho_{i,\,high} - \rho_{i,\,low}}{l} \qquad (19)$$

The proportionality factor D is called diffusion coefficient, with SI unit [m²/s]. The index i in Eq. (19) indicates that Fick's law applies to components of a mixed phase as well. In biological systems, mixed systems occur frequently as membranes separate liquid solutions, such as cytoplasm from the extracellular fluid; or membranes separate gaseous and liquid solutions, such as blood and air in the lung. For such systems the mass of the ith component, m_i, is usually rewritten as n_i in unit [mol], and the density is rewritten as a concentration c_i, using the definitions:

$$n_i\,[mol] = \frac{m_i\,[kg]}{M\,[kg/mol]}$$
$$c_i\,[mol/m^3] = \frac{\rho_i\,[kg/m^3]}{M\,[kg/mol]} \qquad (20)$$

Using these definitions, Fick's law of diffusion can also be written in the form:

$$j_i = \frac{n_i}{t} = D\,A\,\frac{c_{i,\,high} - c_{i,\,low}}{l} \qquad (21)$$

in which j_i is the material flux (a flux is a change in a property with time) with unit [mol/s] and is equal to the number of moles of component i, n_i, crossing the membrane from the side of higher concentration to the side of lower concentration during the time interval t.

The term $\Delta c/l$ is the concentration step from one side of the membrane to the other. This term can be interpreted as the change of the concentration with position across the membrane, $\delta c/\delta x$. This is then called a concentration gradient. The concept of a concentration gradient is more useful when we do not want to refer to a particular membrane thickness. For example, concentration gradients of morphogens are thought to define the body axes in embryos (gradient hypothesis in embryology). In this case you are interested in the local change of a concentration, not a concentration step across the entire embryo.

Concentration gradients need not to be constant; $\delta c/\delta x$ will often be a function of the position x. In the current chapter, we confine our discussion, however, to constant gradients in which case $\delta c/\delta x = \Delta c/l$.

Like Fourier's law, Fick's law of diffusion in Eq. (21) only applies when transport occurs in a steady state, which means that no essential parameter of the system varies with time. In particular, the concentration of component *i* on both sides of the membrane must be constant and the profile of the diffusing component across the membrane must not change with time. A steady state therefore excludes any initial, transient period after the experiment has started. During the early transient period the concentration profile across the membrane varies, eventually approaching the steady state profile. The steady state is an important state because the system will develop toward this state if it cannot develop toward an equilibrium state. As an example, the concentration difference across the membrane is always maintained in a human cell, preventing the cell to approach a chemical equilibrium. The unique role of the steady state for non–equilibrium systems is discussed in more detail in the next chapter.

Since material flows continuously from one side to the other in a steady state diffusion process, independent processes are required to ensure that the concentration of component *i* does not decrease on the incoming side of the membrane (continuous supply) and that the concentration does not increase on the outflowing side of the membrane (continuous consumption). Thus, whenever a concentration gradient is maintained across a semipermeable biological membrane, additional physiological processes are involved. These include:
(i) passive chemical processes, such as the buffer effect regulating the acidity (pH–value) of blood by using the chemical reaction $CO_2 + H_2O \rightleftharpoons HCO_3^- + H^+$,
(ii) active biosynthesis of components such as immuno-globulin (antibodies in blood), or
(iii) active transport across the membrane against the concentration gradient as discussed in Chapter 13 for nerve cells.

Example 7.5

We consider sucrose diffusing along a 10 cm long tube filled with water. The cross–sectional area of the tube is 6.0 cm². The diffusion coefficient is 5.0×10^{-10} m²/s and a total amount of sucrose of 8.0×10^{-14} kg is transported in a steady state along the tube in 15 s. What is the difference in the density levels of sucrose at the two ends of the tube?

Solution: We use Fick's law in the form given in Eq. (19). This equation is rewritten to isolate the unknown density difference:

$$\Delta\rho = \left(\frac{m}{t}\right) \frac{l}{D\,A} \quad (22)$$

Now we substitute the given data into Eq. (22):

$$\Delta\rho = \frac{8 \times 10^{-14}[kg]\ 0.1[m]}{15[s]\ 5 \times 10^{-10}\left[\frac{m^2}{s}\right]\ 6 \times 10^{-4}[m^2]} \quad (23)$$

This yields:

$$\Delta\rho = 1.8 \times 10^{-3} \left[\frac{kg}{m^3}\right] \quad (24)$$

7.4.2. Countercurrent exchange processes in diffusion

We discussed heat–exchangers in section 7.3.5. These systems are based on two adjacent tubes with good thermal contact. When fluids pass through the tubes, heat exchange between the two fluids occurs. In the same fashion, if we establish good diffusive contact between the two tubes, exchange of matter occurs if there are concentration differences across a semipermeable membrane. Such exchangers work most effective in the countercurrent mode as illustrated above for heat–exchange.

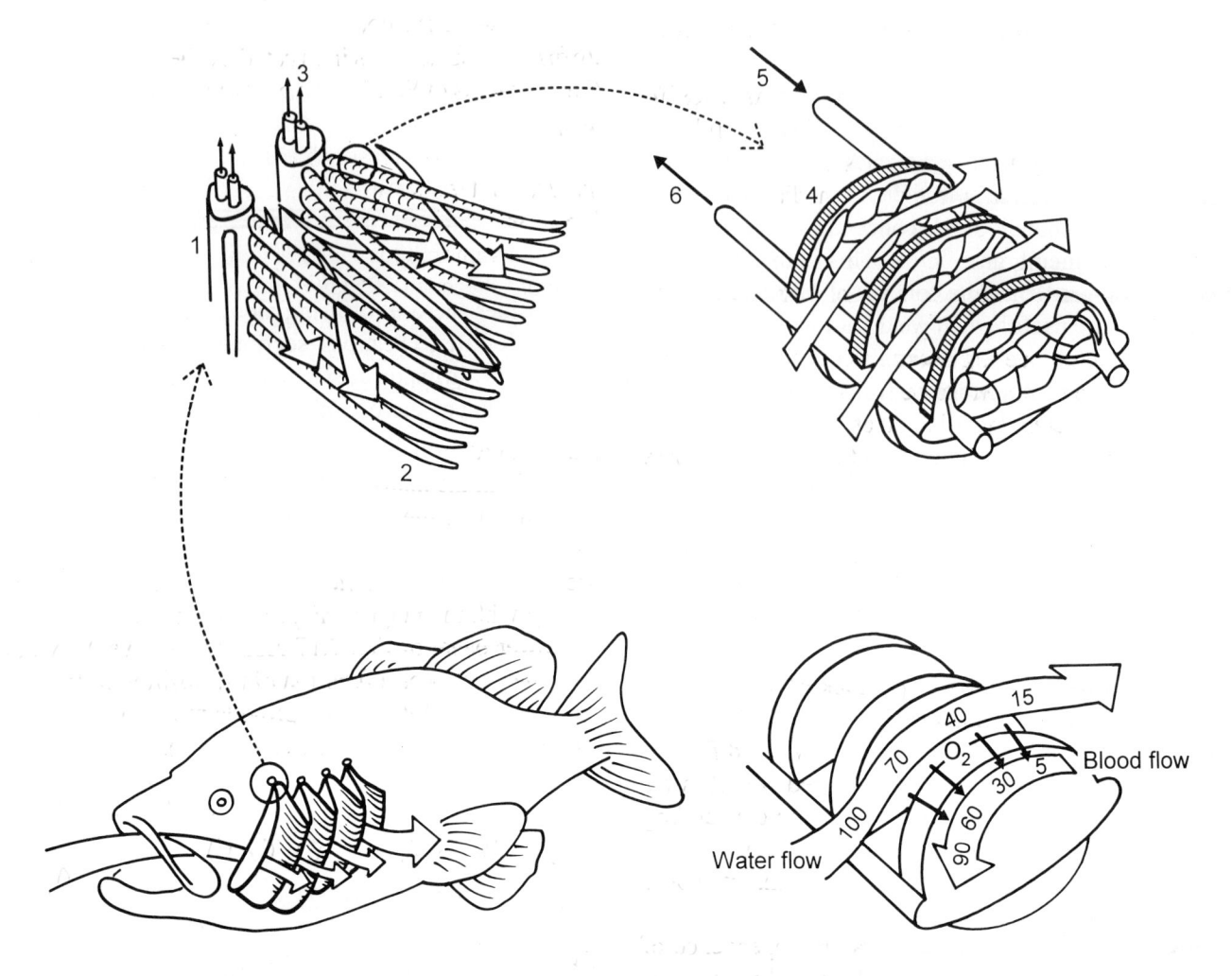

Fig. 7.16: Illustration of the function of fish gills. Fish require a continuous flow of water over their gill arches (1). These arches contain blood vessels (3) which branch into capillaries absorbing oxygen from the water in the lamellae (4) of the gill filaments (2). To maximize the oxygen harvesting, blood flow and water flow are arranged in a countercurrent pattern with (5) oxygen–poor blood entering the lamella upstream of the water flow (5) and oxygen–rich blood leaving the lamella downstream (6).

Countercurrent exchange is often applied in nature. It allows for example seabirds such as the albatross to drink seawater. The birds use a pair of nasal glands which produce a fluid more salty than seawater. That fluid is then disposed of through the beak. In a countercurrent exchange, salt is removed from blood vessels into tubules which collect the salty fluid in the glands. Thus, the salt is removed from the bird's body without the need of fresh water.

A second example is highlighted in Fig. 7.16, which illustrates the respiratory action of fish. Fish extract oxygen from air dissolved in water. They continuously let water stream through their mouth and over the gill arches highlighted for the fish in the figure. Each gill arch has two rows of gill filaments illustrated in the magnified inset above the fish. These filaments are composed of flat plates (lamellae). As illustrated in the panel at the top right, the lamellae contain a mesh of blood capillaries which absorb oxygen from the water passing through the flat plates. Note that the blood flow direction in the capillaries is opposite to the flow direction of the passing water. The inset at the bottom right in Fig. 7.16 highlights how this countercurrent flow enhances the oxygen absorption from the flowing water. The numbers indicated on the two flow arrows correspond to the percentage of oxygen in the fluid; the arrow toward the right shows the percentage of O_2 in the water (100% corresponds to oxygen saturated water) and the arrow along a flat plate toward the left shows the percentage of oxygen in the blood in the capillaries (100 % corresponds to oxygen saturated blood). This elaborate countercurrent flow approach is necessary as the total amount of oxygen dissolved in water is much less than the fraction of oxygen in air. Thus, efficient methods of harvesting oxygen from water is necessary for aquatic animal life.

7.4.3. Temperature dependence of diffusion

Table 7.4 shows several diffusion coefficients D for biologically interesting systems at 20°C. The data indicate some interesting trends, e.g. that the same molecule (e.g. oxygen) diffuses faster in less dense media, i.e., fastest in gases and slowest in solid tissue. The data also show that bigger diffusing species diffuse slower in a given medium, for example sucrose is faster than hemoglobin in water.

When wondering about such observations and the fact that they seem not to be predicted by Fick's law, we need to keep in mind that Fick's law is a phenomenological law. This means that it is an adequate description of experimental observations of the relation between the flux of matter across a membrane and the corresponding concentration change, but it is not derived from any fundamental laws of physics, e.g. the three laws of thermodynamics or Newton's three laws of mechanics. Empirical laws usually contain constants, such as the diffusion coefficient in Fick's law, for which a fundamental origin is not revealed by the empirical law itself. Consequently, although we know the diffusion coefficients in Table 7.4, we cannot predict values for other diffusion coefficients based on our understanding of nature in general, nor can we explain the temperature dependence of D in spite of our intuition that it should be significant.

To understand the temperature dependence of diffusion, a microscopic look at the membrane is necessary. Since diffusion is based on the motion of single atoms or molecules, the membrane model has to be developed at the atomic length scale. We used this approach before, when we extended the macroscopic, empirical definition of temperature using an atomic scale model in section 6.3 to link temperature and the root–mean–square speed of individual particles.

The microscopic model for the matrix in which diffusion is observed is illustrated by the open circles in the top panels of Fig. 7.17: we assume that it consists of a regular array of atoms or molecules with fixed relative positions. This is a reasonable first model for crystalline solids, but it is also suitable to describe systems without long–range order in the context of diffusion. For such systems as amorphous solids, liquids and most biological systems, the open circles represent at least the local environment for a diffusing particle (solid dot).

The microscopic model of diffusion was first introduced quantitatively by Svante August Arrhenius in 1889. Diffusion means microscopically that a foreign particle, the solid dot in Fig. 7.17, propagates from one open site in the matrix to the next by passing through a zone in which the matrix particles are more crowded. For each of the sites which the foreign atom passes in the matrix it is possible to determine its interaction energy with the neighboring matrix atoms. The plot in the lower panel of Fig. 7.17 results when we draw the potential energy as a function of the position of the diffusing particle. Sites which provide more space for the diffusing particle are associated with a smaller potential

Table 7.4: Biologically interesting diffusion coefficients at T = 20°C. The value of water self–diffusion applies at T = 25°C.

System	Diffusion coefficient
Oxygen (O_2) in air	6.4×10^{-5} m²/s
Oxygen (O_2) in water	1×10^{-9} m²/s
Oxygen (O_2) in tissue	1×10^{-11} m²/s
Water in water	2.4×10^{-9} m²/s
Sucrose in water	5×10^{-10} m²/s
Hemoglobin in water	7×10^{-11} m²/s
Tobacco mosaic virus in water	5×10^{-12} m²/s

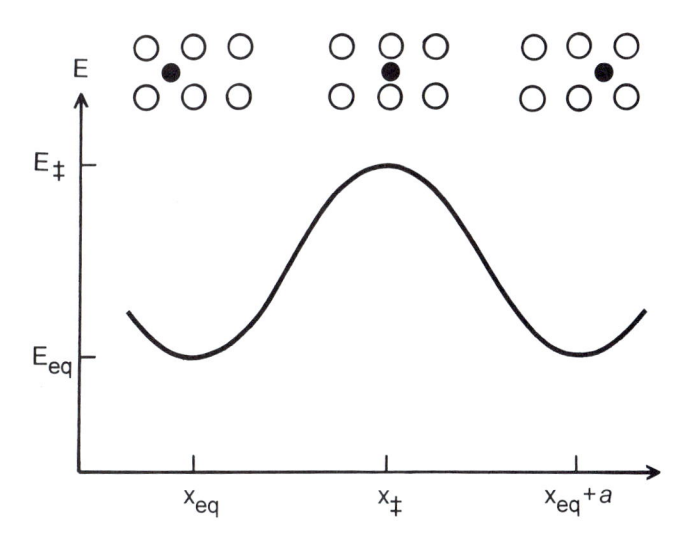

Fig. 7.17: Top panel: three sequential sketches for the microscopic diffusion mechanism in an ordered matrix. The matrix particles are indicated by open circles. The diffusing foreign particle (solid dot) hops from one wide–open site within the matrix to another, passing through a zone in which the matrix particles are located in a denser array. The wide–open sites are equilibrium sites for the foreign particle in which it spends most of the time.
Bottom panel: the corresponding plot of the potential energy of the foreign atom as it moves from its initial site at x_{eq} to the final site of the jump at $x_{eq} + a$. At the equilibrium sites the energy of the atom is E_{eq}. The atom has a maximum energy $E_{\ddagger}$ in the transitional state while it jumps from one equilibrium site to another.

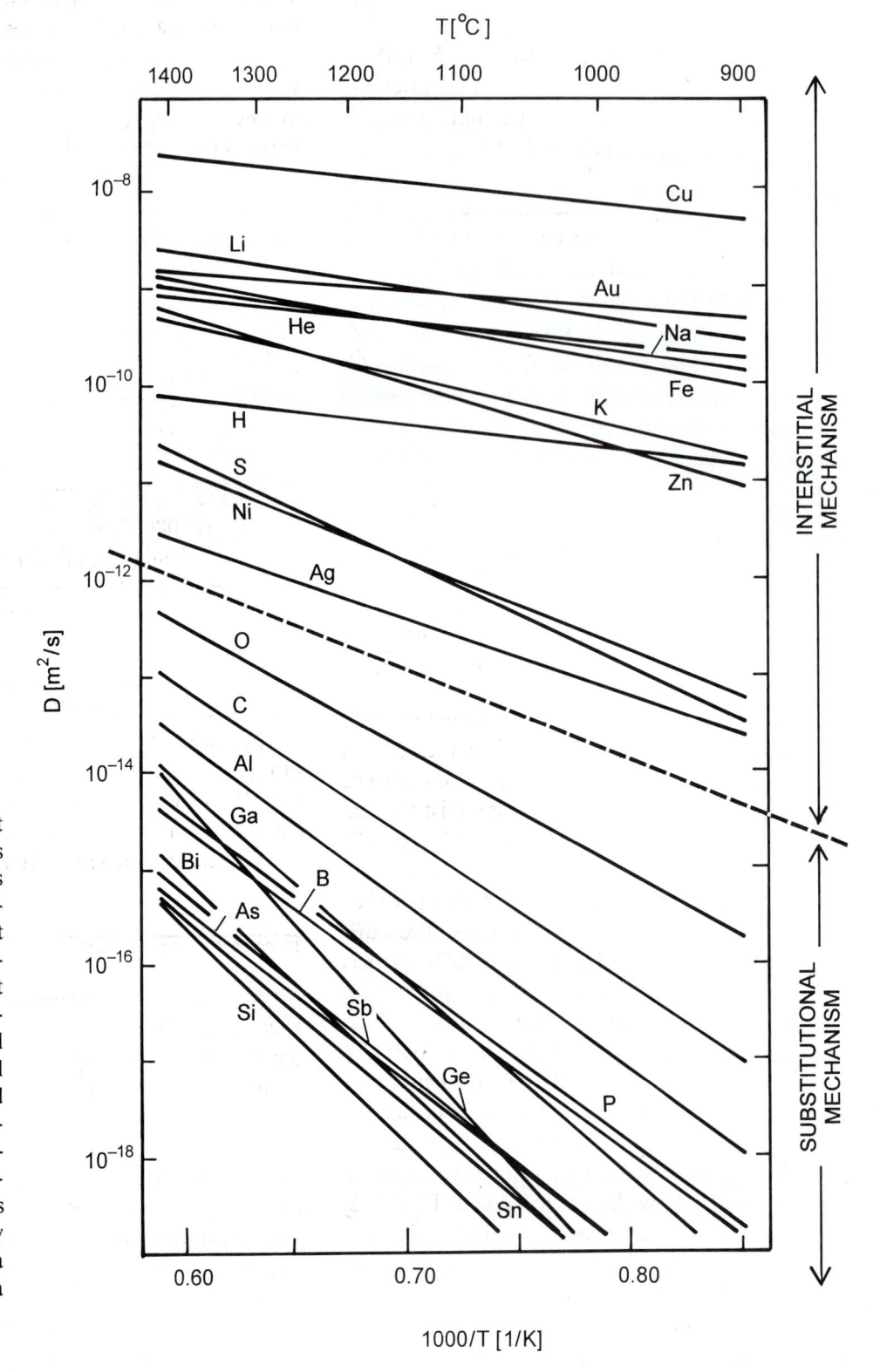

Fig. 7.18: Arrhenius plot of diffusion coefficients (in unit [m²/s]) for various elements in silicon. Temperatures are given in unit [°C] at the top and inversely as 1000/T in unit [1/K] at the bottom. Elements above the dashed line follow an interstitial diffusion mechanism and elements below the dashed line follow a substitutional mechanism of diffusion. Both mechanisms are properly described by Arrhenius' equation for a diffusion coefficient as a function of temperature.

energy. Such sites are shown in the first and last panel at the top of the figure and correspond to positions x_{eq} and $x_{eq} + a$ where a is a typical spacing for a given matrix. Since the potential energy of the diffusing particle has a minimum value at x_{eq} we call this an equilibrium position and label the corresponding energy E_{eq}.

Foreign particles moving in the matrix are in thermal equilibrium with the matrix, which means that they will not have a sufficiently high total energy to move through the matrix like gas particles move in a box as discussed for the kinetic gas theory model. Instead, the total energy of the particle is much smaller than the energy barrier between positions x_{eq} and $x_{eq} + a$ in Fig. 7.17 and the particle is confined to the equilibrium position for most of the time.

When an atom moves, it must pass through an area of higher potential energy. The state in which the foreign atom reaches the maximum potential energy is called the transition state and its potential energy is labelled $E_\ddagger$. $\Delta E = E_\ddagger - E_{eq}$ is then called the *activation energy* since this energy difference must be provided to the atom in order for it to be able to cross into the neighboring equilibrium site. How can particles ever pass the energy barrier when the transition state energy exceeds the total energy of the diffusing particle? The atom jumps successfully when its kinetic energy is higher than the activation energy at the instant it attempts to jump. For atoms at a given temperature the Maxwell–Boltzmann distribution from Fig. 6.16 allows us to determine the fraction of foreign atoms which have enough kinetic energy to pass the barrier. These will be the particles in the tail of the velocity distribution at high velocities. It is apparent from Fig. 6.16 that more atoms have enough energy to overcome the activation energy barrier if the system is at a higher temperature. This explains why diffusion coefficients are larger at higher temperatures.

This qualitative prediction is tested in Fig. 7.18, which displays the diffusion data for many elements in silicon. The crystalline silicon matrix is chosen because by far the best established diffusion data exist for that system. Shown in the figure are the diffusion coefficients as a function of temperature (the temperature scale is shown above the panel). We see that copper has the highest diffusion coefficient, i.e., it is the fastest diffusing element in silicon, and silicon self–diffusion has the smallest diffusion coefficient, i.e., silicon diffuses slower than any other element in silicon. The wide range of diffusion coefficients in the silicon system is partially due to the existence of two different diffusion mechanisms. Fast diffusors like copper move in the fashion indicated in Fig. 7.17, which is called interstitial diffusion. Elements which diffuse more slowly, i.e., those which are located below the dashed line in Fig. 7.18, diffuse substitutionally, i.e., they move from lattice site to lattice site displacing silicon atoms. Arrhenius' model applies to both types of diffusion.

Based on the model in Fig. 7.17, Arrhenius predicted the following temperature dependence of the diffusion coefficient:

$$D = D_0 e^{\left(-\frac{\Delta E}{kT}\right)} = D_0 \exp\left(-\frac{\Delta E}{kT}\right) \quad (25)$$

in which k is the Boltzmann constant first introduced in Chapter 6 and D_0 is called a pre–exponential factor. The label *e* indicates the exponential function, which is also often written as exp(...). Thus, the diffusion coefficient depends on the temperature in a non–linear fashion. As we have done with power law relations before, we want to linearize Eq. (25). This is done by taking the logarithm on both sides of Eq. (25):

$$\ln(D) = \ln(D_0) - \frac{\Delta E}{kT} \quad (26)$$

Eq. (26) states that plotting the logarithm of the diffusion coefficient, ln(D), versus 1/T yields a linear plot of the type $y = a + bx$. Here, $\ln(D_0)$ is the constant offset term *a* and $\Delta E/k$ is the slope *b*. This is called an *Arrhenius plot*. Alternatively, the ordinate can be plotted as a logarithmic scale. This is done in Fig. 7.18 for the diffusion coefficients in silicon. Note that the scale of the abscissa is 1000/T, not T.

Arrhenius' result provides a more detailed explanation of the diffusion coefficient. Eq. (25) shows that the diffusion coefficient decreases as the ratio of the activation energy, ΔE, to the term kT increases. kT is an energy term related to the temperature of the matrix. Therefore, diffusion coefficients become larger at higher temperatures. A careful evaluation of Arrhenius' theory also provides a physical explanation for the factor D_0 in Eq. (25): D_0 is associated with the frequency of attempts by the particle to overcome the activation energy barrier and is therefore related to its vibration frequency.

===

Example 7.6
Using Fig. 7.18, determine the activation energy ΔE and the pre–exponential factor D_0 for
(a) the diffusion of germanium (Ge) in silicon, and
(b) the diffusion of copper (Cu) in silicon.

Solution: The approach to analyzing logarithmic plots is discussed in detail in the General Appendix (Chapter 24). The simplest way to analyse a logarithmic plot such as Fig. 7.18 is to first replace the D–axis (ordinate) by a linear ln(D) axis. This is achieved by replacing each value along the axis by the logarithm of that number, e.g., the value 10^{-14} m²/s is assigned a new value of –32.24 and 10^{-8} m²/s is assigned a new value of –18.42. The new ordinate is linear with an increment of 2.303 for each decade of the original axis.

Solution part (a): From this modified plot, two pairs of ordinate and abscissa values, ln(D) and 1000/T, are taken to determine the unknown parameters in Eq. (26).

Table 7.5. Parameter sets for Ge diffusion in Si.

ln(D)	1/T [1/K]
−44.74	8.0 × 10⁻⁴
−32.80	6.0 × 10⁻⁴

Table 7.5 shows such data from the curve labelled Ge. We substitute the data from Table 7.5 into Eq. (26):

$$(I) \quad -44.74 = \ln(D_0) - \frac{\Delta E}{k} 8.0 \times 10^{-4}$$

$$(II) \quad -32.80 = \ln(D_0) - \frac{\Delta E}{k} 6.0 \times 10^{-4} \qquad (27)$$

The two formulas in Eq. (27) are subtracted from each other to solve for the unknown variable $\Delta E/k$. We find:

$$\frac{\Delta E}{k} = 59700 \ K$$

$$\Rightarrow \quad \Delta E = 8.24 \times 10^{-19} \ J \qquad (28)$$

in which the second line follows from the first line after multiplying with the Boltzmann constant k. Diffusion activation energies are often reported in another energy unit, the electron–volt [eV]. The conversion is 1 eV = 1.6×10^{-19} J (see also Chapter 9). With this conversion we find that the activation energy for diffusion of Ge in Si can be expressed as 5.1 eV. In comparison, the average thermal energy of a particle at room temperature is kT = 0.025 eV, i.e., 0.5 % of the energy needed for a Ge atom to overcome the diffusion barrier between neighboring sites in silicon.

A value for $\ln(D_0)$ is obtained from Eq. (27) by substituting $\Delta E = 8.24 \times 10^{-19}$ J into either one of the two formulas. This leads to $D_0 = 2 \times 10^1$ m²/s.

Solution part (b): This part is solved in an analogous fashion to part (a). Table 7.6 shows the data pairs chosen from the curve labelled Cu.

Table 7.6. Parameter sets for Cu diffusion in Si.

ln(D)	1/T [1/K]
−19.17	8.5 × 10⁻⁴
−17.71	6.0 × 10⁻⁴

The data in Table 7.6 are again substituted into Eq. (26):

$$(I) \quad -19.17 = \ln(D_0) - \frac{\Delta E}{k} 8.5 \times 10^{-4}$$

$$(II) \quad -17.71 = \ln(D_0) - \frac{\Delta E}{k} 6.0 \times 10^{-4} \qquad (29)$$

Eq. (29) leads to $\Delta E = 8.06 \times 10^{-20}$ J = 0.5 eV. This is an energy barrier which is an order of magnitude smaller than the energy barrier in the case of germanium diffusion. We further find $D_0 = 6.8 \times 10^{-7}$ m²/s.

7.4.4. Diffusion length

Albert Einstein developed Arrhenius' model further, considering particles that make not one but many jumps. For each jump a particle selects randomly from its neighboring equilibrium sites. This means, for example, that two consecutive jumps can bring the atom back to its initial position. Thus, the atom does not move a total distance of N a after N jumps of length a. From a statistical analysis of this problem, Einstein found a very useful formula for the diffusion length. The diffusion length Λ at a given temperature is defined as the average distance a diffusing particle moves during a time period t:

$$\Lambda \ [m] = \sqrt{2 \ D \ [m^2/s] \ t \ [s]} \qquad (30)$$

Example 7.7

Fig. 7.19 shows the alveolar sacs at the end of the bronchial tree. The alveoli are in direct contact with blood capillaries. In the alveoli, the inhaled air gets in closest contact to the red blood cells which carry oxygen. Fig. 7.20 highlights the transport process barrier in a single alveolus in contact with a blood capillary. The membrane width between the gas phase inside the alveolus and the blood in the capillary is 1 – 2 μm. An erythrocyte passes through the contact zone in about 0.75 s. As shown in Fig. 7.20, the narrow capillary forces the erythrocyte to deform in order to tightly squeeze through the capillary. Thus, the erythrocyte is in close contact with the membrane and can take up oxygen diffusing across the membrane in that time.

(a) How long do oxygen molecules need to diffuse from the gas phase in the alveolus to a passing erythrocyte in an adjacent blood capillary?

Fig. 7.19: At the end of each bronchial branch in the lungs, small bubbles of about 0.3 mm diameter form an interface between the inhaled air volume and the blood capillaries. These bubbles are called alveoli. Oxygen transfer from the air into the blood system occurs across the alveolar membranes. The inset at the top left shoes an overview of the lung with the bronchial tree.

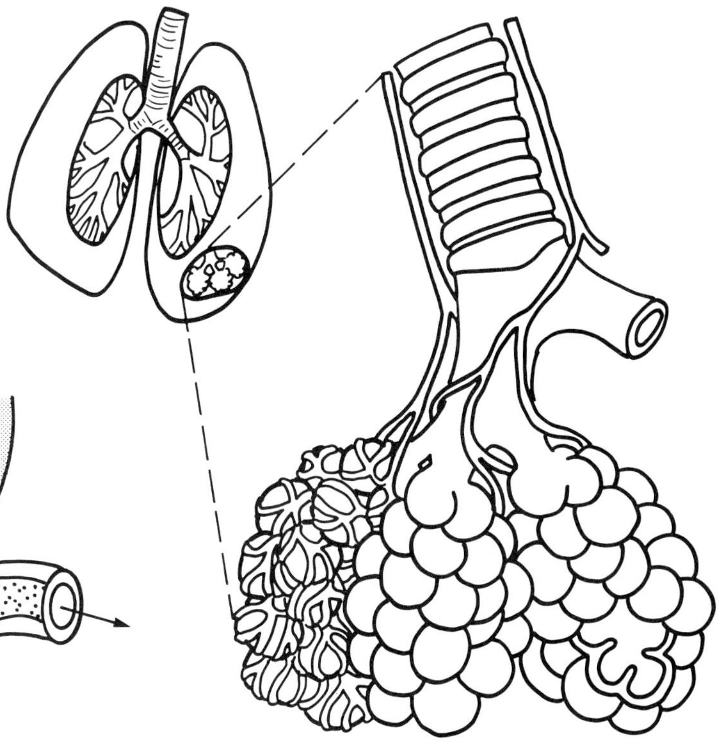

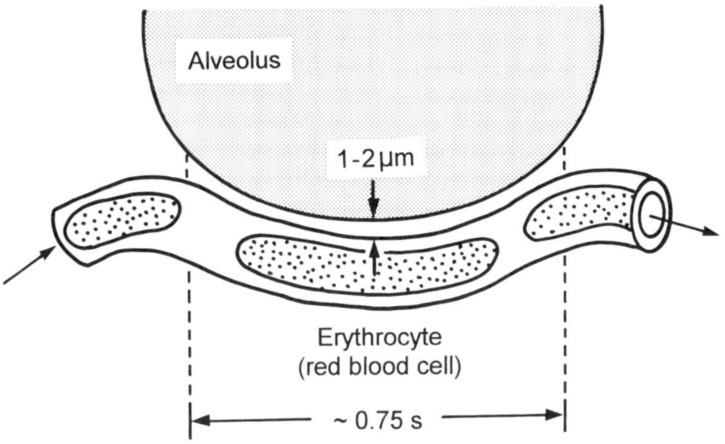

Fig. 7.20: Sketch of a blood capillary in contact with an alveolus across a 1 – 2 µm wide membrane. The capillary has a diameter of about 9 µm (see also data discussed in Chapter 10). An erythrocyte, which is about 7.5 µm wide and 1 to 2 µm thick, passes through the contact area in 0.75 s. A healthy red blood cell can deform to squeeze through the capillary because it does not contain a nucleus.

(b) How thick may the membrane tissue between alveolus and capillary become before the oxygen transfer is significantly reduced? This occurs when the oxygen cannot diffuse to the erythrocyte during the time period an erythrocyte passes the alveolus.

Solution part (a): We use Eq. (30) with the diffusion coefficient for oxygen in tissue taken from Table 7.4. The diffusion length is taken as the maximum distance in healthy tissue, i.e., 2 µm. Eq. (30) is rewritten to express the time for diffusion:

$$t = \frac{\Lambda^2}{2D} = \frac{(2 \times 10^{-6} \,[m])^2}{2 \cdot 1 \times 10^{-11} \,[m^2/s]} = 0.2 \, s \quad (31)$$

Oxygen diffusion occurs without problem across the membrane between alveolus and blood capillary in the allotted time.

Solution part (b): We use the same diffusion coefficient as before and t = 0.75 s. This time, Eq. (30) is used as written since the diffusion length is sought:

$$\Lambda = \sqrt{2Dt} = \sqrt{2 \cdot 1 \times 10^{-11} \left[\frac{m^2}{s}\right] 0.75 \,[s]} \quad (32)$$

$$\Rightarrow \quad \Lambda = 3.9 \times 10^{-6} \, m$$

Doubling of the membrane width between alveolus and blood capillary from 2 µm to 4 µm already shifts the diffusion barrier into a physiologically dangerous range.

We can now compare the respiratory effort of fish as illustrated in Fig. 7.16 and that of humans as discussed in Example 7.7. Breathing in air has the obvious advantage of access to the medium oxygen. Water in most fish habitats contains about 4 – 8 milliliter [ml] of O_2 per liter of water, while each liter of air contains 210 ml O_2. Indeed, a resting fish must actively pump water through its gills to not suffer from oxygen deprivation. Because oxygen and CO_2 diffuse much faster in air than in water, ventilation of the internal surfaces of the alveoli for us is a much lesser concern. However, there is a problem with air breathing that had to be addressed before life on land became possible: the humidity of air changes often which would lead to varying degrees of water vapor inhalation. The inner surfaces of alveoli would change (dry versus moist) causing significant variations in the physiological effectiveness of the respiration process. As a solution, the respiratory system of land living animals operates always with completely water saturated air. The humidity of the air is controlled by a turbulent flow of the inhaled air through the trachea which has a moist inner surface.

7.5. Problems

P–7.1
We quantify Fourier's experiment, shown in Fig. 7.4, for a cylindrical copper rod of a length of 1.2 m and a cross-sectional area 4.8 cm². The rod is insulated to prevent heat loss through its surface. A temperature difference of 100 K is maintained between the ends. Find the rate at which heat is conducted through the rod.

P–7.2
We confirm the concept of the geothermal effect in an alternative fashion to the discussion in the text (Example 7.3). We know that the average rate at which heat is conducted through the surface of the ground in North America is 54.0 mJ/(s m²). Assuming a surface temperature of 10°C, what is the temperature at a depth of 35 km (near the base of the Earth's crust)?
Hint: Ignore the heat generated by the presence of radioactive elements and use 2.5 J/(m s K) for the average thermal conductivity of the near-surface rocks. Start with Fourier's law.

P–7.3
For poor heat conductors a thermal resistance R has been introduced. The thermal resistance of a piece of material of thermal conductivity λ and thickness l is defined as:

$$R = \frac{l}{\lambda} \quad (33)$$

(a) Show that Eq. (33) allows us to rewrite Fourier's law in the form:

$$\frac{Q}{t} = A \frac{T_{high} - T_{low}}{R} \quad (34)$$

in which A is the cross-sectional area of the piece of material.
(b) What is the SI unit of the thermal resistance R?

P–7.4
In a table you find $\lambda = 2.9 \times 10^{-3}$ cal/(cm s K) for the thermal conductivity of Pyrex glass at 0°C.
(a) Express this value in standard units.
(b) What is the thermal resistance of a Pyrex glass sheet of thickness 0.635 cm (or ¼ inch)?

P–7.5
If it takes two days to defrost a frozen 5 kg turkey, estimate how long it would take to defrost a 2 tonnes Siberian Mammoth from the same initial temperature.
Hint: treat both animals as spherically shaped and use the same approach we applied in Example 7.3.

P–7.6
We want to measure the thermal conductivity of an unknown insulator material. For this we use the following set-up: A 3 mm thick plate of the unknown material is placed between two iron plates of thickness 2 cm each. All three plates are 20 cm by 20 cm in size. The upper iron plate is heated to 80°C and the lower iron plate is kept at 20°C. Once a stationary temperature profile has developed across the insulator, the heater is removed from the upper iron plate. We observe that the temperature of the upper iron plate drops by 2.7 K after 1 min. Neglecting any loss of heat to the environment, what is the thermal conductivity coefficient λ for the unknown insulator material?
Hint: approach this problem in the same fashion as we solved Example 7.3. The density of iron is $\rho = 7.9$ g/cm³, the specific heat capacity of iron is c = 450 J/(kg K).

P–7.7
Fig. 7.21 shows a block which consists of two materials with different thicknesses l_1 and l_2 and different thermal conductivities, λ_1 and λ_2. The temperatures of the outer surfaces of the block are T_{high} and T_{low}, (see figure). Each face of the block has a cross-sectional area A.

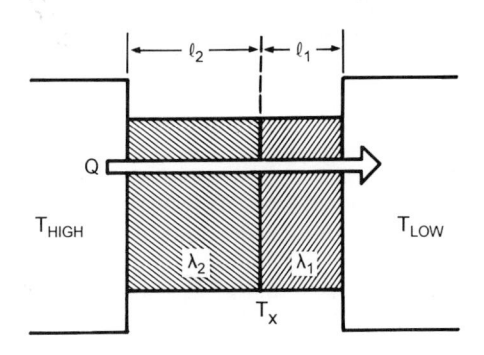

Fig. 7.21 for problem P–7.7.

(a) Show that the formula

$$\frac{Q}{t} = \frac{A\,(T_{high} - T_{low})}{(l_1/\lambda_1) + (l_2/\lambda_2)} \qquad (35)$$

correctly expresses the steady state rate of heat transfer. Hint: in the steady state the heat transfer through any part of the block must be equal to the heat transfer through the other part of the block. Introduce a temperature T_x at the interface of the two parts as shown in Fig. 7.21, and in the first step express the rate of heat transfer for each part of the block separately.
(b) Rewrite Eq. (35) using Eq. (33), which introduces R_1 and R_2 as the thermal resistances for the two parts of the block. By comparing the result with Eq. (34), determine how thermal resistances are combined for materials in sequence.

P–7.8
Show that the temperature T_x at the interface of the block in Fig. 7.21 is given by:

$$T_x = \frac{R_1 T_{high} + R_2 T_{low}}{R_1 + R_2} \qquad (36)$$

P–7.9
Four square pieces of insulation of two different materials, all with the same thickness and cross–sectional area A, are used to cover an opening of total area 2A. This can be done in either of the two ways shown in Fig. 7.22. Which arrangement, (a) or (b), gives the lower heat flow if $\lambda_1 \neq \lambda_2$?

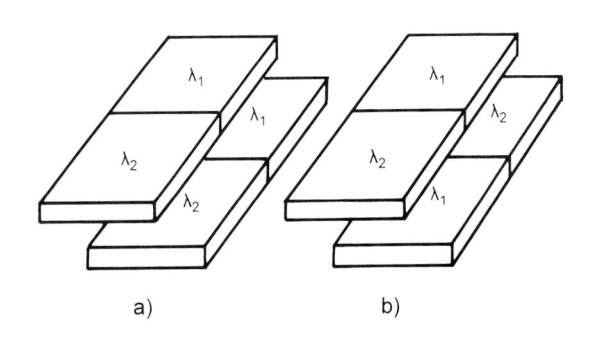

Fig. 7.22 for problem P–7.9.

P–7.10
Two identical rectangular rods of metal are welded end to end, as shown in Fig. 7.23(a), and 1 J of heat is conducted in a steady state process through the combined rod in 2.0 minutes. How long would it take for 1 J to be conducted through the rods if they were welded together as shown in Fig. 7.23(b)?

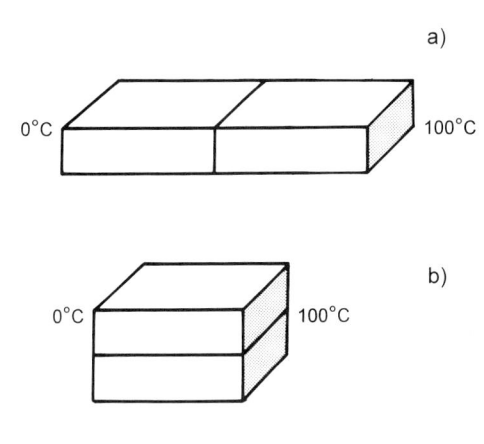

Fig. 7.23 for problem P–7.10.

P–7.11
Heat loss via convection occurs only when heat is carried by a moving fluid. For example, when heating water in a beaker from below, the increase of the water temperature at the bottom leads to a decrease of the water density and causes the warmer water to rise due to buoyancy. The rising water carries excess heat to the surface.
(a) Compare bare skin to skin covered with clothes. Why is the heat loss of the body significantly reduced when wearing clothes?
(b) At temperate lakes and ponds it is often observed that algae bloom for a short period during spring and autumn. Consider Fig. 7.24 which shows the stratification during summer (top) as well as the seasonal turnover in spring and autumn (bottom), how can the convection driven turnover cause algal blooms?

P–7.12
Determine the diffusion coefficient for glycerine in H_2O using the following observations: glycerine diffuses along a horizontal, water–filled column that has a cross–sectional area of 2.0 cm². The density step from one end to the other is $\Delta \rho / l = 3.0 \times 10^{-2}$ kg/m⁴ and the steady state diffusion rate is 5.7×10^{-15} kg/s.

P–7.13
We want to test a statement we will make in Chapter 12: carbon–dioxide diffuses easier than oxygen across the membrane between the lung's alveoli and the blood capillaries. To show this, calculate the ratio of the diffusion coefficient of CO_2 and the diffusion coefficient of O_2 in tissue at 37°C.
Hint: Start with Eq. (21). Rewrite the concentration difference as a pressure difference using the ideal gas law. Applying this equation for both gases separately, deter-

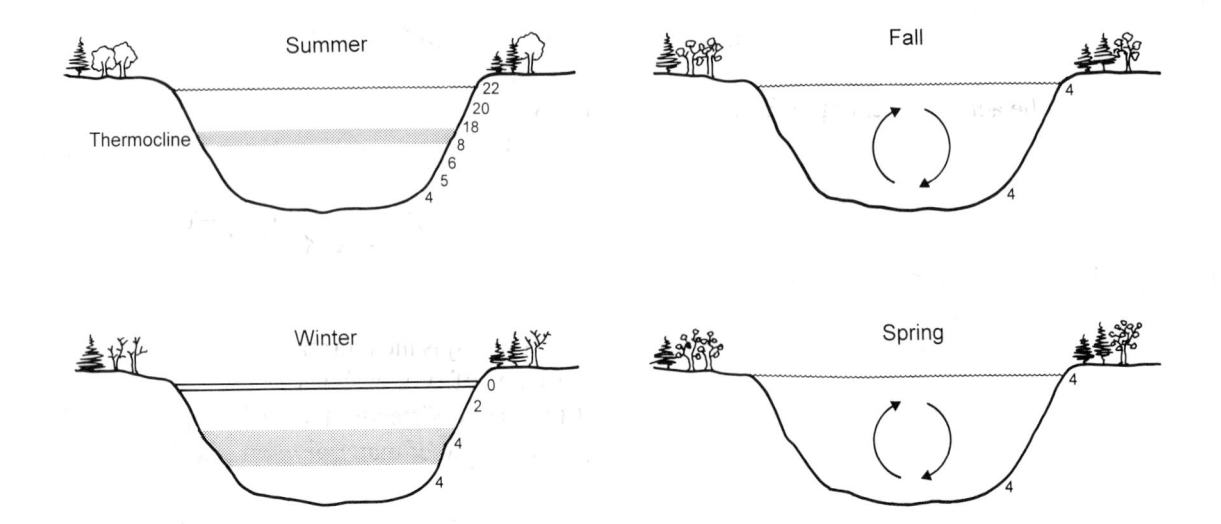

Fig. 7.24 for problem P–7.11(b). Lakes and ponds in temperate climates usually stratify by temperature and water density in winter and summer. In the summer, the warmer water is above the thermocline (water zone between 8°C and 18°C) with temperatures below the thermocline near 4°C (temperature of water at its highest density). In the winter, the water above the thermocline is cooler (between 0°C and 4°C) than the water below. The seasonal turnover occurs biannually as denser water sinks to the bottom of the lake.

mine the ratio of the diffusion coefficients. For the pressure differences across the membranes in the lungs use the values $\Delta p(CO_2) = 0.8$ kPa and $\Delta p(O_2) = 8.0$ kPa. The number of moles of both gases diffusing across the interface alveoli/capillaries can be determined from the data given in Example 6.3.

P–7.14
Why can bacteria rely on passive diffusion for their oxygen supply but not human beings?
Hint: Calculate from Eq. (30):
(a) the time it takes for oxygen to diffuse from the interface with the environment to the center of a bacterium of radius r = 1.0 µm, and
(b) the time it takes for oxygen to diffuse from the external air to an organ 10 cm below human skin.
Note: for an upper limit use the diffusion coefficient of oxygen in water and for a lower limit use the diffusion coefficient of oxygen in tissue from Table 7.4. These two values give you a good approximation since humans consist roughly of 10 liters [l] of extracellular fluid and 30 l of cells.
(c) *If you are interested*: why can many relatively large invertebrates such as hydras survive without a cardiovascular system?

P–7.15
We want to determine the relation between the diffusion coefficient and the molecular mass of macromolecules. Using a double–logarithmic plot of the data listed in Table 7.7, determine the coefficients a and b in

$$D = a \cdot M^b \quad (37)$$

P–7.16
(a) How far does a Tobacco mosaic virus move in water at 20°C in 1 hour?
(b) Using the ratio of the diffusion coefficients for oxygen and carbon–dioxide in tissue from problem P–7.13, what is the ratio of diffusion lengths for these molecules in tissue at 20°C?

P–7.17
Determining the pre–exponential factor D_0 in the manner shown in Example 7.6 leads to a large uncertainty of the value. To illustrate this, we focus on the diffusion of carbon (C) in silicon. Fig. 7.25 shows the Arrhenius plot

Table 7.7: Diffusion coefficients in solution at 20°C.

Protein	D [cm²/s]	M [g/mol]
Insulin	8.2×10^{-7}	41 000
Haemoglobin	6.3×10^{-7}	67 000
Catalase	4.1×10^{-7}	250 000
Urease	3.5×10^{-7}	470 000
Tobacco mosaic virus	5.3×10^{-8}	31 000 000

of the available data (note that silicon melts at about 1400°C). Use the solid line and the dashed line to determine
(a) the variation of the activation energy ΔE, and
(b) the variation of the pre–exponential factor D_0.

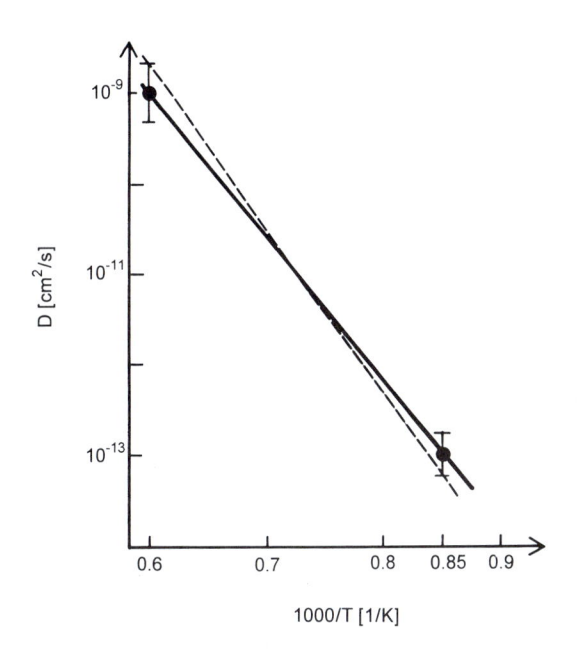

Fig. 7.25 for problem P–7.17.

Summary

Definitions:
● Amount in [mol] and concentration of a component in solution in [mol/m³]:

$$n_i \ [mol] = \frac{m_i \ [kg]}{M \ [kg/mol]}$$

$$c_i \ [mol/m^3] = \frac{\rho_i \ [kg/m^3]}{M \ [kg/mol]}$$

Units:
Molar mass: M [kg/mol]

Laws:
● Fourier's law of steady state heat conduction:

$$\frac{Q}{t} = \lambda \, A \, \frac{T_{high} - T_{low}}{l}$$

λ [J/(s m K)] is the thermal conductivity coefficient, l is the length of the membrane, A is its cross–sectional area.
● Fick's law of steady state diffusion for the transport of
(i) an amount of material in unit [kg]:

$$\frac{m_i}{t} = D \, A \, \frac{\rho_{i,\,high} - \rho_{i,\,low}}{l}$$

D [m/s²] is the diffusion coefficient, ρ is the density.
(ii) an amount of material in unit [mol]:

$$j_i = \frac{n_i}{t} = D \, A \, \frac{c_{i,\,high} - c_{i,\,low}}{l}$$

j_i [mol/s] is the material flux of the ith component.
● Temperature dependence of the diffusion coefficient:

$$D = D_0 \, e^{\left(-\frac{\Delta E}{kT}\right)} = D_0 \, \exp\left(-\frac{\Delta E}{kT}\right)$$

k is the Boltzmann constant, ΔE is the **activation energy**. This is equivalent to:

$$\ln(D) = \ln(D_0) - \frac{\Delta E}{kT}$$

● Einstein's formula for the diffusion length Λ:

$$\Lambda \ [m] = \sqrt{2 \cdot D \ [m^2/s] \cdot t \ [s]}$$

Chapter VIII

Order and Evolution

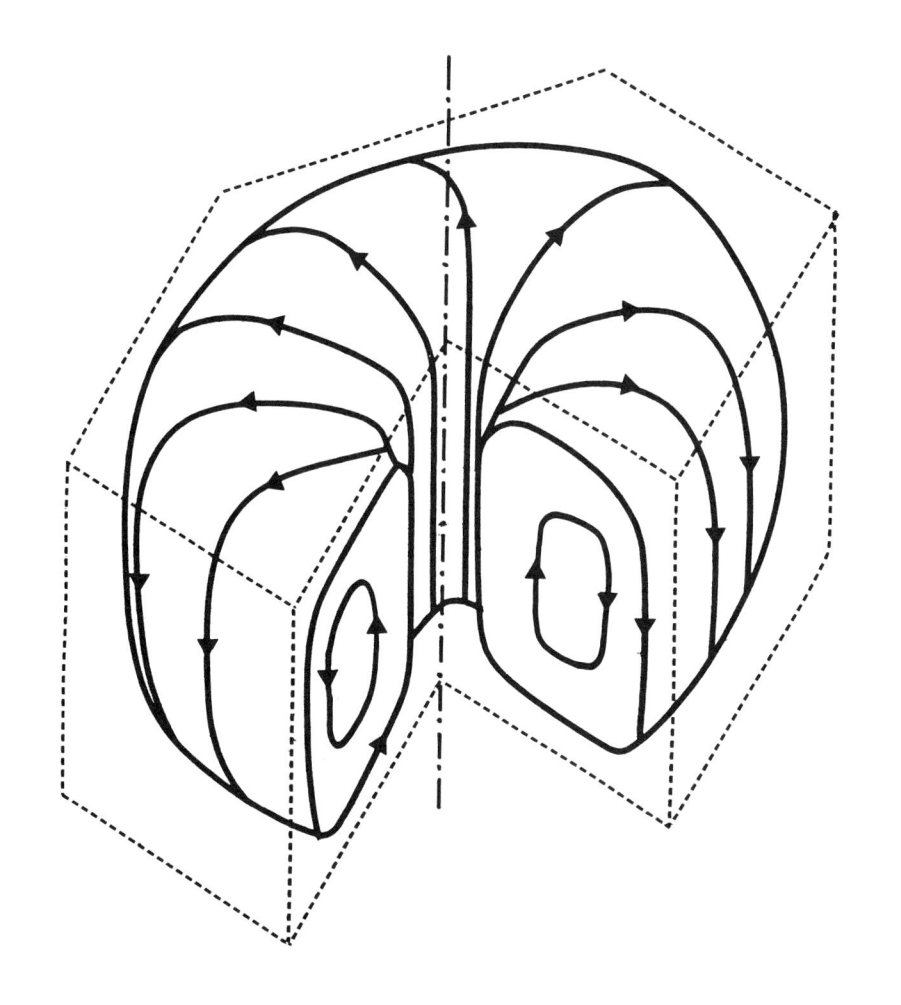

The dynamics of processes

ORDER AND EVOLUTION
THE DYNAMICS OF PROCESSES

The first law of thermodynamics is insufficient to fully characterize systems in thermal equilibrium. It distinguishes possible and impossible processes based on their agreement with the conservation of energy, but it does not allow us to identify the spontaneous direction of a possible process between two system states. The second and third laws of thermodynamics fill this gap: the second law establishes the entropy as a parameter of the state of a system that remains constant in an isolated system with reversible processes (processes which proceed exclusively via equilibrium states) but increases for spontaneous irreversible processes. Based on a statistical interpretation, entropy is a measure of the order of a system; a fully ordered system at T = 0 K has an entropy of S = 0 J/K (third law of thermodynamics).

In a closed or open system at constant pressure, the Gibbs free energy G combines the enthalpy and entropy to predict the dynamics of the system: G remains constant if the process occurs between two states which are in equilibrium with each other ($\Delta G = 0$ e.g. for melting of ice at 0°C) and G approaches a minimum value during a spontaneous irreversible process ($\Delta G < 0$).

The entropy in an isolated system, or the Gibbs free energy in a closed or open system identify the propensity of the system toward a new equilibrium state. However, these parameters do not allow us to describe non–equilibrium processes because time is not a parameter in equilibrium thermodynamics. We introduce the time dependence for systems outside the equilibrium in the form of an entropy production. Near the equilibrium (called the linear regime) the steady state is the stable process with a minimum entropy production.

The study of heat conduction and diffusion as isolated non–equilibrium phenomena in the previous chapter must leave particularly a biologist still wondering about three key questions:

(I) Is it possible to extrapolate such phenomenological processes to the much more complex and intertwined processes occurring in a living organism?

(II) Can diffusion processes, which we linked to simple concentration gradients, combine with other processes, such as chemical reactions, to generate the order of complex structures we find in living organisms?

(III) Can a complicated time dependence of biological processes as postulated in modern evolutionary theory be explained by a combination of non–equilibrium processes such as the transport phenomena we have introduced in the previous chapter?

Obviously we will not give a definite final answer to either one of these questions: they are still subject of ongoing research throughout the biological and medical disciplines. However, we can lay a much stronger foundation for such studies than we have done with the experiments of Fourier, Fick and Arrhenius.

8.1. Protein synthesis

From a biologist's point of view, the ultimate answers to the questions we asked above must come from the study of the living cell. Although the physical approach in this chapter cannot yet reach this level of complexity, it is worthwhile to establish the key features of the biological system to illustrate the ultimate objective. These features center around two main observations: the cell's propensity toward order (both in structure and, as a function of time, in reproducibility) and its susceptibility to evolutionary change.

8.1.1. Processes at the cellular level

In 1665, Robert Hooke was the first to see dead cells in cork, but it was only in the 1830s that Matthias von Schleiden and Theodor Schwann realized that all living organisms consist of cells. Fig. 8.1 is an artist's sketch of a typical human cell. With living cell we mean a physiological entity that displays (i) metabolism and growth, (ii) irritability and mobility, and (iii) reproducibility. The cell is pre–programmed to perform these functions. The necessary know–how is contained in the cell nucleus, which is labelled (1) in Fig. 8.1. It is stored in chemical form in a variable number of chromosomes. Human cells in particular contain 46 chromosomes which carry the blue–print for genes which are in turn construction plans for proteins. Each chromosome consists of a roughly 7 cm long string of deoxyribonucleic acid (DNA). James Dewey Watson and Francis Harry Crick recognized in 1953 that the DNA is folded into a 10 μm long structure and that its molecular structure resembles a twisted ladder (double–helix) containing a pair of bases for every 0.34 nm of length. Sequences of bases (adenine, thymine, cytosine and guanine) contain genetic information in the same fashion as a binary code contains the information stored in a computer.

In the cell nucleus, the genetic code of the DNA is continuously copied (transcription process) onto the messenger–RNA (ribonucleic acid). The m–RNA is then transferred out of the cell nucleus through pores in the nuclear membrane ((2) in Fig. 8.1) and into the cytoplasm of the cell. The m–RNA reaches the ribosomal apparatus which is the rough endoplasmic reticulum ((3) in Fig. 8.1) where the protein synthesis occurs. In the mid–1950's Marshall Warren Nirenberg identified the method by which the living cell decodes the information stored in the DNA. At the ribosomal apparatus, transfer-

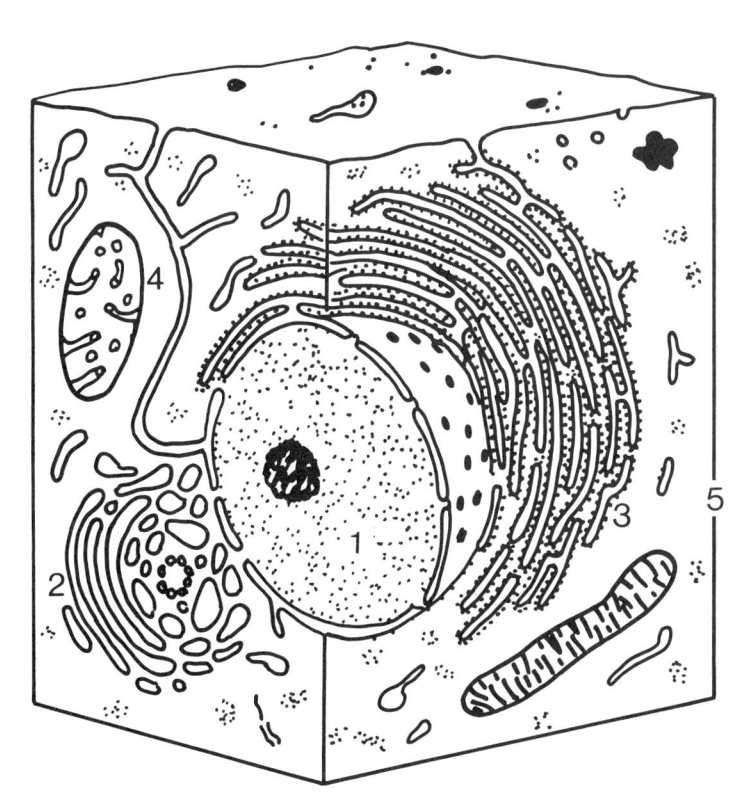

Table 8.1: Genetic code. Numbers 1, 2 and 3 identify the position of each base in the codon triplet. E.g. the triplet containing at first position an uracil (U), and an adenine (A) at positions 2 and 3 leads to the termination of the amino–synthesis ("stop"). Note that a genetic code based on duplets could encode only $4^2 = 16$ amino acids with no redundance.

	2	U	C	A	G
1	3				
U	U	Phe	Ser	Tyr	Cys
	C	Phe	Ser	Tyr	Cys
	A	Leu	Ser	**Stop**	**Stop**
	G	Leu	Ser	**Stop**	Trp
C	U	Leu	Pro	His	Arg
	C	Leu	Pro	His	Arg
	A	Leu	Pro	Gln	Arg
	G	Leu	Pro	Gln	Arg
A	U	Ile	Thr	Asn	Ser
	C	Ile	Thr	Asn	Ser
	A	Ile	Thr	Lys	Arg
	G	**Start**	Thr	Lys	Arg
G	U	Val	Ala	Asp	Gly
	C	Val	Ala	Asp	Gly
	A	Val	Ala	Asp	Gly
	G	Val	Ala	Asp	Gly

RNA bases: A = adenine, C = cytosine,
G = guanine and U = uracil

Amino acids (essential acids underlined):
1. Ala = alanine   2 Arg = arginine
3 Asn = asparagine   4 Asp = aspartic acid
5 Cys = cysteine   6 Gln = glutamine
7 Gly = glycine   8 His = histidine
9 Ile = isoleucine   10 Leu = leucine
11 Lys = lysine   12 Phe = phenylalanine
13 Pro = proline   14 Ser = serine
15 Start = methionine   16 Stop = glutamic acid
17 Thr = threonine   18 Trp = tryptophan
19 Tyr = tyrosine   20 Val = valine

Fig. 8.1: An artists' conception of the three–dimensional organization of an eukaryotic cell. All cellular organisms are formed by eukaryotic cells, with the exception of bacteria which have a much simpler cell structure called a prokaryotic cell. Indicated by numbers are: (1) the nucleus, first observed in 1831, with its porous membrane, (2) the Golgi apparatus, (3) the ribosomal apparatus (with a connected maze of tunnels stretching across the entire cell), (4) mitochondria, and (5) the cell membrane (plasma membrane), which is about 10 nm thick.

RNA molecules supply 20 different amino acids, each connected to a triplet of bases, called codons. All amino acids contain an NH_2 functional group ("amino") and a COOH functional group ("acid"). By matching the codons of a t–RNA to the sequence of bases on the m–RNA using Table 8.1, the genetic code is translated into an amino acid sequence. Such amino acid chains are called peptides if the molecule contains less than 100 amino acids, and are called proteins when they contain more than 100 amino acids. Peptides and proteins are polymers and usually have specific structural and/or catalytic properties that enable them to serve a unique biological purpose. These peptides and proteins are called enzymes. For example, the hemoglobin molecule possesses a delicate structural arrangement capable to accommodate loosely adsorbed oxygen.

In the last step, the synthesized peptides and proteins are transported out of the cell by lysosomes. Lysosomes are lipoid containers that enclose the complete macromolecule at the ribosomal apparatus and/or at the Golgi apparatus (named after Camillo Golgi) to protect it from chemical destruction. As illustrated in Fig. 8.2, the lysosomes travel to the outer cell membrane and release their content into the extracellular space via an inverse pinocytosis process.

8.1.2. Evolution

The processes described above illustrate that a combination of chemical reactions and diffusion constitute the key processes of a living cell. We stressed already in the previous chapter that both chemical reactions and diffusion are non–equilibrium processes. Thus, at the very core, life requires systems which are far from the thermodynamic equilibrium. In this statement the thermodynamic equilibrium is defined as a combination of thermal and chemical equilibrium. The combination of chemical processes in the nucleus with transport across the nuclear membrane prevents feedback mechanisms to optimize the DNA, i.e., environmental factors cannot lead directly to a modification of the DNA to improve the survival chances of the individual, as Jean Baptiste de Lamarck had proposed in 1809.

Disallowing a direct feedback mechanism is vital to maintaining a high reproducibility between sequential generations of cells. Thus, we notice that our first key observation, the high degree of order and reproducibility of structures, can only be safeguarded by nature through a complex combination of processes.

The genetic code and its use as described above are universally in use on Earth since more than two billion years. Thus, we have a tremendous amount of data to test its perfection. These data clearly show that the reproduction is not perfect: we have a continuous change of species for the entire period in which life exists on Earth.

In 1859, Charles Darwin summarized the evidence and the apparent causes for this continuous change in five principles, which we call Darwin's theory of evolution:
(I) Organisms evolve steadily over time (evolution principle),
(II) different kinds of organisms descend from common ancestors (common descent),
(III) species multiply over time (speciation), and
(IV) populations change gradually (gradualism).
(V) The mechanism of evolution is a competition among individuals for limited resources, leading to differences in survival and reproduction (natural selection).

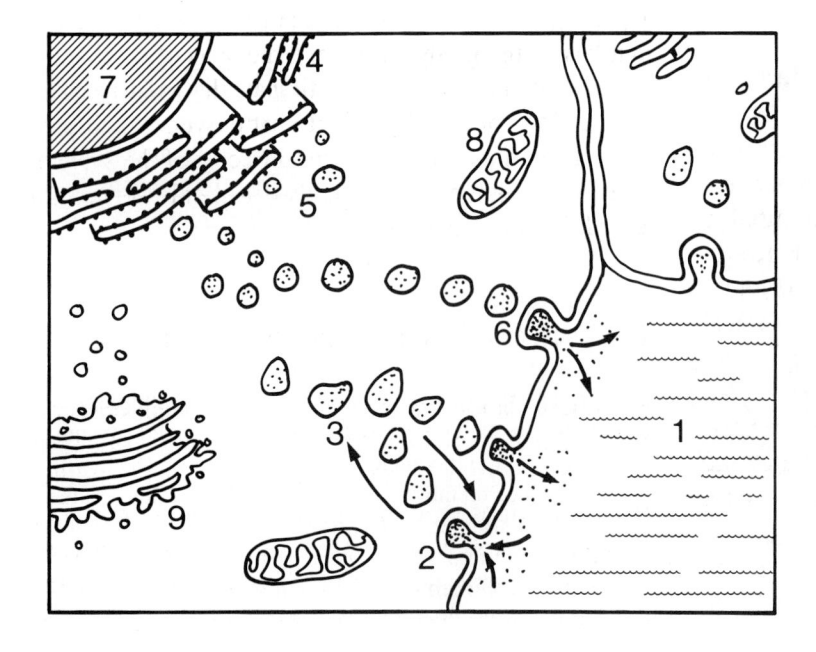

Fig. 8.2: Pinocytosis illustrated for a human cell. Molecules dissolved in the interstitium (1) are enclosed in a protrusion of the cell membrane (2) and are then transported into the cell (3). In the inverse process, proteins formed at the ribosomal apparatus (4) are enclosed by lysosomes (5) and transported to the cell membrane for release (6). Shown are also the cell nucleus with its membrane (7), a mitochondrion (8) and the Golgi apparatus (9). The Golgi apparatus contributes to the production of lysosomes.

These five principles implicitly require a continuous change of traits, but do not identify the mechanism of inheritability of traits. The modern evolution theory, developed by Theodosius Dobzhansky and Ernst Mayr and fully adopted since the 1950s, adds to Darwin's principles the concept of random mutations of the DNA.

In 1972 scientists succeeded in reprogramming the DNA of an E. coli bacterium for the first time, leading to the production of proteins previously foreign to the bacterium. By 1999, about 50 different pharmaceutical drugs were manufactured by bacteria with artificially altered genes, including erythropoietin (supporting the biosynthesis of erythrocytes) with a worldwide annual market share of about 2.4 billion dollars. What humans have only been able to do since 1972, nature must have been doing since the dawn of time. Otherwise, if DNA could not be altered, the evolution of species on Earth would never have been possible, and, as discussed in section 8.5, life on Earth might well have been wiped out by now.

How do we explain the orderly fashion in which life forms reproduce themselves? And how do we explain the continuous evolutionary change to which this process is susceptible?

8.2. Reversibility

To tackle these questions, we cannot proceed with our discussion of the transport phenomena from the previous chapter because they were developed phenomenologically. Instead we must return to our systematic discussion of thermal physics left off at the end of Chapter 6, and identify the issues from which to develop a fundamental theory for the non–equilibrium.

8.2.1. Time invariance of the first law

The concept which will guide us beyond the equilibrium is the reversibility of processes. A process is reversible if we can use it first to move a system from an initial to a final state and then invert the process such that the system returns to the initial state with all parameter changes the same but with opposite signs. Thus, the biological and evolutionary processes discussed above are not reversible, which we call irreversible. Further, we note that all processes we witness in our daily life are not reversible. Once you take fresh eggs from the refrigerator and prepared your breakfast of scrambled eggs, you cannot undo this change of the state of the system "egg" even if you would like to do so. Even simpler things cannot be reversed. For example, you heat a cup of cold coffee in your microwave oven. If you decide afterwards that you do not want the hot coffee, you cannot reverse the process. Even though you can let the cup cool down, you are not recovering the electric energy the microwave oven consumed while heating the coffee. Thus, we conclude that there are no reversible processes in the real world.

This were not really worrisome were it not for the fact that all the fundamental physical laws we discussed in the first six chapters imply that the processes they describe are reversible. In the case of a law, this is identified as time invariance: the law remains unchanged whether time moves from the past to the future or whether time would move from the future toward the past. Let us take the first law of thermodynamics as an example. That law is invariant under time reversal because it's formulation remains the same even if a process is run backwards in time. We confirm this by looking at the equation of the first law:

$$\Delta U = U_{final} - U_{initial} = Q + W \quad (1)$$

Reversing the time in this equation means that the initial state of the system becomes the final state and vice versa. Thus the term $U_{final} - U_{initial}$ becomes $U_{initial} - U_{final}$, which is the same magnitude but carrying the opposite sign. On the right hand side of Eq. (1) the heat term changes under time reversal from Q to – Q (the heat flows in the opposite direction) and the work term changes from W to – W (work is undone). Thus, Eq. (1) looks exactly the same; we cannot distinguish the direction of time (past to future or future to past) using that law.

If we cannot distinguish past and future, the laws are certainly not sufficient to describe time dependent processes. In turn, because we believe that the first law of thermodynamics and the laws of mechanics are scientifically sound, we anticipate that there must be another law, one we have not written yet, which provides us with a time dependent property of the system. Thus, we seek that law, which we will call the second law of thermodynamics.

8.2.2. Reversible and irreversible processes

But where should we look for this law, what observations are there which we haven't taken into account so far? This brings us back to the concept of reversibility, which is obviously closely related to the time–invariance of physical laws. We must seek the new law in the context of observations of irreversible processes. For the simplicity of the description, these should be processes

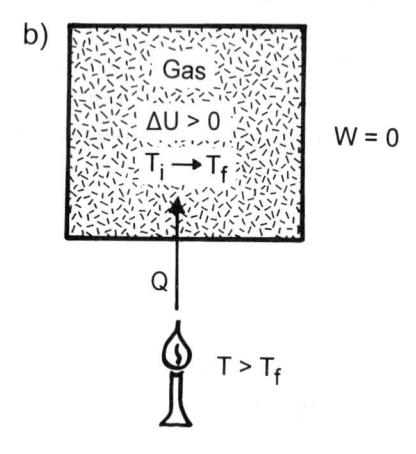

Fig. 8.3: Comparison of isochoric heating and isothermal expansion. Heat Q is taken up by the system in both processes. (a) In the isothermal case, heat flows to the gas from a heat reservoir at the same temperature as the gas. We assume that the piston moves without friction. (b) In the isochoric case, heat is provided by a flame that is much hotter than the system.

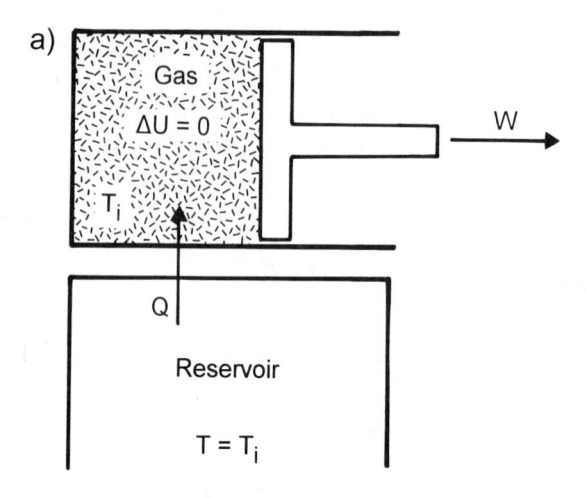

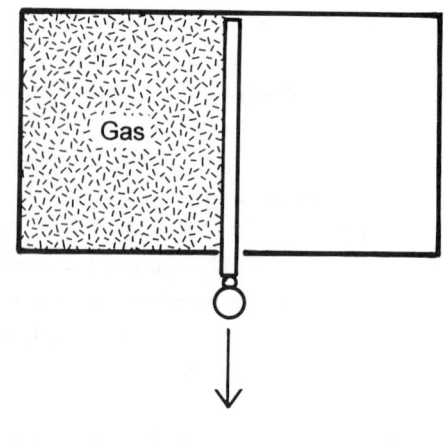

Fig. 8.4: An irreversible isothermal expansion. The chamber at the right is initially evacuated. The shutter is pulled down, allowing the gas to expand.

much less complex than the metabolism of a living cell.

We begin with reviewing two of the idealized pro esses we discussed in the later parts of Chapter 6: the isothermal and isochoric processes as shown in Fig. 8.3. The isothermal expansion illustrated in Fig. 8.3(a) is a reversible process because it can be reversed by pushing the piston back to its original position while the system remains in thermal contact with the same heat reservoir. When the initial expansion is reversed through compression, the gas in front of the piston returns to exact y the same state in which it started.

This is an idealization as both an ideal heat reservoir with a fixed temperature, T, and an ideal piston moving without friction are assumed. However, we can come close to these assumptions with a real system. The assumption of an ideal heat reservoir is reasonable when we consider a reservoir which is much bigger than the system. In this case the temperature of the reservoir changes only negligibly when heat is transferred between the system and the reservoir.

Other processes are intrinsically irreversible, that means that even when making idealizing assumptions no reversibility can be achieved. An example is the isochoric heating in Fig. 8.3(b). This process cannot be reversed because the propane gas burned cannot be recovered by forcing an isochoric cooling of the gas.

Whether a given process, which is not intrinically irreversible, is reversible or irreversible depends on the way the experiment is done. For example, with a different experimental set–up it is possible to conduct an isothermal expansion irreversibly. This is shown in Fig. 8.4 which shows a container with a shutter which sepaates a gas from a vacuum. When the shutter is pulled, the gas expands isothermally to fill the whole container. The initial and final state of the gas are the same as for the isothermal expansion in Fig. 8.3(a), but pushing the shutter back does not reverse the process in Fig. 8.4 as the gas remains expanded.

In section 6.6 we calculated the work done in each of the two processes shown in Fig. 8.3. We found that no work is done in the isochoric heating ($W = 0$) while the reversible isothermal expansion allowed us to obtain work from the system ($W = -nRT \ln(V_f/V_i)$). It turns out that this result can be generalized:

Reversible processes are processes which allow a maximum amount of work to be done.

Put another way, reversible processes are those with the greatest efficiency. In particular, the efficiency calculated for the Carnot process in Eq. (6.115) is the maximum possible efficiency for any cyclical process because the Carnot process is done in a reversible fashion.

In turn, the process shown in Fig. 8.4 does not do any work (W = 0) during the expansion. This is consistent with the process being irreversible. We notice further that work and heat exchange cannot be determined for a process by just specifying the initial and final state. In addition, a detailed knowledge of the history of the system is needed, e.g. whether it undergoes reversible or irreversible processes.

The concepts of reversible and irreversible processes are also fundamentally connected to the concepts of equilibrium and non–equilibrium. A system undergoing a reversible process can be returned to its original state at any instant because at each instant it is in an equilibrium state. Because such a process is not practically possible, reversible processes are idealisations. An irreversible process includes steps which require a non–equilibrium. For example, in the case of the isochoric heating the propane flame must be hotter than the gas. Creating contact between parts of a system which are at different temperatures means that the system is not in thermal equilibrium.

8.3. The second law of thermodynamics

In order to develop a unifying model for the transport phenomena, we have to resume our discussion of the Carnot process from section 6.7. It is important to keep in mind, however, that the Carnot process is an application of the first law of thermodynamics, i.e., an application of the very law we dismissed in the introduction of the current chapter as insufficient to allow us to describe non–equilibrium systems.

We can still start with the Carnot process because we will introduce a time dependence in two steps. The second law of thermodynamics, which will result from generalizations of the observations we made for the Carnot process, will allow us to introduce a new parameter for thermodynamic systems, which is called the entropy. Once we have established the features of this new parameter of the system we proceed in section 8.5 with the formulation of relations explicitly describing the changes of entropy with time.

8.3.1. Formulation of the second law

The Carnot cycle consists of an isothermal expansion followed by an adiabatic expansion, an isothermal compression and a final adiabatic compression. We calculated the efficiency coefficient for this process which is defined as the ratio of the useful work to the heat input per cycle (Eqs. (6.114) and (6.115)):

$$\eta \equiv \frac{|useful\ work|}{heat\ input} = \frac{|W_1+W_3|}{Q_b} = \frac{T_b-T_a}{T_b} \quad (2)$$

In Eq. (2) the two work contributions result from the two isothermal steps and the heat term in the denominator is the heat supplied during the first isothermal step by the higher temperature heat reservoir.

The result that all heat cannot be converted into work in a cyclic process (i.e., $\eta < 1$), implies that there is something unique about heat since all other energy forms can be converted freely. We saw this for the kinetic and potential energy when a ball is thrown straight upwards. The ball has initially kinetic energy based on its speed. At the instant the ball reaches its highest point it comes momentarily to rest and the entire mechanical energy of the ball is in the form of potential energy. As the ball falls down the potential energy is converted back into kinetic energy again.

Following Carnot's work, it became evident that his findings are not only applicable to the specific cyclic process he studied. Rudolf Clausius and Lord Kelvin generalized in 1850 the implications of our discussion of the Carnot process to formulate the second law of thermodynamics. In the form as stated by Lord Kelvin it reads:

> *In a cyclic process it is impossible to take heat from a reservoir and change it into work without releasing a fraction of the heat to a second reservoir at lower temperature.*

It is useful to keep in mind that a system with two heat reservoirs at different temperatures is intrinsically a non–equilibrium system. The Carnot process is idealized insofar as its reversible character allows us to treat it conceptually as an equilibrium process.

8.3.2. Definition of entropy

For applications we need to find a way to express the second law of thermodynamics quantitatively. To do this, we re–examine the efficiency coefficient η of the Carnot process. Combining Eq. (2) and Eq. (6.111) we find:

$$\eta = \frac{|W|}{Q_b} = \frac{Q_a + Q_b}{Q_b} = \frac{T_b - T_a}{T_b} \quad (3)$$

In Eq. (3) we sort the terms associated with the temperature of the upper and the lower heat reservoir, which then leads to:

$$\frac{Q_a}{T_a} + \frac{Q_b}{T_b} = 0 \quad (4)$$

We want to generalize Eq. (4) for any reversible cyclic process, i.e., not limit it to the Carnot process for which it was derived. How we can do this is illustrated in Fig. 8.5 which shows an arbitrary cyclic process in a p–V diagram. We assume that the arbitrary cycle represents a reversible process. A net of thin lines is shown overlapping the cycle. These thin lines are isothermal lines and steeper adiabatic lines like those drawn in Fig. 6.25. This net of isothermal and adiabatic lines divides the arbitrary cycle into a large number of very small Carnot processes, each with a very small temperature difference between the higher and lower temperature heat reservoir. One small Carnot cycle created by the net of thin lines is highlighted near the center for illustration. Following each small Carnot cycle we notice that its four contributing steps are compensated by neighboring Carnot cycles, except for the segments which run along the outer, large arbitrary cycle. Thus, the sum over all Q/T terms for all Carnot cycles in Fig. 8.5 provides a value corresponding to Eq. (4) for the arbitrary reversible cycle:

$$\sum_i \frac{Q_i}{T_i} = 0 \quad (5)$$

We find that the quotient of heat transfer and temperature returns to the same value whenever the system returns to its initial state, in the same way in which the internal energy returns to its initial value when the system undergoes a cyclic process (see Eq. (6.112)). Any quantity which has a well defined value for each equilibrium state of a system, i.e., a value independent of the history of the system, is called a *variable of the state* of the system. Thus the ratio Q over T is a variable of the state, while Q separately is not a variable of the state. To fully describe a system, such variables of the state have to be measured. A complete description of the state of a system includes therefore temperature, volume, pressure, the amount of material in [mol] or [kg], as well as the internal energy and the newly introduced ratio of heat transfer and temperature. With this importance attached to the new quantity, Q/T is given a name, *entropy S* with unit [J/K]. Eq. (5) then represents the change of the entropy for a cyclic process. More generally, for any processes we can define the entropy change ΔS between an initial and a final state of the system in the form:

$$\Delta S = S_{final} - S_{initial} = \sum_i \frac{Q_i}{T_i} \quad (6)$$

This definition also provides for a method to measure entropy: the system is brought into a "standard" initial state for which the entropy is known. Then the state of the system is changed to the final state for which the entropy value is sought. Measuring the heat transfer at each temperature during the change of state allows us to quantify the change in entropy between the two states. This procedure is discussed in detail in section 8.4.4.

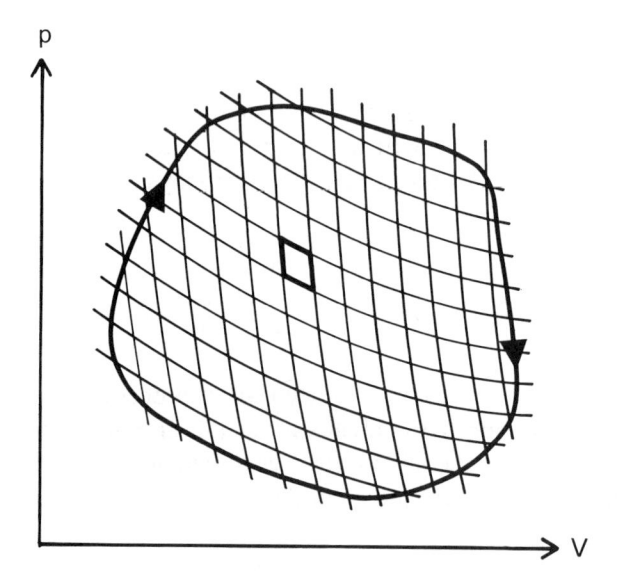

Fig. 8.5: A p–V diagram for an arbitrary cyclic process. To quantify the properties of such a process, it is divided into a very large number of Carnot processes, which are operated in adjacent cycles with very small temperature differences between the two heat reservoirs (thin lines). One such Carnot process is highlighted near the center of the figure. The approach taken in the figure allows us to quantify the entropy change in the process.

Example 8.1
1.0 mol nitrogen gas is initially confined to the left side of the container shown in Fig. 8.6. Assume that the volume of the gas is doubled when the valve is opened and that the temperature of the gas is held constant.
(a) Is the expansion process reversible or irreversible? If

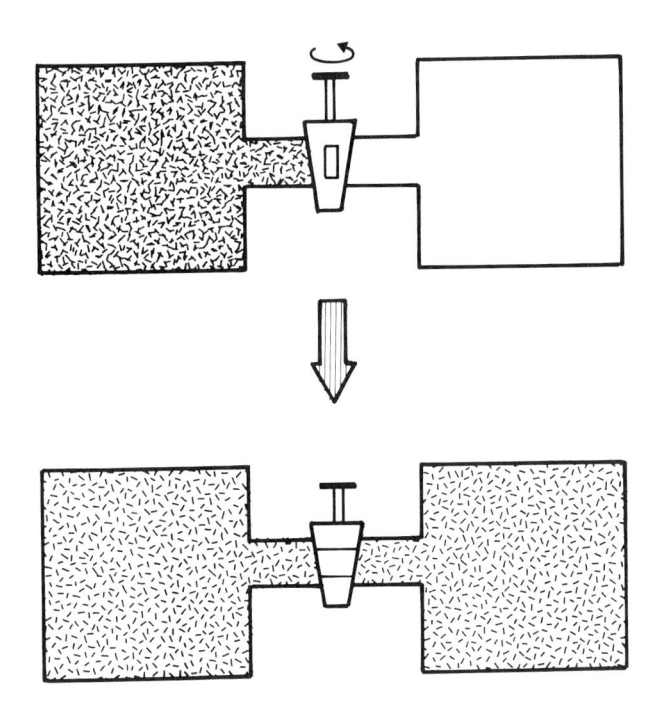

Fig. 8.6: Expansion of 1 mol of nitrogen, which is initially confined to the half-space at the left.

it is irreversible, what is the corresponding reversible process?
(b) Show that the entropy change for this process is:

$$\Delta S = nR \ln\left(\frac{V_{final}}{V_{initial}}\right) \quad (7)$$

(c) Quantify ΔS for the case of Fig. 8.6.
(d) Does the formula in part (b) depend on whether the process is reversible or irreversible?

Solution part (a): The process is irreversible since it cannot be reversed. Closing the valve will not drive the gas back into the chamber where it was at the beginning of the experiment. The corresponding reversible process is a gas expansion with a mobile frictionless piston (Fig. 8.3(a)).

Solution part (b): The heat added to an ideal gas when it expands isothermally is given in Eq. (6.79). Note that the irreversibility of the process has no bearing on this question, as discussed in part (d). Thus:

$$Q = nRT \ln\left(\frac{V_{final}}{V_{initial}}\right) \quad (8)$$

and with the definition of the entropy in Eq. (6), we find for the entropy change for an isothermal process:

$$\Delta S = \frac{Q}{T} = nR \ln\left(\frac{V_{final}}{V_{initial}}\right) \quad (9)$$

Solution part (c): We use n = 1.0 mol for an ideal gas with a ratio of final to initial volume of $V_{final}/V_{initial} = 2$. Thus:

$$\Delta S = 1[mol]\, 8.314\left[\frac{J}{K\,mol}\right] \ln 2$$

$$\Delta S = +\,5.76\,\frac{J}{K} \quad (10)$$

Solution part (d): When going from a reversible to an irreversible process, the amount of heat exchange is not affected, but the maximum work (as calculated for the reversible process) is not obtainable in the irreversible process. The calculation in part (b) does not include a work term and is therefore not affected by the fashion in which the process is conducted.

The following three sections focus on key properties of entropy which we will use later in the textbook and which you find often referred to in biophysical or biochemical studies.

8.3.3. Entropy and work

Based on the discussion of the Carnot process in sections 8.3.1 and 8.3.2 we note that the entropy is associated with the fraction of heat which cannot be utilized as work during a cyclic process, i.e., the heat which is lost to a lower temperature part of the environment. This is one interpretation of the concept entropy. We will expand on this interpretation later when we introduce the Gibbs free energy in section 8.4.5: the total energy of a system can be diminished by the entropy-related useless energy to determine the energy available from the process to do work (to which the term free energy then refers).

227

8.3.4. Entropy and reversibility

We want to compare the values of the change of entropy ΔS for reversible and irreversible spontaneous processes, in which a spontaneous process is a process which progresses on its own. The explosive formation of water from oxygen and hydrogen gases is such a spontaneous process, while the opposite process, the splitting of water to obtain hydrogen and oxygen gases is not spontaneous as it never happens without external effort.

Fig. 8.7 shows idealized reversible and irreversible processes to equilibrating the temperature of two identical bodies (B1 and B2) which differ only in temperatures T_1 and T_2 with $T_1 > T_2$. The top sketch shows the reversible approach, and the bottom sketch shows an irreversible approach.

In the simpler irreversible case, the two bodies are brought into direct thermal contact. As a result, an amount of heat Q flows from the hotter to the colder body until both have the same temperature. This process is irreversible as no mechanism is provided in the isolated superstructure to reverse the process, i.e., to re-establish different temperatures for both bodies after the temperature equilibrium has been established.

The reversible approach is more complex. The two bodies are not brought into direct contact; instead, each is brought into thermal contact with a heat reservoir which is slightly (infinitesimally) warmer in the case of body 2 or slightly colder in the case of body 1 than the respective body itself. The slight temperature difference of body and respective reservoir are called ΔT. We assume that the temperature difference ΔT is the same in both cases. Heat exchange with the heat reservoirs oc-

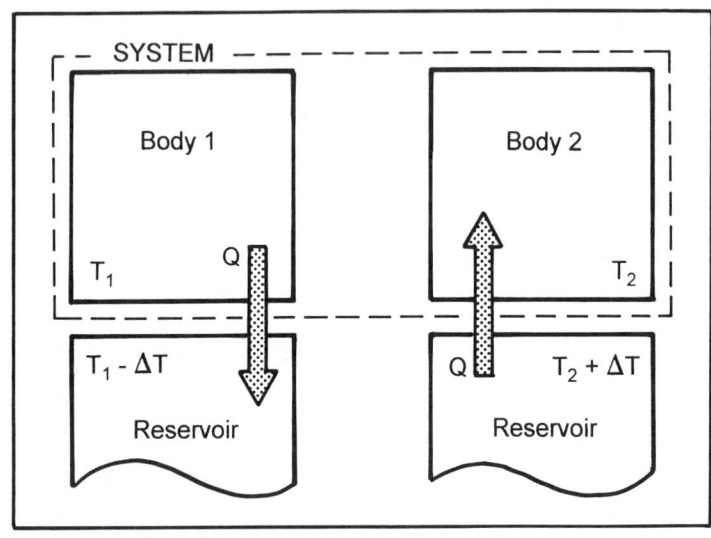

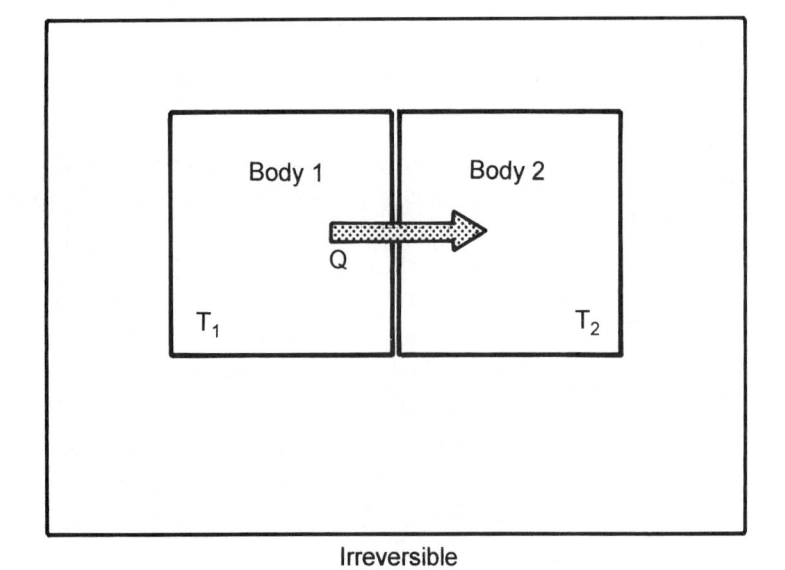

Fig. 8.7: Comparison between a reversible (top) and an irreversible experiment (bottom) to equilibrate the temperature of two bodies.

curs. For simplicity we assume that the initial temperatures of the two bodies also differ only by $T_1 - T_2 = \Delta T$. Otherwise, a very large number of heat reservoirs would have to be lined up for each body, with each one having a temperature smaller or higher than the previous heat reservoir by a difference of ΔT. Even though such a reversible approach is obviously not practical, we use it for argument's sake.

For the reversible approach we carefully distinguish the system, which consists of the two bodies B1 and B2, and the environment, which consists of the two heat reservoirs R1 and R2 within the isolated superstructure of Fig. 8.7. For the respective changes of entropy we find with Eq. (6):

$$\Delta S_{system} = \Delta S_{B1} + \Delta S_{B2} = -\frac{Q}{T_1} + \frac{Q}{T_2} > 0$$

$$\Delta S_{environ.} = \Delta S_{R1} + \Delta S_{R2} = \frac{Q}{T_1} - \frac{Q}{T_2} < 0$$

(11)

Eq. (11) yields for the isolated superstructure:

$$\Delta S_{isol.\ superst.} = \Delta S_{system} + \Delta S_{environ.} = 0 \quad (12)$$

The reversible process is characterized by a zero change in entropy for the isolated superstructure. This allows for an increase of the entropy of the system if concurrently the entropy of the environment is reduced. Note that no entropy is created or destroyed in this case. Fig. 8.7 indicates that the entropy flows across the interface between system and environment. This characterizes reversible processes in general, including also systems which are in equilibrium as these undergo no processes: the entropy remains constant, $\Delta S = 0$.

Next we study the irreversible process shown in the bottom sketch of Fig. 8.7. In this case, the isolated superstructure contains only the system, which again consists of the two bodies B1 and B2. No heat reservoirs are needed as no heat exchange with the environment occurs. The entropy change of the system is the same as in the reversible case as the same amount of heat flows out of body 1 and into body 2. However, no entropy change occurs in the environment as no interaction with the environment takes place:

$$\Delta S_{system} = -\frac{Q}{T_1} + \frac{Q}{T_2} > 0$$

$$\Delta S_{environ.} = 0$$

(13)

Eq. (13) yields for the isolated superstructure:

$$\Delta S_{isol.\ superst.} = \Delta S_{system} + \Delta S_{environ.} > 0 \quad (14)$$

This result is different from the result of the reversible case in Eq. (12): in a spontaneous, irreversible process the entropy of an isolated system increases. Entropy is created in the system! Interpreting the results from Eqs. (12) and (14) we note that an isolated system which is not in equilibrium will undergo spontaneous irreversible processes which increase its entropy. Such processes cease when the system reaches equilibrium and when the entropy does not increase any further. Therefore:

> *The entropy reaches a maximum value*
> *for a system in equilibrium:*
> S_{eq} = *maximum.*

Two interesting consequences are noted:

(a) Because the entire universe is an isolated superstructure displaying all the time irreversible processes, it has an ever-increasing entropy. Since entropy is linked to the amount of useless heat as discussed in section 8.3.3 we conclude that the universe transfers heat continuously into reservoirs at lower temperatures. This can only continue until all energy has been transferred in this way and a final equilibrium is reached. For this final equilibrium state the term heat death of the universe has been coined.

However, it is important to keep in mind that the statement of Eq. (14) only applies to an isolated system. In the next section we discuss how an open or closed system within an isolated superstructure can develop highly complex patterns without violating the second law of thermodynamics.

(b) The second law of thermodynamics is distinguished among all laws of physics as it defines the direction of time. *Future* is the direction of time in which the entropy of an isolated system increases, and *past* is the direction in which the entropy of an isolated system decreases. Therefore, we may one day be able to travel into the future as H. G. Wells suggested in 1895 in his book "The Time Machine," because this would not violate the second law of thermodynamics, but we will never be able to travel into the past!

This discussion shows that the entropy concept applies to non-equilibrium processes because irreversible processes are characterized by the system passing through non-equilibrium states. Thus, we anticipate that entropy is a useful property of the system to distinguish equilibrium and non–equilibrium processes. It is indeed Eq. (14) which will allow us to use the entropy concept when describing quantitatively non–equilibrium processes.

8.3.5. Entropy and order

The laws of thermodynamics can be derived in two ways. The approach we discussed in Chapters 5, 6 and in the current section is called the phenomenological approach since it is based solely on experimental evidence. The alternative approach is called statistical physics because one begins with a large number of particles in a system and then describes their properties in a statistical fashion. This approach is cumbersome for describing the ideal gas and the first law of thermodynamics. It does, however, provide useful, additional insight into the concepts of temperature and entropy.

For temperature, it provides a broader basis for the equilibrium definition than the Maxwell–Boltzmann velocity distribution, because the Maxwell–Boltzmann distribution applies only to gases. Statistical physics reconfirms that temperature is a collective property of a large number of atoms or molecules and cannot be defined for a single particle or a few particles.

The greatest benefit of the statistical physics approach to thermodynamics is the interpretation of entropy. Ludwig Boltzmann showed that entropy is proportional to the number of accessible microscopic states of a system. The number of accessible states is quite complicated to determine even for simple systems. Looking for example at the system we introduced in the kinetic gas theory, calculating the number of accessible states means that for each particle we must count the number of possible values for each of the three position components and for each of the three velocity components. The greater this sum for all the particles in the system the greater the entropy.

While such calculations go beyond what we want to discuss in the current context, we can use the concept qualitatively to judge whether processes are associated with an increase in entropy. Fig. 8.8 shows five processes, each associated with an increase of entropy when followed from the left box to the right box:
(a) Adding particles (i.e., an open system with material influx) increases the entropy since each of the previously present particles has as many accessible states as before, but the new particles contribute additional states for the combined system.
(b) Adding energy to a closed system leads to an increase of the entropy. If the system is a gas, the molecules all gain speed, i.e., the range of accessible velocity components becomes larger. We note that no low–speed

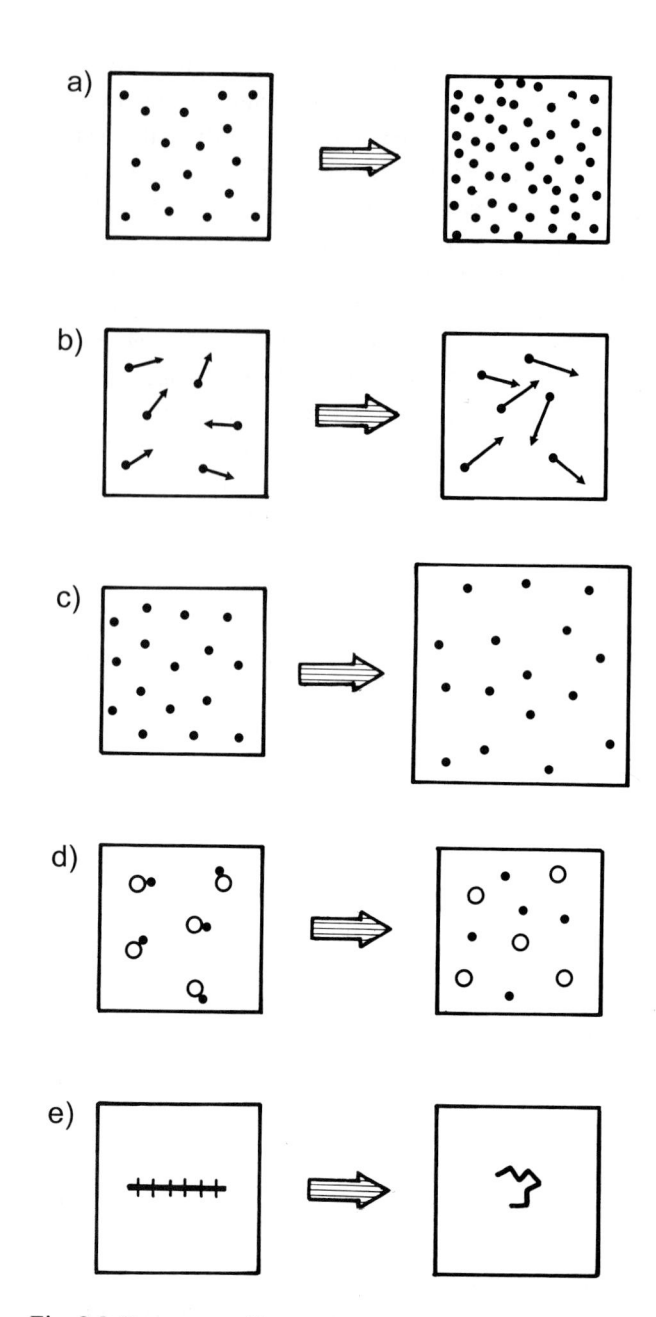

Fig. 8.8: Processes with entropy increase. (a) Increase of particle number, (b) increase of internal energy, (c) isothermal expansion, (d) dissociation, and (e) polymer relaxation.

components are lost since a very fast particle for example can move mostly in the xy–plane and have still a small z–component of velocity.
(c) Increasing the volume can be done in two ways: by holding the internal energy constant (isothermal process, see section 6.6.2) or by isolating the system (adiabatic process, see section 6.6.4). An isothermal expansion increases the entropy since after the expansion, the particles can resume all their previous positions but have access to additional positions with the number of acces-

sible velocity components unchanged.

Adiabatic expansions obey the entropy equation $\Delta S = 0$ since no heat exchange occurs, $Q = 0$. Therefore adiabatic processes are also called *isentropic processes*. Why does the volume increase in this case not lead to an entropy increase? During an adiabatic expansion each particle gains new accessible positions, but, as the temperature drops sharply, it loses the same number of accessible states linked to its speed.

(d) There are also a number of processes we can qualitatively evaluate without a proper, often difficult quantitative description. The two last examples in Fig. 8.8 illustrate such cases. The first one is the dissociation of molecules. If there are N molecules initially, then the system has 6N free parameters (3 spatial and 3 velocity components per particle). In addition, the molecule may resume various states of rotation and various states of vibration. Dissociation is favored because it doubles the number of free parameters to 12N since the number of independent particles doubles while the loss of vibrational and rotational states is much less. The same reasoning applies to salt precipitate formation from aqueous ionic solutions. Each ion added to the precipitate releases a large number of water molecules from its hydration shell. Now independent, these water molecules gain access to a larger number of speed and position states. Therefore, precipitate formation from aqueous solutions is an example of a process with increasing entropy.

(e) The last example is a polymer consisting of a large number of repetitive units, e.g. a DNA string. If these units are connected with flexible chemical bonds, e.g. C–C single bonds, then the relaxation of the polymer represents an increase of entropy. This is due to the fact that only the direction in space of the fully stretched polymer varies, while a very large number of relative positions of twisted repetitive units is possible for the relaxed polymer.

What these processes have in common is that the *degree of disorder* of the system increases as the entropy increases. Thus, entropy can be understood as a measure of the disorder in a system. Again, the second law does not prohibit a system from becoming ordered (e.g. crystals growing from solution or patterns developing in biological systems) unless it is an isolated system. If the system is open or closed, the total entropy or disorder of the isolated superstructure must increase in spontaneous processes, but the entropy or disorder of the system itself can decrease.

8.4. Chemical thermodynamics

Chemical reactions are an example of non–equilibrium processes. However, like for all the processes we have discussed up to Chapter 6, it is possible to quantify some aspects of chemical reactions using equilibrium thermodynamics concepts. For example, chemists are often interested in whether or not a chemical reaction as proposed is possible, or which parameter ranges of temperature, pressure and concentration will favor the reaction. These questions can be answered with the concepts we have developed so far, and their practical application to these questions are summarized in this section.

We need both the internal energy and the entropy to judge whether a chemical reaction is possible. The internal energy allows us to separate chemical reactions into endothermic reactions, which are reactions which require the supply of thermal energy, and exothermic reactions, which are reactions which release thermal energy. The entropy allows us to separate spontaneous reactions from reactions which have to be forced externally.

8.4.1. Internal energy and enthalpy

We start with the internal energy of a chemical process. For oxidation reactions (used for example to determine the energy content of food components for metabolic processes), the internal energy is measured with a calorimeter. This is possible because the change of the internal energy is equal to the heat exchange of a system at constant volume (see section 6.6.1). A calorimeter is a device in which the oxidation occurs at constant volume. The instrument is sketched in Fig. 8.9. The chemical compound is placed in a small container pressurized with oxygen. The small container is immersed in a water bath, which is brought into thermal equilibrium with the small container after the chemical compound has been ignited and the oxidation has been completed. The thermal energy released by the oxidation is determined from the change of the water temperature.

Most chemical processes, including biochemical processes, occur at constant pressure, i.e., atmospheric pressure. We discussed in section 6.6.3 that the enthalpy is better suited than the internal energy to describe the heat exchange in such processes. The reason for this follows from Eq. (6.92): we often observe a change in the volume during a reaction at constant pressure. That volume change is associated with a work term of the form $p_{atm} \Delta V$, this work is done against (expansion) or by the external atmospheric pressure (compression). The change of the internal energy of the system is a combination of this work and the heat which is exchanged between the system and the environment. The heat exchange at constant pressure is defined as the enthalpy change ΔH.

Solution: The internal energy is calculated from the definition of the enthalpy in Eq. (6.87): H = U + pV. Comparing the initial components and the reaction products for the isobaric decomposition of $CaCO_3$ we rewrite this formula in the form:

$$\Delta H = \Delta U + p \Delta V$$
$$\Rightarrow \quad \Delta U = \Delta H - p \Delta V \quad (15)$$

in which p ΔV is calculated from the ideal gas law for the only gaseous component in this reaction (CO_2) with $p = p_{atm}$ and T = 900°C = 1173 K:

$$p \Delta V = n R T =$$
$$= 1.0 [mol] \; 8.314 \left[\frac{J}{K\,mol}\right] 1173 [K] \quad (16)$$
$$\Rightarrow \quad p \Delta V = 9750 \; J$$

in which n = 1 mol because 1 mol of CO_2 is formed for every mol of $CaCO_3$. We further know from the heat required that ΔH = + 42 kcal = + 175.7 kJ. Thus,

$$\Delta U = 175.7 \; kJ - 9.75 \; kJ = +166.0 \; kJ \quad (17)$$

i.e., of the 175.7 kJ supplied to the system, 9.75 kJ is required for the volume expansion of the gaseous product. The balance of + 166 kJ represents the increase of the internal energy of the system.

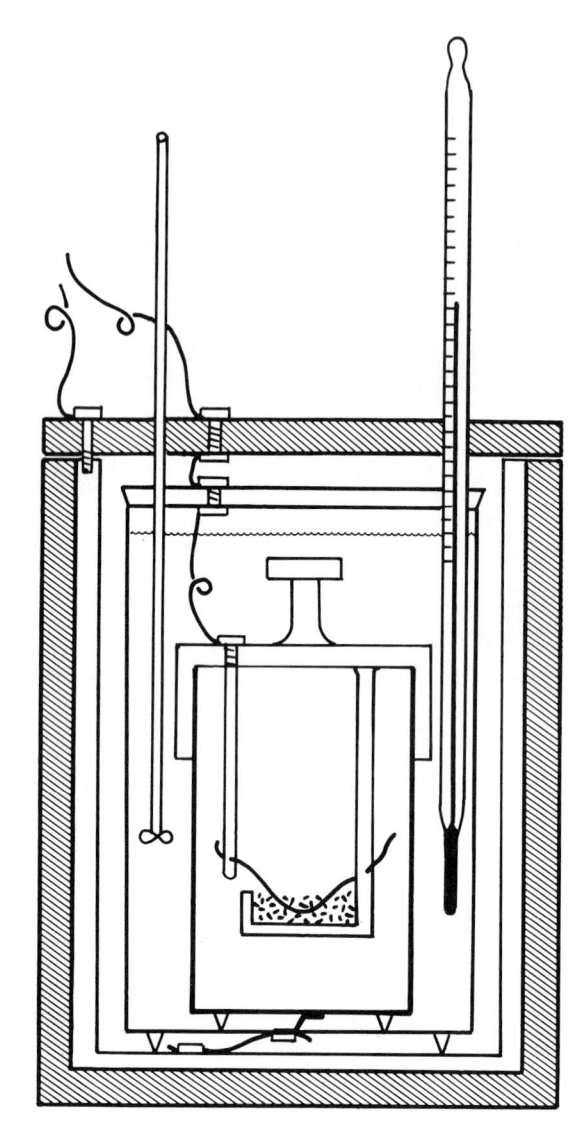

Fig. 8.9: Sketch of a calorimeter used to determine the amount of heat released in a combustion process at constant volume. The probe material is placed in an inner steel container with a high–pressure oxygen atmosphere. The reaction is electrically ignited. The steel container is immersed in a water bath in which the temperature change is measured after the reaction is completed. The water bath in turn is isolated from the environment to prevent measurement errors due to heat loss through the outer wall.

Example 8.2
We study the thermal decomposition of $CaCO_3$ into CaO and CO_2. A CO_2 pressure of 1 atm is reached in this process at 900°C. For each mol of the reaction, 42 kcal of heat are absorbed by the system. What is the change of the internal energy for 1 mol of $CaCO_3$?
Hint: Neglect the volume change of liquid and solid components.

8.4.2. Heat capacity of chemical compounds

When heating a system, which needs not to be an ideal gas, the internal energy or enthalpy increases. To quantify the change in internal energy or enthalpy, the heat capacity is needed. If the system is a gas, we use either C_V for processes at constant volume (see Eq. (6.77)) or C_p for processes at constant pressure (see Eq. (6.92)). If the system is a liquid or solid, $C_V \simeq C_p$ and the subscript of the heat capacity parameter can be dropped (see Eq. (5.43)). The two previously discussed results, $C_V = 3R/2$ with R the universal gas constant, and $C_p = C_V + R$ apply only for the ideal gas. For any other system, we need to use tabulated values of the heat capacity. These numerical values usually depend on the temperature. As an example, the molar heat capacity of solid and liquid water is listed as a function of temperature in Table 8.2.

Table 8.2: Molar heat capacity of liquid and solid water. Compare to the specific heat capacity of liquid water as shown in Fig. 5.33.

State	Temperature	C_p [J mol^{-1} K^{-1}]
solid	-34 °C	33.30
solid	-2.2 °C	37.78
liquid	0 °C	75.86
liquid	25 °C	75.23
liquid	100 °C	75.90

Example 8.3

We want to bring 100 g of water, initially at -10 °C, to a final temperature of $+15$ °C. What is ΔH for this process if the latent heat of melting is 1.44 kcal/mol? Hint: use the heat capacity value at -2.2 °C from Table 8.2 for ice and the value at 0 °C for liquid water. The molecular mass of water is M = 18 g/mol.

Solution: We divide the process into three steps:
(I) heating ice from -10 °C to the freezing point,
(II) transforming ice to liquid water at that temperature,
(III) and heating liquid water from the freezing point to $+15$ °C. The amount of water we express in unit [mol]:

$$n = \frac{100\ [g]}{18\ [g/mol]} = 5.55\ mol \quad (18)$$

Assuming constant pressure conditions (although this needs not to be stressed as no gases are involved), the following are the three enthalpy contributions based on Eqs. (5.43) and (6.92):
(I) Heating ice by 10 degree to the freezing point:

$$\Delta H = 5.55[mol]\ 37.78\left[\frac{J}{K\ mol}\right]\ 10[K] \quad (19)$$

$$\Rightarrow \quad \Delta H = 2100\ J$$

(II) Melting ice, using the latent heat provided in the problem text:

$$\Delta H = 5.55[mol]\ 1440\left[\frac{cal}{mol}\right]\ 4.184\left[\frac{J}{cal}\right] \quad (20)$$

$$\Rightarrow \quad \Delta H = 33440\ J$$

(III) Heating liquid water by 15 degree:

$$\Delta H = 5.55[mol]\ 75.86\left[\frac{J}{K\ mol}\right]\ 15[K] \quad (21)$$

$$\Rightarrow \quad \Delta H = 6320\ J$$

Thus, the total increase in enthalpy is $\Delta H = 41.86$ kJ.

8.4.3. Standard enthalpy of formation

The result of Example 8.3 indicates that enthalpy values vary with several system parameters. For consistency in calculations, a standard state of the system is chosen at T = 25 °C = 298 K and p = 1 atm. This standard state is then used to tabulate reference values for enthalpy (and later entropy). We recall from the discussion of the gravitational potential energy in section 5.5.3 that absolute values of the total energy of a system are meaningless because we can freely choose a reference height for the potential energy. The internal energy and enthalpy of a system are its total energy. Thus, absolute values for the internal energy or the enthalpy of a chemical system are similarly meaningless values. We use this fact to freely choose a reference point for these energies: the internal energy or enthalpy of an elementary system in its most stable form at standard conditions (25 °C and 1 atm) are set equal to zero: H = 0 J. For any other system, we determine the enthalpy relative to this reference state. Of particular use for such calculations is the standard enthalpy of formation of a compound, which is the energy needed to chemically form 1 mol of the compound from the elements at standard conditions. Standard enthalpy of formation values are tabulated and are usually labelled ΔH_f^0, in which the subscript f stands for formation and the superscript 0 indicates the standard state.

Most standard enthalpy of formation values cannot be obtained experimentally. For example, it is impossible to mix carbon, oxygen, hydrogen and nitrogen and hope for igniting the mixture to obtain isoleucine, which is a specific essential amino acid (see Table 8.1). In such cases, the theorem of Hess is applied which states that the enthalpy of formation is independent of the actual reaction by which the product is formed. Thus, we can combine the enthalpies of several known processes, including chemical reactions, to obtain a value for a particular process we want to study. This is illustrated in Example 8.4 for the standard enthalpy of formation of carbon–monoxide, CO.

Example 8.4

We determine the standard enthalpy of formation of CO. This value cannot be obtained experimentally, as oxidation of carbon always leads to the formation of (some) CO_2. However, the following processes yield experimentally accessible values:

$$C + O_2 \rightarrow CO_2 \quad \Delta H_f^0 = -393.5 \frac{kJ}{mol}$$
$$CO + \frac{1}{2}O_2 \rightarrow CO_2 \quad \Delta H_f^0 = -283.0 \frac{kJ}{mol} \quad (22)$$

Use Eq. (22) to find the standard enthalpy of formation of CO.

Solution: Using the theorem of Hess, the standard enthalpy of formation for CO_2 as given in the first formula of Eq. (22) remains unchanged whether carbon and oxygen react directly to carbon–dioxide or whether CO is formed as an intermediate product:

$$C + O_2 \rightarrow CO + \frac{1}{2}O_2 \rightarrow CO_2 \quad (23)$$

For the process in Eq. (23) we know that ΔH_f^0 for the step from left to right is -393.5 kJ/mol and that ΔH_f^0 for the step from the compounds in the middle to the products is -283.0 kJ/mol. Therefore, for the step from the left to the compounds in the middle of Eq. (23), we find:

$$\Delta H_f^0 = -393.5 \frac{kJ}{mol} - \left(-283.0 \frac{kJ}{mol}\right)$$
$$\Rightarrow \Delta H_f^0 (CO) = -110.5 \frac{kJ}{mol} \quad (24)$$

Note that the standard enthalpy of oxygen refers to O_2 because the molecule is the most stable form of oxygen at 25°C and 1 atm. The standard enthalpy of formation for atomic oxygen requires the dissociation of the molecule and leads to a value of $\Delta H_f^0 = +247.3$ kJ/mol. Thus, the formation of CO from the elements is an exothermic process (heat is released), but the dissociation of oxygen into atomic oxygen is an endothermic process (heat is required).

Table 8.3: Combustion heat at 25°C for reaction to CO_2 and H_2O. This type of reaction is called a catabolic reaction, i.e., the breakdown of complex chemicals accompanied by the release of energy. The opposite case is called an anabolic reaction. These include all biosynthesis processes requiring energy.

Compound	ΔH [kJ/g]
Fat	−38.9
Carbohydrates	−17.2
Protein*	−17.2
C_nH_{2n+2}, $1 \leq n \leq 7$ (Methane to heptane)	−55.7 to −48.1
Ethanol	−29.7
Benzene	−42.3
Acetic acid	−14.5

* ΔH for reaction to urea since urea is the final combustion product of proteins in the human body.

In chemical and biological processes, the energy stored in a molecule (e.g. a sugar molecule) may be used in two ways. It can be turned completely into heat. This is the case when a human body responds to undercooling by shivering. For such cases, the knowledge of the change in internal energy in the reaction is sufficient (more precisely, the change of the enthalpy since biological processes occur under isobaric rather than isochoric conditions). Table 8.3 compares enthalpy values for the combustion of the main food components and some other organic compounds.

Note that only part of the energy listed in Table 8.3 can be used to do work. This is relevant when we study processes such as the dissociation of an ATP to ADP molecule at a myosin head to provide the energy for muscle contraction. In that case the distinction between useful and useless energy matters as the latter increases only the temperature of the muscle (like in the shivering case) but does not contribute to the work of muscle contraction. The enthalpy is not sufficient to describe such a process; the change in entropy needs to be taken into account.

8.4.4. Standard entropy

The enthalpy of formation of a chemical compound tells us nothing about the spontaneity of the process. The reason for this limitation is the fact that the internal energy and enthalpy are system properties obtained from the first law of thermodynamics. The conservation of energy does not reveal the direction in which a process evolves. Thus, we need to include one more parameter to completely describe a system: entropy. The entropy characterizes the state of a system (see section 8.3.2) and allows us to distinguish spontaneous from non–spontaneous processes (see section 8.3.4).

When we know the change of entropy for a given process, we know that the process is spontaneous if $\Delta S > 0$. Example 8.1 serves as an example how such entropy changes are calculated for physical processes. Equally, we are interested in the change of the entropy for chemical reactions as these values indicate whether the chemical reaction is spontaneous. Standard entropy values at 25°C and 1 atm are tabulated for a wide range of chemical compounds. It is interesting to note that these values are obtained in a different fashion than the standard enthalpy of formation. In the case of the entropy, there is no material (nor any elements) with a zero–value at the standard state. This is due to the physical meaning of entropy as discussed in section 8.3.5: entropy is related to the degree of order in the system. Therefore, all absolute values of entropy are positive, or zero for a perfectly ordered system. Walther Nernst stated that perfectly ordered systems only exist at T = 0 K because the thermal energy of a system at T > 0 K causes at least some disorder. He therefore formulated the *third law of thermodynamics*:

> *The entropy of a perfect crystal of a chemical element or compound at T = 0 K is zero, S = 0 J/K.*

Thus, the standard entropy at 25°C and 1 atm for 1 mol of any compound has a well–defined value. We find this

Table 8.4: Standard entropy values (at 25°C, 1 atm) for various materials. Note an increase of the standard entropy with a decreasing order of the system: hard solids are more ordered than complex salts, solids are more ordered than liquids, and gases are ordered the least.

Material	Standard entropy S^0 [J K^{-1} mol^{-1}]
1. Solids	
Diamond (C)	2.5
Calcium (Ca)	41.6
CaO	39.7
CaCO$_3$	92.9
NaCl	72.4
2. Liquids	
Mercury (Hg)	76.0
Water (H$_2$O)	70.0
Benzene (C$_6$H$_6$)	175.3
3. Gases	
Hydrogen (H$_2$)	130.6
Oxygen (O$_2$)	205.0
Nitrogen (N$_2$)	191.2
Water vapor (H$_2$O)	188.9
CO$_2$	213.8
NH$_3$	192.6
Ozone (O$_3$)	237.7

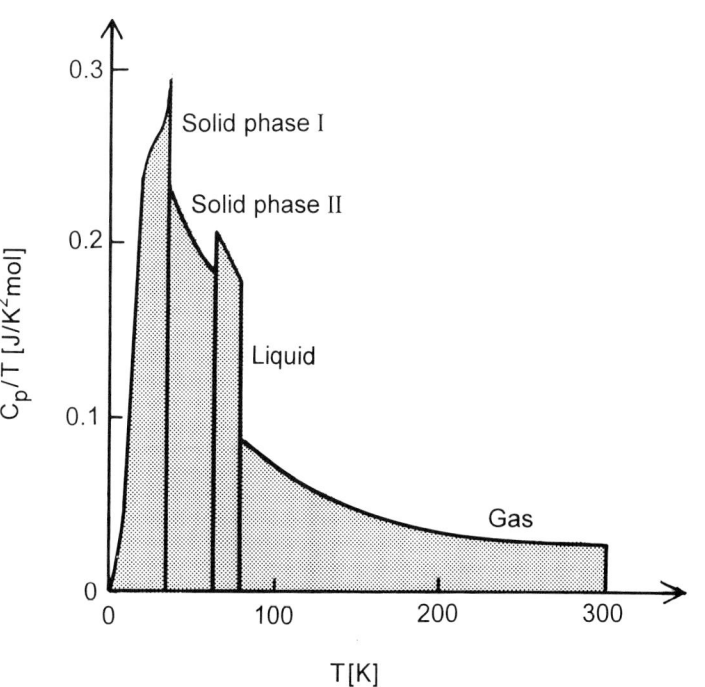

Fig. 8.10: Plot of C_p/T between 0 K and 298 K for nitrogen N$_2$. The area under this curve is the standard entropy for the compound, S^0_{N2}. In this temperature interval, nitrogen passes through two solid phases, melts at 63.14 K and evaporates at 77.32 K. These phase transitions are visible in the figure as discontinuities of the heat capacity function. At each phase transition, a term for the latent heat divided by the transition temperature must be added.

value from Eq. (6) with the initial state at T = 0 K and the final state at T = 25°C. The right hand side of Eq. (6) requires us to sum over all heat exchange contributions from 0 K to 298 K, each divided by the respective temperature at which it occurs. These heat contributions in turn are written for 1.0 mol in the form $Q = C_p \Delta T$ (Eq. (5.44)). Thus, we can determine the standard entropy from the area under the curve of C_p/T versus T. An example is shown in Fig. 8.10 which illustrates the C_p/T versus T curve for N_2 from 0 K to 298 K. From the area under the curve we find $S_{N_2}^0 = +191.2$ J/(K mol). Standard entropy values are lower for pure crystals and higher for more complex solids (which allow for more disorder based on vibrations and rotations); this is illustrated by comparing diamond with some of the solid salts in Table 8.4. Standard entropy values increase also when we go from solid to liquid to the gaseous state, illustrated by the subdivision of Table 8.4.

The standard entropy change for a given chemical reaction is then determined from values such as those in Table 8.4 by adding the entropy values of the products and subtracting the entropy values for the initial compounds. The stoichiometric factors have to be included in this calculation. In the same fashion, the standard entropy of formation of a chemical compound can be determined from the standard entropy of the compound minus the standard entropy of the elements.

To summarize, the following properties for the change of entropy are noted for the later discussions:

$\Delta S > 0$ irreversible process, can occur spontaneous
$\Delta S = 0$ reversible process, the system is continuously in equilibrium with its environment
$\Delta S < 0$ process which requires a significant increase in the environmental entropy such that the entropy change of the superstructure is $\Delta S \geq 0$

8.4.5. Gibbs free energy

The summary statement at the end of the previous section is in principle sufficient to predict the outcome of any process we are interested in. However, for practical purposes, the entropy has the disadvantage that it requires a combined study of the system and its environment. As the statement for a process with $\Delta S < 0$ indicates, such processes can be achieved if appropriate processes occur concurrently in the environment. It would be more convenient to find a thermodynamic system parameter which allows us to make statements about the system and its propensity with respect to a certain process without considerations of the environment.

Initially, it was suggested to use the enthalpy for this purpose. However, there are spontaneous processes which are endothermic. Thus, even though most systems have a propensity toward a low energy state, this is not the sole driving force for chemical processes.

Josiah Willard Gibbs resolved this issue in 1875 by introducing the Gibbs free energy:

$$G = H - TS$$
$$\Delta G = \Delta H - T \Delta S \quad (25)$$

in which the second formula is used for the change of state of a system. The product TS represents the amount of heat lost in a cyclic process to the lower temperature heat reservoir at temperature T. Thus, the Gibbs free energy represents the maximum obtainable work. The obtainable work is a maximum since a reversible process is required to actually gain this amount of work.

Eq. (25) allows us to summarize the properties of the Gibbs free energy for a chemical process:

All natural phenomena are governed by the propensity of the system to lower its internal energy or enthalpy and, secondly, by the propensity of the system to increase its entropy.
$\Delta G < 0$ represents a spontaneous process
$\Delta G = 0$ represents a process in which the products and the initial compounds coexist in equilibrium
$\Delta G > 0$ represents a process which does not occur spontaneously.

Table 8.5 summarizes the basic processes which occur in physics and chemistry and the respective thermodynamic functions we need to study for a full characterization of the properties of the system during the pro-

Table 8.5: The fundamental physical and chemical processes and the respective thermodynamic functions needed to fully characterize the process.

Processes	constant are	Property to study
isolated system	U	Entropy S
isothermal/isochoric	T, V	Free energy F*
isothermal/isobaric	T, p	Gibbs free energy G
adiabatic/isochoric	S, V	Internal energy U
adiabatic/isobaric	S, p	Enthalpy H

* The Helmholtz free energy has not been introduced since we do not further discuss isochoric processes.

cess. For example, a process in an isolated system is fully described by studying the change in entropy as the internal energy of an isolated system is constant (first law of thermodynamics). On the other hand, a combination of isothermal and isobaric processes requires us to calculate the Gibbs free energy as both the enthalpy and the entropy may vary during the process.

For most known organic and inorganic chemical processes values of the standard Gibbs free energy are tabulated or can be calculated from tabulated values for the standard enthalpy and standard entropy.

The concept of maximum obtainable work as related to the Gibbs free energy further allows us to define the *chemical equilibrium*. If a system is in chemical equilibrium then the Gibbs free energy G resumes a minimum value. As a result, nothing happens. If G is not a minimum, then the system spontaneously decreases its Gibbs free energy to the minimum value. If the process to reduce the Gibbs free energy is reversible, then a maximum of work is obtained.

The parameters of state of a system, p, V, T, n, ΔU, ΔH, ΔS, and ΔG, are all linked with well-defined relations. We do not discuss these relations in the textbook; they are found in the physical chemistry literature when needed. Two exceptions are provided:
(i) the dependence of the Gibbs free energy on the pressure for a process in which the temperature is constant:

$$\Delta G = nRT \ln\left(\frac{p_f}{p_i}\right) \quad (26)$$

This relation is needed in Chapter 12 to define a chemical equilibrium between a solution and its vapor phase, and in Chapter 13 to discuss the electrochemical equilibrium across a nerve membrane.
(Ii) The dependence of the entropy on the temperature for a process in which the pressure is held constant:

$$\Delta S = n\, C_p \ln\left(\frac{T_f}{T_i}\right) \quad (27)$$

This relation is needed to solve some of the problems.

Example 8.5
An instructive example of the role of the Gibbs free energy is the comparison of the formation of carbonates of group II elements from aqueous solutions. Table 8.6

Table 8.6: Standard enthalpy and entropy data for four carbonate formation reactions in aqueous solution.

Element X	ΔH^0 [kJ/mol]	$T\,\Delta S^0$ [kJ/mol]
Mg	+ 25.1	+ 71.1
Ca	+ 12.3	+ 59.0
Sr	+ 3.3	+ 55.6
Ba	− 4.2	+ 46.0

provides the standard enthalpy and standard entropy for four carbonate formation reactions of the type

$$X^{2+}_{aq} + [CO_3^{2-}]_{aq} \rightarrow [XCO_3]_{solid} \quad (28)$$

What predictions can we make about the four processes?

Solution: We determine the Gibbs free energy for each of the four processes: for the four reactions in Table 8.6 we find from the second formula in Eq. (25) values from $\Delta G = -46.0$ kJ/mol to $\Delta G = -50.2$ kJ/mol. Thus, all values are negative and quite similar: the four reactions occur spontaneously when mixing a solution of the metal ions with a carbonate solution.

However, the first three reactions have a positive ΔH^0 value. This means that they are endothermic processes, i.e., the chemical reaction requires heat. This is illustrated in Fig. 8.11 which shows the enthalpy of the

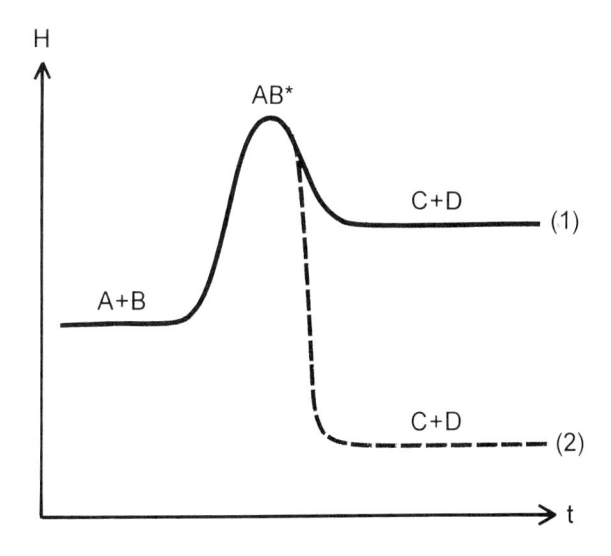

Fig. 8.11: The enthalpy as a function of time for a chemical reaction. The reactants A and B form a transition state AB* which then decomposes into the products C and D. Case 1 shows an endothermic process and case 2 shows an exothermic process.

chemical reaction at constant pressure as a function of time. The reactants A and B form a transition state AB* which leads to products C and D which are either energetically less stable than the reactants (case 1) or more stable (case 2). In case 1 the reaction is endothermic, in case 2 the reaction is exothermic.

Comparing the two columns in Table 8.6 shows that the four reactions are all driven by the entropy term. The reason is the existence of a hydration shell of the ions which must be removed to form a solid precipitate. The elimination of the hydration shell allows the involved water molecules to move more freely after their release which represents a higher degree of disorder in the system after the reaction.

8.5. Non–equilibrium thermodynamics

In the late 19th century, similarities between the four transport phenomena, diffusion, heat conduction, viscous flow and electric conduction, were recognized. In particular, scientists noted a striking similarity in the underlying formulas, Fick's law of diffusion, Fourier's law of heat conduction, the formula for viscosity we will discuss in Chapter 11 and Ohm's law for the electric current which we introduce in Chapter 13. All four laws can be written in the same general form:

$$J = \frac{\Delta x_1}{\Delta t} = c \cdot A \cdot \frac{x_2}{l} \quad (29)$$

in which J is a flux (change of property x_1 with time), x_2/l is the driving force based on a change of property x_2 across a membrane of length l (called a gradient), A is the cross–sectional area and c is a proportionality coefficient. The gradient creates the non–equilibrium in the system and the flux is driven by the gradient. For this reason, the gradient is called a driving force. In each of the four laws the parameters x_1 and x_2 have different physical meaning as highlighted in Table 8.7. In the table, viscosity and the electric flow are included even though we cover the underlying physics only later in the textbook.

Eq. (29) is a linear relation between flux and driving force. For each of the four transport phenomena in Table 8.7 exist thresholds toward regimes where other, more complex relations hold, i.e., where the flux is no longer linearly proportional to the driving force. In the case of heat conduction, the corresponding non–linear effect is convection. In the case of diffusion, the non–linear regime occurs when D becomes concentration dependent.

Once these similarities were noticed, it also became evident that chemical reactions display many similarities to the transport phenomena. Although chemical reactions do not follow Eq. (29) since they do not have spatial gradients to act as a driving force, the transition state model of Arrhenius is successfully used to describe the kinetics of chemical reactions. Chemical reaction rates are therefore often displayed in Arrhenius plots.

In the first half of the 20th century is was then understood that the four transport phenomena are dynamic processes near the equilibrium. Lars Onsager showed in 1931 that fluxes and driving forces near the equilibrium are always connected linearly with each other. In 1945, Ilya Prigogine and H. B. G. Casimir showed further that the *steady state* plays a particularly important role in this linear regime as it represents the state with minimum entropy production toward which all systems near the equilibrium develop.

Beyond this linear regime near the equilibrium things become more complex. In 1954, Prigogine and Glansdorff proposed a first attempt at a model for systems far from the equilibrium (called non–linear non–equilibrium thermodynamics). They derived evolution criteria for systems which allow us to make some predictions. Despite the great interest in non–linear phenomena in biological processes we still do not have a complete formalism to describe all observations in this regime in a comprehensive fashion.

The remainder of this chapter, therefore, is divided into a brief but complete discussion of the linear regime (section 8.5) and a selection of a few interesting results of the work of the last 50 years on the non–linear regime (section 8.6).

8.5.1. Entropy in non–equilibrium systems

To connect the non–equilibrium state of a system to the concept of entropy we must investigate further the irreversible character of the process in Fig. 8.7(b). Fig. 8.12 shows the same system with a zero–width membrane and additional parameters of interest. The system consists of two homogeneous parts at each side of the membrane, labelled I and II, which are each uniform in all parameters but differ in temperature with $T_I < T_{II}$. The system (part I, part II and membrane) is closed toward the environment (ENV), i.e., only heat exchange with the environment is allowed.

Three heat fluxes must be considered as indicated by the arrows in Fig. 8.12: a heat flow between the system and the environment at part I shown at the left, labelled Q_{E1}, a heat flow between the system and the en-

Table 8.7: Summary of the transport phenomena. Viscosity and electric current are discussed later in the textbook.

Phenomenon	x_1	x_2	Coefficient c
Heat conduction	Heat Q	Temperature T	thermal conductivity λ
Diffusion	Mol number n	Concentration c	diffusion coefficient D
Viscosity	Momentum **p**	Flow velocity **v**	viscosity coefficient η
Electric Current	Charge Q	Electric potential V	Resistance R

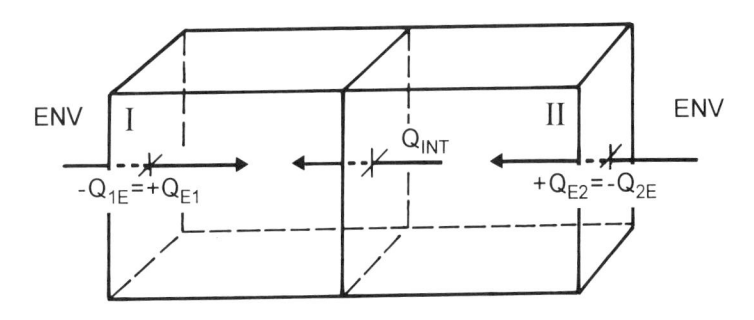

Fig. 8.12: Model of a closed system with two parts separated by a zero–width membrane. Three heat fluxes are studied, heat exchange between either system part with the environment (ENV) and heat transfer between the two system parts.

vironment at part II shown at the right, labelled Q_{E2}, and a heat flow across the membrane toward the lower temperature part of the system, labelled Q_{int} (with index *int* for internal flow). The heat balance for each of the system parts I and II is given as:

$$Q_I = Q_{E1} + Q_{int}$$
$$Q_{II} = Q_{E2} - Q_{int} \qquad (30)$$

Using Eq. (30), we write the entropy change:

$$\Delta S_{system} = \Delta S_I + \Delta S_{II} = \frac{Q_I}{T_{low}} + \frac{Q_{II}}{T_{high}} =$$
$$\frac{Q_{E1}}{T_{low}} + \frac{Q_{E2}}{T_{high}} + Q_{int}\left(\frac{1}{T_{low}} - \frac{1}{T_{high}}\right) \qquad (31)$$

The last line of Eq. (31) contains three terms. The first two represent an *entropy flux* between the system and its environment. This flux is not of particular interest because we showed already in Eq. (12) that entropy flux between the system and the environment occurs.

The last term in Eq. (31) represents an *entropy production* within the system due to a heat flow across the membrane. This is a term we have not seen before. It is zero when the temperatures are the same on both sides of the membrane. It resumes a non–zero value only for systems outside the equilibrium.

At this point we introduce an explicit time dependence by dividing Eq. (31) on both sides by time interval Δt. This defines the entropy production as $\Delta S/\Delta t$ [J/(s K)], i.e., the amount of entropy produced per second in the irreversible process. On the right hand side of the equation we combine the time interval term with the heat amount flowing between the two system parts:

$$\frac{\Delta S_{int}}{\Delta t} = \frac{\Delta Q_{int}}{\Delta t}\left(\frac{1}{T_{low}} - \frac{1}{T_{high}}\right) \qquad (32)$$

The right hand side of Eq. (32) is positive, thus the label entropy production as opposed to entropy annihilation is justified. We can further generalize this finding. Two factors contribute to the entropy production: the difference in inverse temperatures, which is identified as a driving force across the membrane (we use the variable X for such driving forces) and the time change in the internal heat which is identified as a flux (we use the variable J for such fluxes). The flux occurs always in response to a non–vanishing driving force. The entropy production in Eq. (32) is therefore given in the form:

$$\frac{\Delta S_{int}}{\Delta t} = J \cdot X \qquad (33)$$

This formula explains why we found the similarity between the transport phenomena discussed earlier in this section, and why the forces and fluxes are combined in the way observed. Each driving force has a corresponding flux, such that the two together, as shown in Eq. (33), represent the entropy production of the system.

An open system can be treated in an analogous fashion. For an open system the zero–width membrane is permeable for some chemical components, and internal fluxes for the heat and the permeating components have to be considered. Again, only the exchange across the membrane contributes to the production of entropy. For such a system it can be shown that Eq. (33) holds again, except that the flux J and the driving force X are now more complicated functions.

8.5.2. Force–flux relations near the equilibrium

The second law of thermodynamics allows us to study the entropy function near the equilibrium. We know from Eq. (14) that S has a maximum value in the equilibrium and that it has a smaller value if any parameter describing the system is not at its equilibrium value. If the equilibrium is not yet reached, irreversible processes will take place and the entropy rises until the system is in equilibrium. When the system is in equilibrium, Eq. (12) applies and no further processes can occur.

Let us consider α to be a variable parameter of the system which we define such that $\alpha = 0$ when the system is in equilibrium. α could for example be the temperature difference to the equilibrium temperature value, $\alpha = T - T_{eq}$. Fig. 8.13 shows then a sketch of the entropy as a function of this parameter, $S = f(\alpha)$. The entropy at the equilibrium is S_{eq} which is the value we introduced in the context of the second law of thermodynamics. We know that the entropy is a maximum at $\alpha = 0$; thus the sketch in Fig. 8.13 shows properly that the entropy function bends downwards both for $\alpha > 0$ and $\alpha < 0$.

We want to write a mathematical formula which describes the entropy function near $\alpha = 0$. Note that we do not know the entropy function outside the equilibrium, the downward bending is the only feature we know due to the second law of thermodynamics. We want to use the simplest possible function which is sufficient to describe the curve in Fig. 8.13. For the part of the curve near the equilibrium, i.e., for small α values, a parabolic function opening downwards is a good approximation. Introducing a coefficient c_0 to describe the curvature of the function, we write *for the entropy near the equilibrium*:

$$S = S_{eq} - \frac{1}{2} c_0 \alpha^2 \quad (34)$$

The regime of α values near the equilibrium in which this equation applies is called the *linear regime* (for the origin of the name see below). This regime is indicated by the light, vertical-dashed lines in Fig. 8.13. Note that

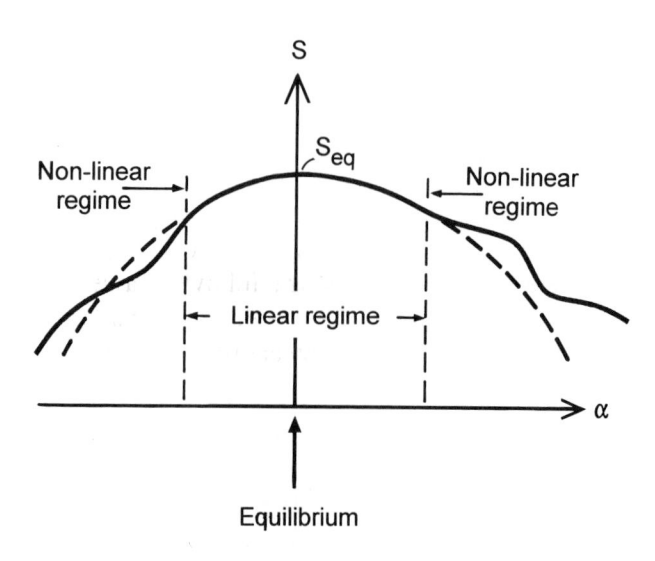

Fig. 8.13: The dependence of the entropy on parameter α (which could e.g. be the temperature), shown near the equilibrium. The parameter interval for which a parabolic function (dashed line) fits the actual entropy function (solid line), is called the linear regime (indicated by the two light, vertical dashed lines). Beyond this interval the parameter range is called the non–linear regime.

this is the first time in this course that we are making a statement which is true beyond the equilibrium based on the fundamental laws of physics! All we have to do for a specific parameter α is to determine c_0 and we have derived a genuine non–equilibrium law.

Now we want to connect Eq. (34) to the previous discussion on entropy production. For this we calculate from Eq. (34) how the entropy changes with time (assuming a very short time interval Δt):

$$\frac{\Delta S_{int}}{\Delta t} = - c_0 \alpha \frac{\Delta \alpha}{\Delta t} \quad (35)$$

The entropy production is proportional to the product of the variable α and the change of parameter α with time.

Comparing Eq. (35) with Eq. (33) we identify the first term as a driving force, $X = -c_0 \alpha$, and the second term as a flux, $J = \Delta \alpha / \Delta t$. Thus, near the equilibrium, the driving force and the flux are both linear in α and, therefore, are linked in a linear fashion with each other. This leads to *Onsager's equation*, in which L is introduced as Onsager's phenomenological coefficient:

$$J = L \cdot X \quad (36)$$

Eq. (36) can be compared with the transport phenomena equations developed in the previous chapter. As an example, the equivalence with Fourier's law of heat conduction is illustrated in the first Appendix (section 8.7).

Onsager's equation is the central law in the discussion of non–equilibrium thermodynamics. In addition to unifying the four empirical transport phenomena equations, it allows us to define the conditions under which these empirical laws apply. It also allows us to classify some previously known observations as well as predict new phenomena. In the following a selective number of these conclusions from Onsager's law are illustrated qualitatively as they are relevant to the biological sciences.

8.5.3. Transport phenomena interference effects

In real physical, chemical and biological systems more than one parameter of the system may deviate from the equilibrium value. For example, across the membrane of a cell, there can be a concentration step of different components capable to permeate the membrane. Or, during fast breathing at very low external temperatures, the air may not reach body temperature before reaching the alveoli, causing a combined thermal and concentration gradient across the membrane toward the blood capillaries. In this respect, Fig. 8.13 is only a special case, and a more general plot has to be drawn which allows for several parameters, α_i, α_k, ... of the system to have values outside of the equilibrium.

Such a plot for two parameters is shown in Fig. 8.14. The equilibrium of the system is given at $\alpha_i = \alpha_k = 0$ with $S = S_{eq}$ a maximum due to the second law of thermodynamics. The same arguments can be repeated which we used in the discussion of Fig. 8.13. In particular, there is a linear regime near the equilibrium in which the function $S = f(\alpha_i, \alpha_k)$ is a paraboloid that opens toward negative S values. Further away from the equilibrium, that approximation does not hold and the entropy function deviates from the paraboloid shape.

Fig. 8.14 predicts the same behavior of a system with two variables as Fig. 8.13 does for one variable: near the equilibrium Onsager's equation holds for both parameters; in other words, the system displays a linear relation between two driving forces and the corresponding fluxes. For example, in a system with a concentration step across a membrane and a concurrent temperature difference, both heat conduction and diffusion occur at the same time. However, a set of new phenomena become possible where the driving force of one phenomenon causes a flux associated with another phenomenon. This possibility arises since Eq. (34) reads for multiple variables:

$$S = S_{eq} - \frac{1}{2} \sum_{i,k} c_{ik} \, \alpha_i \cdot \alpha_k \qquad (37)$$

with $c_{ik} > 0$ for all indices i and k. The following four combinations of driving forces X and fluxes J can be extracted from Eq. (37):

$$\begin{aligned}
(I) & \quad X \propto \alpha_i & \Rightarrow & \quad J \propto \alpha_i \\
(II) & \quad X \propto \alpha_k & \Rightarrow & \quad J \propto \alpha_k \\
(III) & \quad X \propto \alpha_i & \Rightarrow & \quad J \propto \alpha_k \\
(IV) & \quad X \propto \alpha_k & \Rightarrow & \quad J \propto \alpha_i
\end{aligned} \qquad (38)$$

The first two cases are the individual transport phenomena discussed above; the last two cases are cases in which transport phenomena interfere with each other. In 1931, Onsager showed that a reciprocity for cases (III) and (IV) applies, i.e., that studying one case (and finding the Onsager phenomenological coefficient L_{ik} in Eq. (36) for it) allows us to predict the inverse phenomenon because it has the same coefficient $L_{ki} = L_{ik}$. These interference effects are usually weaker than the primary transport phenomena.

One special case is illustrated here: the thermomolecular pressure difference, in which a heat flux through a closed system causes a pressure difference

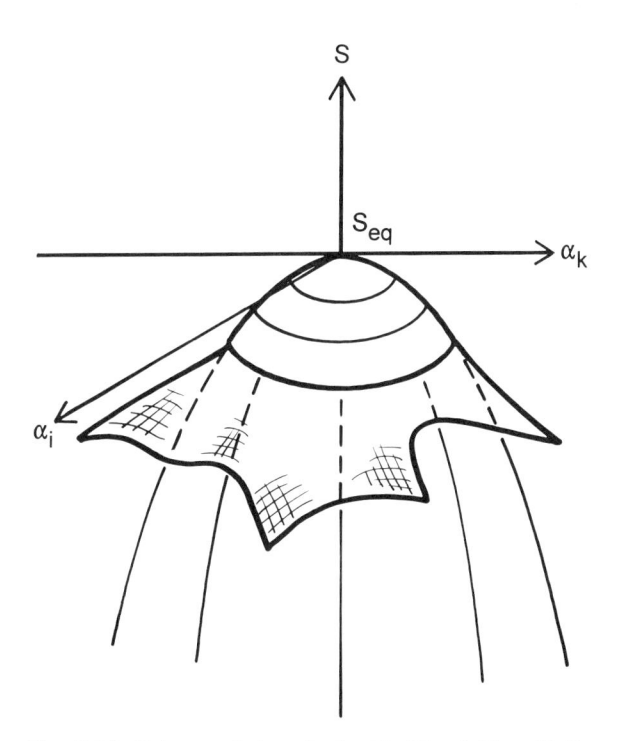

Fig. 8.14: Entropy plot equivalent to Fig. 8.13, with the exception that more than one system parameter varies. In this particular plot we assume that two parameters, α_i and α_k, vary. Linear and non–linear regimes for these parameters are defined in the same fashion as for Fig. 8.13.

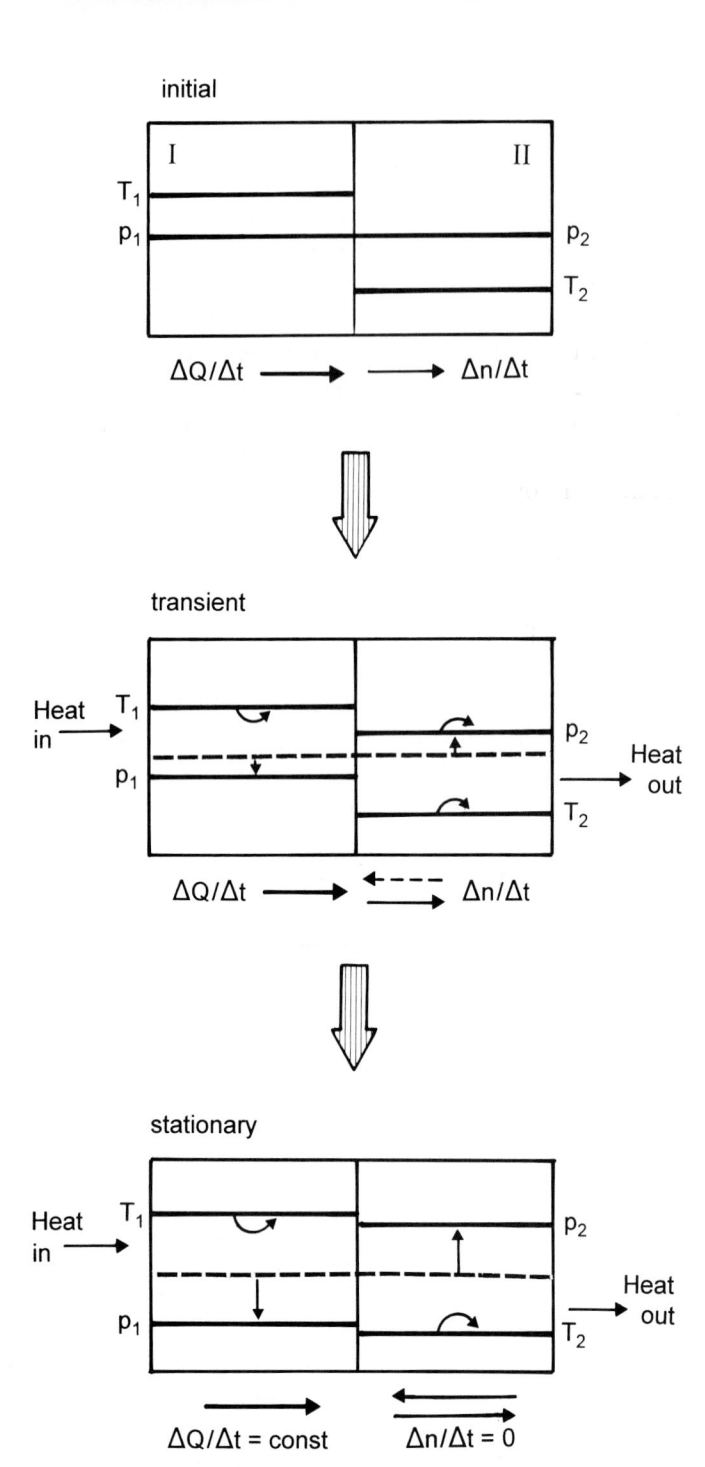

Fig. 8.15: Thermomolecular pressure difference: an initial temperature difference between the two system parts is maintained by a continuous heat flow through the system. During a transient time a pressure difference between the two parts of the system builds up and becomes stationary in the steady state.

across the membrane, as shown in Fig. 8.15. At t = 0 a temperature difference $\Delta T = T_1 - T_2 \neq 0$ is established across the membrane and is maintained by providing a continuous flow of heat through the system (indicated by the arrows on the left and right of the system). The bold arrow below the system indicates that the heat flux is the dominant transport effect in this case. Consequently, at t > 0 matter is pulled through the membrane in the same direction as the heat flows, decreasing the pressure on the left side and increasing the pressure on the right side. In this transient stage the pressure difference rises while the temperature difference is kept constant by externally regulating the heat flow. A small flow of matter ($\Delta n/\Delta t$) toward the right is observed. Eventually the matter flow ceases as the pressure difference leads to an increasing diffusion driven counterflow. At that point the pressure difference between the two system parts becomes stationary, that is, $p_1 - p_2 \neq f(t)$. Thus, a continuous heat flow leads to a pressure difference across the membrane.

This example shows that a continuous external effort is needed to maintain a non–equilibrium. This external effort can take the form of a material flux and/or heat flux across the system and its membrane. The same is true for membranes of finite width, as illustrated by two examples in the second Appendix (section 8.7).

8.5.4. The steady state

The stationary state or steady state has been mentioned several times in the discussion of non–equilibrium processes. So far, it was mostly used as a convenient simplification since all transport phenomena become time independent when the steady state is reached, i.e., the mathematical formalism becomes easier to handle. For example, in the case of diffusion, only the first of two laws by Fick, the one applicable to the steady state, was introduced. However, mathematical convenience is not a sufficient justification to focus on a particular case.

The steady state is important for more fundamental reasons. It plays the same role for open or closed systems near the equilibrium as the equilibrium plays for a homogeneous system. We found in our discussion of thermodynamics in Chapters 5 and 6 that the equilibrium state is unique in two respects: (i) that a system not in equilibrium approaches the equilibrium spontaneously, and (ii) that the equilibrium is a stable state, i.e., a system in equilibrium immediately returns to the equilibrium if a perturbation has occurred.

As early as 1922 in pioneering biological studies, and then since 1933 for physical systems, it was recognized that the steady state plays a very similar role outside the equilibrium as long as the system is near to the equilibrium, or, more specifically, in the linear regime. The steady state is the state toward which any system, that is not yet in the steady state, develops. The steady state is also a stable state of the system, i.e., the system always returns to the steady state in response to a perturbation. In 1945, Prigogine discovered the underlying property which drives this behavior:

> *The steady state is the state for which the entropy production is a minimum.*

Thus, outside the equilibrium this principle replaces the second law of thermodynamics and the entropy production replaces the entropy as the property which determines the dynamics of the system. Prigogine's principle is the reason why the secondary flux in the two examples of interference effects in the previous section ceases in the stationary case.

Thus we make the following statements for a system in the linear regime near the equilibrium:
(I) a system with no constraints goes to the equilibrium as this state has a zero entropy production,
(II) a system with a driving force constraint (i.e., with a non–zero driving force) goes to the steady state with minimum entropy production, and
(III) a system, that is in a steady state responds to a perturbation such that the perturbation is compensated (Le Châtelier's principle of moderation).

8.5.5. Homeostasis

> *Homeostasis is the state of dynamic stability of the internal environment of the body that is maintained by the ever–changing processes of feedback and regulation in response to external changes.*

The unique role of the steady state for biological systems was recognized by Claude Bernard when he distinguished the external environment of a living organism and its internal environment. He noted that many animals maintain quite constant internal conditions even when the conditions outside of the body change. This observation applies to several critical parameters in the human body: the body temperature is allowed only to vary by less than a degree at 37 °C, the pH of blood and other interstitial fluids is held at pH = 7.4, and the sugar concentration in the blood is held at 0.1 %. We refer to this state of the animal body as homeostasis.

There are significant benefits to maintain homeostasis in the animal body. Translated homeostasis means "steady state." Cells in an organism with stable temperature and/or chemical conditions operate in an unperturbed steady state. Individual chemical processes, such as enzyme synthesis, are performed at a steady rate, and the entire cell works like a well–coordinated plant capitalizing on the thermodynamic benefits of the steady state outlined above. Cells for which such an environment is not established display fluctuating productivity which at times may idle other bodily functions for lack of supplies.

The benefits of maintaining steady state conditions in the body are significant enough for the evolutionary development of coupled feedback–mechanisms to control these conditions. These are so complex that modern biological research is still trying to piece the complete network of processes together. Part of this complexity stems from the fact that nature does not want to establish a too rigid steady state, but leaves open the option for non–linear processes we discuss in the next section. Allowing for change is necessary for a healthy development of individual organisms, e.g. the balance of hormones in the blood varies significantly during puberty or pregnancy.

8.6. Non–linear non–equilibrium processes

Reading the previous section we note that the linear regime of non–equilibrium phenomena is not sufficient to explain a large number of complex features of biological systems. In particular, what remains elusive is the formation of complex spatial patterns already at the cellular level. The most complex feature that can develop in an initially homogeneous system near the equilibrium, i.e., in the linear non–equilibrium regime, is a simple gradient, as discussed in the context of the thermomolecular pressure difference.

The inability of linear non–equilibrium concepts to explain biological processes is not too surprising since chemical reactions are dynamic non–equilibrium processes with no, or only a negligible, linear regime. Since chemical reactions are vital to the formation of biological systems, we have to study the non–linear regime far from the equilibrium to find the mechanisms which form more complex patterns. This field is still an area of intensive research, and we do not yet fully understand all the existing observations. Therefore, only two issues are discussed in order to illustrate the type of observations and applications possible in this regime, the spatial pattern formation in hydrodynamic Bénard cells and the temporal pattern formation of evolutionary systems.

8.6.1. Convection and Bénard cell formation

The top part of Fig. 8.16 shows Bénard's set–up for a heat conduction experiment far from the equilibrium which he conducted in 1900. A thin layer of thickness l

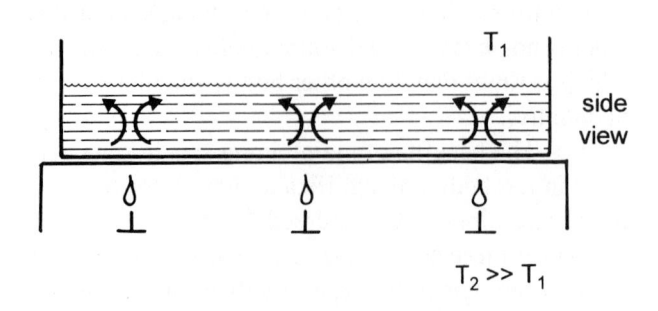

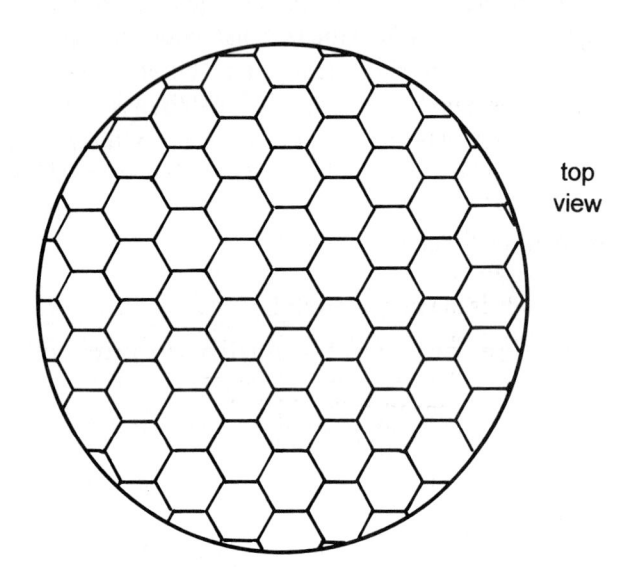

Fig. 8.16: (top) Experimental set–up for Bénard's convection experiment. The side view shows a thin oil layer which is heated from below by a high–temperature heat source. The oil dissipates heat to the air above the oil layer. The heat transport occurs by convection. Convection requires the flow of oil leading to highly ordered honeycomb patterns when viewed from above (bottom sketch).

parabola. Calculating the entropy production from Eq. (39) no longer leads to a linear Onsager equation, i.e., fluxes and forces are no longer connected in the linear form of Eq. (36). With Eq. (36) no longer applicable, new phenomena become possible, which we refer to as non–linear effects.

In the specific case of Bénard's experiment, the last term in Eq. (39) allows for an accelerated heat transport, which is necessary because oil cannot transport heat quickly via Fourier's heat conduction. The new heat conduction mechanism is called *convection*. Convection differs from Fourier's heat conduction in that the heat conducting medium itself moves, with hot oil going up and cooler oil down. This is indicated by arrows in the top part of Fig. 8.16. Such convection flow of oil can be observed for cooking oil in a pan on your stove. Ordered Bénard patterns, however, cannot form in cooking oil as it cannot be heated strongly enough. Using silicon oil, Fig. 8.17 shows that the convection flow is circular. The most intriguing feature is shown in the bottom part of Fig. 8.16. In a top view of the thin oil film, a highly ordered hexagonal pattern is observed. The hexagons are called cells. The boundaries of the hexagonal structure are coincident with the outer boundaries (dashed lines in Fig. 8.17) around each convection seed. Bénard cells were an early example of the transition from linear to non–linear behavior, with Fourier's heat conduction the linear process and convection the non–linear process that leads to the highly complex patterns in Fig. 8.16.

of a temperature resistant oil is heated from below while its surface is cooled by air. This leads to a large temperature gradient $T_2 - T_1/l$. This gradient shifts the system far enough from the equilibrium that the entropy equations (34) or (37) have to be re–evaluated. Without knowing a mathematical form for the entropy formula in the non–linear regime far from the equilibrium, we write for the case when only one parameter α is not in equilibrium:

$$S = S_{eq} - \frac{1}{2}|c_2|\alpha^2 + O(\alpha^3) \qquad (39)$$

This equation is equivalent to Eq. (34) in the linear regime except for a term $O(\alpha^3)$ which stands for "terms of at least the order of α^3," i.e., terms of third, fourth and higher power. When this term begins to dominate on the right hand side of Eq. (39) the function is no longer a

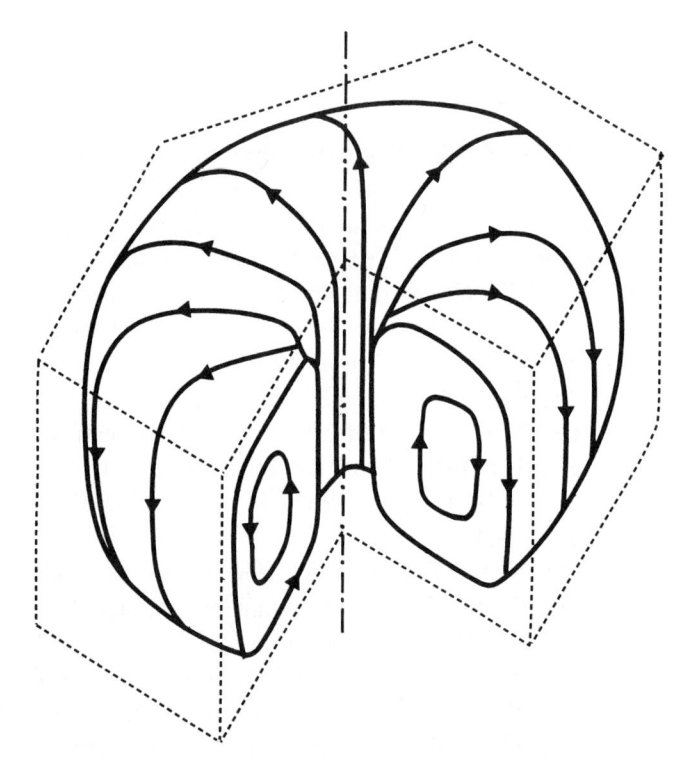

Fig. 8.17: Side view of a single (honeycomb) convection cell indicating the flow pattern in Bénard's experiment.

244

Work on non-equilibrium thermodynamics by Prigogine and Glansdorff in the 1950's showed how difficult it is to describe these non-linear processes. It was found that even entropy is not a system property useful for characterizing the non-linear regime since no general rules apply. In particular, the steady state is no longer stable, i.e., perturbations cause the system to leave such states and drift away. Even minor fluctuations in the parameters of a system can cause major effects. In some cases the entire dynamics of the system is driven by unpredictable random fluctuations.

In other cases, the system starts to oscillate between different steady states which are close to each other in the parameter space. This has been observed for the Belousov–Zhabotinskii reaction (discovered in 1964) which is a catalytic oxidation of bromine–malonic acid. The reaction is written in the form:

$$2\ HBrO_3 + 3\ H_2C(COOH)_2 \rightleftharpoons$$
$$HOBr + HO\text{--}CH(COOH)_2 + ... \quad (40)$$
$$... + BrCH(COOH)_2 + 2\ CO_2 + 2\ H_2O$$

with cerium–sulfate as the catalyzer. When starting this reaction, temporal patterns evolve. This means that the reaction continuously jumps back and forth between different oxidation states of the cerium ions on a time scale of minutes. Since 1964 other reactions have been discovered showing the same oscillatory behavior.

8.6.2. Eigen's theory of evolution

The concepts of non-equilibrium thermodynamics can also be applied to evolutionary theory. Due to the highly mathematical character of the theory only an outline of the early development is provided as a first glimpse at population studies.

The mathematical concept at the root of population studies are rate equations. Rate equations are equations which describe the time dependence of a parameter as a function of all parameters affecting its change. Chemical rate equations may serve as an example. The rate at which the various concentrations change in even the simplest reactions, e.g. $H_2 + I_2 \rightleftharpoons 2\ HI$, depends on the concentrations of the three molecules and a set of kinetic coefficients for the reaction progressing toward the right and toward the left. Among these, the three concentrations are in turn time dependent, leading to differential equations. With the development of powerful computers in the last part of the twentieth century, solving such rate equations has become a fast routine procedure.

In 1971 Manfred Eigen developed rate equations describing the time change in the number of bacteria living on a petri dish. We begin with an equation for the rate of a single species of bacteria which we identify with the index *i*. The species of bacteria is defined by its specific DNA sequence. Assuming that no mutations occur, the rate equation is written as:

$$\frac{\Delta N_i}{\Delta t} = (F_i - A_i)\, N_i \quad (41)$$

in which N_i is the number of our chosen bacteria species. Eq. (41) is a rate equation because the left hand side of the equation describes the change of the number of bacteria with time, $\Delta N_i/\Delta t$. The equation allows us to judge whether or not our bacteria species is well adapted to its environment as an increase or decrease of the number N_i is dependent on the two factors in the bracket, F_i and A_i.

F_i is the rate of formation factor of bacteria, containing species–independent contributions, e.g. the rate of duplication of cells, and species–dependent contributions, e.g. the speed with which the needed amino acids can be supplied to the ribosomal apparatus. The larger the term F_i, the more successful are our bacteria, i.e., the faster does the population grow.

A_i, in turn, is the rate of annihilation factor, which is also based on species–independent contributions, such as the mortality rate of cells, and species–specific contributions, such as the chemical stability of the DNA molecule. The larger the term A_i, the less successful are the bacteria, i.e., the faster do bacteria of this species disappear.

Eq. (41) allows us to decide which bacteria will prosper in the biotope while the biotope is sparsely populated (competition–free biotope). To survive, a bacteria species must fulfil the condition $F_i - A_i \geq 0$ because only in this case is the rate term $\Delta N_i/\Delta t \geq 0$. This applies not only to the fittest but to a range of bacteria with different DNA, defining an interval of successful adaptation, as shown in Fig. 8.18.

Were $F_i - A_i$ a positive constant number, the number of bacteria would grow exponentially. There are two reasons why this cannot occur indefinitely: (I) any biotope is finite in size and resources (such as amino acids), and (II) usually more than one species lives in a biotope and the various species compete for the resources. In the latter case, one equation like Eq. (41) has to be written for each species of bacteria in the biotope, and the formation factors and annihilation factors have to be modified for contributions due to other species (e.g., toxic components in the membrane of one species of bacteria may lead to the death of other bacteria living close by). Instead of exponential growth, the population of the various surviving bacteria species now approaches

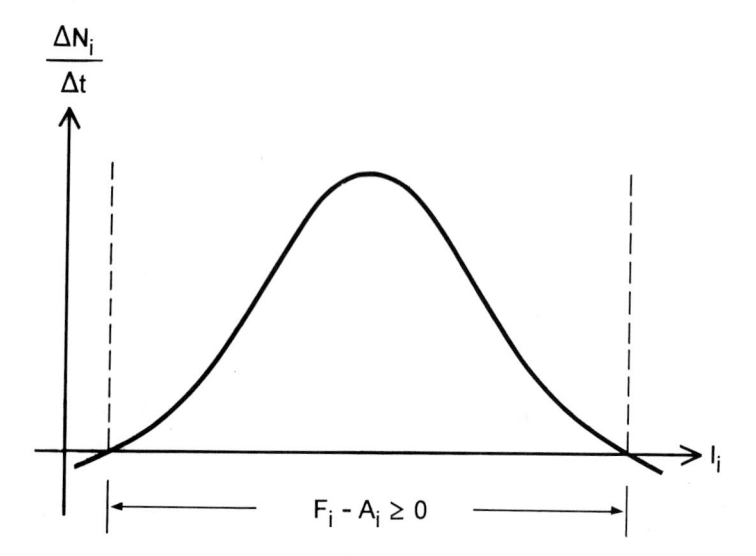

Fig. 8.18: Sketch of the term $F_i - A_i$ in Eq. (41) for each species of bacteria in a competition–free biotope as a function of the DNA (expressed as the DNA of information I_i). Dependent on the information carried on the bacteria's DNA the term $F_i - A_i$ is positive (the bacteria species grows exponentially) or negative (the bacteria species becomes extinct). The interval of surviving species defines the composition of life in the biotope.

a stable steady state distribution. The evolutionary concept of struggle for survival leads to the ecological concept of carrying capacity of an ecosystem. Thus in a world where Eq. (41) applies to each species, all species must be present at time $t = 0$ as no new ones can emerge. On the other side, the extinction of ill–adapted species is possible as their term $F_i - A_i$ may become negative. Eq. (41) can be called the rate equation of "creationism."

We want to test Eq. (41) and see, whether it describes the experiment "life on Earth." One troubling feature of Eq. (41) is the fact that it does not allow for life as a whole to adjust to environmental changes. If the environment changes and causes $F_i - A_i$ to become negative for a species, it becomes extinct. On Earth we know that environmental conditions are not fixed and that these changes lead indeed to species extinctions. In the course of time, environments change gradually (e.g. as ice–ages come and go or, at a much smaller pace, as continents drift across geographic latitudes), and sometimes catastrophically. The consequences for life on Earth are illustrated in Fig. 8.19. The figure shows the number of marine families of species on Earth as a function of time for the last 550 million years (marine species are simpler to quantify as their fossil record is more complete). Identified in Fig. 8.19 are 5 major mass extinctions, the most catastrophic being the Permian extinction 250 million years ago. The Permian extinction claimed more than 90% of all marine animals. The extinction at the end of the Cretaceous was the most recent. It wiped out not only all of the dinosaurs, but 2/3 of all living animals with them.

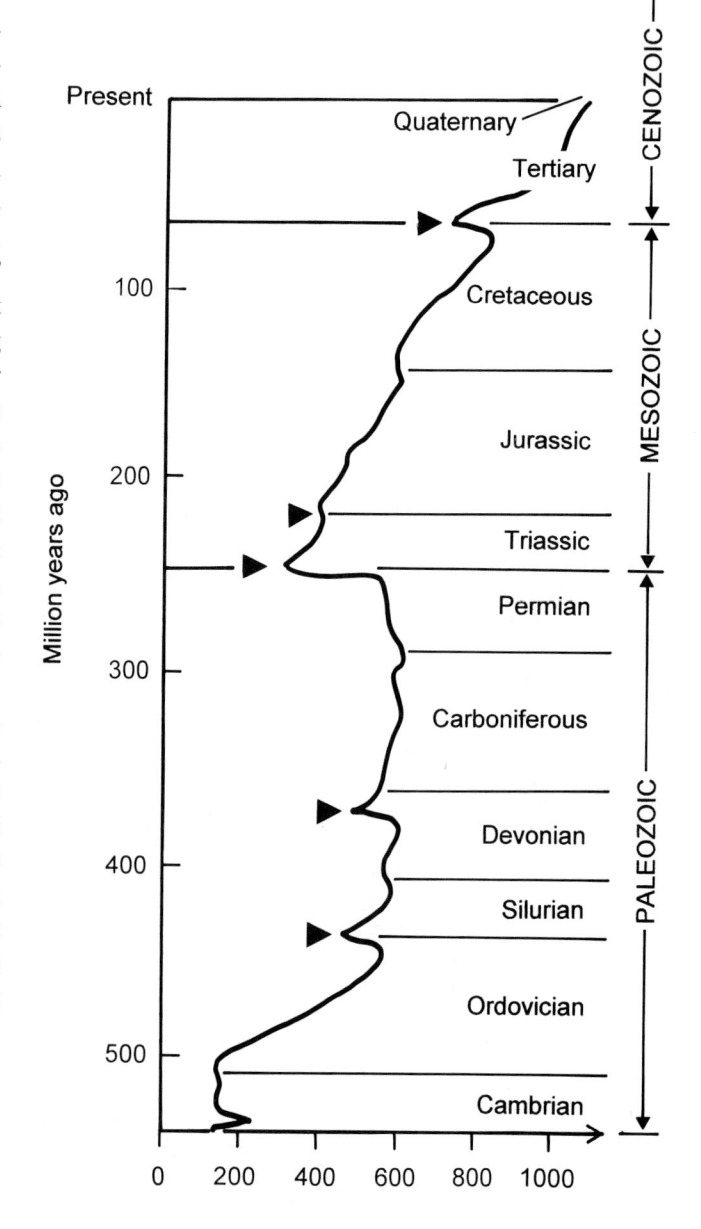

Fig. 8.19: Number of marine families as a function of time for the past 550 million years concurrently living on Earth. The data identify five catastrophic mass extinctions (solid arrow heads).

As indicated above, Eq. (41) is consistent with such mass extinctions due to rapid changes in the environment. However, Fig. 8.19 also shows that a continuous increase in the number of species or families of species is observed between the mass extinctions. Eq. (41) cannot explain the observed increase in species, i.e., the equation must be flawed or incomplete. Indeed, we (as part of life on Earth) are quite lucky that Eq. (41) is not a proper description of the history of life on the planet, because successive changes of the environment between the occurrence of life and the present time might well have led to non–overlapping intervals of conditions for $F_i - A_i \geq 0$. Thus, life in a world governed by Eq. (41) would be wiped out entirely by now!

Eq. (41) can be modified to allow for a continuous increase in species. For this we must include terms which account for the occurrence of mutations, i.e., the random formation of new DNA. Eq. (41) is modified in the form:

$$\frac{\Delta N_i}{\Delta t} = (F_i - A_i) N_i + \sum_{k \neq i} \varphi_{ki} N_k - \sum_{k \neq i} \varphi_{ik} N_i \quad (42)$$

in which the second term on the right hand side allows mutations from any other DNA molecule (index k) to the DNA molecule with index i, and the third term allows mutations from the DNA molecule with index i to DNA molecules of any other index. The second term is positive as it contributes to the amount of DNA molecules of index i and the third term represents a loss of that DNA.

Both mutation coefficients, φ_{ik} and φ_{ki}, are extremely small numbers as mutations happen very infrequently. If no DNA molecules with index i previously existed, then a new species has been created and may either grow or be annihilated based on its $F_i - A_i$ value. At the same time, a new species with a positive value of $F_i - A_i$ competes with all previously established DNA molecules for environmental resources, e.g. amino acids, and can therefore alter the entire balance in the biotope even without any change in the external environmental conditions. As was already properly discussed by Charles Darwin himself, a new species competes particularly strongly with similar DNA molecules, which obviously includes the DNA molecule from which it evolved. This phenomenon generates the so–called missing link problem that it is more likely that direct ancestors of existing species become extinct than more remotely related species.

Is Eq. (42) the formula that describes the evolutionary development of life on Earth? It is a good model for the evolution until about 1 billion years ago. That is the time when nature progressed from single cell organisms to more complex organisms. The slower reproduction rate of higher organisms poses a serious problem in protection against elimination by catastrophic environmental change. It can take many thousands of generations to obtain the mutations necessary for adaptation. If the succession of generations takes more than a few minutes, such a mutation may come too late! Nature solved this problem about one billion years ago by introducing sexual reproduction. Ever since then, the genetic pool of more complex species has hidden apparently neutral mutations, thus, building a stock of mutations which (hopefully) will enable some individuals of the species to adapt quickly to future environmental changes. Eq. (42) only holds for asexual reproduction.

Modern, highly sophisticated mathematical rate equation models of evolution take further aspects of the theoretical developments of the past 30 years into account. As computers become more powerful, complex interactions can be integrated in the rate equation algorithms. One of the issues tested in this fashion is the idea of punctuated equilibria for species evolution. This idea is based on the observation that the fossil record seems not to support the gradual evolution of species but a sudden occurrence, followed by a long period of anatomical stability. The punctuated equilibria model assumes that species tend to be genetically stable for long periods. They disappear only when they are replaced suddenly by newer and more adapted life forms.

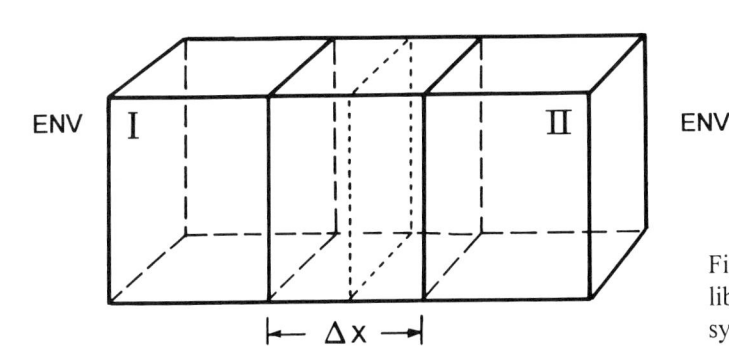

Fig. 8.20: Model sketch used to extend a non–equilibrium zero–width membrane model to describe systems with a finite membrane width.

8.7. Appendix

Fourier's law and the Onsager equation

Eq. (32) is written for a zero–width membrane. To compare the driving force and flux from this formula with Fourier's law, we need to use Fig. 8.20 to rewrite Eq. (32) for a finite width membrane. The finite membrane has then a width of $\Delta x = l$. Fig. 8.20 shows therefore essentially the same system as Fig. 8.12, except that the zero–width membrane (indicated by the dashed lines in the figure) has been replaced by two interfaces, separated by a distance Δx.

The entropy production in Eq. (32) is localized for the system in Fig. 8.12 at the zero–width membrane because the temperature drop occurs at that point and nowhere else in the system. For the system in Fig. 8.20 in turn the entropy production is distributed broader, across the entire length of the finite membrane. Thus, it is more useful to express the entropy production for such a finite–width membrane as an entropy production density; this is achieved by dividing the entropy production as calculated before by the volume in which the entropy production occurs:

$$\frac{1}{V}\left(\frac{\Delta S_{int}}{\Delta t}\right) = \frac{1}{V}\frac{\Delta Q_{int}}{\Delta t}\left(\frac{1}{T_{low}} - \frac{1}{T_{high}}\right) \quad (43)$$

The last term in this equation is then rewritten in the form $T_{high} = T + \tfrac{1}{2}\Delta T$ and $T_{low} = T - \tfrac{1}{2}\Delta T$, assuming that the temperature difference between system part I and system part II is not too large, i.e. $T \gg \Delta T$. Substituting the two temperatures in the last bracket of Eq. (43) leads to:

$$\frac{1}{T_{low}} - \frac{1}{T_{high}} = \frac{T_{high} - T_{low}}{T_{high} \cdot T_{low}} \cong \frac{\Delta T}{T^2} \quad (44)$$

We substitute the result of Eq. (44) into the entropy production density in Eq. (43). This leads to a new formula for the entropy production density:

$$\frac{1}{V}\left(\frac{\Delta S_{int}}{\Delta t}\right) = \frac{1}{A}\frac{\Delta Q_{int}}{\Delta t} \cdot \frac{1}{T^2}\frac{\Delta T}{l} \quad (45)$$

in which $V = A\,l$ is used to split the volume of the membrane into the cross–section A and the length l on the right hand side of the equation. Using Eq. (35), we identify the driving force X and the flux J:

$$J = \frac{1}{A}\frac{\Delta Q_{int}}{\Delta t}$$

$$X = \frac{1}{T^2}\frac{\Delta T}{l} \quad (46)$$

This allows us to compare Onsager's phenomenological coefficient L in Eq. (36) with the thermal conductivity defined in Fourier's equation, which is Eq. (7.1):

Onsager: $\quad \dfrac{1}{A}\dfrac{\Delta Q_{int}}{\Delta t} = L\left(\dfrac{1}{T^2}\dfrac{\Delta T}{l}\right)$

Fourier: $\quad \dfrac{Q}{t} = \lambda\, A\, \dfrac{T_{high} - T_{low}}{l} \quad (47)$

$\Rightarrow \quad L = \lambda\, T^2$

Thus, the Onsager phenomenological coefficient and the thermal conductivity differ by a temperature–dependent factor. Because the Onsager coefficient is a constant due to Eq. (36), the phenomenologically found thermal conductivity constant λ in Fourier's law is indeed not a constant, but temperature dependent.

Interference for finite membrane width

Fig. 8.21 shows a continuous flow of heat through a permeable membrane of finite width. The dominant heat flow leads to a temperature profile across the membrane as shown. A flux of matter occurs in the same direction as the heat flow, like in the thermomolecular pressure difference case. This flow of matter builds up a concentration gradient, which in turn causes diffusion in the opposite direction. In the steady state the material flux ceases, because a stationary state is reached between thermally driven material flux to the right and diffusive flux of matter to the left. This effect is called thermodiffusion or Soret–effect. It allows for the formation of a concentration gradient in a uniform system.

The inverse effect, called the Dufour–effect, is shown in Fig. 8.22. In this case, a dominant flow of matter through the system leads to a concentration profile. The continuous diffusion through the open system builds up a concurrent flow of heat which establishes a temperature gradient. The system becomes stationary when the diffusive heat transport is balanced by a heat conduction in the opposite direction, occurring along the temperature gradient.

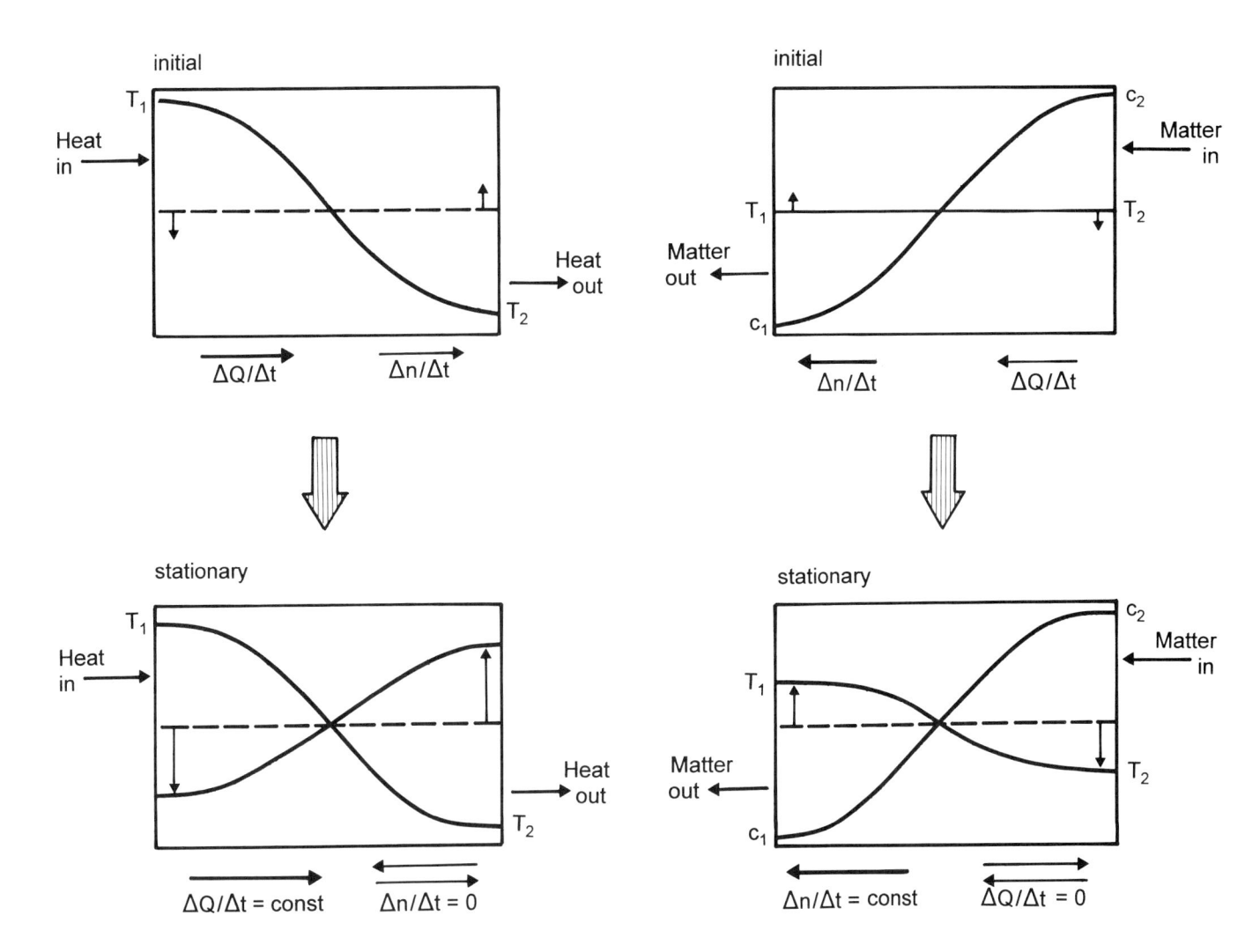

Fig. 8.21: Illustration of the Soret–effect (thermodiffusion). The top panel shows the initial system (with a temperature gradient). The bottom panel shows that a steady state develops if the temperature gradient is maintained by a non–zero heat transport through the system. The steady state is characterized by both a temperature and a concentration gradient.

Fig. 8.22: Illustration of the Dufour–effect. At an initial time (top panel) a concentration profile exists. If this concentration gradient is maintained by a continuous flow of matter through the system, a steady state develops with both a concentration and a temperature profile (lower panel).

8.8. Problems

P–8.1
We revisit the Carnot process discussed in P–6.12. This process is operated with 1.0 mol of an ideal gas of heat capacity $C_V = 3R/2$. The pressure of the gas is 10.0 atm and the temperature is 600 K in the most compressed state. From there, an isothermal expansion leads to a pressure of 1.0 atm. The lower process temperature is 300 K. Draw this Carnot process in an S–T diagram.

P–8.2
(a) Calculate the entropy change of 5 mol of an ideal gas which is isothermally and reversibly expanded from a pressure of 2 atm to 1 atm at 25°C.

(b) How large is the entropy change in the environment within the isolated superstructure?
(c) How large is the entropy change if the expansion is done adiabatically instead?

P–8.3
Calculate the entropy change during melting of 1.0 mol benzene.
Hint: the melting point of benzene at 1 atm pressure is $T_m = 5.4°C$ and the latent heat of melting is 126 kJ/kg.

P–8.4
Calculate the entropy of evaporation for 1 mol of the materials listed in Table 8.8.

Table 8.8: Boiling point T_b and latent heat of evaporation for various materials.

Material	$T_b[°C]$	ΔH [kJ/mol]
Argon (Ar)	–185.7	7.86
Mercury (Hg)	356.6	64.85
CCl_4	76.7	30.0
C_6H_6 (benzene)	80.1	30.75

P–8.5
10 g ice at 0°C are placed in a calorimeter with 20 g water at 90°C. For the latent heat of melting of ice use 5980 J/mol. The molar heat capacity of liquid water is 75.3 J/(K mol), assume that this value is temperature independent.
(a) What is the final temperature of the water?
(b) If the process is done reversibly, what is the entropy change of the combined system ice/water?
(c) What is the entropy change in the environment for the reversible process.
(d) What is the entropy change if the process is done irreversibly in an isolated beaker?
Hint: use Eq. (27) for the temperature dependence of ΔS.

P–8.6
Calculate the entropy of 1 mol nitrogen gas (N_2) at p = 1 atm and T = 150°C. Use for the molar heat capacity of nitrogen C_p = 28.8 J/(K mol).

P–8.7
Determine graphically the standard entropy of silver from the data given in Table 8.9.

Table 8.9: The molar heat capacity C_p of silver (Ag) at temperatures between 15 K and 290 K. The range 0 K to 15 K is extrapolated linearly.

T[K]	C_p [J/(K mol)]	T[K]	C_p [J/(K mol)]
15	0.67	170	23.61
30	4.77	190	24.09
50	11.65	210	24.42
70	16.33	230	24.73
90	19.13	250	25.02
110	20.96	270	25.31
130	22.13	290	25.44
150	22.97		

P–8.8
The standard entropy of diamond is S^0 = 2.5 J/(K mol), the standard entropy of graphite is S^0 = 5.7 J/(K mol). Both are phases of elementary carbon. Which of the two phases is more stable if we establish a thermal equilibrium between them in an isolated system?

P–8.9
For a certain chemical reaction we find ΔH = –94.5 kJ and ΔS = –189.1 J/K. Neglect the temperature dependence of these two values. What is the Gibbs free energy for the reaction at
(a) 300 K, and
(b) 1000 K?

P–8.10
Calculate ΔS and ΔG for the evaporation of 1 mol of water at T = 100°C and p = 1 atm. The latent heat of evaporation of water is 9.7 kcal/mol.

Summary

Definitions:
• Standard state for chemical processes (superscript 0): p = 1 atm, T = 25°C = 298 K
• Enthalpy: standard enthalpy of formation ΔH_f^0: Difference between the enthalpy of a compound and the enthalpy of its elements.
• Entropy:
(i) change of entropy with the state of a system:

$$\Delta S = S_{final} - S_{initial} = \sum_i \frac{Q_i}{T_i}$$

(ii) Standard entropy ΔS^0 is the entropy of a chemical element or compound at the standard state.
• Gibbs free energy:

$$G = H - TS$$

Laws:
• Second law of thermodynamics: In a cyclic process it is impossible to take heat from a reservoir and change it into work without releasing a fraction of the heat to a second reservoir at lower temperature.
• Third law of thermodynamics: The entropy of a perfect crystal at T = 0 K is zero, S = 0 J/K.
• Entropy change for
(i) reversible process: ΔS = 0
(ii) spontaneous irreversible process (system and environment): ΔS > 0
• Gibbs free energy change for
(i) coexisting systems in equilibrium: ΔG = 0
(ii) spontaneous processes ΔG < 0
• Steady state is non–equilibrium process with minimum entropy production.

Chapter IX

Water and Aqueous Solutions

Adenine — Thymine

Guanine — Cytosine

Static electricity

WATER AND AQUEOUS SOLUTIONS
STATIC ELECTRICITY

Biological systems are electrically active at the molecular level. Many of the phenomena we observe can only be explained when such electric effects are included, starting from the unique role of water in aqueous solutions to the conduction of nerve signals along the membrane of an axon.

Electric charge is a property of matter like mass. Different from mass, charges come in two flavors: two equal electric charges repel each other while two dissimilar charges attract each other. The force between charged objects is a long–range field force which decreases in magnitude with the inverse square of the distance (Coulomb's law).

The electric field is introduced to allow us to handle the large number of important and/or practical charge arrangements. It is derived from Coulomb's law by distinguishing the majority of fixed charges from mobile charges. The electric field then represents the net electric effect of all fixed charges in the system at any position in space. Combined with the electric charge of a mobile particle the net force on the particle results.

The magnitude of the electric field of a single fixed point charge is proportional to the square of the distance from the fixed charge; the magnitude of the electric field of a dipole is proportional to the cube of the distance. Therefore, dipoles interact more strongly at close proximity while they show a significantly lesser interaction with charged particles at longer distance. An example is the formation of tight hydration shells around ions in aqueous solutions.

The electric field has its simplest form for a parallel plate arrangement with uniform areal charge densities on each plate. In this case, the field is constant in magnitude and direction for all positions between the two plates. This simple form of the electric field makes the charged parallel plate arrangement a preferred model for many biological membrane systems.

Electric potential energy is introduced in analogy to the gravitational potential energy. It also resumes its simplest form for the parallel plate arrangement, for which the electric energy is linearly proportional to the distance of the test charge to the oppositely charged plate.

The concept of potential is introduced to accompany the electric energy in the same fashion the electric field is introduced to simplify calculations of electric forces in systems with a large number of fixed charges.

At this point we have reached an important milestone in the discussion of physics: thermal physics, which Albert Einstein once identified as its most unshakeable pillar, has allowed us to travel the entire distance from the simple equilibrium to the complex pattern formations in living systems. We have developed many powerful concepts along the way, but we have done it with an incredibly simple model system: the ideal gas.

Now it is time to shift gear and use these tools to develop the properties of the many different physiological systems we recognize to play important roles in our body, including liquids like blood, elastic materials such as tissues, vibrating fluids like the perilymph in the inner ear, electrically active solutions at the surfaces of nerves and optically active materials like the lenses in our eyes or the rods and cones in the retina.

What will guide us in the discussions of these systems in the following chapters is the approach we used with the ideal gas: to establish the equilibrium properties with the first law of thermodynamics, then bridge into the dynamic properties by seeking linear near–equilibrium phenomena first and more complex non–linear properties last.

The current chapter is the first of a group of four

chapters which we dedicate to the most important biological system: water. We will approach this topic from four different directions: the microscopic structure of the molecule as an electric dipole; the macroscopic properties of stationary water with its many unusual features; flowing water as a dynamic non–equilibrium phenomenon; and water as a solvent and main constituent of mixed phases such as blood. New and exciting phenomena will emerge at each of these four levels of study of the water system.

In the first step we note that there exists a wide range of processes in which particles are not sufficiently characterized by their mass. Such processes include acidity regulation of the blood, water and salt countercurrent filtration in the kidneys. In order to describe these processes, a second, mass–independent property of matter has to be introduced: the electric charge. The physical laws which govern the behavior of objects carrying electric charge are distinct from the laws of mechanics because a new fundamental force is associated with electric charges, the electric force. This force is the second fundamental force we discuss in this textbook, following our earlier discussion of the gravitational force.

9.1. Water in the body fluids

The water molecule is shown in Fig. 9.1. It consists of one oxygen atom and two hydrogen atoms, which are arranged with an angle of 104.5°. The molecule forms in an exothermal reaction from the elements (which is the energy–supplying process in the production of ATP in the mitochondria) and is the byproduct of many chemical reactions, including the main metabolic processes in our body (see Table 8.3). The water molecule does not gain its unique role from its chemical properties, however, as water does usually not participate in chemical reactions. Instead, it serves as a solvent, i.e., as a medium for chemical processes.

What makes water unique? We have already ruled out its chemical properties. There are two physical properties we need to focus our attention on: water is liquid across the entire range of temperatures relevant for life on Earth, and water can dissolve a wide range of biologically active compounds, most notably many salts. Both of these properties will be connected in this chapter to the electric properties of the water molecule. The electric effects of water are not due to the formation of a water ion, however, but result from the water molecule polarizing its charge internally, which leads to an electric dipole. To understand what a dipole is and what electric properties it has, we must start from the simplest electrically active unit: the electric charge.

9.2. Electric charge and force: Fundamental concepts

Electric charge is an intrinsic property of the particles which make up matter, in the same fashion as mass is an intrinsic property of the same particles. We use the same concept we used in the context of mass, the point mass, to describe charges as point charges. Mass and charge are, however, independent properties. In our discussion of mechanics we established that there is only one type of mass; objects may have more or less of it but none can have a different type of mass, e.g., a negative mass. The concept of a negative mass had indeed been discussed for a while in the scientific community. It was postulated in 1697 as part of Georg Ernst Stahl's phlo-

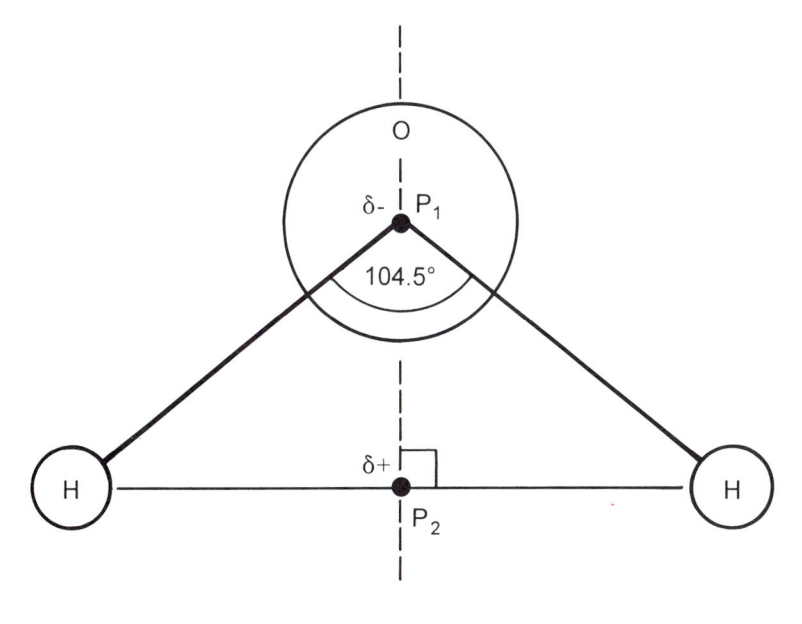

Fig. 9.1: The water molecule consists of two hydrogen atoms and one oxygen atom. The hydrogen atoms are connected to the oxygen atom with covalent bonds. The electrons in these bonds are drawn closer to the oxygen atom, leading to a net negative charge of δ_- near the oxygen–end of the molecule (point P_1) and a net positive charge δ_+ near the hydrogen–end of the molecule (point P_2).

giston theory to explain combustion. He claimed that combustion is the loss of particles with negative mass, these particles he called phlogiston. This theory was finally dismissed in 1777 by Antoine Laurent de Lavoisier when he properly described combustion as a chemical reaction with oxygen.

This is different for charges. Two point charges of the same type interact differently with each other than two point charges of opposite types. To distinguish these two kinds of charges we call one type of charge a positive charge, q_+, and the other type a negative charge, q_-. One could have called them blue and red charges instead, but invoking the notation of mathematical signs turned out to be convenient as opposite charges indeed offset each other in their physical effects: an amount of electric charge of one type is shielded by the same amount of the opposite electric charge in close proximity, which explains the apparent electric neutrality observed for matter.

To see point charges of either type display their physical properties, the electric charges in a system must be separated. This can be achieved in experiments, e.g. by rubbing an insulator such as felt. It also happens in nature, e.g. causing lightning.

9.2.1. The magnitude of the electric force

We define charge quantitatively in terms of the force which occurs between separated charges. The relation between electric force and charge was discovered by Charles Augustin de Coulomb in 1784 and is called Coulomb's law. He experimented with metal spheres carrying electric charges. When the metal spheres were electrically charged, Coulomb observed that:

> *The magnitude of the electric force between two charged spheres is proportional to the amount of charge on either sphere, and is proportional to $1/r^2$ with r the distance between the spheres.*

Coulomb's law quantifies the electric force in the form:

$$F = k \frac{q_1 q_2}{r^2} \quad (1)$$

Note that the magnitude of the force is proportional to the value of the two charges q_1 and q_2. We also see that the force is reduced to 1/4 when the distance r between the charges is doubled.

Coulomb's law is conceptually very different from Newton's law of gravity as discussed in Eq. (2.4), despite a superficial mathematical similarity (both contain the same $1/r^2$ dependence). Gravity is always attractive. In turn, Coulomb's force leads to an attractive or a repulsive interaction between charges, depending on the type of charges in the system, i.e., whether q_1 and q_2 are both positive, both negative or mixed positive and negative. An attractive force results only between charges with opposite signs and is indicated by a negative value for the force in Eq. (1).

Comparing the use of Eq. (1) in electrostatics to the use of Eq. (2.4) in mechanical applications of Newton's laws highlights a practical difference between both forces. In all applications of gravity on the surface of the Earth, the Earth is by far the most massive object in the environment of the object of interest. This allows us to neglect all other gravitational interactions and simplify gravity to F_{grav} = mg. In the case of Coulomb's law, we cannot make such a simplification because the electric force is much stronger than the gravitational force; all charges in a system have to be included in electric problems.

When Coulomb wrote his law, charge had not been defined before. He was, therefore, able to write the law without a constant as he used it at the same time to define charge:

$$F\ [dyn] = \frac{q_1\ [esu]\ q_2\ [esu]}{r^2\ [cm^2]} \quad (2)$$

In this equation, [dyn] is a force unit which is converted to the standard unit [N] using 1 dyn = 1×10^{-5} N. [esu] (which stands for electrostatic unit) is a unit for charge which is converted to the standard unit Coulomb [Cb] using 1 Cb = 3×10^9 esu. Physicists have abandoned the old units and write Coulomb's law now in the form given in Eq. (1). The unit Coulomb [Cb] is defined such that two equal charges of 1 Cb, placed 1 m apart, attract each other with a force of 9×10^9 N. With this definition, the constant in Eq. (1) is $k = 9 \times 10^9$ [N m²/Cb²].

In most applications the constant k is replaced by another constant, $1/4\pi\epsilon_0$, in which ϵ_0 is called the permittivity of vacuum. Coulomb's law is then written in the form:

$$F = \frac{1}{4\pi\epsilon_0} \frac{q_1 q_2}{r^2} \quad (3)$$

ϵ_0 has the value 8.85×10^{-12} Cb²/(N m²). In the course of the later discussions we find that the use of the permittivity of vacuum ϵ_0 instead of the constant k simplifies the formulation of several laws. Therefore, the constant k does not bear a name and is usually not found

Table 9.1: Elementary particles in the atom

Particle	Mass [kg]	Charge [Cb]
Electron	9.11×10^{-31}	-1.6×10^{-19}
Proton	1.673×10^{-27}	$+1.6 \times 10^{-19}$
Neutron	1.675×10^{-27}	0

in the modern literature.

A very important difference between mass and charge is the fact that the latter is quantized. What does this mean? The idea of quantization can be illustrated with our use of money. Goods you buy at a store cannot cost any amount of money, they can only cost a multiple of the smallest unit of currency, which is 1 cent in North America. Even when taxes are added to a bill, you will never be asked to pay 7.5 cents. Any payment will always be an amount which is an integer multiple of one cent. In nature, no such limitation exists for mass; any amount of mass can occur. However, with respect to charge, all processes are based on the transfer of an integer multiple of a smallest amount of charge, which we call the elementary charge.

Table 9.1 demonstrates this for the mass and charge of the fundamental particles in the atoms: the electron (e⁻), the proton (p⁺) and the neutron (n⁰). While the masses of elementary particles vary, all charges have the same magnitude, regardless of whether it is a positive or a negative charge.

The value of the elementary charge was first determined by Robert Andrews Millikan in 1909 with the experiment sketched in Fig. 9.2. The experiment consists of a large chamber into which oil is sprayed through a metallic nozzle of an oil–vaporizer. The oil mist consists of microscopic droplets which may carry an electric charge due to the interaction of the oil with the inner surface of the metallic nozzle during spraying. All oil droplets sink slowly downwards due to their weight. Some fall through a hole in a plate which separates the upper and lower parts of the chamber. In the lower part the oil droplets can be observed with a microscope. The separating plate with the hole and a second plate at the bottom of the lower chamber are electrically isolated and form a parallel plate capacitor when charged with a battery. As we discuss later in this chapter, this arrangement of parallel charged plates allows us to exert an electric force on a charged particle. In the case of Fig. 9.2, we choose the electric force such that it is directed upwards, i.e., counteracting the gravitational force. The amount of charges on the two plates is regulated such that a particular oil droplet, which we selected with the microscope, levitates at a fixed height. This means that the electric force F upwards and the weight of the droplet W downwards are balanced (application of Newton's first law). From the amount of charges needed on the two plates in Fig. 9.2 the charge of the droplet is determined. This experiment has been done numerous times and an oil drop with a charge other than an integer multiple of the elementary charge $e = 1.6 \times 10^{-19}$ Cb has never been found. We return to Millikan's experiment with a quantitative example later when we have introduced the necessary electric concepts.

As the discussion of Millikan's experiment suggests, in a Newtonian approach the electric force is treated like any other force that we discussed in the early chapters of the textbook. For example, if objects are charged in a system, the acceleration of an object is based on a free–body–diagram which must include all electric forces which act on the object. The net electric force acting on a charged object is calculated as the sum of all Coulomb force terms between the charge of the particular particle of interest, Q, and the N other charges in

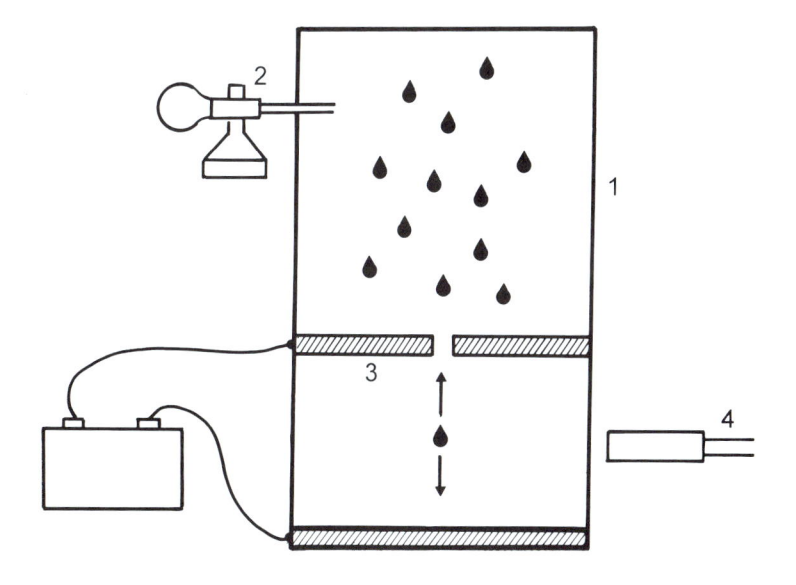

Fig. 9.2: Robert Millikan's experiment. Oil mist, consisting of microscopic oil droplets, is sprayed into a chamber (1). Many of the oil droplets carry charges due to the friction of the oil when leaving the metallic nozzle of the vaporizer (2). The droplets sink downwards due to their weight. It is possible to levitate individual oil droplets between two charged metallic plates (3) forming a horizontal parallel plate arrangement (shaded). This mechanical equilibrium is observed with a microscope (4) and is due to the balance between the gravitational and the electric forces, as indicated on one oil droplet by two arrows. From this experiment the electric charge on the oil droplet is determined. This charge is always a multiple of the elementary charge due to the quantization of electric charge.

the system. If all of these forces are collinear, we write:

$$F_{net} = \sum_{i=1}^{N} F_i = \frac{1}{4\pi\epsilon_0} \sum_{i=1}^{N} \frac{Q\, q_i}{r_i^2} \quad (4)$$

in which r_i is the distance between the i-th point charge and the particle with charge Q. Forces acting in opposite directions are entered with opposite signs based on a pre–selected coordinate system. Fig. 9.3 illustrates with what sign each force is entered depending on the position of the charged particle relative to the point charge of interest Q for a horizontal (middle row) and a vertical case (bottom row).

> *In the calculation of a net electric force for collinear point charges*
> *(I) the electric force is entered negative if the charge of interest is located at a negative position relative to the charge which exerts the force, and*
> *(II) the electric force is entered positive if the charge of interest is located at a positive position relative to the charge which exerts the force.*

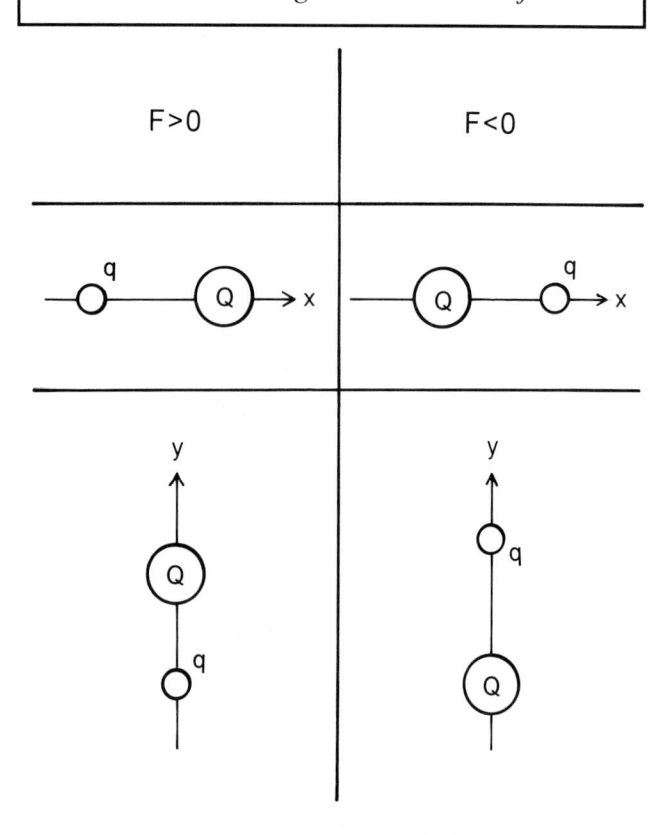

Fig. 9.3: Sign convention for the electric force on a particle with charge Q (which is the point charge of interest) *due to the chosen coordinate system*. Note that this convention applies independent of the sign of the charge of the two point charges. The charges enter the formula only when numerical values are substituted for q and Q.

Fig. 9.3 is used to set up the forces for quantitative calculations. Fig. 9.3 is not a free–body–diagram (and does not show forces as arrow for that reason) because we must still include the charges Q and q_i with the appropriate sign, i.e., – for negative charges and + for positive charges. Because we are dealing with two types of charges, the number of possibilities of directions in which a force has to been drawn in the free–body–diagram is large. Fig. 9.4 provides an overview.

Example 9.1
(a) Find the magnitude of the electric force F exerted on a point charge $+3e$ by a point charge $-5e$ which is located 7 nm away.
(b) In which direction does this force act on the point charge $+3e$?

Solution part (a): We use Coulomb's law in the form of Eq. (1). To find the magnitude of the force only the magnitudes of both charges are entered:

$$F = k\frac{q_1 q_2}{r^2} = \frac{9\times 10^9 \left[\frac{Nm^2}{Cb^2}\right] 4.8\times 10^{-19}[Cb]\, 8\times 10^{-19}[Cb]}{(7\times 10^{-9}[m])^2} \quad (5)$$

which leads to $F = 7.1 \times 10^{-11}$ N.

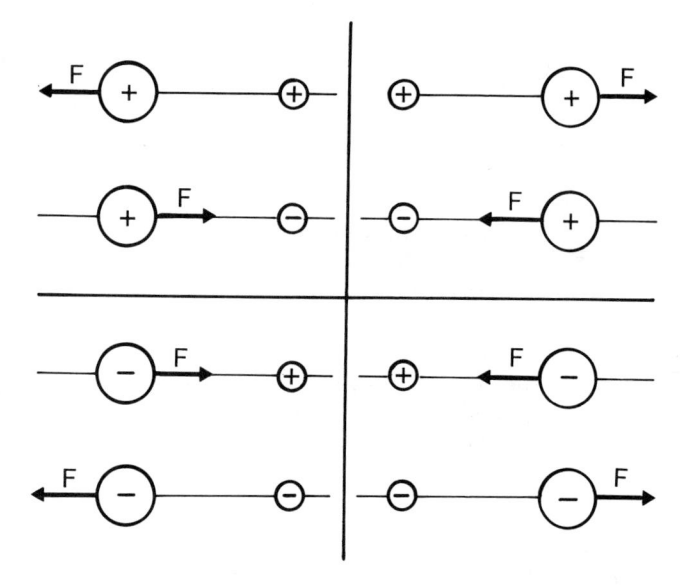

Fig. 9.4: Eight cases showing the direction of the electric force on a point charge of interest (large circle) due to a second point charge (smaller circle) in its vicinity.

Solution part (b): We determine the direction of the force separately by using the information we discussed for Fig. 9.4: the force between two charges acts along the line between the two charges. It points towards the second charge or away from the second charge depending on the signs of the two charges. In the present problem the charges are of opposite signs, thus the force is attractive, and the force points towards the –5 *e* point charge.

Example 9.2

We consider 3 point charges which are positioned along an axis as illustrated in Fig. 9.5(a). Two of these point charges carry positive charges: $q_1 = 20$ μCb, $q_2 = 5$ μCb, and are separated by a distance $L = 1.5$ m. At what distance x_0 from q_2 must the negative point charge q_3 be positioned such that the resulting force on it is zero?

Solution: The sketch in Fig. 9.5(b) shows the same point charge arrangement as Fig. 9.5(a) but highlights the two forces acting on q_3. Using Fig. 9.4, q_3 is attracted toward each of the other two point charges since q_3 is negative while q_1 and q_2 are positive. As a consequence, the two forces shown in Fig. 9.5(b), F_{13} and F_{23}, point in opposite directions. The circle for charge q_3 and the two forces acting on that point charge constitute the free–body–diagram for this problem. Mechanical equilibrium is established when the net force on q_3 is zero:

$$F_{net} = -k \frac{q_1 q_3}{r_{13}^2} + k \frac{q_2 q_3}{r_{23}^2} = 0 \quad (6)$$

i.e., when $F_{23} = F_{13}$ based on Newton's first law and the sign convention for the forces from Fig. 9.3. We substitute the given values for the charges and distances and cancel the charge q_3 on both sides of the equation:

$$\frac{20 \times 10^{-6} \, [Cb]}{(L - x_0)^2} = \frac{5 \times 10^{-6} \, [Cb]}{x_0^2} \quad (7)$$

Note that we need not to define the origin of the axis along which the three point charges are placed because only the distance between the point charges enters Coulomb's law. Eq. (7) leads to a quadratic equation which is solved for the distance x_0 between q_2 and the central point charge:

$$5(1.5 - x_0)^2 = 20 \, x_0^2$$
$$\Rightarrow 0 = 15 x_0^2 + 15 x_0 - 11.25 \quad (8)$$

which yields:

$$x_0 = \frac{-15 \pm \sqrt{15^2 + 4 \cdot 15 \cdot 11.25}}{2 \cdot 15} \quad (9)$$

$$\Rightarrow x_{0,1} = -1.5 \, m \quad ; \quad x_{0,2} = +0.5 \, m$$

Since q_3 must lie between the other two point charges, the second solution in Eq. (9) is the proper answer. We can easily convince ourselves that this result makes sense. Coulomb's law contains the charge and the square of the distance. Thus, a doubling of the distance is compensated by a fourfold increase of the charge.

---

a)

b)

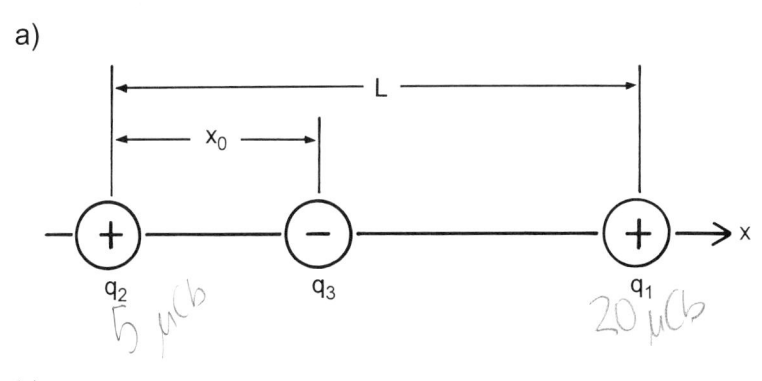

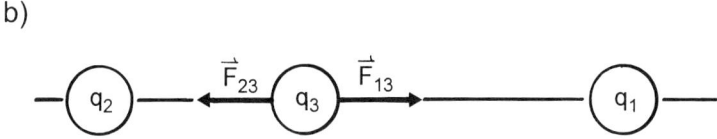

Fig. 9.5: (a) Three charged particles are positioned along the x–axis as shown. (b) Two forces act on the charged particle q_3 which is positioned between the other two point charges.

9.2.2. The direction of the electric force

Two or more electric forces acting on a particular point charge need not to be collinear. If the forces act in other directions, we have to apply the same vector algebra based formalisms we introduced when studying non–collinear mechanical forces in Chapter 3. We illustrate that approach just with an example in the current section as no other new issues of interest arise when studying non–collinear electric forces.

Coulomb's law is written in vector notation in the form:

$$F = k \frac{q_1 q_2}{r^2} r^0 \qquad (10)$$

in which r^0 is a vector of length one pointing in the direction diametrically away from the other charge. This is true regardless of the type of charges in the system, i.e., whether q_1 and q_2 are both positive, both negative or mixed positive and negative.

When N forces act on a point charge of interest Q, the net force is written in vector notation:

$$F_{net} = \sum_{i=1}^{N} F_i = \frac{1}{4\pi\epsilon_0} \sum_{i=1}^{N} \frac{Q q_i}{r_i^2} r_i^0 \qquad (11)$$

in which r_i is the distance between the i–th point charge and the charge Q and r_i^0 is a vector of length one along the connecting line between the i–th point charge and the charge Q pointing away from the i–th point charge.

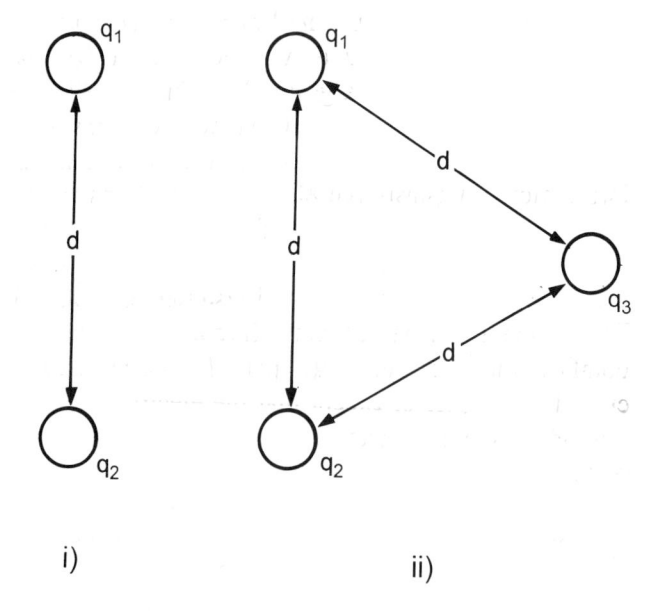

Fig. 9.6: (i) Two point charges interact at a distance d. (ii) A third point charge q_3 is brought close to the first two point charges such that all three form an equilateral triangle.

Example 9.3
Initially, two charged objects with charges q_1 and q_2 are held at a fixed distance d apart from each other, as illustrated in Fig. 9.6(i).
(a) What is the magnitude of the electrostatic force that acts between the two objects? Assume $q_1 = q_2 = 20$ μCb and d = 1.5 m.
(b) A third charged object with a charge of $q_3 = 20$ μCb is brought in and placed as shown in Fig. 9.6(ii). What is now the magnitude of the net electrostatic force on the object with charge q_1?

Solution part (a): This part is again a straight forward application of Coulomb's law because we seek the force between two charged objects. We find:

$$F = k \frac{q_1 q_2}{r^2} = \frac{9\times 10^9 \left[\frac{Nm^2}{Cb^2}\right](2\times 10^{-5}[Cb])^2}{(1.5[m])^2} \qquad (12)$$

which leads to F = 1.60 N.

Solution part (b): The net force on point charge q_1 consists of two forces, one due to the object of charge q_2 and one due to the object of charge q_3. These two forces are not parallel to each other, as illustrated in Fig. 9.7. We solve the problem using Eq. (11). We first note that the magnitude of the two forces, F_{13} and F_{23}, are equal because the charges q_2 and q_3 are equal and each is at a distance d from charge q_1. We also note that the angle θ in Fig. 9.7 is θ = 60° because the triangle formed by the three objects is an equilateral triangle.

Next we chose a coordinate system to write the two forces in component form. The choice we use is shown in Fig. 9.7: the x–axis is directed toward the right and the y–axis is directed up. With this coordinate system we express the components of the net force based on the components of the two forces F_{13} and F_{23}. For the x–component of the net force we find:

$$F_{net, x} = -F_{13} \sin\theta = -1.6[N] \sin 60^0 = -1.4 \ N \qquad (13)$$

and for the y–component of the net force we get:

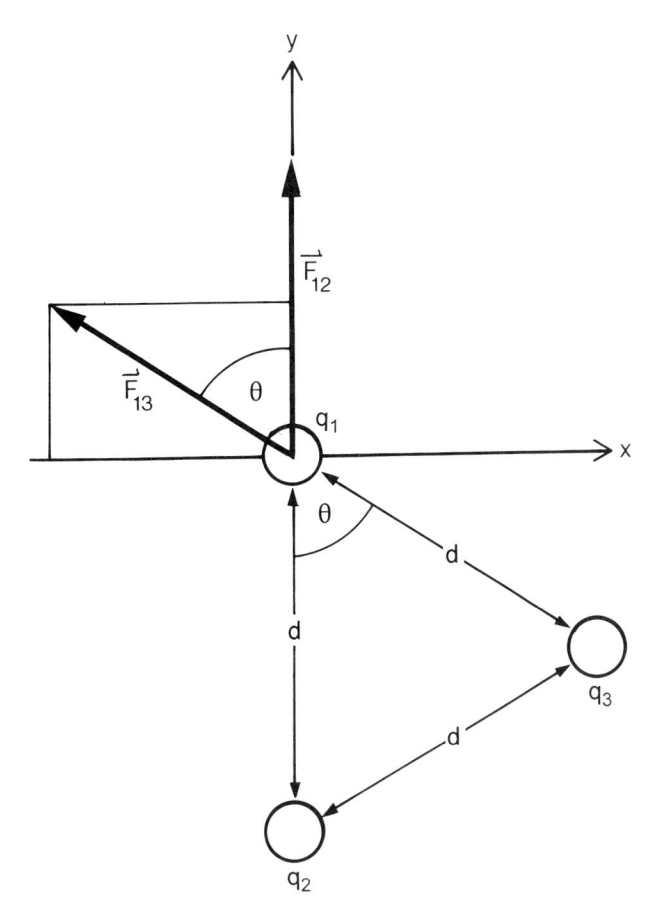

Fig. 9.7: The same three point charges as shown in Fig. 9.6(ii) forming an equilateral triangle. Two electric forces act on the point charge q_1 at the top, labelled $\vec{F}_{12}$ and $\vec{F}_{13}$ to indicate which point charge exerts the respective force. These two forces form an angle θ; vector algebraic methods are used to calculate the net force acting on point charge q_1.

$$F_{net, y} = F_{12} + F_{13} \cos\theta = \qquad (14)$$
$$1.6[N] + 1.6[N] \cos 60^0 = +2.4 \ N$$

Using the Pythagorean theorem allows us to combine the two components:

$$F_{net} = \sqrt{F_{net, x}^2 + F_{net, y}^2} = 2.78 \ N \qquad (15)$$

9.3. Electric charge and force: occurrence in physics and biology

A point charge is an elusive concept, like the point mass. In the case of charges we usually think of one of two possibilities when referring to a point charge in this textbook: in a physical model we think of a single electron in a metal or in vacuum, and in a chemical model we think of an ion in an aqueous solution.

The physical model is conceptually simpler. Electrons are much smaller than atoms, and are therefore properly treated as point objects when travelling through a neighborhood of atoms. We challenge this simplicity later in Chapter 21 when we discuss that the electron behaves sometimes not as a particle but as a wave. In the current context, however, the electron is looked at as both a point mass and point charge with the values given in Table 9.1.

The physical model allows for two environments of the electron: either a vacuum or a metal. A vacuum environment is a reasonable case because the electric force is a field force and thus we do not need a physical contact between charged objects to obtain an electric effect. However, the idea of an electron travelling in a vacuum is rather remote for most applications (an exception is a TV tube) and thus not leading us to the concepts we want to establish. Therefore, the physical model we use in this chapter consists of electrons in a metal.

To proceed we must define what we mean with the term "metal." This requires a brief discussion of the three types of chemical bonds: the metallic bond, the ionic bond and the covalent bond. Which of these is formed depends on the position of the involved atoms in the periodic table. Fig. 9.8 shows the periodic table with each element represented by a circle sized proportional to its actual atomic size. All elements left of a line from boron (B) to iodine (I) are called metals. Metallic atoms consist of a tightly bound shell of inner electrons and one or a few loosely bound outer electrons, called valence electrons. When a large number of metal atoms are brought together in a piece of matter, the atoms bond with each other by releasing these outermost electrons into a cloud of quasi-free electrons. Electrons in this state are mobile relative to the rigid lattice of rump metal ions. Thus, valence electrons in a piece of metal are considered to move freely, as illustrated in Fig. 9.9. When there is no external force, the electron moves randomly in the metal like a gas particle in a box as discussed in Chapter 6, except that the electron not only hits other free electrons, but is also scattered by the rump metal ions.

In living organisms on the other hand, freely moving electrons are not observed. Instead, physiological processes depend strongly on the concentration of various ions in solution. The ions important in biology differ significantly in size. For atomic ions this is illustrated in Fig. 9.8 in which the ionic size for many ions is compared to the respective atomic size.

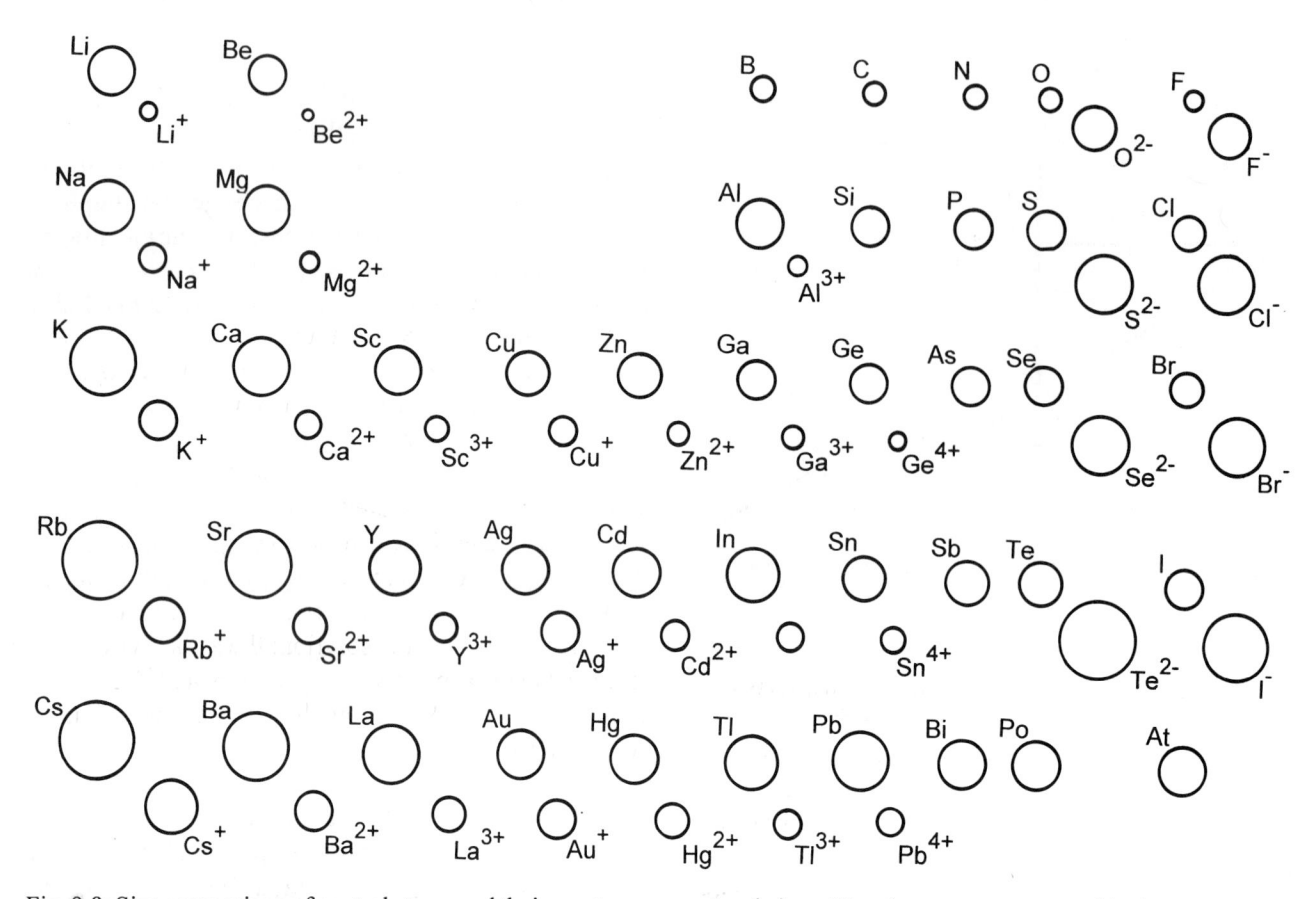

Fig. 9.8: Size comparison of neutral atoms and their most common atomic ions. The elements are arranged in the same fashion as in the periodic table. Sizes are shown by the size of the circles.

A second major difference is the medium in which these ions are studied. The ions in our body are contained in aqueous solutions, i.e., with the water molecule defining the solvent. The water molecule is of comparable size to most inorganic ions and it is smaller than organic ions.

These two differences allow us to define a chemical model for our later discussions. In the chemical model we envisage a point charge to be a positive or negative ion in an aqueous solution. This is a more complicated model than the physical model for three reasons:
(I) the similarity in size between the mobile charge and the particles forming the medium for the moving charge limits the usefulness of the simplification sought with the point character of the charged particle,
(II) the environment of the charged particles is liquid with covalent and ionic chemical bonds instead of metallic bonds, and
(III) the liquid state of water allows for a greater variety of interactions between the particles of the medium and the charged particle than in the case of a rigid solid metal environment for the electron.

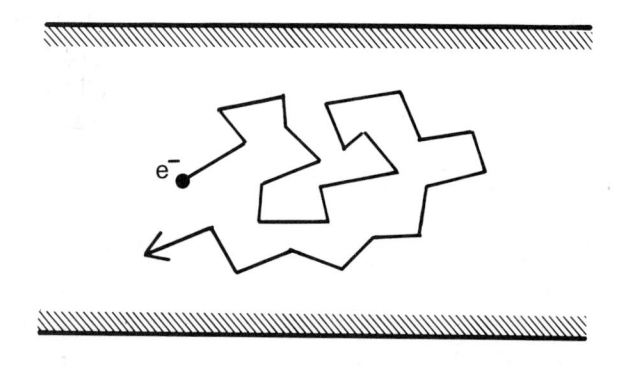

Fig. 9.9: Model of an electron in a piece of metal. The electron moves freely, similar to a gas particle in a box filled with gas. However, the electrons scatter frequently off the densely packed immobile rump metal ions.

To illustrate the chemical differences between the physical model and the chemical model we use in this chapter, we continue our brief discussion of chemical bonds with a look at ionic and covalent bonds. Ionic bonds are formed by salts. A salt consists of a metal atom and an atom to the right of the line from boron to iodine in the periodic system (a non–metal). The metallic atom releases one or more valence electrons; however, these are now not released to a common sea of electrons, but specifically to the neighboring non–metallic atom. Then the metallic atom is positively charged (called a cation) and the non–metallic atom is negatively charged (called an anion). Salt forms large crystals because, due to Coulomb's law, all the negative and positive ions attract each other electrostatically.

If both the metallic and non–metallic atoms forming the bond are close to or on the line from boron to iodine in the periodic table, the character of their chemical bond changes from ionic to covalent. In the covalent case, electrons are not transferred to another atom but are shared between both rump atoms. Carbon–carbon or carbon–hydrogen bonds in organic molecules are an example. These bonds are spatially directed along the connecting line between the two atoms, leading to well characterized bond angles like the tetrahedron angle in CH_4.

Many molecules contain a mixed type of bond which has some ionic and some covalent characteristics. An example is the water molecule in Fig. 9.1, in which the bond between oxygen and hydrogen is essentially covalent with a well–defined bond angle H–O–H of 104.5°, but the molecule is highly polarized with a large negative excess charge (δ_-) localized at the oxygen side of the molecule and a large positive excess charge (δ_+) localized at the hydrogen side of the molecule.

This mixed state of covalent and ionic bonds in the water molecule lies at the root of the unique role of water in biological systems. It allows the molecules to play an active role in the electric properties of physiological systems. When salt is dissolved in water, the polarized water molecules attack the salt crystal and attach themselves to the separated ions. For rock salt we write this in the form:

$$NaCl + n\ H_2O \to Na^+_{aq} + Cl^-_{aq} \qquad (16)$$

The index aq stands for aqueous. It indicates that each ion is embedded in a shell of polar water molecules. This structure is called a *hydration shell* and has a specific morphology for each of the salt ions: the positive side of water molecules points toward the chlorine ion, and the negative sides of water molecules points toward the sodium ion, i.e., the oxygen of the water molecule is closer to the sodium ion and the hydrogens are closer to the chlorine ion, as illustrated in Fig. 9.10.

When the ion moves, the hydration shell is dragged along, as indicated for Na^+ and Cl^- ions in Fig. 9.10. Dragging the hydration shell along leads to a slowing of diffusion of the ions. The hydration shell in turn leads to a screening effect lowering the electric interactions of the ions in the solution: the attractive electric force between a positive sodium ion and a negative chlorine ion in Fig. 9.10 is much weaker than Coulomb's law predicts. This has been quantified in the Debye–Hückel theory.

While we will find some useful similarities between the physical and the chemical model, the additional properties of the chemical model are essential in understanding the physiological relevance of water and aqueous solutions. The physical model will prove very helpful in isolating and quantifying fundamental properties while the chemical model will allow us to establish the important electric properties of the body fluids. The latter model allows us also in Chapter 13 to develop a model for the nerves.

Fig. 9.10: Sketch of a positive sodium ion and a negative chlorine ion in an aqueous solution. The polar water molecules form a hydration shell around each ion as it moves through the solution, screening the ion's charge and, thus, reducing the interaction between the ions.

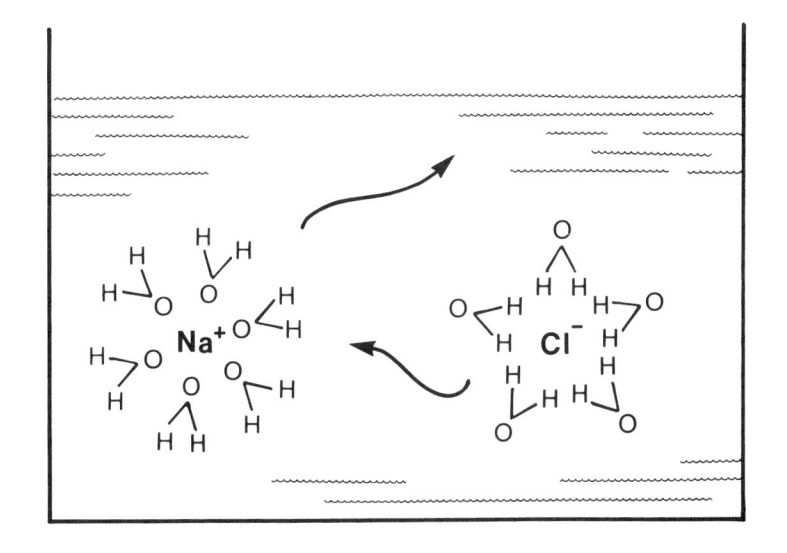

9.4. Electric field

As Eqs. (4) or (11) indicate, applying Coulomb's law to a system with several charged objects becomes easily an extensive and difficult mathematical task. Thus, we seek an approach which subdivides this effort into steps. In the current section the widely applied approach of introducing an electric field is described, which is based on:

(I) dividing the charges in two groups: charges fixed at given positions in the system and mobile charges. For most technical and scientific applications, the number of fixed charges outnumbers by far the number of mobile charges. Also, mobile charges often move in similar fashion, allowing us to calculate the path of a single mobile charge to predict the motion of all others.

(II) For the fixed charges we determine an electric field. The term field implies that we assign in this step a value to each position in the system. For example, a temperature field can be described for a house in winter, which could consist of values near 20 °C at positions far from an open window, and values down to 0 °C near the open window. As long as nobody goes to any of these positions the value may not matter; however, a person anticipating moving to a position close to the open window may use the knowledge of the temperature field to take precaution. An electric field attributes in a similar fashion to each position in the system a value for the strength of an anticipated electrical interaction. This value does not matter as long as no mobile charged particle reaches this position, however, when such a charge passes that position, the resulting electric force acting on the moving particle will be known from the electric field. Thus, knowing a field allows you to predict the outcome of a physical effect before it happens.

(III) In the last step, the dynamics of the system is studied by allowing a charged particle (called a test charge) to move through the system. Its motion is fully determined by the field and Newton's second law, which predicts the acceleration of the particle at every position based on the net force acting on the particle at that position. For an engineered device, we therefore get in this last step the predicted performance; e.g. the mobile electrons in a TV tube indeed hit the screen based on the static charges of the various electric components in the tube. The same applies to a natural system. For example, for a charged nerve membrane we get in the last step the nerve pulse travelling to the brain based on the static charges along the membrane. In both cases, studying a single charged particle allows us to predict the outcome which is based on a larger number of charged particles moving in a similar fashion.

In the current section, we focus on the second step: calculating the electric field for a given arrangement of charges which are fixed at given positions in the system.

Despite the simplification implied in this approach, determining actual electric fields turns out to be a cumbersome mathematical effort. Luckily, there are just three arrangements of fixed charges which we need to consider to deal with the vast majority of practical cases in biology and physiology:

(I) The electric field of a single point charge, e.g. an isolated ion in a solution.

(II) The electric field of two point charges carrying equal but opposite charges, which is called a dipole. Many molecules, such as water, are dipoles.

(III) The electric field between two parallel plates which carry equal but opposite charges, which is called a capacitor. Charged membranes, such as nerve membranes, are modelled as parallel plate arrangements.

The electric fields for these three cases are discussed in turn in the remainder of this section.

9.4.1. Electric field: magnitude for a single point charge

We start with the simplest case in which just two electric charges interact. Coulomb's force as given in Eq. (3) describes this interaction. The field is determined from the electric force between the two particles.

This electric field is ultimately a vector quantity, i.e., it has a magnitude and a direction at every point in the vicinity of the fixed charged objects we study. However, we have repeatedly in this textbook separated the discussion of the magnitude of vectors from their directional features, for example for mechanical forces in Chapters 2 and 3, and for electric forces in sections 9.2.1 and 9.2.2. We maintain this approach by discussing in this section quantitatively the magnitude of the electric field for a single charge. The directional aspects are then considered in the next section. To avoid confusion, the magnitude of the electric field is always labelled $|\mathbf{E}|$ to distinguish it from the labels used for energy.

To develop a formula for the magnitude of the electric field for a single isolated point charge q we start with the magnitude of the electric force between two charged particles 1 and 2. For clarity, we switch from labelling the two objects as 1 and 2 to calling one the "fixed charge" and the other, which is the mobile object, the "test charge." With this provision Coulomb's law takes the form:

$$F = \frac{1}{4\pi\epsilon_0} \left(\frac{q_{fixed}}{r_{fixed/test}^2} \right) (q_{test}) \quad (17)$$

with $r_{fixed/test}$ the distance between the charges.

In the next step we remove the test charge from the system. The distance, which we labelled $r_{fixed/test}$ in Eq. (17) then refers to the distance between the fixed charge and the position at which the test charge previously was. Since Eq. (17) applies for any possible position of the test charge, we can interpret Eq. (17) such that it applies at any point in space. Dropping therefore the index on the distance parameter r means that it now represents the distance r from the fixed charge to any position in space. This yields the magnitude of the electric field |**E**| at that position:

$$|\boldsymbol{E}| = \frac{1}{4\pi\epsilon_0} \frac{q_{fixed}}{r^2} \quad (18)$$

This is the magnitude of the electric field due to a single, fixed point charge. The field varies with distance from the fixed point charge as $1/r^2$. The unit of the magnitude of the electric field |**E**| is [N/Cb], which is even more evident when we rewrite Eq. (17) using Eq. (18):

$$F_{net} = |\boldsymbol{E}| \, q_{test} \quad (19)$$

9.4.2. Electric field: direction for a single point charge

We discussed in the previous section that the electric field is obtained from the electric force by eliminating the mobile test charge. This leaves us with an arrangement of fixed charges in the problem; the electric field is then an expression of the electric interaction due to the fixed charges at any given point in their vicinity. The magnitude of the electric field is sufficient for applications in which we study only one fixed point charge or when we study several fixed point charges located along a common axis, as illustrated for a dipole arrangement in the next section. For more general cases we need to include the vector character of the electric field.

Proceeding in an analogous fashion from Eq. (10) as we did from Eq. (17) to Eq. (18), we find for the electric field of a single fixed charge:

$$\boldsymbol{E} = \frac{1}{4\pi\epsilon_0} \frac{q_{fixed}}{r^2} \boldsymbol{r}^0 \quad (20)$$

Eq. (20) represents a vector field. This means that we assign to each position in the vicinity of the fixed charge a vector which represents both the magnitude and direction of a force acting on a test charge at that position if a test charge is brought there. Eq. (20) shows further that the electric field of a fixed point charge is a radial field, i.e., the electric field vector **E** points at every position in space along the connection line of that point and the fixed point charge. The magnitude of the electric field is still proportional to $1/r^2$ as seen already in Eq. (18). The electric field for a fixed positive point charge is illustrated in Fig. 9.11: each arrow in the figure represents the electric field vector at the point where the foot of the arrow is placed. Note the directional change and the change in magnitude, which is quantified by the length of the arrows.

Since the electric field is a vector, a convention for the direction must be used. We formulate this convention based on Fig. 9.11; it is sketched in Fig. 9.12:

The electric field vector is always directed away from the positive point charge or toward the negative point charge.

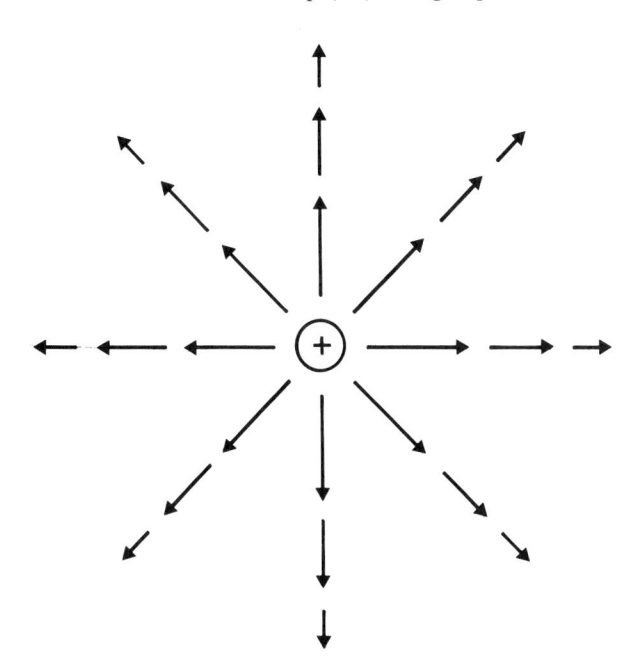

Fig. 9.11: The electric field of a single, positive point charge. The arrows represent the vectors of the electric field. The length of each vector indicates the magnitude of **E** at the respective position. The electric field of a point charge has a radial (in three dimensions therefore spherical) symmetry.

a)

b)

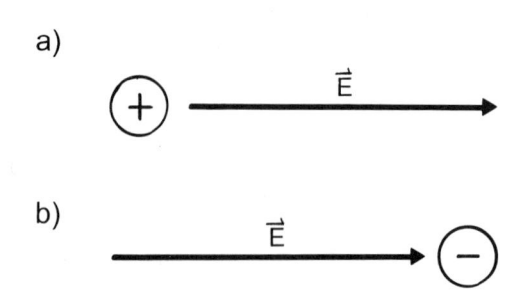

Fig. 9.12: The electric field vector is always pointing away from a positive charge or toward a negative charge. This convention is used often throughout the discussion of electrostatics. As a consequence, if a positive test charge is brought into the system, a force in the direction of the electric field will act on it.

Thus, a positive test charge brought into an electric field feels a force in the direction of the field; a negative test charge in an electric field feels a force in the direction opposite to the field.

9.4.3. Electric field of a dipole

If we consider more than one fixed point charge, Eq. (20) has to be rewritten as a sum of all contributions due to each single fixed point charge in the system. Assuming N fixed point charges q_i which can be located at as many different positions in space, we obtain in vector notation:

$$E = \frac{1}{4\pi\epsilon_0} \sum_i q_i \frac{r_i^0}{r_i^2} \quad (21)$$

in which we consider all particles with index from 1 to N to form the fixed configuration of charges. To apply Eq. (21), we use the same approach we discussed previously for vector sums, such as in Chapter 3: the equation consists of three component equations for the three cartesian coordinates, each representing the respective component of the net electric field:

$$E_{x,\,net} = \sum_i E_x(q_i)$$

$$E_{y,\,net} = \sum_i E_y(q_i) \quad (22)$$

$$E_{z,\,net} = \sum_i E_z(q_i)$$

To apply Eq. (22), the electric field due to each fixed point charge has to be written as three cartesian components. In the Appendix of this Chapter we see how the components of the electric field are determined for a single point charge. Then all components in each cartesian direction are added for the net component. As a specific example for N = 2 the electric field of a dipole is studied in Example 9.4.

Example 9.4
Two charges of equal magnitude q but opposite sign, are separated by a distance d, as shown in Fig. 9.13. This configuration is called an electric dipole. Find the electric field as a function of position along the dipole axis, i.e., the line through the two charges labelled x–axis in the figure.

Supplementary chemical information: The restriction in this problem to study only the electric field along the axial direction of the dipole is sufficient to discuss the physical consequences of the role of the water molecule in aqueous solutions, particularly the formation and structure of the hydration shell. This is evident from Fig. 9.1. A net negative charge is present near the oxygen atom (at point P_1) and a net positive charge near the hydrogen atoms (at point P_2). Due to Coulomb's force, such a dipole approaches a negative ion always with the positively charge end of the molecule because that end is attracted to the negative ion while the other end of the water molecule is repelled. Equally, a positively charged ion in the solution always is approached by a water molecule with its negative end first. Thus, considering the

Fig. 9.13: Dipole configuration: a dipole consists of two point charges separated by a distance d that carry opposite charges of equal magnitude. The figure illustrates the axis of the dipole (x–axis) and identifies a point P at a distance x_0 from the center of the dipole. The electric field is calculated at point P.

ion as our test charge, it is sufficient to know the electric field along the axial direction of the dipole as a water molecule, which can freely rotate in liquid water, will never approach an ion such that the ion is at any positions other than along this axis.

In the solution of this problem we introduce a simplifying assumption that the points for which we determine the electric field are located far from the dipole. This simplification does not diminish the usefulness of the result as the ions in an aqueous solution are usually far from the water molecule compared to the charge separation distance within the molecule.

Solution: Because both point charges and the point P in Fig. 9.13 are located along a single axis, Eq. (18) is sufficient to determine the contributions to the electric field at point P. The directional information is straight forward in this case as all contributions occur along this axis: the next electric field will be directed along the x–axis. The only directional consideration left stems from Fig. 9.12. Choosing the origin of the axis at the center of the two dipole charges we find for the two separate field contributions at point P:

$$E_{+q} = \frac{+q}{4\pi\epsilon_0 x_{+q}^2} = \frac{q}{4\pi\epsilon_0 \left(x - \frac{d}{2}\right)^2}$$

$$E_{-q} = \frac{-q}{4\pi\epsilon_0 x_{-q}^2} = \frac{-q}{4\pi\epsilon_0 \left(x + \frac{d}{2}\right)^2} \quad (23)$$

in which the first formula is the electric field due to the positive charge, +q, and the second formula is the electric field due to the negative charge, –q. The net electric field is the sum of both contributions:

$$E_{net} = \frac{q}{4\pi\epsilon_0}\left(\frac{1}{(x-\frac{d}{2})^2} - \frac{1}{(x+\frac{d}{2})^2}\right) \quad (24)$$

Several algebraic operations are applied to simplify Eq. (24). First, the two terms in the bracket are combined with a single denominator:

$$E_{net} = \frac{q}{4\pi\epsilon_0}\left(\frac{(x+\frac{d}{2})^2 - (x-\frac{d}{2})^2}{(x-\frac{d}{2})^2 (x+\frac{d}{2})^2}\right) \quad (25)$$

The numerator and denominator in the bracket of Eq. (25) are further analyzed. For the numerator we write:

$$(x+\frac{d}{2})^2 - (x-\frac{d}{2})^2 =$$
$$= x^2 + xd + \frac{d^2}{4} - x^2 + xd - \frac{d^2}{4} = 2xd \quad (26)$$

and for the denominator:

$$(x+\frac{d}{2})^2 (x-\frac{d}{2})^2 = \left[(x+\frac{d}{2})(x-\frac{d}{2})\right]^2$$
$$= \left[x^2 - (\frac{d}{2})^2\right]^2 = x^4 - \frac{x^2 d^2}{2} + \frac{d^4}{16} \quad (27)$$

Thus, the magnitude of the electric field of a dipole at point P is:

$$E_{net} = \frac{q\, x\, d}{2\pi\epsilon_0} \frac{1}{x^4 - \frac{x^2 d^2}{2} + \frac{d^4}{16}} \quad (28)$$

This is the proper answer to the question asked in the Example text. Obviously, nobody would wish to deal with dipoles if we were stuck with Eq. (28) every time the properties of dipoles would have to be considered. Luckily, most applications of dipoles don't require Eq. (28) because most applications have one simplifying feature in common: we are only interested in the electric field of the dipole at large distances from the dipole.

Thus, we rewrite Eq. (28) for the limiting case $x \gg d$, i.e., for the case that the point of interest at which we evaluate the electric field of the dipole is farther away than the size of the dipole. In this case, the leading x^4 term dominates the sum in the denominator on the right hand side of Eq. (28). Neglecting the other two terms in the denominator yields a formula for the field that is applicable far from the dipole:

$$\lim_{x \gg d} E_{net} = \frac{q}{2\pi\epsilon_0} \frac{d}{x^3} \quad (29)$$

> *The electric field of a dipole drops in all directions proportional to $1/r^3$, i.e., faster than the electric field of a single charge for which the field is proportional to $1/r^2$.*

This is not surprising since a dipole looks like two very close charges that compensate each other from a position far away.

Had the problem text not limited the positions for which we sought the electric field to those points along the axis of the dipole, electric field components would have had to be calculated at each point and would have had to be combined to a net effect, as shown in Eq. (22). How such a calculation is done is shown for the electric field of a single charge in the Appendix of the current chapter.

Fig. 9.14 shows electric field lines for three cases to illustrate the variety of possible directional patterns of electric fields for just two charges. A plot of electric field lines primarily illustrates the direction of the electric field: the electric field at any given point is directed in the direction of the field line at that position. The plot shows the magnitude of the electric field only in an indirect fashion; it is represented by the local density of field lines.

Fig. 9.14(a) expands on the case of a dipole. The electric field lines point away from the positive charge and/or toward the negative charge as required by the sign convention we introduced in Fig. 9.12. A significant directional variation is noted, which has the radial symmetry of the electric field of a single charge only very close to either of the two charges. The electric field lines along the dipole axis are straight lines, indicating that the vector character of the electric field needs not to be considered along this line. This has already been discussed in Example 9.4.

Fig. 9.14(b) shows the electric field lines for two equal positive point charges. The electric field lines between these charges do not form closed curves like in Fig. 9.14(a). Fig. 9.14(c) indicates that electric field lines can easily become quite complex patterns. In the figure, the electric field lines are shown for a positive and a negative point charge with the positive charge twice the magnitude of the negative charge. Far from the pair of point charges the positive charge dominates the pattern as is evident from following the electric field lines leaving the positive charge.

In Eq. (29), the product of charge and distance defines the *electric dipole moment* μ of the two charges forming a dipole:

$$\mu = q\, d \quad [Cb\, m] \qquad (30)$$

Electric dipole moments characterize the chemical and physical properties of molecules. Table 9.2 lists the elec-

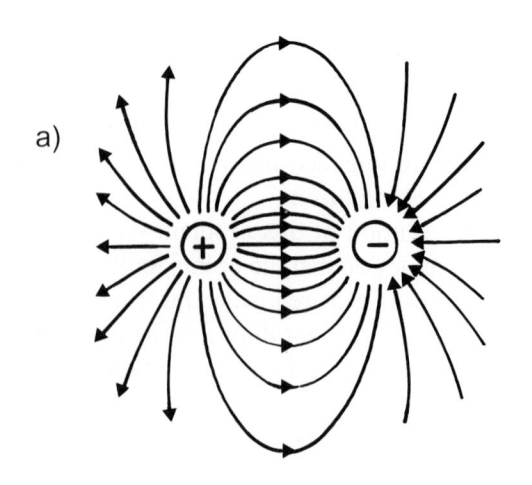

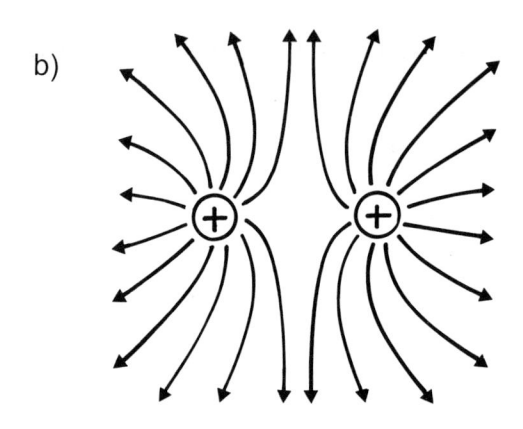

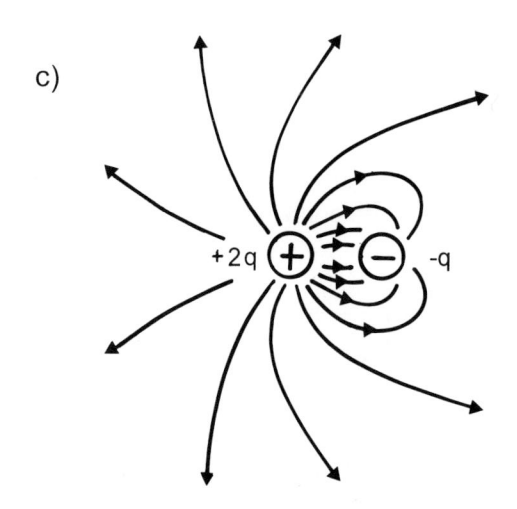

Fig. 9.14: Plots of the electric field lines for three charged systems. An electric field line illustrates the direction of the electric field. At any given point the field points in the direction of the field line.
(a) The electric field lines of a dipole.
(b) The electric field lines for two equal positive point charges.
(c) The electric field lines for two unequal charges.

Table 9.2: The correlation of the dipole moment and the temperature interval between melting point and boiling point at 1 atm pressure for several common small molecules. The data show that higher melting and boiling temperatures are associated with larger dipole moments. Water, and not hydrofluoric acid, plays a central role in the life sciences because HF is chemically very aggressive.

Molecule	Dipole moment [Cb m]	Melting temperature [°C]	Boiling temperature [°C]
HF	6.37×10^{-30}	-84	$+20$
HCl	3.57×10^{-30}	-114	-85
H$_2$O	6.17×10^{-30}	± 0	$+100$
H$_2$S	3.67×10^{-30}	-86	-61
NH$_3$	4.80×10^{-30}	-78	-33
PH$_3$	1.83×10^{-30}	-134	-88
AsH$_3$	7.33×10^{-31}	-117	-62
CH$_4$	0	-182	-161
SiH$_4$	0	-185	-112

tric dipole moment, the melting temperature and the boiling temperature for some common small hydrogen–containing molecules. Fig. 9.15 is a plot of the dipole moment of these molecules versus the range between melting temperature and boiling temperature at atmospheric pressure. The figure shows that water is distinct from the other molecules because its very large electric dipole moment yields melting and boiling points which are unusually high for such small molecules.

The electric dipole moment causes these high temperatures by allowing water molecules to form relatively strong *hydrogen bonds* with neighboring molecules, as sketched in Fig. 9.16. In the figure, the large spheres represent oxygen atoms and the small spheres represent hydrogen atoms. Each water molecule is highlighted with dashed lines. Note that the central oxygen atom is symmetrically surrounded by four hydrogen atoms, two with which it forms covalent bonds and two which be-

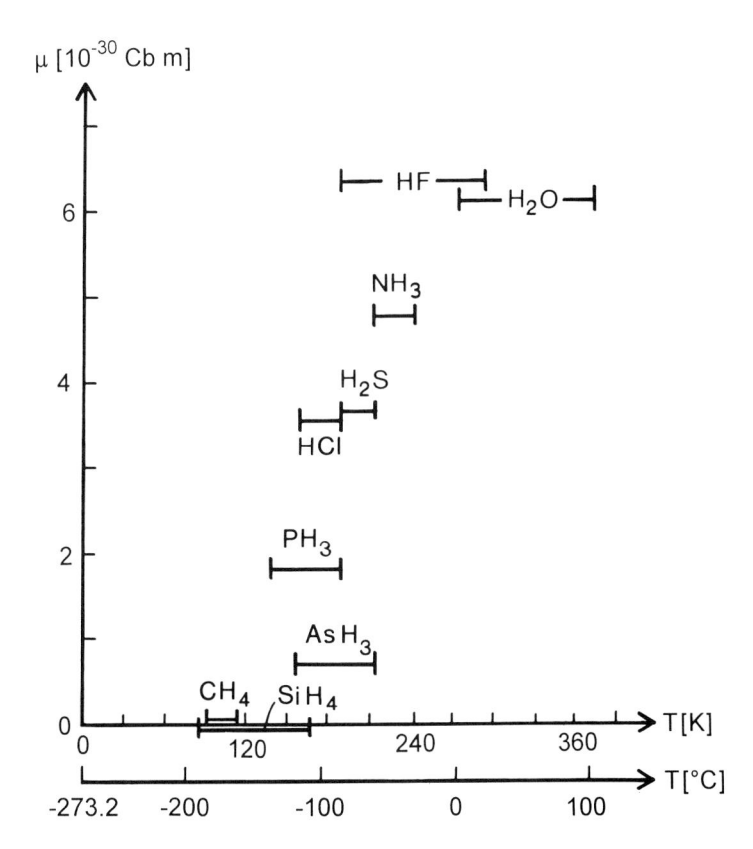

Fig. 9.15: Graphic representation of the data of Table 9.2. The temperature axis is shown in units [K] and [°C]. For each molecule, the shown horizontal bar stretches from the melting point to the boiling point. Both phase transition temperatures increase with increasing dipole moment of the molecule.

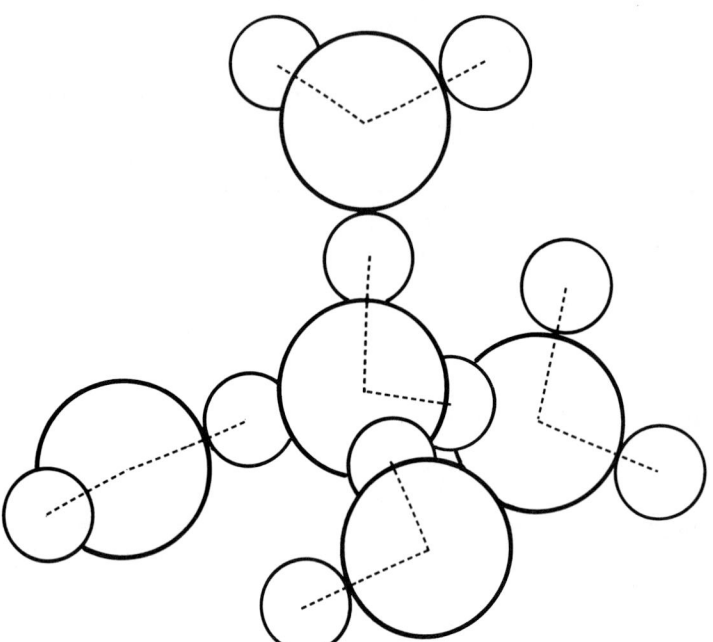

Fig. 9.16: Typical arrangement of four neighboring water molecules (each highlighted by dashed lines) in solid water (ice). The larger spheres represent oxygen atoms and the smaller spheres hydrogen atoms. Four hydrogen atoms are arranged tetrahedrally around each central oxygen atom. In liquid water, hydrogen bonds break frequently and the local order of molecules is less regular. The hydrogen bonds are about 5 to 10 % as strong as chemical O–H bonds (dashed lines).

long to neighboring water molecules. The extra energy needed to break such hydrogen bonds, typically 1 % to 10 % of the energy needed to break a covalent bond, causes higher melting and boiling temperatures. The morphology shown in Fig. 9.16 illustrates the local organization of water molecules in solid ice. Note that extensive long–range order exists in ice due to the fixed directions of the hydrogen bonds. In liquid water, the same structure develops to a lesser extend as hydrogen bonds are frequently broken and newly re–arranged.

Its large electric dipole moment, therefore, enables water to play such a pivotal role in creating suitable conditions for life. If a planet or moon carries liquid water, we believe it may support life. In our solar system, only few bodies qualify, Earth and Jupiter's moon Europa carry liquid water, Mars likely did so in the past. Unfortunately, Mars' atmosphere is only 1 % as thick as Earth's atmosphere and, therefore, no liquid water can be found on its surface at present.

Hydrogen bonds play also a crucial role in other biologically important molecules. The DNA molecule consists of nucleotides, which in turn contain a nitrogenous base, a pentose sugar and a phosphate group. The nitrogenous groups are either cytosine or thymine (pyrimidine compounds), or adenine or guanine (purine compounds). These nitrogenous groups can bond in pairs as shown in Fig. 9.17 to form the DNA double–helix structure. The DNA molecule is quite stable as each base pair forms two or three hydrogen bonds.

Fig. 9.17: Hydrogen bonds play also a crucial role in the formation of DNA molecules. The nitrogenous bases of the nucleotides include either cytosine or thymine (pyrimidine compounds), or adenine or guanine (purine compounds). These groups bond in pairs to form the DNA double–helix structure.

Example 9.5

Calculate the ionic character for the water molecule. Determine the maximum dipole moment for the molecule by allowing each of the two hydrogen atoms to transfer one electron to the oxygen atom. The bond length O–H is 0.096 nm and the bond angle H–O–H is 104.5°.

Supplementary chemical information: using the dipole moment from Table 9.2 and the distance between the positive and negative centers of a molecule allows us to define an *ionic character Ic* for the molecule:

$$Ic\ [\%] = 100\ \frac{\mu_{actual}}{\mu_{max}} \qquad (31)$$

For example, for the HCl molecule the maximum dipole moment is based on the transfer of a single electron from the hydrogen atom to the chlorine atom across the separation distance of the atoms in the molecule. The bond length of the HCl molecule is 0.127 nm. This allows us to calculate the maximum dipole moment for a fully ionized HCl molecule:

$$\mu_{max} = 1.6 \times 10^{-19}[Cb]\ 1.27 \times 10^{-10}[m]$$
$$\Rightarrow \mu_{max}(HCl) = 2.05 \times 10^{-29}\ [Cb\ m] \qquad (32)$$

where we used a single elementary charge for the transferred electric charge. Thus, the ionic character of the HCl bond is:

$$Ic\ (HCl) = 100\ \frac{3.57 \times 10^{-30}[Cb\ m]}{2.05 \times 10^{-29}[Cb\ m]} \qquad (33)$$
$$\Rightarrow Ic\ (HCl) = 17.4\ \%$$

i.e., the HCl molecule is polar, but with a predominantly covalent bond character.

Solution: Fig. 9.1 illustrates the geometry of the water molecule and allows us to determine the maximum separation of the positive and the negative charges during polarisation of the molecule. This maximum separation would be reached when the single electron of each hydrogen atom is fully shifted to the oxygen atom. This corresponds to a double negative charge ($2e$) at point P_1 and a double positive charge at point P_2 due to the symmetry of the molecule. The distance between points P_1 and P_2 is obtained geometrically from the figure:

$$\frac{P_1 P_2}{r} = \cos\left(\frac{104.5°}{2}\right) \qquad (34)$$
$$\Rightarrow P_1 P_2 = r\cos(52.25°) = 0.059\ nm$$

Next we determine the maximum dipole moment of the water molecule using the distance value calculated in Eq. (34):

$$\mu_{max}(H_2O) = (2e)\ P_1 P_2 =$$
$$3.2 \times 10^{-19}[Cb]\ 0.059 \times 10^{-9}[nm] \qquad (35)$$

which leads to:

$$\mu_{max}(H_2O) = 1.89 \times 10^{-29}\ [Cb\ m] \qquad (36)$$

The ionic character of the water molecule follows now from the definition in Eq. (31) by comparing the value determined in Eq. (36) with the value given in Table 9.2:

$$Ic\ (H_2O) = 100\ \frac{6.17 \times 10^{-30}[Cb\ m]}{1.89 \times 10^{-29}[Cb\ m]} \qquad (37)$$
$$Ic\ (H_2O) = 32.6\ \%$$

Note that this value significantly exceeds the value for HCl, which is one of the stronger acids known in chemistry. It is this highly ionic character of the water molecule which leads to those properties of the molecule which establish its distinguished role for all living organisms.

9.4.4. Electric field of charged parallel plates

When there are more than a few fixed point charges, it is no longer feasible to calculate the electric field from Eq. (21). The equation must be rewritten in a more suitable form to reduce the mathematical effort required. This can only be done if two conditions are met: the fixed charges have a uniform density in the system, and the arrangement of these fixed charges is symmetric.

Although this sounds like restrictive conditions, they are actually applicable to most real charge distributions of interest. If the charge distribution is the result of a manufactured device, the design of the device is always based on a simple geometry. When describing natural structures, the system can at least locally be characterized by a simple geometry.

Our approach to systems with many charges is analogous to the approach taken when we studied extended bodies or fluids. We no longer identified the system as a large number of point masses but expressed the mass of the system as its volume and density. In the same fashion, we now describe the large number of charged particles in the system with just three parameters: the total charge, $Q = \Sigma_i q_i$; the volume; and the charge density. If the charges are distributed in three dimensions, we define the charge density as $\rho^* = Q/V$ with unit [Cb/m³], in which V is the volume; if the charges are distributed on a two-dimensional surface, we define the areal charge density as $\sigma = Q/A$ with unit [Cb/m²], in which A is the area. In the discussion of real electric systems, the areal charge density σ plays a more prominent role since charges are usually uniformly distributed across the surface of the conducting components of the system as they repel each other due to Coulomb's law. An example is the nerve membrane: the charges which are relevant for the nerve signal transport are located on the inside and outside surfaces of the nerve membrane, leading to a uniform areal charge density of 700 µCb/m².

Calculating the electric field for systems with large numbers of charged particles is complicated, even for uniform and highly symmetric charge distributions. Considering the mathematical effort required to determine the electric field in these cases, it is advisable to first survey existing literature when you require an electric field for a given charge distribution for your future work. Most of the geometries that you encounter in biological applications have already been studied for unrelated engineering purposes.

There is one case, however, in which the resulting field has an extremely simple form: the case of the electric field between two infinitely large parallel plates, each with a uniform areal charge density. The magnitude of the electric field between the charged parallel plates is given by:

$$|E_\parallel| = \frac{\sigma}{\epsilon_0} \tag{38}$$

> The electric field between charged parallel plates is independent of the position and is proportional to the area charge density of the plates.

Example 9.6
What is the electric field between two parallel flat plates, where one plate is charged positively and the other plate is charged negatively with $\sigma = 700$ µCb/m²? This value is a typical areal charge density for nerve membranes.

Solution: Using Eq. (38) we find:

$$|E_\parallel| = \frac{7 \times 10^{-4} \, [Cb/m^2]}{8.85 \times 10^{-12} \, [Cb^2/Nm^2]} \tag{39}$$

$$\Rightarrow |E_\parallel| = 7.9 \times 10^7 \, \frac{N}{Cb}$$

We will use this value frequently in Chapter 13.

Example 9.7
A large flat plate has a surface charge density with a value $\sigma = +5$ µCb/m² on its surface. What is the electric field very close to the surface of the plate?

Solution: The electric field of a single, flat plate is half of the value of the parallel plate arrangement discussed in Eq. (38), i.e., $|E| = \sigma/2\epsilon_0$ and is directed away from a positive plate. With the values given in the example text we substitute into this formula:

$$|E| = \frac{\sigma}{2\epsilon_0} = \frac{5.0 \times 10^{-6} \left[\frac{Cb}{m^2}\right]}{2 \cdot 8.85 \times 10^{-12} \left[\frac{Cb^2}{Nm^2}\right]} \tag{40}$$

$$\Rightarrow |E| = 2.8 \times 10^5 \, \frac{N}{Cb}$$

This is the correct value for the electric field at any point near the surface of the flat plate except close to the edges where fringe effects require corrections.

Note: fields of the magnitude calculated in Eq. (40) occur in commercial photocopiers. Air breaks down electrically at an electric field of 3×10^6 N/Cb. When this threshold is reached, air is ionized and becomes conducting. Thus, electric fields in photocopiers are limited to values up to a factor 10 below the break-down threshold for air due to safety concerns.

Example 9.8

In Robert Millikan's experiment as illustrated in Fig. 9.2 a constant electric field along the vertical axis is obtained with two charged plates, one located above and one below the experimental set–up. The electric field is directed downwards. An oil drop of radius 1.64 μm and density 0.851 g/cm³ is levitated in the chamber when an electric field of 1.92×10^5 N/Cb is applied. Find the charge on the drop as a multiple of the elementary charge *e*.

Solution: When the drop levitates, it is in mechanical equilibrium; therefore, the two forces on the drop, the electric force upwards and the gravitational force downwards are equal (Newton's first law):

$$m_{drop}\, g = q_{drop}\, |E| \qquad (41)$$

Eq. (41) allows us to express the charge of the droplet in the form:

$$q_{drop} = \frac{m_{drop}\, g}{|E|} = \frac{4\pi r_{drop}^3\, \rho\, g}{3|E|} \qquad (42)$$

in which the mass of the droplet has been replaced by its volume and density. Substituting the given values into Eq. (42) leads to:

$$q = \frac{4\pi(1.64\times 10^{-6}[m])^3\, 851[\frac{kg}{m^3}]\, 9.8[\frac{m}{s^2}]}{3 \cdot 1.92\times 10^5[\frac{N}{Cb}]} \qquad (43)$$

$$\Rightarrow \quad q_{drop} = 8.0 \times 10^{-19}\, Cb$$

Because the electric field **E** is directed down and the electric force **F** is directed up, the oil drop must have a net negative charge. The benefit of a constant, position independent electric field in this experiment is obvious. In terms of the elementary charge we find:

$$\frac{q_{drop}}{e} = \frac{8.0 \times 10^{-19}\,[Cb]}{1.6 \times 10^{-19}\,[Cb]} = 5 \qquad (44)$$

i.e., the droplet carries five elementary charges.

9.4.5. Detection of electric fields by living organisms

Most organisms, including humans, cannot detect electric fields in their environment. You know this from walking below power lines: unless you identify their location visually you do not notice where they are. The lack of receptors for electric fields is due to the fact that few natural electric fields occur to which an organism should respond. Most such fields are very weak and would require a very elaborate detection system.

Sharks have developed a pair of regions in the skin of their heads which can detect the weak electric fields generated by the muscle action of nearby animals. These regions are called ampullae of Lorenzi. Sharks benefit from this sense in hunting prey even though they have good (colorless) vision, olfaction and bone–conduction hearing (discussed in Chapter 1). They also sense vibrations in their vicinity with the lateral line system we discussed in Fig. 3.17.

9.5. Electric energy concepts

In Chapter 5 we discovered that the concept of energy is often more powerful than the concept of force. Therefore, we want to extend the discussion of electric effects by introducing an electric energy that is associated with the force term in Coulomb's law.

9.5.1. Electric potential energy: charged parallel plates

The electric energy is introduced analogous to the gravitational potential energy in mechanics in section 5.5. We start with the general definition of work W for the cases in which a force **F** and the resulting displacement **Δs** are co–linear:

$$W = F\, \Delta s \qquad (45)$$

In the electric case, we consider a charged particle which is moved by an external force $\mathbf{F}_{ext}$ from an initial equilibrium position to a final equilibrium position within a system of other fixed charges. The external force is chosen such that it creates the mechanical equilibrium for the mobile test charge. The work required is equal to the difference in electric potential energy E_{el}:

$$W = E_{el,\, final} - E_{el,\, initial} \qquad (46)$$

Remember that we can use Eq. (45) only if the force does not vary with the position of the charged particle along the displacement. In mechanics, this condition was met by all contact forces. Also, by replacing Newton's law of gravity with the relation F = mg, gravity became position independent. In the case of the electric force, the force is usually *not* independent of the position as the $1/r^2$ dependence in Eq. (1) indicates. This requires a more detailed discussion, similar to the one for the work in an isothermal expansion of a gas in Chapter 6. Before considering this general case, however, we note that there is one case in which the electric force is position independent, i.e., in which Eq. (45) allows us to determine the electric energy: the parallel plate arrangement for which Eq. (38) applies. Therefore we consider this case first.

The electric energy for a parallel plate arrangement is derived from Fig. 9.18. The plate at the top is charged positively and the plate at the bottom is charged negatively. This leads to a downwards directed electric field between the plates. We further assume that a positive test charge is moved from close to the positive plate to a position close to the negative plate, i.e., from position $y_{initial}$ to y_{final}. Moving a positive test charge from one equilibrium position to another in this fashion requires an external force F_{ext} to prevent the charged particle from accelerating toward the negative plate. Consequently, the external force is positive and the displacement is negative. A negative work follows when the external force and the displacement are anti–parallel, i.e., the test charge releases in Fig. 9.18 work to the source of the external force:

$$W = F_{ext} \Delta s = q_{test} |E| (y_{fin} - y_{init}) < 0 \quad (47)$$

Using Eq. (46), we derive from Eq. (47) the formula for the electric potential energy:

$$E_{el} = q_{test} |E| y = q_{test} \frac{\sigma}{\epsilon_0} y \quad (48)$$

in which we used Eq. (38) for the magnitude of the electric field.

> *The electric energy in a parallel plate arrangement is a linear function of distance from the plate with the opposite charge as the test charge.*

Note that Eq. (48) is similar to the formula derived for the gravitational potential energy, which is a linear function of height above ground ($E_{pot, grav}$ = mgh). The simple form of Eq. (48) is the reason why parallel plate arrangements are a convenient and often used system for studying electric phenomena.

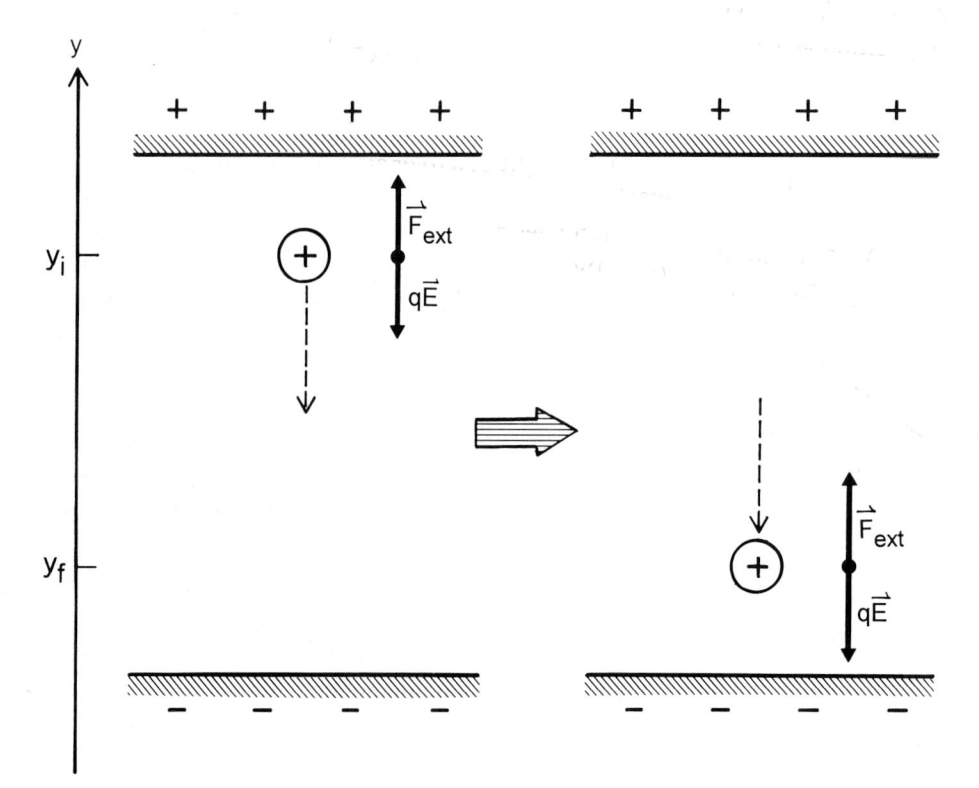

Fig. 9.18: A parallel plate arrangement with an electric field **E** pointing downwards. The forces acting on a positive test charge are shown in a free–body–diagram at the right of the test charge. The sketch at the left side shows the test charge at its initial position y_i and the sketch at the right side shows the same charge in its final position y_f. Note that the test charge is in both cases in mechanical equilibrium.

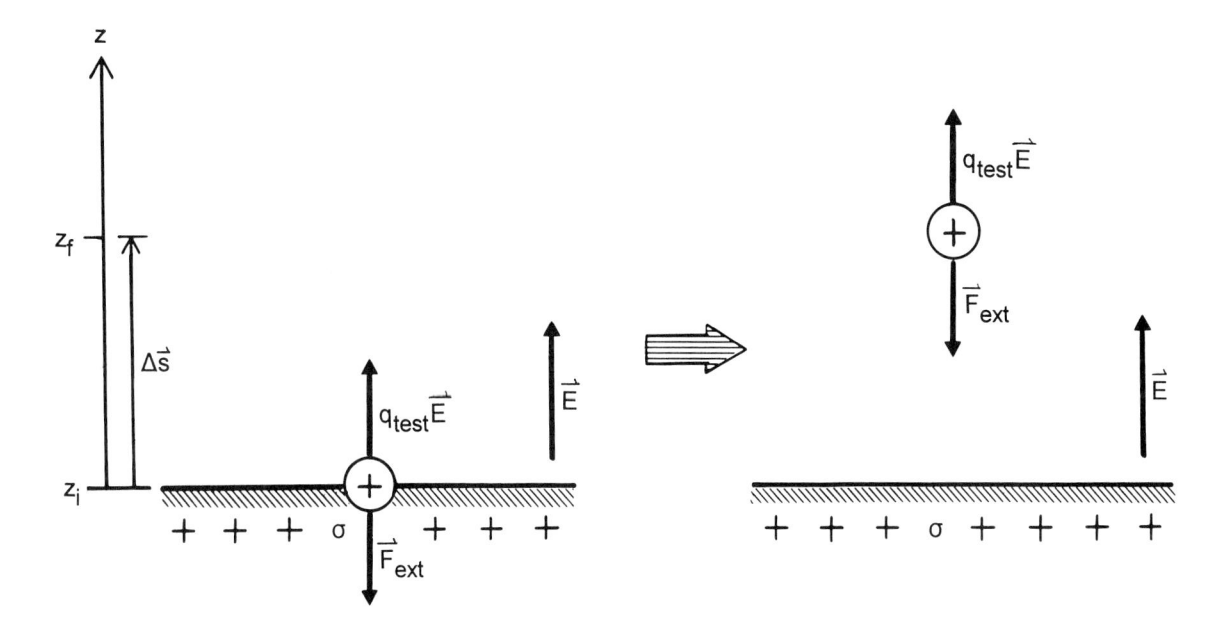

Fig. 9.19: A positive test charge moving from the surface of a single plate (position z_i) with a positive areal charge density σ (at left) to a final position z_f (at right). The electric field of the plate points upwards. The total displacement of the test charge is Δs. The test charge is in both positions in mechanical equilibrium.

Example 9.9
In Fig. 9.19 we are given a single infinite, non–conducting sheet with a positive surface charge σ.
(a) How much work is done by the external force as a positive test charge q_{test} is moved perpendicularly from the surface of the sheet at z_i to a final position at z_f?
(b) How much work is done by the electric field of the sheet during the same displacement?

Solution: The electric field of a single flat plate is given in the form $|\mathbf{E}| = \sigma/2\epsilon_0$.
Solution part (a): The external force needed to create an equilibrium is directed in the opposite direction to the Coulomb force, and is, therefore, antiparallel to the displacement. Thus, the work is negative, i.e., work is done by the test charge on the source of the external force. With the magnitude of the external force $F_{ext} = q|\mathbf{E}|$:

$$W = -\frac{q_{test}\sigma}{2\epsilon_0} z_f < 0 \qquad (49)$$

Solution part (b): Since Coulomb's force is opposite but equal in magnitude to the external force, we find:

$$W(Coulomb) = -W(external) \qquad (50)$$

The absolute value of the work done by the charged particle on the sheet is the same as the work done on the test charge in part (a).

9.5.2. Electrophoresis (Example 9.10)

A blood sample of a liver cirrhosis patient is analyzed by electrophoresis. A γ–globulin molecule from this blood sample moves during the protein separation a distance of 7 cm toward the negative plate of the set–up. The electric field between the parallel plates is $|\mathbf{E}| = 2000$ N/Cb. How much work has been done on the γ–globulin molecule?

Supplementary physiological information Electrophoresis is widely used to separate and identify charged components in a solution such as blood. Two types of experimental set–up exist. In forensic science, DNA fragments are routinely separated across a gel after the original DNA molecule has been split by restriction enzymes. Such a set–up is shown in Fig. 9.20: the sample is brought onto the gel close to the negative plate at left (cross–shaded zone). Electrophoresis separates the charged molecule fragments on the basis of their rate of movement through the gel in a given electric field.

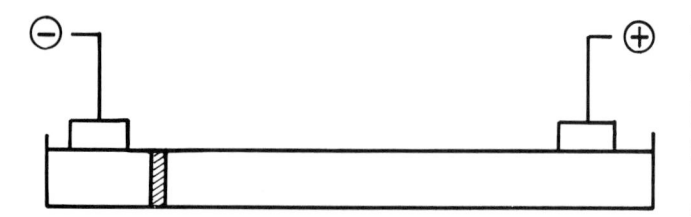

Fig. 9.20: Electrophoresis set–up used in forensic sciences. DNA fragments are separated across a gel after the original DNA molecule has been split by restriction enzymes. The sample is embedded in the gel (cross–shaded zone). Electrophoresis separates the molecule fragments on the basis of their drift rate in the electric field. The DNA sample is brought close to the negative plate as the fragments carry negative charge due to phosphate groups.

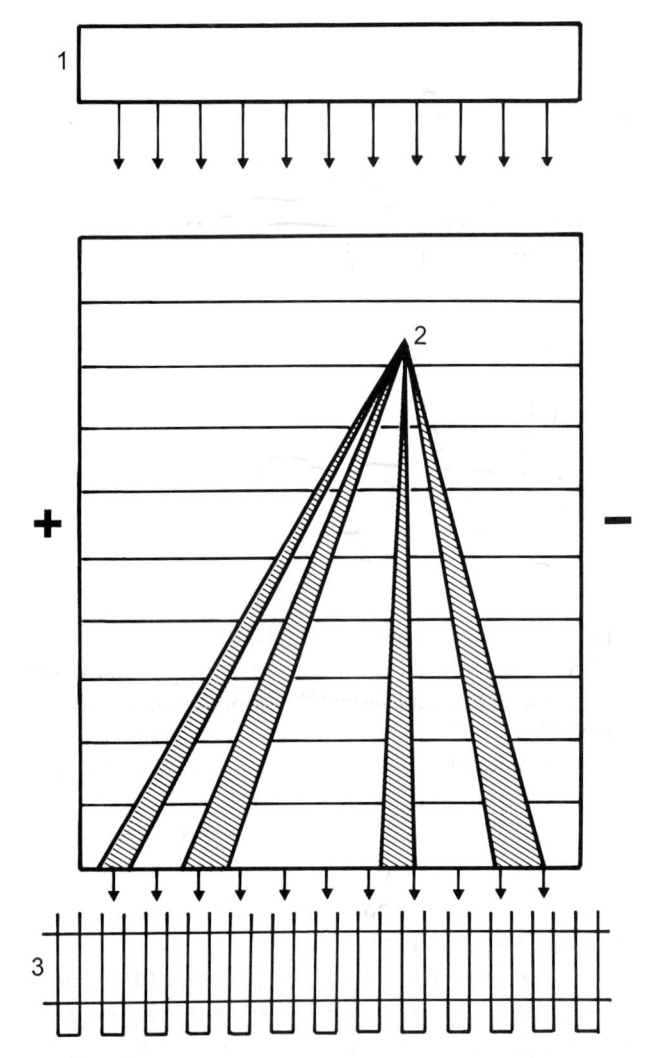

Fig. 9.21: A second electrophoresis set–up often used for blood sample analysis. The proteins in the sample travel downwards in a cellulose matrix in a vertical arrangement, driven by the steady flow of a buffer solution from a reservoir at the top (1). The components of the blood sample drift in the electric field; e.g. the negative plate at the right causes positive ions to drift to the right. Separation of the ions occurs due to their molecular sizes. The components of the sample are collected in test tubes (3).

Typically, larger fragments travel slower than smaller ones. The DNA sample is brought close to the negative plate because the fragments carry negative charge due to phosphate groups.

Fig. 9.21 shows a second set–up which is more suitable to recover the separated components. This approach is used for blood sample analysis for protein composition. In this case, the sample travels downwards in a cellulose matrix in a vertical arrangement, driven by the steady flow of a buffer solution from a reservoir at the top (1). The components of the blood sample drift toward left or right, driven by the electric field applied horizontally across the matrix. In the figure, the negative plate is shown at the right, causing positive ions to drift to the right; the positive plate is shown at the left, causing negative ions to drift to the left. Separation of equally charged ions occurs again on the basis of molecular size as smaller ions travel easier along the cellulose matrix. Thus, the mixture applied at point (2) to the matrix separates as it is washed downwards, and the various components can be collected in test tubes at the bottom of the cellulose sheet (3). Note that a similar process is used without the electrical set–up to separate dyes; in that case the process is called chromatography.

Fig. 9.22 shows the result of electrophoretically separated blood samples for (a) a normal and (b – f) pathological cases. The components of blood identified are albumin (labelled A) and five different globulin proteins, labelled α_1, α_2, β_1, β_2 and γ. The relative concentration of these proteins in the blood sample allows the physician to detect various diseases as indicated.

Solution: The electrophoresis set–up is electrically identical to an arrangement of oppositely charged parallel plates. Thus, Eq. (47) represents the work done on a charged particle between the two plates when that particle moves closer to one of the plates. The electric field between the plates in Fig. 9.22 points toward the negative plate at the right due to the convention we introduced in Fig. 9.12. γ–globulin is a positively charged ion because it drifts toward the negative plate. Therefore, the electric force on the protein ion is directed toward the right and the external force to hold it in mechanical equilibrium, F_{ext}, must be directed toward the left. The displacement of the protein ion occurs toward the right. If we define the positive y–axis toward the right, then $F_{ext} < 0$ and $\Delta y > 0$. Thus, the work calculated from $W = F_{ext} \Delta y$ is negative, $W < 0$.

For the numerical value of the work, we substitute the given values into Eq. (47). An elementary charge is carried by the γ–globulin: $q_{test} = e = 1.6 \times 10^{-19}$ Cb. The magnitude of the field is $|\mathbf{E}| = 2.0 \times 10^3$ N/Cb and the displacement is $\Delta y = 7.0 \times 10^{-2}$ m:

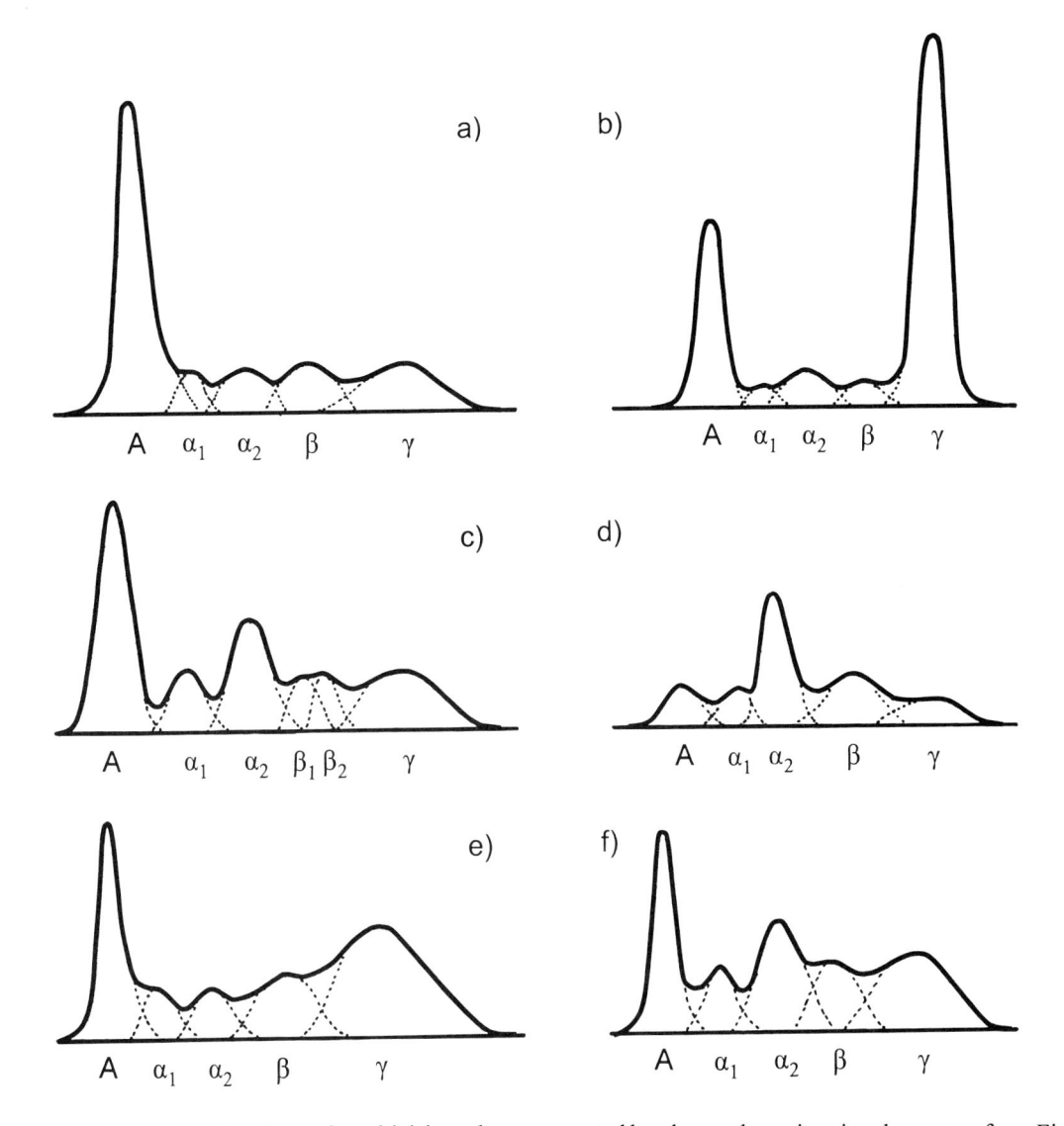

Fig. 9.22: Typical results for blood samples which have been separated by electrophoresis using the set–up from Fig. 9.21. The components of blood identified are albumin (labelled A) and five different globulin proteins, labelled α_1, α_2, β_1, β_2 and γ. The relative concentration of these proteins in the blood sample allows the physician to detect various diseases. (a) Is a comparison sample for a healthy patient, (b – f) are pathological cases: (b) plasma cell tumor, (c) acute inflamation, (d) severe nephrosis, (e) cirrhosis of liver, (f) liver parenchyma damage (parenchyma refers to the essential and distinctive tissue of an organ).

$$W = -1.6 \times 10^{-19}[Cb]\, 2 \times 10^3 \left[\frac{N}{Cb}\right] 0.07[m] \quad (51)$$

$$\Rightarrow \quad W = -2.2 \times 10^{-17}\ J$$

We want to discuss the sign in Eq. (51) a little further. Why is the work negative? Let's start with a positive ion between two charged plates in vacuum, i.e., we remove the cellulose matrix of the electrophoresis set–up. In that set–up the ion accelerates toward the negative plate. The ion and the charged plate represent an isolated system for which the conservation of energy applies in the form given in Eq. (5.4). Thus, the potential energy of the ion decreases during the acceleration but its kinetic energy increases by the same amount so that the internal energy (total energy) remains unchanged.

In the case of the electrophoresis experiment we discussed above, the positive ion does not accelerate. It moves with a small constant speed toward the negative plate. This is due to the cellulose matrix which acts as the origin of an external force. Thus, in the electrophoresis experiment, the system ion and charged plates is not an isolated system and the conservation of energy applies in the form of Eq. (5.5): $\Delta U = Q + W$. Specifically, no heat exchange is observed and the particle changes only its potential energy, but not its kinetic energy. Thus, $\Delta E_{el} = W$; the negative work is due to the decrease in potential energy of the ion.

9.5.3. Electric potential energy: single charged particle

Unfortunately, the parallel plate arrangement is not the only arrangement of charges with practical relevance. In this textbook, we will only consider two other cases, the electric energy of a single point charge Q and later the electric energy for a dipole.

In the first case, we consider a positive test charge which is brought closer to a positive, central point charge Q, as illustrated in Fig. 9.23. The position of the central charged particle is given as r = 0. The electrostatic force acting on the test charge at its initial position is q**E** (Eq. (19)). To bring the test charge closer to the central charge an external force is needed to push it from the initial to the final position, across a distance **Δs**. Bringing the test charge closer requires work, i.e., the work is positive.

Note that we study only cases where the test charge moves directly towards or away from the fixed charge. Then the force and the displacement are parallel and we need not to include vector algebra concepts.

Since the electric force varies along the displacement Δs, we cannot use Eq. (45) to calculate the work. Instead, we have to graph the magnitude of the external force as a function of position and determine the work as the area under the curve from $r_{initial}$ to r_{final}, as shown in Fig. 9.24. The work is then obtained from the shaded area under the curve and is written in the form:

$$W = \frac{q_{test}\, Q}{4\pi\epsilon_0}\left(\frac{1}{|r_{final}|} - \frac{1}{|r_{initial}|}\right) \quad (52)$$

From Eq. (52) we derive the electric potential energy for a single fixed point charge:

$$E_{el} = \frac{1}{4\pi\epsilon_0}\frac{q_{test}\, Q}{|r|} \quad (53)$$

Note that the result is independent of the sign of the position of the test charge. This is indicated by the absolute–bars of the variable r in the denominator of Eqs. (52) and (53), |r|.

The existence of positive and negative charges also distinguishes the electric potential energy from the gravitational potential energy. The gravitational force is always attractive; therefore, the external force vector establishing mechanical equilibrium always points away from the fixed mass (the Earth) when the test mass is brought closer, as illustrated in Fig. 5.9. However, whether the electric force is attractive or repulsive depends on whether the fixed charge at position r = 0 is positive or negative. In Fig. 9.23 this charge is positive; therefore, the electric force is repulsive because the test charge is by default considered to be positive. Thus, the external force points toward r = 0, as shown in the figure. If the charge at r = 0 were negative in turn, then the electric force would be attractive and the external force needed to establish a mechanical equilibrium would point away from the origin.

Eq. (53) illustrates that the electric interaction between two particles with opposite charges leads always to a negative electric potential energy, which is an energy we have to overcome to separate the two charges. This energy is particularly large if the initial separation

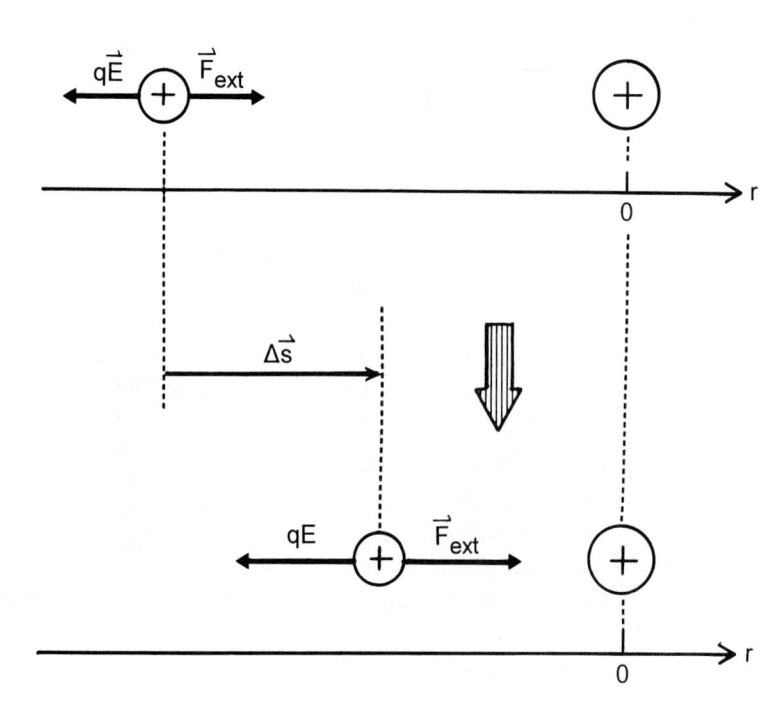

Fig. 9.23: Sketch to illustrate the work associated with moving a positive test charge (small circle) by a distance Δs closer to a positive fixed charge (large circle, positioned at r = 0). Both the initial (top) and final position (bottom) of the test charge are at negative positions along the axis. The electric force q**E** and the external force **F**$_{ext}$ for the mechanical equilibrium increase in magnitude as the test charge moves towards the fixed charge.

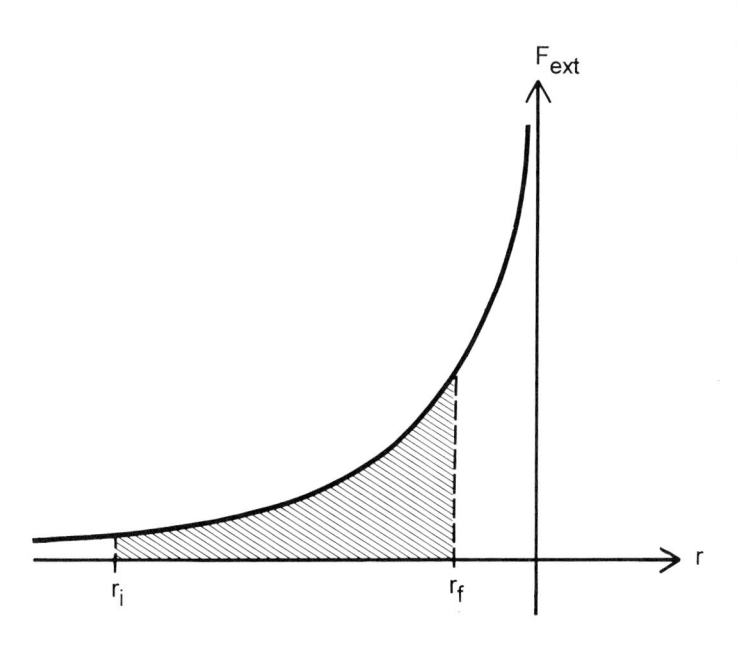

Fig. 9.24: The electric potential energy for the system shown in Fig. 9.23 is obtained from the area under the curve for the electric force as a function of position. This leads to the mathematical form of Eq. (52).

of the two charged particles is small, for example between ions in rock salt (NaCl). Still, these ions occur always separated. In a physiologically active environment we don't find rock salt crystals but only electrolyte solutions. Where does the energy come from to break up a rock salt crystal?

Again, water plays the crucial role in establishing the physiological balance of salt in our body. That role is associated with its electric dipole moment. The dipole moment provides the means of separating salt ions, such as Na^+ and Cl^-: without water, separating Na^+ and Cl^- ions turn neutral (via an electron exchange) at a distance of about one nanometer, as depicted in Fig. 9.25. The figure compares the total energy of a combination of a neutral Na atom and a neutral Cl atom (dashed line) with the total energy of a Na^+ ion and a Cl^- ion (solid line). At large distances, the energy difference results from the following thermodynamic relations:

Na	$\rightarrow Na^+ + e^-$	$\Delta U = +498$ kJ/mol
$Cl + e^-$	$\rightarrow Cl^-$	$\Delta U = -351$ kJ/mol
Na + Cl	$\rightarrow Na^+ + Cl^-$	$\Delta U = +147$ kJ/mol

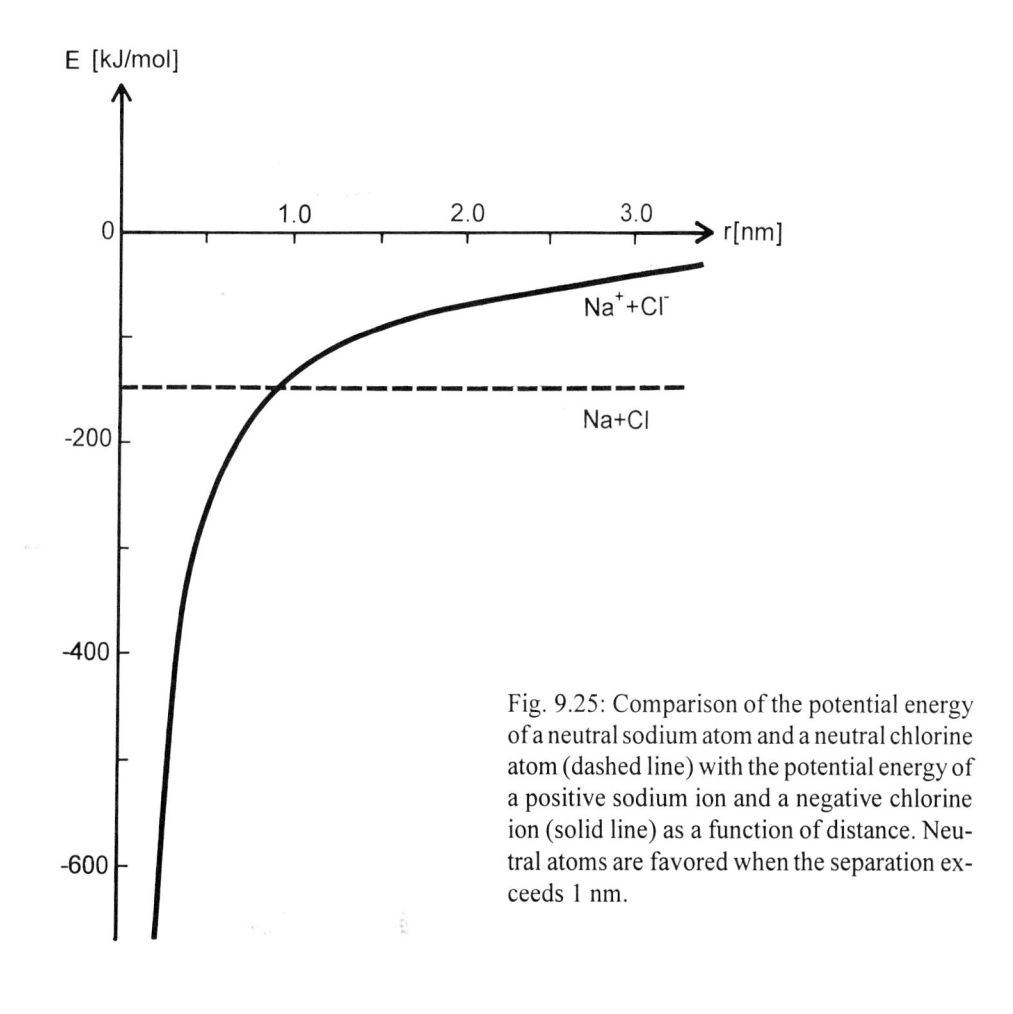

Fig. 9.25: Comparison of the potential energy of a neutral sodium atom and a neutral chlorine atom (dashed line) with the potential energy of a positive sodium ion and a negative chlorine ion (solid line) as a function of distance. Neutral atoms are favored when the separation exceeds 1 nm.

277

Remember, a positive change in the internal energy means that the system requires energy from its environment. Thus, the transfer of one mole of electrons from one mole of sodium atoms to one mole of chlorine atoms requires +147 kJ. However, when the atoms are at a distance of less than 1 nm from each other, Fig. 9.25 shows that the ions are energetically favored due to the electric potential energy, and an electron exchange occurs.

As a consequence, rock salt ions can only be separated by distances greater than 1 nm if this neutralizing electron exchange is prevented. A separation of ions across a typical 6 nm nerve membrane would be impossible. In order to do this, the energy of the separating ions must be lowered. In an aqueous solution, this is achieved by the formation of the hydration shell illustrated in Fig. 9.10. The hydration shell screens the central charge, an effect which reduces the interaction with other ions. It also lowers the energy by redistributing the charge over a larger volume, stabilizing the ion.

Example 9.11
Fig. 9.25 compares the potential energy of a pair of neutral Na and Cl atoms (dashed line) and the potential energy of a Na^+/Cl^- ion pair (solid line). Calculate the distance between the two ions at which the two curves cross, i.e., the point where the potential energy of the neutral Na/Cl pair equals the electric potential energy of the Na^+/Cl^- pair.

Solution: The electric energy of a pair of charges at infinite distance is 0 J, as follows from Eq. (53). At any closer distance, the energy between a positive and a negative particle is negative. We want to find in particular the distance at which the electric energy is equal to the change of the internal energy in the neutralization process of the Na/Cl pair, $\Delta U = -147$ kJ/mol. This energy is converted into an energy $\epsilon_{Na/Cl}$ for a single pair of neutral atoms by dividing ΔU by the Avogadro number. This yields $\epsilon_{Na/Cl} = -2.45 \times 10^{-19}$ J. We rewrite Eq. (53) to find the distance at which this energy equals the electric potential energy of the system:

$$r = \frac{q_{Na^+} q_{Cl^-}}{4\pi\epsilon_0} \frac{1}{E_{el}} =$$

$$\frac{(1.6 \times 10^{-19} [Cb])(-1.6 \times 10^{-19} [Cb])}{4\pi \cdot 8.85 \times 10^{-12} \left[\frac{Cb^2}{Nm^2}\right](-2.45 \times 10^{-19} [J])} \quad (54)$$

which yields:

$$r = 9.4 \times 10^{-10} \ m = 0.94 \ nm \quad (55)$$

This calculation confirms a value near 1 nm which we read off Fig. 9.25 above.

For systems with more than one fixed point charge, the electric energies of each pair-interaction with the point charge of interest are added to obtain the total energy of the point charge of interest:

$$E_{el} = \sum_{i=1}^{n} E_{el,\,i} \quad (56)$$

9.6. Electric potential

When studying the electric force we noted that the variability of positions of charges in a given set–up causes mathematical complexity. We dealt with this problem by splitting the electric force to define the electric field. The same difficulties arise for the electric energy because Eq. (53) still contains a 1/r dependence. Thus, we separate the electric energy into
(I) a field due to all fixed charges in the system. This field is called the *electric potential*, which should not be confused with the electric potential energy.
(II) a test charge.

As before, this is a more general description that allows us to reduce the number of calculations necessary in applications. The potential is usually labelled V. The definition of V follows from the electric potential energy of Eq. (53):

$$V = \frac{E_{el}}{q_{test}} \quad (57)$$

> The electric potential is defined as the electric potential energy per unit charge.

A new unit is introduced for the potential, called Volt [J/Cb] = [V], named for Alessandro Count Volta.

Two specific cases are studied further: the potential of a parallel plate arrangement and the potential of a fixed point charge. For the parallel plate arrangement we obtain:

$$V_\parallel = \frac{E_{el}}{q_{test}} = |E| \, y = \frac{\sigma}{\epsilon_0} y \quad (58)$$

in which σ is the areal charge density on the plates. For a single point charge we get:

$$V = \frac{E_{el}}{q_{test}} = \frac{1}{4\pi\epsilon_0} \frac{q}{|r|} \quad (59)$$

We can now compare with the force and energy concepts we developed in mechanics. Remember, it was the attempt to extend the discussion beyond classical mechanics which brought us to the energy concept in the first place. We may ask the same question here again: for electric problems, should we use the energy approach with the electric potential energy and the potential, or the force approach with the electric force and the electric field?

The answer is that, again, the energy approach is more useful. From a life sciences point of view, the first reason is the same as in mechanics: in order to describe nature at the molecular level, force is a more elusive concept than energy. In the case of electricity, a second reason has to be added: potentials can be measured while electric fields are experimentally inaccessible. The instrument allowing us to measure the potential is called a voltmeter. All we have to do is to position two metallic electrodes (wires) at two chosen points in a system and the voltmeter registers the potential difference between these two points. This measurement method involves magnetic concepts we have not discussed yet and we postpone therefore the discussion of the principles of the voltmeter. It is important to notice, however, that there is no equivalent instrument to measure electric fields.

Example 9.12
A potential difference of 80 mV exists between the inner and outer surfaces of the membrane of a cell. The inner surface is negative relative to the outer surface. How much work is required to eject a positive potassium ion (K$^+$) from the interior of the cell?

Solution: Fig. 9.26 shows the environment of the diffusing potassium ion. Initially the ion is inside (as shown) where it is in close proximity to the negative surface charge on the membrane. Work is required to transfer

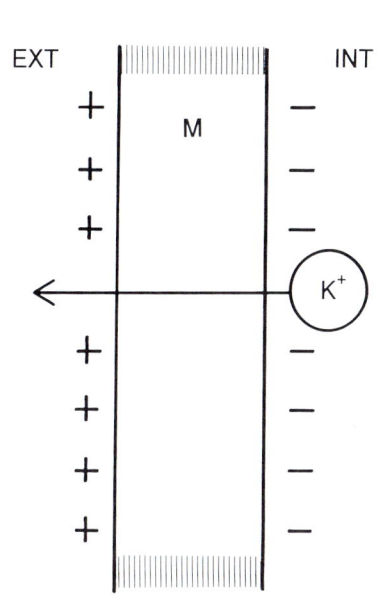

Fig. 9.26: A positively charged potassium ion is ejected from the interior of a cell through the cell membrane carrying surface charge density.

the potassium ion through the membrane as the ion leaves a negative environment and approaches a positive environment. The work is calculated using Eq. (58) noting that a potassium ion carries a single positive elementary charge e:

$$W = q \, \Delta V = 1.6 \times 10^{-19}[Cb] \; 80 \times 10^{-3}[V]$$
$$\Rightarrow \quad W = 1.28 \times 10^{-20} \, J \quad (60)$$

The work is positive for a process into which work has to be invested.

Example 9.13
Find the potential at point P which is located at an arbitrary position relative to a dipole, as shown in Fig. 9.27(a). Assume that the point P is far from the dipole.

Solution: For more than one fixed point charge, electric potentials have to be added in the same fashion as we discussed for the electric potential energy in Eq. (56). In particular, the electric potential at point P in Fig. 9.27(a), V_p, is:

$$V_P = V_{P,+q} + V_{P,-q} = \frac{1}{4\pi\epsilon_0}\left(\frac{q}{r_+} + \frac{-q}{r_-}\right) \quad (61)$$

with P a distance r_+ from the positive charge and P a distance r_- from the negative charge of the dipole. Eq. (61) is rewritten with a common denominator for the term in the bracket:

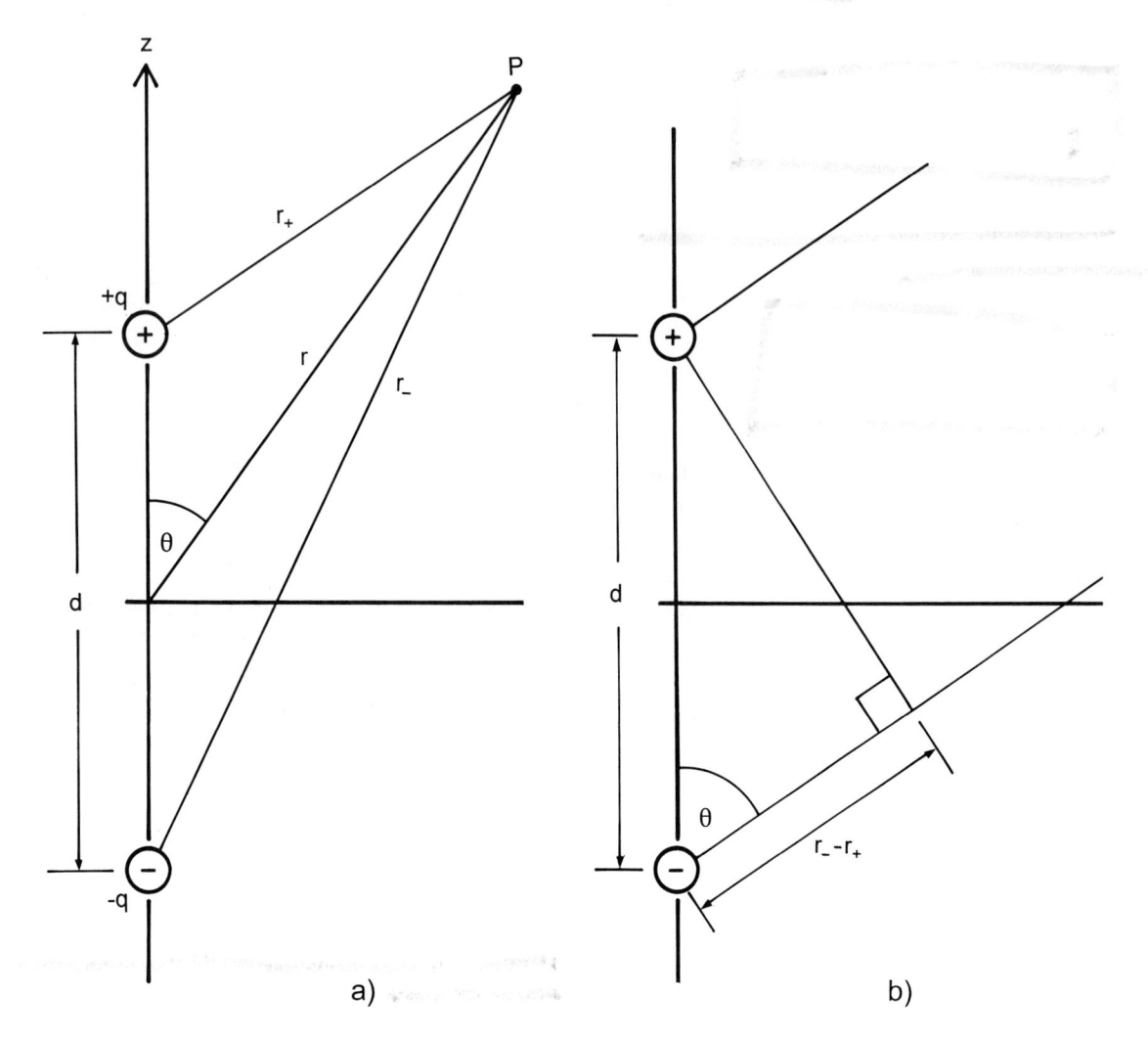

Fig. 9.27: (a) A dipole oriented along the z–axis. The point P is located at an arbitrary position relative to the dipole. (b) Geometric plot to determine the difference in the distances from each of the two charges of the dipole in part (a) to a distant point P.

$$V_P = \frac{q}{4\pi\epsilon_0} \frac{(r_- - r_+)}{r_- r_+} \tag{62}$$

If P is close to the dipole, Eq. (62) cannot be simplified further and is therefore our final result. However, if P lies far from the dipole with $r_+, r_- \gg d$, then both numerator and denominator of the last term in Eq. (62) are rewritten by using geometrical relations obtained from Fig. 9.27(b). In that figure, the two lines which extend from the dipole charges to point P are parallel. The difference in distance from the two charges to point P is a side in a right–angle triangle. This triangle allows us to express the term $r_- - r_+$ as a function of the length d and the angle θ with θ the angle between the dipole axis and the position vector to point P:

$$r_- - r_+ = d\cos\theta \tag{63}$$

We further use $r_- \cong r_+ \cong r$ with r the distance of the point P from the center of the dipole. This simplifies the denominator to:

$$r_- r_+ = r^2 \tag{64}$$

Inserting Eqs. (63) and (64) in Eq. (62), we find:

$$\lim_{r \gg d} V_P = \frac{q}{4\pi\epsilon_0} \frac{d\cos\theta}{r^2} = \frac{\mu}{4\pi\epsilon_0} \frac{\cos\theta}{r^2} \tag{65}$$

in which μ is the electric dipole moment of the dipole in

280

Fig. 9.27, as defined in Eq. (30). Thus, the electric potential of a dipole diminishes faster with distance than the electric potential of a point charge. The same qualitative behavior was observed for the electric field in Eq. (29).

The electric potential for more complex arrangements of charges is often visualized by using *equipotential lines* in a graphical sketch. Equipotential lines are lines which connect points of equal value of the electric potential. These lines are always perpendicular to electric field lines. Fig. 9.28 illustrates the equipotential lines for the three types of systems we discussed in the current chapter: Fig. 9.28(a) shows horizontal electric field lines (dashed arrows) and vertical equipotential lines (solid lines) for a uniformly charged parallel plate arrangement. Neither the electric field lines nor the equipotential lines indicate a complicated position dependence in this case.

Fig. 9.28(b) shows radial electric field lines and concentric equipotential lines for a single positive point charge. To illustrate the non–linear r dependence, the equipotential lines are chosen with a constant difference ΔV between neighboring lines.

Fig. 9.28(c) shows the more complex structure of electric field lines (dashed arrows) and equipotential lines (solid lines) for a dipole. Note that the electric field lines are straight only along the dipole axis while a straight equipotential line exists perpendicular to the dipole axis at the center of the dipole.

9.7. Conservation of energy

The electric energy is a form of energy that was not considered in Chapter 5. Therefore, we must determine whether it has the same properties as the previously defined forms of energy. We are particularly interested to see how it relates to the two major characteristics of the energy of a system:
(I) that the internal energy is conserved in an *isolated system*, and
(II) that the Gibbs free energy is equal on both sides of a separating membrane in a *closed or open system* in chemical equilibrium.

We consider the first issue in this chapter; the equilibrium for two electrically charged closed or open systems is then considered at the beginning of Chapter 13.

We established in Chapter 5 that the internal energy of an isolated system is constant (conservation of

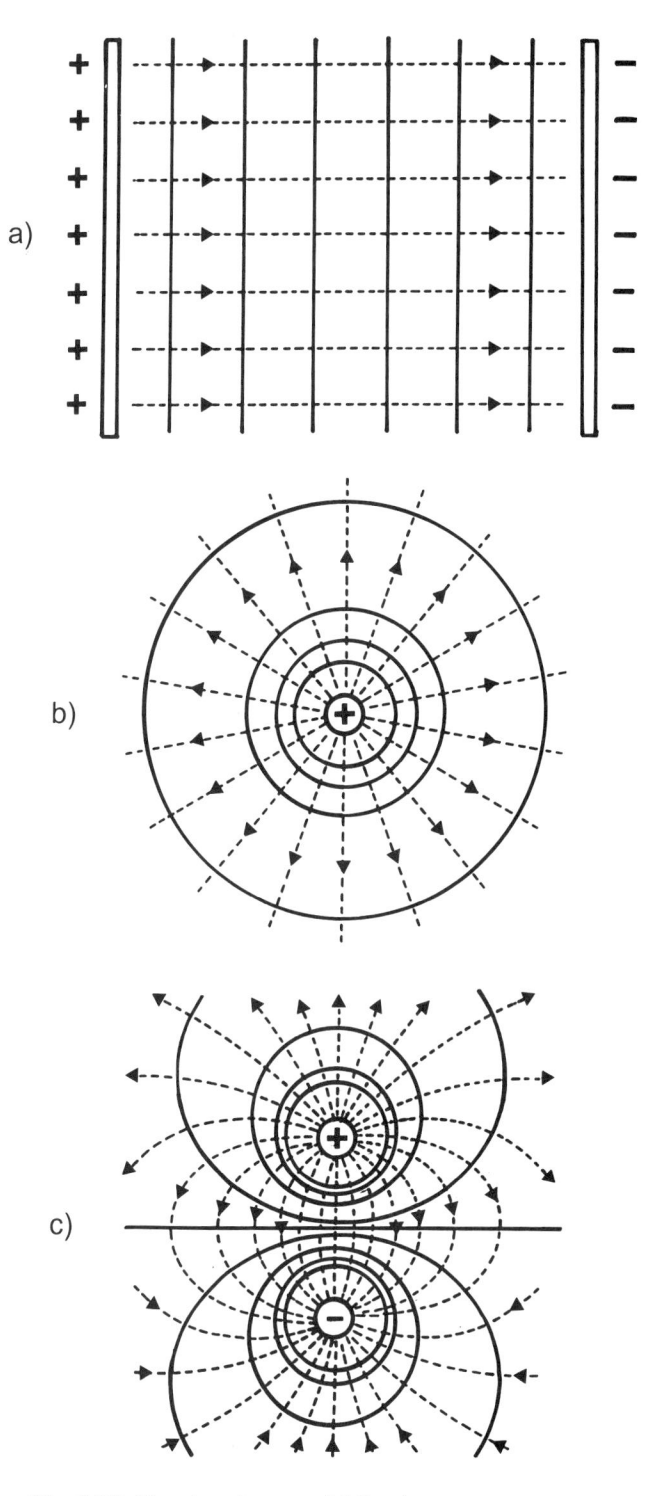

Fig. 9.28: The electric potential for charge arrangements is often visualized by using equipotential lines in a graphical sketch. Equipotential lines are lines which connect points of equal value of the electric potential. They are shown as solid lines in the figure. These lines are always perpendicular to electric field lines, shown as dashed lines in the figure. Examples include:
(a) a uniformly charged parallel plate arrangement,
(b) a single positive point charge, and
(c) a dipole.

energy). The same result is found in all experiments which include electric effects, i.e., electricity does not contradict the laws of thermodynamics.

In a *closed system* of charged particles which interact with their environment, the total work exchanged with the environment includes an electric work contribution in the form:

$$W = \Delta E_{el.\ pot} = E_{el,\ final} - E_{el,\ initial} \quad (66)$$

The inclusion of a new contribution to the total energy does not complicate the calculations as the number of energy terms which are relevant for a given system is usually small. For example, in most biological systems gravitational potential energy is negligible. The kinetic energy plays a role only when parts of the system are mobile, e.g. in respiration and blood circulation, as discussed in Chapter 11. For example, kinetic energy needs not be included in the discussion of signal transport in nerves because no motion of charged particles along the nerve is involved, as we will see in Chapter 13.

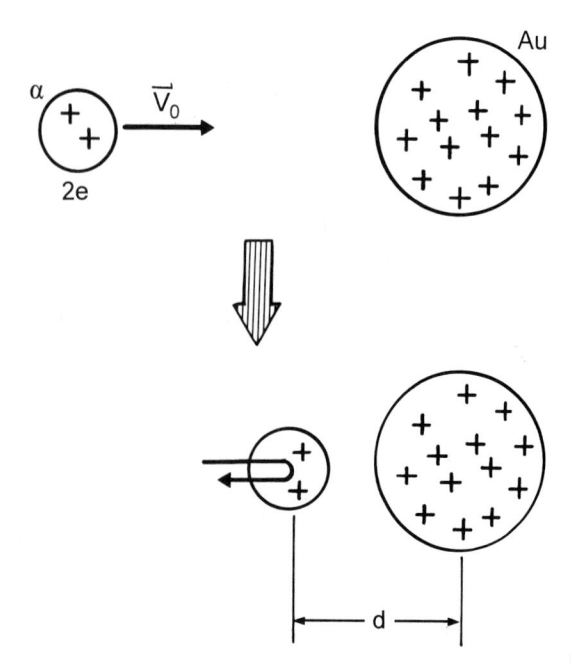

Fig. 9.29: Microscopic sketch of Ernest Rutherford's experiment: a helium nucleus (α–particle with two positive charges) approaches at high speed a gold nucleus at rest in the target.

Example 9.14

In 1911, Ernest Rutherford conducted an ion scattering experiment that allowed him to postulate a planetary model for the atom (see also Chapter 21). In the experiment he studied fast alpha particles of charge $+2e$ and mass 6.6×10^{-27} kg, which penetrated into a gold target as sketched in Fig. 9.29. If an alpha particle in a head–on collision with an Au nucleus has a speed of 2.0×10^7 m/s while still far from the Au nucleus, how close does it get to the Au nucleus before turning around? Use for the charge of the Au nucleus $+79e$.

Solution: We solve this problem with the conservation of energy. In the particular case, the kinetic energy and the electric potential energy are the only two energy forms which vary during the process. Thus, we write the conservation of energy in the form:

$$E_{kin,\ init} + E_{el,\ init} = E_{kin,\ fin} + E_{el,\ fin} \quad (67)$$

in which the kinetic energy is related to the speed of the moving particle in the usual form (½mv²) and the electric potential energy is given by Eq. (53) since the interaction occurs between two point charges.

We choose the initial state where the α–particle is still far away from the gold nucleus. In this context "far" means essentially farther than the radius of the gold atom. This very short distance is sufficient as the negative electrons in the atomic shells of a neutral gold atom screen the positive charge centered in the nucleus. In the initial state the electric potential energy of the α–particle is zero as obtained from Eq. (53) for $d = \infty$. The speed of the particle is determined from the acceleration process available in the laboratory.

The final state is given where the α–particle reaches the closest proximity to the gold nucleus (distance d_{min}). The particle is now well within the innermost shell of atomic electrons and thus facing the unscreened charge of the Au nucleus. At that point, the kinetic energy of the particle becomes zero. The particle comes momentarily to rest before accelerating away from the nucleus. Its entire energy has been shifted into its electric potential energy. Substituting these two states into Eq. (67) yields:

$$\frac{1}{2} m\ v_{init}^2 = k\ \frac{q_\alpha\ q_{Au}}{d_{min}} \quad (68)$$

which is equivalent to:

$$d_{min} = \frac{2\ k\ q_\alpha\ q_{Au}}{m_\alpha\ v_{init}^2} \quad (69)$$

With the data given in the Example text this yields for

the closest proximity of the α–particle:

$$d_{min} = \frac{2 \cdot 9 \times 10^9 \left[\frac{Nm^2}{Cb^2}\right] 2e \cdot 79e}{6.6 \times 10^{-27}[kg] \left(2 \times 10^7 \left[\frac{m}{s}\right]\right)^2} \quad (70)$$

which yields as the final result:

$$d_{min} = 2.8 \times 10^{-14} \; m \quad (71)$$

We compare this value to the radius of the gold nucleus, which is $r = 7 \times 10^{-15}$ m. Thus, the α–particle approaches the gold nucleus to within a distance twice the diameter of the nucleus!

9.8. Appendix: Electric field of a fixed point charge

Fig. 9.30 shows a fixed positive point charge at the origin. The task is to calculate the electric field at point $P = (x_0, y_0)$. Note that the problem is set up in two dimensions to reduce the required mathematical effort. We determine the two components of the electric field in two steps. First, the magnitude of the electric field $|\mathbf{E}|$ is calculated at point P. Then the geometric properties of the system from Fig. 9.30 are used to write its x– and y–components.

The magnitude of the electric field at point P is calculated from Eq. (18). If we label the charge of the fixed point charge Q, we obtain:

$$|\mathbf{E}| = \frac{1}{4\pi\epsilon_0} \frac{Q}{x_0^2 + y_0^2} \quad (72)$$

in which the denominator in the second term on the right hand side equals the square of the distance between the charge Q and the point P due to the Pythagorean theorem.

The components E_x and E_y are derived from Eq. (72) and trigonometric considerations of Fig. 9.30 as indicated in the figure:

$$E_x = \frac{1}{4\pi\epsilon_0} \frac{Q}{x_0^2 + y_0^2} \cos\theta$$

$$E_y = \frac{1}{4\pi\epsilon_0} \frac{Q}{x_0^2 + y_0^2} \sin\theta \quad (73)$$

with

$$\sin\theta = \frac{y_0}{\sqrt{x_0^2 + y_0^2}} \;\; ; \;\; \cos\theta = \frac{x_0}{\sqrt{x_0^2 + y_0^2}} \quad (74)$$

9.9. Problems

P–9.1
We study 3 point charges at the corners of a triangle, as shown in Fig. 9.31. The charges are $q_1 = 5.0 \times 10^{-9}$ Cb, $q_2 = -4.0 \times 10^{-9}$ Cb, and $q_3 = 2.5 \times 10^{-9}$ Cb. Two distances of separation are also given, $l_{12} = 4$ m and $l_{13} = 6$ m. Find the net electric force on q_3.

P–9.2
In Fig. 9.32(a) we study two identical, electrically isolated spheres A and B. The surface of each sphere is conducting which allows for a uniform charge distribution. The spheres are separated by a distance a that is large compared to the diameter of each of the two spheres. Sphere A has initially a positive charge of $+Q$ and sphere B is electrically neutral ($q = 0$). Thus, there is no electrostatic force acting between the spheres.

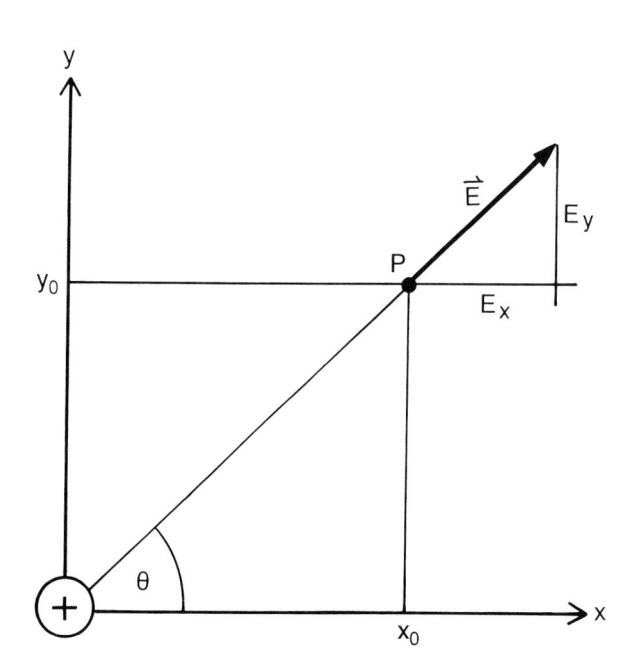

Fig. 9.30: The electric field and electric field components in a cartesian coordinate system at point $P = (x_0, y_0)$ with a positive point charge at the origin.

Fig. 9.31 for problem P–9.1.

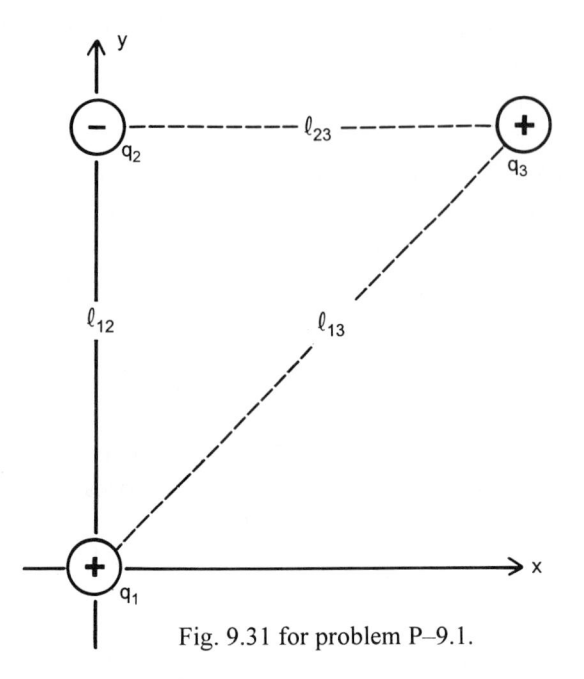

Suppose the spheres are now connected with a conducting wire as shown in Fig. 9.32(b). We assume that the wire is thin enough so that any net charge on it can be neglected. However, the repulsive force between the charges on sphere A leads to an equal distribution of charges between the two spheres, i.e., all the charges move to a maximum mutual distance. What is the electrostatic force between the spheres after the wire is removed?

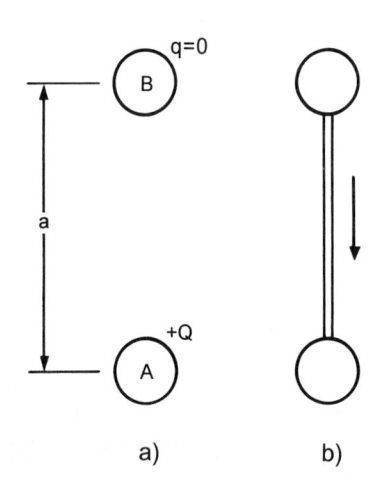

Fig. 9.32 for problem P–9.2.

P–9.3
The radius of atomic nuclei follows closely the formula

$$r\ [m] = 1.2 \times 10^{-15}\ A^{1/3} \qquad (75)$$

in which A is the atomic mass in unit [g/mol].

(a) Confirm that the density of the material in the nuclei is independent of the type of atom studied. This density is 2×10^{17} kg/m³!
(b) Using Eq. (75) and A(Bi) = 209.0 g/mol, find the magnitude of the repulsive electrostatic force between two of the protons in a bismuth nucleus when they are separated by the diameter of the nucleus.

P–9.4
How much negative charge is in 1.0 mol of neutral helium gas? Each He atom has two electrons in its atomic shell.

P–9.5
A CsCl (cesium chloride) salt crystal is built from unit cells, as shown in Fig. 9.33. Cl⁻ ions form the corners of the cube and the Cs⁺ ion is at the center of the cube. The edge length of the cube, which is called the lattice constant, is 0.4 nm.
(a) What is the magnitude of the net electrostatic force exerted on the cesium ion by its eight shown Cl⁻ neighbors?
(b) If the Cl⁻ in the lower left corner is removed, what is the magnitude of the net electrostatic force exerted on the cesium ion at the center by the seven remaining chlorine ions? In what direction does this force act on the cesium ion?

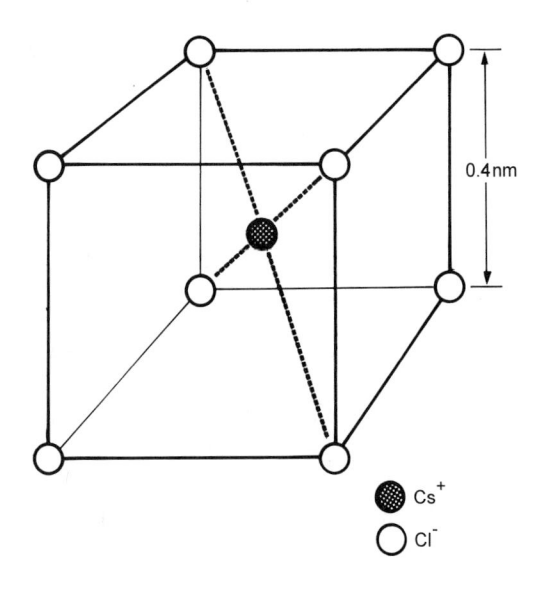

Fig. 9.33 for problem P–9.5.

P–9.6
Fig. 9.34 shows three positive charges, two charges of magnitude q at a distance a along the x– and the y–axis, and one charge of magnitude 2q at the origin. Calculate the electric field at point P for q = 1.0 nCb and the distance a = 1.0 m.

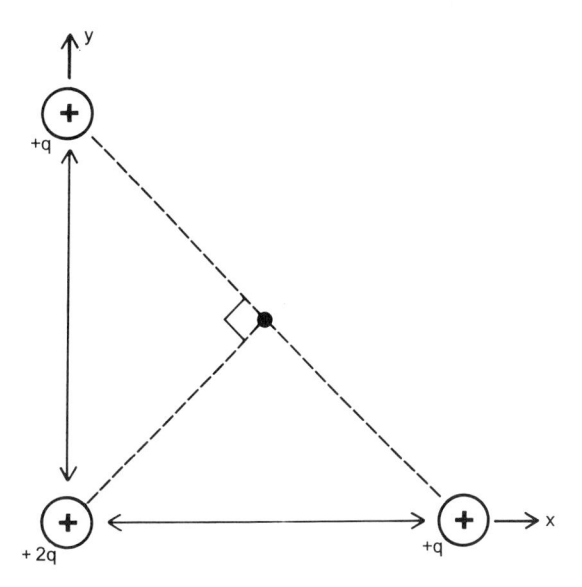

Fig. 9.34 for problem P–9.6 and P–9.15

P–9.7
Calculate the electric field half way between two charges, where one charge is $+10.0 \times 10^{-9}$ Cb and the second charge is
(a) $+5.0 \times 10^{-9}$ Cb at a distance of 20 cm;
(b) -5.0×10^{-9} Cb at a distance of 20 cm.

P–9.8
In the Millikan oil–drop apparatus of Fig. 9.2 a drop of radius r = 1.9 μm has an excess charge of two electrons. What are the magnitude and direction of the electric field that is required to balance the drop so it remains stationary in the apparatus? Use for the density of oil the value $\rho = 0.925$ g/cm³.

P–9.9
An electron is released into a uniform electric field of magnitude 1.5×10^3 N/Cb. Calculate the acceleration of the electron, neglecting gravitation.

P–9.10
Determine the magnitude of the force between an electric dipole with a dipole moment of 3×10^{-29} Cb m and an electron. The electron is positioned 20 nm from the center of the dipole, along the dipole axis.
Hint: assume that the given distance is large relative to the charge separation of the dipole.

P–9.11
Humid air breaks electrically down when its molecules become ionized. This happens in an electric field $|\mathbf{E}| = 3.0 \times 10^6$ N/Cb. In that field, calculate the magnitude of the electrostatic force on
(a) an electron, and
(b) an ion with a single positive charge.

P–9.12
A constant electric field is experimentally obtained with the set–up shown in Fig. 9.35: a 12 V battery is connected to two parallel metal plates separated by a distance of d = 0.25 cm. Calculate the magnitude of the electric field between the plates.

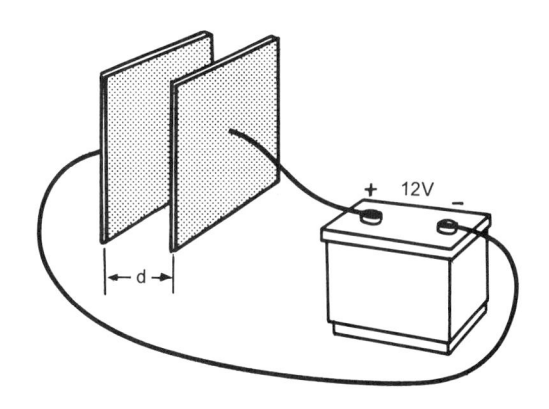

Fig. 9.35 for problem P–9.12.

P–9.13
A large number of energetic cosmic–ray particles (more on these in Chapter 20) reach the Earth's atmosphere continuously and knock electrons out of the molecules in the air. Once an electron is released, it responds to an electrostatic force which is due to an electric field **E** that is produced in the atmosphere by other charged particles. Near the surface of the Earth this electric field has a magnitude of E = 150 N/Cb and is directed downwards, as shown in Fig. 9.36. Calculate the change in electric potential energy of a released electron when it moves vertically upward through a distance d = 650 m.

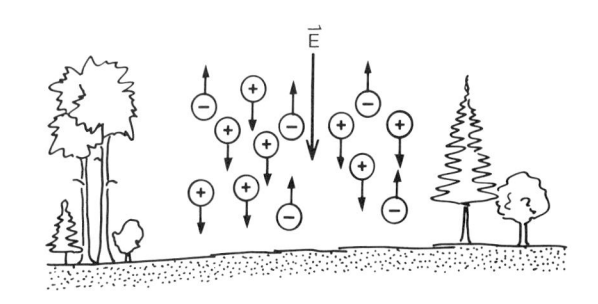

Fig. 9.36 for problem P–9.13.

P–9.14
(a) What is the electric potential V at a distance of r = 2.1×10^{-8} cm from a proton?
(b) What is the electric potential energy in units [J] and [eV] of an electron at the given distance from a proton?

(c) Why is this value close to the potential energy of an hydrogen atom?
(d) If the electron moves closer to the proton, does the electric potential energy increase or decrease?

P–9.15
(a) For the arrangement of charges in Fig. 9.34, calculate the electric potential at point P. Use q = 1.0 nCb and a = 1.0 m, and assume that V = 0 V at infinite distance.
(b) If a charge – 2q is brought to point P, what is the electric energy of this charge? Assume again that the electric potential energy is zero at infinite distance.

P–9.16
We study the three point charges shown in Fig. 9.37. The point charges are held at fixed positions of distance $l = 0.2$ m by forces that are not shown. What is *the electric potential energy of the system of 3 point charges*? Use for the three charges: $q_1 = +2Q$, $q_2 = -3Q$ and $q_3 = +Q$ where Q = 100 nCb.
Hint: The solution is done in steps. Assume that you bring first one of the point charges from a very large (infinite) distance to its position. Then repeat the procedure for the second, and lastly for the third point charge.

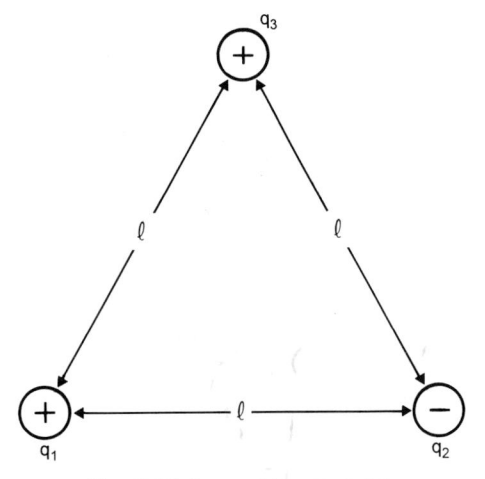

Fig. 9.37 for problem P–9.16.

Summary

Definitions:
- Dipole moment: $\mu = q\,d$ [Cb m]
  d is distance between charges q in dipole.

Units:
- Charge q [Cb], electric field **E** [N/Cb]
- Electric potential V [V]

Laws:
- Coulomb's law:

$$F = \frac{1}{4\pi\epsilon_0} \frac{q_1 \cdot q_2}{r^2} r^0$$

- Electric field:
(i) for a single point charge:

$$E = \frac{q_{fixed}}{4\pi\epsilon_0} \frac{r^0}{r^2}$$

The electric field vector is directed toward a negative charge or away from a positive charge.
(ii) for small number of point charges:
first calculate the field components for each charge. Then the components are added for all charges:

$$E_{x,\,net} = \sum_i E_x(q_i)$$

$$E_{y,\,net} = \sum_i E_y(q_i)$$

$$E_{z,\,net} = \sum_i E_z(q_i)$$

(iii) far from a dipole in axial direction (magnitude):

$$\lim_{x \gg d} |E_{at\,P}| = \frac{q}{2\pi\epsilon_0} \frac{d}{x^3}$$

(iv) for a parallel plate capacitor (magnitude): $|E| = \sigma/\epsilon_0$
σ is areal charge density $\sigma = q/A$.
- Electric energy for 2 point charges at distance r:

$$E_{el} = \frac{1}{4\pi\epsilon_0} \frac{q_1 q_2}{|r|}$$

- Electric potential: (i) for a point charge:

$$V = \frac{1}{4\pi\epsilon_0} \frac{q}{|r|}$$

(ii) for a dipole:

$$\lim_{r \gg d} V = \frac{q}{4\pi\epsilon_0} \frac{d\cos\theta}{r^2}$$

(iii) for a parallel plate capacitor:

$$V = |E|\,y = \frac{\sigma}{\epsilon_0} y$$

Chapter X

A second look at Water

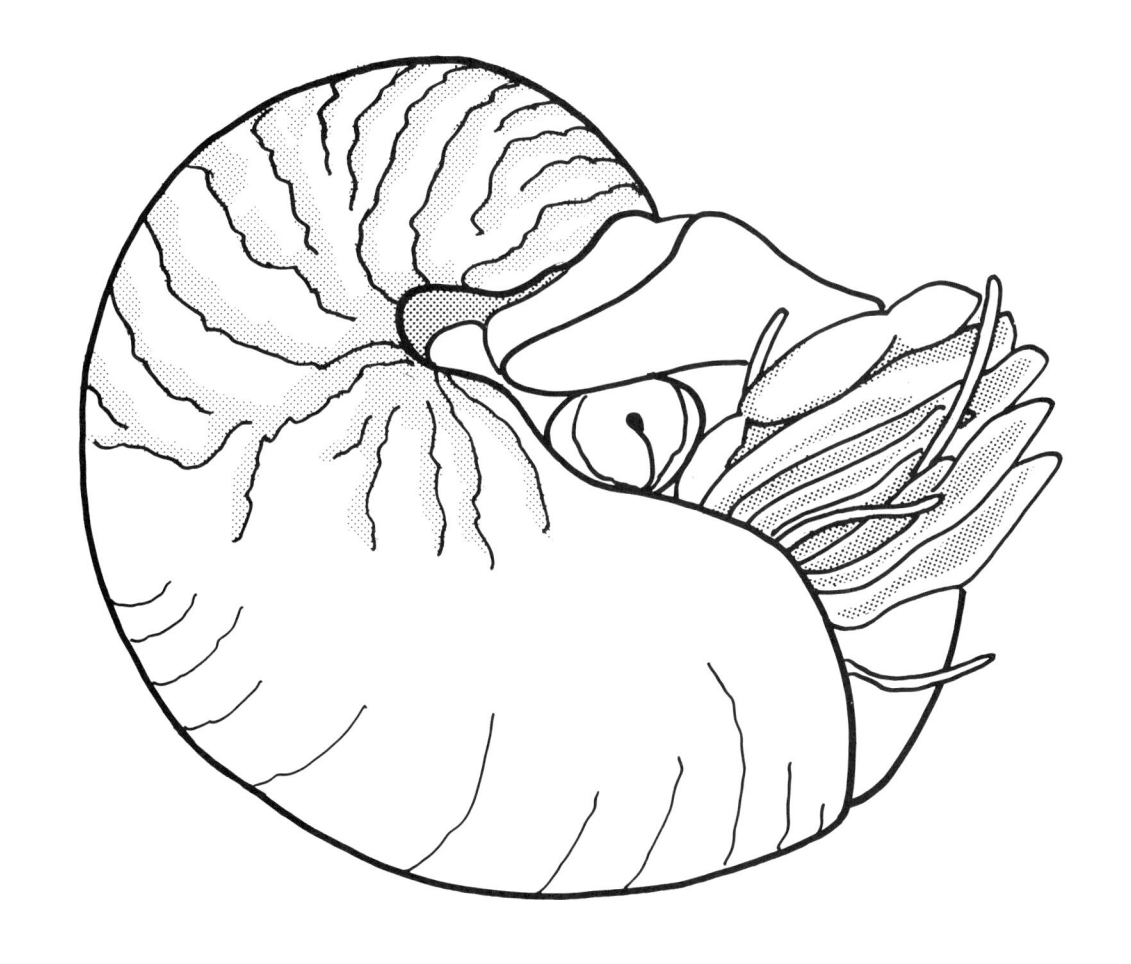

Static fluids

A SECOND LOOK AT WATER
STATIC FLUIDS

The term fluid includes liquids and gases. Fluids are deformable which allows them to develop toward a mechanical equilibrium in a given space. When intermolecular forces dominate, the fluid condenses and forms the liquid state. When the thermal energy of the system dominates its properties the fluid remains in the gaseous state. Liquids occupy a well–defined volume, it forms a surface when the dimensions of the accessible space exceeds the liquid's volume.

The ideal fluid model assumes that the fluid is incompressible. If such a fluid is in mechanical equilibrium it is called an ideal stationary fluid. If the ideal stationary fluid is in the condensed liquid state, Pascal's law states that the pressure increases linearly with depth below the surface. The mechanical equilibrium at the surface requires the pressure at the liquid surface to be equal to the pressure of the gas above.

Fluids support immersed objects by a buoyant force. This force counteracts the weight of the object and is proportional to the volume of the object and the density of the fluid.

The surface of a condensed ideal stationary fluid has properties which are distinct from the those of the bulk material. This is due to an excess amount of energy required to form a surface, called surface tension or surface energy. Surface energy causes a pressure difference across a bubble/droplet surface which is inversely proportional to the radius of the bubble/droplet.

Fluid surfaces facing a substance other than air are called interfaces. Interfacial energies are conceptually similar to surface energies and are related to the wetting properties at the interface. A consequence of interfacial interactions is capillarity. Capillarity is the action by which the surface of a liquid is elevated or depressed in a tube based on its surface energy and the tube/liquid interfacial energy.

10.1. Why water?

Life on Earth began in water and remained there exclusively for more than three billion years. Even life on dry land maintains close ties to water. The importance of water is evident from its abundance throughout the human body. The fraction of our body mass made up by water is about 75 % for a baby, decreases to about 60 % for young adults and as low as 50 % for seniors. Two thirds of the water in an adult's body is located in the cells with the last third in extracellular fluids, including the blood plasma.

Our bodies also operate a careful budgeting of the intake and disposal of water. The primary mechanisms of H_2O disposal are urine excretion (1500 ml/day) and perspiration through skin or lungs (900 ml/day). The water intake of an adult consists of 1500 ml/day as beverages and 700 ml/day with solid food. An additional 300 ml/day result from the metabolic processes in the body.

Water is so common that we often overlook the fact that it has many extraordinary qualities, all emerging from its electric dipole structure. Some of these properties were already mentioned in previous chapters; in the current chapter we want to study the macroscopic properties of liquids like water in a systematic fashion. We start with an overview of the features which make macroscopic amounts of water so unique.

Hydrogen bond formation
The bonds that hold together the atoms in a water molecule are polar covalent bonds, with the oxygen end of the molecule carrying a partial negative charge and the hydrogen end carrying a partial positive charge, as shown in Fig. 9.1. At the molecular level, these dipoles interact electrically with ions and other polarized neutral molecules. The interaction is strongest at short range and more effective along the dipole axis than in other directions (directional anisotropy).

At the next higher level of organization, water molecules form hydrogen bonds with other water molecules (illustrated in Fig. 9.16). With ions the formation of a hydration shell is observed (illustrated in Fig. 9.10). Both of these effects indicate a strong propensity of water molecules to form larger complexes.

Hydrogen bonds lead to cohesion
Water molecules stick to each other as a result of hydrogen bonding. When water is in its liquid form, its hydrogen bonds are fragile: they are only about 5 % to 10 % as strong as covalent bonds. Each hydrogen bond lasts only for a time period of about 1×10^{-12} s, but there are so many of these bonds in a droplet of water at any given time that the net effect is profound. Thus, we have found a collective property: hydrogen bonds hold water together at a macroscopic scale. This effect is called cohesion.

Related to cohesion is the effect of surface tension, which is a measure of how much effort is needed to increase the surface area of a liquid. Water has a greater surface tension than most other liquids due to the cohesion between the water molecules in its surface. We note the large surface tension of water when observing some animals, such as water striders, standing on water without breaking the surface. Surface tension is a macroscopic property of the fluid we discuss later in detail in this chapter.

Large cohesion and surface tension allow water to be liquid at room temperature. Most other small molecules are in the gaseous state at room temperature; the closest molecule to allow as a solvent the development of life is ammonia which boils at $-33°C$. In an ammonia solution, chemical processes would be severely slowed down as chemical reaction rates roughly double for every additional 10 degrees of temperature.

The large heat capacity of water moderates temperature changes
We saw already in Chapter 5 that water has a large heat capacity. It can therefore stabilize air temperatures as it absorbs or releases a relatively large amount of heat with only a slight change in its own temperature. This is the reason coastal regions usually have a milder climate than continental regions. The high heat capacity of water also stabilizes the temperature of ocean water which causes favorable conditions for marine life. The same reasoning applies also to individual organisms. Because we are made primarily of water, our bodies are able to better resist changes in their temperature.

The high latent heat of vaporization of water favors evaporative cooling
The transformation of a system from the liquid to the gaseous state is called evaporation. Some evaporation occurs at any temperature but if a liquid is heated it evaporates more rapidly. The amount of thermal energy required to evaporate a liquid is called the latent heat of vaporization. The latent heat of vaporization of water is very high; to convert 1 mol of liquid water to vapor, nearly double the amount of thermal energy is needed than to evaporate 1 mol of an alcohol or ammonia. This property is again caused by cohesion: hydrogen bonds must be broken before the molecules can leave from the liquid. On a global scale, the high latent heat of vaporization of water helps moderate the climate: a significant fraction of the solar heat absorbed by equatorial oceans is stored in the water vapor formed in evaporation of surface water. This moisture then circulates toward the poles and releases the stored thermal energy when it condenses to form rain or snow. On the level of individual organisms, evaporating water cools the skin surface because the evaporation requires a significant amount of thermal energy drawn from the body. Thus, perspiration prevents terrestrial organisms from overheating. This mechanism also works for plants. Water evaporation from the leaves keeps the tissues in the leaves from overheating in the sunlight.

Ice floats on the surface of liquid water
Water is one of the few substances that are less dense in solid form than in the liquid state. While most substances contract when they solidify, water expands to accommodate the peculiar hydrogen bond structure shown in Fig. 9.16. At temperatures above $4°C$, water behaves like other liquids: it expands when heated and it contracts when cooled. Below $4°C$ more and more hydrogen bonds remain stable which pushes the molecules further apart from each other. At $0°C$ water then freezes as the thermal energy of the molecules is no longer sufficient to break the hydrogen bonds. Ice is fully ordered as shown for the central water molecule in Fig. 9.16. This local order is a morphologically wide open arrangement, leading to a 10 % reduction in the density compared to liquid water at $4°C$. The ability of ice to float is due to buoyancy which we discuss in the current chapter. It is biologically important, because if ice sank, then sooner than later ponds, lakes, and oceans would freeze solid, making life as we know it impossible. Instead, floating ice thermally insulates the liquid water below, allowing life to exist under the frozen surface.

Water is an effective solvent in chemistry
Sugar thrown in a beaker of water dissolves. The beaker then contains a uniform mixture of sugar and water. A liquid that is completely homogeneous but contains two or more substances is called a solution. An aqueous solution is one in which water is the solvent. Water is a very

versatile solvent, a property we traced to its dipole character in the previous chapter. We saw that a sodium chloride crystal would not dissolve if the water molecules could not form a hydration shell, which represents an electric interaction to lower the potential energy of the parting ions. Aqueous solutions are wide–spread: from seawater to the cytoplasm in cells, a great variety of dissolved ions are found. A compound does not need to be ionic to dissolve in water, sugar for example dissolves because it is a polar molecule (dipole structure). Even molecules as large as proteins dissolve in water as they often have ionic and/or polar regions.

10.2. Model system: the ideal stationary fluid

We discuss the macroscopic properties of water in this and the next chapters. However, we don't focus exclusively on water but study a more general model system which displays many of the same properties. This model system is called a fluid. Fluids are systems that yield to any force that alters their shape, causing the system to flow until it reaches a mechanical equilibrium at which it conforms to the shape of the container. Based on this definition, the term fluid refers to both liquids and gases, but distinguishes these substances from solids, which remain unaltered when placed in a container.

There are, however, differences between liquids and gases we have to take into account. The molecules in a liquid are in a condensed state of matter, i.e., they maintain a fixed intermolecular distance. If the liquid is brought into a container with a volume larger than the volume the liquid occupies, the liquid forms a surface. In contrast, gases adjust their intermolecular distance and fill any provided volume uniformly. Gases have no natural surfaces. We focus first on fluids in mechanical equilibrium; in that state we call the fluid stationary.

Remember that we defined the term equilibrium such that it refers to the state in which all essential parameters of the system are time independent. What we mean with essential parameters in the current context is illustrated with a glass filled with water. The water is in equilibrium: no obvious changes occur while we observe the system. However, like in a gas, there is a tremendous amount of motion of the particles at the microscopic level. Thus, the equilibrium of a macroscopic fluid does not include as an essential parameter the microscopic motion of the fluid molecules. The properties which are essential for an ideal stationary fluid are:

(I) The ideal stationary fluid is incompressible. This means that both the volume of the fluid, V, and its density, $\rho = m/V$, are constant, i.e., they particularly do not depend on the pressure. This is a good approximation for liquids, but does not apply to gases. Therefore, we have to apply the concepts of this chapter with some caution to gases and cannot abandon the ideal gas model introduced in the previous chapter.

(II) The ideal stationary fluid is deformable under the influence of forces and seeks a mechanical equilibrium. Only after the mechanical equilibrium is established does the fluid become stationary. This applies equally to liquids and gases. This condition is obviously very useful because we already know a great deal about mechanical equilibria.

10.3. Basic parameters of the model system: the pressure

We are well aware of pressure variations in the atmosphere. These are most notable when travelling to large altitudes, e.g. in mountaineering or during air travel. In comparison, pressure variations in liquids are much more profound. Many diving–related accidents and the need of life–guards in all public pools are a clear sign that we are exposed to unexpectedly strong effects once we immerse our bodies in a liquid. But how can we express this strong effect quantitatively? The idea goes back to Blaise Pascal and the year 1653, i.e., 34 years before Sir Isaac Newton laid the foundation of mechanics.

10.3.1. Pascal's law

Instead of following Pascal's original reasoning, we use the mechanics concepts introduced in Chapter 2 to study a deep ideal stationary fluid. The approach is illustrated in Fig. 10.1. We can use the mechanics concepts because we required the ideal stationary fluid to be in mechanical equilibrium. The pressure dependence on depth in the fluid is established by selecting a small fluid element at a certain depth as highlighted in Fig. 10.1 by a small box. The sketch at the right side of Fig. 10.1 shows the free–body–diagram for this fluid element. Three collinear forces act on the element:

(I) the weight of the fluid element W, which is directed downwards;

(II) the contact force of the fluid below the element, F_{up}, which pushes the fluid element upwards; and

(III) the contact force of the fluid above the element, F_{down}, which pushes the fluid element downwards.

The fluid element neither rises nor sinks because it is in mechanical equilibrium. Thus Newton's first law

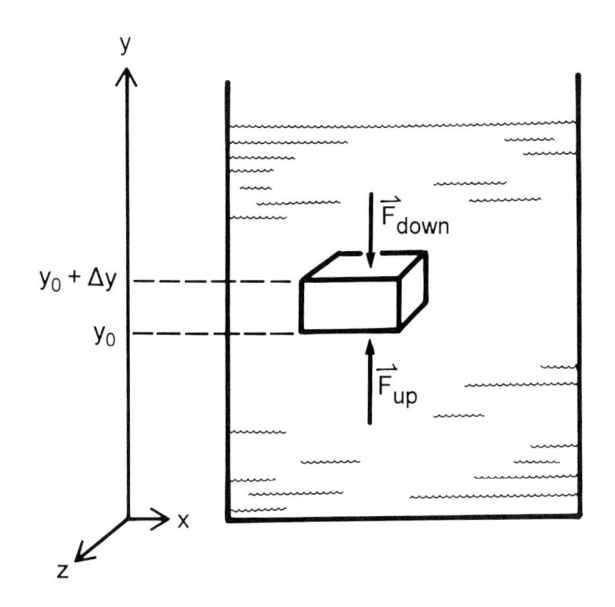

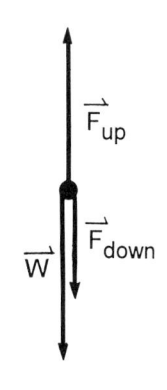

Fig. 10.1: A small element of fluid is identified in a beaker. Three forces act on this element: two contact forces due to the remaining fluid and the weight of the fluid element. The corresponding free–body–diagram for the fluid segment is shown at the right. Note that such a fluid element is at rest in an ideal stationary fluid.

applies:

$$\sum_i F_{i,y} = 0 = F_{up} - W - F_{down} \qquad (1)$$

We use Eq. (1) to find a relation between pressure and depth. All three forces are rewritten; the weight to show density and volume, and the two contact forces to show the pressure. Because density is mass divided by volume, the mass of the fluid element is given as:

$$\Delta m = \rho \, \Delta V = \rho \, A \, \Delta y \qquad (2)$$

in which A is the horizontal surface area of the water element and ρ is the density of the fluid. Thus the weight of the fluid element in Fig. 10.1 is:

$$W = g \, \Delta m = \rho \, g \, A \, \Delta y \qquad (3)$$

The two contact forces in Eq. (1) are replaced by the respective pressure terms since the forces do not act on a point mass but on an extended object. For this we first note that the fluid element stretches vertically from y_0 to $y_0 + \Delta y$. At the position y_0 we label the pressure p and at the position $y_0 + \Delta y$ we label the pressure $p + \Delta p$. This allows us to express the magnitudes of the forces acting on the two horizontal surfaces of the fluid element:

$$|F_{up}| = p \cdot A$$
$$|F_{down}| = (p + \Delta p) \cdot A \qquad (4)$$

Using Eqs. (3) and (4) we rewrite Eq. (1) in the form:

$$p A - (p + \Delta p) A - \rho \, g \, A \, \Delta y = 0 \qquad (5)$$

after dividing by A this leads to:

$$\Delta p = - \rho \, g \, \Delta y \qquad (6)$$

Note that Eq. (6) applies for any depth difference Δy since neither the density ρ nor the gravitational constant g vary with depth. Thus, choosing two arbitrary depths y_1 and y_2 with respective pressures p_1 and p_2, Eq. (6) is written in the form:

$$p_2 - p_1 = - \rho \, g \, (y_2 - y_1) \qquad (7)$$

> *Pascal's law states that the difference between the pressures at two different positions in a fluid is proportional to the vertical distance between these two positions. The proportionality factor is the product of the density of the fluid and the gravitational acceleration.*

Eq. (7) is the first of two formulations we introduce for Pascal's law. It is used in this general form when the surface of the fluid cannot be identified and thus cannot be used as a reference point. Examples include studies of the blood pressure because the cardiovascular system is a closed system and no surface of the blood toward air exists. For an application of the law in the form of Eq. (7) see the example given in the next section.

In systems with an identifiable surface of the fluid, e.g. for water in a glass, index 1 in Eq. (7) is chosen to refer to the surface of the liquid. Therefore, we set $y_1 = 0$ and $p_1 = p_{atm}$. The atmospheric pressure is the proper value for the pressure of the fluid surface since it is in mechanical equilibrium. The force pushing the surface upwards equals the force caused by the air pressure pushing downwards. Note that we used this argument before when we introduced Boyle's law in Chapter 6.

It is also more convenient in this case to define the position axis downwards, i.e. to define the depth below the surface as a positive distance. This changes the negative sign on the right hand side of Eq. (6) into a positive sign. Writing $y_2 = d$ with d the depth below the surface of the fluid in unit [m] we get:

$$p = p_{atm} + \rho g d \quad (8)$$

Eq. (8) is the second formulation of Pascal's law. It expresses the pressure at a depth d below the surface as a function of the pressure at the surface and the weight of the water column above depth d. The following comments on the two formulations of Pascal's law are useful:

(I) Pascal's law does not apply to the fluid *air*, i.e., Eq. (7) does not describe pressure variations in the atmosphere. This is illustrated by trying to calculate the height of the upper end (surface) of the atmosphere by substituting for the height $y_2 = y_{max}$, the maximum height y_{max} of the atmosphere:

$$\left(p_{y_{max}} - p_{ground}\right) = -\rho g \left(y_{max} - y_{ground}\right) \quad (9)$$

At the maximum height the pressure drops to a value of $p_{y_{max}} = 0$ atm, i.e., y_{max} is the height where the vacuum of outer space would begin. The ground level values are $y_{ground} = 0$ m and the pressure $p_{ground} = p_{atm}$. We find from Eq. (9):

$$-1.01 \times 10^5 [Pa] = -1.2 [\frac{kg}{m^3}] \, 9.8 [\frac{m}{s^2}] \, y_{max} \quad (10)$$

in which we used $\rho = 1.2$ kg/m³ for the density of air at sea level. Eq. (10) yields:

$$y_{max} = \frac{1.01 \times 10^5 [Pa]}{1.2 \left[\frac{kg}{m^3}\right] 9.8 \left[\frac{m}{s^2}\right]} = 8614 \text{ m} \quad (11)$$

The assumption of a constant density throughout the atmosphere is clearly inadequate as the atmosphere would terminate at 8614 m height which is 234 m below the peak of Mount Everest! Thus, Pascal's law does not apply to gases because gases are compressible and have densities which depend on pressure. The dependence of the gas density on the pressure was discussed in detail in Example 6.2. The data for carbon–dioxide in Table 6.1 provide a specific example.

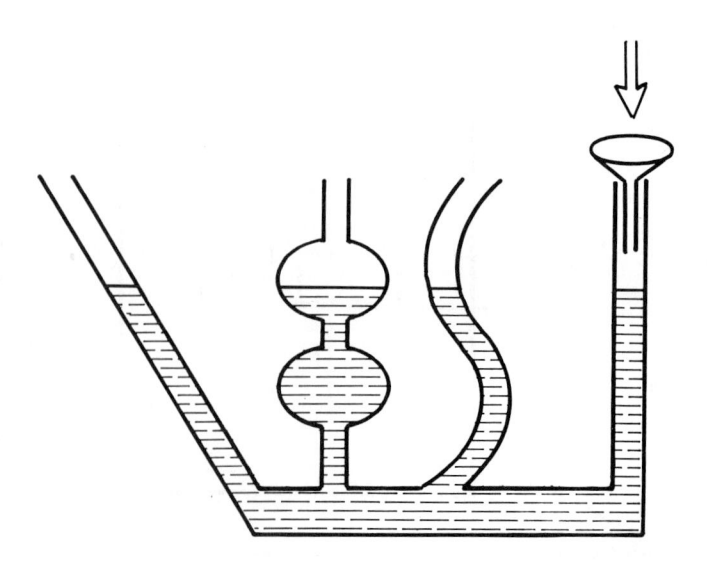

Fig. 10.2: Experimental illustration of the result of Pascal's law (Eq. (8)) that the pressure at various depth in a fluid does not depend on the shape of the fluid container.

(II) Pascal's law does not contain any information about the shape of the container. Thus, regardless of the shape of the container, the pressure increases below the surface and results in a fixed value at a given depth. This is illustrated in Fig. 10.2, in which the fluid surface is located at the same height above the bottom of the glass container in each tube. Note that deviations from this behavior may occur for fluid containers with tiny diameters. We discuss such observations as capillarity later in this chapter.

(III) Pressure data are often given in non–standard units. Blood pressure, for example, is usually recorded in unit [mmHg]. For calculations it is advisable to convert such units to standard units. The standard unit of pressure is [Pa]. Frequently used conversions are included in a conversion table in the General Appendix (Chapter 24). Some pressure data, such as blood pressure, are reported relative to air pressure. Pressure values relative to air pressure (called gauge pressure values) can have either positive or negative values. For example, the term $\rho g d$ in Eq. (8) represents a gauge pressure.

Example 10.1
What is the pressure in water 10 m below the surface?

Solution: The density of fresh water has a value of $\rho = 1.0$ kg/l = 1×10^3 kg/m³. Using further g = 9.8 m/s² and p_{atm} = 1 atm = 1.01×10^5 Pa, we get at 10 m depth from Eq. (8):

$$p_{10m} = 1.01 \times 10^5 [Pa] + ...$$

$$... + 1000[\frac{kg}{m^3}]\, 9.8[\frac{m}{s^2}]\, 10[m] \quad (12)$$

which yields:

$$p_{10m} = 1.993 \times 10^5\ Pa = 1.97\ atm \quad (13)$$

This result shows that the pressure below the water surface rises fast, doubling at just 10 m depth. In Fig. 10.3, Eq. (13) is used to illustrate the pressure in water as a function of depth. The fast pressure increase is a critical issue for diving, as discussed in several problem sets and in greater detail in the next chapter.

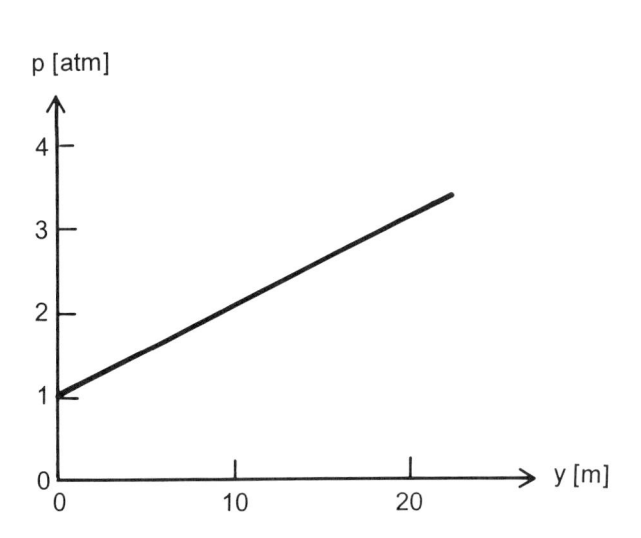

Fig. 10.3: The water pressure as a function of depth from the surface to 20 m below the surface.

Fig. 10.4: Blood pressure variations along the cardiovascular system. (1) left ventricle of the heart, (2) aorta, (3) peripheric arteries, (4) arterioles, (5) capillaries, (6) vena cava, (7) right atrium of heart, (8) right ventricle of heart, (9) pulmonary artery, (10) left atrium of heart. Note that the pressure values are gauge pressures, i.e., values given relative to the atmospheric pressure.

10.3.2. Blood pressure
(Example 10.2)

Calculate the additional blood pressure difference between the brain and the feet in a standing person of height 1.8 m, relative to the blood pressure for the person in supine position. Use $\rho = 1.06$ g/cm³ for the density of blood.

Supplementary physiological information : We distinguish high and low pressure circuits in the cardiovascular system. The blood pressure varies significantly along the human cardiovascular system as illustrated in Fig. 10.4. The high–pressure circuit includes the aorta, the arteries and arterioles, and the capillaries. The blood pressure in the arteries varies between 10.7 kPa (diastolic pressure) and 16.0 kPa (systolic pressure). The low–pressure circuit includes the veins and the pulmonary system; in this system the pressure varies only between 1.3 kPa and 3.3 kPa. Since all blood pressure values in

Table 10.1: Blood pressure as a function of age.

Age	normal blood pressure	
	[mmHg]	[kPa]
Newborn[†]	60 – 80	8.0 – 10.7
Baby[†]	80 – 90	10.7 – 12.0
Up to 10 years[‡]	90/60	12.0/8.0
10 – 30 years[‡]	110/75	14.7/10.0
30 – 40 years[‡]	125/85	16.7/11.3
40 – 60 years[‡]	140/90	18.7/12.0
> 60 years[‡]	150/90	20.0/12.0

[†] systolic blood pressure only
[‡] systolic/diastolic blood pressure

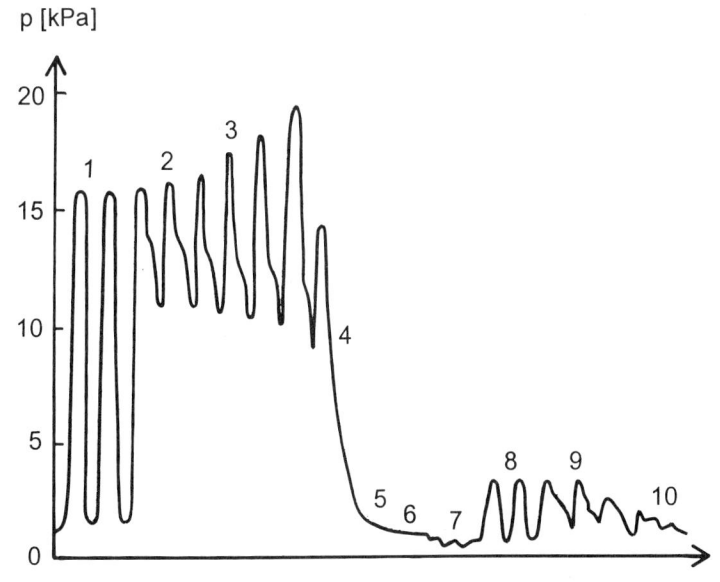

Fig. 10.4 are positive gauge pressure values, we note that the pressure in our cardiovascular system is always above air pressure.

The pressure in the high pressure system varies also with age as illustrated in Table 10.1.

The term *supine position* in the problem text refers to the case that the person is lying as shown in Fig. 10.5(a). In supine position the blood pressure is fully described in Fig. 10.4, with a maximum variation of about 15 % of atmospheric pressure. When the person stands as shown in Fig. 10.5(b), an additional difference between the blood pressure in the feet and in the brain is due to the extra column of blood which rests on the blood in the feet.

Solution: To quantify the additional difference for the standing person, we use Pascal's law in the general form as given in Eq. (7) because there is no blood surface:

$$p_{brain} - p_{feet} = -\rho_{blood}\, g\, (y_{brain} - y_{feet}) \qquad (14)$$

Eq. (14) is rewritten by introducing $\Delta p = p_{feet} - p_{brain}$ for the pressure difference and the term $\Delta h = y_{brain} - y_{feet}$ for the height of the person. This choice for Δp eliminates the extra minus–sign on the right hand side of Eq. (14):

$$\Delta p = \rho_{blood}\, g\, \Delta h \qquad (15)$$

Substituting the given values in Eq. (15) yields:

$$\Delta p = 1.06 \times 10^3 \left[\frac{kg}{m^3}\right] 9.8 \left[\frac{m}{s^2}\right] 1.8 [m] \qquad (16)$$

$$\Rightarrow \Delta p = 1.87 \times 10^4\ Pa$$

This difference is about 20 % of the atmospheric pressure; it is of the same order of magnitude as the pressure variation in the circulatory system in supine position.

For medical applications, it is more useful to refer to pressures which are measured relative to the pressure at the height of the heart. For a standing person of 1.8 m height, the heart is at a height of 1.26 m and the arterial and venous pressures in the feet are increased relative to the pressures at the height of the heart by:

$$\Delta p = \rho\, g\, h =$$

$$= 1.06 \times 10^3 \left[\frac{kg}{m^3}\right] 9.8 \left[\frac{m}{s^2}\right] 1.26 [m] \qquad (17)$$

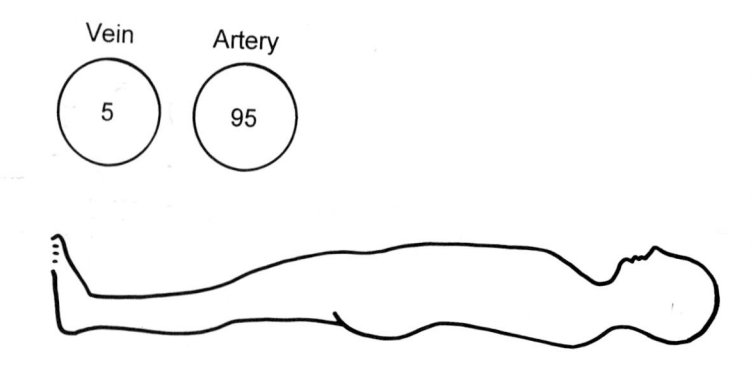

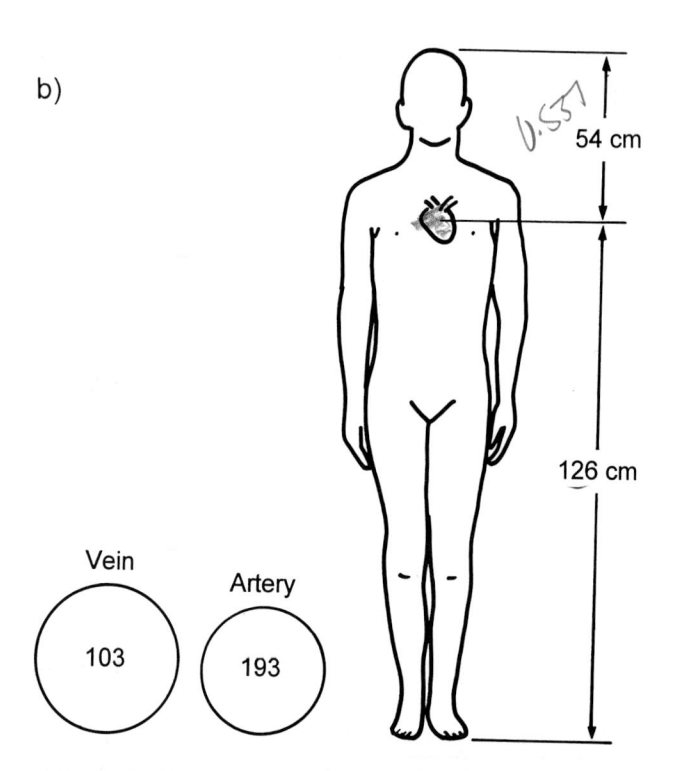

Fig. 10.5: Blood pressures and blood vessel sizes in the feet of a person (a) in supine position and (b) standing upright. The vessel sizes are indicated by the area of the shown circles. The numbers in the vessels are the respective blood pressures in [mmHg].

which yields:

$$\Delta p = 13.1\ kPa = 98\ mmHg \qquad (18)$$

The pressure is increased to an average arterial value of 193 mmHg and an average venous value of 103 mmHg. This is illustrated in Fig. 10.5. The figure shows two pairs of circles which indicate the relative size of veins and arteries in the feet. The numbers in the circles refer

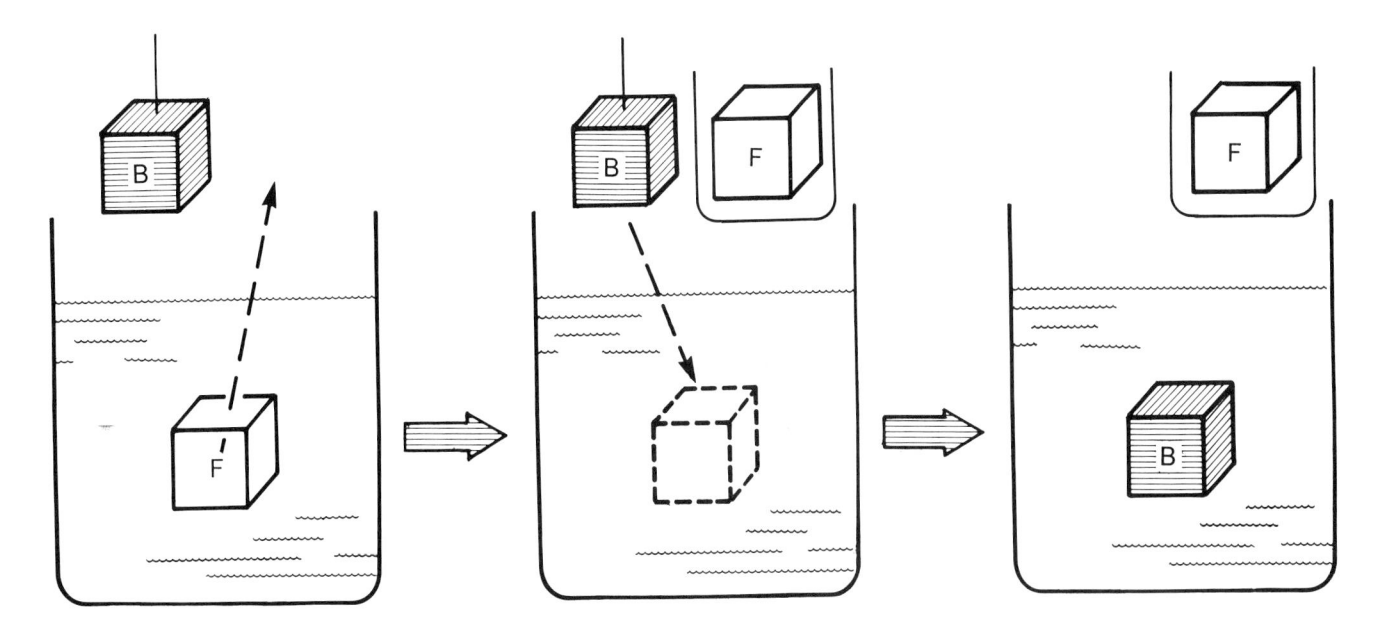

Fig. 10.6: Illustration of Archimedes' principle. The principle is introduced in two steps: first a fluid element with the same shape as the object is removed. In the second step the object is placed in the void.

to blood pressures in the respective vessel in [mmHg]. In the scalp, the pressures decrease at the same time by:

$$\Delta p = 1.06 \times 10^3 \left[\frac{kg}{m^3}\right] 9.8 \left[\frac{m}{s^2}\right] (-0.54 [m]) \quad (19)$$

which yields:

$$\Delta p = -5.6 \; kPa = -42 \; mmHg \quad (20)$$

The average arterial pressure drops to 53 mmHg and the average venous pressure becomes −37 mmHg. This low venous value does not lead to the closing of the veins in the skull, though, since the blood vessels in the brain are surrounded by cerebrospinal fluid and the pressure in that fluid also drops by a corresponding amount relative to the extracellular fluid in the chest when the person is standing upright.

In large land animals, this effect can be much more profound than in humans. The additional pressure required when blood must be pushed above the level of the heart can only be generated with the four–chambered heart of mammals. Of these, the pumping challenge is greatest for animals with long necks. A standing giraffe needs to pump blood as much as 2.5 m above the heart to the brain. That requires significantly more of an additional blood pressure in the left ventricle; the normal systolic pressure at the heart of a giraffe is therefore more than 250 mm Hg. Such a systolic pressure would be extremely dangerous for humans. Special valves and a feedback mechanism reduce cardiac output when the giraffe bends its neck down to drink. In this position the brain is suddenly almost 2 m below the heart and would otherwise be exposed to a tremendous blood pressure due to the height difference.

Another group of animals which had similar issues to deal with were the dinosaurs. With their upright gait and long necks (up to 10 m), cardiovascular adaptations were needed to compensate blood pressure variations as a function of body posture.

10.4. Important properties of ideal stationary fluids

Ideal stationary fluids display a range of physical properties which are important for biological applications. Of these properties, we discuss buoyancy, surface tension and capillarity in this section.

10.4.1. Buoyancy (Archimedes principle)

The density of an ideal stationary fluid in which an object is released has a profound effect on the resulting motion: a piece of wood released above a table falls down onto the table, but floats up to the surface when released from a submerged position in a beaker of water. Even an object which accelerates downwards in both air and water, such as a piece of metal, displays a different apparent weight when suspended from a spring scale and held below the surface of water.

Fig. 10.6 illustrates how the effect due to the

surrounding fluid is quantified. A beaker with a fluid and a block B, suspended above the fluid, are shown in the left sketch. A fluid element F with the same shape and volume as the block B is identified below the fluid surface. For the fluid element F, mechanical equilibrium conditions apply in the same fashion as discussed for Fig. 10.1. Choosing the positive y–axis to be directed upwards, the mechanical equilibrium condition for the fluid element F is written as:

$$F_{up} - F_{down} - W_F = 0 \qquad (21)$$

In the first step, we assume that the fluid element F is removed from the beaker and placed in a small container, leaving a void in the beaker of the same shape and volume as the block B. This is obviously not possible in a real experiment, thus we call these considerations a gedanken–experiment which implies that the experiment is only done in our thoughts. After creating the void, the void is not in mechanical equilibrium since its weight is zero but the two contact forces remain unaltered as the fluid around the void, which exerts these forces, has not changed:

$$F_{up} - F_{down} = W_F > 0 \qquad (22)$$

As a result, an acceleration of the void would occur as required by Newton's second law. Indeed, for a system similar to the void, such as an air bubble, an acceleration to the surface is observed. In our gedanken–experiment, however, we now place block B in the void. This leads to the following net force acting on the block:

$$F_{net} = F_{up} - F_{down} - W_B = W_F - W_B \qquad (23)$$

Three cases are distinguished for Eq. (23):
(I) $F_{net} > 0$. The weight of the block is less than the weight of the displaced fluid and the block B rises to the surface. The force causing the object to accelerate upwards is called the buoyant force. Examples of this case are ice or wood in water. The wood fibres are denser than the displaced water but wood contains a large fraction of enclosed air. Ice has a lower density than liquid water due to its peculiar structure in the solid state at atmospheric pressure.
(II) $F_{net} = 0$. The block floats at its current depth below the fluid surface. The weight of the block equals the weight of the displaced fluid. This case describes a submerged submarine or a diver with breathing equipment.
(III) $F_{net} < 0$. The weight of the block is larger than the weight of the displaced fluid and the block sinks to the bottom of the container.

These findings were first reported by Archimedes in antiquity. Based on Eq. (23) the principle is usually stated in the following form:

> *Archimedes principle: When an object is immersed in a fluid, the fluid exerts an upward force on the object equal to the weight of the fluid displaced by the object.*

We express the magnitude of the buoyant force in the form:

$$F_{buoy} = \rho_{fluid} V_{body} g \qquad (24)$$

in which the density is the value for the fluid but the volume is the value for the immersed object. The buoyant force is directed upwards, i.e., in the opposite direction of the weight.

Mechanical equilibrium applies in one of the three cases; the system accelerates toward a new equilibrium in the other two cases: in case (I), in which the buoyant force exceeds the weight, the object floats to the surface of the fluid. When a sufficient fraction of the object reaches above the fluid surface, the body's volume that displaces fluid is reduced and the weight of the displaced fluid becomes equal to the weight of the block. Note that for an object floating at the surface of a fluid, only the fraction of the volume below the surface of the fluid enters Eq. (24). In case (III) the object sinks to the bottom of the beaker. There, a mechanical equilibrium is reached due to an additional normal force acting on the object upwards.

Buoyant forces are observed in many contexts. In Example 3.8, we calculated the force on the central dendrite in a Pacinian corpuscle (shown in Fig. 3.23). The example illustrates how the buoyant force is taken into account in a mechanical problem involving a floating object in a fluid. Buoyancy can also be illustrated in many macroscopic experiments. A simple experiment with biological implications consists of a freshly cut piece of lemon peel placed in a bottle filled with fluid. The bottle is closed with a plastic cap and variable pressure is exerted on the cap with the thumb. The lemon peel rises or sinks depending on the pressure exerted on the plastic cap. The lemon peel floats in the first place due to very small air bubbles in its porous structure. The varying force acting on the cap causes variations of the water pressure. The air bubbles vary significantly in size with these changes (air as a gas is highly compressible), changing the volume of the peel in Eq. (24).

Example 10.3

The envelope and basket of a hot–air balloon have a combined mass of 250 kg. The spherical envelope of the balloon has a diameter of 16 m when fully inflated. To what temperature must the enclosed air be heated for the balloon to carry four passengers of 70 kg each? Assume that the surrounding air is at 20°C and is treated as an ideal gas.

Supplementary chemical information The molar mass of air is 29 g/mol, This value results from the composition of air: 75 % of the air volume is nitrogen at 28 g/mol and 25 % is oxygen at 32 g/mol.

Solution: Buoyancy also occurs in gases such as air. In the case of a hot–air balloon, the hot air displaces cold air in the enclosed volume. The hot air in the balloon has the same pressure as the cold air outside since the balloon is open at the bottom.

In the example, we want to lift a total mass of 530 kg, which corresponds to a weight of 5200 N. The volume of the balloon is $V = 4\pi r^3/3$; thus, the volume is $V = 2145$ m³ for a radius of r = 8 m. If the air in the fully inflated balloon were at the same temperature as the surrounding air, the balloon would enclose the following amount of air:

$$n_{cold} = \frac{pV}{RT} = \frac{1.013\times10^5[Pa]\ 2145[m^3]}{8.314[J/K\ mol]\ 293[K]} \quad (25)$$

$$\Rightarrow n_{cold} = 89200\ mol$$

This amount is calculated with the assumption that the air can be treated as an ideal gas. When the air in the balloon has reached its operating temperature, the number of moles of air in the balloon must be reduced by an amount equivalent to 530 kg (or more). The needed reduction in [mol] is 530 kg divided by the molar mass of air with 29 g/mol, which yields 18280 mol. Thus, we require $n_{hot} = 70920$ mol (or less). Using the ideal gas law with a fixed pressure and volume, we find for the temperature:

$$T_{hot} = T_{cold}\frac{n_{cold}}{n_{hot}} = 293[K]\frac{89200[mol]}{70920[mol]} \quad (26)$$

$$\Rightarrow T_{hot} = 369\ K = 96\ °C$$

Another vehicle designed for lighter–than–air travel is the zeppelin (named for Ferdinand von Zeppelin; this term is used for an airship with a rigid framework while blimp refers to a non–rigid design where the shape of the airship is a result of the gas pressure). A famous airship of this type was the 250 m long Hindenburg. Zeppelins carry large tanks of either hydrogen (H_2, M = 2 g/mol) or helium (He, M = 4 g/mol). While lighter when using hydrogen gas and, therefore, allowing 70 passengers on a trans–Atlantic trip instead of 40 passengers, the hydrogen filling of the Hindenburg was dangerous as hydrogen is explosive when mixed with oxygen. Such an explosion caused the Hindenburg disaster in 1937 at Lakehurst, New Jersey.

Example 10.4

Greek mythology reports the story of the Argonauts. Under Jason's leadership they had to travel to Aeëtes, king of Colchis, in their quest for the Golden Fleece. On the way, the story claims, they had to throw significant amounts of gold overboard when passing from the Mediterranean Sea into the Black Sea and then again when passing from the Black Sea into the Sea of Azov. Can this story be true?

Solution: There is a significant change in the salt concentration between these three bodies of water. The Mediterranean Sea, the most southern of them stretching from 30° to 40 ° northern latitude, loses water through evaporation the fastest. It receives fresh water from only four major rivers: the Po (Italy), the Rhône (France), the Ebro (Spain) and the Nile (Egypt). Thus, the salt content in the Mediterranean Sea is high at 38 g/ l NaCl, which corresponds to a density of $\rho = 1.028$ g/cm³. The Black Sea is smaller than the Mediterranean Sea, but receives fresh water from two major rivers, the Danube (Romania) and the Dnieper (Ukraine). Thus, its salt content is lower at 16 g/l NaCl and its density is $\rho = 1.014$ g/cm³. The Sea of Azov is a very small body of water separated from the Black Sea by the Crimean peninsula. Because it receives fresh water from a major river, the Don (Russia), it is almost like an inland lake with a salt content of only 3 g/l NaCl and a density of $\rho = 1.003$ g/cm³, i.e., just 0.3 % denser than tab water.

The Archimedes principle predicts that the Mediterranean Sea can carry 2.5 % more weight than the Sea of Azov. Thus, an overloaded ship must reduce its cargo when travelling between these bodies of water. Cargo ships travelling across the Atlantic and continuing through the St. Lawrence river to Montréal are affected in the same way.

Average sea water in the Earth's oceans contains 25.5 g/l NaCl with a density of $\rho = 1.02$ g/cm³. With the molar mass of sodium M = 23 g/mol and chlorine M =

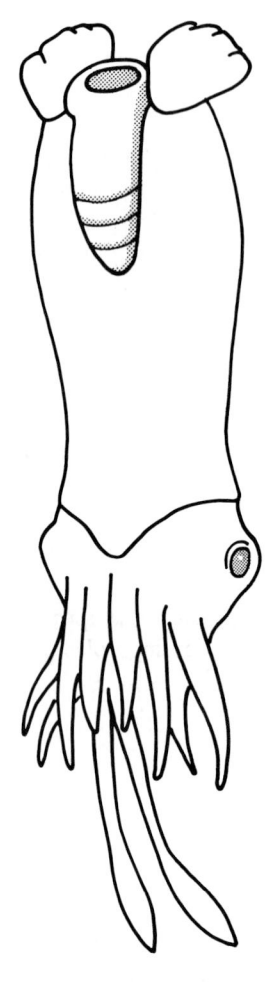

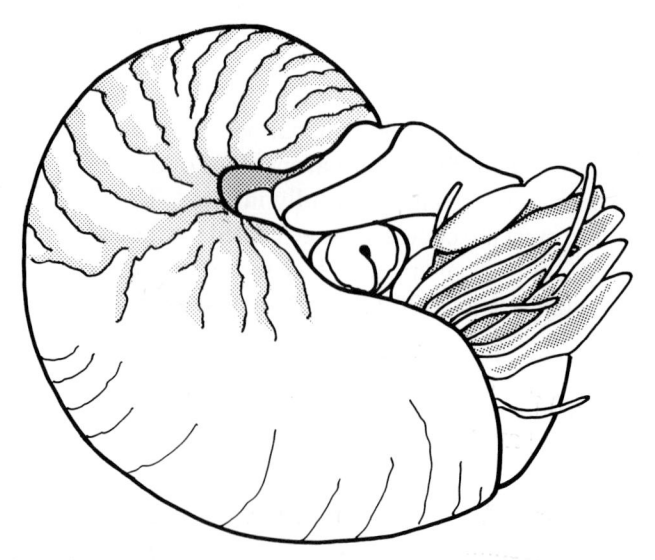

Fig. 10.8: The nautilus is a relative of the long extinct spiral–shelled ammonites. Its shell not only protects the soft–bodied mollusk but also provides the animal with perfect control over the buoyant force acting on its body. The mollusk inhabits the last chamber inside the shell and fills the other chambers with a mixture of air and seawater to adjust its overall density.

Fig. 10.7: As described in the "Report on the scientific results of the voyage of the H.M.S. Challenger during the years 1873 – 1876," one of the more remarkable events during the long voyage to chart the world's oceans was the discovery of spirula, a cephalopod that was thought from fossil evidence to have died out 50 million years earlier. It swims head down because it has a buoyant, gas–filled shell at the posterior end.

35.5 g/mol, the NaCl salt concentration of average sea water corresponds to 435 mmol/l. The extracellular fluid in our body has a NaCl concentration of 165 mmol/l, i.e., the NaCl concentration in the interstitium is 40 % of that of sea water. However, this comparison does not allow to rule out a widely held belief that the salt concentration in the interstitium resembles the salt concentration of the sea from which life on land emerged (as, for example, stated in a famous interview by the late American president John F. Kennedy), since this evolutionary step happened about 420 million years ago when the salt level in sea water may have been lower.

The effect discussed in this Example can easily be verified in a simple experiment. In your kitchen, fill a jar about halfway with water and dissolve a large amount of salt in it. Then add more salt–free water, pouring it into the jar carefully such that the two liquids don't mix. If you place a chicken egg in the water, it will sink to the interface between both liquids. The reason for this is the same effect we just discussed for ships on the high seas: the egg displaces a fixed volume of water equal to its own volume; the weight of the displaced tap water is less than the weight of the egg but the weight of the same volume of salt water is greater than the weight of the egg.

10.4.2. Buoyancy in human physiology (Example 10.5)

The human brain is immersed in the cerebrospinal fluid of density 1.007 g/cm³. This density is slightly less than the average density of the brain, which is 1.04 g/cm³. Thus, most of the weight of the brain is supported by the buoyant force of the surrounding fluid. What fraction of the weight of the brain is not supported by this force?

Solution: This problem is an application of Archimedes' principle. The magnitude of the weight of the brain is:

$$W = \rho_{brain} V_{brain} g \qquad (27)$$

The buoyancy force in turn for the brain fully immersed in the cerebrospinal fluid is:

$$F_{buoy.} = \rho_{cereb. fluid} V_{brain} g \qquad (28)$$

We know that these two forces do not balance each other as the brain is connected through the medulla oblongata to the spinal cord which exerts an additional force on the brain. To determine the fraction of the weight of the brain which is not balanced by the buoyant force we calculate:

$$\frac{W - F_{buoy}}{W} = \frac{\rho_{brain} - \rho_{cereb\,fluid}}{\rho_{brain}} =$$

$$\frac{1.04\left[\frac{g}{cm^3}\right] - 1.007\left[\frac{g}{cm^3}\right]}{1.04\left[\frac{g}{cm^3}\right]} = 0.032 \quad (29)$$

Just 3.2 % of the brain's weight is not balanced by the cerebrospinal fluid, requiring only a small force to be exerted by the spinal cord on the brain.

Buoyancy is used by many marine animals to float, rise or sink in seawater without effort. A famous example is spirula, shown in Fig. 10.7. Spirula is a cephalopod that was thought to have died out 50 million years ago but was then discovered by a scientific expedition of H.M.S. Challenger during its voyage around the world in 1873 – 1876. The animal swims head down because it has a buoyant, gas–filled shell at the posterior end. Another living fossil is the nautilus (Fig. 10.8), a relative of the spiral–shelled ammonites. Nautilus' shell not only protects the soft–bodied mollusk but also provides the animal with perfect control over the buoyant force acting on its body. The mollusk inhabits only the last of a spiralling series of chambers inside the shell. It fills the inner chambers with a mixture of air and seawater to adjust its overall density. Decreasing the density allows the nautilus to rise during its nightly migration from the depths of the Pacific Ocean to the surface.

Most bony fish possess a swim bladder to control buoyancy. The swim bladder is an air sac which allows gas exchange with the fish's blood. This gas exchange leads to a variation in size of the swim bladder, which in turn adjusts the density of the fish. Bony fish can therefore conserve energy by remaining motionless at a chosen depth in the water. Sharks don't have swim bladders and must swim all their life to prevent their body from sinking.

10.4.3. Surface Tension

Surface tension is a fluid property associated with the existence of a surface toward air. The term interfacial tension is used to describe analogous phenomena for fluids with interfaces toward solids or immiscible liquids. Surfaces and interfaces have properties distinct from the bulk of the fluid as the symmetry of the interactions of molecules with their immediate neighbor molecules is broken. This is shown in Fig. 10.9 for a liquid such as water. Sufficiently far below the surface, each water molecule has attractive interactions in all directions with its nearest neighbor molecules. The attractive forces cancel each other and the molecule is in equilibrium. When such a water molecule comes to within one nanometer of the surface, the sphere of neighboring water molecules is not complete anymore and a net force acts on the water molecule pulling it away from the surface. This resulting force is greatest when the water molecule reaches the surface because at this point about half of the neighboring molecules have vanished.

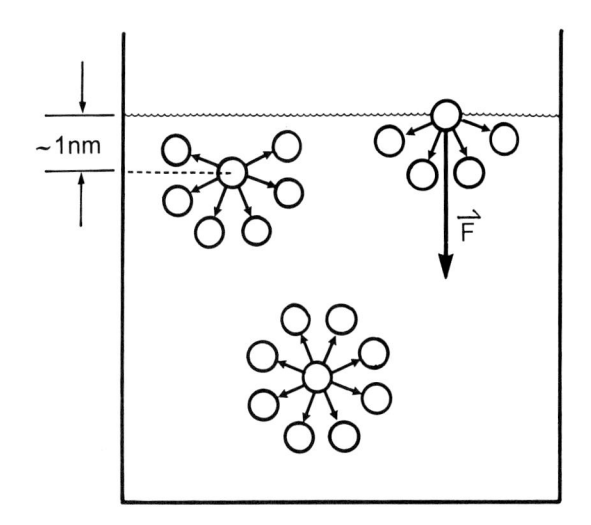

Fig. 10.9: Three water molecules, shown as open circles, are shown with their respective neighboring molecules. Any molecule which is 1 nm or farther below the surface has a symmetric cloud of other water molecules around it. Only molecules at the surface encounter a net force downwards due to an incomplete cloud of attractive neighboring molecules.

The resulting force tends to pull molecules away from the surface. However, molecules cannot leave the surface toward the bulk as the surface cannot shrink. Since the molecules in the surface layer have to be brought to the surface against the net force shown in Fig. 10.9, there is an energy associated with the formation of a surface. We define the surface energy σ in the form:

$$\sigma \equiv \frac{\Delta E}{\Delta A} \left[\frac{J}{m^2}\right] \quad (30)$$

in which ΔE is the energy needed to increase the surface of a fluid by an area ΔA. Thus σ is the energy required to form 1 m² of new surface.

There is a second way to interpret σ. If we interpret σ in Eq. (30) as the work done to achieve a surface increase of area ΔA then we write:

$$W = \Delta E = \sigma \Delta A \quad (31)$$

As you recall from Chapter 5, the work is related to a force by W = F d, in which d is the displacement. We use the device shown in Fig. 10.10 to derive a relationship between the magnitude of the force F and σ. The device consists of a fixed U–shaped wire and a mobile wire with a handle which may be pulled with force **F** to enlarge the surface enclosed by the wires. We consider an increase in area A from $A = l_x l_y$ to $A = l_x(l_y + \Delta l_y)$. The enclosed area is spanned by a film, e.g. a soap film, for which the work needed to change the surface is to be calculated. The work associated with enlarging the area is $W = F \Delta l_y$. Note that the force and the displacement are parallel. The resulting change in area is $\Delta A = l_x \Delta l_y$. These terms are substituted in Eq. (31):

$$\sigma \Delta A = \sigma l_x \Delta l_y = W = F \Delta l_y$$

$$\Rightarrow \quad \sigma = \frac{F}{l_x} \left[\frac{N}{m}\right] \quad (32)$$

Thus, σ also represents the *tangential force* needed to increase the surface per length unit. For this reason, σ is also called surface tension. This double interpretation of σ as energy to increase a surface or force to stretch a film is possible because the units for an energy per surface area and for a force per unit length are the same, $[J/m^2] = [N/m]$.

Fig. 10.10 illustrates one way in which the surface of a fluid can be increased. This instrument is particularly suitable for soap films due to their high cohesiveness. Surface tensions of other fluids such as water cannot be measured this way. For such fluids an alternative set–up exists where the surface area is reduced by bringing a flat solid surface of known area into contact with the fluid surface such that the solid surface covers the respective fluid surface. The surface tension is then determined from the force needed to lift the solid surface off the fluid. An external force is needed to achieve this separation because it leads to a surface increase of the fluid.

10.4.4. Bubbles and droplets

Two major consequences of the existence of surfaces and the associated surface tension will be discussed: the

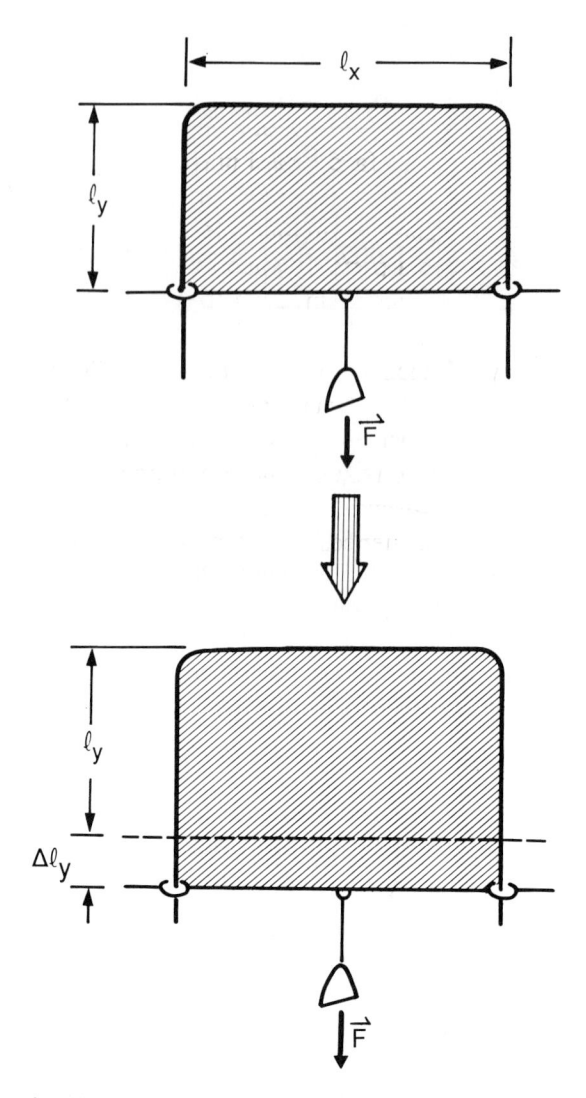

Fig. 10.10: Sketch of a device to measure surface tension as the force **F** acting per unit length on a film. The U–shaped wire and the mobile bar enclose the film. The mobile bar has length l_x and is pulled in the lower frame from the dashed line down to the solid line by a distance Δl_y.

equilibrium shape of bubbles and droplets, and the pressure in small bubbles, droplets and cylindrical capillaries.

We first study a free system, i.e., a fluid that is not confined by any external surface. An example is a rain drop. Since work has to be done to increase the surface of a liquid, the liquid minimizes its surface to achieve its equilibrium state. The equilibrium shape of the rain drop is the geometrical figure which has the least surface for a fixed volume; this is the sphere. Due to Eq. (30) we conclude that a spherical droplet has the least total energy. If a drop is not spherical, it releases energy while reshaping toward a sphere. When the drop is spherical, external energy would have to be provided to change the shape of the drop.

If we introduce additional boundary conditions, e.g. a droplet sitting on a surface, the mathematical requirements to find solutions for the shape of the droplet become more complex. However, some simpler cases should be noted. For any flat frame, like in Fig. 10.10, the minimum energy surface for a film is a flat layer, not a bent structure. For droplets on inert surfaces, such as water droplets on glass, a circular interface forms and the droplet assumes a partially spherical shape with a well defined contact angle. This contact angle is discussed in section 10.4.6.

A physiological example are the 300 to 400 million alveoli at the end of the bronchial tree in the lungs. Each alveolus is a partial sphere with a diameter of about 0.3 mm placed on top of a narrow bronchial tube. Two examples are discussed in the next section which deal with the consequences of the surface energy of alveoli in the lungs. However, before we can discuss these effects we need to find the radial dependence of the pressure in a bubble.

10.4.5. Pressure in a bubble: Laplace's law

Even though the soap film forming a bubble is less than a micrometer thick, it is able to retain compressed air inside. To illustrate that there is indeed an enhanced pressure inside a bubble, blow some bubbles for example with a soap solution available in most toy stores, and catch one soap bubble on a pipe-bowl while covering the mouthpiece with your finger. Then hold the mouthpiece close to the flame of a burning candle and remove your finger. The candle flame is blown to the side while the bubble shrinks and vanishes into the pipe-bowl.

We want to quantify by how much the pressure inside a bubble exceeds the atmospheric pressure. The top part of Fig. 10.11 shows a (close to square) segment selected on the spherical surface of a bubble. In the center panel a coordinate system is chosen for the small segment. The z-axis is perpendicular to the surface. The x- and y-axes are parallel to the edges of the selected segment. They intersect with the z-axis at the same point where the z-axis intercepts the bubble surface. Thus, edges 1 and 3 of the segment lie in the yz-plane and edges 2 and 4 lie in the xz-plane. The four arrows in the figure indicate the directions in which the remaining bubble surface in the top sketch pulls on the selected segment. Since the segment bends downwards from the origin, these four forces are all directed below the horizontal.

The bottom part of Fig. 10.11 shows the free-body-diagram for the bubble segment. The four forces discussed above are identified as $\mathbf{F}_i$ with i = 1 to 4. If these were the only forces acting on the bubble segment, then the segment would not be in mechanical equilibrium as a net force downwards would result, which

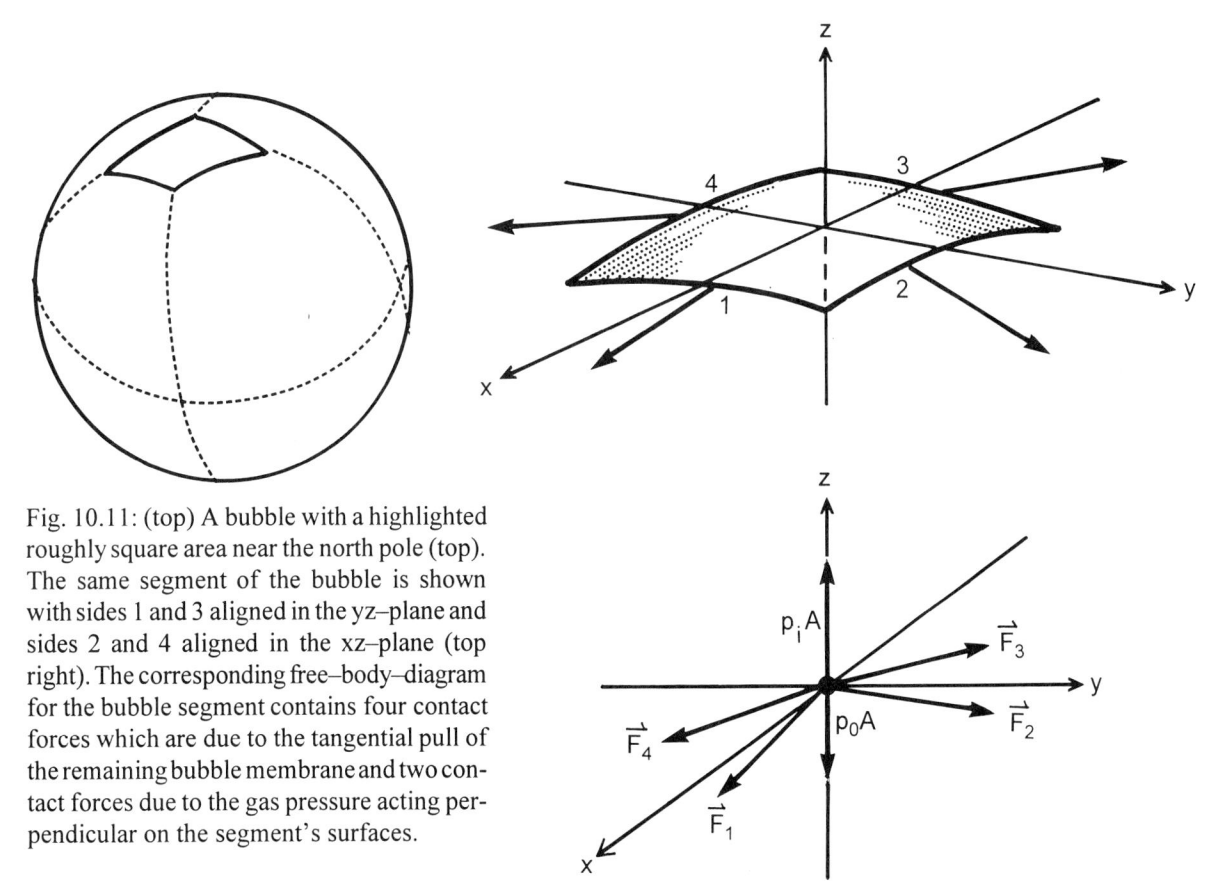

Fig. 10.11: (top) A bubble with a highlighted roughly square area near the north pole (top). The same segment of the bubble is shown with sides 1 and 3 aligned in the yz-plane and sides 2 and 4 aligned in the xz-plane (top right). The corresponding free-body-diagram for the bubble segment contains four contact forces which are due to the tangential pull of the remaining bubble membrane and two contact forces due to the gas pressure acting perpendicular on the segment's surfaces.

301

would cause the segment to accelerate downwards. Thus, for a bubble in mechanical equilibrium more forces must be taken into account. These are the forces pushing on the bubble segment due to the pressure inside of the bubble, p_i, and the pressure outside of the bubble, p_o. To yield a force, each pressure is multiplied with A, where A is the area of the bubble segment shown in the figure.

Due to the symmetry of the surface segment in Fig. 10.11 the following relations between the components of the four forces $\mathbf{F}_i$ apply:

$$F_{1,x} = -F_{3,x} \; ; \; F_{2,x} = F_{4,x} = 0$$

$$F_{2,y} = -F_{4,y} \; ; \; F_{1,y} = F_{3,y} = 0 \quad (33)$$

$$F_{1,z} = F_{2,z} = F_{3,z} = F_{4,z}$$

The force components in the x– and y–directions (first two lines in Eq. (33)) compensate each other. Only the z–components in the third line of Eq. (33) enter the calculation. Newton's first law describes the mechanical equilibrium of the bubble segment in the z–direction:

$$\sum_{i=1}^{6} F_{i,z} = 0 = 4F_{1,z} + p_i A - p_o A \quad (34)$$

Eq. (32) is used to quantify $F_{1,z}$. If l is the length of each edge of the segment, i.e., $l^2 = A$, then $|\mathbf{F}_1| = 2\sigma l$. The factor 2 in this relation is due to the fact that the bubble has an inner and an outer surface. We use Fig. 10.12 to determine the z–component of this force. In the figure, r is the radius of the bubble and ϕ is the opening angle of the segment of length $l/2$. The thick solid line in Fig. 10.12 corresponds to a side view of the segment shown in Fig. 10.11. Applying trigonometric rules to express $\sin\phi$ in Fig. 10.12 we find:

$$\sin\phi = \frac{l/2}{r}$$

$$\sin\phi = \frac{F_{1,z}}{|\mathbf{F}_1|} \quad (35)$$

Eq. (35) contains two relations because the angle ϕ occurs twice in Fig. 10.12. We equate the right hand sides of the two formulas in Eq. (35) to express $F_{1,z}$:

$$F_{1,z} = 2\sigma l \frac{l/2}{r} = \sigma \frac{l^2}{r} = \frac{\sigma A}{r} \quad (36)$$

in which we replaced $l^2 = A$. Substituting the z–component of the force from Eq. (36) into the mechanical equilibrium condition of Eq. (34) we find:

$$\sum_{i=1}^{6} F_{i,z} = 0 = -\frac{4\sigma A}{r} + A\Delta p \quad (37)$$

which leads to:

$$\Delta p = \frac{4\sigma}{r} \quad (38)$$

In Eq. (38) the term $\Delta p = p_i - p_o$ is called the *transmural pressure*. Thus, the internal pressure in a small bubble is larger than the external pressure. This pressure difference maintains the curved surface of the bubble.

Formulas equivalent to Eq. (38) can also be derived for homogeneous droplets or other shapes of hollow or homogeneous liquids. The derivation of such formulas follows the exact same approach we took with Fig. 10.11 and Eqs. (33) to (38), except that for a homo-

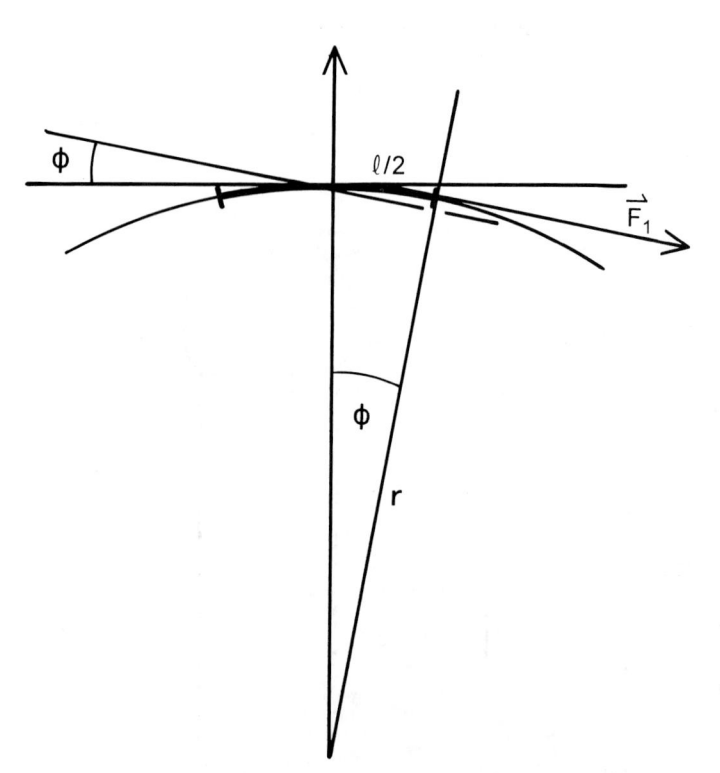

Fig. 10.12: Geometric sketch of the z–components of the forces shown in Fig. 10.11. The bold solid line segment indicates the side view of the square area from Fig. 10.11.

geneous droplet only one surface exists while the bubble has two, an outer and an inner surface.

Alternatively, we can replace the spherical fluid droplet with a cylindrical fluid in a tube. A surface element of a cylinder, cut in the same fashion as the element in Fig. 10.11, has one less pair of curved edges.

Either of these changes eliminates a factor of 2; for the droplet the factor of 2 is eliminated from the magnitude of the force $\mathbf{F}_1$, i.e., $|\mathbf{F}_1| = \sigma l$. For the cylinder, only two instead of four z–components occur in the last line of Eq. (33). Either of these changes are carried through the calculation to Eq. (38). Thus we find three formulations for Laplace's law:

bubble: $\quad \Delta p = p_i - p_o = \dfrac{4\sigma}{r}$

droplet: $\quad \Delta p = p_i - p_o = \dfrac{2\sigma}{r}$ (39)

homog. cylinder: $\Delta p = p_i - p_o = \dfrac{\sigma}{r}$

Laplace's law states that the pressure difference inside and outside of a fluid with a curved surface is inversely proportional to the radius of curvature of the curved surface. This means that a smaller bubble, droplet or cylinder has a larger pressure difference Δp.

Each of the formulas in Eq. (39) has physiological applications. The formula for the bubble applies to membrane encapsulated systems with a hollow interior such as the alveoli in the lungs.

The formula for the homogeneous cylinder applies to blood vessels: the elastic tissue of the blood vessel must be capable to sustain this pressure difference. We compare blood capillaries and small arterioles to illustrate the consequences of Eq. (39). The transmural pressure values between blood in blood vessels and the surrounding tissue are essentially equivalent to the values given in Fig. 10.4. From the figure we find that essentially the same pressure differences Δp apply for the smallest arterioles (between labels 4 and 5 in Fig. 10.4) and the capillaries (labelled 5). This leads to:

$$\frac{\sigma_{arteriole}}{r_{arteriole}} \cong \frac{\sigma_{capillary}}{r_{capillary}} \quad (40)$$

Therefore, the surface tension for a capillary of small radius must be smaller than the surface tension of an arteriole with a larger radius:

$$r_{arteriole} \gg r_{capillary} \quad \Rightarrow \quad \sigma_{arteriole} \gg \sigma_{capillary} \quad (41)$$

This result is physiologically important, because it allows the walls of the capillaries to be thinner; this in turn improves the efficiency of diffusive transport of small ions and oxygen from the blood into the surrounding tissue.

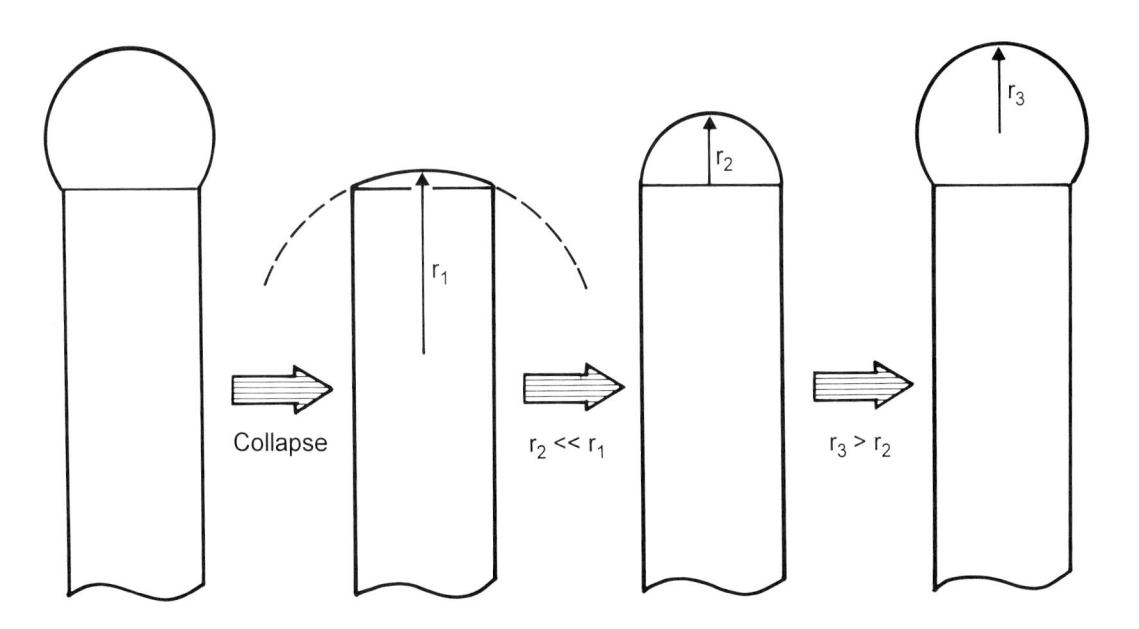

Fig. 10.13: Left panel: healthy alveolus sealing the end of a bronchial tube. Three right panels: stages of the inflation of a collapsed lung. Initially, (second panel) the lungs resist inflation until the alveoli reach an intermediate, smallest radius (third panel). Thereafter, the completion of the inflation does not require further pressurizing (last panel).

Example 10.6
A lung has collapsed when the alveoli have retracted so that they lie almost flat on the end of the bronchial tubes, as shown in the second sketch from left in Fig. 10.13. What happens when we try to inflate the collapsed lung?

Solution: When the alveoli are collapsed as shown in the second sketch from left in Fig. 10.13, the corresponding radius of the alveolus surface, r_1, is large and the transmural pressure in the alveolus is low due to the inverse relation between radius and pressure difference in Eq. (39). When trying to inflate such a collapsed lung, a significant resistance must be overcome. Initially, the tissue resists the inflating of the lung, because pushing the alveoli out of the bronchial tubes reduces their radii significantly, $r_1 \gg r_2$. Thus, pressurizing the lung has initially very little effect until an external pressure has been reached which causes the transmural pressure needed for alveoli of radius r_2. When this radius is reached the external pressure must be lowered suddenly because inflating the alveoli from r_2 to r_3 in Fig. 10.13 requires a decreasing pressure based on Eq. (39) since $r_2 < r_3$. Thanks to the great elasticity of human tissues the risk of rupturing the lungs during inflation is not too high.

Example 10.7
We study two alveoli in competition at closely connected bronchial tubes as shown in Fig. 10.14. As shown, the actual size of any two adjacent alveoli may vary slightly. Why does this create a problem?

Solution: We assume two different radii for the alveoli, $r_1 > r_2$. As a consequence, the corresponding internal pressures between the two alveoli would vary because the external pressure in the surrounding tissue is the same for both alveoli:

$$r_1 > r_2$$
$$\Downarrow$$
$$\Delta p_1 = \frac{4\sigma}{r_1} < \frac{4\sigma}{r_2} = \Delta p_2 \quad (42)$$

Because of Eq. (42), the actual pulmonary pressure would not sufficiently pressurize the smaller alveolus and it would collapse. This should not happen since the air exchange in the lungs is proportional to the contact area with the adjacent blood capillaries, i.e., small alveoli contribute more effectively than larger ones.

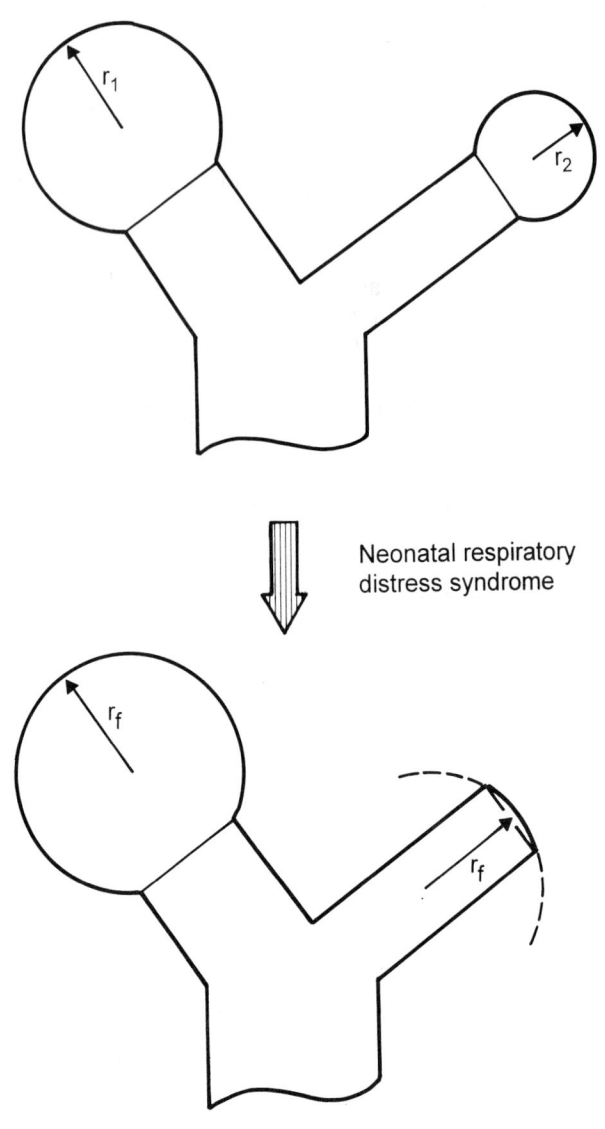

Fig. 10.14: Sketch of two alveoli of different sizes located near a bronchial branching point. The smaller alveolus requires a larger pressure difference, therefore it should collapse in favor of the bigger alveolus. After collapsing, both alveoli have the same radius r_f, but the previously smaller alveolus is essentially completely retracted into the bronchial tube. A healthy lung has means of preventing this effect using pulmonary surfactants to modify the surface tension in the alveoli. However, prematurely born babies lack these surfactants, and the collapsing of small alveoli is observed. This neonatal respiratory distress syndrome was in the past a major cause of death of prematurely born babies.

To prevent this problem, alveolar cells produce a phospholipid which wets the alveolar surface to counterbalance the radius effect in Eq. (42) by lowering the surface tension σ for smaller alveoli. The phospholipid is called a pulmonary surfactant. Pulmonary surfactant is formed late in fetal life. For this reason, it is often the case in premature births that insufficient pulmonary surfactant is present, which causes neonatal respiratory distress syndrome. For a baby with this syndrome, the lung is stiff, with some alveoli collapsed and others likely to be filled with fluid. Immediate medical attention is required.

We can easily demonstrate that the competitive effect between small and large bubbles discussed in this problem indeed exists by adding some soap to a bottle filled with water. When pouring the water out of the bottle, air streams in and bubbles are formed. You observe that the smaller bubbles arch into larger, more stable bubbles.

10.4.6. Capillarity

Capillarity is an effect closely related to surface tension. This effect is illustrated in Fig. 10.15, which compares the results of two simple experiments. A small, hollow glass tube is immersed into water (left sketch) or liquid mercury (right sketch). It is observed that the water rises in the tube and its surface bends up slightly at the water/glass/air interface. In turn, the mercury level in the tube is lower than the surface of the surrounding mercury and the mercury bends downwards at the mercury/glass/air interface. This indicates that not only the surface tension of the liquid plays a role in this experiment but also the interfacial tension at the water/glass or mercury/glass interfaces, respectively. Surface tension values are always positive since forming a surface toward air requires energy to reduce the number of attractive neighboring molecules in the liquid, as indicated in Fig. 10.9. Interfacial tensions can be positive or negative since a solid or liquid surface contains a similar density of molecules for interaction as the studied liquid. The attractive interaction with equal molecules may be replaced by a stronger attractive interaction with the molecules on the other side of the interface. This is the case for water and glass. Consequently, water wets glass because forming this interface requires less energy than forming a surface with air. Mercury, in turn, does not wet glass as formation of the glass/mercury interface requires a large amount of energy.

A second experiment illustrating the effect of capillarity is shown in Fig. 10.16. A system of connected tubes with decreasing diameters is filled with water. The water level in each tube is related to the tube diameter such that the smaller tubes have the highest level. This is due to the total energy required in each tube to form surfaces toward air and interfaces along the glass walls as quantified in Example 10.8. Capillarity is an essential part of many life processes. In higher animals, blood is pumped through arteries and veins, but capillarity is important in the smallest blood vessels, which are therefore called capillaries. We address this issue in part (b) of Example 10.8.

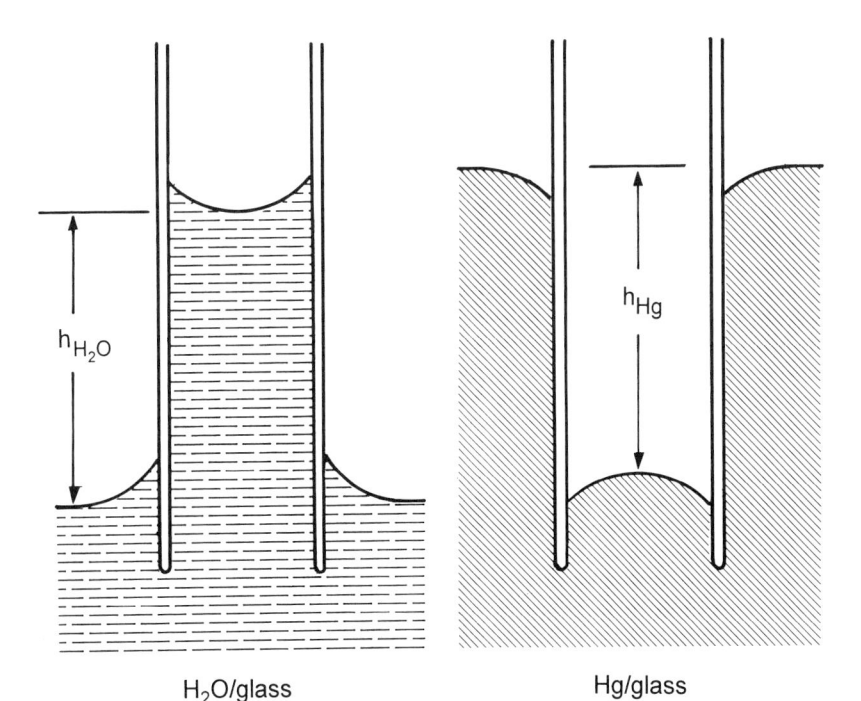

Fig. 10.15: Comparison between the wetting of an hollow glass tube immersed in water (left panel) and immersed in mercury (right panel). The two final equilibrium states shown indicate that water wets glass, which leads to an upward force on the water in the tube. This effect is called capillarity (capillary action). Mercury does not wet glass, leading to a mercury level in the tube below the mercury surface in the remaining beaker.

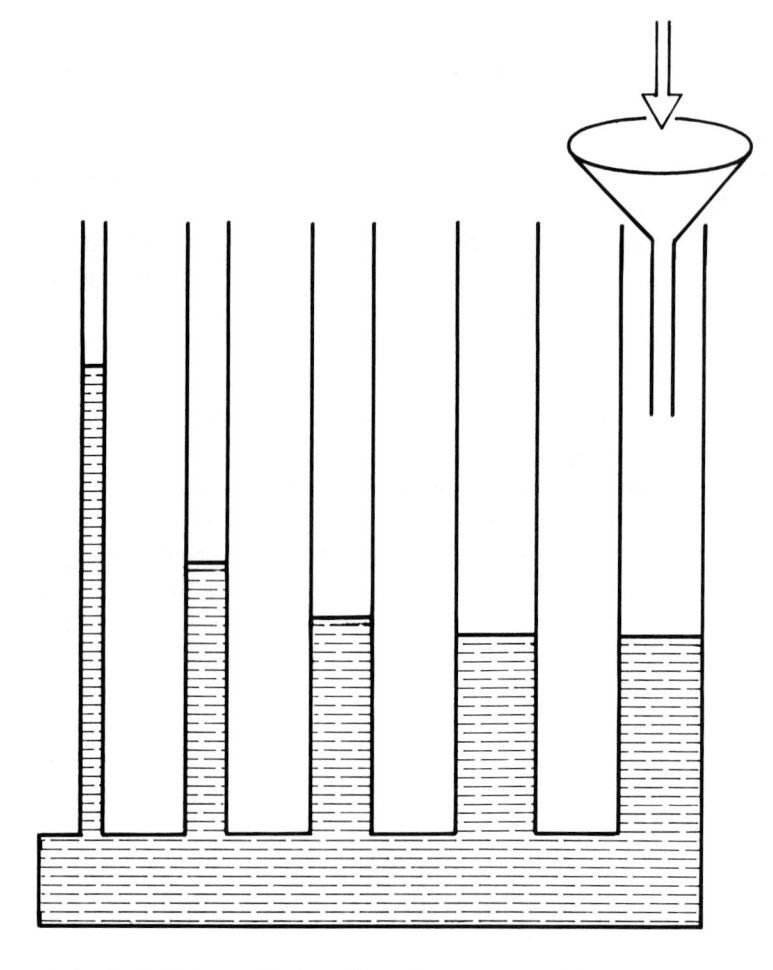

Fig. 10.17: Sketch of a liquid column rising in a narrow capillary of radius r to a height h_{liquid}. The curvature of the meniscus of the liquid is defined by the radius of curvature, R, which leads to a contact angle θ of the liquid with the inner capillary wall. The force related to the surface tension is indicated.

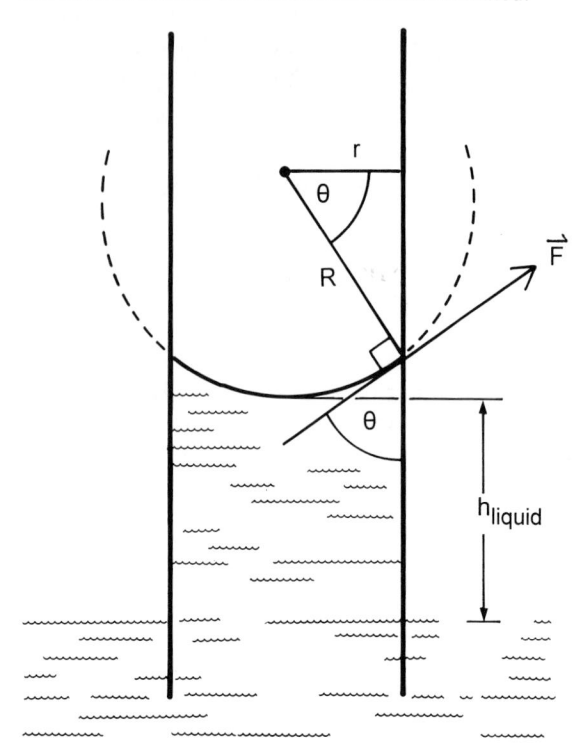

Fig. 10.16: The capillarity effect of water. Water is brought into a system of connected glass tubes with decreasing diameter. The smaller the tube diameter, the more advantageous the interaction between the water and the glass surface, which allows the water to rise to higher levels before reaching equilibrium.

Example 10.8

(a) Using Fig. 10.17 for a liquid that has risen in a capillary to height h_{liquid} and forms a contact angle θ with the inner surface of the capillary of radius r, show that the height of the liquid column in the capillary is expressed in the form (Jurin's law):

$$h_{liquid} = \frac{2\,\sigma_{liquid}}{\rho_{liquid}\,g}\frac{\cos\theta}{r} \qquad (43)$$

(b) For whole blood with a surface tension value of $\sigma = 0.058$ N/m and a density of 1.06 g/cm³, calculate the maximum height to which it can rise in a capillary blood vessel that has a diameter of 4.5 μm.

Solution part (a): In Fig. 10.17 you notice that the meniscus of the liquid surface is not flat but curved like an inverse sphere. This is due to the capillarity effect in the tube as described by Eq. (39). We use the formula with the proportionality factor 2 for the droplet because there is only one interface between liquid and air. Eq. (39) describes the pressure difference in the liquid at the meniscus in the tube and the outside air as:

$$p_{liquid\ surface} - p_{atm} = -\frac{2\sigma_{liquid}}{R} \qquad (44)$$

in which R is the radius of curvature of the meniscus as shown in Fig. 10.17. Eq. (44) has a negative sign on the right hand side since the meniscus is curved upwards (as opposed to the curvature of the bubbles in Figs. 10.13 and 10.14). The radius of curvature in Eq. (44) is related to the inner radius of the capillary in the form:

$$R = \frac{r}{\cos\theta} \quad (45)$$

Pascal's law enables us to write a second equation for the same pressure difference since we know that the surface pressure of water and the air pressure are the same at the water/air interface outside of the tube, i.e., at a height h_{liquid} below the meniscus in the capillary. Thus, at the meniscus in the tube we find:

$$p_{liquid\ surface} - p_{atm} = -\rho_{liquid}\, g\, h_{liquid} \quad (46)$$

Equating the right hand sides of Eqs. (44) and (46), and substituting Eq. (45) for R, leads to:

$$-\frac{2\sigma_{liquid}}{r/\cos\theta} = -\rho_{liquid}\, g\, h_{liquid} \quad (47)$$

which is written as Jurin's law:

$$\frac{2\sigma_{liquid}\cos\theta}{r\, \rho_{liquid}\, g} = h_{liquid} \quad (48)$$

Solution part (b): This part of the Example is an application of Eq. (43). First, we need to interpret the term "maximum height" in the Example text. Note that we do not identify the contact angle θ. The range of possible contact angles between 0° and 180° allows for the range of cosine–values $-1 \le \cos\theta \le +1$ in Eq. (43). Thus, a maximum height is reached when $\cos\theta = 1$:

$$h_{max,\ blood} = \frac{2\,\sigma_{blood}}{r\, \rho_{blood}\, g} \quad (49)$$

We substitute the values given in the Example text and obtain:

$$h_{max,\ blood} = \frac{2 \cdot 5.8 \times 10^{-2}\left[\frac{N}{m}\right]}{1.06\times 10^{3}\left[\frac{kg}{m^{3}}\right] 9.8\left[\frac{m}{s^{2}}\right] 2.25\times 10^{-6}[m]} \quad (50)$$

which leads to:

$$h_{max,\ blood} = 4.96\ m \quad (51)$$

Significant amounts of water are transported upwards in trees: a full grown birch evaporates from its leaves about 350 liters of water per summer day. It is still a matter of research to what extent the effect shown in Fig. 10.16 plays a role in this transport of water and sap in high trees. In order to transport water by capillarity into the canopies of even the highest trees, e.g. eucalyptus trees of 150 m height, capillary diameters of smaller than 0.1 μm would be required. However, the xylem fibres, in which water has been shown to rise in trees, have typically diameters of 20 μm to 300 μm.

Clearly other effects play a role in the transport of water from the ground to the leaves. We study the wood anemone as an example. The wood anemone is a flower that stands erect and opens only when the sun shines. When a cloud covers the sun or when we create an artificial shade for the flower, the flower closes and the stem bends down. This is a sign of reduced water pressure in the stem. When the shade is removed, the flower resumes its erect posture as the water pressure in the stem rises again. In the anemone, the water pressure is regulated by chemical reactions which operate only under sunny and warm conditions.

10.4.7. Wetting

Different liquids wet glass (or any other surface) differently as Fig. 10.15 indicates. Some, like water on glass, like to form an interface and rise in the tube (with an upwards curved meniscus) and others, like mercury, do not like to form an interface with glass. In that case the meniscus drops and is curved downward. Any liquid forming an upward curved interface with glass, as shown in the left sketch in Fig. 10.15, is referred to as wetting the surface, and any liquid forming a downward sloped interface as shown in the right sketch of Fig. 10.15, is referred to as non–wetting the surface.

Wetting versus non–wetting is an important concept, e.g. for clothes, where fluorinated clothes (Gortex) cause a non–wetting condition for water, i.e., the clothes allow air to penetrate but keep water out. However, wetting is often not complete, leading to a range of contact angles of the liquid with the glass surface, with values between 0° (complete wetting) and 180° (complete non–wetting).

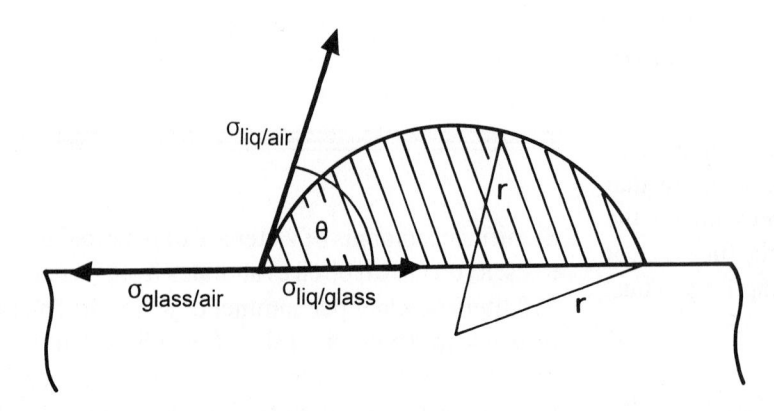

Fig. 10.18: A partially spherical droplet of radius r on a flat surface. The three surface and interface tensions indicated are connected by the Young–Dupré equation which allows us to calculate the contact angle θ.

The forces acting at a point where the three materials in the tube, air, water and glass, meet, are illustrated for a partially wetting droplet on a surface in Fig. 10.18. A mechanical equilibrium between the three interfacial or surface tensions, which are forces per unit length of contact line, must exist along the surface, since the common point would accelerate otherwise along the surface (and the droplet would change its shape). We obtain the condition for mechanical equilibrium from Fig. 10.18 (called the Young–Dupré relation):

$$\sigma_{glass/air} = \sigma_{glass/liquid} + \sigma_{liquid/air}\cos\theta \quad (52)$$

10.5. Problems

P–10.1
The sphere is the shape with the smallest surface for a given volume. To prove this statement properly requires variational analysis. Here we only want to confirm this result for a selection of highly symmetric shapes by calculating the ratio of surface and volume. Find these ratios for (a) sphere, (b) cylinder, (c) cube, (d) pyramid, (e) tetrahedron, and (f) cone. Does the statement hold for these six shapes?

P–10.2
A diver thinks that if a typical snorkel tube of 25 cm length works, a tube of length 7.0 m should also work. When trying to use such a tube, what is the pressure difference between the external pressure on the diver's chest and the air pressure in the lungs of the diver?
For those interested: what happens to the diver if this new snorkel were tested?

P–10.3
A scuba diver takes a deep breath from an air–filled tank at depth L, then abandons the tank. During the subsequent ascent to the surface the diver fails to exhale. When reaching the surface, the pressure difference between the external pressure and the pressure in the lung is 76 torr. From what depth did the diver start?
For those interested: what potentially lethal danger does the diver face?

P–10.4
The U–shaped glass tube in Fig. 10.19 contains two liquids in mechanical equilibrium: water of density ρ_w = 1.0 kg/l, and an unknown liquid of density ρ_l. The unknown liquid is in the left tube, floating on top of the water with a clearly visible interface. Use h_1 = 150 mm and h_2 = 15 mm with the heights as labelled in Fig. 10.19. What is the density ρ_l?

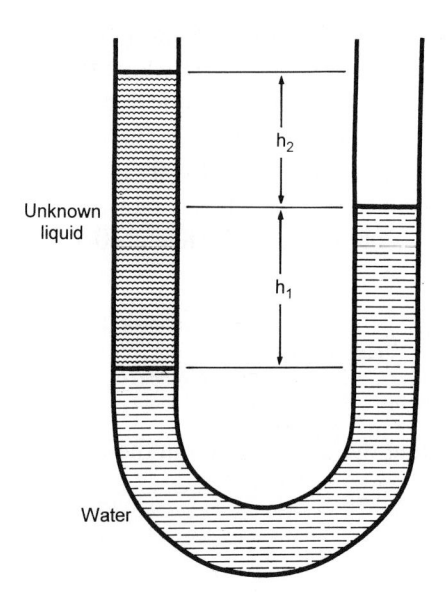

Fig. 10.19 for problem P–10.4.

P–10.5
What is the pressure increase in the fluid in a syringe when a force of 50 N is applied to the circular piston of the syringe, which has a radius 1.25 cm?

P–10.6
We often say the tip of an iceberg when we want to refer to a small visible fraction of something that is otherwise hidden. For a real iceberg, what is that fraction? The density of ice is $\rho_{ice} = 917$ kg/m³ and the average density of seawater is $\rho_w = 1.025$ g/cm³.

P–10.7
To suck water up a straw to a maximum height of 10 cm, what minimum gauge pressure must be produced in the lungs? Note: the gauge pressure is defined as the pressure relative to atmospheric pressure, $p_{gauge} = p - p_{atm}$.

P–10.8
Collapsible plastic bags are used in hospitals for infusions. We want to use such a bag to infuse a electrolyte solution into the artery of a patient. For this we mount the bag at a height h above the arm of the patient, as shown in Fig. 10.20. Assuming that the average gauge pressure in the artery is 13.3 kPa and the density of the electrolyte solution is 1.03 g/cm³, what is the minimum height h in order for the infusion to work?

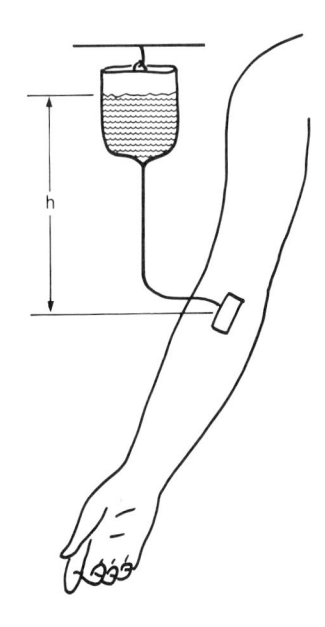

Fig. 10.20 for problem P–10.8.

P–10.9
A helium–filled blimp cruises slowly at a low altitude. Its maximum useful payload, including crew and cargo, is 1500 kg. How much more payload can be carried if the blimp were filled with hydrogen? Use for the volume of the gas–filled interior space a value of 6000 m³. The density of helium gas is 0.16 kg/m³ and the density of hydrogen gas is 0.08 kg/m³.

P–10.10
Water is transported upwards in plants through xylem tissue, which consists of cells of 1 mm length and a species dependent diameter between 40 μm and 400 μm. The xylem cells are attached to each other to form a channel. To what maximum height can water rise in these xylem channels due to the capillarity effect?
Hint: the surface tension of water is $\sigma = 0.073$ N/m at 20˚C.
Note: if you only believe what you can see, cut and split the stem of a flower with white petals (e.g. a dahlia or a carnation) and place one half of the stem in a glass with dilute red ink and the other half in a glass with dilute blue ink. After several hours the flower will be half red and half blue.

P–10.11
(a) Fig. 10.21(a) shows a wooden sphere with a diameter of d = 10 cm (density $\rho = 0.9$ g/cm³) held under water by a string. What is the tension in the string?
(b) Fig. 10.21(b) shows a sphere of radius r = 10 cm and density of $\rho = 2.0$ g/cm³ suspended in water. What is the tension in the sting?
Hint: draw the free–body–diagram in each case.

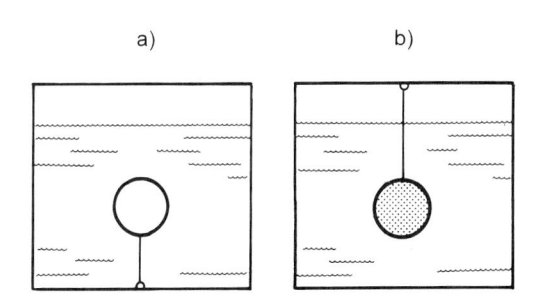

Fig. 10.21 for problem P–10.11.

P–10.12
Surface tension supports insects such as water–striders on the water surface. Assume that an insect's foot is spherical as shown in Fig. 10.22 and that the insect stands with all of its 6 feet on the water. Each foot presses the water surface down while the surface tension of the water produces upwards forces to restore the normal flat shape of the water surface. As a result a characteristic profile of the water surface results as shown in the figure. The mass of the insect is 15 mg and the diameter of the insect's foot is 250 μm. Find the angle θ as indicated in the figure.
Hint: the definition of the surface tension provides for a tangential force along the depressed surface of the water, shown as force **F** in the figure. The surface tension of water at 20˚C is $\sigma = 0.073$ N/m.

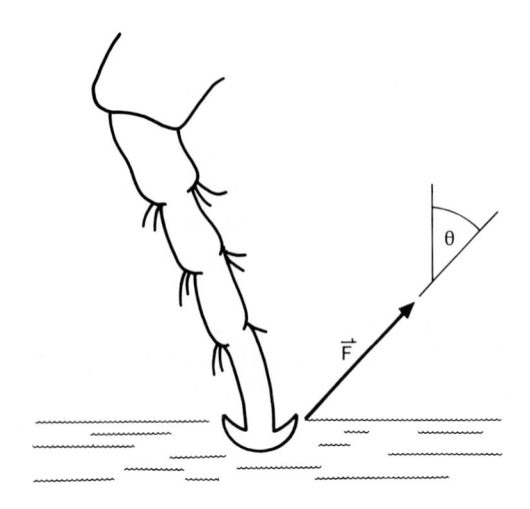

Fig. 10.22 for problem P–10.12.

Summary

Definitions:
- Atmospheric pressure: $p_{atm} = 1.01 \times 10^5$ Pa.
- Surface energy σ is the energy required to form an area of 1 m² of new surface:

$$\sigma \equiv \frac{\Delta E}{\Delta A} \left[\frac{J}{m^2}\right]$$

- Surface tension (equivalent to surface energy):

$$\sigma = \frac{F}{l_x} \left[\frac{N}{m}\right]$$

l_x is the length along which the force acts tangentially to the surface.

Laws:
- Pascal's law (depth d measured from surface downwards):

$$p = p_{atm} + \rho g d$$

- Buoyancy force (Archimedes' principle):

$$F = \rho_{fluid} V_{body} g$$

- Laplace's formula for pressure difference across the surface for (r is radius)
(i) hollow bubble: $\Delta p = 4\sigma/r$
(ii) homogeneous droplet: $\Delta p = 2\sigma/r$
(iii) homogeneous cylinder: $\Delta p = \sigma/r$
- Jurin's law for capillarity:

$$h_{liquid} = \frac{2\sigma_{liquid}}{\rho_{liquid} g} \frac{\cos\theta}{r}$$

r is radius, θ is contact angle of fluid with wall.

Chapter XI

Cardiovascular System

Fluid flow

CARDIOVASCULAR SYSTEM
FLUID FLOW

Fluid flow results when a fluid system is not in mechanical equilibrium. Different aspects of fluid flow are described in this chapter with three models introduced for dynamic fluids: the (non–viscous) ideal dynamic fluid, the (viscous) Newtonian fluid, and the non–Newtonian fluid. All three models are idealized because we assume that the fluid of interest is incompressible and free of turbulences. The flow under these conditions is called laminar flow.

For the ideal dynamic fluid we further neglect inter–molecular interactions, including interactions with the container walls. Two laws determine the properties of the resulting non–viscous flow: the Equation of continuity is an expression of the conservation of mass in the system and Bernoulli's law represents the conservation of energy. These two laws predict that the flow through a tapering tube accelerates, and that the pressure in the fluid decreases with increasing speed.

In a viscous fluid inter–molecular interactions become important. The fluid can no longer be treated as an isolated system as its interactions with the walls of the confining container lead to energy loss. While the Equation of continuity (conservation of fluid mass) remains in effect, Bernoulli's law is replaced by Poiseuille's law. This law states that fluid flow is the result of a forward directed force due to a pressure difference along the tube and a force directed against the motion of the fluid due to viscosity. This leads to a parabolic velocity distribution of the fluid across a cylindrical tube with the volume flow rate proportional to the fourth power of the radius of the tube. When a fluid obeys Poiseuille's law we call it a Newtonian fluid.

Real fluids often show non–Newtonian behavior. Mixed systems such as blood in the cardiovascular system or air in the respiratory system are important physiological examples. Non–Newtonian fluids are discussed in Chapter 12.

When viscous fluids flow faster than a certain threshold speed, the flow becomes turbulent. For turbulent flow, a further pressure difference increase along the tube yields only a negligible increase in the volume flow rate. Turbulent flow is therefore dangerous for physiological systems which rely on large volume flow rates, but it is beneficial when a significant fluid–tube wall interaction is required such as in respiration.

11.1. Fluids in the human body

To provide a physiological motivation for the study of fluids, we introduce a specific system: the cardiovascular system containing the fluid system blood. The respiratory system is a second system that will serve as a comparison case because it operates with a gas instead of a liquid.

The generalized circulatory schemes of fish, amphibians and mammals are compared in Fig. 11.1. Fish have a two–chambered heart which provides blood to a single circuit. Amphibians have a three–chambered heart with two circuits of blood flow. These are called the pulmocutaneous and the systemic systems. The systemic system delivers blood under high pressure to the systemic organs. The pulmocutaneous system delivers blood to the skin and to the lungs. Mammals have a four–chambered heart and a double circulation system. Oxygen–rich blood from the lungs is kept separate in the mammalian heart from oxygen–poor blood flowing back from the organs. The two blood circulation systems are called the pulmonary circuit (delivering oxygen–poor blood to the lungs) and the systemic circuit (high–pressure system delivering oxygen–rich blood to all organ systems).

A quantitative schematic overview of the human

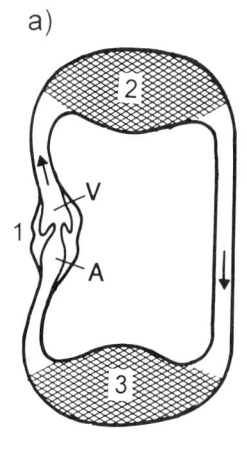

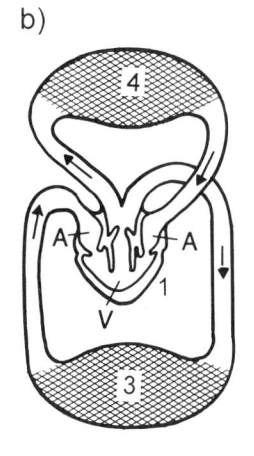

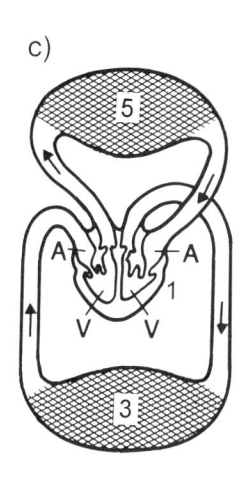

Fig. 11.1: Comparison of the circulatory systems of various vertebrates.
(a) Fish have a two–chambered heart with a single circulatory system.
(b) Amphibians have a three–chambered heart with two circulatory systems, the pulmocutaneous and the systemic systems.
(c) Mammals have a four–chambered heart with two circulatory systems, the systemic and the pulmonary systems. This heart fully separates oxygen–rich blood from the lungs and oxygen–depleted blood from the systemic circuit.

cardiovascular system as a specific example of the mammalian circulatory system of is shown in Fig. 11.2. The heart pumps blood from its left ventricle into the arteries of the greater cardiovascular or systemic system. The arteries carry the blood to the capillaries, where it supplies the organs with oxygen. From the organs the blood returns to the right ventricle through veins. Next it is pumped through the lesser cardiovascular or pulmonary system to the lungs. After the oxygen/carbon–dioxide exchange is completed in the capillaries of the lungs, the blood returns to the left ventricle.

The organs are arranged in parallel for blood supply which allows the body to prioritize the supply based on the vital relevance of the organ and the current demand for oxygen. The pulmonary system is arranged in sequence with the systemic system because the blood must pass through the lungs for gas exchange.

For the major organs, Fig. 11.2 also shows the fraction of the blood flow passing through the organ, I/I_0. $I = \Delta V/\Delta t$ is the volume flow rate through an organ and I_0 is the total volume flow rate through the cardiovascular system. A volume flow rate corresponds to a volume ΔV which flows through a tube per time interval Δt. I_0 is determined from the amount of blood pumped out of the heart ventricle per heart beat, which is 0.07 liters.

With the repetition rate of 70 heart beats per minute, a total volume flow rate of $I_0 = 5$ l/min results.

Fig. 11.2 also shows the fraction of oxygen consumption for each organ. The oxygen consumption is labelled O_2 in the figure. The oxygen supply rate to the blood system is 0.25 l/min. Of this amount, the figure shows the fraction of oxygen consumption by each organ in percent. Sufficient blood supply to the brain has the highest priority as the brain is very sensitive to oxygen deficiency (hypoxia). In turn, the brain is efficient in retrieving oxygen from the blood: it requires only 13 % of the blood flow to consume 23 % of the total oxygen. The same priority is given to the heart muscle, which receives about 5 % of the blood, because blood circulation is a vital function.

A high priority is also given to the kidneys, which receive 20 % to 25 % of the blood even though they contribute less than 0.5 % to the body weight. This preferred supply is due to the filtration function of the kidneys, as discussed in an example later in the chapter.

Supply to the skeletal muscles and the gastrointestinal tract with the liver varies significantly with demand. While physically active, up to 2/3 of the blood flux is distributed to the skeletal muscles. While digesting, a similarly high fraction of blood flows through the

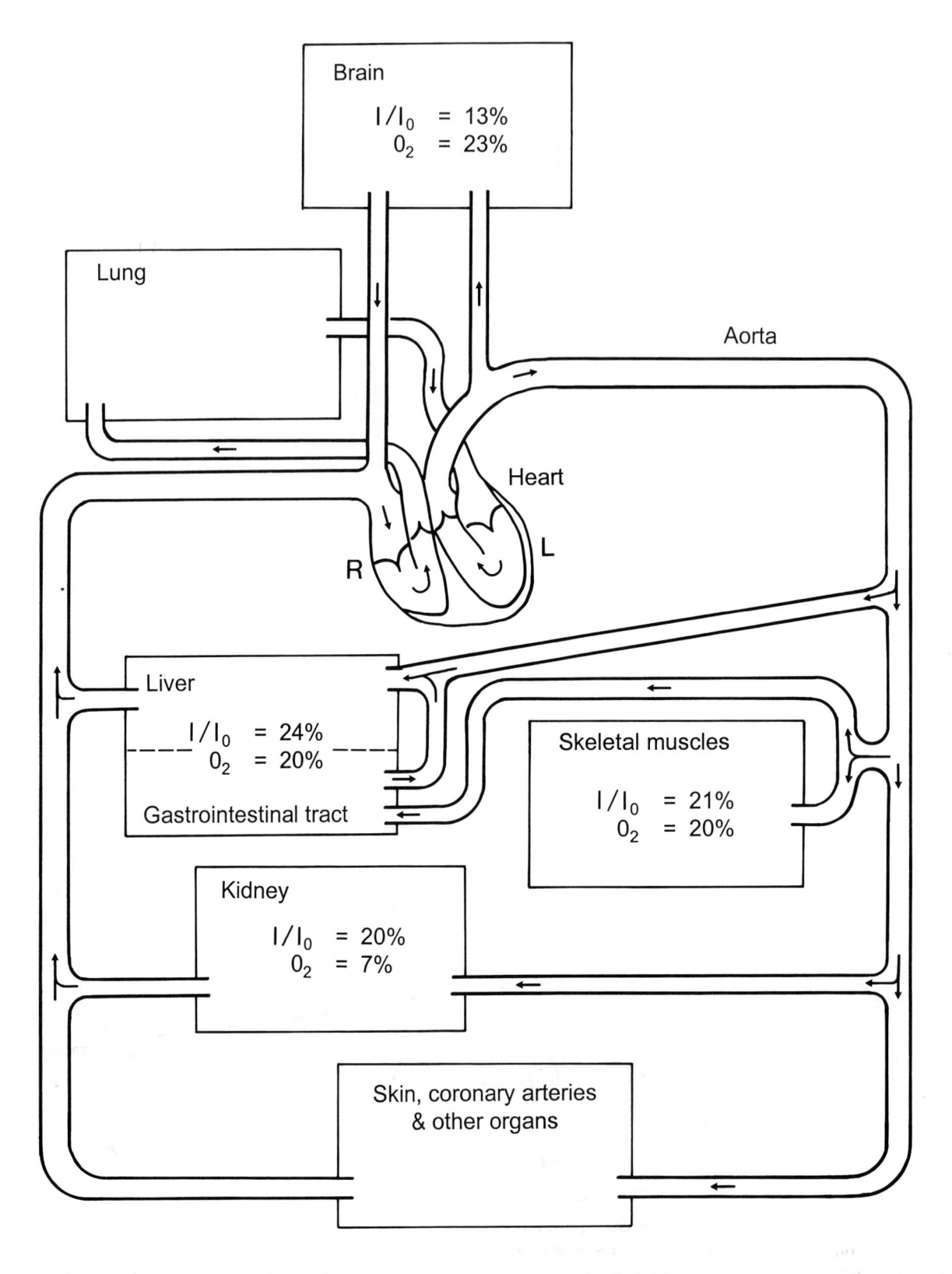

Fig. 11.2: Quantitative overview of the flow diagram of the human cardiovascular system. For each major organ, the fraction of the volume flow rate, I/I_0, and the fraction of oxygen consumed (labelled O_2) are listed.

gastrointestinal tract. Thus, it is sensible not to force both organ systems to work at the same time, e.g. by eating just before physical work!

The lungs receive blood through the lesser cardiovascular system to arterialize it (to add oxygen), and through the greater cardiovascular system to provide the lung tissue with oxygen. Both input streams leave the lungs together through the pulmonary vein.

The blood flow through the various organs is controlled by two mechanisms. The first mechanism is based on a smooth muscle layer in arterioles near the capillary bed. When these muscles are contracted, the blood vessel is constricted and blood flow is reduced. The second mechanism is illustrated in Fig. 11.3. Rings of smooth muscles called precapillary sphincters close off capillaries near the arteriole. As a result, a reduced blood flow occurs directly from the arteriole into the nearby venule through a throughfare channel, which is a single capillary which remains always open.

The total volume of blood is 5 liters (about 7 % of total body mass). Fig. 11.4(a) shows the volume distribution of the blood in the cardiovascular system. At any time, at least 80 % of the blood is in the veins, the right ventricle and the lesser cardiovascular system. This part of the cardiovascular system is called the low–pressure system since the blood pressure is usually only 2 kPa. Note that all blood pressure data are given relative to atmospheric pressure, which is about 101.3 kPa. The main purpose of the low–pressure system is the storage of blood. This part of the system can accommo-

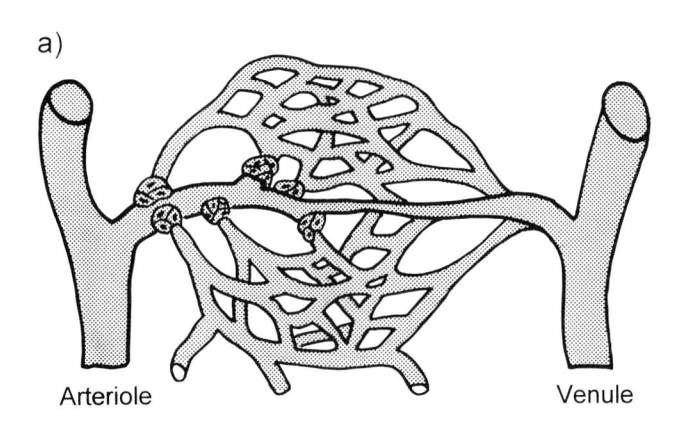

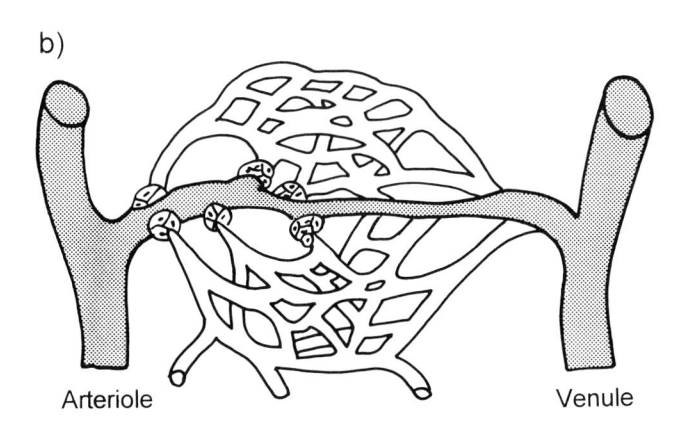

Fig. 11.3: Regulation of blood flow in capillary beds. Rings of smooth muscles called sphincters are located at the entry point from arterioles to the capillary bed. When these muscles close the blood flow, the flow is limited to a throughfare channel to keep the circulatory system open.

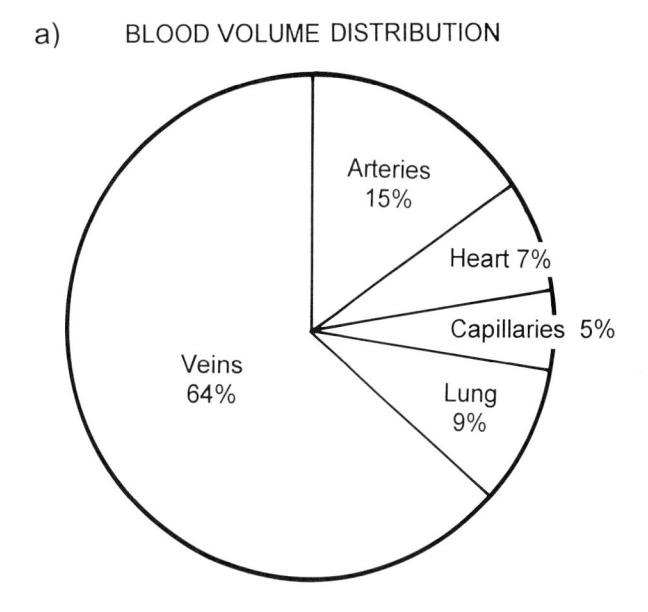

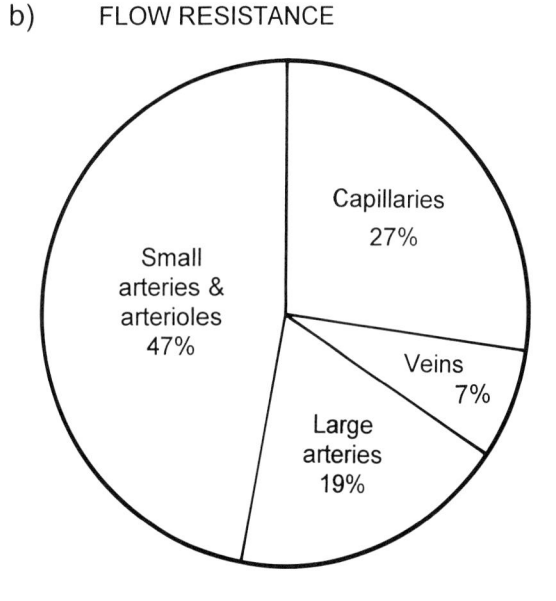

Fig. 11.4: (a) The blood volume distribution and (b) the contribution to the flow resistance for the main components of the cardiovascular system. While the veins accommodate a major fraction of the blood, it is the small arteries and arterioles which produce the largest contribution to the flow resistance of blood.

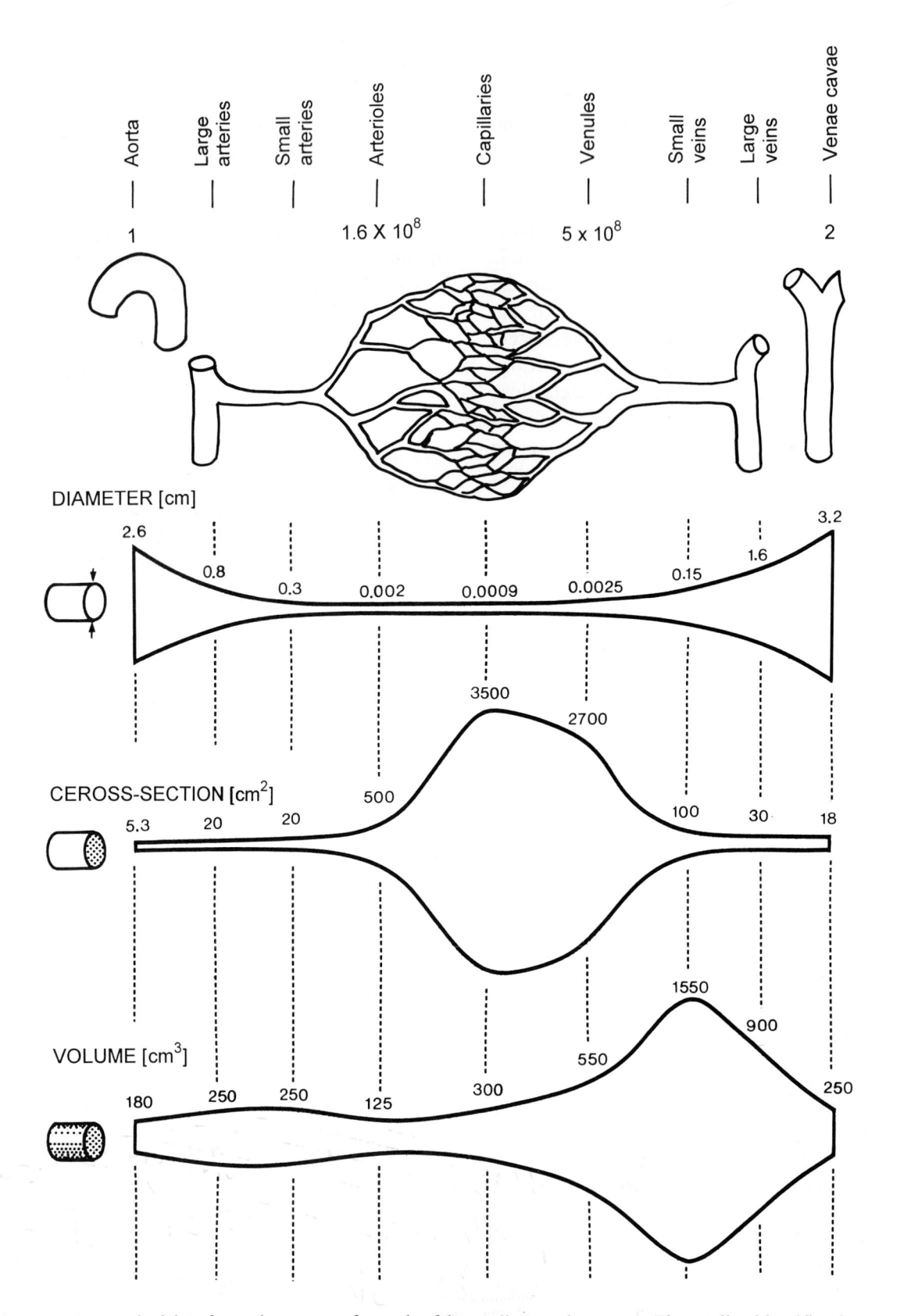

Fig. 11.5: Anatomical data for various types of vessels of the cardiovascular system. The top line identifies the type of blood vessel. The second line gives numbers of blood vessels for some types. For each type, the outer diameter of a single vessel, the outer cross–sectional area and the volume of all vessels of this type are illustrated. The numerical values are given in the indicated units.

date as much as 98 % of the blood in the human body, e.g. when the total blood volume is increased during blood transfusion.

The main purpose of the high pressure system is to supply the organs with oxygen. Since this involves pushing the blood through tiny capillaries, this part of the system represents more than 90 % of the flow resistance, as shown in Fig. 11.4(b). Blood pressure variations during blood flow and blood flow resistance are key issues for the cardiovascular system and are discussed in detail in this chapter.

Fig. 11.5 illustrates how the respective volumes in Fig. 11.4(a) are accommodated by the various parts of the cardiovascular system. The numbers at the top indicate how many blood vessels of each type are found in our body. These numbers vary from one aorta to 5×10^9 capillaries. Below these numbers are three sketches for
(I) the individual diameter of a vessel of a given type in [cm],
(II) the total cross–section for all vessels of this type in [cm²], which is important for determining the flow resistance, and
(III) the total capacity of all vessels of this type in [cm³]. Since the graph in Fig. 11.5 is not drawn to scale, numbers are shown to permit a quantitative comparison. Note that a quantitative discussion of the physical properties of the cardiovascular system depends on the anatomical data shown in Fig. 11.5.

11.2. Non–viscous flow

In the previous chapter several fundamental properties of fluids were defined. With these established we want to leave the stationary equilibrium in the current chapter and study non–equilibrium situations which occur when fluids flow.

11.2.1. Ideal dynamic fluid model

To describe a fluid in motion the assumption of a mechanical equilibrium is dropped, but we retain the incompressibility of the fluid as a useful simplification. To limit the possible complexity of the behavior of a flowing fluid, three additional assumptions are made:
(I) no turbulences occur during flow,
(II) no sound waves develop in the flowing fluid, and
(III) no friction occurs with the walls of the tube.
A system fulfilling these assumptions is called an ideal dynamic fluid.

The first assumption is satisfied when fluids flow sufficiently slowly. Toward the end of this section we will examine that limit more carefully as it is of crucial importance for the flow of blood and the breathing of air. The second assumption is automatically true as long as the fluid is incompressible since sound waves are the result of localized compressions in the fluid. We study sound when this assumption is dropped in Chapter 16. The third assumption is the most restrictive and is therefore already lifted in section 11.3 when the effects of viscosity and flow resistance are introduced.

The flow pattern of a fluid which satisfies the assumptions for an ideal dynamic fluid is called *laminar flow* and is illustrated in Fig. 11.6. Shown is an amount of fluid entering the field of view through the shaded area at the left side. If we divide the fluid into small fluid elements, then we can follow each element as a function of time. The path the element takes is called a flow line and can be envisaged to lie fully within a given flow tube as indicated for one flow line in the lower part of Fig. 11.6. With flow lines and flow tubes defined, laminar flow requires that (I) flow lines never cross each other, and that (II) flow tubes never penetrate each other.

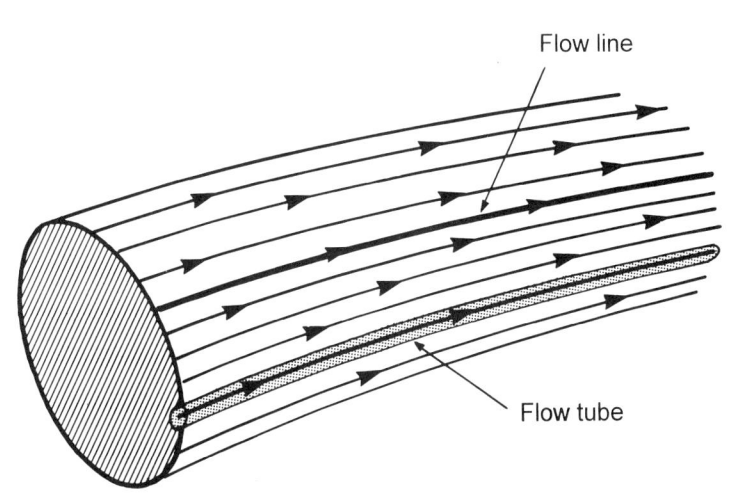

Fig. 11.6: Sketch of laminar flow through an arbitrarily chosen shaded area. The path taken by each fluid element is drawn as a flow line. One of the lower flow lines in the sketch is enclosed in a flow tube (dotted cylinder). Flow lines cannot cross each other during laminar flow. Laminar flow occurs for non–viscous and viscous flow. Ideal dynamic fluids cannot display other flow patterns. Newtonian fluids can alternatively display turbulent flow.

11.2.2. Equation of continuity

We now establish the laws applying to ideal dynamic fluids under laminar flow. The first relation is developed for a fluid that moves through a tube of varying cross–sectional area, as illustrated in Fig. 11.7. In the figure, the fluid flows from left to right. The cross–sectional area of the tube changes from A_1 to A_2, where $A_1 > A_2$. From experience we know that fluid is neither created nor lost across the narrowing of the tube. Thus, the same mass of fluid that enters through area A_1 (shaded area in upper sketch) must leave through area A_2 (shaded area in lower sketch) during the same time interval:

$$\frac{\Delta m_1}{\Delta t} = \frac{\Delta m_2}{\Delta t} \qquad (1)$$

Since the fluid is incompressible, the conservation of fluid mass in Eq. (1) extends to the volumes of fluid that passes the cross–sectional areas A_1 and A_2 per time interval. Using ρ for the density of the fluid, the conservation of fluid is quantified for the shaded areas in Fig. 11.7:

$$\rho \frac{\Delta V_1}{\Delta t} = \rho \frac{\Delta V_2}{\Delta t} \qquad (2)$$

The term $\Delta m/\Delta t$ in Eq. (1) is called the mass flow rate and the term $\Delta V/\Delta t$ in Eq. (2) is called the *volume flow rate*. The volume of a fluid element at any point in Fig. 11.7 can be written as the product of the cross–sectional area and the length of the element. Thus Eq. (2) is rewritten in the form:

$$\rho A_1 \frac{\Delta l_1}{\Delta t} = \rho A_2 \frac{\Delta l_2}{\Delta t} \qquad (3)$$

Δl can be interpreted as a displacement of the fluid along the tube. In the form $\Delta l/\Delta t$ it then represents a speed $|\mathbf{v}|$ of the fluid in the tube. Based on this argument, Eq. (3) is written in the form:

$$A_1 |\mathbf{v}_1| = A_2 |\mathbf{v}_2| \qquad (4)$$

Eq. (4) is called the Equation of continuity and applies to laminar flow of an ideal dynamic fluid:

> *The Equation of continuity states that the volume flow rate of an ideal dynamic fluid is constant along a tube. The fluid flows faster when it passes through a section of the tube with a smaller cross–section.*

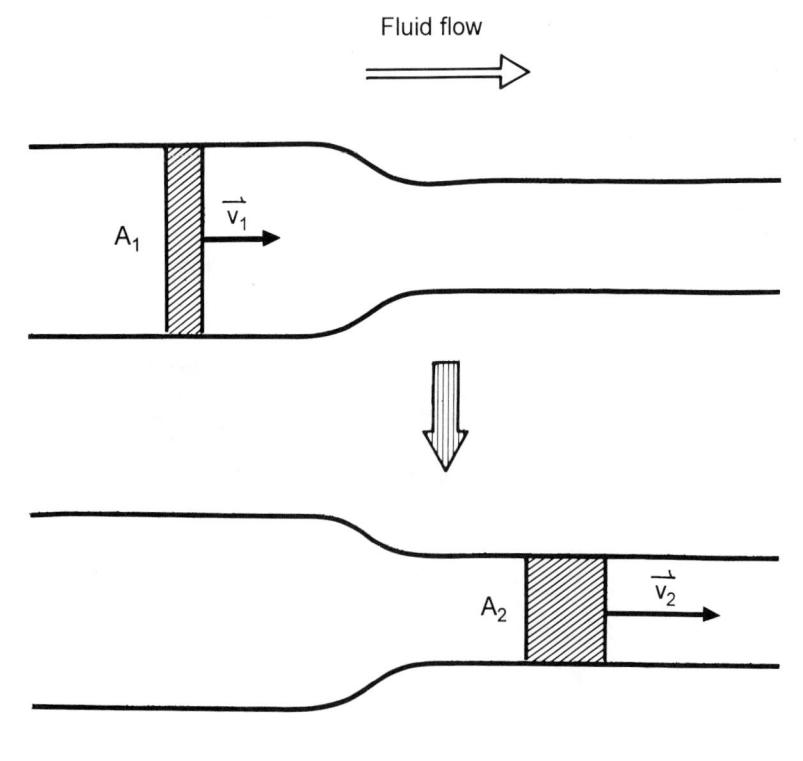

Fig. 11.7: Model of a tapering tube which we use to derive the Equation of continuity. Fluid flow occurs from left to right.
(Top) the fluid element is initially represented by the shaded area at the left with cross–sectional area A_1 and fluid speed v_1.
(Bottom) later the fluid element is positioned in the shaded area at the right with cross–sectional area A_2 and flow speed v_2.

Because Eq. (4) applies at any point along the tube, we can rewrite it in a generalized form:

$$A \, |\mathbf{v}| = const \qquad (5)$$

The reasoning which led from Eq. (2) to (4) also establishes a second useful equation for the volume flow rate:

$$A \, |\mathbf{v}| = \frac{\Delta V}{\Delta t} \qquad (6)$$

which applies at any point along the tube, including at the cross–sectional areas with index 1 and 2 in Fig. 11.7.

11.2.3. Speed of blood in capillaries (Example 11.1)

Our heart pumps 5 liters blood per minute into the aorta.
(a) What is the volume flow rate in unit [cm³/s]?
(b) What is the speed of blood in the aorta?
(c) If we assume that the blood passes through all capillaries in our body in sequence, how fast would the blood have to flow through each capillary? Would this speed make physiologically sense?
(d) What is the speed of blood in a capillary if blood flows in parallel through all capillaries in the body?

Solution part (a): The amount of blood flowing through the aorta per minute corresponds to a volume flow rate of 5000 cm³ per 60 s = 83 cm³/s.

Solution part (b): The diameter of the aorta is given in Fig. 11.5 as d = 2.6 cm, which leads to an outer cross–sectional area of the aorta of A = π(d/2)² = 5.3 cm² (also shown in the figure). The inner diameter defines the *lumen*, which is the open volume inside a blood vessel. To calculate the inner diameter of the blood vessel, the wall thickness has to be taken into account. The fraction of the total diameter due to the blood vessel wall lies between 15 % and 20 %; thus a typical inner diameter of the aorta is d_A = 2.2 cm. This leads to a cross–sectional area of the lumen of $A_A = \pi(d_A/2)^2 = 3.8$ cm². The speed of the blood in the aorta is obtained from the inner cross–sectional area of the aorta and the volume passing per second. Using Eq. (6) we obtain:

$$|\mathbf{v}_A| = \frac{\frac{\Delta V_A}{\Delta t}}{A_A} = \frac{83 \left[\frac{cm^3}{s}\right]}{3.8 [cm^2]} = 21.8 \, \frac{cm}{s} \qquad (7)$$

This is a frequently used result: blood flows through the aorta at an average speed of about 20 cm/s.

Solution part (c): Let's assume that blood passes through each single capillary at the rate found in part (a). For the outer diameter of a capillary we use 9 μm from Fig. 11.5. This value leads to an inner diameter of d_C = 7 μm (capillary wall thickness is about 1 μm, see Fig. 7.20). The cross–sectional area of the capillary is then $A_C = \pi(d_C/2)^2 = 3.8 \times 10^{-7}$ cm². We use the Equation of continuity to find the blood speed in a capillary, $|\mathbf{v}_C|$:

$$|\mathbf{v}_C| = \frac{A_A \, |\mathbf{v}_A|}{A_C} = \frac{83 \, cm^3/s}{3.8 \times 10^{-7} \, cm^2} \qquad (8)$$

$$\Rightarrow |\mathbf{v}_C| = 2150 \, km/s$$

Even if the capillaries could sustain blood flow at such speeds, exchange of chemicals between the blood and the surrounding tissue would no longer be possible.

Solution part (d): A slow flow of blood in the capillaries is achieved by arranging all capillaries parallel to each other with a combined cross–section which is larger than the cross–section of the aorta. Fig. 11.5 suggests that this is the case with 3500 cm² for the capillaries, compared to 5.3 cm² for the aorta. The Equation of continuity allows us to determine the actual speed of blood in the capillaries once we have corrected the cross–sectional areas from Fig. 11.5 to represent the cross–sectional areas of the lumen. This correction factor k is defined as the ratio of the lumen cross–sectional area to the outer cross–sectional area and is derived from the ratio of inner and outer diameter for a typical capillary:

$$k = \frac{A_{lumen}}{A_{outer}} = \frac{(7 \, \mu m)^2}{(9 \, \mu m)^2} = 0.6 \qquad (9)$$

The two diameters are squared because the area is proportional to the square of the radius. With this factor we obtain for the lumen cross–sectional area of the capillaries $A_C = 0.6 \cdot 3500$ cm² = 2100 cm². Thus:

$$|\mathbf{v}_C| = \frac{(\Delta V/\Delta t)_A}{A_C} = \frac{83 \, cm^3/s}{2100 \, cm^2} \qquad (10)$$

$$\Rightarrow |\mathbf{v}_C| = 0.4 \, mm/s$$

Again, this is a frequently used value. Blood flows very slowly through the capillaries, at less than 1 mm/s.

11.2.4. Bernoulli's equation

The changes in speed of a flowing fluid due to changes in the cross–section of the tube also lead to changes in the pressure in the fluid. This can be illustrated experimentally with an instrument called Venturi–meter, which is shown in Fig. 11.8. The instrument consists of a tube with a central constriction zone. A W–shaped tube is connected at the left and at the right side to the wide sections of the main tube; in the middle the W–shaped tube is open to the constriction zone. The W–shaped tube is partially filled with a liquid to indicate the pressure in the section of the horizontal tube above each column. Initially, while the fluid in the main horizontal tube is at rest, the liquid in the W–shaped tube rises to the same level in all three sections, indicating that the pressure is the same. When the fluid flows through the main tube, a pressure difference is observed: the liquid in the middle column rises highest, indicating that the pressure in the constriction zone is lower than in the wider sections. Thus, the speed of the fluid, which is higher in the central section due to the Equation of continuity, is inversely related to the pressure.

Daniel Bernoulli quantified this observation. He started with Fig. 11.9. Shown is a horizontal tube which tapers from cross–section A_1 to A_2. We assign a pressure p_1 to the wider section of the tube and p_2 to the narrower section. With these definitions, we study the shaded volume of fluid. We want to determine its kinetic energy at an initial and a final instant and then relate the change in the kinetic energy to the work needed to move the shaded volume across the constriction. We specifically choose the initial time (index 1) when the fluid volume occupies the shaded area shown in the top part of Fig. 11.9. At that instant the volume of the fluid element is identified as $\Delta V = A_1 \Delta x_1$. The final instant is shown in the bottom part of Fig. 11.9 (index 2). At this point the volume is given as $\Delta V = A_2 \Delta x_2$.

The cross–sectional areas and lengths are related by the Equation of continuity, Eq. (4). A force $\mathbf{F}_1$ has to be applied to push the fluid element through the tube against an opposing force $\mathbf{F}_2$, which is exerted on the fluid element by fluid further downstream. The change in the kinetic energy of the fluid element is:

$$\frac{1}{2} \Delta m\ v_2^2 - \frac{1}{2} \Delta m\ v_1^2 = \Delta E_{kin} \qquad (11)$$

in which Δm is the mass of the fluid element. With ρ the density of the fluid, we rewrite the mass of the fluid element as $\Delta m = \rho \Delta V$ and obtain for the change of the kinetic energy:

$$\Delta E_{kin} = \frac{1}{2} \rho \left(v_2^2 - v_1^2\right) dV \qquad (12)$$

Since the tube becomes narrower, the speed must increase and thus the kinetic energy of the fluid element increases. To achieve this increase of kinetic energy, work must be done on the fluid element. The work is obtained from transferring the fluid element from its initial to its final position. We can split the work in two contributions: removing the fluid element in the part of the tube with pressure p_1 and adding the fluid element to the part of the tube with pressure p_2. Quantitatively, this means that the volume of the element is changed from ΔV to 0 in the top part of Fig. 11.9, and, concurrently, the volume of the fluid element is changed from 0 to ΔV in the bottom part of the figure. The work is:

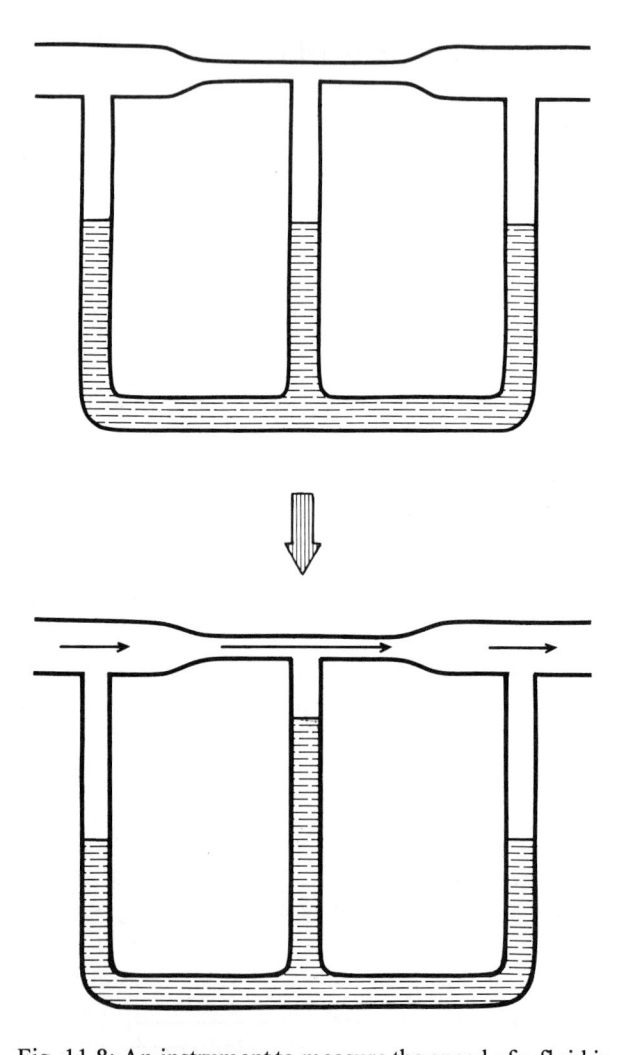

Fig. 11.8: An instrument to measure the speed of a fluid in a horizontal tube. This instrument is called a Venturi–meter. (Top) the Venturi–meter indicates the same pressure in every section of the tube while the fluid is at rest.
(Bottom) when the fluid flows as indicated by the arrows in the tube, pressure variations become evident: the pressure is higher where the speed of the fluid is slower.

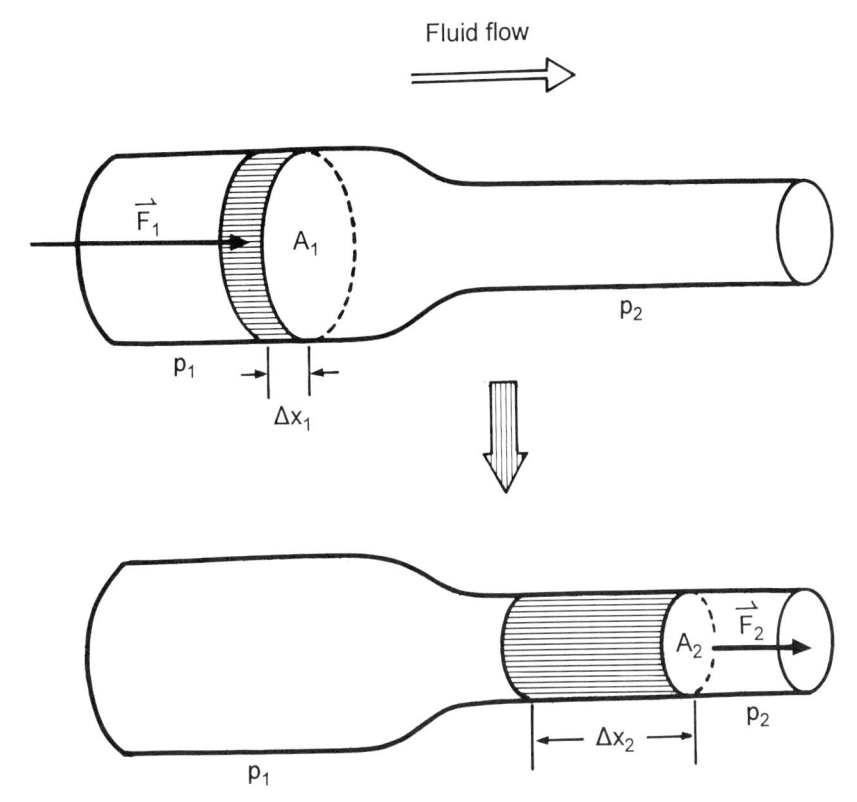

Fig. 11.9: A sketch defining the parameters needed to derive Bernoulli's law. We study a shaded fluid which occupies initially the volume $A_1 \Delta x_1$ (top) and later the volume $A_2 \Delta x_2$ (bottom). Fluid flow in the sketch occurs from left to right through a tapering tube. The fluid pressure varies from p_1 to p_2 across the constriction. The change in the speed of the fluid causes a change in the kinetic energy which is accounted for by a work term which is associated with the transfer of fluid across the constriction.

$$W = -p_2 \Delta V - p_1(-\Delta V) = \\ = -(p_2 - p_1)\Delta V \quad (13)$$

The conservation of energy formula for the fluid element as a closed system requires that $\Delta U = W$ because no temperature change occurs and thus no heat exchange takes place. The only form of energy changing in Fig. 11.9 is the kinetic energy and thus $\Delta U = \Delta E_{kin}$. We therefore find $\Delta E_{kin} = W$, i.e.:

$$-(p_2 - p_1)\Delta V = \frac{1}{2}\rho(v_2^2 - v_1^2)\Delta V \quad (14)$$

In the last step we separate all the terms related to position 1 on the left side of the equation and all the terms related to position 2 on the right side of the equation:

$$p_1 + \frac{1}{2}\rho v_1^2 = p_2 + \frac{1}{2}\rho v_2^2 \quad (15)$$

Eq. (15) states that the sum of the pressure and the term $\frac{1}{2}\rho v^2$ is constant at any position along the tube. This leads to Bernoulli's law:

$$p + \frac{1}{2}\rho v^2 = const \quad (16)$$

Bernoulli's law states that an increase in the speed of an ideal dynamic fluid in a tube is accompanied by a drop in the pressure during laminar flow.

Bernoulli's law, as usually reported in the physics literature, includes one more term which accommodates a change in the height of the tube when the tube is not oriented horizontal. That equation is not required for most applications. Example 10.2 provides an alternative approach to include height differences via Pascal's law.

A well–known application of Bernoulli's law during summer or early fall is the quaking of the leaves of the aspen tree. In a gentle breeze, the leaves of the aspen tree move up and down, or left and right, depending on the direction of the wind. Fig. 11.10 shows an aspen leaf. Notice that these leaves are slightly arched. Wind blowing through the tree splits above and below the leaves. It has to travel different path lengths above and below the leaf. This causes different wind speeds. From Bernoulli's law we find that the difference in the speed of the wind causes a difference in the pressure above and below the leaf. This causes a net force on the leaf and is the origin of the motion you observe.

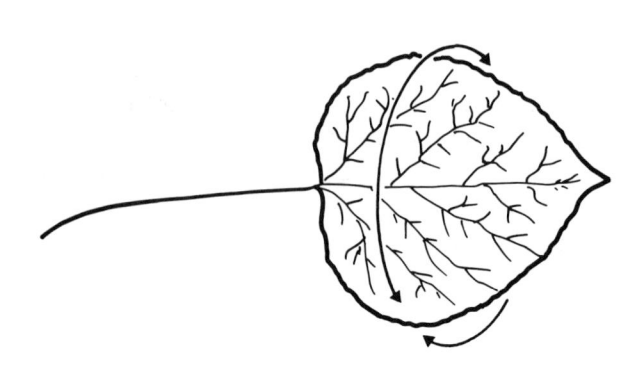

Fig. 11.10: The leaves of the aspen tree are slightly curved. A mild breeze blowing over the leaf causes a difference in wind speed above and below the leaf. This causes a variation in air pressure across the leaf, which causes in turn a lift force. This force sets the leaves in vibrating motion.

Example 11.2
Ethanol flows smoothly through a horizontal pipe that tapers in cross–sectional area from $A_1 = 1 \times 10^{-3}$ m² to A_2 with $A_2 = A_1/2$, similar to the case illustrated in Fig. 11.9. The pressure difference Δp between the wide and the narrow sections of the pipe is 5.0 kPa. What is the volume flow rate $\Delta V/\Delta t$ of the ethanol? The density of ethanol is $\rho = 790$ kg/m³.

Solution: We start with Bernoulli's law. Index 1 in Eq. (15) refers to the wide section and index 2 refers to the narrow section of the pipe. From the Equation of continuity we know that the flow is faster in the narrow section, i.e., $v_2 > v_1$. Inserting this inequality in Eq. (15) leads to $p_1 > p_2$. Thus, we predict that the pressure drops from section 1 to section 2. This must be taken into account when rewriting the pressure difference in the form $\Delta p = p_1 - p_2$. In this form, $\Delta p > 0$ and we use $\Delta p = +5.0$ kPa. Note that we could have chosen to define Δp as $p_2 - p_1$, in which case Δp would be a negative value.

Eq. (6) allows us to specify the two speeds, v_1 and v_2, since we know how the two cross–sectional areas differ: $A_2 = \frac{1}{2}A_1$. Thus, we write for the two speeds:

$$v_1 = \frac{\Delta V/\Delta t}{A_1} \tag{17}$$

and:

$$v_2 = \frac{\Delta V/\Delta t}{A_2} = \frac{2\,\Delta V/\Delta t}{A_1} \tag{18}$$

Substituting Eqs. (17) and (18) into Eq. (15) we find:

$$\Delta p = \frac{1}{2}\rho\left(\frac{4\,(\Delta V/\Delta t)^2}{A_1^2} - \frac{(\Delta V/\Delta t)^2}{A_1^2}\right) \tag{19}$$

which leads to:

$$\Delta p = \frac{3\,\rho\,(\Delta V/\Delta t)^2}{2\,A_1^2} \tag{20}$$

This equation is solved for the unknown volume flow rate $\Delta V/\Delta t$:

$$\frac{\Delta V}{\Delta t} = A_1 \sqrt{\frac{2\,\Delta p}{3\,\rho}} \tag{21}$$

which gives the final result:

$$\frac{\Delta V}{\Delta t} = 1 \times 10^{-3}[m^2] \sqrt{\frac{2 \cdot 5000[Pa]}{3 \cdot 790\left[\frac{kg}{m^3}\right]}} \tag{22}$$

$$\Rightarrow \frac{\Delta V}{\Delta t} = 2.05 \times 10^{-3} \left[\frac{m^3}{s}\right]$$

11.3. Viscous flow

In section 11.2 we have limited the discussion to an idealized fluid for which the interactions with the walls of the tube are negligible. The experiment illustrated in Fig. 11.11 shows that this is too severe a restriction. The figure shows a tube with a liquid flowing from left to right (direction of arrow). Three smaller, vertical tubes

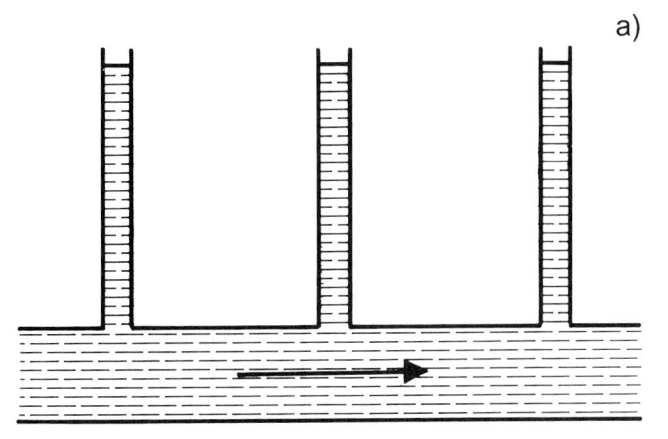

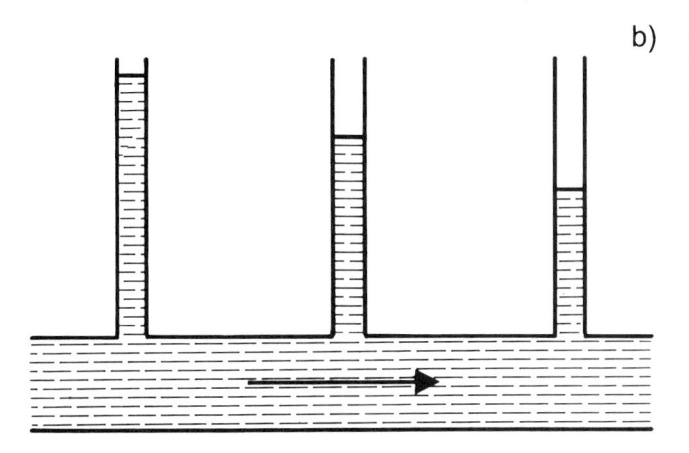

Fig. 11.11: Comparison of (a) an ideal dynamic fluid and (b) a Newtonian fluid (viscous fluid) flowing through a horizontal tube. Viscous flow leads to a pressure drop along the tube in the flow direction, as indicated by the lower column height of the fluid above the tube at the right in part (b).

Thus, the experimental result differs fundamentally from the prediction in Fig. 11.11(a): either the liquid speed and/or the pressure along the tube must change; i.e., either the Equation of continuity or Bernoulli's law is not applicable. We will find in this section that the problem rests with Bernoulli's law. Introducing first the concept of viscosity, we show that there is a change in the pressure along the tube which causes the observation in Fig. 11.11(b).

11.3.1. Viscosity

Viscosity introduces an interaction between neighboring layers of fluids in a direction perpendicular to the flow lines. This is shown in Fig. 11.12 in which two layers of area A in the fluid are highlighted. The lower layer is at rest. This could be, for example, due to close proximity to the resting walls of the tube. The upper layer, a distance Δy away from the lower layer, moves with velocity $\Delta \mathbf{v}$ toward the right. We assume that the moving layer encounters a force **R** which tries to slow it down. To maintain a constant velocity, Newton's first law requires the presence of a second force, $\mathbf{F}_{ext}$, with which the upper layer of fluid is pushed forward. Thus, if a fluid encounters flow resistance, an external force must be applied to push the fluid forward in the tube. The magnitude of the external force is found empirically by submerging thin plates into a resting fluid and moving one plate relative to the other as Fig. 11.12 suggests. From such experiments $\mathbf{F}_{ext}$ is found to be proportional to
(I) the area of the submerged plates, A, and
(II) the relative speed of the plates to each other, $\Delta \mathbf{v}$. The force is also inversely proportional to
(III) the distance between the two plates, Δy:

$$\mathbf{F}_{ext} = \eta \, A \, \frac{\Delta \mathbf{v}}{\Delta y} \qquad (23)$$

Since the needed external force further varies from fluid to fluid, with smaller forces typically needed in gases and larger forces in liquids, a materials constant is introduced, which is called the viscosity coefficient η. Based on Eq. (23) the unit of η is [Ns/m²]. Table 11.1 lists viscosity coefficients for several fluids.

Note that the third column in Table 11.1 gives the temperature at which the reported values apply, implying that these values change with temperature. Viscosity is one of the non–equilibrium effects we call transport phenomena; as we saw for diffusion in Chapter 7, a microscopic model is needed in addition to the phenomenological law in Eq. (23) to quantify the temperature dependence of the viscosity coefficient.

are placed at different positions along the tube. The height to which the liquid rises in each of the small tubes depends on the air pressure and the weight of the liquid column as well as the pressure in the flowing liquid below. For a liquid that can be described as an ideal dynamic fluid (with no flow resistance), the liquid columns in all three small tubes are equally high. This case is shown in Fig. 11.11(a) and is in agreement with the prediction of the Equation of continuity and Bernoulli's law: the Equation of continuity states that the speed of an incompressible, ideal fluid does not change when the cross–section of the tube does not change. Bernoulli's law then states that the pressure in the fluid does not change when the speed of the fluid does not change.

The observation for a real liquid is shown in Fig. 11.11(b). The further the liquid progresses along the tube, the lower the liquid column in the small tubes.

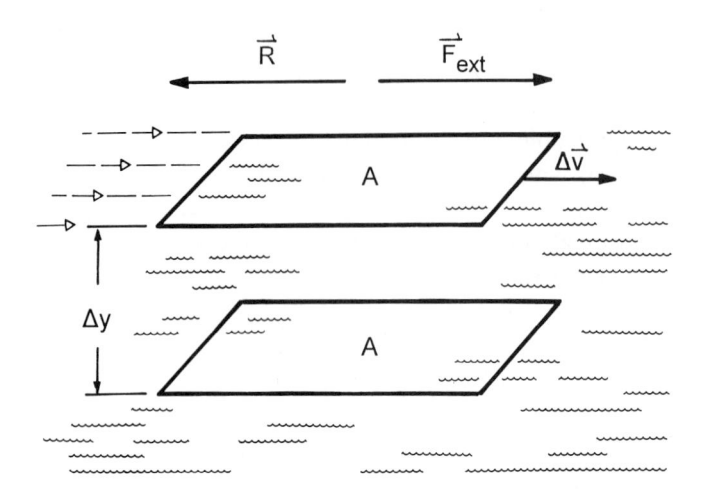

Fig. 11.12: Experimental set–up of the experiment used to determine viscosity. Two parallel plates are immersed in a fluid at a distance Δy from each other. The lower plate is held at rest and the upper plate is pushed by the external force **F**$_{ext}$. The resistance force of the fluid **R** balances the external force, leading to a constant speed **Δv** of the plate toward the right.

Table 11.1: Viscosity coefficients

Fluid	Viscosity coefficient η [Ns/m^2]	Temperature [°C]
1. Gases		
N$_2$	1.78×10^{-5}	25
O$_2$	2.08×10^{-5}	25
Air	1.71×10^{-5}	0
H$_2$	9.0×10^{-6}	25
H$_2$	8.4×10^{-6}	0
H$_2$O	9.8×10^{-6}	25
2. Liquids		
H$_2$O	1.79×10^{-3}	0
H$_2$O	1.01×10^{-3}	20
H$_2$O	2.8×10^{-4}	100
(whole) blood	$2.3 - 2.7 \times 10^{-3}$	37
Blood serum	$1.6 - 2.2 \times 10^{-3}$	20
Ethanol	1.19×10^{-3}	20
Glycerin	1.5	20

Viscosity in gases

Comparing first some of the values given in Table 11.1 for gases, we note that the viscosity coefficient increases with temperature. A more precise measurement of this effect reveals that the viscosity coefficient for gases is proportional to the square–root of the temperature, $\eta \propto \sqrt{T}$. This is explained with the ideal gas model when the distance between the plates in Fig. 11.12 is chosen to be roughly the mean free path between collisions of gas molecules. In this case, a particle encountering a collision in one plate of Fig. 11.12 will have the next collision in the neighboring plate. During each collision the particle equilibrates its speed with the average speed of its environment, thus accelerating the other particles in a slower plate and slowing the particles in a faster plate. The microscopic formula for the viscosity coefficient, as derived using the ideal gas law, reads:

$$\eta = \frac{1}{\pi d^2} \sqrt{\frac{mkT}{\pi}} \qquad (24)$$

in which d is the diameter of the gas molecule, m is the mass of the molecule and k is the Boltzmann constant. Thus, the gas becomes more viscous at higher temperature because the gas molecules become faster and penetrate neighboring layers more effectively. This interlocks the neighboring sections of the gas more strongly.

Viscosity in liquids

Again, we first study Table 11.1 to see what temperature effect we need to explain. The data show that for liquids the viscosity decreases with temperature, with the temperature dependence of the viscosity coefficient given by $\eta \propto \exp(\text{const}/T)$. Thus, in liquids a different microscopic model is needed. As discussed in detail in the context of the temperature dependence of diffusion in Chapter 7, an exponential dependence with a factor 1/T in the exponent indicates that an energy barrier has to be overcome. For the motion of two liquid layers this is qualitatively sketched in Fig. 11.13. Liquids are much denser than gases; their molecules are tightly packed. The three boxes in the figure show how one row of molecules in the liquid squeezes past the molecules below. To squeeze by energy is required. This is illustrated in the plot of the potential energy as a function of position of the particles in the layer in the lower part of Fig. 11.13.

Example 11.3

A 1.0 mm thick coating of glycerine is placed between two microscope slides of width 2 cm and length 7 cm. Find the force required to move the microscope slides at a constant speed of 20 cm/s relative to each other. The coefficient of viscosity of glycerine is found in Table 11.1.

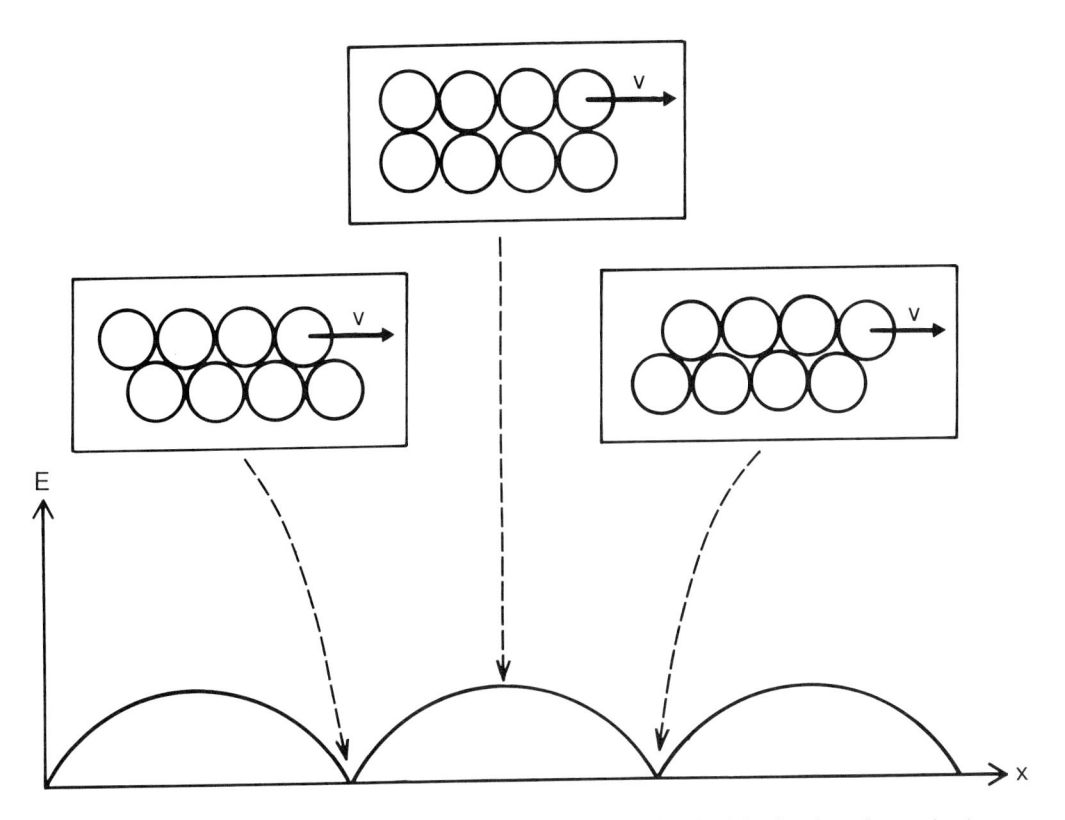

Fig. 11.13: Microscopic model and energy profile for the viscous flow of a liquid. The three boxes in the upper part of the sketch illustrate how tightly packed spheres representing the molecules in the liquid move past each other. The corresponding energy profile of the motion is given below.

Solution: This problem is solved using Eq. (23). Each of the terms on the right hand side of the equation is given in the Example text: the area is given as A = 0.02 m 0.07 m = 1.4×10^{-3} m², the difference in speed as $\Delta v = 0.2$ m/s and the distance as $\Delta y = 1.0 \times 10^{-3}$ m (coating thickness). Using the viscosity coefficient $\eta = 1.5$ Ns/m² we find:

$$F = \frac{1.5 \left[\frac{Ns}{m^2}\right] 1.4 \times 10^{-3}[m^2] \, 0.2\left[\frac{m}{s}\right]}{1.0 \times 10^{-3}[m]} \quad (25)$$

$$\Rightarrow \quad F = 0.42 \ N$$

11.3.2. Poiseuille's law

For viscous flow the velocity of the fluid in a tube is no longer uniform across the tube. The actual velocity profile depends on the geometry of the tube. Of particular biological interest is a cylindrical tube and a time independent flow pattern. This state was defined in section 8.5 as the steady state.

We know from Newton's second law that accelerations occur when forces are not balanced. Acceleration is associated with the time dependent change of velocity and, therefore, the velocity profile in the tube would change. Thus, to obtain a steady state velocity profile in a cylindrical tube, all forces on the fluid in the tube must be balanced.

Two forces act on the fluid in a tube. In the direction of the motion of the fluid there is a force due to a pressure difference along the tube. This force pushes the fluid through the tube. The viscosity of the fluid causes a resistance force acting in the direction opposite to the direction of motion of the fluid. This force counteracts therefore the flow and tries to slow down the moving fluid. The mechanical equilibrium between these two forces varies with the position of the fluid element in the tube: near the outer wall viscosity dominates and the fluid flows very slowly (with the speed vanishing directly at the wall), whereas towards the center of the tube the force pushing the fluid dominates and the fluid moves relatively fast. The velocity profile is written quantitatively in the form:

$$v = \frac{r_t^2 - r^2}{4\eta} \frac{\Delta p}{l} \qquad (26)$$

in which r_t is the radius of the tube and Δp is the pressure difference along a segment of the tube of length l. η is the viscosity coefficient of the fluid. Eq. (26) corresponds to a parabolic velocity distribution, as shown in Fig. 11.14. Jean Leonard Poiseuille used Eq. (26) to determine the volume flow rate through a cylindrical tube, called Poiseuille's law:

$$\frac{\Delta V}{\Delta t} = \frac{\pi}{8\eta} \frac{r_t^4}{l} \Delta p \qquad (27)$$

Poiseuille's law states that the volume flow rate of a viscous fluid through a tube is proportional to the fourth power of the radius of the tube.

Thus, a narrower tube reduces the flow severely. When the diameter of a tube is reduced by a factor of 2 the flow through the tube is diminished by a factor of 16!

When a fluid obeys Eq. (27) we call it a *Newtonian fluid*. The properties of some familiar fluids differ significantly from this behavior. These fluids include blood and are discussed in the next chapter.

Eq. (27) can be generalized for other geometries than cylindrical tubes in the form called Ohm's law:

$$\Delta p = R \frac{\Delta V}{\Delta t} \qquad (28)$$

R in Eq. (28) is the *flow resistance* with unit [Pa s/m³].

Ohm's law states that the volume flow rate of a Newtonian fluid is proportional to the pressure difference for a viscous fluid, and that the proportionality constant is the flow resistance.

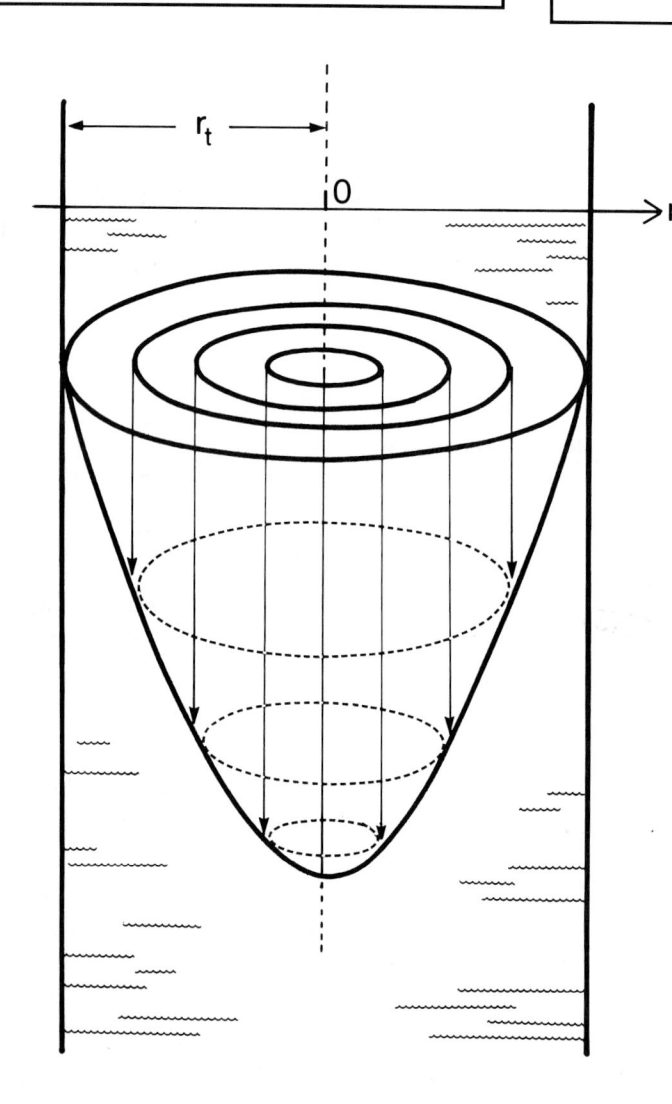

Fig. 11.14: The steady state velocity profile of a viscous liquid flowing through a cylindrical tube. The highest speed is reached at the center, while the fluid layer directly in contact with the wall does not move. Note that the figure shows a physical sketch of the system, which includes the walls of the tubes, and a diagram with the velocity–axis pointing downwards and the position–axis pointing to the right.

This relates to the everyday use of the word resistance since a large pressure difference leads to only a small volume flow rate if the resistance is high. In our discussion on nerves in Chapter 13, we will compare Eq. (28) to Ohm's law as applied to the flow of electric charges.

For a cylindrical tube, the flow resistance is defined by Eq. (27). It is directly proportional to the viscosity coefficient η of the fluid:

$$R = \frac{8 l}{\pi r_t^4} \eta \quad (29)$$

Example 11.4
What is the pressure gradient (the drop of pressure per length unit) in the aorta?
Hint: assume that blood can be treated as a Newtonian fluid. The viscosity coefficient of blood is taken from Table 11.1 as $\eta_{blood} = 2.5 \times 10^{-3}$ Ns/m².

Solution: The volume flow rate in the aorta is $\Delta V/\Delta t = 8.3 \times 10^{-5}$ m³/s as we have discussed in Example 11.1. The aorta is assumed to be cylinder-shaped with an inner diameter of 2.2 cm. We apply Poiseuille's law for the pressure gradient $\Delta p/l$:

$$\frac{\Delta p}{l} = \frac{\Delta V}{\Delta t} \frac{8 \eta}{\pi} \frac{1}{r_t^4} \quad (30)$$

This formula yields with the values given in the problem text:

$$\frac{\Delta p}{l} = \frac{8.3 \times 10^{-5} \left[\frac{m^3}{s}\right] \cdot 8 \cdot 2.5 \times 10^{-3} \left[\frac{Ns}{m^2}\right]}{\pi \left(1.1 \times 10^{-2} [m]\right)^4} \quad (31)$$

This is a convenient place to check the units. Note that the pressure gradient does not have the same units as the pressure, but carries an additional m⁻¹. The final result then follows from Eq. (31):

$$\frac{\Delta p}{l} = 36 \frac{Pa}{m} \quad (32)$$

11.3.3. Flow in parallel and sequential tubes: Kirchhoff's laws

Kirchhoff's laws describe the way in which flow resistances have to be combined in cases in which we are interested in the fact that blood passes through more than one vessel as it contributes to the flow resistance before returning to the heart. There are two laws to be formulated, one for vessels in series (e.g. the aorta and an artery leading to the liver) and one for vessels in parallel (e.g. a bed of capillaries between an arteriole and a venule in the liver).

Robert Gustav Kirchhoff derived these laws in 1845 originally not for fluids but for flowing electric charges. In the physics literature, you find them therefore most frequently applied in electricity. However, in physiological systems they are more important for fluid flow.

Blood vessels in series
Let's assume that a given amount of blood passes a vessel 1 with a given flow resistance R_1 and then passes a vessel 2 with a flow resistance R_2. We assume further that the blood vessel does not branch between vessel 1 and vessel 2.

The volume flow rate of each of the two vessels obeys Ohm's law as given in Eq. (28). In other words, the respective drop in blood pressure along the vessel is equal to the product of the flow resistance in the vessel and the volume flow rate of blood through the vessel:

$$\Delta p_1 = R_1 \frac{\Delta V}{\Delta t}$$
$$\Delta p_2 = R_2 \frac{\Delta V}{\Delta t} \quad (33)$$

Note that the volume flow rate is the same in both vessels because the volume of blood is conserved for an incompressible fluid and does not change because there are no branching points between the two vessels in the combined system.

On top of studying each vessel separately, we can also describe the combined system by Eq. (28):

$$\Delta p = R_{eqiv} \frac{\Delta V}{\Delta t} \quad (34)$$

in which we introduced an equivalent flow resistance, R_{eqiv}, which must be a combination of the two individual flow resistances in Eq. (33). The term $\Delta V/\Delta t$ in Eq. (34) is equal to the same terms in Eq. (33) because it is the same volume flow rate in each case. We can combine Eqs. (33) and (34) to relate the equivalent flow resistance to the individual flow resistances by recognizing that $\Delta p = \Delta p_1 + \Delta p_2$, i.e., that the pressure drop along the first vessel and the pressure drop along the second vessel combine to the total pressure drop along the two vessels in series. This leads to:

$$R_{eqiv} \frac{\Delta V}{\Delta t} = (R_1 + R_2) \frac{\Delta V}{\Delta t}$$
$$\Rightarrow R_{eqiv} = R_1 + R_2 \quad (35)$$

This is Kirchhoff's first law.

> *Kirchhoff's first law states that flow resistances in series are added to obtain the equivalent flow resistance.*

Blood vessels in parallel
In the second case we study a blood vessel which branches into two vessels, a vessel with flow resistance R_1 and a vessel with flow resistance R_2. Downstream, the two vessels recombine to a single vessel. No further branching occurs.

In this case, the pressure drop along the two separated vessels must be the same because there can only be one particular pressure value in the vessel before branching and there can also only be one particular pressure value in the vessel after they reunite.

Thus, we write Eq. (28) for the two parallel vessels in the form:

$$\Delta p = R_1 \left(\frac{\Delta V}{\Delta t} \right)_1$$
$$\Delta p = R_2 \left(\frac{\Delta V}{\Delta t} \right)_2 \quad (36)$$

Eq. (36) shows that the fraction of the blood passing through each of the two vessels depends on their respective flow resistances. We can alternatively study the two vessels as a combined system. For this we apply Eq. (28) to the combined system by assigning an equivalent flow resistance, R_{eqiv}:

$$\Delta p = R_{eqiv} \frac{\Delta V}{\Delta t} \quad (37)$$

Eqs. (36) and (37) are combined to determine the dependence of the equivalent flow resistance on the two individual flow resistances. First we note that the total amount of blood flowing into the branching point per time, $\Delta V/\Delta t$, must be equal to the sum of blood passing the two vessels during the same time interval, i.e.:

$$\frac{\Delta V}{\Delta t} = \left(\frac{\Delta V}{\Delta t} \right)_1 + \left(\frac{\Delta V}{\Delta t} \right)_2 \quad (38)$$

Were this not so, either blood would have to accumulate in vessel 1 and 2 or blood would have to accumulate upstream. Substituting Eqs. (36) and (37) in (38) we find:

$$\frac{\Delta V}{\Delta t} = \frac{\Delta p}{R_{eqiv}} =$$
$$= \left(\frac{\Delta V}{\Delta t} \right)_1 + \left(\frac{\Delta V}{\Delta t} \right)_2 = \frac{\Delta p}{R_1} + \frac{\Delta p}{R_2} \quad (39)$$

From Eq. (39) we conclude Kirchhoff's second law:

$$\frac{1}{R_{eqiv}} = \frac{1}{R_1} + \frac{1}{R_2} \quad (40)$$

> *Kirchhoff's second law states that flow resistances in parallel are added inversely to obtain the equivalent flow resistance.*

Example 11.5
Fig. 11.15 shows a blood vessel A of radius r_1 in which blood flows from point P_1 to point P_2 with the two points a distance l_1 apart. At point P_2 the blood vessel splits into

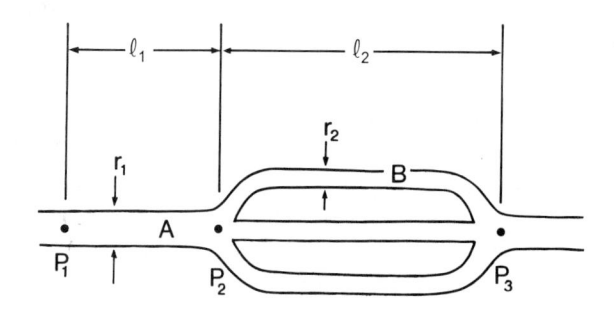

Fig. 11.15: Example for Kirchhoff's law. Shown is a single blood vessel A which splits into three capillaries of type B. The capillaries reunite to form a single vessel at point P_3. Note the various geometric data shown in the figure.

three vessels, one of which we label vessel B. Each of the parallel vessels has a radius $r_2 = \frac{1}{2} r_1$. The three vessels merge at a distance $l_2 = \frac{1}{2} l_1$ downstream from point P_2; this position we define as point P_3.
(a) What fraction of the blood volume passing through vessel A is passing through vessel B?
(b) What fraction of the drop in pressure between points P_1 and P_3 is occurring in vessel A?

Solution part (a): The volume flow rate at point P_1 and the volume flow rate at point P_3 are equal. Using Eq. (29) for the flow resistance we note further that the three parallel vessels have the same flow resistance because they are equal in all parameters. Using Eq. (28) we find therefore that the volume flow rate in each of the three parallel vessels is the same. With this information we calculate the ratio of the volume flow rate in vessel A and in vessel B:

$$\frac{\left(\frac{\Delta V}{\Delta t}\right)_B}{\left(\frac{\Delta V}{\Delta t}\right)_A} = \frac{\frac{1}{3}\left(\frac{\Delta V}{\Delta t}\right)_A}{\left(\frac{\Delta V}{\Delta t}\right)_A} = \frac{1}{3} \quad (41)$$

Solution part (b): Using Eq. (28) for both, the entire system in Fig. 11.15 and for vessel A, we write:

$$\Delta p_{P_1 P_3} = R_{P_1 P_3} \left(\frac{\Delta V}{\Delta t}\right)$$
$$\Delta p_A = R_A \left(\frac{\Delta V}{\Delta t}\right) \quad (42)$$

These two formulas are combined:

$$\frac{\Delta p_A}{\Delta p_{P_1 P_3}} = \frac{R_A}{R_{P_1 P_3}} \quad (43)$$

Thus, we obtain the fraction of the drop in pressure on the left hand side of Eq. (43) once the equivalent flow resistance for the system in Fig. 11.15 has been determined to evaluate the right hand side of Eq. (43).
The equivalent flow resistance for Fig. 11.15 is calculated in three steps:
(I) First we calculate R_A and R_B,
(II) then we combine the three parallel vessels and calculate the equivalent flow resistance for this section.
(III) Finally, the equivalent flow resistance for the three parallel vessels and the flow resistance for vessel A are combined to obtain the equivalent flow resistance.

Step (I): The flow resistances for sections A and B are calculated from Eq. (29). We obtain:

$$R_A = \frac{8 \, l_1 \, \eta}{\pi \, r_1^4} \quad (44)$$

and

$$R_B = \frac{8 \, l_2 \, \eta}{\pi \, r_2^4} = \frac{8 \, \frac{1}{2} l_1 \, \eta}{\pi \, (\frac{1}{2} r_1)^4} = 8 \, R_A \quad (45)$$

Step (II): We combine the contributions of the three parallel vessels to an equivalent flow resistance for the part of Fig. 11.15 which lies between points P_2 and P_3. For this equivalent flow resistance we use Kirchhoff's law for parallel vessels from Eq. (40):

$$\frac{1}{R_{P_1 P_3}} = \frac{1}{R_B} + \frac{1}{R_B} + \frac{1}{R_B} = \frac{3}{R_B} \quad (46)$$

Step (III): In the last step we combine the flow resistance for the section between points P_1 and P_2 (vessel A with R_A) and the equivalent flow resistance for the section between points P_2 and P_3. The equivalent flow resistance for the entire system in Fig. 11.15 is obtained from Kirchhoff's law for vessels in series, which is Eq. (35):

$$R_{P_1 P_3} = R_A + R_{P_2 P_3} = R_A + \frac{R_B}{3} =$$
$$= R_A + \frac{8 \, R_A}{3} = \frac{11 \, R_A}{3} \quad (47)$$

in which we used Eq. (45) to replace R_B. By substituting Eq. (47) in Eq. (43) we find:

$$\frac{\Delta p_A}{\Delta p_{P_1 P_3}} = \frac{R_A}{R_{P_1 P_3}} = \frac{R_A}{\frac{11 \, R_A}{3}} = \frac{3}{11} \quad (48)$$

Thus, about 27 % of the drop in pressure occurs in vessel A.

11.4. The Newtonian fluid applied in physiology

11.4.1. Flow resistance in the human cardiovascular system (Example 11.6)

50 % of the flow resistance in the circulatory system is caused in the arterioles (small arteries), a higher fraction than either in the aorta or the capillaries (see Fig. 11.4). Using the viscosity of blood from Table 11.1 in Eq. (29) and the data from Fig. 11.5 (with 5×10^9 capillaries in the human body), confirm that the total flow resistance is greatest in the arterioles.

Hint: calculate first the flow resistance for a single vessel, then the flow resistance for all vessels of the same type by using Kirchhoff's second law:

$$\frac{1}{R_{total}} = \sum_i \frac{1}{R_i} \qquad (49)$$

Solution: We first go through the calculations for the aorta. The average length $<l>$ of any vessel of a given type is determined from Fig. 11.5 by dividing the total cross–sectional area of this type of vessels by the total volume of the same type. For the aorta this leads to:

$$<l> = \frac{V}{A} = \frac{180\ [cm^3]}{5.3\ [cm^2]} = 34\ cm \qquad (50)$$

The radius of the tube is half the inner aorta diameter, $r_t = 1.1$ cm. The flow resistance follows from Eq. (29):

$$R_{aorta} = \frac{8 \cdot 0.34[m]\ 2.5 \times 10^{-3}\left[\frac{Ns}{m^2}\right]}{\pi\ (0.011[m])^4} \qquad (51)$$

$$\Rightarrow R_{aorta} = 1.5 \times 10^5\ \frac{Pa\ s}{m^3}$$

Since there is only one aorta in our body, we have the summation parameter i = 1 in Kirchhoff's law, i.e., we find:

$$\frac{1}{R_{total}} = \sum_i \frac{1}{R_{aorta}} \qquad (52)$$

$$\Rightarrow R_{total} = R_{aorta}$$

The calculations of the corresponding values for the other blood vessel types proceed in the same fashion. For the capillaries we have a summation parameter i = 5×10^9. Thus:

$$\frac{1}{R_{total}} = \sum_i \frac{1}{R_{capillary}} = \frac{5 \times 10^9}{R_{capillary}} \qquad (53)$$

$$\Rightarrow R_{total} = \frac{R_{capillary}}{5 \times 10^9}$$

The results for all vessels are summarized in Table 11.2. We learn from this exercise and the data of Table 11.2 that there are two factors which give rise to the domination of the arterioles among the flow resistances in our body:
(I) the arterioles are significantly longer than the capillaries, and
(II) there are twenty times fewer arterioles than capillaries.

What consequence does this large flow resistance of the arterioles have for the systemic circuit of the cardiovascular system? To answer, we study the pressure–current relation of Eq. (28). The current $\Delta V/\Delta t$ is constant throughout the systemic system since otherwise blood would collect or disappear somewhere. Thus, a section with a large flow resistance R must have a large pressure difference Δp. The blood pressure drops significantly in the arterioles. This is an effective means for protecting the capillaries, where a significant pressure drop is undesirable due to the thinner and more fragile nature of the blood vessels.

Table 11.2: Length, radius, individual and cumulative flow resistance for vessels of type (I) arterioles, (II) aorta and (III) capillaries. The arterioles contribute most to the flow resistance in the cardiovascular system.

Vessel type	length [m]	radius [m]	R_{single} [Pa s/m³]	R_{total} [Pa s/m³]
Arterioles	2.5×10^{-3}	8.0×10^{-6}	3.9×10^{15}	2.4×10^7
Aorta	3.4×10^{-1}	1.1×10^{-2}	1.5×10^5	1.5×10^5
Capillaries	8.5×10^{-4}	3.5×10^{-6}	3.6×10^{16}	7.2×10^6

11.4.2. Diving in water (Example 11.7)

(a) How deep can a snorkel diver dive if the maximum gauge pressure on the thorax cannot exceed 11 kPa? Near the depth calculated in part (a), which effects cause breathing problems when
(b) the breathing tube to the surface is wide, and
(c) when the breathing tube is narrow?

Solution part (a): The role of the flow resistance of air in the respiratory system becomes evident when we study diving with a breathing tube. With a maximum gauge pressure of 11 kPa on the thorax, the maximum depth for diving is calculated from Pascal's law, Eq. (10.8):

$$p_{max} - p_{atm} = \Delta p = \rho g d$$

$$d = \frac{\Delta p}{\rho g} = \frac{1.1 \times 10^4 [Pa]}{1 \times 10^3 \left[\frac{kg}{m^3}\right] 9.8 \left[\frac{m}{s^2}\right]} = 1.1 \ m \quad (54)$$

At a depth of 1.1 m a pressure difference of $\Delta p = 11$ kPa must be generated in the lung to open the thorax against the water pressure from outside to inhale (see Fig. 10.3). This is the maximum pressure a human can withstand as illustrated in Fig. 11.16. Defying this physical limitation leads to anoxia (lack of O_2 supply to the body).

Solution parts (b) and (c): At around 1 m depth, the diver struggles with either one of two problems. If the breathing tube is too wide, it creates too much dead–space. Dead–space in respiration refers to any space which is filled with air during inhalation but does not contribute to the exchange of oxygen with the blood. Thus, any space between the outside air and the lungs excluding the alveoli is part of the dead–space. The diver inhales hard but only a small fraction of the inhaled air reaches the alveoli in the lung; the rest is stuck in the trachea and its plastic–extension.

If the diver uses a narrower breathing tube to reduce the dead–space, then the flow resistance for the inhaled air increases dramatically because $R \propto 1/r_t^4$ in Eq. (29). Thus, pulling air through the breathing tube becomes an exhaustive effort.

11.4.3. Filtration in the kidneys (Example 11.8)

(a) Quantify the volume flow rate $\Delta V/\Delta t$ which passes through a single pore in the basement membrane in the kidneys, using for the pressure difference across the membrane the value $\Delta p = 1.3$ kPa and a viscosity coefficient of $\eta = 1.4 \times 10^{-3}$ Ns/m². Note that this value lies between the values of blood serum and water and has been chosen due to the composition of the actual filtrate.

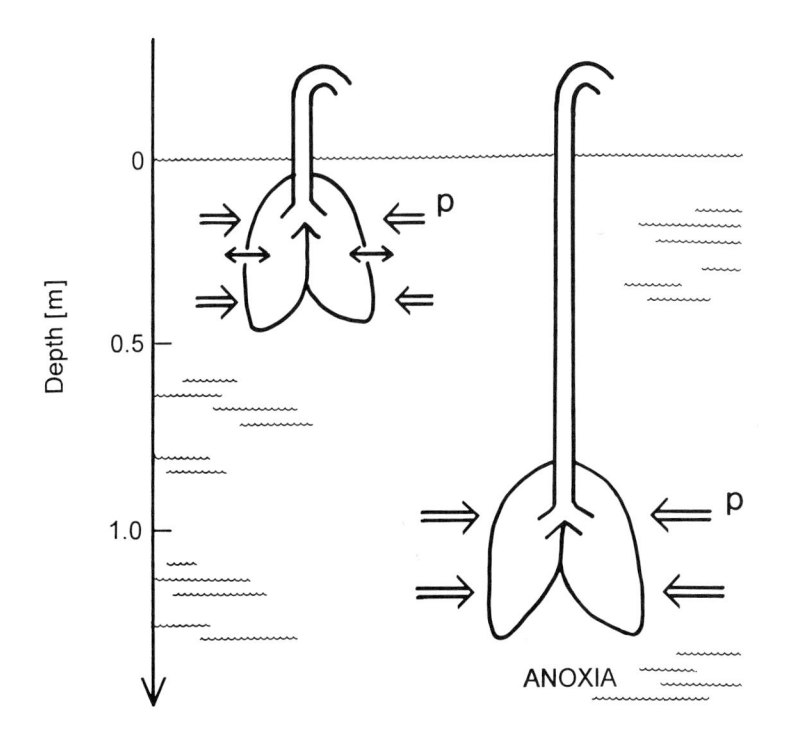

Fig. 11.16: A conceptual sketch of the lungs, the trachea and an artificial breathing tube extension used during diving. Below 1.1 m (as shown at the right) breathing becomes impossible due to the water pressure. Trying it leads to anoxia.

(b) How many pores are needed in the kidneys of a human body and how many pores are then needed per nephron?

Supplementary anatomical information: The kidneys serve two purposes: to regulate the total water volume and the pH (acidity) of the blood, and to filter the end products of the metabolism, especially urea and uric acid, out of the blood. Both purposes are accomplished in the functional unit of the kidneys which is called the *nephron*.

A kidney contains about 1.2 million nephrons. An overview of the nephron is shown in Fig. 11.17. The filtration process in the nephron is a two-step process. An arteriole branches into the glomerulus which is embedded in Bowman's capsule. The glomerulus filters the blood by holding only proteins and blood cells back. About 180 liters/day of filtrate reach the renal tube. There, more than 99 % of the fluid is resorbed into the cardiovascular system. The remainder reaches the collecting tube and is eliminated from the body, leading to about 1.5 liters/day excretion in the form of urine.

A detailed view of the glomerulus in Bowman's capsule is shown in Fig. 11.18. The figure shows from left to right three successive magnifications of details of the glomerulus. In the left sketch, the supplying arteriole is shown at the top left. It leads to tangled loops of capillaries (resembling a skein of wool) embedded in a capsule and finally leaves as a blood vessel at the top right. The renal tubule, which collects the filtrate, is shown at the bottom where it leaves Bowman's capsule, which serves as the primary fluid collection container. One section of the capillary loops, highlighted by a rectangular box in the left sketch, is shown in detail in the middle sketch.

The middle sketch shows that the capillary membrane in Bowman's capsule, called squamous epithelium, is porous, but enclosed by the basement membrane. The basement membrane is embraced by podocytes, which are cells with arm-like extensions, leaving only narrow slits open between these arms.

The right sketch in Fig. 11.18 illustrates the serial filtration effect of the three layers of the membrane structure of the glomerulus. The sketch is a magnification of the highlighted rectangular box in the lower part of the middle sketch. The pores in the capillary membrane (on the blood side, 1) are typically 20 nm in diameter. The basement membrane at the center (2) is 50 to 80 nm thick and contains pores of typical 12 nm diameter. The podocytes on the urine side (3) leave slits of typically 7.5 nm spacing.

The actual value for the pressure drop across the basement membrane varies between zero and 1.3 kPa to allow the body to regulate the flow by using variations in the blood plasma pressure.

Solution: We use $r_t = 6$ nm for the radius of the pores in the basement membrane, the given pressure difference across the membrane of $\Delta p = 1.3$ kPa, a length of the pore of 50 nm, which is equivalent to the thickness of the basement membrane, and the viscosity coefficient as $\eta = 1.4 \times 10^{-3}$ Ns/m². With these values we find from Eq. (27) the volume flow rate of a single pore:

$$\frac{\Delta V}{\Delta t} = \frac{\pi \left(6\times 10^{-9}[m]\right)^4 \; 1.3\times 10^3 [Pa]}{8 \cdot 1.4\times 10^{-3}\left[\frac{Ns}{m^2}\right] 5\times 10^{-8}[m]} \quad (55)$$

$$\Rightarrow \quad \frac{\Delta V}{\Delta t} = 9.5 \times 10^{-21} \frac{m^3}{s}$$

To handle the daily filtration of 180 liters, the two kidneys together must have more than $N = 2 \times 10^{14}$ pores. This number is obtained from Eq. (55):

$$\left(\frac{\Delta V}{\Delta t}\right)_{body} = \left(\frac{\Delta V}{\Delta t}\right)_{pore} \cdot N \quad (56)$$

which leads to:

$$N = \frac{180\left[\frac{l}{day}\right]}{9.5 \times 10^{-21}\left[\frac{m^3}{s}\right]} = 2.2 \times 10^{14} \quad (57)$$

The number of pores per nephron, the unit shown in the left panel of Fig. 11.18, is obtained from N in Eq. (57) by dividing N by the number of nephrons in our body. Two kidneys together have about 2.4 million nephrons. Thus, we need about 9×10^7 pores per nephron, which is a number close to 100 million. We see that the physiological performance of the kidneys on a macroscopic scale is based on the physical properties of a tremendous number of microscopic functional units.

11.5. Transition from laminar to turbulent flow

When local variations in the speed of a fluid become too big, turbulences occur. Turbulent flow is a superposition of laminar flow (discussed above) and vortex formation/vortex motion. The different flow patterns for laminar

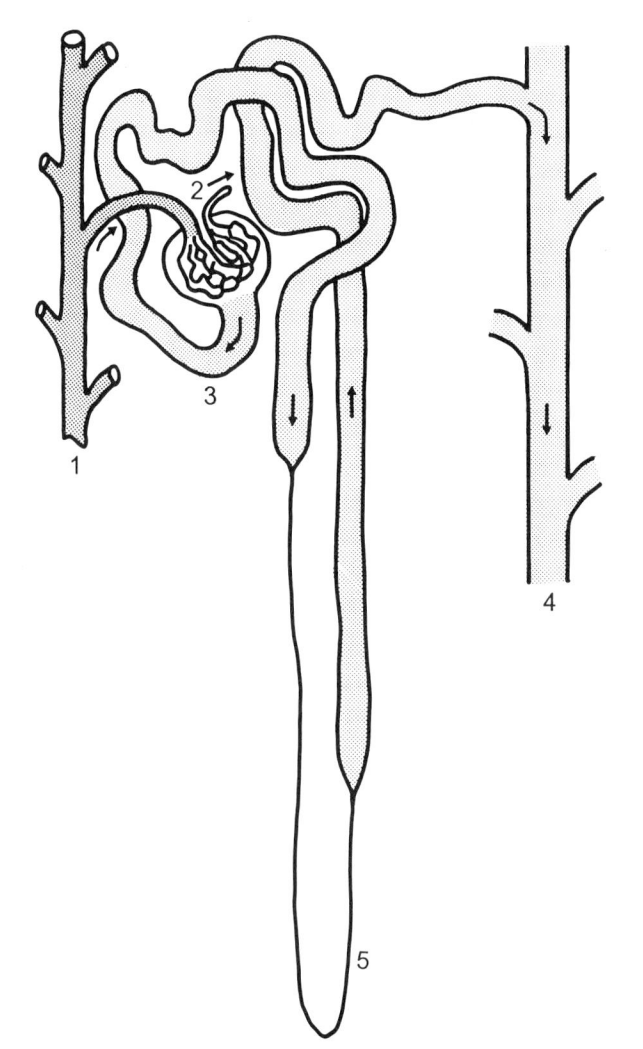

Fig. 11.17: Overview of a nephron showing the blood supplying arteriole (1), the glomerulus in Bowman's capsule (2), the renal tube (3), the urinary tract collection tube (4) and the loop of Henle (5).

Fig. 11.18: Detailed sketches of Bowman's capsule at three different magnifications. (a) At the lowest magnification, Bowman's capsule is shown with the blood supply at the top and the filtrate removal at the bottom. (b) A single vessel in Bowman's capsule. (c) A cross–section of the wall with the capillary membrane (1), the basement membrane (2) and the podocytes (3). In this sketch the blood is on the left and the urine is on the right.

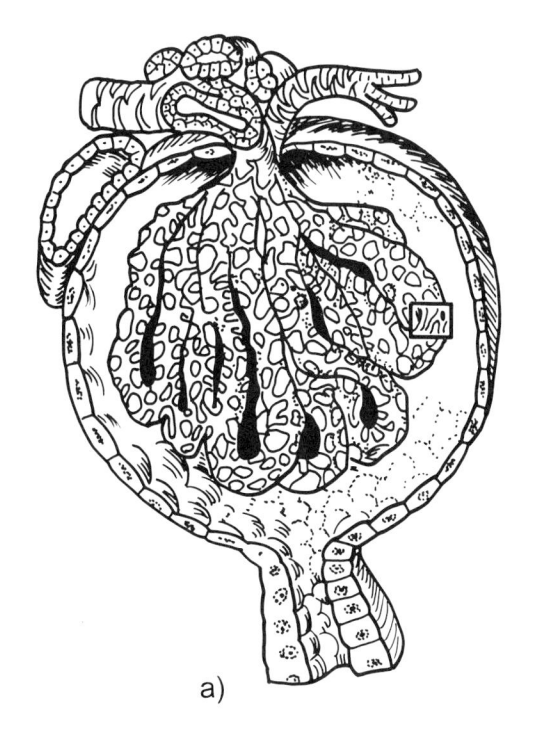

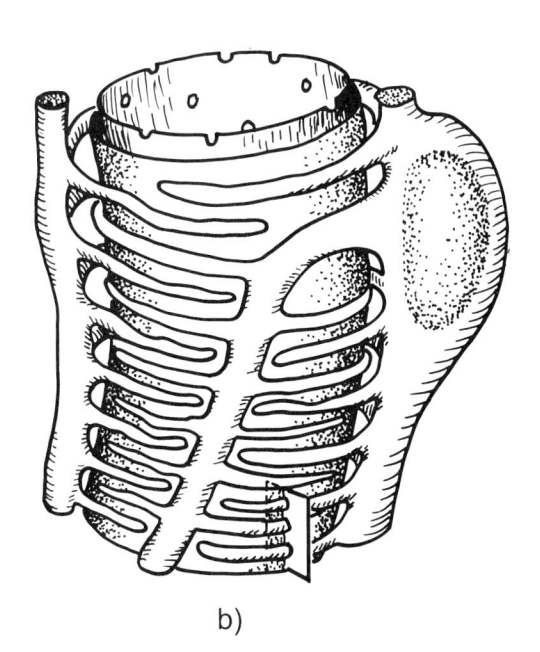

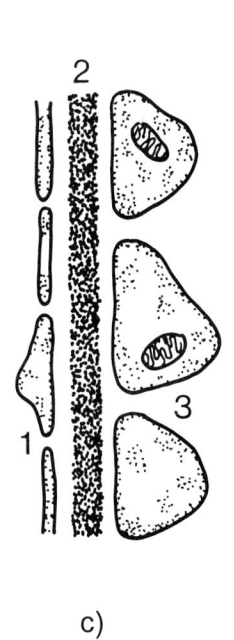

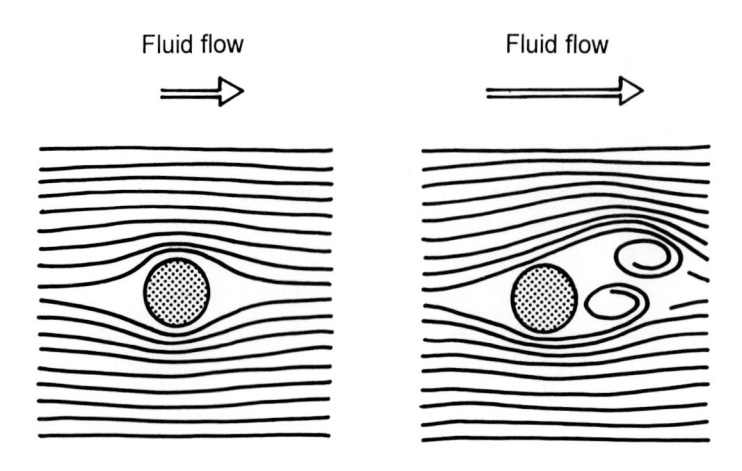

Fig. 11.19: Two flow patterns: laminar flow (left) and turbulent flow (right) around a solid cylinder immersed in the fluid. Note the vortex formation for turbulent flow.

Fig. 11.20: Transition of the volume flow rate as a function of pressure difference along a tube from laminar to turbulent flow (dashed threshold line). Turbulent flow is characterized by negligible volume flow increases for increasing pressure differences.

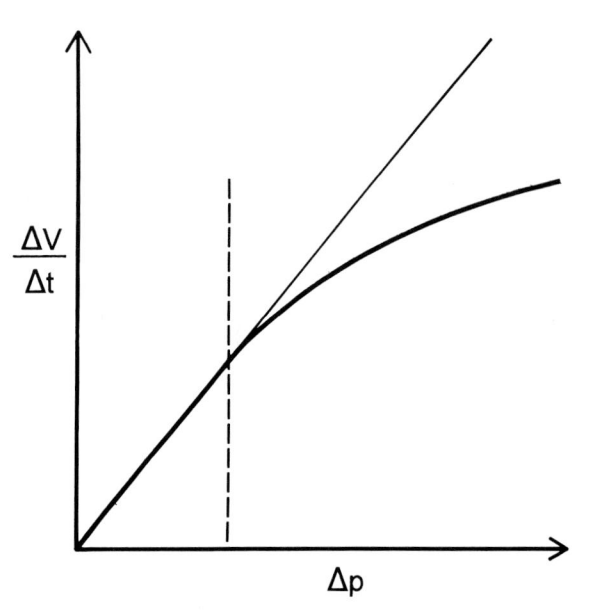

flow and turbulent flow around a solid cylinder are shown in Fig. 11.19. In turbulent flow, flow lines are not continuous, but terminate or start in vortices.

Turbulent flow has a major effect on the volume flow rate. This is illustrated in Fig. 11.20. The figure shows the volume flow rate as a function of pressure difference along a given tube. At low pressure differences Ohm's law applies, i.e., the volume flow rate is proportional to the pressure difference. The vertical dashed line indicates the pressure difference at which the flow undergoes the transition from laminar to turbulent flow. At larger pressure differences Ohm's law no longer applies. Increasing the pressure difference to obtain a volume flow rate increase beyond the transition line is ineffective. Thus, once the flow has become turbulent, no significant increase of the volume flow rate can be achieved.

To determine whether flow is laminar or turbulent, a semi–empirical threshold number is introduced, which is called the Reynolds number Re. The present discussion is limited to flow in a cylindrical tube. For that geometry, the Reynolds number is given by:

$$Re = \frac{\rho <v> d}{\eta} \qquad (58)$$

in which $<v>$ is the average speed of the fluid, d is the diameter of the tube, η is the viscosity coefficient and ρ is the density of the fluid. Re is a dimensionless number. For a cylindrical tube, laminar flow is predicted for Reynolds numbers of $Re < 2000$ and turbulent flow for Reynolds numbers of $Re > 2000$.

The need to minimize turbulences around airplane wings is well established. These wings are designed such that the air above the wing travels faster and the air below the wing travels slower. Due to Bernoulli's law, a lower air pressure results above the wing. The net effect is a lift force sufficient to compensate the effect of gravity on the airplane. We discussed this effect for the aspen leaf in Fig. 11.10. The flow of air around an airplane wing is, however, never perfectly laminar. The design of airplane wings shifts the turbulences behind the wing (wake turbulences), where such turbulences have little adverse effect on the airplane itself. Extensive turbulences are frequently the cause of major accidents, such as the crash of an American Airlines jet in New York City in 2001.

Birds are animals with a good sense for turbulences. Interestingly, this does not only apply when they are airborne. When frigid winds blow along the seashore in winter, you can see seagulls on the beach all facing in the same direction. As illustrated in Fig. 11.21, the birds align their streamlined bodies such that they offer the least resistance to the oncoming breeze. This leads to a laminar flow of air around their bodies, avoiding the ruffling of their feathers due to turbulences which would expose their body to the low temperatures and possibly cause hypothermia.

There are cases in turn, in which turbulences are desirable. Some physiological examples highlight this in Example 11.9.

Fig. 11.21: When cold winds blow over the shore, seagulls align their bodies with the wind to allow a laminar air flow. Minimizing turbulences is essential for these animals as the air vortices would lift some of their feathers and allow the body to lose heat.

Example 11.9
Determine for the following four systems the Reynolds number: (a) water flow in a creek, (b) water flow in a water pipe in a residential neighborhood, (c) air flow through the trachea, and (d) blood flow in the aorta.

Solution part (a): In most creeks of 1.0 meter width water flows at speeds of 1.0 to 10.0 m/s. The density of water is 1.0×10^3 kg/m³ and its viscosity coefficient is 1.8×10^{-3} Ns/m² (see Table 11.1). This leads to a Reynolds number of $1.0 \times 10^6 \leq Re \leq 1.0 \times 10^7$, i.e., the flow in a creek is always turbulent.

Solution part (b): For water piping in houses, v = 0.1 to 1.0 m/s and d ≈ 1.0 cm. Using the same density and viscosity coefficient as in part (a), we find for the Reynolds number $1 \times 10^3 \leq Re \leq 1 \times 10^4$, i.e., water flow is at the transition between laminar and turbulent flow.

Solution part (c): Air flow through the trachea. We base the calculation on 15 inhalations per minute of 0.5 liter each. The air speed is obtained from the volume flow rate. The volume flow rate is:

$$\frac{\Delta V}{\Delta t} = 2 \cdot 15 \cdot 0.5 \left[\frac{l}{\min}\right]$$

$$\Rightarrow \quad \frac{\Delta V}{\Delta t} = 2.5 \times 10^{-4} \frac{m^3}{s}$$

(59)

An extra factor 2 is introduced since each inhalation is followed by an exhalation, doubling the volume flow through the trachea per breath. Using the diameter of the trachea as d = 1 cm, the average speed of air is determined from Eq. (6):

$$v = \frac{1}{A}\frac{\Delta V}{\Delta t} = \frac{2.5 \times 10^{-4}\left[\frac{m^3}{s}\right]}{(5 \times 10^{-3}[m])^2 \pi} = 3.2 \frac{m}{s} \quad (60)$$

With the air density ρ = 1.3 kg/m³ and a viscosity coefficient η = 2×10^{-5} Ns/m² (from Table 11.1) we get $Re \approx$ 2000, i.e., air flow in the trachea is almost turbulent. This increases the contact of the dry air with the walls of the trachea to allow moistening.

Solution part (d): Blood flow in the aorta. The speed of blood in the aorta is 20 cm/s (see Eq. (7)). Using 2.2 cm for the inner diameter of the aorta, 2.5×10^{-3} Ns/m² for the viscosity coefficient of blood, and 1.05×10^3 kg/m³ for the density of blood, we find that the Reynolds number is $Re \approx$ 2000, i.e., blood flow in the aorta is at the transition laminar to turbulent. Nature therefore maximizes the efficiency of the aorta based on Fig. 11.20: it goes to the maximum volume flow rate without requiring an excess effort by progressing into the turbulent regime.

Pathological vasoconstriction, i.e., vessels becoming narrower due to illness, may cause turbulent blood flow. Based on the Equation of continuity, the blood speed <v> increases in this case, because the heart still pumps the same amount of blood through the aorta. This leads to a potentially dangerous increase in the Reynolds number even though the diameter of the blood vessel, d, is reduced. To illustrate the net effect, we use the Equation of continuity to determine the dependence of the blood speed on the vessel diameter:

$$|\mathbf{v}| A = |\mathbf{v}| \pi \left(\frac{d}{2}\right)^2 = const$$

$$\Rightarrow \quad |\mathbf{v}| \propto \frac{1}{d^2}$$

(61)

Fig. 11.22: Instruments needed to measure blood pressure. The stethoscope is used to listen to the sound of the flowing blood while the cuff, rubber bulb and manometer allow us to measure the pressure exerted on the arm.

Fig. 11.23: Four panels illustrating the blood pressure measurement with a sphygmomanometer. The recording of the blood flow is based on the health practitioner's listening to the artery with a stethoscope (3). The cuff (1) and the rubber bulb (2) are used to vary the pressure on the artery. When the artery is partially open, turbulent flow of the blood causes a characteristic sound.

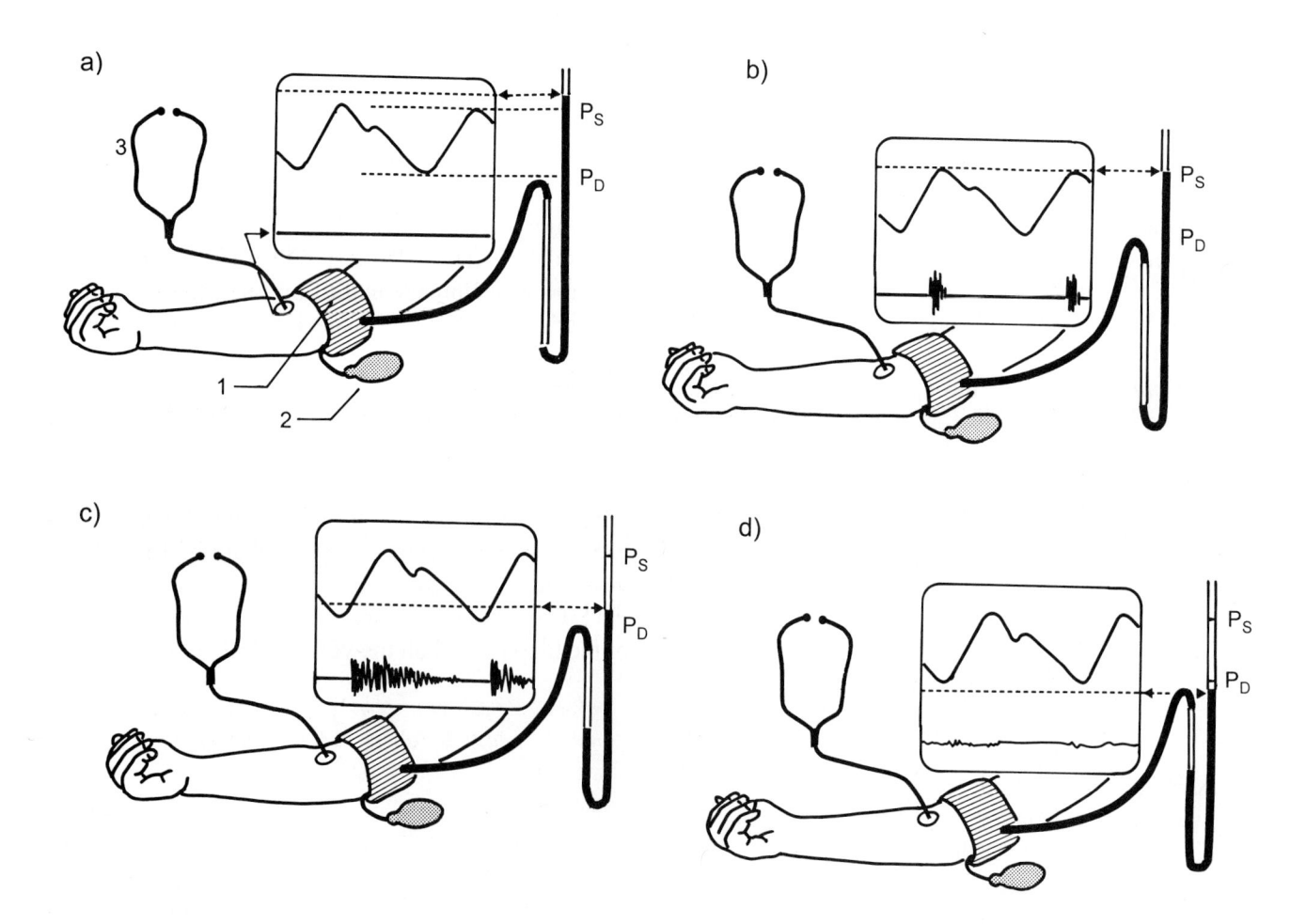

Thus, even though the diameter of the blood vessel is reduced in the case of pathological vasoconstriction, the overall effect on the Reynolds number is an increase:

$$Re = \frac{\rho \langle v \rangle d}{\eta} \propto \frac{1}{d} \quad (62)$$

A local reduction in aorta diameter easily shifts the blood flow through the vessel into the transition regime between laminar and turbulent flow!

The sphygmomanometer is an instrument to measure the blood pressure, using the acoustic difference audible for blood streaming laminar or turbulent through a blood vessel. The set–up of this instrument is shown in Fig. 11.22. A rubber bulb is used by the health practitioner to force air simultaneously into both a cuff wrapped tightly around the upper arm and a standard manometer.

Fig. 11.23 illustrates what the health practitioner hears with a stethoscope as a function of pressure. Each sketch shows the pressure relative to systolic and diastolic pressure at the right, the normal variation of the blood pressure in the boxed diagram and the audible sound along the line below. Initially (Fig. 11.23(a)) the pressure in the cuff is increased until the flow of blood through the brachial artery is stopped. At that point the practitioner hears nothing at a point just below the cuff. A valve on the bulb is then opened to lower the pressure in the cuff. When the pressure in the brachial artery falls just below the maximum pressure generated by the heart (which is the systolic pressure, where systole refers to the contraction of the heart muscle, see Fig. 11.23(b)) the artery opens momentarily on each beat of the heart. The velocity of the blood in the artery is high and the blood flow is turbulent during the momentary openings of the artery. This leads to a noisy blood flow easily recognizable by the health practitioner. The manometer reads now 120 mmHg for a 30 year old person with a healthy heart.

When the pressure in the cuff is lowered further (Fig. 11.23(c)), intermittent sounds are heard until the pressure in the cuff falls below the minimum heart pressure (which is the diastolic pressure, where diastole refers to the expansion of the heart muscle). Then a continuous background sound is heard, as illustrated in Fig. 11.23(d). The transition to the continuous sound occurs at about 80 mmHg for a 30 year old person with a healthy heart.

11.6. Problems

P–11.1
During flight, air flows over the top of an air plane wing of area A with speed v_t and past the underside of the wing with speed v_u. Show that Bernoulli's law predicts that the magnitude F of the upward lift–force on the wing is given by (ρ is the density of air):

$$F = \frac{1}{2} \rho A \left(v_t^2 - v_u^2 \right) \quad (63)$$

P–11.2
The instrument shown in Fig. 11.8 (Venturi–meter) is used to measure the flow speed v of a fluid in a pipe of cross–sectional area A. This is done by integrating the instrument into the tube with the entry and exit cross–sectional areas identical to the primary tube. Between the entry and exit points, the fluid flows through a narrow constriction of cross–sectional area a. At the constriction the speed of the fluid is v_{con}. A manometer tube, connecting the two parts of the main tube, shows a difference Δh in the liquid levels in its two arms.
(a) Using Bernoulli's law and the Equation of continuity, show that:

$$v = \sqrt{\frac{2 a^2 g \Delta h}{(A^2 - a^2)} \frac{\rho_{liquid}}{\rho_{fluid}}} \quad (64)$$

(b) What is the volume flow rate $\Delta V/\Delta t$ if we use water for the fluid in the pipe? The pipe diameter is 0.8 m, the diameter of the constriction is 20 cm, and the pressure difference is 15 kPa.

P–11.3
Confirm the data shown in Table 11.2 for the average length, radius, individual and total flow resistance in (a) arterioles, (b) the aorta and (c) capillaries.
Hint: use $\eta = 2.5 \times 10^{-3}$ Ns/m² as an average value for the blood viscosity coefficient from Table 11.1 at 37°C.

P–11.4
(a) In a person with advanced arteriosclerosis (artery constriction due to accumulated plaque on the inner walls, as shown in Fig. 11.24), the Bernoulli effect produces a symptom called vascular flutter. To maintain a constant volume flow rate in this situation, the blood must travel faster than normal through the constriction. At a sufficiently high blood speed, the artery collapses and immediately reopens, leading to a repetitive interruption of the blood flow which can be heard with a stethoscope. Why does this vascular flutter occur?

(b) An aneurysm is a weakened spot of an artery where the artery walls balloon outward. Blood flows slowly through this region, resulting in an increased blood pressure. This is dangerous because the artery may rupture. Why does the blood flow slow down at an aneurysm?

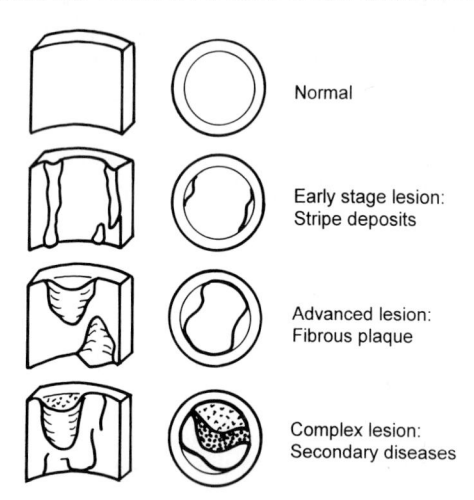

Fig. 11.24 for problem P–11.4(a).

P–11.5

The hypodermic syringe in Fig. 11.25 contains water. The barrel of the syringe has a cross–sectional area $A_1 = 30$ mm². The pressure is 1.0 atm everywhere while no force is exerted on the plunger. When a 2.0 N force is exerted on the plunger, water squirts from the needle. Determine its flow speed through the needle, v_2. Assume that the pressure in the needle remains at $p_2 = 1.0$ atm and that the syringe is held horizontal. The final speed of the water in the barrel is negligible.

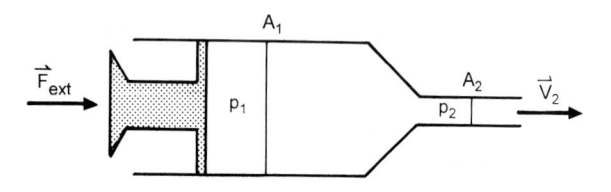

Fig. 11.25 for problem P–11.5.

P–11.6

A hypodermic needle is 4.0 cm long and has an inner diameter of 0.25 mm. What excess pressure is required along the needle so that the flow rate of water through it is 1.0 g/s? Use $\eta = 1.0 \times 10^{-3}$ Ns/m² for water.

Summary

Definitions:
• Laminar flow: flow tubes (around flow lines) are not created in the flow, they do not intersect or vanish in the flow.

• Viscosity is the force needed to move a plate at speed Δv parallel to a plate at rest at distance Δy in a fluid:

$$F_{ext} = \eta \, A \, \frac{\Delta v}{\Delta y}$$

A is the area of the plates, η is the viscosity coefficient.
• Newtonian fluid is a fluid that obeys Ohm's law.
• Reynolds number for transition laminar to turbulent flow in a cylindrical tube (Re < 2000 is laminar, Re > 2000 is turbulent):

$$Re = \frac{\rho \, <v> \, d}{\eta}$$

$<v>$ is the average fluid speed, d is the tube diameter, η is the viscosity coefficient and ρ is the fluid density.

Units:
Volume flow rate: $\Delta V/\Delta t$ [m³/s]
Mass flow rate: $\Delta m/\Delta t$ [kg/s]
Viscosity coefficient η: [Ns/m²]
Flow resistance R: [Pa s/m³]

Laws:
• Equation of continuity (fluid mass conservation):

$$\frac{\Delta V}{\Delta t} = A \, |\mathbf{v}| = const$$

$|\mathbf{v}|$ is the speed of the fluid.
• Bernoulli's law for ideal flow along a horizontal pipe:

$$p + \frac{1}{2} \rho \, v^2 = const$$

• Poiseuille's law of viscous flow in a cylindrical tube:

$$\frac{\Delta V}{\Delta t} = \frac{\pi}{8\eta} \frac{r_t^4}{l} \Delta p$$

r_t is the radius of the cylindrical tube, Δp is the pressure difference along the length l of the tube.
• Ohm's law (R is the flow resistance):

$$\Delta p = R \, \frac{\Delta V}{\Delta t}$$

The flow resistance in a cylindrical tube is:

$$R = \frac{8l}{\pi r_t^4} \eta$$

Chapter XII

Blood and Air

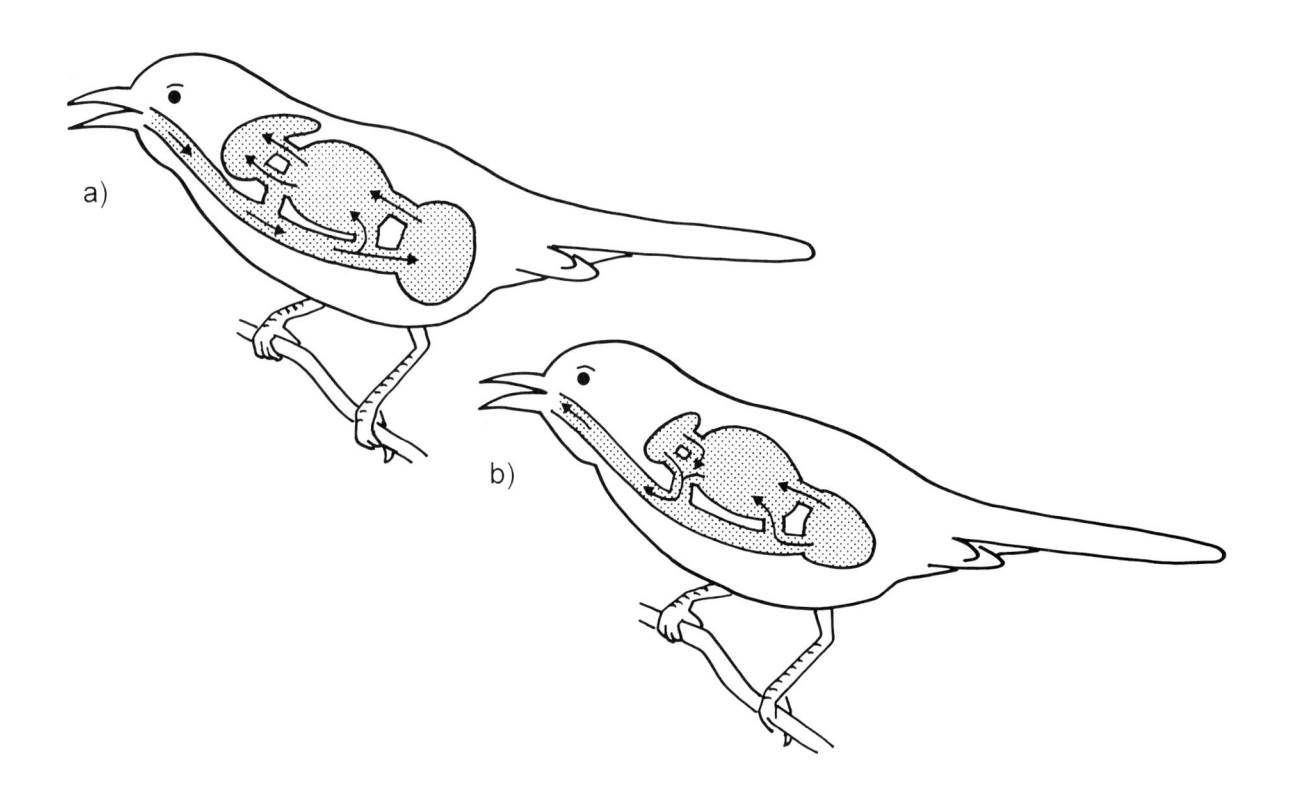

Mixed phases

BLOOD AND AIR
MIXED PHASES

A mixed system in equilibrium is characterized by its composition. If the system is a gas, we define the partial pressure of each component as the pressure of this component as if it were alone in the container. Using the ideal gas law, Dalton demonstrated that the partial pressure is proportional to the molar fraction of the respective component.

If the mixed system is a liquid solution, we describe its properties by studying the vapor phase which is in thermodynamic equilibrium with the solution. The solution is called an ideal solution if no heat is released or required when mixing the fluids; thus, ideal solutions are conceptually equivalent to the ideal gas because inter–molecular interactions are negligible in both systems. Raoult showed that the partial pressure of a component in the vapor phase is proportional to the molar fraction of the same component in the corresponding ideal solution. This means that a complete characterization of the liquid solution is obtained from studying the parameters of the vapor phase.

The interaction of solutions across membranes leads to a range of important biological and chemical phenomena. In particular, osmosis is the movement of a solvent through a semi-permeable membrane toward the side with the higher solute concentration. This effect tends to equalize the concentration of the solute on both sides of the membrane while causing a pressure difference across the membrane. This pressure difference is called the osmotic pressure.

The heterogeneous composition of blood leads to novel properties which we cannot explain with the models developed in the previous chapters. We illustrate this point for the viscosity coefficient of blood η, as listed in Table 11.1, and the flow resistance R, which we defined in Eq. (11.29). As that equation showed, both parameters are closely related in the form $R \propto \eta$. In the discussion in the previous chapter, we noted that the viscosity coefficient is a materials constant, which depends on the temperature. This was illustrated in Eq. (11.24) for a gaseous system and then also for a liquid. As no dependence on other macroscopic parameters was identified, the blood viscosity in the cardiovascular system of an endothermic species should be constant. Further, Eq. (11.29) showed that the flow resistance R depends on geometric factors, such as the tube length and the tube radius, and the viscosity coefficient η. Thus, for the blood flow in a particular blood vessel of an endotherm, the flow resistance should be constant as well.

Physiological observations illustrate that the opposite is true: the viscosity of blood and its flow resistance in a blood vessel depend strongly on two factors: (I) The hematocrit value, which is the volume fraction of blood cells in the blood. A higher hematocrit value leads to a higher viscosity. This fact is illustrated in Fig. 12.1,

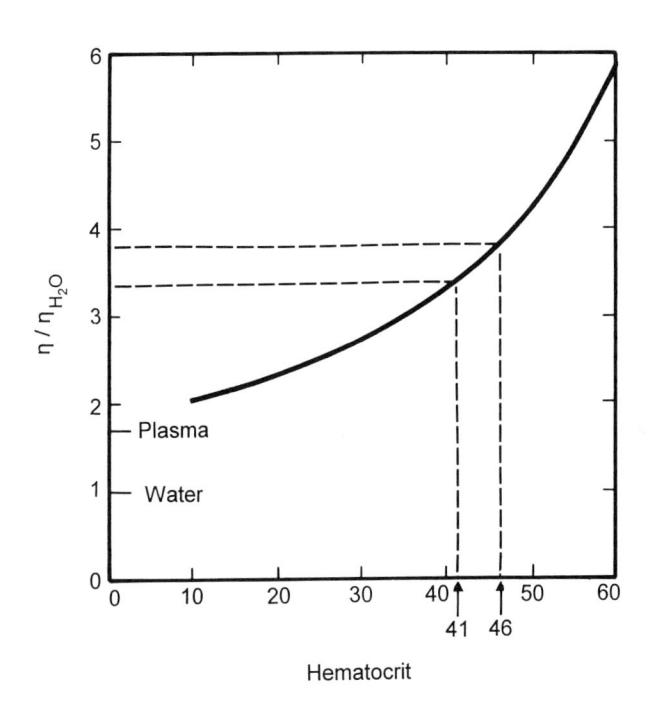

Fig. 12.1: The viscosity for whole blood relative to the viscosity value of water as a function of the hematocrit value, which is a parameter measuring the fraction of blood cells. The average hematocrit value for males is 46 and for females is 41. Thus, males have on average blood of a higher viscosity, as indicated by the two dashed lines.

which shows the viscosity coefficient of blood (relative to the viscosity coefficient of water) as a function of the hematocrit value. With an average hematocrit value of 46 for males and 41 for females we note that the blood of males is more viscous.

(II) The flow velocity of the blood: the viscosity coefficient is inversely proportional to the flow velocity. This is illustrated in Fig. 12.2 which shows the volume flow rate of a Newtonian fluid (1) and the volume flow rate of blood (2) as a function of the pressure difference along a vessel. The viscosity coefficient is part of the flow resistance, which is constant in the case of a Newtonian fluid (straight line in Fig. 12.2) but varies as a function of pressure difference for blood (curve is bent).

As a consequence of Fig. 12.2, blood flow cannot be allowed to fall below a minimum speed, as a dangerous feedback–loop effect may occur, which we illustrate for an anaphylactic shock. An anaphylactic shock is an allergic reaction of the body's immune system in response to a second contact with an antigen to which the body has become sensitized. An example is a severe peanut allergy. The initial reaction of the body is a histamine release which leads to a peripheral vascular dilatation, i.e., blood vessel widening. The increased cross–sectional area of the blood vessels causes the blood flow to slow down (as predicted by the Equation of continuity, Eq. (11.4)). Due to the non–Newtonian behavior of blood, the slower flow leads to an increase of the viscosity. This causes further slowing of the blood flow, which again results in a further increase in the viscosity. In the end, this feedback–loop leads to the cessation of the volume flow rate, $\Delta V/\Delta t = 0$, a state called stasis.

But why does the viscosity change with the flow velocity? The answer lies in the fact that blood is heterogeneous. Normally, blood cells are well immersed in the blood plasma due to the fact that they are nucleus free, contain a low viscosity cytoplasm and have a highly flexible cell membrane. This allows blood to behave like a low viscosity emulsion (mixture of two liquids). When blood flows slowly, however, aggregation of the red blood cells (erythrocytes) occurs in a process called nummulation. The red blood cells form a structure resembling a stack of coins. Nummulation creates a highly viscous suspension (mixture of solid in liquid).

12.1. Fluid composition in the human body

Blood and air are two important fluids in human physiology. For this reason did we discuss in considerable detail the ideal gas model in Chapter 6 and the static and dynamic properties of fluids in Chapters 10 and 11. In the current chapter we supplement the earlier discussions with the air and blood properties which are attributed to their composition of several chemically and physiologically distinct components.

12.1.1. Air in the respiratory system

We noted already that air contains oxygen, which is its chemically most active component and essential for our metabolism. Joseph Priestley isolated oxygen in 1774. But air consists of more than oxygen. John Mayow recognized this already in the 17th century, noting that not all the components of air are essential for living organisms. Antoine de Lavoisier noted in 1776 that nitrogen is the main component in air. He also described carbon–dioxide as a byproduct of respiration. The composition of air is shown in the left column of Fig. 12.3: dry air consists of 79 % nitrogen (N_2), 21 % oxygen (O_2) and traces of other gases, including 0.03 % carbon–dioxide (CO_2).

The composition of the air we breathe changes notably during respiration. This is illustrated in the second and third columns of Fig. 12.3: the center column shows the composition of the air in the alveoli, which are the small bubbles at the end of the bronchial tree where gas exchange with the blood occurs. In the trachea

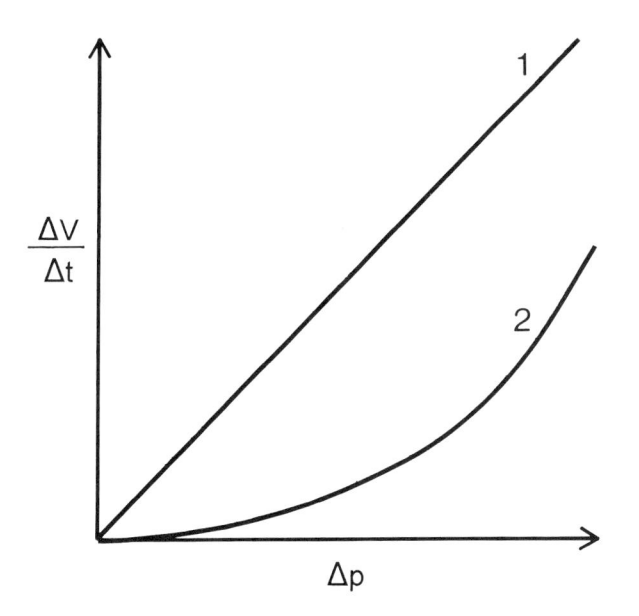

Fig. 12.2: Pumping is required to force Newtonian and non–Newtonian fluids (e.g., water versus blood) at various rates of flow through a straight tube. As the intended volume flow rate increases, the pressure the pump must produce increases as well. Note that for Newtonian fluids (1), the slope of the line relating flow and pressure is constant. However, for non–Newtonian fluids (2) the flow resistance is very high at low flow rates but approaches the value for Newtonian fluids at higher rates.

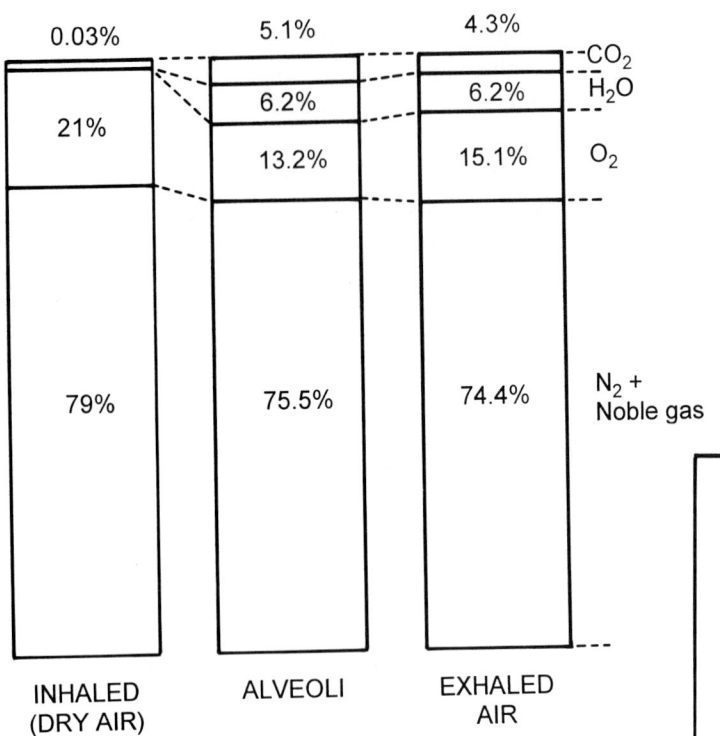

Fig. 12.3: The composition of dry air before inhaling (left panel), the air in the alveoli (center panel) and the exhaled air (right panel). Note the increase of the water fraction due to humidifying the air in the trachea.

Fig. 12.4: The components of human blood. (a) In a first step (centrifuge) the plasma and the blood cells are separated. The total amount of blood (5 liter) contains about 2.5×10^{13} red blood cells (erythrocytes) and 2.5 to 5.0×10^{10} leukocytes. (b) Separating plasma further shows that it contains mostly water, with 70 to 80 g/l proteins, about 3.7 g/l positive ions and 5.6 g/l negative ions (excluding protein ions).

the air is humidified (saturated with water). In the lungs the fraction of CO_2 has noticeably increased, mostly at the expense of the O_2 component. This is due to the diffusive exchange process discussed in section 7.4. The last column in Fig. 12.3 shows the composition of the exhaled air, which displays further changes.

12.1.2. Blood

Blood is a homogeneous mixture of liquids and liquid–like components. Fig. 12.4 shows the main components of the human blood. The large blood cells contained in the blood can be separated by a process called sedimentation (in a centrifuge). The volume fraction of the blood cells is 46 % for males and 41 % for females. The remainder is called blood plasma. As shown in the lower part of Fig. 12.4, the plasma can be separated further. Water is the major component, but there are 70 to 80 g/l proteins, about 3.7 g/l cations (positively charged ions) and about 5.6 g/l anions (negatively charged ions) excluding protein ions. For the later discussion in this chapter it is interesting to compare the concentrations of various ions in the plasma with those in the cells and the extracellular fluids. These data are provided in Table 12.1. Discrepancies between the concentrations in the cell and in the extracellular fluid (interstitium) will be discussed in Chapter 13, when we discuss how the mechanisms of nerve pulse transmission depends on the differences between ion concentrations on the two sides

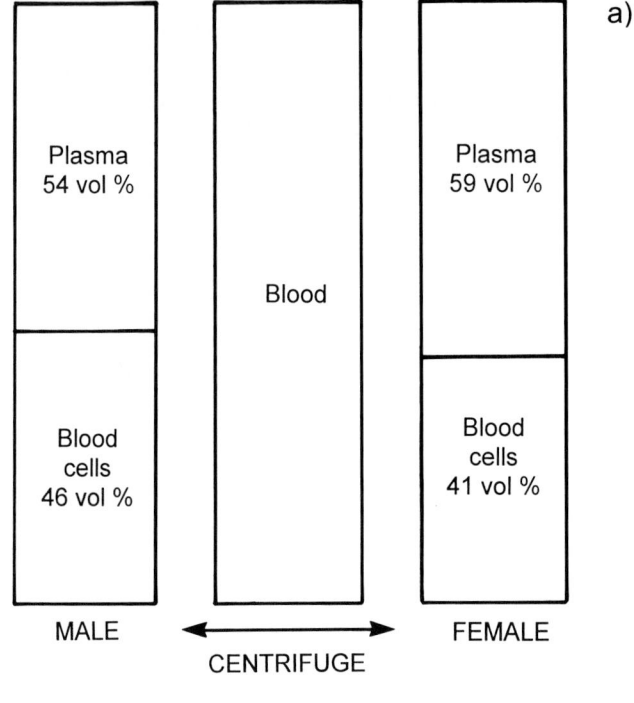

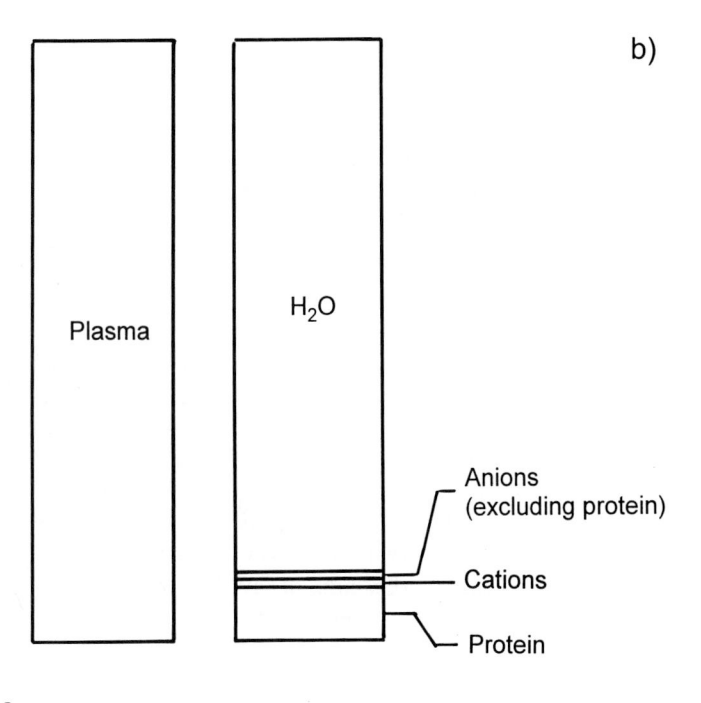

Table 12.1: Concentration of various positive and negative ions in blood plasma, extracellular fluids (interstitium) and cytoplasm (within cells).

Ion [mmol/l]	Na$^+$	K$^+$	Mg^{2+}	Ca^{2+}	Cl$^-$	HCO$_3^-$	Prot.$^-$	HPO$_4^{2-}$	SO$_4^{2-}$
Plasma	150	5	1	1.5	110	27	17	1	0.5
Interstitium	144	5	1	1.5	114	28	4	1	0.5
Cells	10	160	14	—	3	10	65	50	10

of a cell membrane. In the present chapter, the comparison of interest is between the columns plasma and interstitium as it relates to osmotic effects in capillaries. The most important difference occurs in the concentration of proteins, which is 4 times higher in the blood than in the interstitium.

12.2. Mixed phases

We start with a few definitions to clarify the nomenclature used in this chapter.

> *A system which is homogeneous at the molecular level is called a phase.*
> *A phase consists of one or more components.*

Ice and snow, each are single phases and homogeneously mixed chemicals, such as alcohol and water in wine, are also single phases. Mixtures of gases always form single phases, liquid and solid mixtures may be one or several phases depending on their miscibility. Each type of molecule in a mixture is a component, e.g. sugar and water are the two components of a single phase water/sugar solution. However, if the chemical components are reactants and products of a chemical reaction, then they do not count as separate components. An example are singly and doubly charged phosphate ions in a solution, since they are related by a chemical equilibrium in the form $H_2PO_4^- \rightleftharpoons HPO_4^{2-} + H^+$.

> *A system is called a disperse system when it consists of two or more phases but remains macroscopically homogeneous.*

A system that remains macroscopically homogeneous is a system that appears homogeneous when you look at it with the naked eye, but it does not appear homogeneous when it is examined at a microscopic length scale. The different types of disperse systems are listed with examples in Table 12.2. Not included are systems such as a water/oil mixtures, since the two components in this system form two, macroscopically separated phases, so the system is not a disperse system.

Table 12.2: Nomenclature for disperse systems. Examples are provided in brackets.

Disperse Mixtures: phase 1 dispersed in phase 2		Dispersed in phase 2 (dispersion medium)		
^	^	in solid	in liquid	in gas
Phase 1	Solid	Solid suspension (frosted glass)	Suspension (slaked lime)	Smoke
^	Liquid	Solid emulsion (potter's clay)	Emulsion (milk)	Fog
^	Gas	Solid foam (pumice stone)	Foam (soap foam)	—

12.2.1. Dalton's law

Gas mixtures such as air are the simplest case of mixed systems as gases always mix and therefore always form a single phase. The physical behavior of a gas mixture can be modelled with the ideal gas law. To describe gas mixtures we begin with the definition of the *partial pressure*. The partial pressure of a gas component is the pressure which would be measured if all other gas components were removed from the observed volume. John Dalton studied a gas mixture of n components with partial pressures $p_1, ..., p_n$, and found in 1810 that the partial pressures add up to the total pressure of the mixture:

$$p_{total} = \sum_{i=1}^{n} p_i \qquad (1)$$

> *Dalton's law states that the total pressure of a gas is equal to the sum of the partial pressures of all its components.*

Thus, the partial pressure of each gas doesn't depend on the other components (no interactions). To interpret Eq. (1) further, we use the ideal gas law for each component:

$$p_{total} = \frac{n_1 RT}{V} + ... + \frac{n_n RT}{V} \qquad (2)$$

which is equivalent to:

$$p_{total} = \frac{RT}{V} \sum_{i=1}^{n} n_i \qquad (3)$$

Eqs. (2) and (3) state that the ideal gas law applies to an ideal gas mixture when the amounts of the individual gases n_i in [mol] are added. This leads to the definition of the *mole fraction* x_i of the *i–th* component:

$$\frac{n_i}{\sum_i n_i} = \frac{n_i}{n_{total}} \equiv x_i \qquad (4)$$

With this definition, Dalton's law in Eq. (3) is rewritten for each single component of the gas mixture:

$$\frac{p_i}{p_{total}} = x_i \qquad (5)$$

In this form, Dalton's law states that the ratio of the partial pressure of each component of a gas mixture to the total gas pressure is equal to the mole fraction of the same component. Historically, Dalton's discovery of the independent behavior of gas components was one of the first significant indications that matter has a molecular structure.

Dalton's law can also be applied to gases dissolved in liquids if the solution is dilute, i.e., only a small concentration of a dissolved component is contained in the liquid. Three examples are chosen in the following two sections to illustrate the importance of the partial pressure concept in physiological applications.

12.2.2. Two applications: diving

Example 12.1

What is dangerous about diving while holding your breath? Study the case where a person hyperventilates first (to increase the amount of oxygen in the lungs so that it is possible to dive longer) and then dives to a depth of 10 m and back to the surface. Base the arguments on (i) the development of the partial pressures of O_2 and CO_2 in the lungs and (ii) the partial pressures of both gases in the venous blood, as given in Table 12.3.

Physiological information: Table 12.3 provides the normal partial pressures of oxygen and carbon–dioxide in the alveoli and in the blood with respect to an air pressure of $p_{total} = 101.3$ kPa. The higher partial pressure of oxygen in the lungs causes oxygen to diffuse into the blood system. The opposite pressure difference pushes carbon–dioxide from the venous blood into the lungs. The pressure difference for CO_2 is lower since carbon–dioxide penetrates the alveolus membrane more easily than oxygen and, therefore, does not need as high a driving force to pass through it. The diffusion processes for the gas components diffusing between the lungs and the blood were discussed in Chapter 7. From those considerations we know that each component of a gas always transfers from the space with higher partial pressure to the space with lower partial pressure.

Table 12.3: Partial pressures of CO_2 and O_2 in the alveoli and the venous blood. The values in the venous blood are obtained from Eq. (5) using the dissolved concentration of the gases.

Gas component	Alveoli	Venous blood
O_2	13.33 kPa	5.33 kPa
CO_2	5.33 kPa	6.13 kPa

When a person is not breathing, the partial pressure of carbon–dioxide in the blood increases as this gas cannot be removed through respiration. The increase in the partial pressure of CO_2 triggers the central chemoreceptor in the lowest section of the brain (medulla oblongata) to signal respiratory distress.

Solution: Fig. 12.5 illustrates a typical diving attempt.

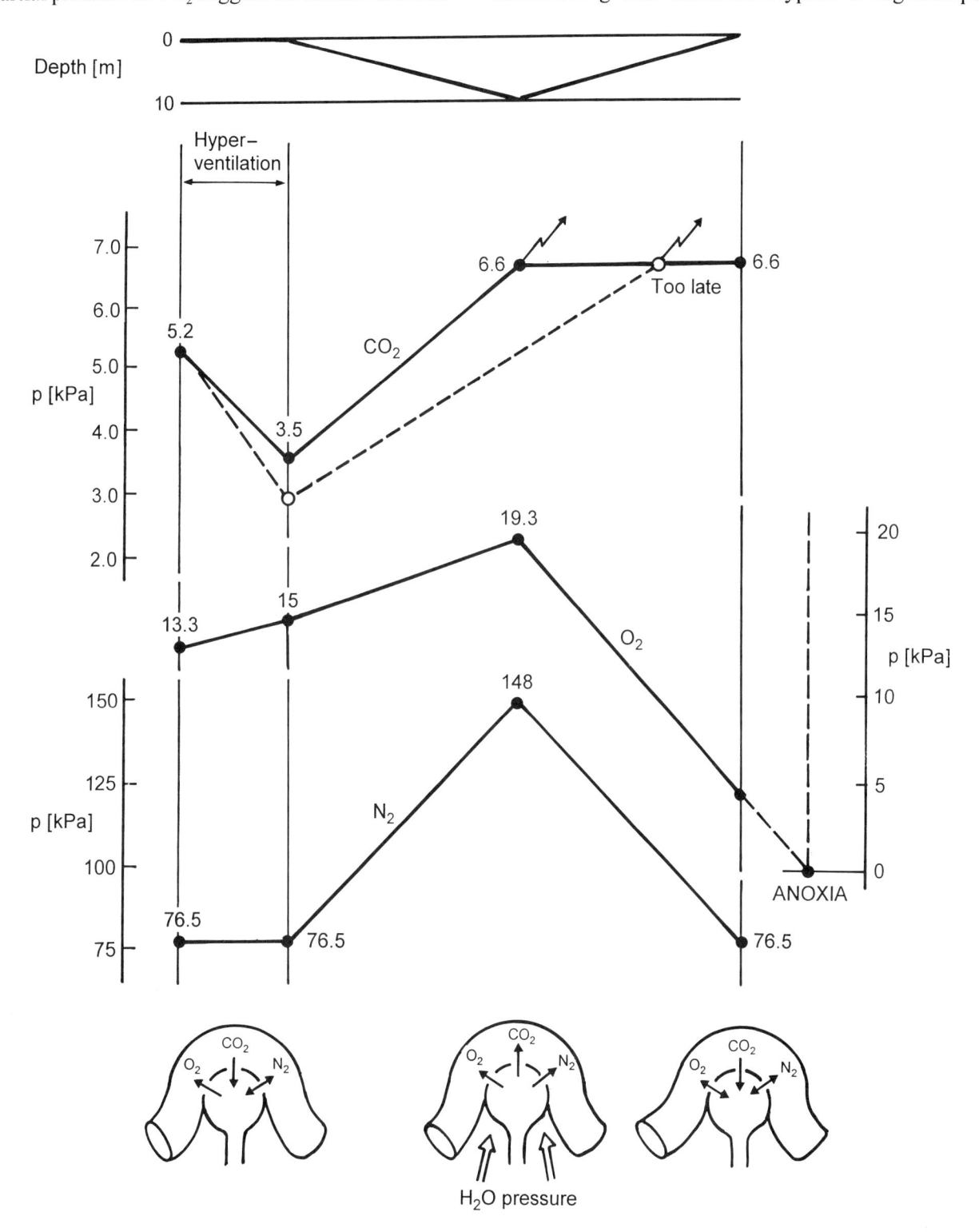

Fig. 12.5: Sketch of a 10 m deep dive after hyperventilation. The depth profile of the dive is shown at the top. Corresponding to the dive and the preceding hyperventilation, the changes of the partial pressures of nitrogen, oxygen and CO_2 in the alveoli are recorded (solid lines). The dashed line corresponds to an even stronger initial hyperventilation, which causes the diver to resurface too late. In this case, anoxia related unconsciousness may cause drowning. The curve for the partial pressure of CO_2 indicates that at 6.6 kPa a signal is triggered forcing the person to resurface to breathe. The pressure scale for the partial alveolar pressure of carbon–dioxide is shown at the upper left, for oxygen at the right and for nitrogen at the lower left.

The diver wants to extend the time to be spent under water and does this by initially hyperventilating (heavy breathing) to artificially decrease the carbon–dioxide partial pressure in the blood. Hyperventilation allows the person to increase the partial pressure of oxygen in the alveoli, e.g. from 13.3 kPa to 15 kPa in the case of Fig. 12.5 (second curve from bottom, labelled O_2). The corresponding pressure scale is shown at the right side. The increase of the partial oxygen pressure is achieved by lowering the partial pressure of CO_2 from 5.2 to 3.5 kPa (upper solid curve, labelled CO_2). The figure also includes a sketch of the alveolus/blood capillary system below the graphs, which shows the resulting exchange of gases with the blood qualitatively. The arrows indicate the dominant direction of gas transfer. During hyperventilation the partial pressure of nitrogen in the alveoli remains unchanged. Hyperventilation allows a healthy diver to stay below the surface for up to one minute.

Now the person dives into the water and reaches a depth of 10 m below the surface. The depth profile of the dive is shown in Fig. 12.5 above the graphs of the partial pressures in the alveoli. As the diver reaches deeper and deeper below the surface, the pressure on the thorax increases significantly. Using Pascal's law (Eq. (10.8)), we find at the greatest depth of the dive:

$$p_{10\,m} = p_{atm} + \rho g d =$$
$$p_{atm} + 1.0 \times 10^3 \left[\frac{kg}{m^3}\right] 9.8 \left[\frac{m}{s^2}\right] 10[m] \quad (6)$$

which yields:

$$p_{10\,m} = p_{atm} + 9.8 \times 10^4 [Pa] \cong 2 p_{atm} \quad (7)$$

This twofold increase of the external pressure on the thorax leads roughly to a doubling of each partial pressure in the lungs due to Eq. (5). However, as shown in the center sketch at the bottom of Fig. 12.5, the increased pressure in the alveoli now pushes all gases into

Table 12.4: Carbon–dioxide concentration in the alveoli and the adjacent blood capillaries at atmospheric pressure and at twice the atmospheric pressure.

CO_2 concentration	p = 1 atm	p = 2 atm
in alveoli	2.1×10^{-3}	4.2×10^{-3}
in blood	2.4×10^{-3}	2.4×10^{-3}

the blood system. CO_2 diffusion in particular is reversed when the CO_2 partial pressure in the lungs exceeds the value of 6.13 kPa from Table 12.3.

The validity of the comparison of the CO_2 partial pressure in the alveoli and the blood capillaries is illustrated with the following argument. When the external pressure on the human body rises during a dive, both the gas in the lungs and the blood in the arteries are subject to a pressure increase. The gas volume in the lungs responds approximately like an ideal gas. Using the ideal gas law for the air in the lungs we estimate the change in the concentration of CO_2 in the gas phase:

$$p_{CO2} = \frac{n_{CO2} RT}{V} \propto c_{CO2} \quad (8)$$

i.e., doubling the partial pressure doubles the concentration of the gas component.

On the other side of the membrane separating the alveolus and the blood capillary, the liquid blood can be treated as an incompressible fluid, for which a pressure increase does not lead to a volume change. Thus, no change in the concentration of dissolved components in the fluid results. For real blood these changes are minor.

Consequently, a doubling of the pressure on the human body inverts the direction of the concentration gradient across the membrane of the alveolus, as illustrated in Table 12.4.

During the dive in Fig. 12.5, the oxygen and carbon–dioxide partial pressures in the alveoli rise by less than a factor of two: O_2 to only 19.3 kPa since it is continuously consumed by the body and CO_2 to 6.6 kPa. The partial pressure of CO_2 cannot rise higher since the blood system is able to take up a large amount of CO_2. The value of 6.6 kPa partial pressure of CO_2 triggers the central chemoreceptor as described above, i.e., the diver now feels a strong urge to resurface.

A diver obeying this urge and approaching the surface from a depth of 10 m encounters a rapid decrease of the water pressure on the thorax accompanied by noticeable adjustments in the partial pressures in the lungs. The nitrogen value comes down to its pre–dive value. The CO_2 partial pressure remains roughly constant as the blood pushes into the alveoli all excess CO_2 it had to absorb due to the high external pressure. At this stage the change of the oxygen partial pressure is critical. It decreases during the resurfacing for three reasons: (I) a drop of the total gas pressure in the lung, (II) a renewed ability of the blood to absorb oxygen to replace the leaving CO_2, and (III) continued oxygen consumption by the body's metabolism. In the case shown as solid lines for CO_2 and O_2 in Fig. 12.5, the final partial pressure of O_2 in the alveoli is 4.2 kPa.

However, the dashed line for CO_2 illustrates the dangers associated with diving for a person misjudging the physical laws of nature: excessive hyperventilation may lower the initial partial pressure of CO_2 below the value considered above. Thus, the person feels comfortable below the surface for a longer time, particularly at 10 m depth where the dangerous decrease of the partial pressure of oxygen in the lungs is not noticed due to its increased partial pressure based on the external water pressure calculated in Eq. (7). This time, following the dashed lines in Fig. 12.5, the signal to surface comes from the central chemoreceptor too late since the partial pressure of oxygen drops to 0.0 kPa during surfacing (anoxia). At that moment the diver loses consciousness and drowns if not rescued by others.

Example 12.2
Diving gear allows diving to depths of about 60 m, since the gas cylinder automatically regulates the air supply so that the pressure of the inhaled air is always equal to the pressure of the surrounding water. Why is it dangerous to resurface from such a dive too quickly?

Solution: During the dive, the overall increase of the pressure leads also to an increase of the partial pressure of nitrogen in the lungs. This follows from Eq. (5) when it is taken into consideration that the mole fraction of nitrogen is constant:

$$p_{N_2} = x_{N_2} \, p_{total} \tag{9}$$

Pascal's law (Eq. (10.8)) and Eq. (9) indicate that there is a sevenfold increase of the partial pressure of nitrogen in the alveoli at 60 m depth. This increase, in turn, leads to about a sevenfold increase of the partial pressure of N_2 in the blood because the gas diffuses across the membrane between the alveolus and the blood capillary as a result of the increased partial pressure in the lungs.

When the diver resurfaces too quickly, the blood cannot push the dissolved nitrogen back into the alveoli fast enough because diffusion is a slow process. As a result, the lower pressure on the human body closer to the surface allows nitrogen to exceed its solubility in blood at atmospheric pressure and to form bubbles. This effect is called embolism, Caisson disease or diver's paralysis.

Even if the diver surfaces slowly, there is still danger looming during deep sea diving. At great depths, the partial pressure of oxygen in the blood is also raised to dangerous levels. A prolonged increase of the partial pressure of O_2 increases the risk of *hyperoxia*, which is

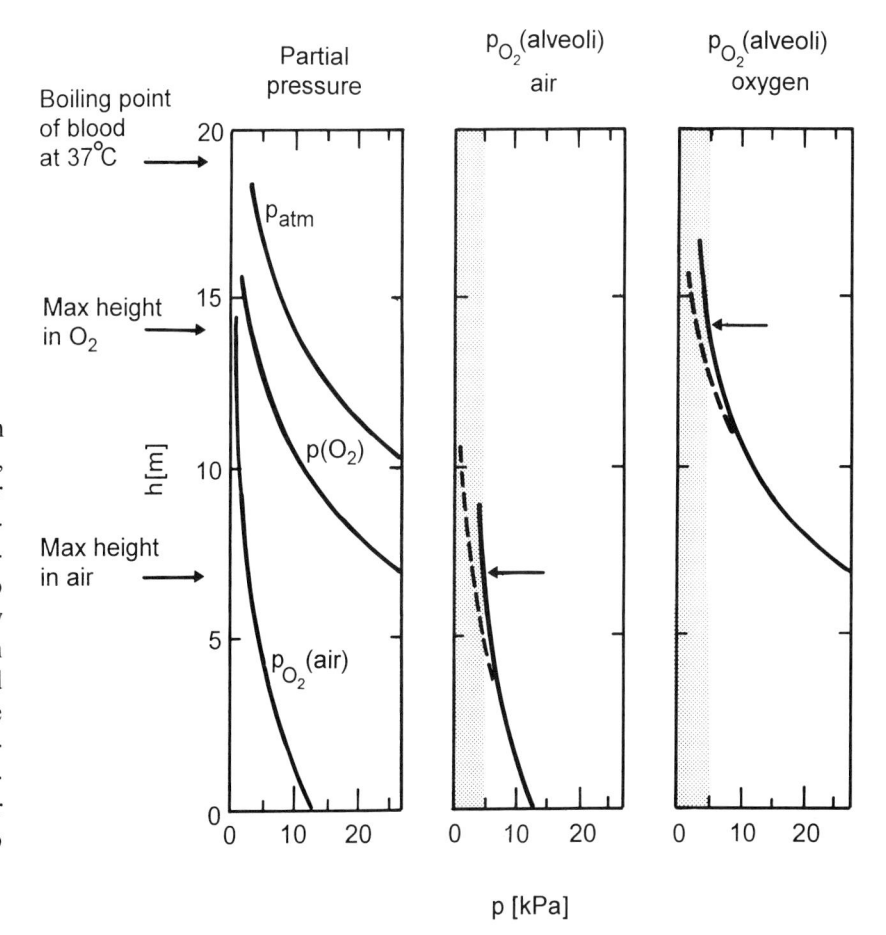

Fig. 12.6: Total pressure and partial oxygen pressure in the inhaled air (left column), partial oxygen pressure in the alveoli for air breathing (center column) and partial pressure for oxygen–mask breathing (right column). Data include heights from ground to 20 km. The two columns at the right show the partial alveolar pressure of oxygen when breathing air (center column) and when breathing oxygen (right column). The shaded area represents partial oxygen pressures below 5 kPa which prohibits breathing. The dashed curves indicate regular breathing, the solid curves correspond to oxygen–deficiency breathing.

the condition caused by excess oxygen in the blood, acting toxic for partial pressures above 40 kPa. A partial pressure for O$_2$ of 70 kPa for several days or 200 kPa for 3 to 6 hours causes the alveolus surface to shrink irreversibly and an O$_2$ partial pressure of 220 kPa or higher results in cramping and unconsciousness. These conditions can occur when diving with compressed air/oxygen tanks at 100 m depth.

12.2.3. Air travel (Example 12.3)

The atmospheric pressure decreases with height above sea level. The left column of Fig. 12.6 shows the total atmospheric pressure as a function of height between sea level and 20 km above sea level.
(a) Above which height is it impossible to survive outside a pressurized aircraft?
(b) Above which height is it deadly to breathe air?
(c) Above which height is it no longer sufficient to breathe with an oxygen–mask?
(d) If great heights are so dangerous to us, how do birds manage to fly at high altitudes?

Solution part (a): At 19 km the air pressure has decreased to about 5 kPa and blood starts to boil at 37°C. This was the cause of death of the crew of the Russian Soyuz

Table 12.5: Boiling point of water as a function of altitude.

Altitude [m]	Pressure [mmHg]	Boiling point H$_2$O [°C]
1000	671	98
2000	592	94
3000	523	91
4000	461	88
5000	407	84
6000	359	80
7000	317	78
8000	280	75

II mission, when returning from their 24 day Salyut I space station visit in June 1971 (first successful USSR space station visit). When a seal of the space capsule broke during re–entry into the Earth's atmosphere the three cosmonauts, Georgi Dobrovolski, Vladislav Volkov and Viktor Patsayev died within seconds since they were not wearing pressurized space–suits.

Boiling of a liquid far below the temperature at which it boils in the laboratory under normal conditions occurs at reduced air pressure. Fig. 12.7 illustrates how the boiling temperature of water depends on pressure. The reason for this observation lies in the thermal equilibrium between the liquid and its vapor at the boiling point. The partial pressure of water reaches the atmospheric pressure earlier when the atmospheric pressure is lowered. In "The travels of Marco Polo" (written in 1299) the Venetian adventurer described how complicated the preparation of food was in 1272 when he camped in the Pamir (Himalayan mountains) more than 4000 m above sea level. At that height, water boils between 80°C and 90°C, as shown in Table 12.5. It is interesting to note that Marco Polo also reported that their camp fires provided much less warmth at that altitude.

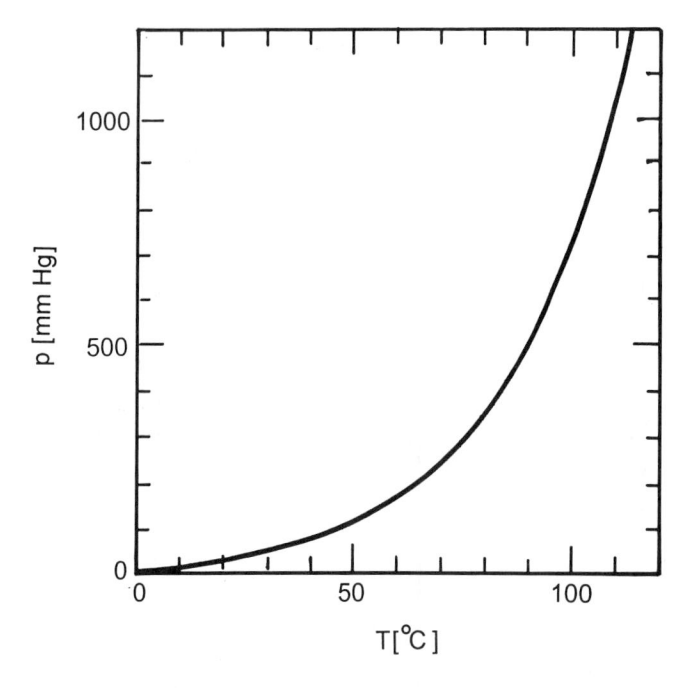

Fig. 12.7: Pressure of water vapor in equilibrium with liquid water at temperatures between 0 °C and 120°C. Water boils when the atmospheric pressure is equal to the vapor pressure of water.

Solution parts (b) and (c): Typical air pressure at sea level is 101.3 kPa. Given that oxygen makes up 21 % of air, a partial pressure of oxygen of 21.3 kPa can be calculated from Eq. (5). As a result of inhaling this air, the partial pressure in the alveoli is 13.3 kPa, as shown in Table 12.3. This value is lower than the atmospheric value since (i) the inhaled air is saturated with water vapor in the trachea, and (ii) the continuous gas exchange in the alveoli increases the CO$_2$ component of the air at the expense of the average oxygen component (see Fig. 12.3). The dependence of the various pressure values important for air breathing, as a function of altitude are shown in the first two columns of Fig. 12.6. The total pressure and the partial pressure of oxygen in air are shown as the top and bottom curve in the first column, and the corresponding partial pressure of oxygen in the alveoli is shown in the middle column (dashed line). As the plot indicates, the partial pressure curves are essentially parallel to the total air pressure since Eq. (5) applies.

Hypoxia, which is an acute respiratory distress disabling normal brain functions, occurs when the partial pressure of O_2 in the alveoli decreases below 4.7 kPa since in that situation oxygen can no longer be absorbed by the blood because a partial pressure of oxygen in the veins of 5.33 kPa must be maintained (see Table 12.3). This limit is indicated by the shaded areas in the two last columns of Fig. 12.6.

Solution part (b): The middle column of Fig. 12.6 shows that the minimum oxygen limit is reached at 4000 m height for a person breathing normally. Increased breathing involving the respiratory reserve volume (called oxygen–deficiency breathing) is triggered automatically by our body when needed. Increased breathing stretches the limit to a maximum height of 7000 m. A well–known accident caused by hypoxia was the death of Payne Stewart (US golf champion) in 1999 when a small aircraft on autopilot suddenly lost cabin pressure at high altitude. Flying between 7 km and 13 km altitude for several hours, the air plane carried the incapacitated passengers and crew until it run out of fuel and crashed.

Solution part (c): Above 7000 m, oxygen equipment must be used. For a person breathing 100 % oxygen (e.g. in large air planes) the center curve in the left column of Fig. 12.6 shows the partial pressure of O_2 before it is inhaled and the last column shows the partial pressure of O_2 in the alveoli for oxygen–breathing. Normal breathing with this equipment allows a person to maintain a partial pressure above 4.7 kPa to a height of 12 km, or, with oxygen–deficiency breathing, to 14 km. Thus, commercial air planes stay below heights of 14 km, since above that height even oxygen masks would not save the lives of the passengers and crew in the case of accidental air pressure loss.

Solution part (d): Birds have adapted to flight at high altitudes as shown in Fig. 12.8. The figure highlights the avian respiratory system, which consists of lungs and several air sacs. Contraction and relaxation of the air sacs pushes the air through the lungs. We distinguish posterior sacs through which the air flows before it reaches the lungs, and anterior sacs which the air reaches after it passes through the lungs. During inhalation, both sets of air sacs expand. The posterior sacs fill with fresh air from the outside, and the anterior sacs fill with used air from the lungs. Later, during exhalation, both the air sacs deflate, pushing air from the posterior sacs into the lungs, and from the anterior sacs out through the bird's

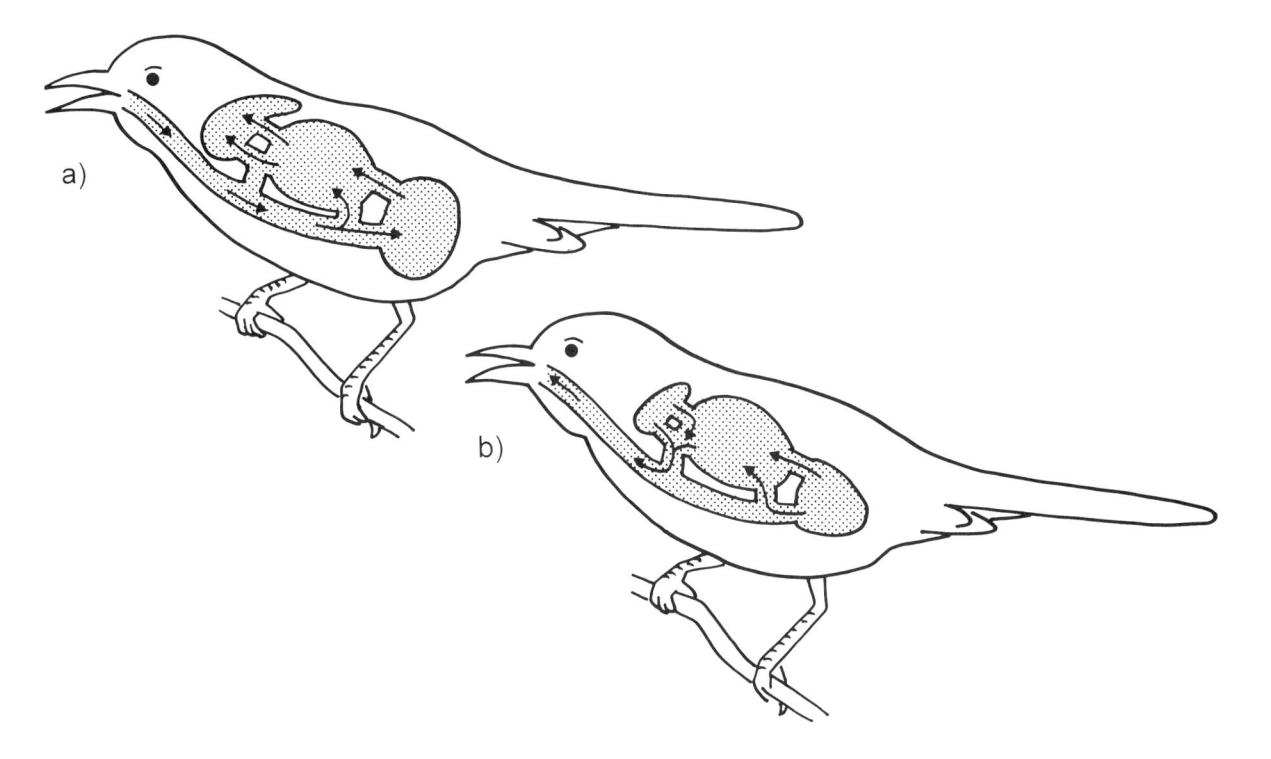

Fig. 12.8: The respiratory system of birds. Air sacs before (posterior air sacs, 1) and behind the lungs (anterior air sacs, 2) ventilate the lungs (3). The lung is not a dead–end organ but allows the air to flow through tiny tubes (parabronchi), in which gas exchange occurs across the membrane walls. During inhalation, both sets of air sacs expand, and during exhalation, both sets of air sacs deflate. Two cycles of inhalation and exhalation are required for the air to pass all the way through the bird's respiratory system.

trachea. Two cycles of inhalation and exhalation are therefore required for the air to pass all the way through.

This system completely exchanges the air in the lungs for every breath, i.e., a lung oxygen concentration much higher than in mammals is maintained. This better use of the partial pressure of oxygen in the air is one reason why birds get away with flying at high altitudes. This adaptation is not a simple one, though. Besides the addition of air sacs, the alveoli had to be reconfigured from a dead–end system to a system allowing for continuous one–directional flow through tiny tubes, which are called parabronchi.

12.3. Liquid solutions

As we move from gases to liquids, Dalton's law is often not appropriate for describing systems because it assumes ideal gas behavior for each component of the mixture, which implies that intermolecular interactions can be neglected. This is an inappropriate assumption because it is these interactions which cause the gas to condense and become a liquid in the first place. Thus, we need other tools to describe liquid mixtures such as blood, extracellular fluid and the cytoplasm in the cell.

Since liquids have surfaces which separate the condensed phase from the vapor phase, it is useful to develop a description of liquid solutions starting at that interface. At the interface, the solution is in mechanical and chemical equilibrium with the vapor phase. This allows us to utilize the gas laws we have already established to characterize the vapor phase and, therefore, the condensed phase indirectly.

An important experimental observation is the fact that in equilibrium a well–defined, non–zero vapor pressure is present above a liquid at any temperature. The pressure of this vapor is called the saturation vapor pressure. If a gas comes in contact with a liquid and is undersaturated, evaporation occurs until saturation is reached. This is the mechanism by which the dry air that we inhale is saturated with water vapor in the trachea before it reaches the alveoli in the lungs.

12.3.1. Ideal solutions and Raoult's law

With the concept of a vapor pressure above a liquid introduced, we can now define and study ideal solutions. An ideal solution is a solution for which the enthalpy of the system (i.e., the quantity corresponding to the internal energy for a system at constant pressure) is the same for the sum of the separated components and for the mixed system. That means that no heat is absorbed or released while mixing the components, except for the energy needed to adjust the volume (due to the pV–term in the definition of the enthalpy H). This definition utilizes the same concept used in Dalton's definition of partial pressures in gas mixtures: ideal means that interactions between the various molecular species in the mixed state are negligible.

François Raoult made the following experimental observation for such a system, called Raoult's law:

$$p_i = x_i \, p_i^0 \qquad (10)$$

> Raoult's law states that the partial pressure p_i of the i–th component in the vapor phase above the solution is equal to the mole fraction x_i of the i–th component in the solution multiplied by the constant vapor pressure of the i–th component above a pure liquid of the same component (p_i^0).

This law is important for the description of solutions as it allows us to predict properties of the solution from measurements in the vapor phase. For an ideal solution of two components A and B, the vapor pressure curves are shown in Fig. 12.9. The vertical axis is the partial pressure of component A or B and the horizontal axis is the mole fraction of component B, ranging from $x_B = 0$ for pure liquid A, to $x_B = 1$ for pure liquid B.

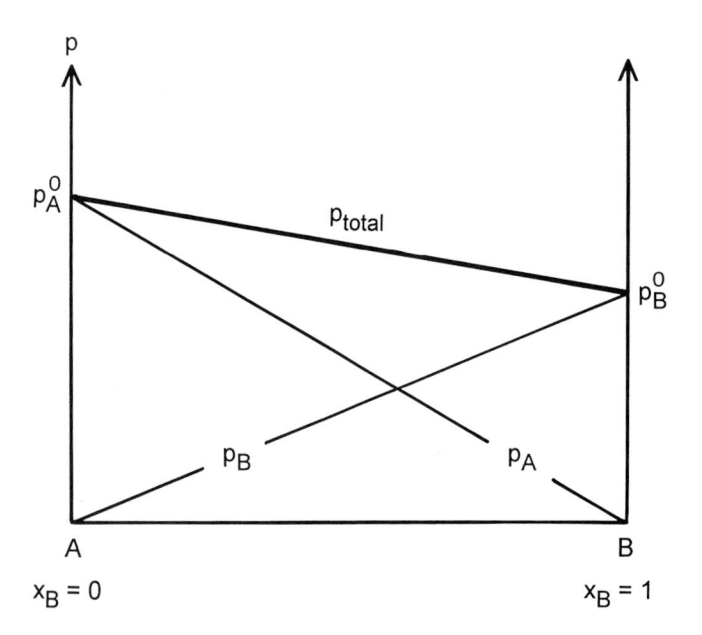

Fig. 12.9: Sketch of a two phase system illustrating Raoult's law. The partial pressures of the two components in the gas phase are linearly proportional to the mole fractions of the components in solution.

Fig. 12.10 shows experimentally measured partial and total vapor pressure data for two real systems. Toluene and benzene, shown in Fig. 12.10(a), behave ideally since the data follow Raoult's law across the entire mole fraction range. This indicates that there is effectively no interaction between the benzene and toluene molecules which differs from the interactions between a pair of toluene molecules or a pair of benzene molecules. Many other systems behave non–ideally. As an example, a system consisting of acetone and chloroform is shown in Fig. 12.10(b). The vapor pressure curves predicted by Raoult's law are shown as dashed lines. The solid lines are extrapolations of the experimental data points and clearly deviate from Raoult's law.

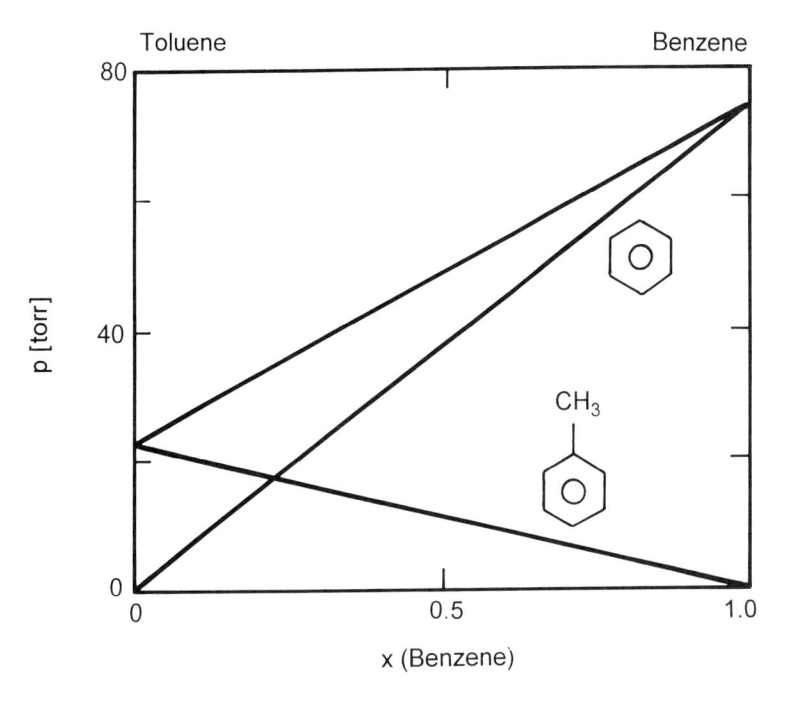

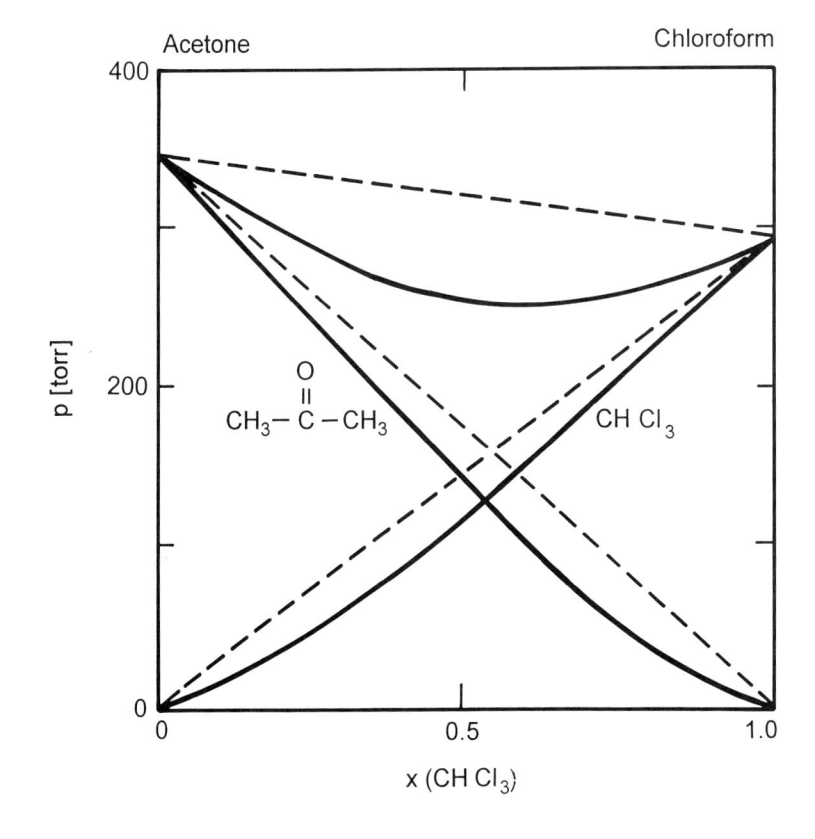

Fig. 12.10: Experimental partial pressure curves over a liquid solution for (a) toluene and benzene (a near–ideal solution following Raoult's law) and (b) acetone and chloroform (a non–ideal solution, following Raoult's law only in the very dilute limit, i.e., where $x \approx 1$ or where $x \approx 0$.

The figure illustrates further that for this and most other systems ideal behavior is still a good approximation if the system is dilute ($x_i \ll 1$). Note that the solid curves and the dashed curves coincide reasonably well near $x(CHCl_3) = 0$ and $x(CHCl_3) = 1$.

12.3.2. Gibbs free energy and chemical potential

Our next objective is to apply the laws of thermodynamics to the vapor/solution systems discussed in this section. Since we are dealing with open systems in which an exchange of matter between the vapor phase and the solution is possible, we connect to our discussion of the basic thermodynamic concepts in section 8.4.5. In particular, we need to focus on the differences in the Gibbs free energy for two states of the system and the dependence of ΔG on the pressure (given as Eq. (8.26)):

$$\Delta G = nRT \ln\left(\frac{p_f}{p_i}\right) \quad (11)$$

This equation is applied to a solution and its vapor phase in the current context. The studied system is sketched in Fig. 12.11: a solution and a vapor phase with one component highlighted (solid dots). If the solution and the vapor phase are in equilibrium the Gibbs free energies must be balanced:

$$G_{mixed\ vapor} = G_{solution} \quad (12)$$

If the Gibbs free energies for both system parts were not the same, evaporation or condensation would occur to establish a chemical equilibrium at the liquid surface. We study the Gibbs free energy because we focus on the pressure and the temperature as the primary system parameters. The solution and the vapor phase are two open systems. Consequently, we have to add one more variable to our consideration: the mole number of the highlighted component in Fig. 12.11 on each side of the liquid surface. This allows us to include the change of the energy of the system as a function of the change in moles, $G = f(p, T, n)$. If p and T are held constant, we define a new variable, called the *chemical potential* μ:

$$G_{total} = \sum_{i=1}^{n} \mu_i n_i \quad (13)$$

Eq. (13) states that the chemical potential of the i–*th* component, μ_i, is the Gibbs free energy per mole for

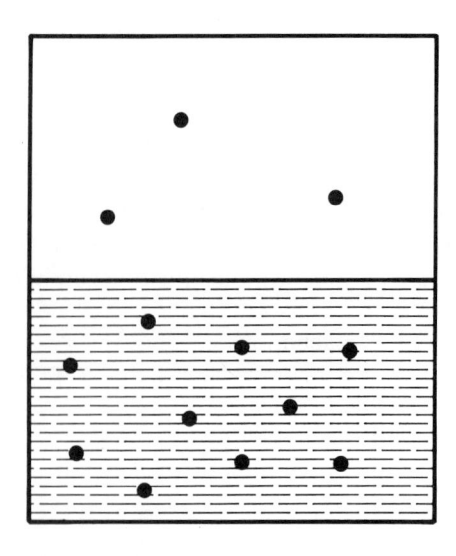

Fig. 12.11: Sketch of a solution and its gas phase in equilibrium. The component of interest is represented by solid dots.

that component in unit [J/mol]. Since the single components in an ideal solution do not interact with each other, the overall equation for the equilibrium of the system, Eq. (12), must apply to each component separately:

$$\mu_{i,\ gas\ phase} = \mu_{i,\ solution} \quad (14)$$

For the gas phase the expression for the Gibbs free energy as a function of pressure in Eq. (11) applies under isothermal conditions, i.e., when the temperature of the solution and the vapor phase are the same. Choosing 1 atm as the reference pressure for the standard state (indicated by the superscript *), the chemical potential of one mol of the i–*th* component in the vapor is written with Eq. (11) in the form:

$$\mu_{i,\ gas} = \mu^*_{i,\ gas} + RT \ln\left(\frac{p_{i,\ gas}}{1\ atm}\right) \quad (15)$$

This equation allows us to study explicitly the pressure related contributions to the chemical potential. Next we rewrite Eq. (15) to replace the pressure dependence with the mole fraction dependence, using Raoult's law in the form $p_{i,\ gas} = p^0_{i,\ gas} x_i$ from Eq. (10):

$$\mu_{i,\ gas} = \mu^*_{i,\ gas} + RT \ln\left(\frac{p^0_{i,\ gas}}{1\ atm}\right) + RT \ln x_i \quad (16)$$

Now we use Eq. (14). The left hand side is replaced with Eq. (16). This leads to:

$$\mu_{i,\,solution} = \mu_i^0 + RT \ln x_i \quad (17)$$

in which μ_i^0 is the chemical potential (free energy per mole) of the vapor of the i–th component over the pure liquid of component i. Thus Eq. (17) allows us to study the explicit dependence of the chemical potential on the mole fraction of the i–th component in the solution.

12.4. Osmosis

An important physiological application of the solution concept is the process of osmosis. Osmosis occurs when some components in a solution cannot pass through an otherwise permeable membrane. This occurs for example in the blood filtration system in the glomerulus of the kidneys, in which the basement membrane blocks proteins and blood cells from leaving the blood system.

Osmosis can also be observed in many other biological systems. Various weeds are often found to break through asphalt surfaces. The plants develop the strength from osmotic transport of water from cell to cell, building up an internal water pressure comparable with the force a jackhammer can exert. The pressure in a cell due to water driven in by osmosis is called turgor pressure. It is this pressure which allows wood–free plants to stand upright.

We quantify the osmotic effect for the system shown in Fig. 12.12. The figure shows two parts of a system separated by a membrane. The left part contains a pure liquid (component 1) and the right part contains the same liquid, which acts as a solvent for a second component (component 2, illustrated by solid dots). The solvent passes the membrane freely and establishes an equilibrium for component 1 between the two parts of the system. Component 2 cannot pass through the membrane, i.e., the membrane is semipermeable and no equilibrium is established for component 2.

> *Osmosis is the movement of a solvent through a semipermeable membrane into a solution of higher solute concentration. This effect tends to equalize the concentrations of the solute on the two sides of the membrane.*

The equilibrium condition for component 1 of the system in Fig. 12.12 requires the chemical potential to be the same on both sides of the membrane:

$$\mu_{1,\,pure} = \mu_{1,\,mix} \quad (18)$$

Since the chemical potential is different for a pure liquid and the same liquid in a solution, some molecules of component 1 diffuse through the membrane, resulting in non–equal amounts of component 1 on the two sides. This leads to a difference in the pressure of component 1 across the membrane. This pressure difference is defined as the osmotic pressure Π (capital letter π):

$$\Pi \equiv p_{mix} - p_{pure} \quad (19)$$

> *The osmotic pressure is the excess pressure we must apply on the side of the solution to prevent the diffusion of solvent through the membrane.*

Jacobus Hendricus van't Hoff calculated the dependence of the osmotic pressure on the concentration of the non–permeable component. As outlined in the Appendix, this yields van't Hoff's law for a dilute solution ($x_2 \ll 1$), i.e., a solution with a very small mole fraction of the non–permeating component:

$$\Pi = \frac{RT}{V_1^0} x_2 \quad (20)$$

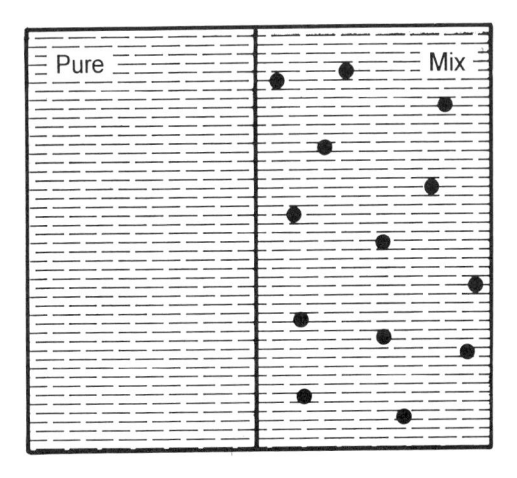

Fig. 12.12: Sketch of a model to describe osmotic effects. A solvent is free to pass through a semipermeable membrane (center line), while a dilute component (solid dots) is blocked by the membrane.

V_1^0 is the molar volume of the solvent (component 1). Thus, the osmotic pressure is directly proportional to the mole fraction (concentration) of the dilute dissolved component, x_2.

Eq. (20) is used to illustrate the osmotic effect experimentally. A vertical tube filled with a sugar solution and sealed with a semipermeable membrane is placed in a beaker with water. The water, which is capable to pass the membrane in both directions, is driven into the tube due to the lower water concentration in the tube. The liquid level in the tube rises until its hydrostatic pressure compensates the osmotic pressure from Eq. (20). The same effect happens on a microscopic scale when cellular systems are immersed in water. You may have observed two well–known examples:

(I) If the stem of a dandelion is split into long stripes and the weed is placed in a glass of water, the stem stripes roll up. This is due to the spongy cells inside the stem that expand due to osmotic uptake of water. In uncut stems the strong outer layer of cells prevents this from happening.

(II) The skin of ripe cherries bursts when they are placed in water. The skin of cherries allows water to diffuse into the cherry while preventing the sugar juice to diffuse outwards. The water pressure in the cherry cells is driven up by the osmotic effect until it causes the fruit to burst.

12.5. Physiological and medical applications

12.5.1. Homeostatic control of the osmolarity of blood

The human body operates a careful budgeting of the intake and loss of water. The primary mechanisms of water loss are urine excretion (1500 ml/day corresponding to 60 %) and perspiration through skin and the lungs (900 ml/day corresponding to 36 %). The water intake of an adult typically consists of 1500 ml/day as beverages and 700 ml/day with solid food. Another 300 ml/day result from the metabolic reactions in the body.

The water balance is measured by a center in the hypothalamus. It does not measure the total amount of body water directly, but analyzes changes in the concentration of various components dissolved in water. The measurement is based on the osmosis effect and takes place in the osmoreceptors of the hypothalamus. Eq. (20) establishes that the osmotic pressure is proportional to the concentration of the dilute components which cannot permeate the membrane in the osmoreceptors. These components in the blood are called osmotically active. Their concentration is used to define the osmolarity with unit [osm/l]. The unit [osm] is related to the unit [mol]. For example, if we dissolve 1 mol glucose in water, we obtain a solution with 1 osm/l. If we dissolve 1 mol of NaCl (rock salt) we obtain a solution of 2 osm/l because the salt molecule dissolves into two separate ions, Na$^+$ and Cl$^-$.

Blood has a osmolarity of 290 mosm/l. A solution with this value is called isotonic, a solution with a smaller osmolarity is called hypotonic and a solution with a larger osmolarity is called hypertonic. The osmoreceptors cause the release of ADH (antidiuretic hormone) when we observe variations in the osmolarity as small as 3 mosm/l (i.e., variations of about 1 %). ADH triggers the kidneys to respond to hypertonic conditions with water retention or to hypotonic conditions with excess water excretion. A hypertonic osmolarity causes also a signal to the brain causing the perception of thirst.

This sensitive water concentration detection system has been developed by the body to protect itself against the rather severe consequences of a water imbalance. Water deficit can lead to diabetes insipidus and hypovolemic shock, excess water can cause intracellular edemas (e.g. brain swelling). Also a too fast intake of water (e.g. by a patient who is dehydrated) is dangerous as it may cause vomiting or even a shock.

12.5.2. Edemas

Edema is an abnormal infiltration and excess accumulation of serous fluid in connective tissue.

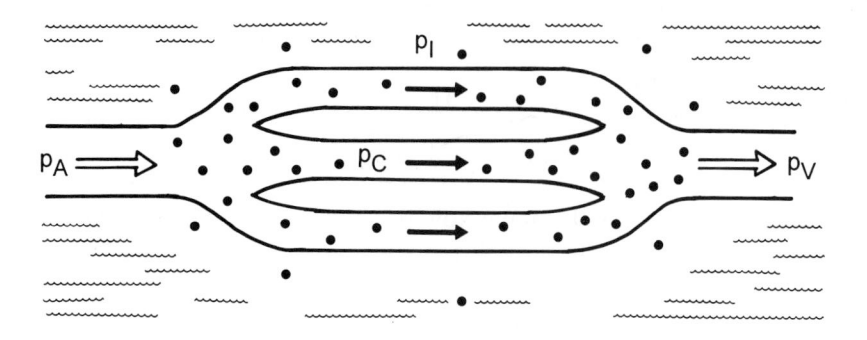

Fig. 12.13: Arteriole (at left) splitting into several parallel capillaries that reunite downstream into a single venule (shown at right). The protein concentration (solid dots) is about 4 times higher in the blood than in the interstitium.

Solutions are found throughout our body. They are often separated by semipermeable membranes, leading to many applications of osmosis. In this section, the concepts introduced above are applied to the special case of edemas, i.e., the collection of liquids (serum) in body tissue (outside of cells and blood vessels). To establish the different factors which play a role in the occurrence of edemas, the osmotic properties of a healthy blood capillary are introduced first.

Fig. 12.13 shows a typical capillary system. A larger arteriole splits into several thin capillaries which reunite in a venule after passing through organ tissue. The capillaries are surrounded by extracellular fluid since the blood vessel membrane is semipermeable, blocking proteins in the blood from leaving while permitting serum to diffuse in and out of the blood system. This semipermeable behavior is reflected in Table 12.1, which compares the concentrations of different components in the interstitium and the blood plasma. Large protein molecules cannot pass through the membrane; all other components can pass through the membrane and establish essentially equal concentrations on both sides.

Pressures at different points in Fig. 12.13 are as follows (all relative to air pressure): $p_A = 3.3$ kPa at the arterial end of the capillaries, $p_V = 1.3$ kPa at the venous end of the capillaries, and $p_I = -0.8$ kPa in the interstitium. Due to the protein concentrations in Table 12.1, the osmotic pressure of the blood is given as $\Pi_C = \Pi_A = \Pi_V = 3.7$ kPa and the osmotic pressure of the extracellular fluid is $\Pi_I = 0.8$ kPa.

Note that the capillary system varies from the simple model in Fig. 12.12 as non–zero protein concentrations are present on both sides of the membrane, which means that the osmotic pressure on both sides must be considered. We check the ratio of the osmotic pressure data for the capillary system by using van't Hoff's law (Eq. (20)) in the form:

$$\frac{\Pi_C}{\Pi_I} = \frac{x_C}{x_I} \qquad (21)$$

The ratio of concentrations of the osmotic active components (proteins) on both sides of the membrane follows from Table 12.1:

$$\frac{x_C}{x_I} = \frac{17 \pm 1 \; mmol/l}{4 \pm 1 \; mmol/l} = 4.3 \pm 1.1 \qquad (22)$$

The osmotic pressure data given in this section lead to:

$$\frac{\Pi_C}{\Pi_I} = \frac{3.7 \; kPa}{0.8 \; kPa} = 4.6 \qquad (23)$$

Eqs. (22) and (23) confirm that the osmotic pressure data used in this section are in agreement with the data reported in Table 12.1.

What are the consequences for the blood passing through a capillary? Fig. 12.14 illustrates the flow of serum in a healthy capillary. Shown is the pressure relative to atmospheric pressure along the capillary from the arterial end (left side) to the venous end (right side). The

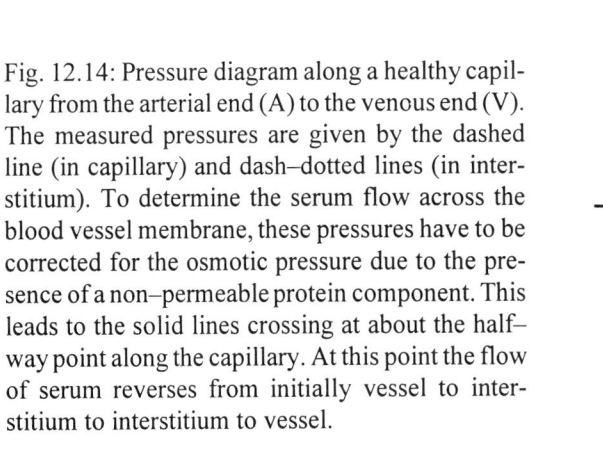

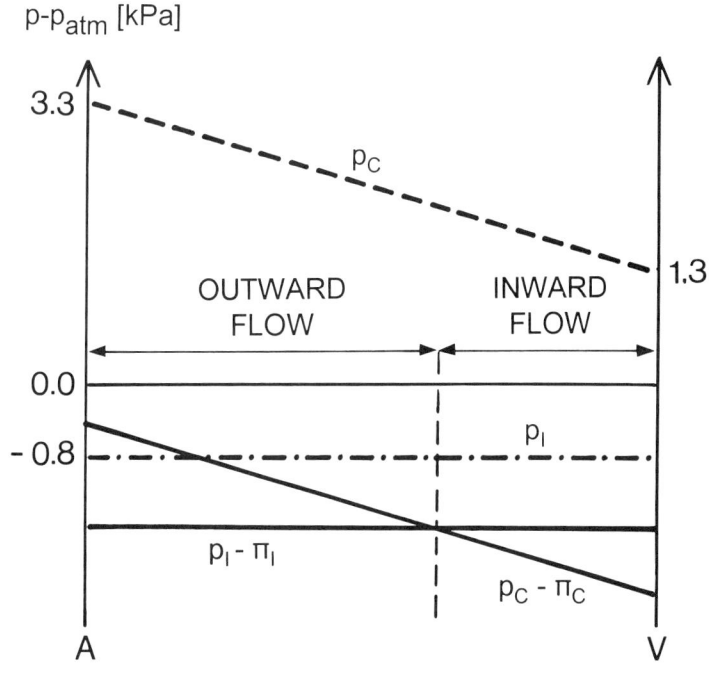

Fig. 12.14: Pressure diagram along a healthy capillary from the arterial end (A) to the venous end (V). The measured pressures are given by the dashed line (in capillary) and dash–dotted lines (in interstitium). To determine the serum flow across the blood vessel membrane, these pressures have to be corrected for the osmotic pressure due to the presence of a non–permeable protein component. This leads to the solid lines crossing at about the half–way point along the capillary. At this point the flow of serum reverses from initially vessel to interstitium to interstitium to vessel.

dashed curve at the top represents the pressure change in the capillary. Due to the high concentration of proteins in the blood, a large osmotic pressure must be taken into account. The apparent pressure in the capillary, after correcting for the proteins, is given by the curve $p_C - \Pi_C$, which decreases left to right from –0.4 kPa to –2.4 kPa.

For the interstitium the pressure is harder to measure but has been estimated to be –0.8 kPa. Again, the calculation of the apparent pressure in the interstitium must include the correction for the osmotic pressure due to the protein concentration, which, however, is lower outside the blood vessel. The apparent pressure in the interstitium is constant at a value of –1.6 kPa, as the curve $p_I - \Pi_I$ in Fig. 12.14 illustrates.

The comparison of the apparent pressures inside and outside the capillary membrane (two solid lines in Fig. 12.14) allows us to predict the direction of serum flow. Serum flows in the direction toward the lower pressure, i.e., it is pushed away by the higher pressure. Since the two apparent pressure curves cross somewhere between the arterial end and the venous end of the capillary, an initial outward flow of serum into the extracellular tissue is compensated by an inward flow from the tissue into the capillary slightly further downstream (a typical capillary length is 0.85 mm). On balance, no increase of serum occurs in the tissue: 90 % actually return into the capillary immediately (resorption) and about 10 % reach the lymphs.

This delicate balance can be disturbed in several ways, leading to clinical problems we can now illustrate by studying Fig. 12.14:
(I) The pressure on the venous end increases, leading to a continuous outflow of serum across the entire organ. This occurs, for example, when a patient has a right heart failure, i.e., when the pumping of blood in the right heart ventricle becomes ineffective. In this case, blood collects in the veins, resulting in a pressure increase. Liquid collects in the tissue of the lowest body parts (legs for a standing patient and back for a patient lying down) until the pressure of the interstitium has built up enough to suppress this outward flow. A left heart failure causes the same effect in the pulmonary veins (the veins leading to the lungs). This results in a pulmonary edema, which literally causes the patient to drown.
(II) The osmotic pressure in the capillary decreases. The clinical term for this is hypoproteinemia. This condition often indicates that the patient is suffering from a nephrotic syndrome, i.e., protein loss due to the diffusion of protein into the urine in the kidneys because the basement membrane has become permeable to proteins. A reduction in the blood concentration of proteins results in a decrease of the osmotic pressure in the entire cardiovascular system that primarily disturbs the balance of in– and outward flow of serum in capillaries.

(III) The osmotic pressure of the capillaries and the osmotic pressure of the interstitium approach each other due to local diffusion of proteins into the extracellular tissue. This is often caused by inflamation. Injured or burned tissue leads to dilation (widening) of capillaries to increase the blood supply as an increased number of immune–response components are needed locally; such as antibodies, macrophages (slow) or granulocytes (fast). Since these rather large units have to enter the tissue, other proteins and blood cells are also enabled to permeate the capillary walls. This secondary effect leads to a local levelling of the osmotic pressures in the interstitium and in the blood vessel, and subsequently serum is leaking into the tissue.

Osmotic effects play also a prominent role in the resorption processes in the nephrons of the kidneys. Water is not directly resorbed because it will follow actively resorbed components, such as sodium ions and HCO_3^-, due to the created osmotic pressure gradient toward the blood side of the membrane.

12.6. Appendix: van't Hoff's law

Consider a pure solvent, labelled 1, which is separated from a solution of component 2 in solvent 1 by a membrane permeable only to solvent 1. In equilibrium, an osmotic pressure Π has developed, as defined in Eq. (19). The condition for equilibrium is that the chemical potential of component 1 is the same on both sides of the membrane, as stated in Eq. (14). Thus, in equilibrium, the value of μ_1 in the solution must equal the value of μ_1 in the pure solvent 1.

There are two factors causing the value of μ_1 in the solution to depart from that in pure solvent 1. These factors must therefore have exactly equal and opposite effects on μ_1. The first is the change in μ_1 produced by dilution of component 1 in the solution. This change causes a lowering of μ_1 equal to Eq. (17).

Exactly counteracting this is the increase in μ_1 in the solution due to the imposed pressure Π. We have discussed two thermodynamic relations, given in Eqs. (8.26) and (8.27). Another such thermodynamic relation states that the change of the chemical potential with pressure at constant temperature is equal to the molar volume of the chemical component. We assume that the partial molar volume of component 1, V_1, is independent of pressure (the solution is incompressible) and that the solution is an ideal solution. Then we find:

$$V_1 \Pi = RT \ln x_1 \qquad (24)$$

The implications of Eq. (24) can be stated as follows: The osmotic pressure is the external pressure that must be applied to the solution to raise the vapor pressure of the solvent 1 to that of the pure component 1.

In most cases, the partial molar volume V_1 of the solvent in the solution can be approximated by the molar volume of the pure liquid V_1^0.

Next we replace x_1 in Eq. (24) by $(1 - x_2)$ and use a mathematical expansion of the logarithm function in the form:

$$-\ln(1 - x) = x + \frac{1}{2}x^2 + \ldots \quad (25)$$

If $x \ll 1$, only the first term on the right side has to be considered. This allows us to rewrite Eq. (24) for very dilute solutions ($x_2 \ll 1$) in the form:

$$V_1^0 \Pi = RT x_2 \quad (26)$$

which is equivalent to Eq. (20).

Table 12.6: Polyisobutylene data for two solutions

concentration [g/cm³]	osmotic pressure Π [atm]	
	in benzene	in cyclohexane
0.020	0.0021	0.0122
0.015	0.00153	0.0068
0.010	0.0010	0.0031
0.005	0.0005	0.0009

12.7. Problems

P–12.1
The osmotic effect is often used to determine the molar mass of macromolecules. This problem illustrates how this is done. The apparatus used is shown in Fig. 12.15: it consists of two chambers which are separated by a semipermeable membrane. One tube is filled with a dilute solution of the macromolecules and the other tube is filled with pure solvent. Additional tubes are mounted vertically on each chamber to measure the osmotic pressure (using Pascal's law).

Assume that the experiment is done at 25°C. We use van't Hoff's law from Eq. (20) as $\Pi = (RT/M)c$, where c is the concentration of the macromolecule in the solution (in [kg/m³]), M is the molar mass (in [kg/mol]) of the macromolecule and Π is the osmotic pressure, as measured with the apparatus in Fig. 12.15. Since van't Hoff's law applies exactly only for very dilute solutions, several measurements are taken for various dilute solutions (i.e., several different values of c) and are then extrapolated. For the extrapolation, we plot Π/c vs. c and obtain the value for Π/c at c = 0 from the plot.

Using the data from Table 12.6 for the osmotic pressure of polyisobutylene in benzene and cyclohexane
(a) plot Π/c versus c for both solutions,
(b) find the extrapolation value of Π/c at c = 0 for each curve,
(c) use van't Hoff's law in the form $\Pi = (RT/M)c$ to determine the molar mass of polyisobutylene.

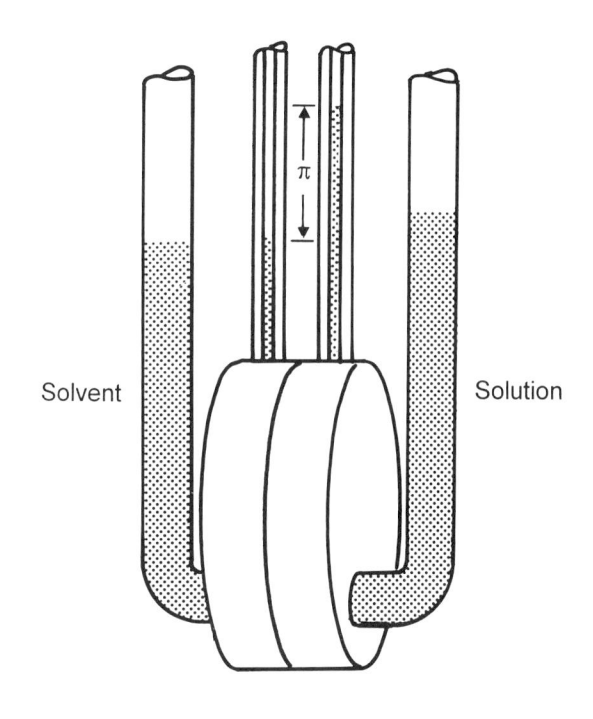

Fig. 12.15 for problem P–12.1

P–12.2
We mix 0.174 g hydrogen gas (H_2) and 1.365 g nitrogen gas (N_2) in a container of 2.83 liters at 0 °C. Assuming that both gases behave ideally, what are (a) the partial pressure of hydrogen,
(b) the partial pressure of nitrogen, and
(c) the total pressure in the container?
Hint: the molar mass of hydrogen is 2.016 g/mol and the molar mass of nitrogen is 28.014 g/mol.

P–12.3
Most extracellular fluids in the human body and the cytoplasm of most human cells have a concentration of osmotically active components of 0.29 mol/kg, e.g. dissolved sugar or dissolved ions such as potassium, sodium and chlorine.
(a) If the body loses water (dehydration) or has a too large intake of salt, both of which affect the extracellular fluid, what consequence does this have on the cells?
(b) What would happen if, instead, a human body were to lose too much salt from the extracellular fluid?

P–12.4
Which is lighter under otherwise equal conditions (same pressure, temperature, volume): humid air or dry air?

P–12.5
In 1965, a French team led by Jacques–Yves Cousteau lived for 28 days in the deep sea station Conshelf III at 108 m below the sea surface. They breathed an oxygen/helium mixture (called helox) instead of air.
(a) Would you agree with their claim that breathing this mixture is easier than breathing air?
(b) Can you think of another reason why they used helox instead of air?
Note: One member of the team reported that among other adverse effects of this exercise the taste is irritated, and he could no longer distinguish caviar from chicken. This, of course, is a disastrous effect for a Frenchman!

Summary

Definitions:
- Partial pressure of component i is the pressure of i–th component with all other components removed from the container.
- Mole fraction x:

$$\frac{n_i}{\sum_i n_i} = \frac{n_i}{n_{total}} = x_i$$

- Chemical potential: the chemical potential of the i–th component, μ_i, is the Gibbs free energy per mole for that component:

$$G_{total} = \sum_{i=1}^{n} \mu_i n_i$$

- Osmotic pressure Π: excess pressure we must apply on solution side to prevent diffusion of solvent through the membrane:

$$\Pi = p_{mix} - p_{pure}$$

Laws:
- Dalton's law for partial gas pressures:

$$p_{total} = \sum_{i=1}^{n} p_i$$

this is equivalent to:

$$\frac{p_i}{p_{total}} = x_i$$

- Raoult's law for ideal solutions:

$$p_i = x_i\, p_i^0$$

p_i is partial pressure in vapor phase, x_i is mole fraction, p_i^0 is vapor pressure of the i–th component.
- Chemical potential of i–th component in solution:

$$\mu_{i,\, solution} = \mu_i^0 + RT\, \ln x_i$$

μ_i^0 is the chemical potential of the vapor above the pure liquid of component i.
- van't Hoff's law of osmosis:

$$\Pi = \frac{RT}{V_1^0} x_2$$

V_1^0 is the molar volume of component 1 (solvent), x_2 is mole fraction of the dilute, non–permeable component.

Chapter XIII

Nerves

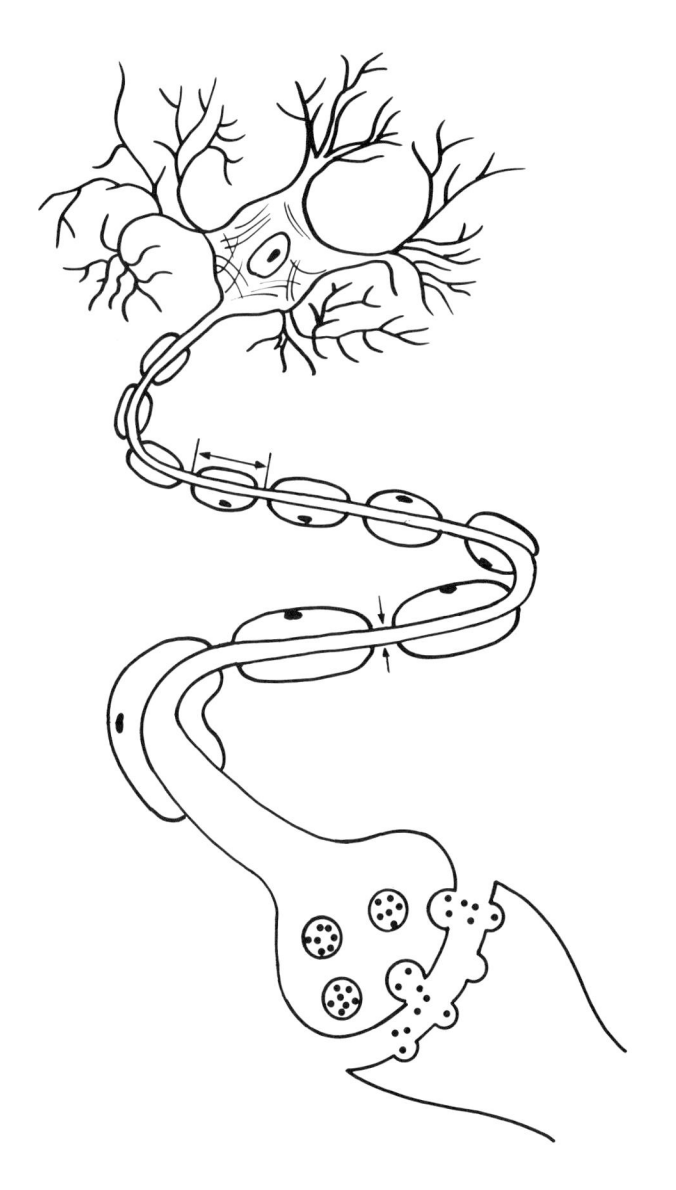

The flow of charges

NERVES
THE FLOW OF CHARGES

Electric currents flow when an electric potential difference is established along a conducting path. The charges move such that they compensate the potential difference. If the moving particles are positively charged they travel in the direction of the electric field along the conductor. The current is proportional to the density of mobile charges in the material, the number of elementary charges carried by each moving particle, the average velocity (drift velocity) of these particles and the cross–sectional area of the conductor. The current per unit area is a materials–specific property and is called the current density.

Flowing charges encounter a resistance against their motion in the conductor. The resistance depends on the material, the length and cross–section of the conductor and is the proportionality factor between electric current and potential near the (electrochemical) equilibrium. The relation between current and potential is called Ohm's law. The resistivity is proportional to the resistance but contains only materials–specific properties. Resistivities at room temperature vary from good conductors (e.g. copper) to good insulators (e.g. quartz glass) by more than 20 orders of magnitude.

The resting nerve is characterized as an electrically active non–equilibrium system. The nerve membrane is modelled as a capacitor with the phospholipid bilayer as the dielectric material between an outer positively charged surface and a parallel inner surface charged negatively. The Na/K pump generates a concentration gradient for K^+ and Na^+, the diffusive and electric drifts of these ions across the membrane then cause a membrane potential of – 70 mV. The flow of ions through the membrane establishes a leakage current.

In the physical sciences, electric effects are often discussed with practical applications in mind, such as power plants, household appliances or consumer electronics. In this textbook, the physiological relevance of electric effects is illustrated instead. In particular, we want to apply the fundamental electric concepts of Chapter 9 to human nerves. Describing the different types of nerves when they are resting and when they are carrying an impulse requires a few additional aspects of electricity.

As in previous chapters, an overview of the relevant anatomical and physiological properties of the model system is presented first. This allows us not only to introduce the notations used later, but also to identify additional fundamental issues that we will have to address.

13.1. Human nerves

Nerves are the most important application of electricity in our body. Already Galen, the physician to Emperor Marcus Aurelius in ancient Rome, had noted the existence of the spinal cord and its connection to the muscle action. Luigi Galvani demonstrated in the late eighteenth century that electricity can trigger the muscles of frogs.

13.1.1. Microscopic nerve anatomy

Nerves serve two purposes: (i) to communicate stimuli to the control centers of the nervous system (e.g. the brain) when they are registered by organs sensitive to the environment, and (ii) to communicate commands from these control centers to various organs, either in response to a stimulus or without any external stimulus, e.g. when controlling the heart beat.

Both types of information transfer must occur within very short times. If you drive your car and an obstacle suddenly appears on the road, your brain's command "hit the breaks" reaches the muscles in your foot in less than 0.1 seconds. In this case, the command has to travel through two of the longest nerves in your body, the nerve from your brain to the lower back synapse and

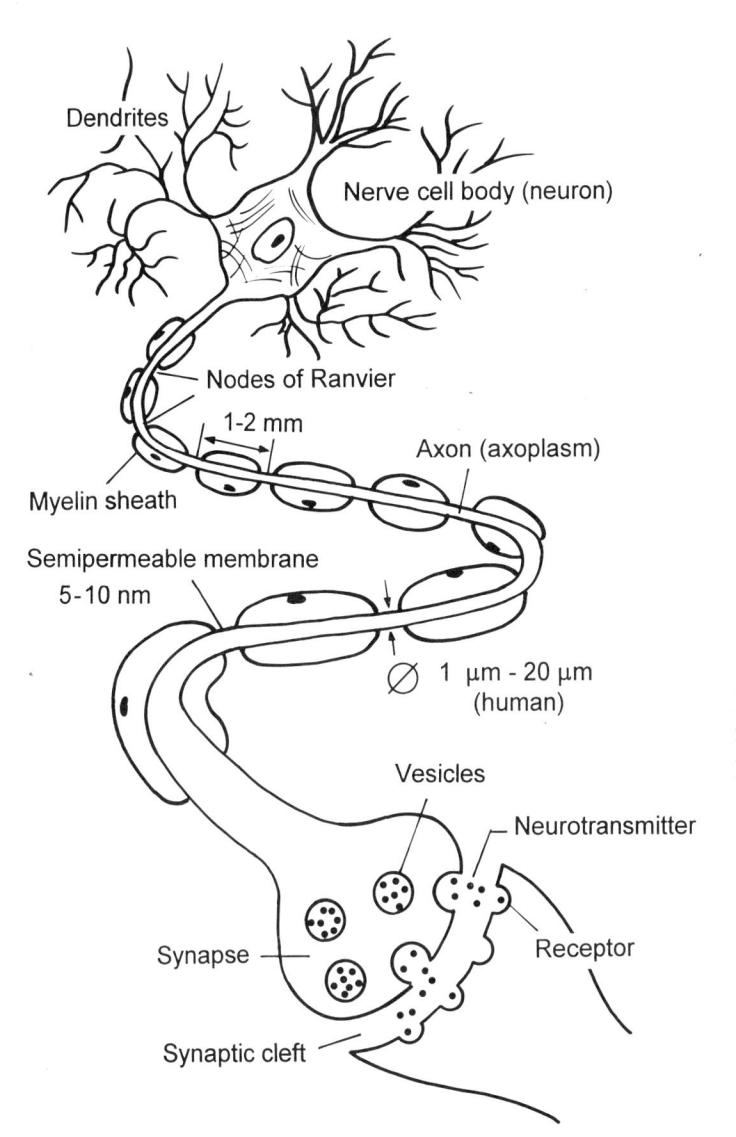

Fig. 13.1: Sketch of a single, myelinated nerve cell. The axon, containing the axoplasm, carries the nerve impulse from the dendrites to the synapse. The myelin sheath plays an important role in the mechanism of the nerve impulse propagation. Note that the myelin sheaths are interrupted about every 1 to 2 mm by a node of Ranvier.

the nerve from there to the toes. These two nerves have a total length of up to 2 meters. Thus, an impulse speed in nerves in excess of 20 m/s is vital in our everyday lives. The evolutionary solution to the problem of communicating information at such high speeds is based on electric and electrochemical effects.

A nerve is a strand of up to 1000 nerve cells (neurons), each stretching from a transducer to a synapse, which is a junction to the transducer of another nerve cell, the brain or a muscle. Nerve cell strands contains two types of nerves, myelinated nerve cells (about 30 %) and unmyelinated nerve cells (about 70 %). We will discuss the differences between these two types in detail later in this chapter.

Fig. 13.1 shows a microscopic sketch of a single, myelinated nerve cell. Nerves have tentacle–like receptors, called dendrites. These respond to a wide range of stimuli, ranging from temperature change to motion parameters (e.g. acceleration in Pacinian corpuscles as discussed in section 3.5). The stimulus causes an electric response which travels along the nerve to the synapse. At the synapse, vesicles are triggered to release neuro–transmitters which pass through the synaptic cleft to a secondary receptor. This cleft is typically 10 to 20 nm wide if the secondary receptor is a dendrite (neural junction) and 50 to 100 nm wide if the secondary receptor is a muscle (myoneural junction).

The neuron and the synapse are connected by the axon. The axons of both the myelinated and unmyelinated nerves are cylindrical tubes filled with a solution called the axoplasm. The axoplasm is separated from the extracellular fluid (also called interstitium) of the human body by a semipermeable membrane of 5 to 10 nm thickness. As illustrated in Fig. 13.1, myelinated nerves are in addition enclosed by a tapelike myelin sheath, called Schwann's cells (discovered by Theodor Schwann). Schwann's cells are 1 to 2 mm long envelopes around the axon and its membrane. Myelin is a phosphorous–based lipoid (fat–type molecules). The myelin sheath is interrupted by short gaps, called nodes of Ran-

Table 13.1: Comparison of physiologically relevant data for myelinated and unmyelinated human nerve cells.

Human nerve cell type	Unmyelinated	Myelinated
Fraction of nerves	70 %	30 %
Cross–section of nerve cell	≈ 1.5 μm	≤ 20 μm*
Axon walls	semipermeable membrane (5 – 10 nm thick)	myelin sheath (2000 nm thick)
Impulse speed	0.6 – 10 m/s	10 – 100 m/s
Purpose	slow information (e.g. temperature stimulation)	motor information

* Giant axon of squid: Cross–section ≈ 500 μm = 0.5 mm

vier (named for Louis Ranvier).

Table 13.1 lists some of the properties of human nerve cells for myelinated and unmyelinated nerves. The table indicates that the presence of the myelin sheath plays an important role in the mechanism of the nerves. Myelinated nerves are vital when high signal speeds are required, e.g. when attempting the emergency stop with a car discussed above.

On the other hand, temperature information is processed by slower unmyelinated nerves. You can establish this in a simple self–experiment. Consciously reach for a mug of coffee. You become aware that you touch the mug clearly before you can tell how warm it is.

13.1.2. Electrochemical processes in nerves

To describe the mechanism of an active nerve, a few additional microscopic observations are needed. We will find that two types of processes are essential for the understanding of nerves: non–equilibrium chemical processes and electric phenomena. On the other hand, neither fluid dynamics nor mechanics are required since signal conduction in nerves occurs without the nerve itself changing shape.

Fig. 13.2 shows the concentrations of various chemical components in both the axoplasm and the ex-

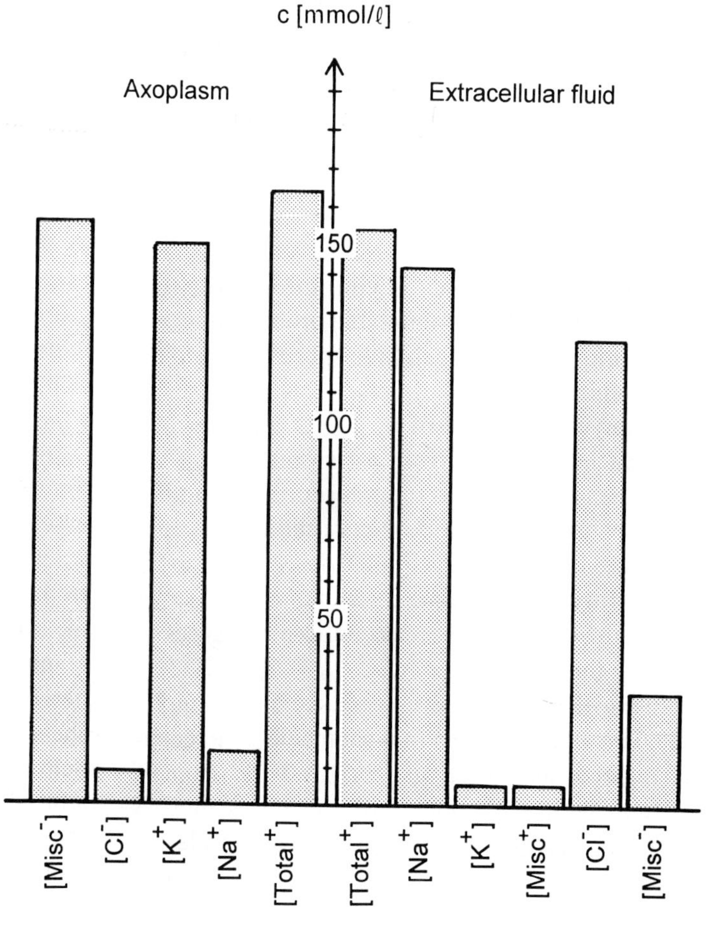

Fig. 13.2: The concentration of various chemical components in the axoplasm (left) and the in extracellular fluid (right). The given values are based on mammalian spinal cord motor neurons.

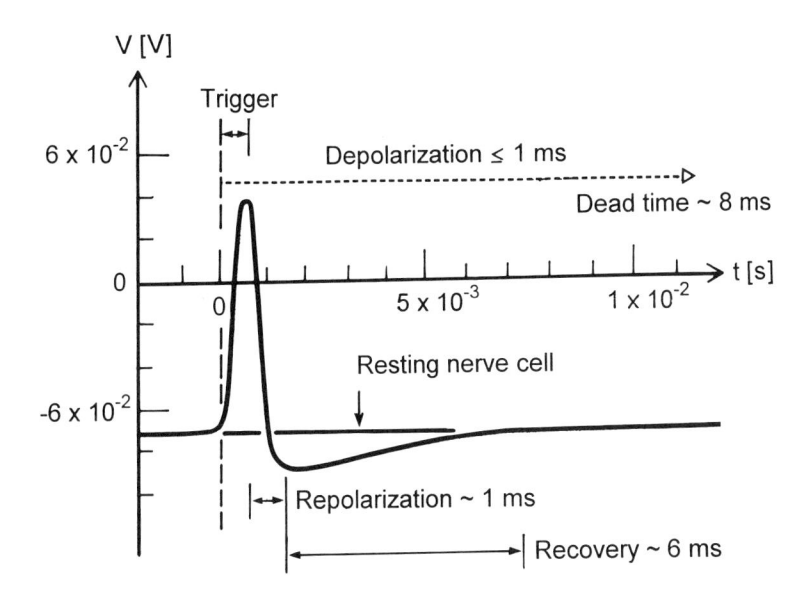

Fig. 13.3: The changes of the electric potential across the membrane of a nerve cell when an impulse passes. The major changes occur within a millisecond, followed by a period of about 6 ms recovery time before the nerve can fire again (i.e., a total of about 8 ms of dead time).

tracellular fluid surrounding the nerves. The data are given in unit [mmol/liter]. We note that in both solutions all important components are either positive or negative ions, with NaCl (rock salt) the dominant species outside the nerve and potassium salts (potassium bound by protein ions and phosphate ions, shown as miscellaneous negative ions in the figure) the major component inside. On either side of the membrane negative and positive ions are respectively balanced, but the axoplasm carries the larger total salt concentration of 165 mmol/liter.

The potential change during an impulse is illustrated in Fig. 13.3. This is the main data set we want to explain in this chapter. The electric potential is a measure of the strength of electric effects, and is often the first information available for a system because potentials are relatively easy to measure. The existence of a non–zero electric potential across the nerve membrane indicates that the numbers of negative and positive ions are not equal on the inside and outside surface of the nerve membrane. In Fig. 13.3 we follow the electric potential while an impulse passes as a function of time. The data in the figure can be described as a sequence of four steps:

(I) *Trigger*: an initial potential change by 10 mV causes an impulse.
(II) *Depolarization*: the nerve is polarized to a positive potential within a millisecond.
(III) *Repolarization*: the depolarization is followed immediately by a repolarization to a potential value which more negative than the resting potential.
(IV) *Recovery*: the nerve returns during a period of about 6 milliseconds to its resting potential. It can now carry another impulse.

Each impulse leads to the same potential profile, i.e., the same shape and intensity of the impulse. Thus, information can only be communicated by the frequency of impulses, i.e., how many impulses occur per second.

13.2. Static properties of a resting nerve

To understand these observations we need to develop a model of the nerve. Let us consider an unmyelinated nerve first. We return to myelinated nerves towards the end of the chapter. A very simple model of a nerve is shown in Fig. 13.4. The figure shows a cross–section through a nerve, with the axoplasm inside a cylindrical tube and the extracellular fluid outside. The nerve membrane separates electric charges. The membrane is modelled as a parallel plate arrangement for which we studied its electrostatic properties in Chapter 9. There is

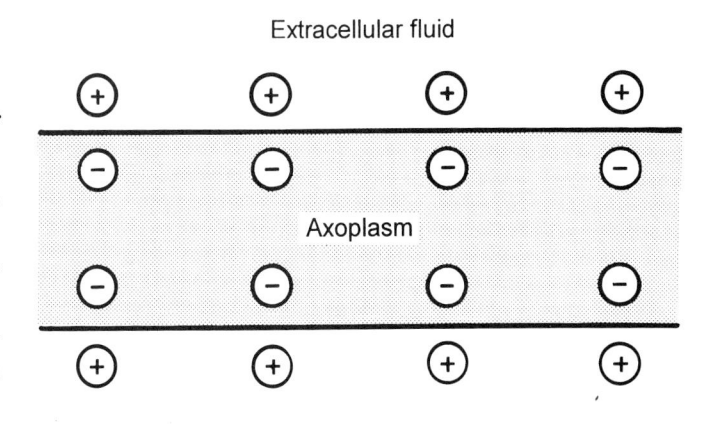

Fig. 13.4: Simplified model of a nerve: the inner surface of the membrane (axoplasm side) carries negative charges, the outer surface of the membrane (extracellular fluid or interstitium side) carries positive charges.

363

an excess number of positive ions outside and an excess number of negative ions inside the nerve. This model is a good starting point to describe a nerve when no impulse is passing through, i.e., a resting nerve. To quantify the model two new concepts are needed: the electrochemical equilibrium and the parallel plate capacitor.

13.2.1. Nernst's equation

We established in Eq. (12.12) that a closed or open system is in thermodynamic equilibrium when the Gibbs free energy (G) is equilibrated between all system parts which are separated by membranes. This equilibrium condition remains true when the electric energy contributes to the enthalpy. Applying the concept of equilibrium across a semipermeable membrane for the specific system of a nerve, i.e., a thin membrane with an extracellular fluid outside and an axoplasm inside, we write:

$$\left(G^* + E_{el}\right)_{interstitium} = \left(G^* + E_{el}\right)_{axoplasm} \quad (1)$$

In this equation, G^* is the part of the Gibbs free energy which is due to the electrically neutral system parts (chemical energy) and E_{el} is the part of the Gibbs free energy which is due to the electric charges (electric energy). The reason that we keep G^* and E_{el} separate is that this allows us to specifically track the electric energy. We derive Nernst's equation from Eq. (1).

Walther Herrmann Nernst started with a system which contains electrolytes (i.e., ionic solutions) of different chemical species on the two sides of a semipermeable membrane. The interaction between electrically neutral solutions across the membrane has already been discussed in section 12.4. Since we made the assumption that both solutions are ideal solutions, and therefore that their components do not interact, the equilibrium condition across the membrane applies to each chemical species separately. Thus, we can replace the Gibbs free energy with the chemical potential defined in Eq. (12.13). The equilibrium condition for ideal, electrically neutral solutions was introduced in Eq. (12.14):

$$\left(\mu_i\right)_{interstitium} = \left(\mu_i\right)_{axoplasm} \quad (2)$$

in which the index i stands for a chemical component in the system. Since the ideal solutions are electrolytes, Eq. (2) must be modified in analogy to Eq. (1):

$$\left(\mu_i + Z_i e N_A V_i\right)_{inter} = \left(\mu_i + Z_i e N_A V_i\right)_{axo} \quad (3)$$

Note that we use the abbreviation "inter" for interstitium and "axo" for axoplasm frequently. In Eq. (3), Z_i is the charge state of the i-th ion species. With e the elementary charge, $Z_i e$ is the charge of the i-th ion species. Since the chemical potential is a molar quantity, i.e., is a value per mol, also all other terms in Eq. (3) must be written per mol. This requires that we multiply the charge per ion with the Avogadro number: $Z_i e N_A$ is the charge per mol for the i-th ion species and V_i is the potential of the i-th ion species. The product of charge and potential equals the electric potential energy as defined in Eq. (9.57).

We will see later in this chapter that only the singly charged ions Na$^+$, K$^+$, and Cl$^-$ play a role in the signal transport in nerves. For these ions $Z_i = 1$. We introduce further the Faraday constant F as the charge per mol for singly charge ions: $F = eN_A = 9.65 \times 10^4$ Cb/mol. This simplifies Eq. (3):

$$\left(\mu_i + FV_i\right)_{interstitium} = \left(\mu_i + FV_i\right)_{axoplasm} \quad (4)$$

Both the interstitium and the axoplasm are modelled as dilute solutions for which the concentration dependence of the chemical potential is given by Raoult's law (Eq. (12.17)):

$$\mu_{i,\,solution} = \mu_i^0 + RT \ln x_i \quad (5)$$

In this equation, the term μ_i^0 represents the constant chemical potential of the vapor of the i-th component over the corresponding pure liquid. Thus, the chemical potential of the i-th species in a solution is equal to a constant term plus a term proportional to the mole fraction of this component in the solution. The standard chemical potential μ_i^0 depends only on the temperature for a given chemical species. Since the nerve is in thermal equilibrium (i.e., the temperatures in the interstitium and in the axoplasm are the same), the standard chemical potential μ_i^0 is the same on both sides of the membrane. Substituting Eq. (5) in Eq. (4) yields:

$$\left(RT \ln \frac{c_i}{c_{tot}} + FV_i\right)_{inter} = \left(RT \ln \frac{c_i}{c_{tot}} + FV_i\right)_{axo} \quad (6)$$

In Eq. (6) the mole fraction x_i has been rewritten as $x_i =$

c_i/c_{tot} where the total concentration for a dilute solution is essentially equal to the water concentration $c_{tot} \cong c_{water}$. In the next step, the logarithmic terms are rewritten, using the mathematical identity $\ln(a/b) = \ln a - \ln b$:

$$\left(RT \ln c_i - RT \ln c_{tot} + FV_i\right)_{inter} = \left(RT \ln c_i - RT \ln c_{tot} + FV_i\right)_{axo} \quad (7)$$

The second term on both sides of Eq. (7) is the same since the water concentration is constant on both sides of the membrane. Thus, this term can be removed from the equation. At this point, we also divide both sides of the equation by the Avogadro number, which yields:

$$\left(kT \ln c_i + eV_i\right)_{inter} = \left(kT \ln c_i + eV_i\right)_{axo} \quad (8)$$

where k is the Boltzmann constant ($R/N_A = k$). In the final step, Eq. (8) is rewritten by combining the concentration terms from both sides:

$$\ln \frac{c_{i,\,inter}}{c_{i,\,axo}} = \frac{e}{kT}\left(V_{i,\,axo} - V_{i,\,inter}\right) \quad (9)$$

We eliminate the logarithm–function to write the concentration ratio as the independent variable. With this last step Nernst's equation is obtained:

$$\frac{c_{i,\,inter}}{c_{i,\,axo}} = \exp\left[-\frac{e}{kT}\left(V_{i,\,inter} - V_{i,\,axo}\right)\right] \quad (10)$$

> *Nernst's equation states that the concentration ratio of the i–th component of a solution is proportional to an exponential term containing the difference of the electric potential between both sides of the membrane.*

Of course, this formula applies only if an equilibrium across the membrane has been established for the *i*–th component of the solution. A necessary condition for this equilibrium is that the membrane is permeable for the respective component.

13.2.2. Resting nerve: An equilibrium model

We use Nernst's equation to determine whether nerves are in thermodynamic equilibrium. As noted before, a resting nerve is not transporting an impulse, thus its state is not changing with time. However, the nerve is an open system in which it is possible for energy and chemical components to be exchanged with the surrounding extracellular fluid. Radioactive tracer experiments have established that sodium and potassium ions penetrate the nerve membrane continuously. Therefore, the nerve is either in a thermodynamic equilibrium state or in a time–independent non–equilibrium state, i.e., a steady state. Our first task is to determine which of these two possibilities is actually the case. In the current section the possibility to describe resting nerves with an equilibrium model is tested. We will find that this model is not suitable. In the next section a non–equilibrium model will then be tested.

To establish an equilibrium model for the resting nerve we use an analogy to a chemical battery. An equilibrium is expected when only passive processes occur in the system. We know from Fig. 13.2 that concentration differences exist across the nerve membrane for most ion species. If we focus for example on potassium, which has a much higher concentration in the axoplasm than in the extracellular fluid, then we expect the following processes to occur passively: potassium ions diffuse through the membrane into the extracellular fluid along the concentration gradient, following Fick's law as discussed in section 7.4. Since potassium is present in the system as a positively charged ion, each potassium ion diffusing outwards causes the axoplasm to become more negatively charged and the extracellular fluid to become more positively charged.

Considering the competing electric and diffusive phenomena, we notice that the motion of potassium ions across the membrane is a self–terminating process: each potassium ion, which diffuses in the direction of the concentration gradient increases the electric potential difference in that direction which makes it harder for the next potassium ion to diffuse as it must move from a negatively charged environment towards a positively charged environment.

These two competing passive processes occur in this form at the surface of the electrodes in a battery. A simple type of battery arrangement is shown in Fig. 13.5. Shown are two electrochemical half–cells: at the left side is a zinc metal strip immersed in an aqueous $ZnSO_4$ solution and at the right side, separated by a porous barrier, is a copper strip immersed in an aqueous $CuSO_4$ solution.

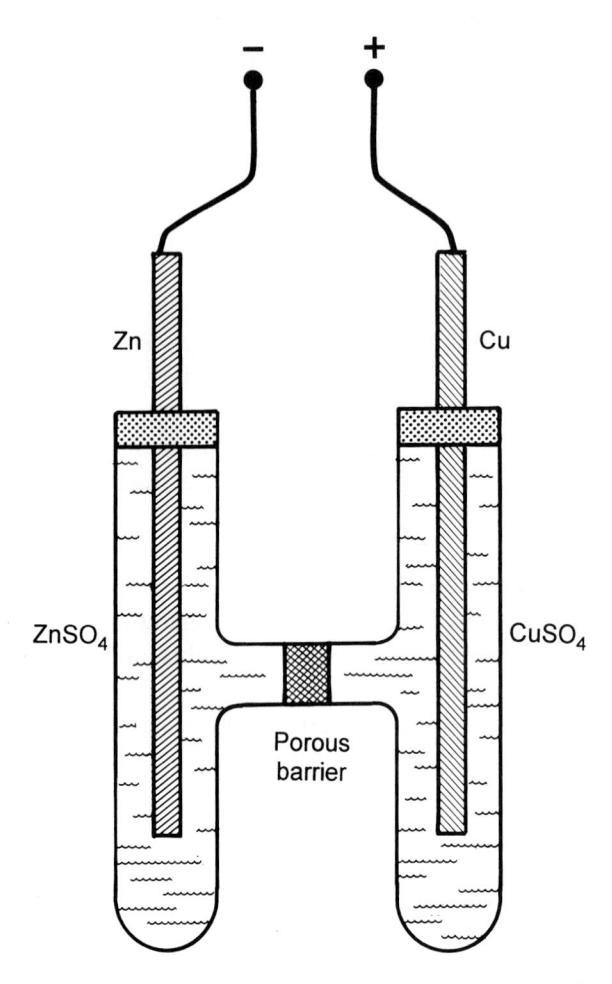

Fig. 13.5: An electrochemical cell consisting of a Zn/Zn²⁺ and a Cu/Cu²⁺ half–cell.

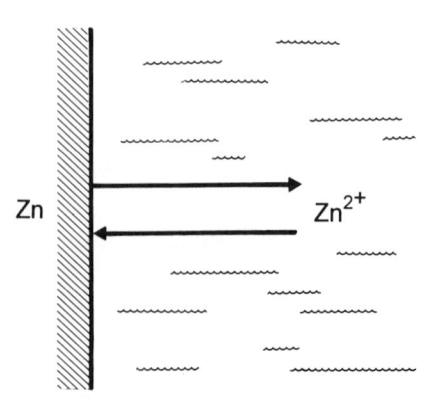

Fig. 13.6: Concept of the microscopic dynamic equilibrium at the Zn metal/solution interface.

To study the phenomena occurring at the metal/solution interfaces, we focus first on the surface of the immersed zinc metal. The fundamental step which takes place at that surface is illustrated in Fig. 13.6: neutral zinc atoms dissolve into the solution as double–positively charged ions, leaving behind two electrons each:

$$Zn \rightleftharpoons Zn^{2+} + 2e^- \quad (11)$$

This process is self–terminating as every zinc atom which becomes an ion in the solution increases the negative charge of the metal, causing an increasing electric potential barrier for subsequent zinc atoms to leave the metal. It is important to note that the term self–terminating is somewhat misleading because microscopically Zn atoms transfer as ions into the solution all the time. However, once the potential reaches a certain value, the electric potential difference causes an electric drift of ions toward the metal strip, as indicated by the double–arrow in Fig. 13.6 and in Eq. (11). Zn ions, which reach the metal surface, pick up two electrons and condense onto the Zn strip as neutral atoms. The final state of the processes at the metal/solution interface is therefore called a dynamic equilibrium. When the dynamic equilibrium is reached, we can use Nernst's equation to quantify the concentration and potential differences across the interface:

$$\frac{c(Zn)}{c(Zn^{2+})} = \exp\left[-\frac{2e\left(V_{Zn} - V_{Zn^{2+}}\right)}{kT}\right] \quad (12)$$

in which the factor 2 in the exponent on the right hand side is due to the double–positive charge of the Zn ions. While the concentration for pure metal does not vary, the concentration of the ions in solution, the temperature and the potential across the metal/solution interface can change in Eq. (12).

Eq. (12) is, however, in the given form not applicable to an experimental set–up since Eq. (11) does not represent a proper chemical reaction. Studying Fig. 13.5 we note that an electrochemical cell always consists of two half–cells, each based on a reaction similar to the one given in Eq. (11). While the potential difference in Eq. (12) is experimentally not measurable, the combination of two half–cells leads to an actual potential difference which we call the electromotive force (emf), $\mathscr{E}$. Since we can vary which half–cells we combine, you find listed in the literature the standard electrode potentials, in which the term standard refers to T = 25°C and a concentration of the solution of c = 1.0 mol/liter. The reference potential, V = 0 V, is assigned to the hydrogen gas half–cell, which is shown in Fig. 13.7. This half–cell consists of an inert platinum foil immersed in a one–molar acid solution and is flooded with hydrogen gas of atmospheric pressure. A few examples of half–cell electrode potentials are listed in Table 13.2.

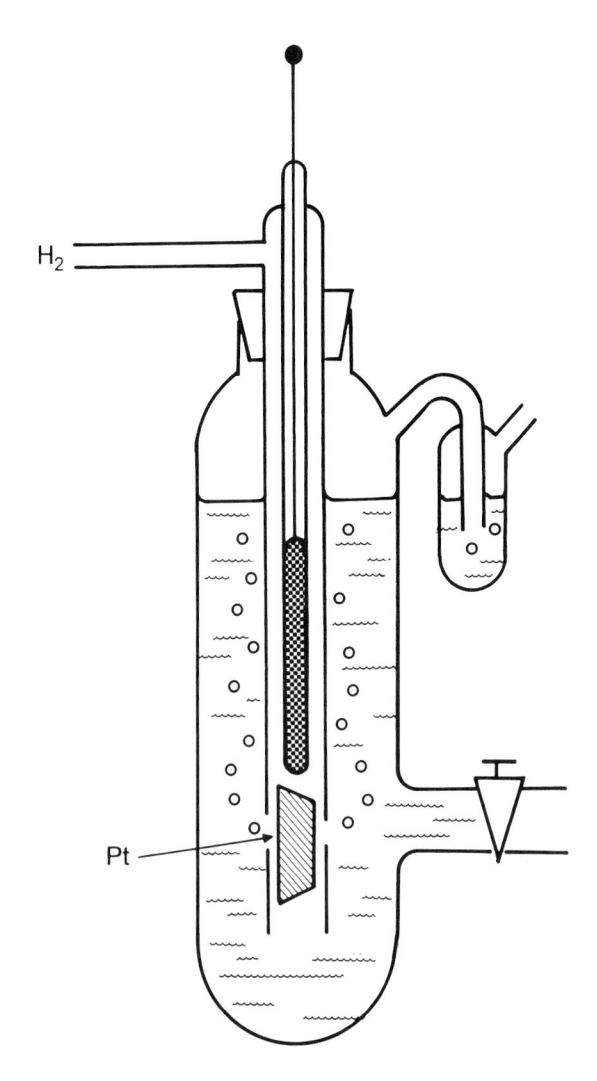

Fig. 13.7: The standard hydrogen gas half–cell to which the potential of 0 V is assigned. An inert Pt metal strip is flooded with hydrogen gas at 1 atm and surrounded by an acid solution. Combining this half–cell with any other half–cell allows us to measure the electromotive force (emf) $\mathscr{E}$ of the second half–cell.

Table 13.2: Selected standard electrode potentials for electrochemical half–cells with acid solutions, calibrated against a standard hydrogen cell H⁺/H₂/Pt (shown in Fig. 13.7).

Electrode	Electrode process	V [V]
Li⁺/Li	$Li^+ + e \rightleftharpoons Li$	−3.045
K⁺/K	$K^+ + e \rightleftharpoons K$	−2.925
Ca²⁺/Ca	$Ca^{2+} + 2e \rightleftharpoons Ca$	−2.865
Na⁺/Na	$Na^+ + e \rightleftharpoons Na$	−2.715
Zn²⁺/Zn	$Zn^{2+} + 2e \rightleftharpoons Zn$	−0.763
H⁺/H₂/Pt	$2H^+ + 2e \rightleftharpoons H_2$	0.0
Cu²⁺/Cu	$Cu^{2+} + 2e \rightleftharpoons Cu$	+0.337
Ag⁺/Ag	$Ag^+ + e \rightleftharpoons Ag$	+0.800

which together constitute a valid chemical reaction. Assuming first that both half–cells are standard electrodes, we calculate from Table 13.2 the electromotive force. Note that the reaction for the Zn cell is included backwards, as written in the chemical reaction:

$$\mathscr{E} = V_{Cu_{2+}/Cu} - V_{Zn_{2+}/Zn} = \\ +0.337[V] - (-0.763[V]) = +1.1 \text{ V} \quad (13)$$

In the second step we correct for the non–standard concentration of the copper solution with Nernst's equation:

$$\frac{c(Cu^{2+})_{standard}}{c(Cu^{2+})_{actual}} = \exp\left[-\frac{2e(V_{st} - V_{act})}{kT}\right] \quad (14)$$

in which V_{st} is the standard potential from Table 13.2 and V_{act} is the actual potential of the given system. Thus:

$$V_{actual} - V_{standard} = \frac{kT}{2e} \ln\left(\frac{c(Cu^{2+})_{st}}{c(Cu^{2+})_{act}}\right) = \\ \frac{1.38 \times 10^{-23}\left[\frac{J}{K}\right] 298[K]}{2(-1.6 \times 10^{-19}[Cb])} \ln 10 = -0.03 \text{ V} \quad (15)$$

This leads to a correction to the value in Eq. (13). The final electromotive force is $\mathscr{E} = 1.1$ V $- 0.03$ V $= 1.07$ V. The electromotive force of an electrochemical cell is governed by the choice of half–cells. Temperature or concentration variations cause only minor corrections.

Example 13.1
Calculate the electromotive force of the electrochemical cell shown in Fig. 13.5. We use T = 25 °C, for the concentration of the ZnSO₄ solution 1.0 mol/liter and for the concentration of the CuSO₄ solution 0.1 mol/liter.

Solution: The underlying chemical processes of the two half–cells are:

(I)   Zn $\rightleftharpoons Zn^{2+} + 2e^-$
(II) $Cu^{2+} + 2e^- \rightleftharpoons$ Cu

    Zn + CuSO₄ $\rightleftharpoons$ Cu + ZnSO₄

The equilibrium model, as we derived it from the properties of an electrochemical cell or battery, is not satisfactory as a model for the resting nerve. Since the nerve has positive ions on both sides of the membrane which are able to diffuse through the membrane, the nerve would not acquire a potential difference because the two diffusing species, potassium and sodium, would seek to balance each other electrically. Nernst's equation would then require the concentration of each species to balance separately on both sides of the membrane to establish a proper electrochemical equilibrium. As a result the nerve could not function.

13.2.3. Resting nerve: An non–equilibrium model

Alternatively to the equilibrium model based on the analogy to an electrochemical cell, a non–equilibrium model for the resting nerve is proposed. This model is shown in Fig. 13.8. We have to go through this complex figure step by step to understand all details of the model. The abbreviations used in Fig. 13.8 are as follows: EXT stands for extracellular fluid (interstitium), INT for interior fluid (axoplasm), M for membrane, Prot for protein, and Phos for phosphate. The concentration of a chemical species is higher on the side on which its chemical symbol is bold faced.

The first of the five columns represents a passive (dead) nerve. The potassium and sodium concentrations inside and outside the nerve cell are equal, the extracellular fluid has a slightly higher chlorine concentration because the negative chlorine ions can permeate the nerve membrane, but the negative phosphate and protein ions inside cannot. There is no potential difference across the membrane of the dead nerve, as indicated at the top of the figure; nor are any ion transport processes active in the nerve membrane. The term dead applies in two ways: (I) this nerve cannot carry a nerve impulse and (II) the system nerve/extracellular fluid is in thermal and chemical equilibrium as the only remaining concentration gradient of the negative ions cannot be compen-

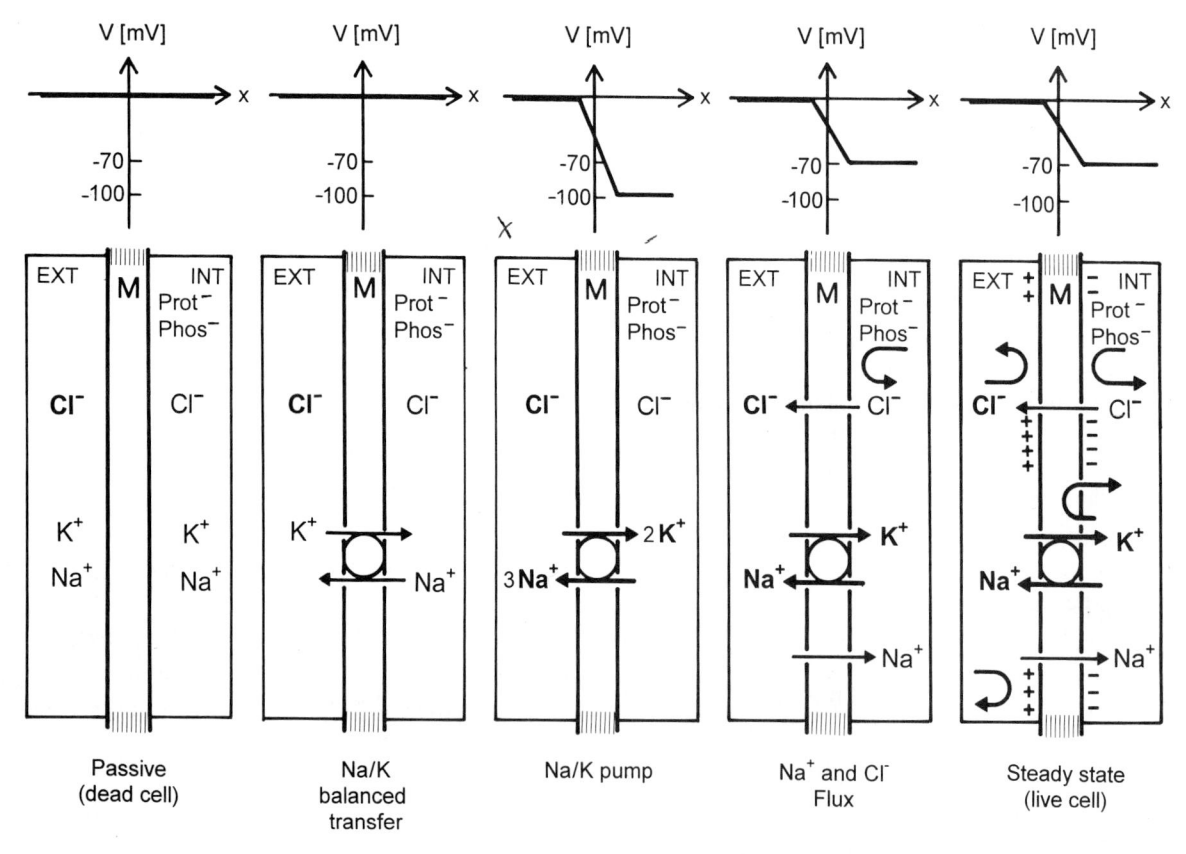

Fig. 13.8: Non–equilibrium model of nerve: a live cell is built up from a dead cell in equilibrium in separate steps. The Na/K pump separates Na^+ and K^+ across the membrane. If the pump would transfer sodium and potassium at an equal ratio, no electric potential would emerge (second frame). The actual biological Na/K pump transfers ions with a ratio $Na^+:K^+ = 3:2$ which would yield an axoplasm potential of -100 mV (third frame). As a result of the electric field across the membrane Na^+ and Cl^- drift across the membrane, lowering the axoplasm potential to -70 mV (fourth frame). These processes lead to a steady state as further cross–membrane drift of ions is hindered by the areal charge densities on the membrane surfaces.

sated because the membrane is impermeable to the large negative protein and phosphate ions.

Starting from the dead cell, we build up a live cell in four steps. First, as shown in the second frame, a non–equilibrium process separates the positive potassium and sodium ions. The resting nerve needs an excess potassium concentration inside and an excess sodium concentration outside. To establish these concentrations, a transport of Na$^+$ and K$^+$ against their concentration gradients is required; therefore, a simple diffusion process cannot achieve the ion separation across the permeable membrane. Instead, an active transport process is needed. This process is called the *Na/K pump*. The energy for the ion pump is provided by ATP molecules. A resting nerve cell consumes 30 % of its ATP to maintain the Na/K ion imbalance across the membrane. The Na/K pump achieves the same result as the external flow of matter through an open system. The only difference is that the Na/K pump is integrated into the membrane and is therefore not external to the system.

If the same number of ions of each type pass through the membrane per time unit as shown in the second panel of Fig. 13.8, the system remains electrically neutral. However, this is not the net result of the actual biological Na/K pump. The net effect of the active ion transport is illustrated in the third panel of Fig. 13.8: for every three sodium ions transferred to the extracellular fluid only two potassium ions are transferred to the axoplasm. This imbalance of charge transfer leads to a potential difference between the axoplasm and the extracellular fluid. Defining the potential of the extracellular fluid as 0 V, we observe the development of a –100 mV potential in the axoplasm. The potential in the axoplasm is negative because the number of positive charges is reduced due to the imbalanced pumping.

The –100 mV potential difference of the axoplasm subsequently has an effect on the chlorine ions that is similar to the effect of the emerging potential in the battery. Unlike the larger negative ions in the axoplasm (phosphate and protein ions), the chlorine ions are driven by the electric field to permeate the membrane, drifting against their concentration gradient toward the more positive potential. Some amount of chlorine passes through the membrane, effectively lowering the potential difference to –70 mV, as shown in the fourth panel of Fig. 13.8. In the same fashion a minor electric drift occurs for the sodium ions towards the inside of the nerve.

At this stage a steady state of the system is reached. It is maintained by the Na/K pump and leads to a –70 mV potential difference between the axoplasm and the extracellular fluid. An imbalance of the potassium, sodium and chlorine ion concentrations across the membrane is also established. The accumulated charge on the membrane walls (negative on the side of the axoplasm and positive on the side of the extracellular fluid) blocks a further net diffusive flow or net electric drift of all ion types across the membrane (indicated by curved arrows in the last panel of Fig. 13.8). However, there is a continuous flow of Na$^+$, K$^+$ and Cl$^-$ across the membrane in both directions to offset the Na/K pumping.

Which of the two models describes the live nerve cell better, the equilibrium model developed in analogy to Fig. 13.5, or the non–equilibrium model of Fig. 13.8? Can we prove that th model in Fig. 13.8 is a better description than Fig. 13.5?

The proof will be provided using Nernst's equation (Eq. (10)). The measured potential difference across the nerve membrane is –70 mV. The temperature of the system is the body temperature of 37°C = 310 K. Thus, a nerve in equilibrium would have the following concentration ratios for (I) positive ions:

$$\frac{c^+_{in}}{c^+_{ax}} = \exp\left[-\frac{1.6\times10^{-19}[Cb]\ 7\times10^{-2}[V]}{1.38\times10^{-23}[J/K]\ 310[K]}\right]$$

$$\frac{c^+_{axoplasm}}{c^+_{interstitium}} = 13.7$$

(16)

and (II) negative ions:

$$\frac{c^-_{in}}{c^-_{ax}} = \exp\left[-\frac{-1.6\times10^{-19}[Cb]\ 7\times10^{-2}[V]}{1.38\times10^{-23}[J/K]\ 310[K]}\right]$$

$$\frac{c^-_{axoplasm}}{c^-_{interstitium}} = 0.073$$

(17)

Note that the result in Eqs. (16) and (17) is written in inverted form.

Now we compare the actual concentration ratios to these values predicted for a nerve in thermodynamic equilibrium. Using the values from Fig. 13.2 we obtain:

$$\frac{[Na^+]_{axoplasm}}{[Na^+]_{interstitium}} = \frac{15[mmol/l]}{145[mmol/l]} = 0.103$$

$$\frac{[K^+]_{axoplasm}}{[K^+]_{interstitium}} = \frac{150[mmol/l]}{5[mmol/l]} = 30.0 \quad (18)$$

$$\frac{[Cl^-]_{axoplasm}}{[Cl^-]_{interstitium}} = \frac{9[mmol/l]}{125[mmol/l]} = 0.072$$

These numbers apply to virtually all mammals, including humans. The ratios for potassium and sodium deviate significantly from the equilibrium values, while the chlorine value is close to the equilibrium ratio. These deviations from the equilibrium are due to the Na/K pump, which affects the two positive ion species, but not chlorine ions. Thus, the battery model cannot be used for the nerve and the more complex model shown in Fig. 13.8 is used for further study of the resting nerve.

Fig. 13.9 gives an overview of the potential (in the top panel) and the electric field across an axon (in the bottom panel). In the interior of the axon, which is about 1 μm wide, the potential is −70 mV relative to the potential outside. The potential changes where charges are separated. This occurs between the inside surface (negative charges) and the outside surface of the membrane (positive charges), across a distance of 6 nm. Inside the axoplasm no uncompensated charges occur.

Example 13.2
Determine the electric field across a human nerve membrane.

Solution: The electric field across the membrane is calculated from the potential of a parallel plate arrangement using Eq. (9.58):

$$|E| = \frac{V}{y} = \frac{7 \times 10^{-2} \, [V]}{6 \times 10^{-9} \, [m]}$$

$$\Rightarrow \quad |E| = 1.17 \times 10^7 \, \frac{V}{m}$$

(19)

As defined before, the electric field points towards the negative charge, i.e., $|E| > 0$ for the membrane at the left in Fig. 13.9 and $|E| < 0$ for the membrane at the right in the figure. The calculated value is used in the lower panel of Fig. 13.9 to sketch the electric field quantitatively. Note that the notion of positive or negative electric fields in Fig. 13.9 is of no practical use as the choice of the direction of the coordinate axis is arbitrary. The important conclusion from the figure is that the electric field points everywhere in the membrane into the nerve (toward the axoplasm side).

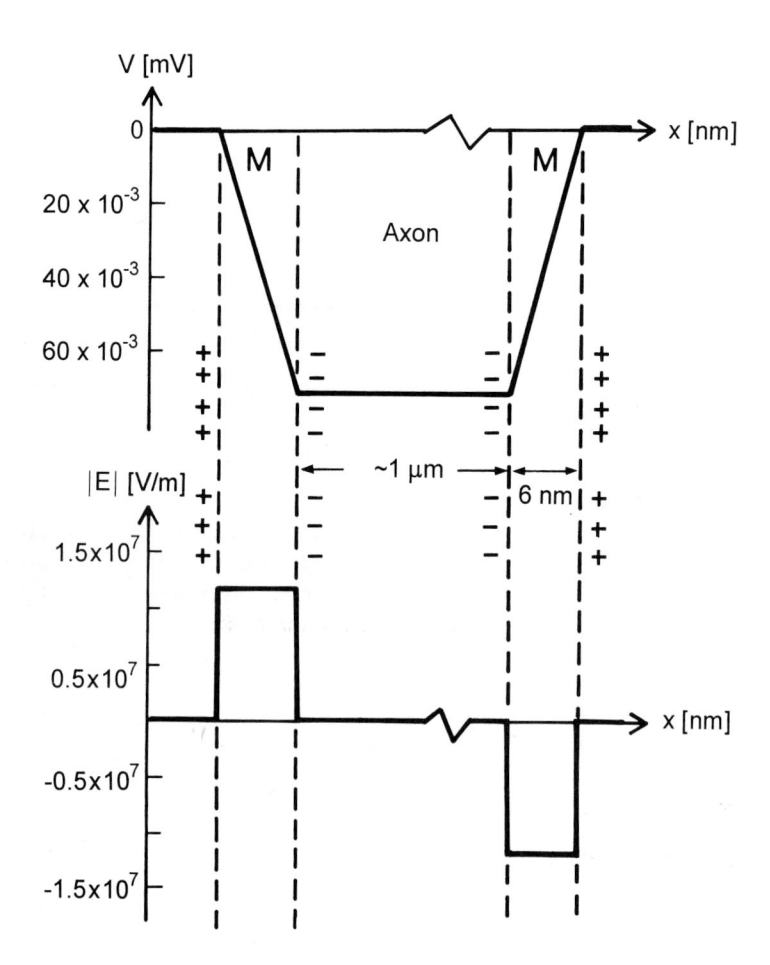

Fig. 13.9: The potential (top panel) and the electric field (bottom panel) across a human nerve cell. Note that the potential always decreases in the direction in which the electric field vector points, which occurs toward the inside of the axon.

13.3. Capacitors

The potential and electric field curves of Fig. 13.9 are the direct consequence of the arrangement of the electric charges at the interior and exterior membrane surfaces: the areal charge density of positive charges on the outside is equal to that of the negative charges on the inside. This arrangement corresponds to two parallel conducting plates, which are separated by an insulator of thickness b, as illustrated in Fig. 13.10. This arrangement is called a capacitor when the two conducting plates are oppositely charged, as sketched in Fig. 13.11. When two initially neutral plates are connected to the two terminals of a battery, positive charge builds up on the plate connected to the positive terminal and an equal amount of negative charge builds up on the plate connected to the negative terminal. Note that we have so far assumed that the insulator is a vacuum, but other insulators like the membrane in Fig. 13.9 are possible and will be considered in this section.

Three quantities characterize a capacitor: the areal charge density σ, the capacitance C and the dielectric constant κ. Of these, only the areal charge density has been introduced so far. Here we define the other two quantities. This allows us to quantify more properties of the resting nerve, including the value of the areal charge density of the axon membrane.

To define capacitance, we start with a parallel plate capacitor as shown in Fig. 13.12. In contrast to previous arrangements, a specific area A is defined for both plates. The upper plate is given a charge +q and the lower plate is given a corresponding charge of −q, generating a symmetric arrangement. The gap between the plates has a width of b and contains a vacuum.

For such a parallel plate capacitor we know that the potential is linear in the charge density and the plate separation, $V = \sigma b/\epsilon_0$ (Eq. (9.58)). Using the definition of the areal charge density, $\sigma = q/A$, we conclude that the potential is proportional to the charge q, $V \propto q$. This proportionality is written as an equation by introducing the capacitance C as a proportionality constant:

$$q = C \cdot V \qquad (20)$$

in which the unit of C is [Cb/V] = [F]. [F] stands for *Farad* (named after Michael Faraday).

> *The potential of a parallel plate capacitor is proportional to the charge on the plates. The proportionality factor is the capacitance.*

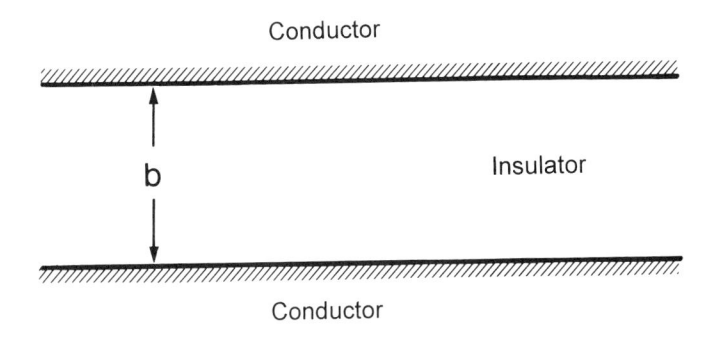

Fig. 13.10: The geometric configuration of a parallel plate capacitor with gap width *b*. Both plates must be electrically conducting, while the gap contains either a vacuum or an insulating material.

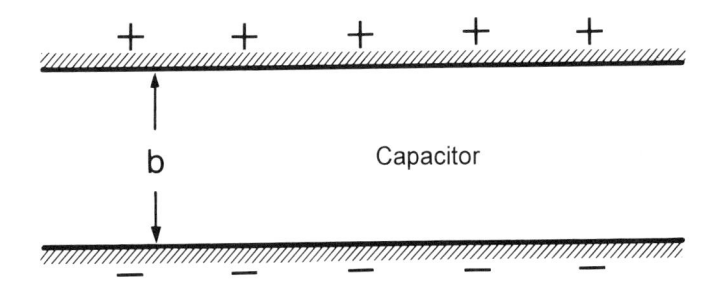

Fig. 13.11: The electric configuration of a charged parallel plate capacitor.

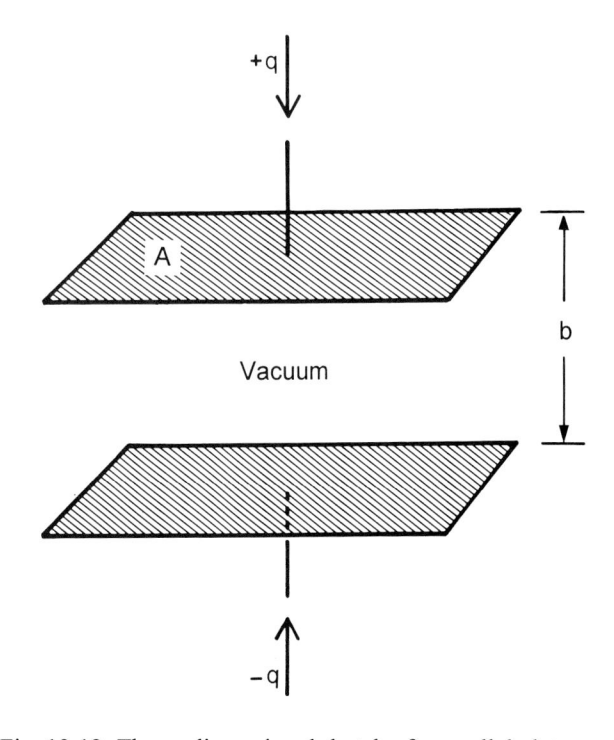

Fig. 13.12: Three–dimensional sketch of a parallel plate capacitor illustrating the finite area A of the plates. Later in the section the vacuum indicated to be inside the gap is replaced with electrically insulating materials.

Therefore, the capacitance of a capacitor is the ratio of charge on each plate to the potential difference across the capacitor. The name capacitance is a fitting choice for C: a large capacitance means that a large amount of charge only causes a small potential, i.e., a system with a large capacitance can accommodate a lot of charges before a significant potential develops between the two plates.

Starting from Eq. (9.58), we derive an explicit expression for the capacitance:

$$V_{\parallel} = \frac{\sigma}{\epsilon_0} b = \frac{q}{\epsilon_0 A} b = \frac{q}{C} \qquad (21)$$

$$\Rightarrow \quad C = \frac{\epsilon_0 A}{b}$$

The capacitance of a parallel plate capacitor depends only on geometric properties: it is proportional to the area of the plates and inversely proportional to the width of the gap between the plates.

Eqs. (20) and (21) also justify the name of ϵ_0, which is called the permittivity of vacuum. For a capacitor of fixed unit area (A = 1 m²) and fixed unit plate gap width (b = 1 m), ϵ_0 is the proportionality factor of the charge brought onto the plates and the resulting potential between the plates. Thus, ϵ_0 is a measure of the ability of charges to reach through vacuum to affect charges on the other plate.

We can change the permittivity of the capacitor by replacing the vacuum with something else. The material that we replace the vacuum with must not allow the transfer of charges between the plates as this would short–circuit the device. Michael Faraday determined in 1837 that all electrically insulating materials qualify. We call an insulating material placed in a capacitor a dielectric material. Faraday was able to show that inserting a dielectric material into a parallel plate capacitor has only a minor effect on the physical formulas describing the device. The change is that ϵ_0 is replaced by $\kappa\epsilon_0$ in any formula in which ϵ_0 appears. κ is called the *dielectric constant*. It is a materials constant that has a well defined value for each insulator. Table 13.3 lists several values at room temperature. The product $\kappa\epsilon_0$ represents then the permittivity of the dielectric.

The larger the dielectric constant, the smaller the potential of a given parallel plate capacitor with a given charge. Thus, materials with large dielectric constants

Table 13.3: Dielectric constants at room temperature

Material	Dielectric constant κ
Vacuum	1.0
Air at 1.0 atm	1.00054
Polystyrene	2.6
Paper	3.5
Pyrex glass	4.7
Porcelain	6.5
Nerve membrane	7.0
Silicon	12.0
Ethanol	25.0
Water	78.5

effectively screen the effect of the charges on the plates. The extremely large dielectric constant of water is due to its dipole moment which we discussed in section 9.4. In the same way that water molecules screen the charges of ions in a solution (Fig. 9.10), they orient themselves in a parallel plate capacitor such that the positive end of the molecule is directed toward the negatively charged plate and vice versa. This effect is called polarization of the dielectric. Ethanol also has a large dielectric constant. This is a result of the same polarization effect due to the dipole moment of the OH–group in the alcohol molecule.

Charged capacitors store electric potential energy. This is illustrated in Fig. 13.13. To determine the potential energy quantitatively, we start with an uncharged capacitor. In the first step a small amount of charge, Δq, is transferred from one plate to the other. In this first step there is no work associated with the charge transfer as the capacitor still has a zero potential difference. However, as we continue to transfer the same amount of charge step by step, work is required. The formula for the work done when moving an amount of charge Δq against an electric force is $W = \Delta q \, \Delta V$. The potential difference ΔV is due to all the previously transferred charges, leading to the step function shown in Fig. 13.13. The total work is then the area under the curve in the figure. This area is described by a triangle for which we find:

$$W = \frac{1}{2} Q \, \Delta V_{final} \qquad (22)$$

in which ΔV_{final} is the final potential difference and Q is the total amount of charge transferred. The result in Eq. (22) represents also the work stored in the capacitor, i.e., the electric potential energy of the device.

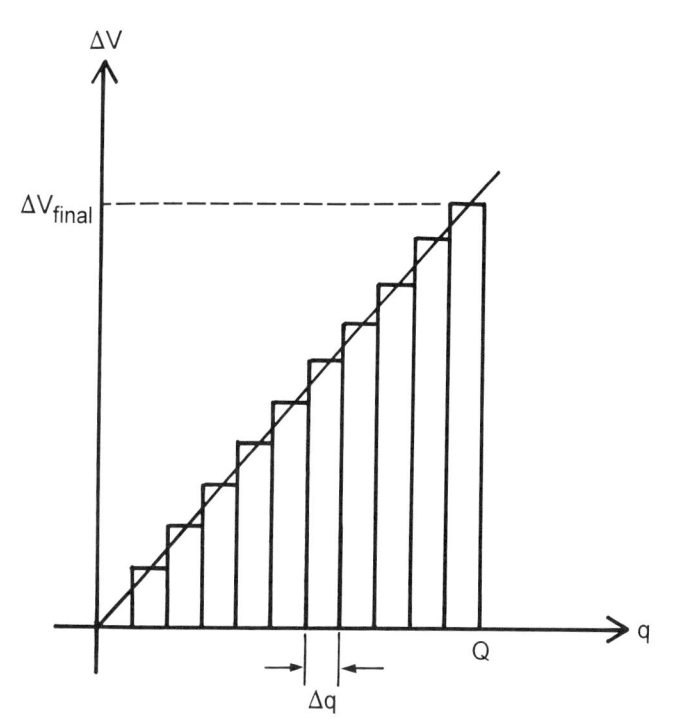

Fig. 13.13: A sketch illustrating how the successive transfer of small amounts of charge from one plate to the other yields a charged parallel plate capacitor. The work required for this charging process is determined from the figure by determining the area under the curve.

===

Example 13.3
A parallel plate capacitor with capacitance C = 13.5 pF is charged to a potential difference of 12.5 V between its plates. The charging battery is then disconnected and a piece of porcelain is placed between the plates.
(a) What is the potential energy of the device before the porcelain piece is added?
(b) What is its potential energy after the porcelain piece has been added?

Solution part (a): In the first part of the problem the electric potential energy after charging is determined from Eq. (22). The work in Eq. (22) is equal to the change of the electric potential energy, $W = \Delta E_{el}$, and thus for the charging process from an initial potential of 0 V we find $E_{el,\,final} = \frac{1}{2} Q V_{final}$.

To calculate $E_{el,\,final}$, Eq. (20) is used to replace the unknown charge with the capacitance and the potential:

$$E_{el} = \frac{1}{2} Q V = \frac{1}{2} (CV) V = \frac{1}{2} C V^2 \quad (23)$$

Eq. (23) allows us to quantify the electric potential energy with the values given in the problem:

$$E_{el} = \frac{1}{2} 13.5 \times 10^{-12} [F] \, (12.5 [V])^2$$

$$\Rightarrow \quad E_{el} = 1.06 \times 10^{-9} \, J \quad (24)$$

Solution part (b): Next a porcelain slab is placed between the capacitor's plates. With the battery disconnected, it is now the charge on the plates of the capacitor and no longer the potential which is fixed. Thus, for this situation Eq. (23) is replaced in the form:

$$E_{el} = \frac{1}{2} Q V = \frac{1}{2} Q \left(\frac{Q}{C} \right) = \frac{Q^2}{2C} \quad (25)$$

When we place a dielectric between the plates of a parallel plate capacitor we change any quantity carrying an ϵ_0 to $\kappa \epsilon_0$ with κ the dielectric constant of the dielectric material. In Eq. (25), the capacitance in the denominator is affected. Identifying the initial state of the capacitor when it is air–filled and the final state when the porcelain is placed between the capacitor plates, we find:

$$C_{init} = \epsilon_0 \frac{A}{b}$$
$$\Downarrow \quad (26)$$
$$C_{fin} = \kappa \epsilon_0 \frac{A}{b} = \kappa C_{init}$$

Thus, Eq. (25) is rewritten for the capacitor with the porcelain in the form:

$$E_{el,\,fin} = \frac{1}{\kappa} E_{el,\,init} = \frac{1.06 \times 10^{-9} [J]}{6.5}$$

$$\Rightarrow \quad E_{el,\,fin} = 1.6 \times 10^{-10} \, J \quad (27)$$

in which the dielectric constant for porcelain is taken from Table 13.3.

Note that the energy with the porcelain slab is less than the energy without it. The energy difference got dissipated into the porcelain slab.

Example 13.4
Determine for a resting nerve,
(a) the capacitance per unit area of membrane, and
(b) the areal charge density on the nerve membrane in unit [Cb/m²].
Hint: Use the dielectric constant from Table 13.3.

Solution part (a): For the capacitance per unit area we find from Eq. (21):

$$\frac{C}{A} = \frac{\kappa \epsilon_0}{b} = \frac{7.0 \cdot 8.854 \times 10^{-12} \left[\frac{Cb^2}{Nm^2}\right]}{6 \cdot 10^{-9} \, [m]} \quad (28)$$

$$\frac{C}{A} = 0.01 \, \frac{F}{m^2}$$

in which b is the membrane thickness of 6 nm and in which the unit [Cb²/Nm³] is equivalent to the unit [F/m²] since [J/Cb] = [V], [Nm] = [J] and [F] = [Cb/V]. Because we haven't discussed many other capacitance values, such a number may mean little. However, from Q = CV we know that a smaller capacitance implies that a smaller charge supports a given potential. We also know that the capacitance is inversely proportional to b, C ∝ 1/b. Later in this chapter we will discuss differences between myelinated and unmyelinated nerves. The myelinated nerves have a membrane that is 300 times thicker (the axon membrane and the myelin sheath together); consequently, they have a significantly smaller capacitance than the unmyelinated nerves. This means that myelinated nerves maintain the same –70 mV potential with significantly smaller charge densities. Operating with a lower number of ions allows for a higher signal speed in myelinated nerves.

Solution part (b): Next we determine the areal charge density on the resting nerve membrane. Starting with Eq. (9.38) and using the electric field across the membrane from Eq. (19) as 1.17×10^7 V/m we find:

$$\sigma = \kappa \epsilon_0 |E| =$$

$$7.0 \cdot 8.85 \times 10^{-12} \left[\frac{Cb^2}{Nm^2}\right] 1.17 \times 10^7 \left[\frac{V}{m}\right] \quad (29)$$

$$\Rightarrow \sigma = 7 \times 10^{-4} \left[\frac{Cb}{m^2}\right]$$

We want to interpret this value a little bit further. The Na⁺, K⁺ and Cl⁻ ions at the nerve membrane are all singly charged, i.e., they carry an elementary charge $e = \pm 1.6 \times 10^{-19}$ Cb. The number of ionized particles per unit area on the nerve membrane, c_{ions}, can therefore be determined as follows:

$$c_{ions} \left[\frac{ions}{m^2}\right] = \frac{\sigma \, [Cb/m^2]}{e \, [Cb/ion]} = \quad (30)$$

$$\frac{7 \times 10^{-4} [Cb/m^2]}{1.6 \times 10^{-19} [Cb/ion]} = 4.4 \times 10^{15} \, \frac{ions}{m^2}$$

This ion concentration is small when compared with the density of atoms at the surface of the nerve membrane, which is about 10^{20} atoms/m²: only one in every 20,000 sites on the membrane is occupied by an ion.

In a hospital or at an emergency scene patients are often revived with a defibrillator machine. How does this machine work?

While the amount of charge stored in a large capacitor is sufficient to kill a person, the flow of these charges through the heart can under appropriate conditions save the life of a heart attack victim. Fibrillation means that the heart produces a rapid, out–of–control pattern of heart beats in response to which the heart muscles contract uncoordinated. A fast discharge of electric energy through such a heart is the only medical approach known to date to return the heart to its normal rhythm and thereby to save the patient.

The device designed to allow a controlled discharge from a capacitor through a patient's body is called a defibrillator. They exist in stationary form in hospitals and in portable form carried by emergency medical units. The portable defibrillator consists of a large capacitor and a set of batteries capable of charging that capacitor to a large potential. When the defibrillator is discharged the charge flows through two electrodes (paddles) that are placed on both sides of the patient's chest.

The emergency paramedics has to wait between successive discharges due to the time delay for charging the capacitor (less than a minute). Typical defibrillators have a capacity of about 70 μF, a potential difference of about 5 kV and thus an electric potential energy of $E_{el} = \frac{1}{2}CV^2 = 875$ J. In an emergency discharge, about 200 J of this energy flow through the heart of the patient, carried by an impulse of about 2 ms duration.

The time which elapses between the occurrence of fibrillation and the application of the defibrillator is critical: if the response time is between 6 and 10 minutes, typically only 8 % of the patients survive. With response times of about 3 minutes, the survival rate can be improved to about 20 %. To shorten the response time, semi–automatic defibrillators have been developed which release an electroshock only after positively identifying fibrillation. Such instruments can in principle be operated by untrained personnel and have been installed in casinos (Las Vegas) and department stores and subway stations (Germany). As such instruments become more common, some basic training with respect to the placement of the electrodes, is beneficial: with the casino personnel in Las Vegas trained a survival rate of 80 % of cases occurring in the casino was achieved!

13.4. Moving charges in a resting nerve

Let us take another look at the non–equilibrium model for the nerve membrane shown in Fig. 13.8. A capacitor model is not quite sufficient because there is a continuous flow of charges across the membrane, as discussed in section 13.2. This is schematically shown in panel (a) of Fig. 13.14. In addition to the charge separation onto the two surfaces of the membrane, a continuous leakage of charges across the membrane must be taken into account. The relevant processes are modelled by their respective electric counterparts in panel (b) of Fig. 13.14. Shown is the parallel plate capacitor with capacitance C and surface charges ±Q, establishing an electric potential difference ΔV. In addition, a flow of charges across the membrane occurs, defined as a current I_m (the index m stands for membrane). To allow charges to flow, an electrically conducting connection between the plates of the capacitor must exist. This cannot be a simple conductor, however, as this would short–circuit the capacitor, which means that all charges would flow across the capacitor gap and neutralize (destroy) the nerve. Thus, along the electric connection between the capacitor plates must lie a resistor R_m, as shown.

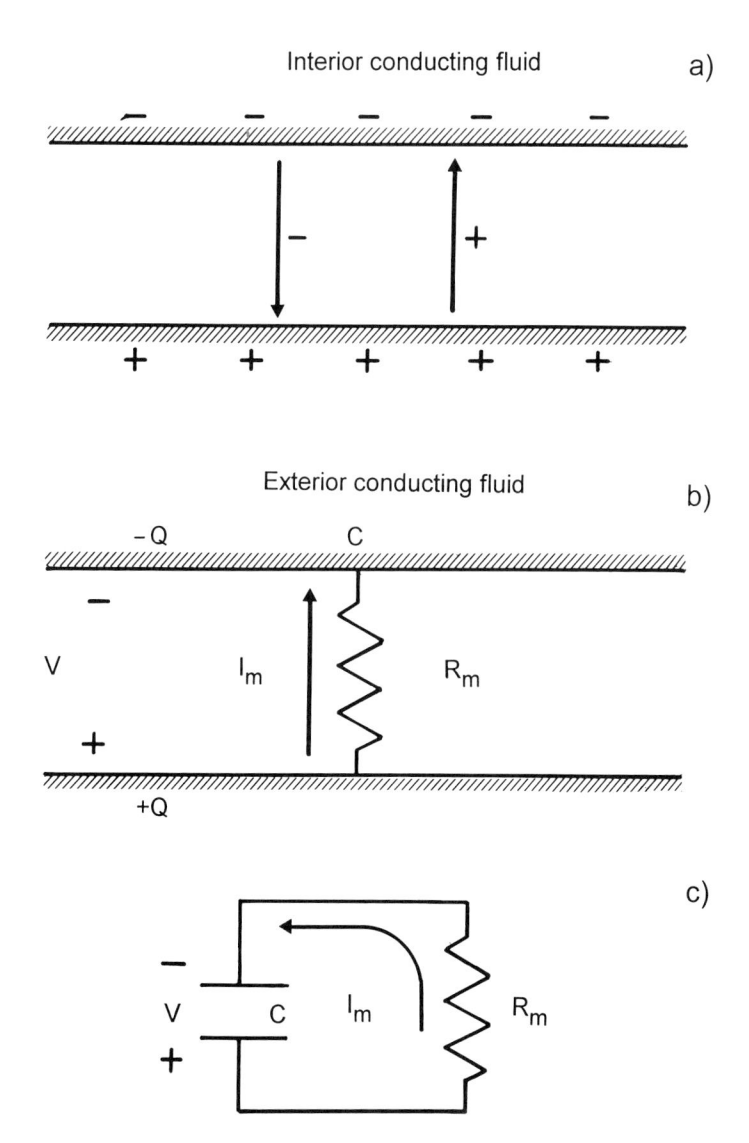

Fig. 13.14: Model for the passive processes in a nerve membrane. (a) A real nerve is not a perfect capacitor as ions continuously flow across the membrane, leading to a leakage current. (b) This phenomenon is modelled electrically by introducing a conducting connection across the membrane. This connection has a resistance R_m leading to a leakage current of I_m. (c) The electric model, as sketched in panel (b), is equivalent to an electric circuit, which we are able to analyze.

Finally, in panel (c) of Fig. 13.14 these electric elements are arranged to form a circuit.

To understand the dynamic properties of charges moving across the membrane in a resting nerve, we have to establish two new concepts in this section: (I) the electric current and (II) the electric resistance.

13.4.1. Electric current

The flow of charge is called an electric current. To introduce the concept of electric current, we return to our physical model of an electron in a metal which we introduced in section 9.2. We may consider for example a good conductor, such as copper. As discussed for Fig. 9.9, such a metal consists of a lattice of stationary, positive rump ions and a mobile sea of very loosely bound electrons. In such a system, the electrons are moving continuously on a microscopic length scale similar to molecules in a stationary gas, but the electrons remain near their respective rump ions on a macroscopic scale.

An electric current is established when these electrons move collectively in a common direction. This requires an electric force acting on the electrons. Such a force causes an acceleration of each electron according to the equation of motion (Newton's second law), F = ma. Surprisingly, we will find that this leads only to very small drift speeds in metallic conductors, e.g. the electrons in household wires typically move at 0.1 mm/s!

This small velocity will allow us to use the model we develop for the electric current to describe also the motion of ions in a solution when an electrochemical force is applied, e.g. in a battery where anions and cations drift toward opposite electrodes or in the resting nerve shown in Fig. 13.14.

> *An electric current I is defined as the amount of charge transferred through an area A per time unit.*

This definition of the current is given in equation form:

$$I\ [A] = \frac{\Delta Q}{\Delta t} \left[\frac{Cb}{s}\right] \quad (31)$$

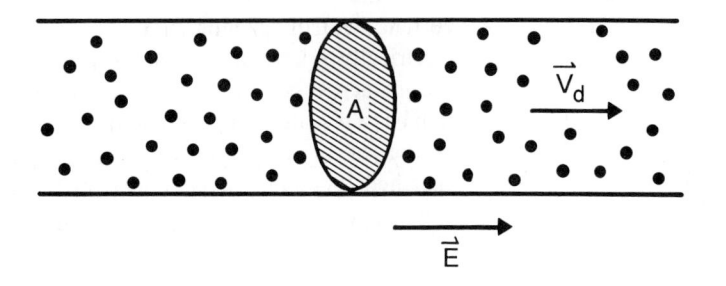

The unit of current is Ampère [A], named for André Marie Ampère. We note that the unit [A] is the electric unit considered a fundamental standard (SI) unit because the current I can easily be measured using the same instrument we mentioned as a voltmeter, now rearranged as an Ampère–meter. Thus, it is preferable to define the unit of the current as a fundamental unit and the unit of the charge, [Cb], as a derived unit.

The actual speed of charges in a piece of metal with an applied electric field is determined using Fig. 13.15. The figure shows a cylindrical conducting wire along the x-axis with a cross-sectional area A. For simplicity we assume that the positively charged particles are mobile within the metal, i.e., they move toward the right if an electric field is applied as shown. Note that this is a conventional choice. Instead, we could have chosen to consider the negatively charged particles as the moving particles because each type of particles is moving relative to the other. A consequence of the convention is that the electrons in a household wire actually move in the opposite direction to the current I.

The density of mobile charges is labelled n with unit [1/m³]. The motion of the charged particles is indicated in Fig. 13.15 by an arrow labelled $\mathbf{v}_d = \Delta \mathbf{x}/\Delta t$, where v_d is the magnitude of the drift velocity with unit [m/s]. By introducing a single drift velocity we assume that the charges move through the wire with an average speed, although they are constantly accelerated by the electric field. This assumption will be justified after the magnitude of the drift velocity is found.

We find the current through area A using Fig. 13.15. During the time interval Δt, all mobile charges which are closer than the distance $|\mathbf{v}_d|\Delta t$ pass through A because charged particles can neither be created nor destroyed in the wire. This defines the volume from which charged particles pass through the area A:

$$\Delta V = A\ \Delta x = A\ v_d\ \Delta t \quad (32)$$

Since each of the charged particles carries an elementary charge e, and the number density of charges is n, a total amount of charge ΔQ passes through the area A during the time interval Δt which is given by:

Fig. 13.15: Simple, atomic scale model for a metallic conductor of cross-sectional area A with an external electric field. In response to the field, positively charged particles move with the drift velocity v_d.

$$\Delta Q = e\, n\, \Delta V = e\, n\, A\, v_d\, \Delta t \quad (33)$$

Now we divide Eq. (33) by Δt to obtain the current:

$$I = \frac{\Delta Q}{\Delta t} = n\, e\, v_d\, A \quad (34)$$

Thus, the current is proportional to the density of mobile charges, the drift velocity and the geometric cross–sectional area of the wire. The density of mobile charges is a materials constant and is a large number for good conductors. I is positive in Eq. (34) for Fig. 13.15.

Due to the dependence on the cross–sectional area, the current is not a parameter characteristic for the conducting material. To classify materials according to their ability to carry electric charges, we define the current density J [A/m²] by dividing Eq. (34) by A:

$$J = \frac{I}{A} = n\, e\, v_d \quad (35)$$

The current density is defined as the current per unit cross–sectional area of the conductor. It is a materials constant.

Although J is a fundamental materials property, many calculations and studies use current instead because the current can be measured directly while the current density can only be calculated from Eq. (35).

Example 13.5
For a typical household copper wire (diameter 1.02 mm) which carries a current of I = 1.67 A, calculate
(a) the current density J, and
(b) the drift velocity v_d.
Use for the density of mobile electrons in copper the value n = 8.5×10^{28} m^{-3}.

Solution part (a): First we need to calculate the cross–sectional area of the wire:

$$A = \pi r^2 = \pi \left(\frac{d}{2}\right)^2 = \frac{\pi}{4}(1.02 \times 10^{-3}[m])^2 \quad (36)$$

$$\Rightarrow A = 8.2 \times 10^{-7}\, m^2$$

With this value, Eq. (35) provides the current density:

$$J = \frac{I}{A} = \frac{1.67\,[A]}{8.2 \times 10^{-7}[m^2]} = 2 \times 10^6\, \frac{A}{m^2} \quad (37)$$

Solution part (b): The drift velocity follows from the last term in Eq. (35):

$$v_d = \frac{J}{n\, e} = \frac{2 \times 10^6 \left[\frac{A}{m^2}\right]}{8.5 \times 10^{28}\left[\frac{1}{m^3}\right] 1.6 \times 10^{-19}[Cb]} \quad (38)$$

which leads to:

$$v_d = 1.5 \times 10^{-4}\, m/s = 0.15\, mm/s \quad (39)$$

A drift velocity of 0.15 mm/s for electrons in a metal wire is a surprisingly small value when we think for example of turning on a light switch and the light fixture operates immediately, despite a distance of several meters between the switch and the light fixture. The explanation of this apparent paradox is evident from Fig. 13.15. All throughout the wire, the same density of mobile electrons is present. When closing the switch, a continuous line of conductive electrons is created from the power plant through the switch and the light fixture, back to the power plant. The power plant causes an electric field in this loop and all electrons start simultaneously to drift along the loop with 0.15 mm/s. Thus, the light fixture operates due to the motion of electrons in the fixture and not the flow of electrons from the switch to the light fixture.

Fig. 13.15 also explain why each electron drifts at such a small speed through the wire. The electric field causes a significant acceleration of the electron. However, before the electron can pick up any significant speed it is scattered by one of the positive rump ions in the metal. Since the electron is much lighter than the rump ion, the impact causes the electron to bounce backwards. It has to slow down and then accelerate again in the direction of the field, only to be scattered again almost immediately by the same rump ion or by one close by. The progress of the electron resembles that of an aggressive Porsche driver during rush hour in downtown Manhattan!

13.4.2. Resistivity and resistance

The electric potential or the electric current are not sufficient to characterize the flux of charges. To see why, we compare the flow of charges with the flow of fluids. For fluids we identified the pressure difference along a tube as the cause of fluid flow. The flow (fluid volume per time unit through the tube) is then related to the pressure difference by the linear equation $\Delta p = R(\Delta V/\Delta t)$ in which R is the flow resistance, which in turn is proportional to the viscosity of the fluid.

A resistance against the flow of charges through a wire is needed to relate current and potential difference in the same fashion. This can be confirmed experimentally. Eq. (34) does not contain the length of the wire, yet, when connecting a light bulb to a battery (which provides a given potential difference) with variable lengths of wires, the bulb is brighter for the shorter wires. Comparing this situation to that for the flow of fluids, we find that the flow resistance in Eq. (11.29) introduces a length dependence. We expect the length dependence in the electric experiment to be caused by an electric flow resistance in the same fashion.

In this section we define two types of flow resistance for the electric flow of charges. One is the *resistivity* ρ, and the other is the *resistance* R. This is due to the same distinction between fundamental materials properties and experimentally observable quantities we noted before for the current density J and the current I.

Resistivity
We observe a current density when we apply an electric field across a piece of conducting material. If the electric field is not too large, the current density increases proportional to the electric field, as illustrated in Fig. 13.16. The slope of the curve in Fig. 13.16 is constant and defines the resistivity ρ. Thus, the data in Fig. 13.16 can be written in the form (Ohm's law):

$$|E| = \rho \cdot J \qquad (40)$$

which has been named for Georg Simon Ohm.

> *The resistivity is the proportionality factor between the magnitude of the electric field, which causes charges to move, and the current density, which represents the flow of charges.*

Both the electric field **E** and the current density **J** are not directly measurable, and thus, the resistivity ρ is also not a quantity we can measure.

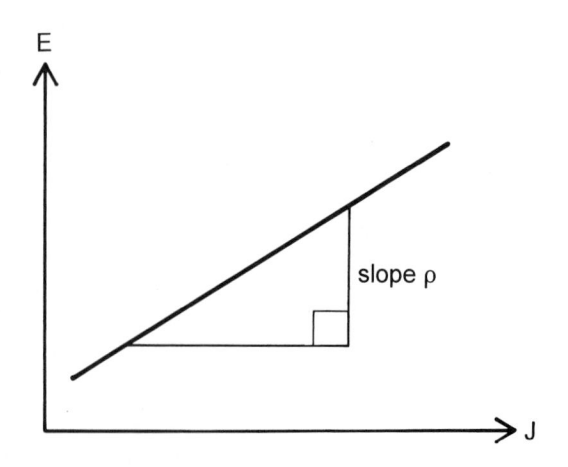

Fig. 13.16: Illustration of Ohm's law: the magnitude of the electric field is proportional to the current density with the slope defining the resistivity ρ.

Technically, Eq. (40) should be written as a vector equation, but we have not introduced the current density as a vector and thus limit the discussion to the scalar form given in Eq. (40). If we extend the experiment to much larger electric fields or to other materials classes, such as semiconductors, we note that Ohm's law does not apply universally: the current density in those cases is not linearly proportional to the applied electric field. We confine our discussion to cases in which the relation between electric field and current density is linear, i.e., follows Ohm's law. The material is then said to behave "ohmic".

The unit of the resistivity follows from Eq. (40) as $[(V/m)/(A/m^2)] = [Vm/A]$. For the ratio Volt to Ampère a new unit is introduced, called the *Ohm* which is abbreviated by the Greek letter Ω. Thus, the unit of the resistivity is $[\Omega m]$. The resistivity is a materials constant with an extremely wide range of values, as illustrated in Table 13.4. At temperatures below 90 K, some materials become superconductors, i.e., perfect conductors in which the flow of charges encounters no resistivity at all, $\rho = 0\ \Omega m$. On the other side, good insulators have extremely large resistivities against charge conduction. At room temperature, resistivities cover a range of 22 orders of magnitude.

Of particular interest is the value of the resistivity for the axoplasm and nerve membranes. The axoplasm is a decent conductor with a resistivity of $1.1\ \Omega m$. For the resistivity of the nerve membrane, a value measured for thin, artificial lipid membranes was initially proposed: $\rho = 1 \times 10^{13}\ \Omega m$. This is a very high value which would make the mechanism of impulse transport in nerves as we describe it later impossible. Luckily, the actual nerve membrane contains additional

Table 13.4: Resistivity values for various materials

Material	Resistivity [Ωm]
Insulators and semiconductors:	
Yellow sulfur	2.0×10^{15}
Artificial lipid membrane	1.0×10^{13}
Quartz	1.0×10^{13}
Nerve membrane	1.6×10^{7}
Silicon	2.5×10^{3}
Axoplasm	1.1×10^{0}
Germanium	5.0×10^{-1}
Metals:	
Mercury	1.0×10^{-6}
Iron	1.0×10^{-7}
Gold	2.4×10^{-8}
Copper	1.7×10^{-8}

proteins which reduce the resistivity significantly to $\rho = 1.6 \times 10^7$ Ωm. The nerve membrane thus remains an insulator, allowing us to use the capacitor model developed in Fig. 13.14.

Resistance
Resistance is used instead of resistivity when an actual conductor is described rather than a generic property of a material. To define resistance, we revisit Eq. (40). To make this equation more accessible to measurement, the electric field is replaced by the potential and the current density is replaced by the current:

$$|E| = \rho J \quad \Rightarrow \quad \frac{V}{l} = \rho \frac{I}{A} \quad (41)$$

in which we used the definition of the current density from Eq. (35). Next, the various parameters in Eq. (41) are grouped such that a new materials constant R is introduced as the proportionality factor of electric potential and electric current:

$$V = \frac{\rho l}{A} I = R I$$

$$\text{with} \quad R = \frac{\rho l}{A} \quad (42)$$

> *The resistance is the proportionality factor of potential and current for a given conductor. It increases with increasing length and decreases with increasing cross–sectional area of the conductor.*

The unit of the resistance R is [V/A] = [Ω]. Eq. (42) is also called Ohm's law.

Why did we use the formula for the potential of a capacitor, Eq. (9.58), to convert the electric field to the potential? Consider Fig. 13.15 once more. A wire can be considered to be a long (very poor) dielectric between two charged plates placed at its ends. Thus, the electric field equals the potential divided by the length of the conductor, l.

Conductivity
The last quantity we introduce in this context is the conductivity γ. The conductivity is simply defined as the inverse value of the resistivity: $\gamma = 1/\rho$ [1/Ωm]. It is used when we prefer to think in quantities describing the current passing through a resistor rather than in terms of hindrance to the motion of charges.

Example 13.6
Considering again the household copper wire of Example 13.5, find
(a) the electric field,
(b) the potential difference over 50 m along the wire,
(c) and the resistance of the same 50 m of wire.
Note: in Example 13.5 we found for the cross–sectional area a value of $A = 8.2 \times 10^{-7}$ m² and for the current density $J = 2 \times 10^6$ A/m² with the given current 1.67 A. The resistivity of copper is $\rho = 1.72 \times 10^{-8}$ Ωm (see Table 13.4).

Solution part (a): the electric field is calculated from Eq. (40):

$$|E| = \rho J = 1.72 \times 10^{-8} [\Omega m] \ 2 \times 10^6 [A/m^2]$$
$$\Rightarrow \quad |E| = 0.034 \ V/m \quad (43)$$

Solution part (b): For 50 m of copper wire, we use the potential formula for a parallel plate arrangement, Eq. (9.58), to find:

$$V = |E| l = 0.034 \left[\frac{V}{m}\right] 50 [m] = 1.7 \ V \quad (44)$$

Solution part (c): The resistance can be obtained in two different ways. One possibility is to use Ohm's law (Eq. (42)):

$$R = \frac{V}{I} = \frac{1.7\,[V]}{1.67\,[A]} = 1.0\,\Omega \qquad (45)$$

A second way is to use the definition of the resistance in Eq. (42):

$$R = \frac{\rho l}{A} = \frac{1.72\times 10^{-8}[\Omega m]\ 50[m]}{8.2\times 10^{-7}[m^2]} \qquad (46)$$

$$\Rightarrow R = 1.0\,\Omega$$

Example 13.7

(a) Calculate the resistance along an axon 1 cm long with a radius of 4 μm.
(b) Repeat the same calculation for an axon radius of 400 μm.
Hint: Use the resistivity value for the axoplasm from Table 13.4.

Solution part (a): For the axoplasm of the axon in this problem we know from Table 13.4 that the resistivity is $\rho = 1.1\,\Omega m$. The cylindrical axon has a cross–sectional area $A = \pi r^2$ with the radius given as $r = 4.0 \times 10^{-6}$ m. For a length of $l = 1.0 \times 10^{-2}$ m we find for the resistance:

$$R = \frac{\rho l}{A} = \frac{1.1[\Omega m]\ 1\times 10^{-2}[m]}{\pi\,(4\cdot 10^{-6}[m])^2} \qquad (47)$$

$$\Rightarrow R = 2.2 \times 10^8\,\Omega = 220\,M\Omega$$

Solution part (b): The only change in the second part of the problem is the modified radius of $r = 4.0 \times 10^{-4}$ m, thus leading to a changed resistance of:

$$R = \frac{\rho l}{A} = \frac{1.1[\Omega m]\ 1\times 10^{-2}[m]}{\pi\,(4\times 10^{-4}[m])^2} \qquad (48)$$

$$\Rightarrow R = 2.2 \times 10^4\,\Omega = 22\,k\Omega$$

A bigger nerve leads to a lesser resistance of the axoplasm.

13.4.3. The signal decay time of a resting nerve

We are now in a position to analyze the electric model of a resting nerve in Fig. 13.14. Qualitatively, we expect that the membrane, acting as a resistor, allows the separated charges to recombine, thus neutralizing the capacitor. However, since the resistivity of the nerve membrane is quite high, it might be the case that the recombination is a slow process which can be neglected. The aim of this section is therefore to establish the time it takes to neutralize the nerve membrane electrically, which is called the decay time of the nerve. Note that Fig. 13.14 does not include the active effect of the Na/K pump but shows only the passive processes.

We obtain the decay time by combining the three equations which govern the motion of charges through the membrane in Fig. 13.14:

(I) The amount of charge on the plates varies when an electric current flows according to Eq. (31):

$$\frac{\Delta Q}{\Delta t} = -I_m \qquad (49)$$

in which I_m is the current across the membrane. Note the minus sign on the right hand side of Eq. (49). A positive current I_m means that the number of uncompensated charges Q on both sides of the membrane in Fig. 13.14 diminishes, i.e., $\Delta Q/\Delta t$ is negative.

(II) A change of the number of charges also leads to a change of the capacitor properties of the nerve membrane. We use Eq. (20), replacing the charge in that equation by the time change of the charge:

$$\frac{\Delta Q}{\Delta t} = \frac{\Delta(CV)}{\Delta t} = C\,\frac{\Delta V}{\Delta t} \qquad (50)$$

In the second step in Eq. (50) the capacitance has been separated because we know that capacitance values do not change with time.

(III) The actual flow of charges across the membrane due to its resistance is governed by Ohm's law in the form introduced in Eq. (42):

$$I_m = \frac{V}{R_m} \qquad (51)$$

in which R_m is the resistance of the nerve membrane.

The three equations, Eqs. (49), (50) and (51), are combined to eliminate the charge and the current and provide us with an equation for the time change of the potential across the membrane. This is mathematically achieved in two steps.

Combining first Eq. (49) and Eq. (50) to eliminate the charge term $\Delta Q/\Delta t$, we obtain:

$$-I_m = C \frac{\Delta V}{\Delta t} \quad (52)$$

Next we use Eq. (51) to eliminate the current in Eq. (52):

$$\frac{\Delta V}{\Delta t} = -\frac{1}{R_m C} V \quad (53)$$

We find this type of a mathematical equation frequently in physics: an equation that combines a parameter (here the potential) with its change as a function of time in a linear fashion, $\Delta V/\Delta t \propto V$. You will find similar equations often in the life sciences, including population growth studies (epidemiology) and applications of radioactive decay (radiology). For this reason, we want to study the equation in more detail while continuing our discussion of the time dependence of the nerve potential.

What does Eq. (53) imply? The rate of change of the potential is proportional to the potential at each time instant. Due to the negative sign on the right hand side of Eq. (53), the potential change is a reduction (potential decay). Therefore, the higher the potential at a given time, the higher the rate of decay of the potential. Since the potential decay and the potential itself are proportional, we know that the mathematical function describing the potential decay must be the same as the function describing the potential itself. There is only one mathematical function with this property: the exponential function. This leads to:

$$V(t) = V_{initial} \exp\left[-\frac{t}{R_m C}\right] \quad (54)$$

$$\text{with} \quad \tau = R_m C$$

Eq. (54) is often written in the form:

$$V(t) = V_{initial} \, e^{-t/\tau} \quad (55)$$

$V_{initial}$ is the potential at the time t = 0, which is $V_{initial}$ = − 70 mV for a life nerve cell. In Eq. (54), we have introduced τ as a new parameter. The unit of τ is [s], thus τ is a time constant. We find out what happens at time τ by substituting $t = \tau$ in Eqs. (54) or (55): $V(\tau) = V_{initial}/e$ with e the Euler number. This means that the potential drops to $1/e \approx 37$ % of the initial potential after this time. After 2τ the potential drops to about 14 % and after 3τ to about 5 %. Thus, τ is a measure of the time to observe a significant but not yet total decay.

The definition of τ in Eq. (54), $\tau = R_m C$, is however not quite satisfactory. The membrane resistance is a quantity which depends on an arbitrary reference area (e.g. 1 m²). It is preferable to replace the resistance with the resistivity as this quantity contains only fundamental properties of the nerve membrane material. We use therefore Eqs. (28) and (42) to rewrite τ:

$$\tau = R_m C = \frac{\rho_m b}{A} \frac{\kappa \epsilon_0 A}{b} = \kappa \epsilon_0 \rho_m \quad (56)$$

Thus, the decay time constant is indeed a fundamental quantity. It does not even depend on the thickness of the membrane, b. We therefore conclude that nature did not invent the myelinated nerve to vary the decay time, since the main difference between myelinated and unmyelinated nerves is the membrane thickness b. Using Eq. (56) we quantify the time constant τ for a nerve:

$$\tau = 7 \cdot 8.85 \times 10^{-12} \left[\frac{Cb^2}{Nm^2}\right] 1.6 \times 10^7 [\Omega m] \quad (57)$$

$$\Rightarrow \quad \tau = 1.0 \times 10^{-3} \, s = 1.0 \, ms$$

Thus, the potential of a nerve tends to decay in the very short time of 1 millisecond! The Na/K pump prevents this, consuming energy (provided by ATP molecules) to maintain a steady state. We note again how thin a line nature has drawn between life and death: we are within a micrometer of suffocating with the given width of the membrane between alveoli and pulmonary blood capillaries, and we are always a millisecond away from a catastrophic failure of our nervous system!

13.5. Stimulated nerve impulses

Having sufficiently characterized the resting nerve, we next consider the response of the nerve to a stimulus. An impulse is triggered when an external stimulus causes the electric potential of a nerve to collapse momentarily at the stimulated point (usually a dendritic receptor). We will study two basic types of response:

(I) In *electrotonus spread* or *passive spread* the nerve membrane behaves ohmically, i.e., the resistivity of the membrane remains constant. This model is valid for smaller potential changes. We will find that the electrotonus spread alone is not sufficient to explain impulse transport in unmyelinated nerves. However, this mechanism still plays an important role in the propagation of nerve impulses.

(II) The *Hodgkin–Huxley model* is based on experimental evidence, originally obtained by Alan Lloyd Hodgkin and Andrew Fielding Huxley. Their observations of the nerve impulse transport in an unmyelinated nerve showed that a significant variation in the permeability of the membrane occurs during a potential change. This causes a non–Ohmic, non–linear dependence of the membrane current I_m on the potential V. We will see in section 13.5.2 that the Hodgkin–Huxley model is sufficient to explain the nerve impulse transport in unmyelinated nerves.

13.5.1. Electrotonus spread

Let us assume a localized drop in the potential difference across an unmyelinated nerve membrane as shown in Fig. 13.17. To quantify the response to such a small potential difference, we assume that the membrane resistivity does not change, i.e., that the membrane acts as a resistor obeying Ohm's law (Eq. (42)). The response of the nerve to a potential perturbation in this case is described in two ways: as a function of time and as a function of distance from the perturbation along the nerve.

Response as a function of time
We established in the previous sections that a resting nerve has a potential $V_{rest} = -70$ mV and is thermodynamically in a steady state due to the continuous operation of the Na/K pump. In Chapter 8 we noted that steady states are stable near the equilibrium. This is the case here since Ohm's law applies in the linear non–equilibrium regime. The system returns to the steady state in response to a perturbation $\Delta V_{init} = V_p - V_{rest}$ with V_p the potential of the perturbation. This electrotonus response is quantitatively described in the same fashion we derived Eq. (57) from Eq. (54), except that the potential does not drop to zero this time but returns back to the steady state value of -70 mV. Therefore, a perturbation diminishes as a function of time as:

$$\Delta V = \Delta V_{init}\, e^{-\frac{t}{\tau}} \qquad (58)$$

$$\text{with} \quad \tau = \kappa\epsilon_0 \rho_m \approx 1.0\ ms$$

This potential change as a function of time is shown in the top panel of Fig. 13.18. The perturbation reduces to $1/e \approx 37\%$ of its initial value after time τ.

Response as a function of distance to the perturbation
To evaluate the spatial spread of a localized perturbation we assume that the perturbation itself is kept fixed, i.e., that the potential deviation ΔV_{init} from -70 mV at the place of the perturbation does not change with time. Consider, for example, the case qualitatively shown in Fig. 13.19. There is a potential of -65 mV on the inside (axoplasm) of the membrane and a potential of -5 mV on the outside of the membrane (extracellular fluid). This means that $\Delta V_{init} = 10$ mV. Because this potential difference is maintained, mobile charges in the vicinity of the perturbation respond. As indicated in Fig. 13.19, positive charges move toward the greater negative potential of the perturbation on the interstitium side, causing a current I_{int} toward the perturbation, and negative charges move toward the greater positive potential of the perturbation on the axoplasm side, causing a current I_{ax} along the nerve away from the perturbation. The latter current is in the direction away from the perturbation since we defined a current to be in the direction of moving positive charges (see section 13.4.1). The currents along the axoplasm or the extracellular fluid flow much easier than a current across the membrane as the resistivity of these fluids is about 7 orders of magnitude

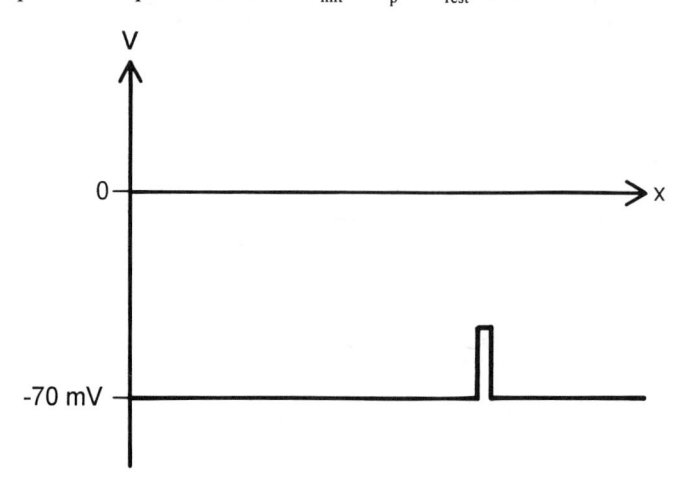

Fig. 13.17: Sketch of a localized, minor perturbation in the electric potential along a nerve cell.

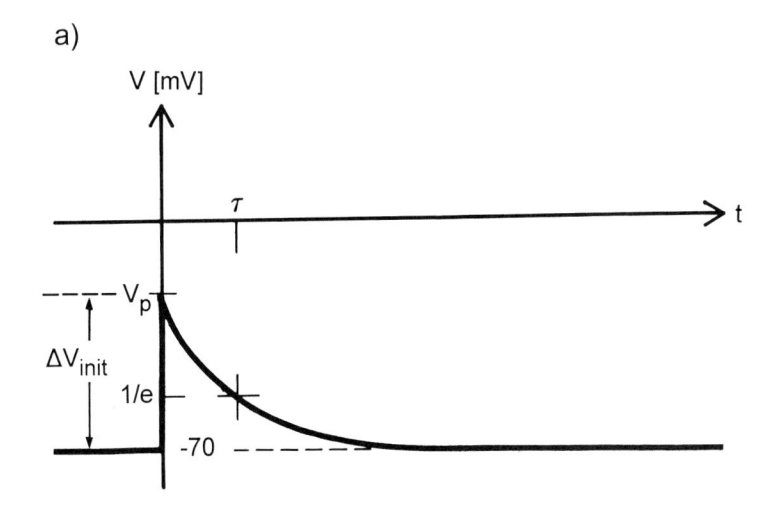

Fig. 13.18: The electrotonus spread for the perturbation in Fig. 13.17 (a) as a function of time, and (b) as a function of distance from the perturbation along the nerve cell. When a small perturbation in the electric potential of a nerve occurs at time t = 0, this perturbation disappears with a time constant τ. A fixed perturbation leads to an exponentially decreasing potential profile along the nerve with a decay length λ. V_p is the potential of the perturbation, $V_{rest} = -70$ mV is the potential of a resting nerve, and $\Delta V_{init} = V_p - V_{rest}$.

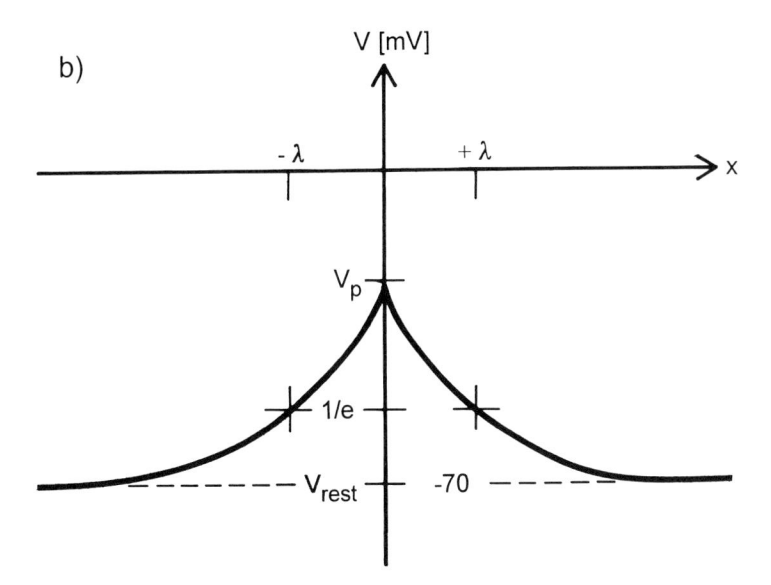

Fig. 13.19: The motion of charged particles and the corresponding electric currents along a nerve cell in response to a potential perturbation occurring between the dashed lines. I_{in} is the current in the interstitium and I_{ax} is the current in the axoplasm.

lower than that of the membrane (see Table 13.4). As charges move along the nerve membrane, the potential perturbation broadens spatially.

It is of interest to see what final potential distribution results from this broadening. In particular, does the perturbation broaden as much as several tens of centimeters to a meter? If so, electrotonus spread would be sufficient to transport a signal (i.e., the potential perturbation) from the dendrite to the synapse of the nerve, and thus to the brain. Instead of fully quantifying the case of electrotonus spread, we study a semi–quantitative model which is sufficient to understand the important aspects.

The model is based on Fig. 13.20, which illustrates in the top sketch the directions and the amounts of charges flowing near the membrane surface in the interstitium when a final, time–independent potential profile is reached, as shown in the lower part of the figure. An equivalent model with currents in the opposite directions can be sketched on the axoplasm side of the nerve membrane.

We consider in Fig. 13.20 three arbitrarily chosen zones, each with a width of Δx. For the zone directly adjacent to the perturbation area, a large deviation of the potential from the steady state value of -70 mV causes the Na/K pump to produce a strong net flow of charges across the membrane. This is indicated by a pair of vertical arrows with the arrow directed upwards drawn much stronger than the arrow downwards. To maintain a potential difference of less than -70 mV across the membrane in this zone a larger amount of charge must flow out of the Δx–zone along the nerve membrane (in Fig. 13.20 horizontally toward the left into the perturbation) compared to the amount of charge entering the Δx–zone along the nerve membrane from the right.

Δx–zones further away from the perturbation, such as the one shown at the center of Fig. 13.20, maintain a potential difference closer to -70 mV because only fewer charges can flow toward the perturbation zone. Lastly, considering a Δx–zone far away from the perturbation, no net flow occurs through the membrane, i.e., the charge exchange across the membrane is balanced as indicated by a pair of equally strong vertical arrows.

The diminishing potential difference with distance from the perturbation is shown in the bottom panel of Fig. 13.18 and is quantified by the formula:

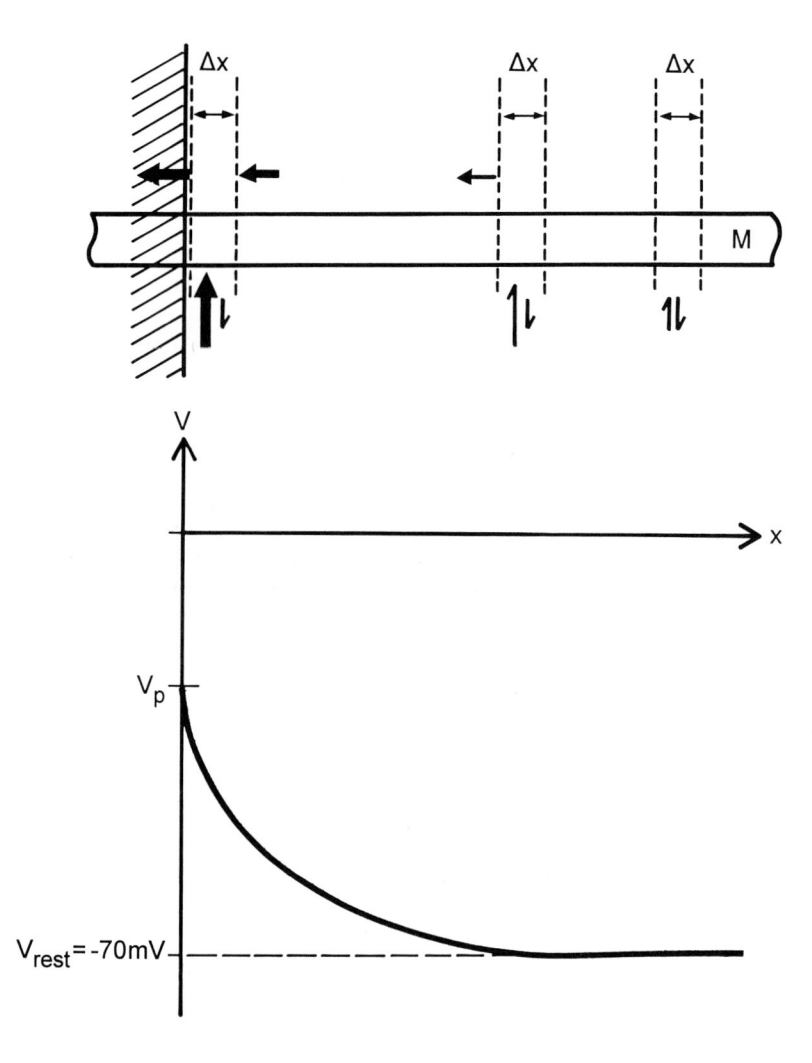

Fig. 13.20: Illustration of the mechanism by which the electrotonus spread along the nerve cell is maintained for a constant perturbation. Both, charge flow across and along the nerve membrane are required.

$$\Delta V(x) = \Delta V(x=0)\, e^{-x/\lambda}$$

$$\text{with} \quad \lambda = \sqrt{\frac{a\,b}{2}\,\frac{\rho_m}{\rho_{ax}}} \tag{59}$$

in which the x–axis is defined along the nerve and the perturbation is located at x = 0. The constant λ has unit [m] and is called a decay length. As the second line of Eq. (59) shows, λ depends on the axon radius, a, the membrane thickness, b, the resistivity of the membrane, ρ_m, and the resistivity of the axoplasm, ρ_{ax}. λ is called a decay length since the perturbation ΔV has dropped to $1/e \approx 37\%$ of its original value at that distance.

Example 13.8

Calculate the decay length for an unmyelinated nerve.

Solution: We use the second line of Eq. (59). The resistivities in the equation are obtained from Table 13.4, the membrane thickness and axon diameter are given in Table 13.1. We choose b = 6 nm and a = 0.6 μm, i.e., values for a large human unmyelinated nerve:

$$\lambda = \sqrt{\frac{6\times 10^{-7}[m]\; 6\times 10^{-9}[m]\; 1\times 10^{7}[\Omega m]}{2\cdot 1.1[\Omega m]}} \tag{60}$$

$$\lambda = 1.28 \times 10^{-4}\ m = 0.13\ mm$$

This mechanism cannot carry a nerve impulse along an entire nerve with l_{nerve} about 10 to 100 cm because the electrotonus spread has a decay length of less than a millimeter.

Example 13.9

In the literature, you find axoplasm resistivities reported from $\rho_{ax} = 0.5\ \Omega m$ to $1.1\ \Omega m$. We want to test what consequence this variability of the value has.
(a) By how much does the time constant for electrotonus spread vary?
(b) Assuming a perturbation changing the potential across a nerve membrane from -70 mV to -60 mV. What is the potential difference across a nerve with axoplasm resistivity of $0.5\ \Omega m$ at the same distance from the perturbation at which the potential has fallen to 20 % for a nerve with axoplasm resistivity of $1.1\ \Omega m$?

Solution part (a): There is no change since the time constant τ does not depend on ρ_{ax}.

Solution part (b): The bottom of Fig. 13.18 illustrates the case discussed in the second part of the problem. The resting nerve potential has the value of -70 mV. The change to -60 mV represents a perturbation of 10 mV. This perturbation of the potential decays toward the resting nerve value with distance from the perturbation as given in Eq. (59).

The example refers to a specific point x_0 along a nerve with axoplasm resistivity of $1.1\ \Omega m$, $\Delta V(x_0) = 0.2\, \Delta V_{max} = 2$ mV. We first determine x_0 for the nerve with the higher axoplasm resistivity $\rho_{high} = 1.1\ \Omega m$. Substituting λ we rewrite Eq. (59):

$$\Delta V(x_0) = \Delta V_{max} \exp\left(-\frac{x_0}{\lambda}\right) =$$

$$= \Delta V_{max} \exp\left(-\frac{x_0}{\sqrt{\dfrac{ab}{2}\dfrac{\rho_m}{\rho_{high}}}}\right) \tag{61}$$

Eq. (61) is solved for x_0:

$$\ln\frac{\Delta V(x_0)}{\Delta V_{max}} = \ln 0.2 = -1.609 = -\frac{x_0}{\lambda}$$

$$\Rightarrow \quad x_0 = 1.609\sqrt{\frac{ab}{2}\frac{\rho_m}{\rho_{high}}} \tag{62}$$

In the second step the potential difference remaining from a 10 mV perturbation is calculated at a distance x_0 from the perturbation for a nerve with the lower value of the axoplasm resistivity, $\rho_{low} = 0.5\ \Omega m$. This is done by substituting the value for x_0 as found in Eq. (62) and the new resistivity ρ_{low} into Eq. (59):

$$\Delta V(x_0) = \Delta V_{max} \exp\left(-\frac{x_0}{\lambda}\right) =$$

$$= 10[mV]\exp\left(-\frac{1.609\sqrt{\dfrac{ab}{2}\dfrac{\rho_m}{\rho_{high}}}}{\sqrt{\dfrac{ab}{2}\dfrac{\rho_m}{\rho_{low}}}}\right) \tag{63}$$

The argument of the exponential function simplifies now greatly, yielding:

$$\Delta V(x_0) = 10[mV] \exp\left(-1.609\sqrt{\frac{\rho_{low}}{\rho_{high}}}\right) \quad (64)$$

$$\Rightarrow \quad \Delta V(x_0) = 3.4 \; mV$$

Thus the potential perturbation has not decayed to a value of 2 mV as before, but only to 3.4 mV at the same distance from the 10 mV perturbation.

13.5.2. Hodgkin–Huxley model

The discussion in section 13.5.1 demonstrated that the electrotonus spread is not sufficient to transport a nerve impulse. Since the electrotonus spread is based on Ohm's law, it is a model which belongs to the linear non–equilibrium regime. In this section, we discuss a more successful model for unmyelinated nerves, the Hodgkin–Huxley model proposed in 1952. The Hodgkin–Huxley model is non–linear, confirming the observation that we made already in previous chapters that phenomena in the biological sciences often include non–linear non–equilibrium concepts.

The Hodgkin–Huxley model was only introduced about fifty years ago because extensive and rather difficult experiments had to be conducted first to put the most important elements of the model in place. The experiments are based on the set–up sketched in Fig. 13.21: two electrodes are inserted into the axoplasm of a nerve and a third electrode runs along the nerve in the extracellular fluid. One of the electrodes inside and the electrode outside are used to measure the potential across the nerve membrane. The way the experiment is then conducted is called a voltage–clamp measurement: the potential between the two electrodes is kept constant by the controller via a feedback connection to a current generator. Whenever a potential change occurs, it is compensated by a current from the current generator, which is sent through the third electrode. Therefore, we can measure the membrane current directly by recording the current output of the current generator.

It is not easy to insert two non–touching electrodes into an axon of a cross–section of 1.5 µm or less. It was only after the discovery of the giant axon of the squid (with diameters of up to 1 mm) in 1936 that experiments with single nerve cells became feasible. However, it is not possible to conduct these experiments on a life squid specimen. Therefore, the next question was whether the nerve could be kept functional after the animal had been destroyed. After dissection, the axoplasm and the extracellular fluid were replaced by various simpler electrolytes. It turned out that the nerve continued to operate for a time period which was sufficient to conduct the experiments that Hodgkin and Huxley had planned.

The most important result of the electrolyte experiments was that the crucial processes in nerve signal propagation occur across the membrane and not within the axoplasm. Therefore, several electrolytes were acceptable, and the ion species that are important for the nerve impulse transport process – sodium, potas-

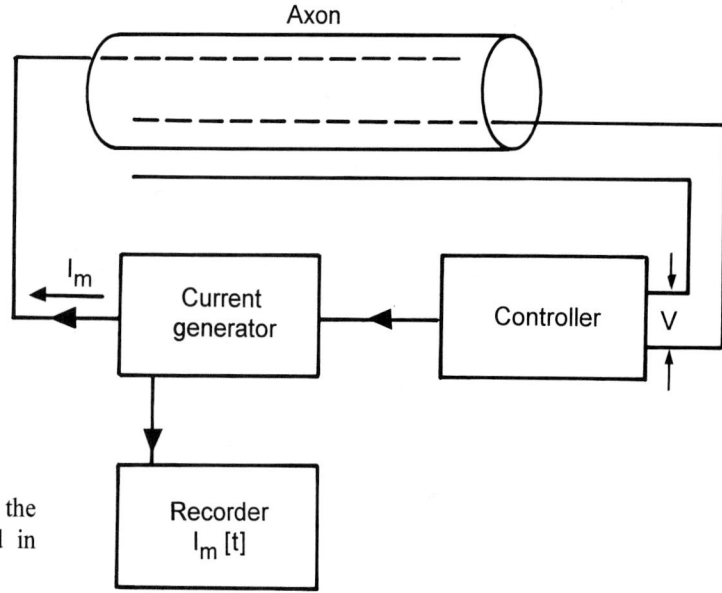

Fig. 13.21: Experimental set–up for the voltage–clamp experiment conducted in 1952 by Hodgkin and Huxley.

sium and chlorine – were identified.

We now study the results of Hodgkin's and Huxley's voltage–clamp experiment. Their experiments showed that only the sodium and potassium contributions have to considered separately, all other ion species can be grouped together. Thus, the current density across the membrane is written as:

$$J_m = J_{Na} + J_K + J_L \quad (65)$$

The label "L" stands for leakage and implies that all other ion species have a fixed resistivity and obey Ohm's law. They therefore establish a leakage current through a fixed resistor in the way presented in Fig. 13.14. The current densities of sodium and potassium, however, respond quite differently because the permeability of these two ion species varies significantly during the transmission of a nerve impulse: J_{Na} and J_K vary on a very short time scale.

The total amount of ions passing through the membrane during a nerve impulse is much smaller than the total amount of charges on either side of the membrane. This is written in the form of an equation as:

$$\frac{\Delta c_{Na+}}{\Delta t} \ll c_{Na+} \quad ; \quad \frac{\Delta c_{K+}}{\Delta t} \ll c_{K+}$$

$$\Downarrow \quad (66)$$

$$c_{Na+, \, interstitium} \cong const \quad ; \quad c_{K+, \, in} \cong const$$
$$c_{Na+, \, axoplasm} \cong const \quad ; \quad c_{K+, \, ax} \cong const$$

This result remains true during the time period when an impulse passes. With Eq. (66) established, it makes sense to define equilibrium potentials for each ion species, using the concentration values from Fig. 13.2 and Nernst's equation (Eq. (10)) at a temperature of 310 K.

(I) We find an equilibrium potential for sodium:

$$\Delta V_{Na+, \, eq} = \frac{kT}{e} \ln\left(\frac{c_{Na+, \, in}}{c_{Na+, \, ax}}\right) =$$

$$\frac{1.38 \times 10^{-23} \left[\frac{J}{K}\right] 310[K]}{1.6 \times 10^{-19}[Cb]} \ln\left(\frac{145 \left[\frac{mmol}{l}\right]}{15 \left[\frac{mmol}{l}\right]}\right) \quad (67)$$

which yields:

$$\Delta V_{Na+, \, eq} = +60 \, mV \quad (68)$$

(II) The equilibrium potential for potassium is:

$$\Delta V_{K+, \, eq} = \frac{kT}{e} \ln\left(\frac{c_{K+, \, in}}{c_{K+, \, ax}}\right) =$$

$$\frac{1.38 \times 10^{-23} \left[\frac{J}{K}\right] 310[K]}{1.6 \times 10^{-19}[Cb]} \ln\left(\frac{5 \left[\frac{mmol}{l}\right]}{150 \left[\frac{mmol}{l}\right]}\right) \quad (69)$$

which yields:

$$\Delta V_{K+, \, eq} = -90 \, mV \quad (70)$$

Nernst's equation indicates that a current is observed unless these equilibrium potentials are established. The results in Eqs. (68) and (70) also enable us to predict the direction of a current when a current occurs. This is illustrated for the steady state potential at – 70 mV. Since neither of the equilibrium potential differences in Eqs. (68) and (70) are equal to – 70 mV, a net current of both ion species across the membrane is observed:

$$\Delta V_{actual} < \Delta V_{Na+, \, eq} \Rightarrow J_{Na+} \, to \, axoplasm$$
$$\Delta V_{actual} > \Delta V_{K+, \, eq} \Rightarrow J_{K+} \, to \, interstitium \quad (71)$$

From the five last equations, Eqs. (67) to (71), we conclude that the actual potential difference during an impulse should not exceed a potential of + 60 mV and should not drop below a potential of – 90 mV since beyond these values both ion species flow in the same direction across the nerve membrane. We conclude further that the current densities predicted in Eq. (71) are exactly compensated by the Na/K pump, since the considered potential difference is that of a resting nerve when a steady state is established.

For any other potential difference, different sodium and potassium current densities follow, and these are then not compensated by the Na/K pump because the pump operates independently of the potential difference. These current densities are of interest as they establish the total membrane current density measured with the Hodgkin–Huxley set–up in Fig.13.21. These current densities are written as:

387

$$J_{Na+} = \gamma_{Na+} \frac{(\Delta V_{actual} - \Delta V_{Na+,\, eq})}{b}$$

$$J_{K+} = \gamma_{K+} \frac{(\Delta V_{actual} - \Delta V_{K+,\, eq})}{b} \quad (72)$$

In Eq. (72), the current densities are related to the conductivities and the potential difference, corrected for the potential difference in equilibrium. The equation contains the fixed membrane width b to compensate for the fact that it should contain the electric field instead of the potential difference, as can be seen when comparing with Eq. (42).

Eq. (72) is different from Ohm's law because the conductivities are not constant, i.e., $\gamma_{Na+} = f(\Delta V_{actual})$ and $\gamma_{K+} = f(\Delta V_{actual})$. This is the particular reason why the Hodgkin–Huxley model is an empiric, experiment–based model. The dependence of the conductivity (or permeability) for each ion species on the potential difference cannot be predicted for a real nerve membrane, but must be measured.

Thus, experimental data are reported next. In Fig. 13.22 the response of a giant axon of a squid to an artificial nerve impulse is shown at 18.5°C (just below room temperature). The top panel shows the potential difference across the nerve membrane. Note the sudden change from −65 mV to a value of about −55 mV. This small change is sufficient to trigger an impulse. During the impulse the potential difference swings all the way to a positive value of + 30 mV, and returns in less than 0.5 ms to negative values, falling first to a negative potential difference of about −75 mV before slowly recovering to the steady state value. The second panel shows the change of the current density of potassium J_K and sodium J_{Na}, and the total membrane current density J_m for the same impulse. From the total membrane current density it is clear that during the early stage of the impulse the net current flows in the opposite direction than it flows during the latter stage of the impulse. The third panel shows the conductivity values associated with the impulse. The immediate response to the onset of the impulse is a strong, but short–lived increase in the conductivity of sodium, followed by a slower, but longer lasting increase of the conductivity of potassium.

To understand the processes seen in Fig. 13.22 qualitatively, we look at an impulse as a function of position along the nerve. Fig. 13.23 shows the potential change and Fig. 13.24 shows the corresponding change of the current along the axon surface in the axoplasm.

We start with Fig. 13.23. This is again a complex figure and we have to go through all the details to

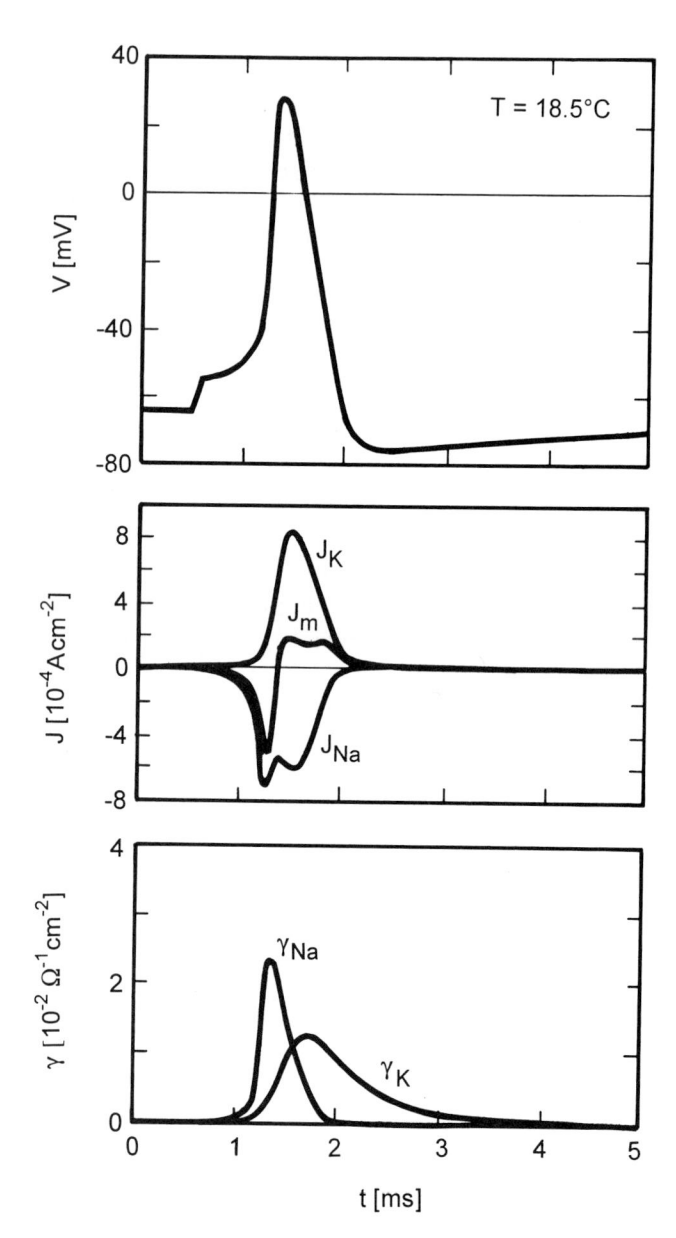

Fig. 13.22: Response of a squid axon to an externally triggered impulse at 18.5°C. The impulse is triggered by a 10 mV change in the potential.
Top panel: change in the potential with time.
Middle panel: variation of current density across the membrane with time.
Bottom panel: conductivity of sodium and potassium as function of time.

understand what happens. The top graph in Fig. 13.23 shows the potential as a function of position for a nerve impulse travelling with a speed of about 1 m/s toward the right (positive x–direction). As noted in Table 13.1, this is an average speed for an unmyelinated human nerve. The shown potential profile can be drawn from the potential profile as a function of time, i.e., the plot in the top panel of Fig. 13.22, and by taking into account that nerve impulses travel in one direction only along a

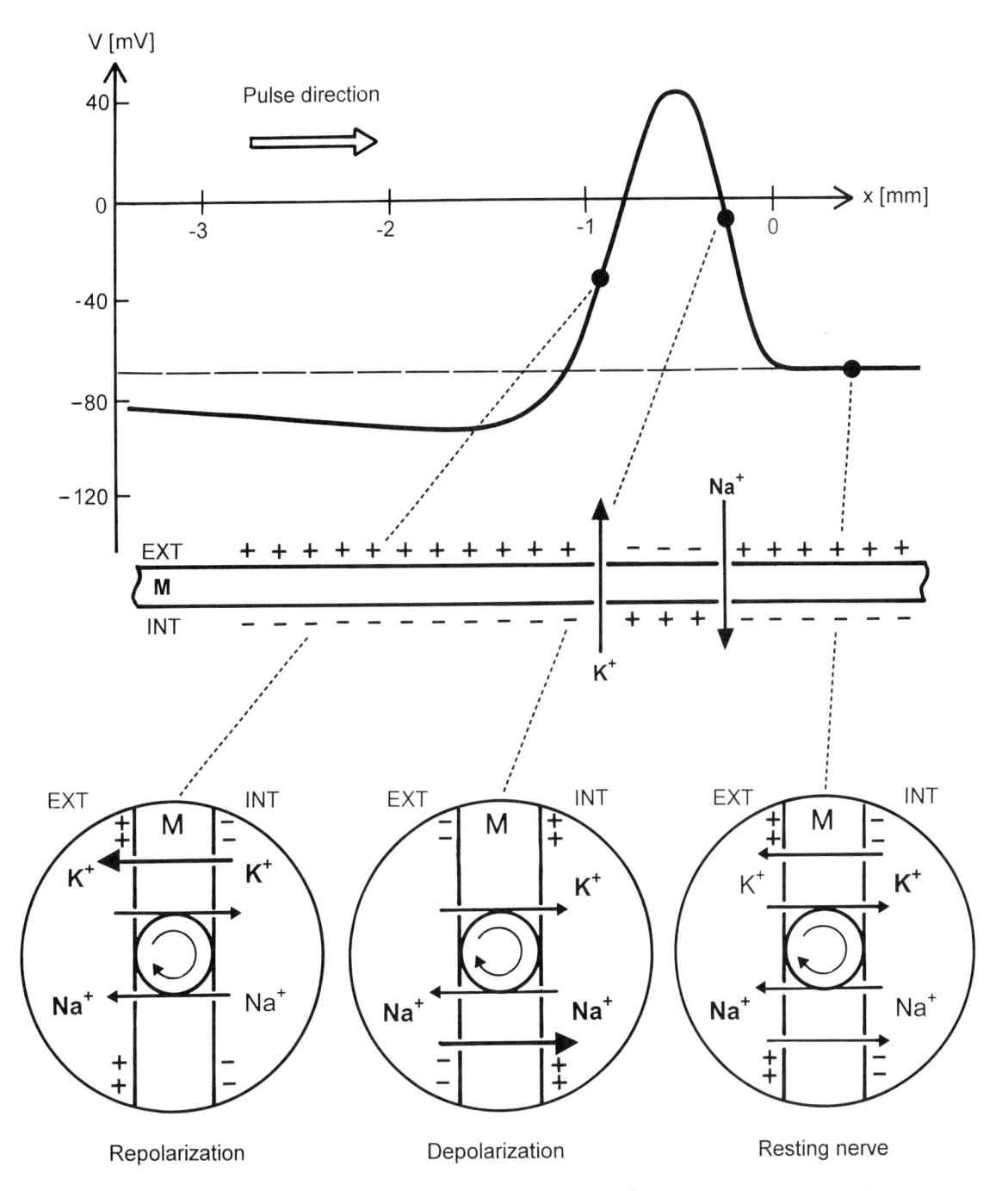

Fig. 13.23: The potential across the nerve membrane as a function of the position along the nerve cell when a nerve impulse passes. The sketch below the curve shows the polarity of the corresponding charges on either side of the membrane. The three circular panels at the bottom illustrate the microscopic processes across the membrane at the highlighted positions.

given nerve cell. For the spatial potential profile shown in the figure, the origin of the x–axis is chosen such that the leading edge of the impulse has just reached this point at the time instant chosen. The nerve impulse has a steep leading slope with the potential raising to a maximum about 0.5 mm behind the onset. At 1 mm behind the leading slope the potential drops sharply back below the initial, steady state potential value. For several more millimeters behind the leading slope the potential is below the resting value.

Fig. 13.23 highlights three points along this curve: (I) for reference, a point in front of the impulse, i.e., a point at which the nerve is still at its steady state value, (II) a point near the maximum potential increase, roughly 0.25 mm behind the impulse front, and (III) a point near the maximum potential decrease 0.9 mm behind the impulse front.

(I) Before the impulse arrives, the nerve is resting and is, therefore, in the steady state. A potential of -70 mV is established between the axoplasm and the extracellular fluid because the Na/K pumping and the passive diffusion of sodium and potassium are properly balanced as discussed in Fig. 13.8. This potential is achieved by an excess negative charge density on the extracellular side of the membrane and an excess positive charge density on the axoplasm side of the membrane, as sketched along the membrane shown below the potential profile in Fig. 13.23.

(II) As the impulse front arrives, an initial, small drop in the potential difference triggers a sudden increase in the conductivity of sodium in the membrane (see third panel of Fig. 13.22), leading to a sodium ion current across the membrane inwards. This step is called depolarization. The sodium concentration in the axoplasm is sufficiently raised to reverse the charge distribution across the membrane, which temporarily establishes a negative areal charge density on the extracellular side of the membrane and a positive areal charge density on the axoplasm side.

(III) In the depolarized state the sodium conductivity falls off sharply and the potassium conductivity increases. As a result, the inward current of sodium ceases, but an outward current of potassium emerges. This quickly returns the charge distribution across the membrane to its original polarity, with excess positive charge on the extracellular side of the membrane and excess negative charge on the axoplasm side of the membrane. The potential difference drops accordingly. After these fast processes are completed, a slower recovery of the steady state follows, i.e., the Na/K pump must transport potassium and sodium back to the side of the membrane they came from in the resting nerve stage. This is associated with the slow approach of the potential difference from values as negative as -90 mV to the steady state value of -70 mV. While the potential has not recovered, the nerve's ability to trigger a new impulse is diminished, which reduces the risk of unintentional secondary impulses.

It becomes apparent how the impulse travels forward along the nerve when the current along the axon membrane is studied as a function of the position of the impulse at a given instant. This is shown in Fig. 13.24. Note carefully that the curve shows a different property of the system compared to Fig. 13.23 even though the two profiles appear superficially similar. The sketch of the membrane below the current density diagram in Fig. 13.24 illustrates once again the currents occurring across the membrane, which are also shown in Fig. 13.23: when the impulse front arrives, a strong sodium ion current occurs toward the axoplasm accompanied by a weaker potassium ion current across a broader zone toward the extracellular fluid a little bit further upstream.

Focus first on the point at which the sodium current across the membrane occurs. The associated reduction of positive charges on the extracellular fluid side of the membrane causes other positive charges from the vicinity to move toward this point. In the same fashion, the sudden increase in positive charges on the axoplasm side of the membrane leads to an outflow of positive charges along the membrane in both directions. (We studied a similar case in Fig. 13.19.) The current parallel to the membrane in the axoplasm is shown in the top diagram of Fig. 13.24. The current is positive in the di-

Fig. 13.24: The electric current along the inner surface of a nerve membrane as a function of position along the nerve. The sketch below the curve illustrates the formation of a current loop behind the crest of the impulse. A reduction in the amount of charge ahead of the impulse lowers the potential there, causing a Hodgkin–Huxley type of response. This leads to a forward motion of the impulse.

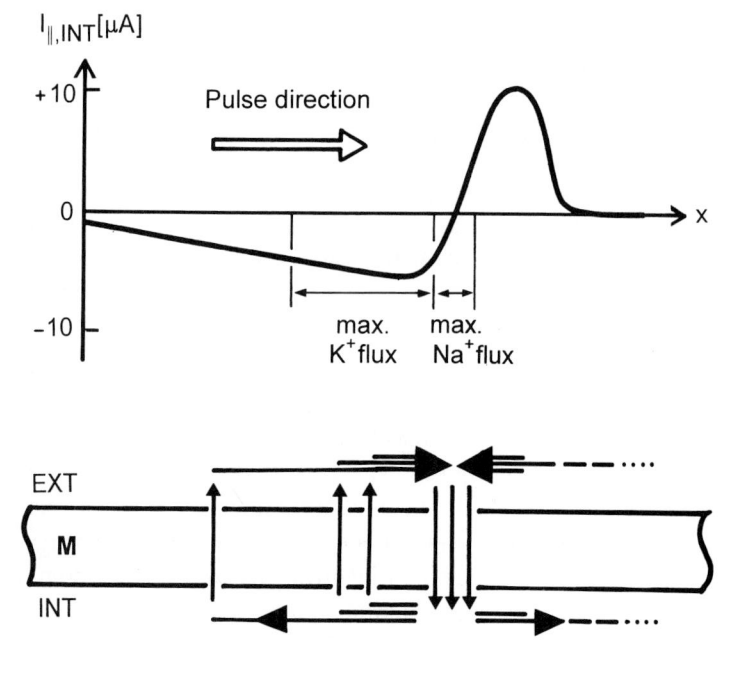

rection downstream of the impulse and is negative in the direction upstream. These currents are very small, e.g., typically below 10 μA.

The current components in the downstream and upstream directions have different consequences. The current toward the left in Fig. 13.24, i.e., toward the side which the impulse front has already passed, is short–circuited by the countercurrent of potassium, leading to a current loop trailing the impulse front.

On the other side of the point where sodium crosses the membrane, i.e., where the parallel current flows ahead of the impulse front, it serves as the trigger for the impulse front to move forward by lowering the potential at the right. As we noted before, a small potential drop is sufficient to cause the sodium conductivity to shoot up, pushing the nerve impulse front forward. This current we identified in Fig. 13.24 downstream is, however, the same current we used in Fig. 13.20 to explain the electrotonus spread. Thus, the signal propagates forward by using the electrotonus spread to trigger the adjacent segment downstream along the nerve.

13.5.3. Impulse transport in a myelinated nerve

The Hodgkin–Huxley model explains most aspects of the impulse transport in unmyelinated nerves, which comprise about 70 % of the nerve cells in a human body.

As Table 13.1 shows, the remaining 30 % of myelinated nerves play an important part as they are responsible for transmission of motor information and response. They are designated for motor response because impulse transport in these nerve cells is much faster than in the unmyelinated nerves.

We first want to establish the difference in the impulse transport speeds of the two nerve types by studying Figs. 13.25 to 13.27. Fig. 13.25 is a linear plot of the signal transport speed of both nerve types as a function of axon radius for human nerves. The first panel shows the range to 0.6 μm axon radius; the second panel shows the range up to 10 μm axon radius, which includes the largest myelinated nerves in the human body. Both graphs show clearly that the impulse transport speed increases with axon radius, although the increase appears to be steeper for the myelinated nerve. The figure also shows that a myelinated nerve of same radius (e.g., 0.5 μm) transports the impulse faster by almost a factor of 10. Thus, from this figure we conclude that two factors play a role in nerve impulse speed: the size of the axon and the presence of a myelin sheath. The linear data representation in Fig. 13.25 is unsatisfactory, however, because it does not allow both curves to be usefully combined in a single plot.

Fig. 13.26 is an improvement. It is a logarithmic plot of the same speed versus axon radius data. This graph allows us to see clearly that for both nerve types a strong dependence on the axon radius exists, a point

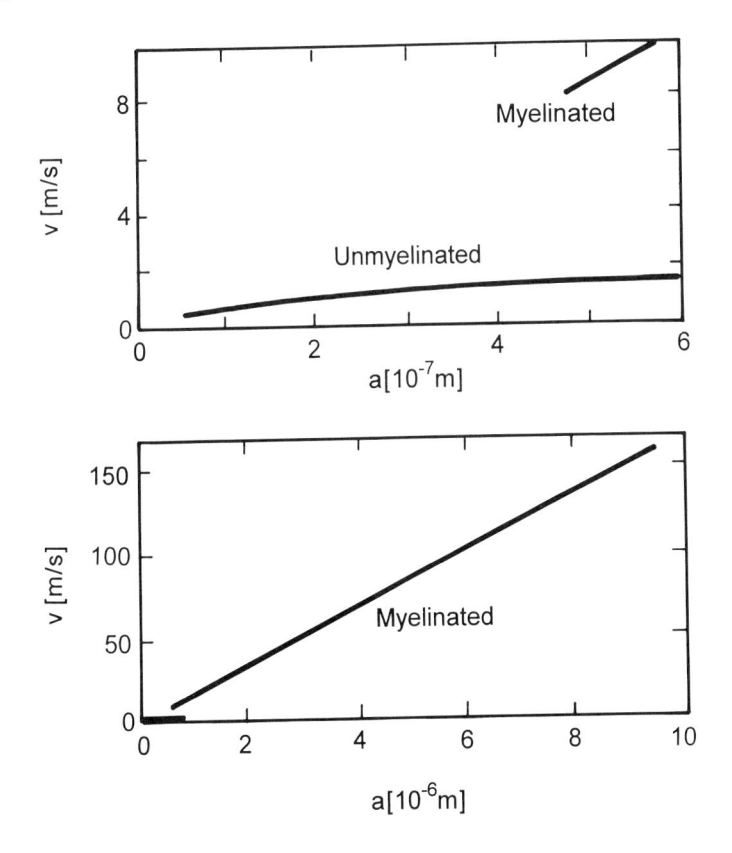

Fig. 13.25: Linear plot of impulse transport speed versus axon radius for myelinated and unmyelinated nerves in the human body. Due to the large range of data, two separate plots are shown.

Fig. 13.26: Logarithmic plot of the same data plotted in Fig. 13.25. The curved slope indicates that the speed v is not an exponential function of the axon radius a.

Fig. 13.27: Double–logarithmic plot of the same data plotted in Fig. 13.25. Different slopes for the two nerve types suggest that different mechanisms have to be found for the impulse transport in myelinated and unmyelinated nerves.

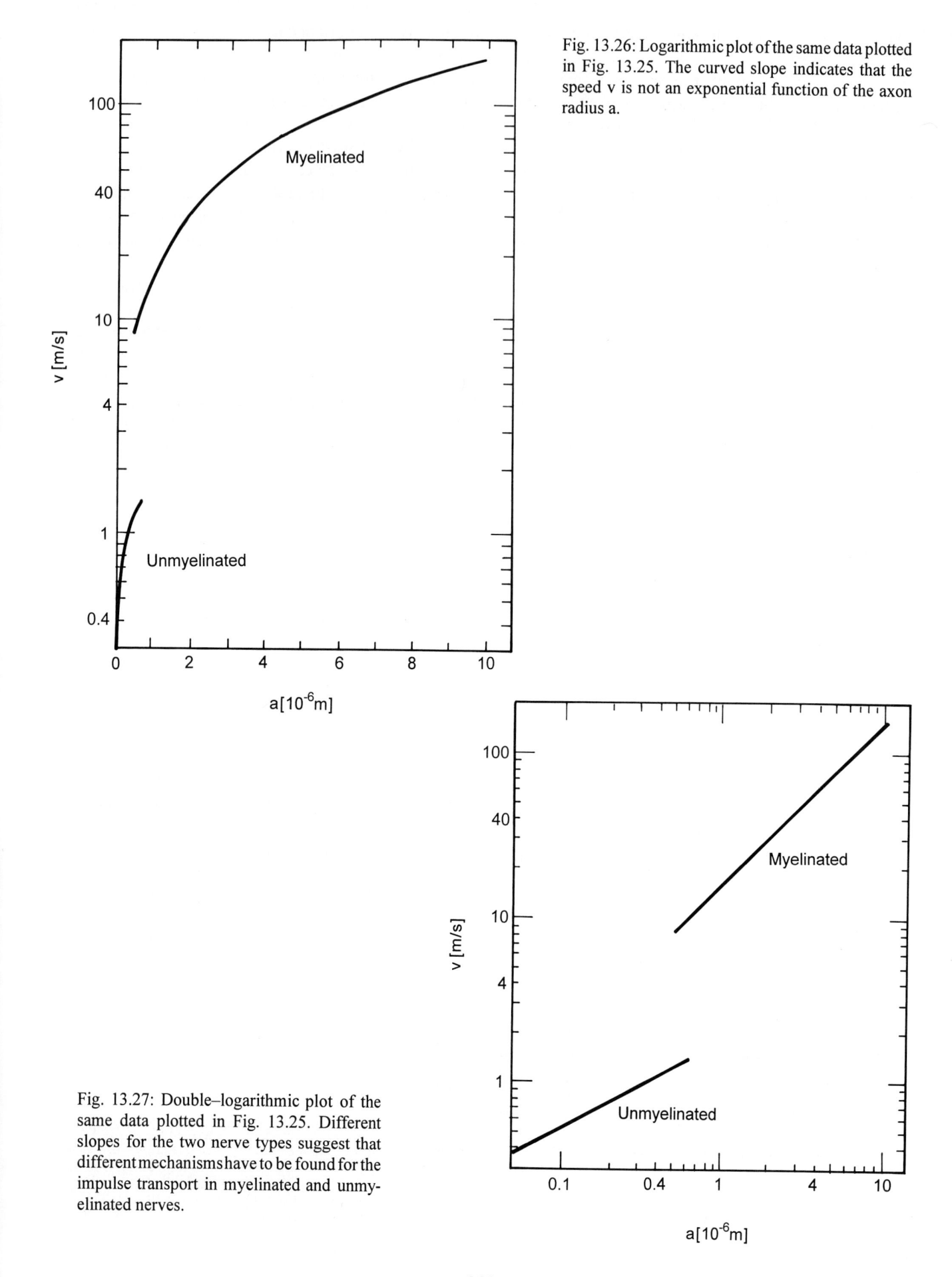

which may get lost in the linear representation of Fig. 13.25. However, Fig. 13.26 is not conclusive on the question whether the same mechanism explains both curves. They are both bent in a similar fashion, but qualitatively it seems that their curvatures do not match in the region of overlap.

Fig. 13.27, a double–logarithmic plot of the same data as in the previous two figures, addresses the question of whether the two types of nerve share the same mechanism. The answer is that, for both the myelinated and the unmyelinated nerve, the impulse transport speed and the axon radius obey a power–law; however, the exponents are different:

$$\begin{aligned}\text{\textit{unmyelinated nerve}}: \quad & v \propto a^{0.5} = \sqrt{a} \\ \text{\textit{myelinated nerve}}: \quad & v \propto a^{1.0} = a \end{aligned} \quad (73)$$

Thus, three main aspects of the impulse transport speed of a myelinated nerve must be explained:
(I) the dependence of the signal speed on the axon radius, i.e., the fact that the signal travels faster for larger nerves,
(II) the increase of speed by about an order of magnitude at the same axon radius relative to an unmyelinated nerve due to the myelin sheath, and
(III) the different mechanism of signal transport as indicated by the different functional dependence on the axon radius in comparison to the unmyelinated nerve. This aspect implies that a novel model must be found for the myelinated nerves which is distinct from the Hodgkin–Huxley model described in the previous section.

The best way to develop a model for the impulse transport in a myelinated nerve is to return to Fig. 13.1: the myelin sheath is too thick to allow ion diffusion or ion currents to pass through it. Therefore, the 1 to 2 mm long myelinated sections are passive elements in which electrically only an electrotonus spread is possible. However, the myelinated sections are interrupted by the nodes of Ranvier. At these points only a 5 to 10 nm thick membrane separates the axoplasm from the extracellular fluid, and the electric behavior is the same as that of an unmyelinated nerve.

The combination of electrotonus spread and Hodgkin–Huxley's all–or–nothing impulses in the nodes of Ranvier is essentially the new model that we propose for the myelinated nerve. This mechanism is called *saltatory conduction* since a Hodgkin–Huxley type impulse, shown in Fig. 13.22, occurring at one node spreads in an electrotonus fashion along the nerve, generating a potential perturbation at subsequent nodes which is sufficient to cause them to fire.

We want to quantify this process by studying the simplified sketch of a section of the myelinated nerve in Fig. 13.28. Myelin sheath segments of length D alternate with nodes of Ranvier of length W. The radius of the axon is a, the width of the membrane and the myelin sheath is b. From microbiological studies we know that the variables a, b and D have fixed ratios for human nerves:

$$\begin{aligned}(I) \quad & a + b = 1.4\, a \\ (II) \quad & D = 280\, a \end{aligned} \quad (74)$$

The width of the nodes of Ranvier, W, is not critical as long as the gap between the sheaths is wide enough to allow a Hodgkin–Huxley impulse to occur in the node.

We want to establish next whether the electrotonus spread is indeed sufficient to cause the next node to fire in response to the firing of the previous node for a myelinated nerve. Remember that we found for the unmyelinated nerve only a decay length of about 0.1 mm in Eq. (60). Would this value apply to myelinated nerves as well, the myelin sheath length of 1 to 2 mm might be too long for a Hodgkin–Huxley event in one node to trigger such an event in the next node.

We use Eq. (59) to determine the decay length of a potential perturbation in a myelinated nerve of typical radius. With a = 5 μm, b = 2 μm (related in this way due to Eq. (74)) and the resistivity data from Table 13.4, we find:

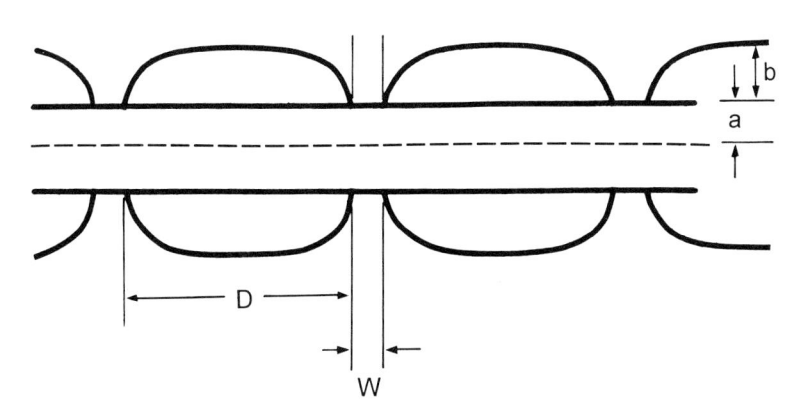

Fig. 13.28: Geometric sketch of a section of a myelinated nerve. Nodes of Ranvier are separated by distance D and have a gap width W. The axon radius is a and the thickness of the myelin sheath and the cell membrane is b.

$$\lambda = \sqrt{\frac{a\,b\,\rho_m}{2\,\rho_{ax}}} =$$ (75)

$$\sqrt{\frac{5\times10^{-6}[m]\;2\times10^{-6}[m]\;1\times10^{7}[\Omega m]}{2\cdot 1.1[\Omega m]}}$$

which yields:

$$\lambda = 7\times 10^{-3}\,m = 7\,mm \quad (76)$$

This decay length is much longer than the corresponding value in the unmyelinated nerve in Eq. (60). It is now compared to the distance D between two nodes of Ranvier for the same nerve (from Eq. (74)):

$$D = 280\,a = 280\cdot 5\times 10^{-6} m = 1.4\,mm \quad (77)$$

Therefore, the distance between two nodes of Ranvier is 20 % of the decay length. Based on this comparison, it is likely that nodes further downstream than just the next node are triggered. To test this possibility, we note that the threshold for a node to fire is about 10 % of the total potential change during a Hodgkin–Huxley impulse ($\Delta V_{HH} = 100$ mV, e.g., in Fig. 13.22). We saw above that a node of Ranvier fires when its potential difference charges to a value of $V_{actual} \geq -60$ mV, which is a variation of $\Delta V = 10$ mV. Based on Eq. (59) we find for the fraction of potential change due to the electrotonus spread for the next twenty nodes of Ranvier the values:

$$\begin{aligned}\Delta V/\Delta V_{HH} &= e^{-D/\lambda} = 0.80 \\ \Delta V/\Delta V_{HH} &= e^{-5D/\lambda} = 0.37 \\ \Delta V/\Delta V_{HH} &= e^{-10D/\lambda} = 0.13 \\ \Delta V/\Delta V_{HH} &= e^{-20D/\lambda} = 0.02\end{aligned} \quad (78)$$

Thus, at least the next 10 nodes of Ranvier fire as a result of a given node firing. This is a good design by nature; with all the things which can go wrong, it is better that we do not depend on each of the several hundred nodes of Ranvier along a nerve firing in sequence.

While this discussion establishes the model for the signal transport in myelinated nerves qualitatively, we want to estimate the speed of impulses for the saltatory conduction. A proper calculation of such a speed is not possible analytically and, therefore, has to be done with computer simulations. It is instructive, however, to estimate a value for both the speed in myelinated and unmyelinated nerves.

Unmyelinated nerve

We start with an unmyelinated nerve since we also have not estimated the signal speed for these nerves before. A speed is generally defined by a distance divided by a time. In the case of the unmyelinated nerve, the decay length in Eq. (59) establishes a characteristic length for how far a perturbation affects a nerve. The decay time in Eq. (58) introduces a characteristic time for how long a perturbation affects a nerve. Thus, we estimate the speed of the impulse by dividing these two numbers:

$$v \approx \frac{\lambda}{\tau} = \frac{\sqrt{\dfrac{a\,b\,\rho_m}{2\,\rho_{ax}}}}{\kappa\,\epsilon_0\,\rho_m} = \frac{1}{\kappa\,\epsilon_0}\sqrt{\frac{a\,b}{2\,\rho_m\,\rho_{ax}}} \quad (79)$$

This formula is satisfactory because it reproduces the proper square–root dependence on the axon radius, $v \propto (a)^{1/2}$, found in Fig. 13.27. Calculating the speed for a nerve of axon radius $a = 0.6$ μm results in a speed of $v = 0.22$ m/s. This value underestimates the proper value in Fig. 13.27 by a factor 6 or 7 since λ is defined for a drop of the potential difference to 37 % but a drop to as much as 85 % is already sufficient to propagate the impulse.

Myelinated nerve

For the myelinated nerve we have two alternative ways of estimating the speed since we have two characteristic length scales for this type of nerve: D and λ. We test both for a typical nerve with axon radius $a = 5$ μm.

If the distance between neighboring nodes of Ranvier controls the speed, we find:

$$v \approx \frac{D}{\tau} = \frac{280\,a}{\kappa\epsilon_0\rho_m} = 2.3\,m/s \quad (80)$$

This formula satisfies the result of Fig. 13.27 which stated that $v \propto a$ for a myelinated nerve. But the speed of 2.3 m/s is more than an order of magnitude too low.

Alternatively, we assume that the speed of the impulse depends on the decay length, as for the unmyelinated nerve. In this case the same formula as in Eq. (79) is used; however, since b and a are related by Eq. (74) for a myelinated nerve, the speed is again a linear function of a, $v \propto a$. Inserting numerical values for the myelinated nerve ($a = 5$ μm and $b = 2$ μm) we find $v = 11.4$ m/s. This value comes closer to the actual value measured. It underestimates the real value again by a factor of 7 to 10, like Eq. (79).

As a consequence, we see that nature gains a second advantage by not relying on the firing of each neighboring node of Ranvier: we gain in speed by a factor 5. What makes the signal transport in myelinated nerves faster than that in unmyelinated nerves of equal axon radius? It is in the end not a difference in mechanism because we used the same formula (Eq. (79)) to estimate the signal speed; electrotonus spread determines in both cases how fast the signal travels along the nerve. The important difference between both types of nerves is the thickness b, i.e., the presence of the myelin sheath. Physically, the thicker myelin sheath reduces the capacitance of the nerve ($C \propto 1/b$, see Eq. (21)), which in turn means that fewer charges must cross the membrane at the nodes of Ranvier than have to cross in the case of an unmyelinated nerve. The impulse propagates faster as lesser time is needed to change the potential at the nodes of Ranvier!

13.6. Problems

P–13.1
We study some capacitor arrangements.
(a) An air–filled parallel plate capacitor has a plate separation of b = 1.5 mm and an area A = 4.0 cm². Find its capacitance.
(b) A capacitor with capacitance of C = 4.5 μF is connected to a 9 V battery. What is the amount of charge on each plate of the capacitor?

P–13.2
The plates of a parallel plate capacitor are 3 cm wide and 4 cm long. The plates are separated by 1.5 mm paper.
(a) Calculate the capacitance of the device using the dielectric constant of paper from Table 13.3.
(b) Any dielectric material other than vacuum has a maximum electric field that can be produced in the dielectric material before it physically or chemically breaks down and begins to conduct. This maximum electric field is called *dielectric strength*. The dielectric strength for paper is reached at a value of 15×10^6 V/m. Calculate the maximum charge that can be placed on the capacitor at this dielectric strength.

P–13.3
An air–filled parallel plate capacitor has a capacitance of 60 pF.
(a) What is the separation of the plates if each plate has an area of 0.5 m²?
(b) If the region between the plates is filled with a material with κ = 4.5, what is the final capacitance?

P–13.4
A simplified model for an erythrocyte is a spherical capacitor with a positively charged liquid interior of surface area A. The interior fluid is separated by a membrane of thickness b from the surrounding, negatively charged plasma fluid. The potential difference across the membrane is 100 mV and the thickness of the membrane is about 100 nm with a dielectric constant of κ = 5.0.
(a) Calculate the volume of the blood cell assuming that an average erythrocyte has a mass 1×10^{-12} kg. From the volume determine the surface area of the erythrocyte.
(b) Calculate the capacitance of the blood cell. For this calculation model the membrane as a parallel plate capacitor with the area found in part (a).
(c) Calculate the charge on the surface of the membrane. How many elementary charges does this represent? Hint: use the density of blood as 1.06 g/cm³.

P–13.5
All electric devices have identifying plates specifying their electrical characteristics. E.g., a typical household device may be specified for a current of 6.0 A when connected to a 120 V source. What is its resistance?

P–13.6
A person notices a mild shock if the current along a path through the thumb and index finger of one hand exceeds 80 μA. Compare the respective maximum allowable potential for the hand with
(a) dry skin with a resistance of $R = 4.0 \times 10^5$ Ω, and
(b) wet skin with a resistance of R = 2000 Ω.

P–13.7
A rectangular piece of copper is 2 cm long, 2 cm wide and 10 cm deep.
(a) What is the resistance of the copper piece as measured between the two square ends? (Use the resistivity of copper from Table 13.4.)
(b) What is the resistance between two opposite rectangular faces?

P–13.8
A current of 6.0 A flows through a 20 Ω resistor for t = 3 minutes. What total amount of charge passes through any cross–section of the resistor in this time?
(a) Express your result in unit [Cb].
(b) Express your result as the number of electrons passing the cross–sectional area.

P–13.9
A conducting, cylindrical wire has a 1.0 mm diameter, a 1.67 m length and a 50 mΩ resistance. What is the resistivity of the material? Identify the material of which this conductor is made by using Table 13.4.

P–13.10
The potential along an axon is shown in Fig. 13.29 at a given time instant. The axon radius is 8 μm, the resistivity of the axoplasm is taken from Table 13.4. What is the longitudinal current in the axon as a function of position? Use $l_1 = 0.8$ mm and $l_2 = 0.4$ mm.

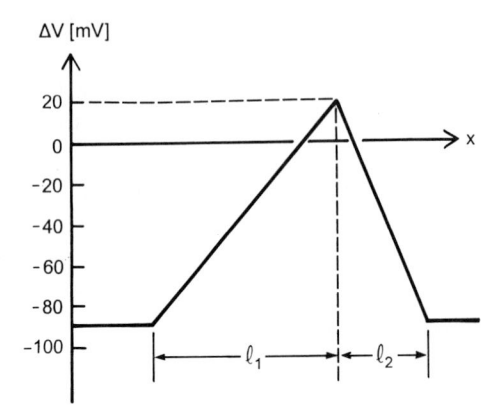

Fig. 13.29 for problem P–13.10.

P–13.11
A current density of 0.8×10^{-4} A/cm² stimulates a membrane for 150 μs. How much does this change the potential across the membrane?
Hint: Use 6 nm for the nerve membrane thickness. Take the dielectric constant of the membrane from Table 13.3.

P–13.12
For the myelinated nerve the axon radius is 10 μm, the membrane resistivity is $\rho_m = 1.0 \times 10^7$ Ωm, the axoplasm resistivity is $\rho_{ax} = 0.5$ Ωm and the myelin sheath thickness is related to the axon radius as given in Eq. (74).
(a) What is its electrotonus spread decay length λ?
(b) Using Eq. (74) for the distance between nodes of Ranvier for this nerve, how many nodes of Ranvier fire along the nerve as a result of a certain node being stimulated. Use a potential difference of $\Delta V = 100$ mV for the maximum potential change in the node which fires initially, and allow other nodes of Ranvier to fire if electrotonus spread causes at their site at least a change from – 70 mV to – 60 mV.

P–13.13
Confirm Eq. (73) graphically by using Fig. 13.27.

P–13.14
Table 13.5 provides approximate values for the intracellular and extracellular concentrations for sodium, potassium and chlorine ions in a frog muscle with resting potential of – 98 mV and for the squid axon with a resting potential – 70 mV. Calculate the equilibrium potential for each ion species in both cases at 20°C.

Table 13.5: Ion concentrations for frogs, squids in [mmol/l].

Ion species	intracellular	extracellular
1. Frog muscle		
Na⁺	9.0 – 13.0	120.0
K⁺	140.0	2.5
Cl⁻	3.5	120.0
2. Squid axon		
Na⁺	50.0	440.0
K⁺	400.0	20.0
Cl⁻	40.0 – 100.0	560.0

Summary

Definitions:
- Capacitance: (i) general definition: $C = q/V$
(ii) parallel plate arrangement: $C = \epsilon_0 A/b$
b is plate distance, A is plate area
- Dielectric constant κ: κ is a dimensionless materials constant, $\kappa = 1$ vacuum. For other materials: $\epsilon_0 \Rightarrow \kappa \epsilon_0$
- Current $I = \Delta q/\Delta t$; Current density $J = I/A$
- Resistivity ρ: $|\mathbf{E}| = \rho J$ (Ohm's law)
- Resistance $R = \rho \, l/A = V/I$

l is length, A cross–sectional area of conductor

Units:
- Capacitance C [F = Cb/V]; Current I [A = Cb/s]
- Resistance R [Ω = V/A]; Resistivity ρ [Ωm = Vm/A]

Laws:
- Nernst's equation, assuming singly charged ions:

$$\frac{c_{i,1}}{c_{i,2}} = \exp\left[-\frac{e}{kT}\left(V_{i,1} - V_{i,2}\right)\right]$$

e is the elementary charge.
- Work stored in a parallel plate capacitor:

$$W = \frac{1}{2} Q \, \Delta V$$

Q is final charge, ΔV is total change of potential.

Chapter XIV

Electrocardiography

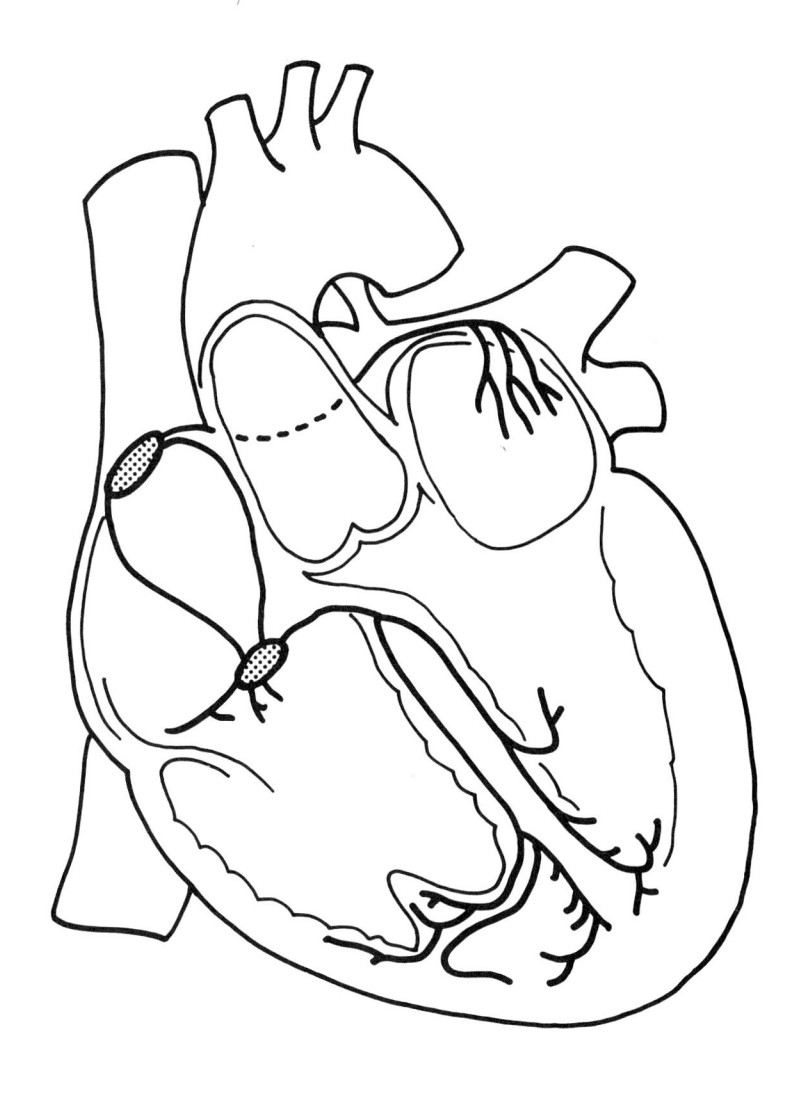

Electric phenomena of the heart

ELECTROCARDIOGRAPHY
ELECTRIC PHENOMENA OF THE HEART

The electrocardiogram (ECG) is a medical diagnosis and observation tool for time resolved measurements of the electric activity of the heart muscle. The heart muscle of higher vertebrates is stimulated by the rhythmic action of the pacemaker cells in the sino–atrial node (SA–node) of the autonomous nervous system of the heart.

The complex human heart is a relatively recent evolutionary development we share only with mammals, birds and some reptiles (as illustrated in Fig. 11.1). Its physiological role has been understood since William Harvey discovered the circulatory flow of blood in the cardiovascular system in 1628. It took almost 300 years until in 1906 Willem Einthoven developed a method to observe the heart while it beats in the human chest. This method is based on the electric properties of the heart. We survey the nervous signals and muscle cell response of the heart first. Then we study the respective electric potential variations which are observable on the skin of the patient. The electrocardiogram (ECG) of a healthy heart is described by studying the time–dependence of the electric potential differences between electrodes placed at specific points on the skin. For illustration, we focus on the most commonly used type of ECG as developed by Einthoven.

14.1. Physiology of the heart

14.1.1. Anatomic overview of the heart

The human heart serves as the pump for two blood circulation systems, the systemic and the pulmonary systems. To provide this function, the heart is divided into two pairs of chambers, which are in turn separated by valves to ensure blood flow in one direction only. Its main anatomical components are shown in Fig. 14.1, including the right atrium (3), the two venae cavae (8), the right ventricle (4), the left atrium (5), the left ventricle (6), and the aorta (7). Fig. 14.2 illustrates how these components cooperate. On the left side, the pulmonary veins feed the blood, which arrives from the lungs, into the left atrium. The blood then passes through the mitral valve into the left ventricle. From there it leaves through the aortic valve into the aorta. In turn, the two venae cavae (venae is the Latin plural form of vena, since there are the inferior vena cava and the superior vena cava) supply blood to the right atrium. From there it passes the tricuspid valve into the right ventricle. The right ventricle ejects the blood into the pulmonary artery.

An interesting feature of the anatomy of the healthy human heart is the complete separation of both sides of the heart by the septum. This allows the heart to

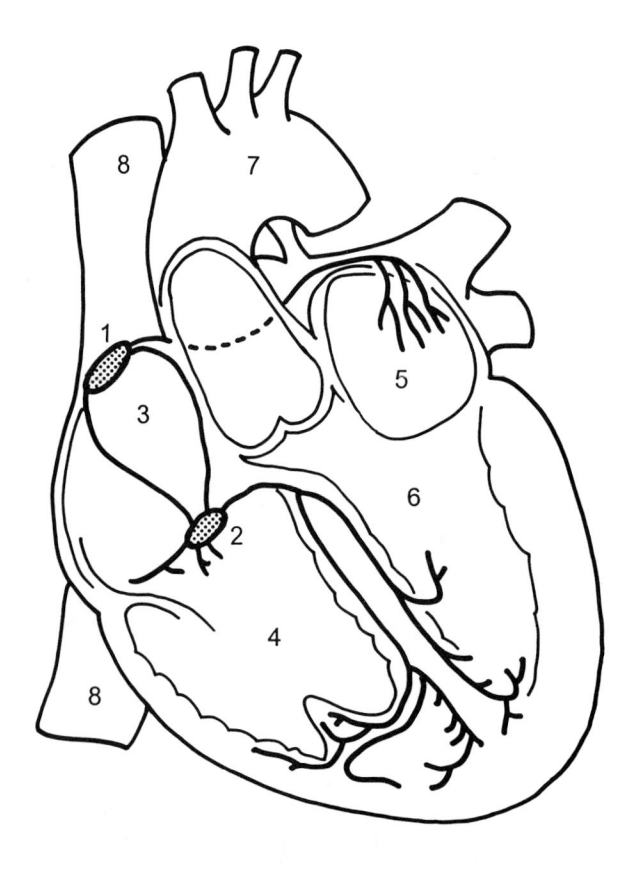

Fig. 14.1: Anatomic sketch of the human heart. Shown are (1) the sino–atrial node (SA–node), (2) the atrio–ventricular node (AV–node), (3) right atrium, (4) right ventricle, (5) left atrium, (6) left ventricle, (7) aorta with aorta bend and (8) the two venae cavae.

398

Table 14.1: Number of heartbeats/min for a resting person.

Age	cycles/min
Newborn	130
2 years	110
8 years	90
Adolescent/adult	70
Senior	60

14.1.2. Electric systems of the heart

Since the operation of the heart is unconditional, it is not controlled remotely by the brain but locally by a nerve center above the right atrium and near the entry point of the superior vena cava ((1) in Fig. 14.1). This center is called the sino–atrial node (SA–node). It has a diameter of 1 to 2 centimeters. Its rhythmic electric action is controlled by pacemaker cells. Note that the number of heartbeats varies with age (Table 14.1). The electric properties of the pacemaker cells are discussed below.

The electric action caused by the pacemaker cells is carried to the muscle cells of the heart like nerve impulses in regular nerves. As illustrated in Fig. 14.3,

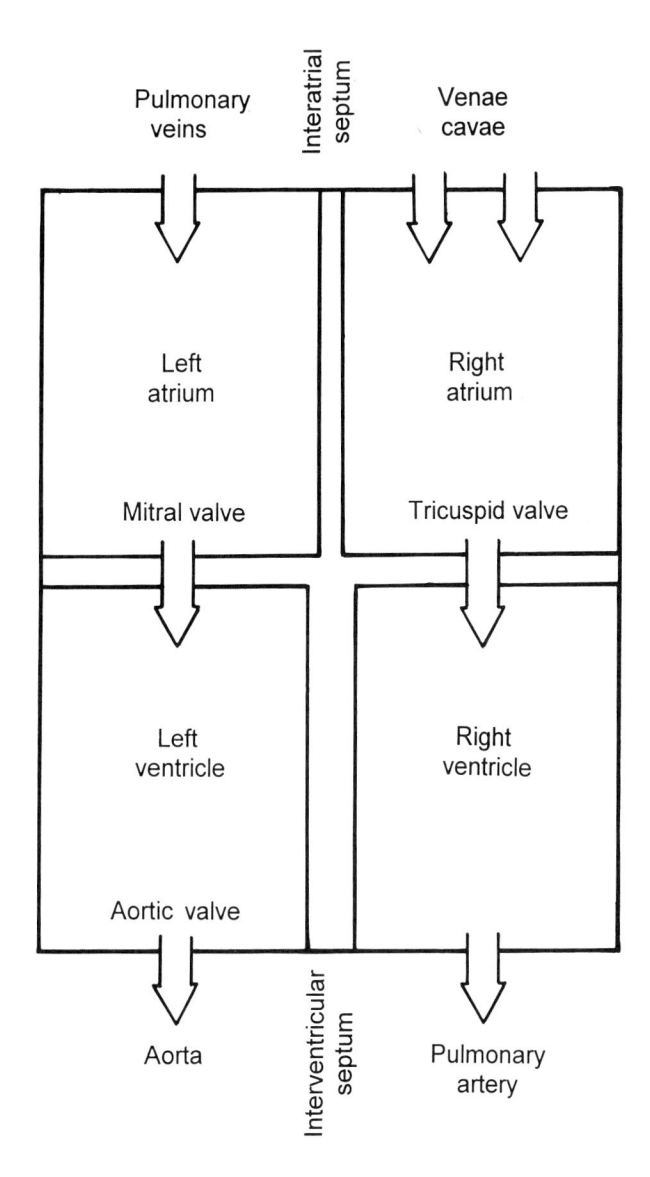

Fig. 14.2: Sketch of the blood flow patterns through the various anatomic components of the heart. Blood from the lungs passes through the left atrium and ventricle to the aorta and blood from the venae cavae flows through the right atrium and ventricle to the pulmonary artery. Both atria and ventricles are separated by valves; the left side and the right side of the heart are separated by the septum.

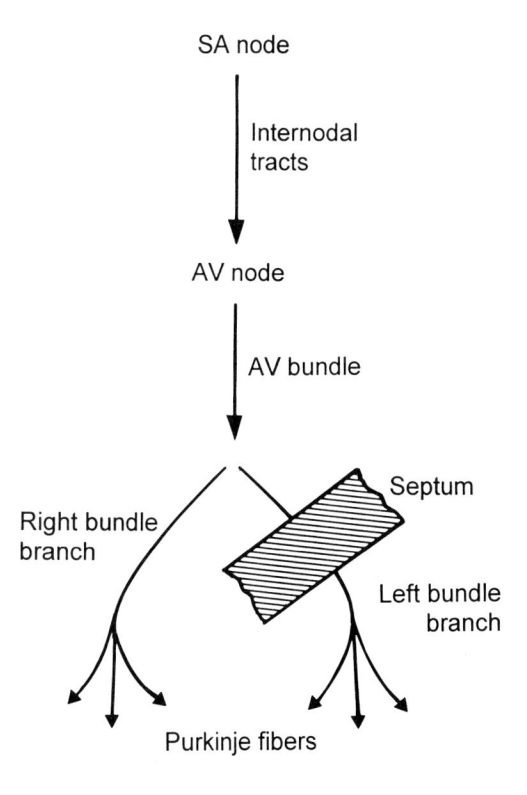

Fig. 14.3: Sketch illustrating the path the electric signals take in the heart as they emerge from the SA–node. Note that the signal is delayed in the AV–node. The signal then passes the septum, spreading on both sides to the muscle fibers (Purkinje fibers).

serve as a single pump for two circulatory systems simultaneously. Both halves of the heart have a similar set of heart muscles with a common electric trigger system to keep their operation synchronous. This indicates the uniqueness of the nervous system of the heart, which is its only component that reaches across the septum, with nerve bundles passing from the right side, where the nervous centers are located, to the left side.

the impulse from the SA–node travels at 0.5 to 1.0 m/s along the internodal tracts to the atrio–ventricular node (AV–node), which is a secondary nerve center located at the bottom of the right atrium near the tricuspid valve. The internodal tract is illustrated in Fig. 14.1 by two thicker lines leading from the SA–node (1) to the AV–node (2).

The atrio–ventricular node operates similar to the SA–node, except at a slower rate of depolarizations. As a result, a healthy SA–node triggers the AV–node every time before it would fire on its own. However, the AV–node still serves an important purpose in that it delays the nerve signal by about 0.1 to 0.2 seconds in reaching the ventricular muscle cells, thus allowing the atria to empty into the ventricles before the blood is pushed out of the ventricles into the blood vessels.

Once the AV–node has fired in response to the impulse from the SA–node, the electric signal leaves through the AV–bundle and splits into two major branches, one spreading along the right side of the heart (right bundle branch) and the other, after passing through the interventricular septum, spreading along the left side of the heart (left bundle branch). The signals reach their final destination in the Purkinje fibers (named for the Czech physiologist Jan Purkyně, with the name usually shown in German spelling), which are the muscle cells of the heart which contract as a result of the stimulation. The mechanism of contraction is essentially the same as discussed in Fig. 2.3. The signal speed from the AV–node to the Purkinje fibers, 1.0 m/s to 4.0 m/s, is slightly faster than from the SA–node to the AV–node.

We noted above that the heart serves two cardiovascular systems. With two atria and two ventricles, we could argue that the heart is actually a combination of two pumps in one place. The fact that only one nervous system operates the heart dismisses the two–pump model. Indeed, the existence of only one nervous control system is vital as the synchronization of the contractions provides for an additional support of the larger systemic system, which obviously needs the stronger push for the blood to circulate. This additional effect is achieved in an interesting way, with the right atrium contracting slightly ahead of the left atrium (due to the location of the SA–node on the right side), but the left ventricle contracting between 10 ms and 30 ms ahead of the right ventricle.

14.1.3. Pacemaker cells and muscle cell response

To establish the properties of the heart, the mechanism of the pacemaker cells must be established first. From our discussion in Chapter 13 we know that these cells cannot be usual nerve cells: if they were, they could only cause a signal if triggered externally.

Fig. 14.4 illustrates how the potential of the pacemaker cells in the SA–node develops as a function of time. Different from normal nerve cells, no resting potential (steady state level) exists for the pacemaker cells. Instead, the potential increases steadily from −80 mV to about −55 mV after the pacemaker cell has fired (undergone a depolarization like other nerve cells, as shown in Fig. 13.3). This steady increase takes just under one second. When a potential of about −55 mV is reached, a new depolarization cycle is triggered. The different behavior shown in Fig. 14.4 is achieved by adding a new ion species to those which are involved in cross–membrane exchange: Ca^{2+} causes the new properties, while Na^+ and K^+ play the same role in the pacemaker cells as they do in regular nerve cells. The presence of the calcium ions allows for a continuous inward flow of charges, i.e., a continuous inward current across the membrane.

The rhythmic action of the pacemaker cells in the SA–node triggers the responses throughout the nervous system of the heart. Fig. 14.5 illustrates the poten-

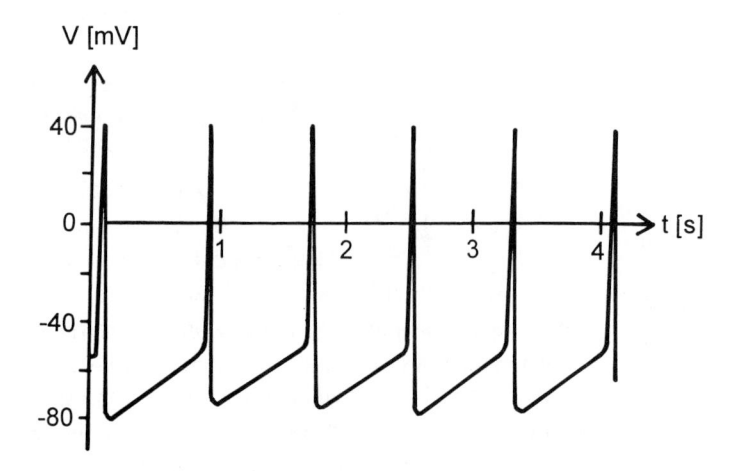

Fig. 14.4: Rhythmic action of the SA–node. Due to the involvement of calcium ions, the pacemaker cells do not have a steady–state potential level to which the nerve cell returns after firing.

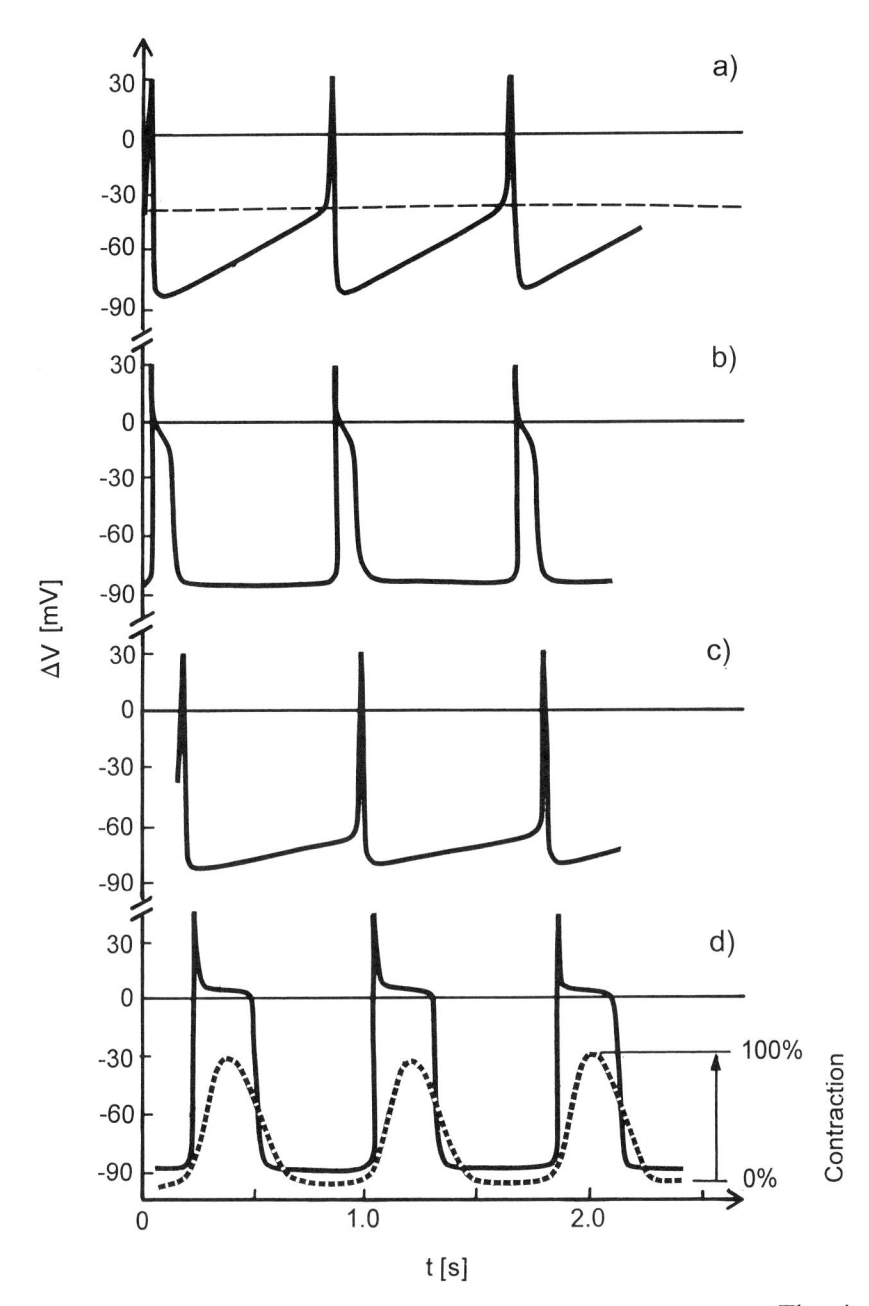

Fig. 14.5: Comparison of the electric potential curves for various nervous and muscle cells in the heart.
(a) Pacemaker cells in the SA–node (see also Fig. 14.4),
(b) atrial muscle cells,
(c) AV–node cells, and
(d) Purkinje fiber cells (solid line). Frame (d) shows also the muscle contraction profile of the fiber cells (dashed line with scale at the right).

tial profile at various points throughout the system in comparison to the potential profile of the pacemaker cells in the SA–node, which is shown in the top frame of the figure. Every time the threshold near − 55 mV is reached, a depolarization signal is sent toward both the AV–node and the muscle cells of the two atrial chambers of the heart. The atrial muscle cells (second frame in Fig. 14.5) depolarize within 50 ms of the depolarization of the SA–node. This is indicated by a slight shift of the potential profile along the time axis to the right. The shape of the depolarization profile of the atrial muscle cells adds another delay of about 50 ms following the initial overshoot to + 30 mV. This shoulder–type feature of the potential profile is typical for heart muscle cells and is due to the role of Ca^{2+} ions as discussed in detail for the ventricular muscle cells below.

The signal from the SA–node also reaches the AV–node and causes a depolarization, which is further delayed relative to the SA–node, as shown in the third frame of Fig. 14.5.

The last frame of Fig. 14.5 illustrates the electric response (solid line) and the contraction (dashed line with a separate scale of relative contraction in [%] at the right side of the figure) of the ventricular cells. The delay varies from 100 ms to 150 ms for the cells close to the septum, which respond first, and those which are located on the outside wall of the heart. Note the characteristic shape of the depolarization and repolarization profile of the ventricular muscle cells, which includes of a delay of up to 300 ms occurring near the 0 mV potential level, compared with a 1 ms period between depolarization and repolarization for regular nerve cells

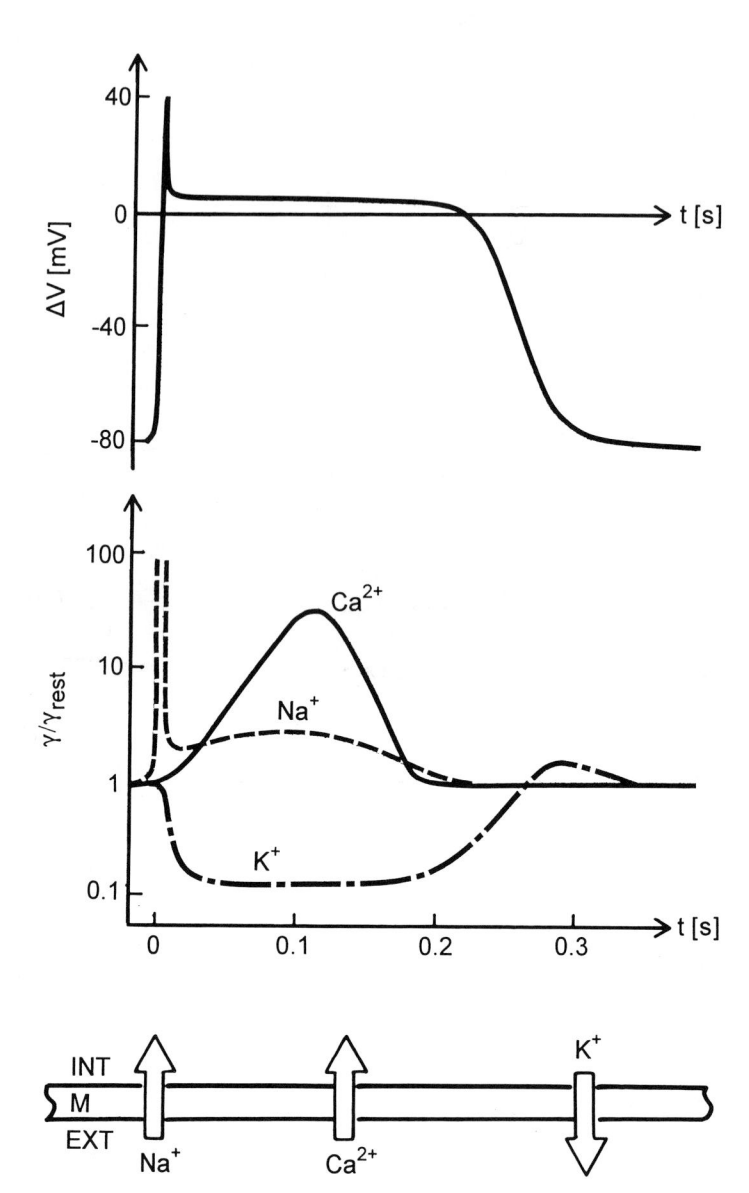

Fig. 14.6: Potential profile (top), relative permeability of the cell membrane (middle) and sketch of the dominant trans–membrane ion flux (bottom) for the Purkinje fiber cells. The figure illustrates how a small calcium ion concentration causes a significant delay of the repolarization of the cells.

(compare Fig. 13.3).

This unusual potential profile is explained in more detail in Fig. 14.6. The top part of the figure shows again a single cycle of the potential of a heart muscle cell as a function of time, taken from the last frame in Fig. 14.5. The lower plot shows the time profile of the relative permeability (relative to a value of 1 for the resting muscle cell) for sodium, calcium and potassium ions. Note that the relative permeability is shown by using a logarithmic scale. The sketch below the two plots identifies the dominant ion transport across the muscle cell membrane for each stage of the signal.

The fast depolarization, initially taking place when the nerve impulse arrives, is due to a steep increase in the permeability of sodium. This leads to the diffusion of sodium along its concentration gradient from the extracellular fluid into the cell (with the concentrations given in Table 14.2). This process is equivalent to the depolarization of a regular nerve cell, as discussed in Chapter 13.

The next stage is unique to the muscle cells of the heart. The changed potential triggers an increased calcium transport across the membrane, leading to the plateau phase of the action potential near 0 mV for about 150 ms, i.e., more than a tenth of a second. The sodium transport across the membrane is significantly reduced at this potential, in the same fashion we already saw for the nerve cells in Chapter 13. However, the calcium diffusion suppresses the trans–membrane permeability of potassium, while transporting little charge across the membrane due to much smaller concentration levels of calcium inside and outside of the cell (see Table 14.2). Note that the very low intracellular calcium concentration increases by up to 50 % during this period, to a maximum of 1.5 $\mu mol/l$. The calcium diffusion into the cell is notably slower than the diffusion of either sodium or potassium, thus leading to the long delay at this stage.

The ongoing change in the concentrations of calcium eventually leads to a reduction of the calcium diffusion rate, favoring the steep increase in the potassium

Table 14.2: Ion concentrations on the extracellular and intracellular sides of the membrane of a heart muscle cell.

Ion species	Intracellular [mmol/l]	Extracellular [mmol/l]
Na^+	12	145
Ca^{2+}	0.0011	1.25
K^+	150	4

permeability. Once potassium flows across the membrane into the interstitium, the potential quickly drops in the repolarization stage to − 80 mV. This last stage is analogous to the repolarization step for regular nerve cells, as discussed in Chapter 13. The electric effect due to the potassium flow is much larger than the effects during calcium diffusion because of the larger potassium concentrations involved in Table 14.2.

14.2. The electrocardiogram

14.2.1. The ECG signal

The long period of the depolarized state of the muscle cells in the heart is advantageous to the external electric measurement of the heart action, leading to electrocardiography. Before we can measure and interpret an electrocardiogram, however, we have to understand how a measurable potential outside the cell membrane is formed.

In Chapter 13, our focus was on the potential across a nerve membrane, i.e., assuming that in a measurement one electrode is placed inside the axoplasm and the second electrode is placed outside the cell in the extracellular fluid. This corresponds to the experimental set–up of the Hodgkin–Huxley experiment discussed in section 13.5. To measure this potential requires obviously an intrusive technique. If such an experiment is done, as illustrated in Fig. 14.7(b), a potential difference of − 70 mV is measured for a resting nerve cell. However, if the measurement is done non–intrusively, i.e., with both electrodes placed outside the nerve cell, no potential difference is observed, as indicated for a second Voltmeter in Fig. 14.7(a).

The non–intrusive measurement in Fig. 14.7(a) can lead to the observation of a non–zero potential when a nerve signal passes through the section along which the two electrodes are placed. This is illustrated in Fig. 14.8. The figure shows in five steps the signal that is observed with two external electrodes placed along a nerve cell. In the first frame, the two electrodes are both located ahead of the nerve section currently carrying the nerve impulse (shaded area), i.e., along a section of resting nerve. Since the nerve is anatomically and electrically in the same stage at both points, i.e., the same potential applies, a zero potential difference is measured, as indicated in the attached display of the potential difference versus time (thick line).

In the second frame, the travelling nerve signal has passed the first electrode, but has not reached the second electrode further downstream. Thus, the electric effect at the two electrodes differs with positive ions near the electrode where the nerve cell is still at rest and negative ions near the electrode where the nerve signal has already arrived. Thus, a potential difference is measured between the two electrodes and is seen on the oscilloscope. Whether a positive or negative deviation from the reference line occurs depends on the polarity of the signal. The polarity of the potential for a passing nerve signal in Fig. 14.8 is based on the definition of the electric field direction as a function of the electric charges, as shown in Fig. 9.12, and the connection between the direction of the field vector and the polarity of the potential, as illustrated in Fig. 13.9. From Fig. 13.9 we find that the potential is lower at the point where negative charges are present. The oscilloscope in the second frame of Fig. 14.8 reads therefore a positive value as it represents the potential at the leading electrode minus the potential at the trailing electrode.

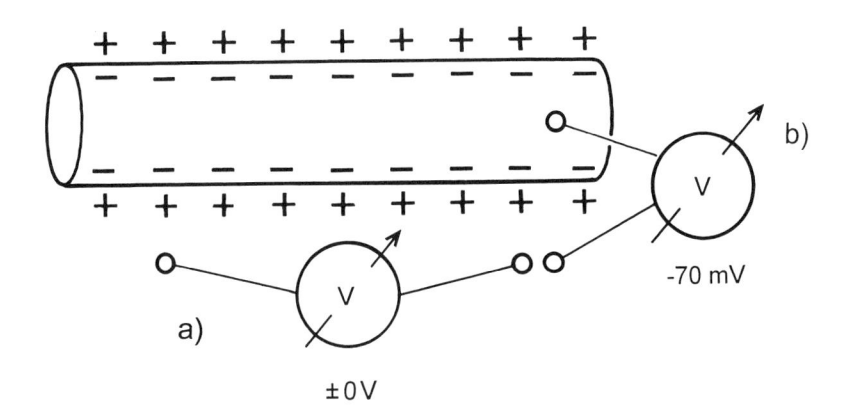

Fig. 14.7: Comparison of a potential measurement (a) along the nerve membrane and (b) across the nerve membrane for a resting nerve cell.

In the third frame of Fig. 14.8 both electrodes are located along the depolarized section of the nerve. Thus, a zero potential difference follows. Looking at the fourth and the fifth frames illustrates that the measured potential difference peaks with opposite polarity when the repolarization passes the electrodes in sequence.

Fig. 14.8 illustrates that the polarity of the signal matters, and that the depolarization and repolarization of a cell lead to signals of opposite polarity. Although a potential difference is a scalar quantity, the polarity and the orientation of the studied nerve tissue allow us to interpret the quantity we observe on the oscilloscope in Fig. 14.8 as the projection of a vector onto the line between the two electrodes. To simplify the later discussion of the ECG we define this vector as the depolarization vector: the depolarization vector is a vector pointing from depolarized tissue toward polarized tissue.

It is important to distinguish the depolarization vector and the electric field vector. This is highlighted in Fig. 14.9, which shows a section of tissue in which the left part is depolarized (negative excess charges in the interstitium) and the right part is polarized or in the resting state, with positive excess charges in the interstitium. Based on the definition in Fig. 9.12, the electric field vector points therefore from the depolarized section toward the resting/polarized section. Thus, the depolarization vector and the electric field vector are anti–parallel.

The discussion of Fig. 14.8 illustrates that non–zero potentials occur during the depolarization process if measured with two electrodes outside the nerve tissue itself. This establishes the possibility for non–intrusive

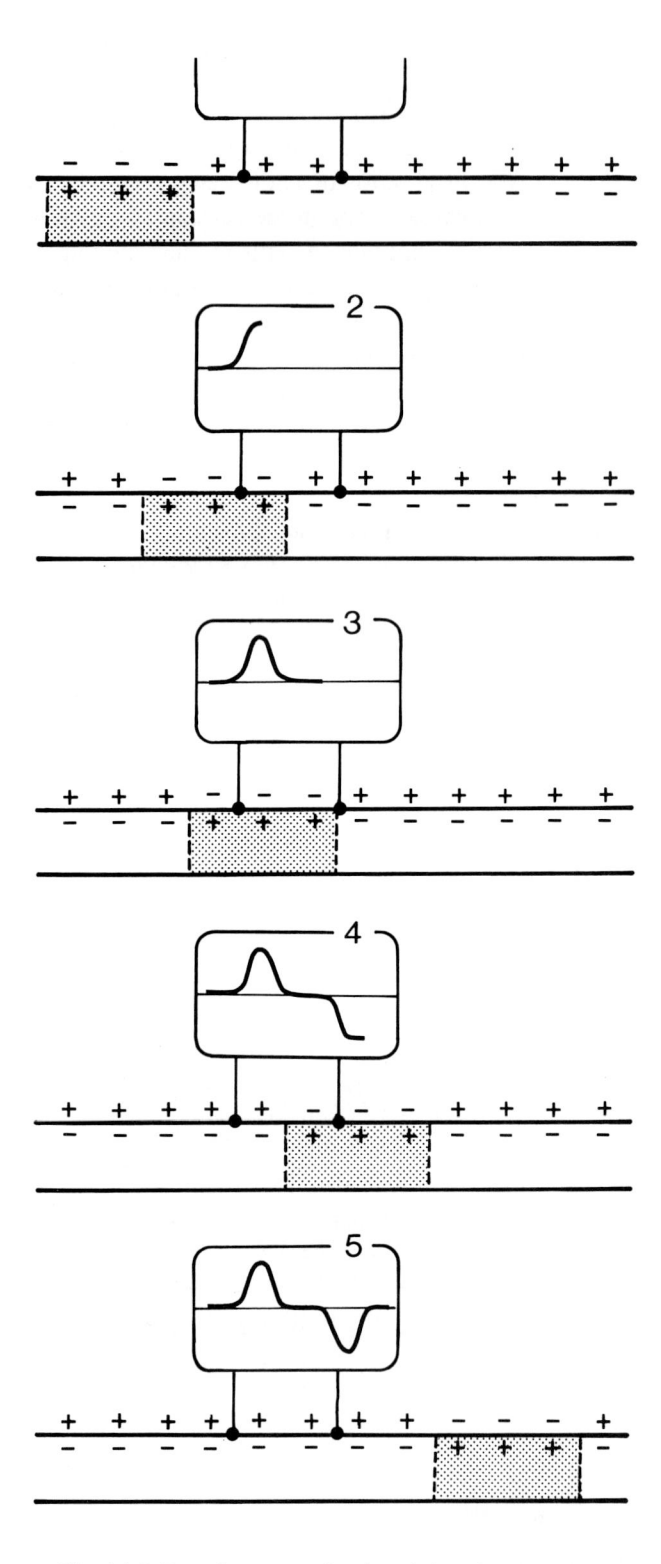

Fig. 14.8: Development of a signal showing a potential change for a passing nerve signal with two external electrodes. No potential difference is detected in frames 1, 3 and 5 as the nerve depolarization (frame 2) and the nerve repolarization (frame 4) have respectively passed both electrodes.

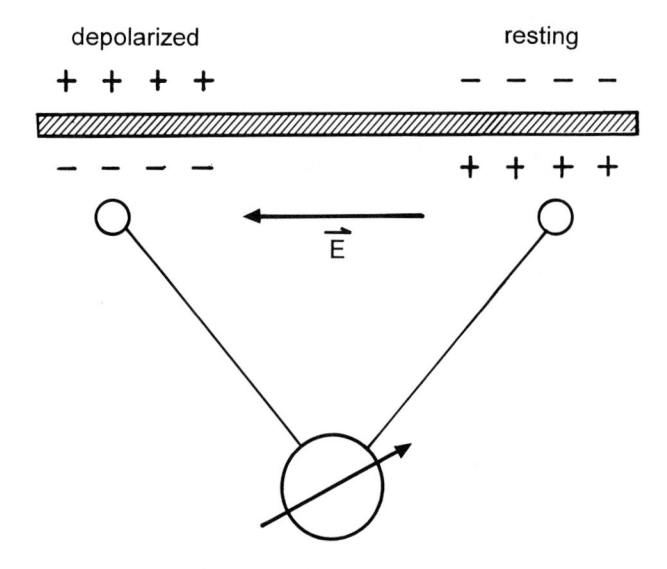

Fig. 14.9: Illustration of the direction of the electric field between two electrodes when a depolarization signal has passed the first but not the second electrode. The depolarization signal travels toward the left in the figure.

measurements of nervous processes in the heart. We also note that the long delay of the repolarization in the muscle cells of the heart simplifies the measurement as it guarantees that significant fractions of the tissue are depolarized for extended periods during the heart's cycle. However, Fig. 14.8 indicates that the potential measurement depends not only on time but also on the location of the two electrodes relative to each other and relative to the nerve.

The variability of a potential measurement as a function of the location of two electrodes is illustrated in Fig. 14.10. The figure illustrates the equipotential lines for the human heart at a given instant in time during the cycle of the heart (during the R–peak of the ECG as defined below). The figure also shows which absolute potential values in [mV] correspond to the equipotential lines when determined on the skin of the patient. Assuming that two electrodes are attached to the skin of the patient, the potential difference measured at this instant would correspond to the difference of the potential value shown for the location of the two electrodes. Comparing the equipotential lines of Fig. 14.10 with those of an electric dipole (solid lines in Fig. 14.11, see also Fig. 9.28(c)) shows that the dipole is a useful model to approximate the skin surface potential due to the heart action.

14.2.2. The ECG method of Einthoven

Fig. 14.10 shows that the measured potential difference depends on the location of the two electrodes attached to the patient's skin. Since equipotential line patterns at other stages of the heart's beating cycle are similar to those of Fig. 14.10, but rotate due to the change of the direction of the depolarization vector as discussed below, it is important to establish a convention for the placing of the electrodes to ensure a consistent reading of the potential difference curves as a function of time. The most widely used convention is based on the work of Willem Einthoven, who developed the ECG method in 1906. Einthoven noted that the potential of the heart action can be detected as far away as the limbs. These are therefore chosen as the locations for the electrodes since their positions relative to the heart are fixed.

Einthoven further decided to connect three electrodes to the patient, one to the right arm, one to the left arm and one to the left leg. This allowed him to measure the potential between any pair of electrodes, i.e., there are three different measurements possible, which are called "leads." Fig. 14.12 illustrates these leads in a conceptual sketch. The three electrodes are configured such that they describe essentially an equilateral triangle. The electrodes must have different po-

Fig. 14.10: Equipotential lines for the human heart as measured on the skin surface during the R–peak of the ECG. The values given in the figure are in unit [mV].

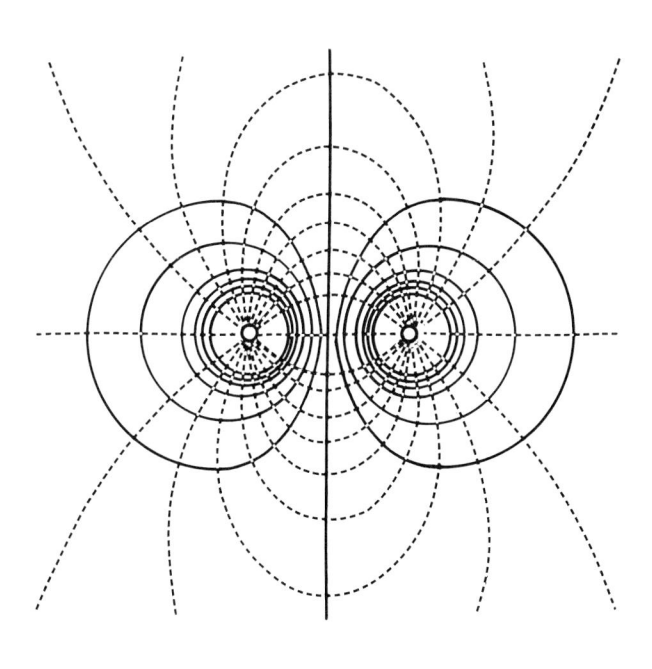

Fig. 14.11: Electric field lines (dashed curves) and equipotential lines (solid lines) for an electric dipole with the two charges indicated by open circles. Comparison with Fig. 14.10 allows us to approximate the electric field of the heart as a changing dipole field.

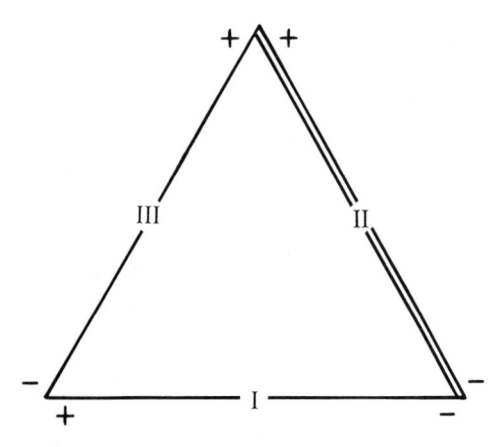

Fig. 14.12: The three leads as defined by Einthoven for the measurement of ECG curves. Lead II is selected for the further discussion in this chapter.

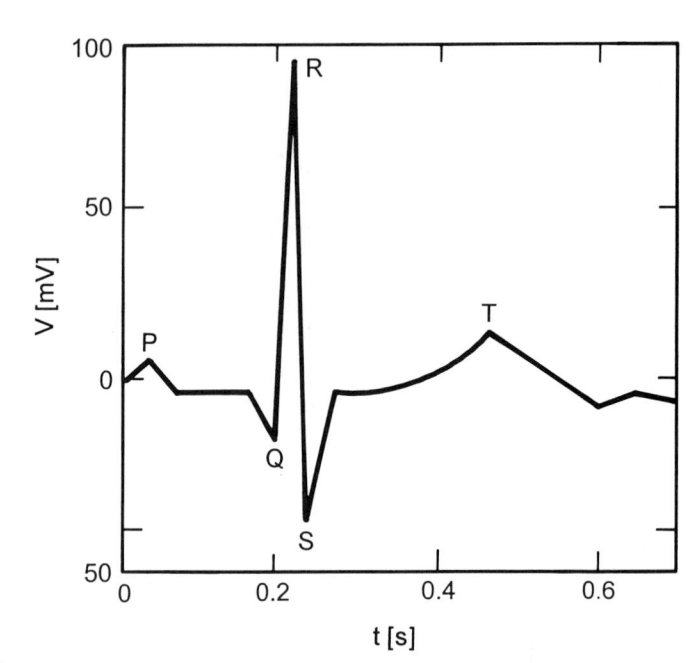

Fig. 14.13: The repetitive section of an ECG signal using lead II from Fig. 14.12. Note the P, Q, R, S and T–peaks which are explained in detail in the text and in the next figure.

larities for each of the three leads. The standard polarities for the three cases are indicated by the respective + and − signs in Fig. 14.12. Highlighted in the figure is lead II, which is the lead for which the electrocardiogram for a full cycle of the healthy human heart is shown in Fig. 14.13.

We want to understand each of the features of the electrocardiogram in Fig. 14.13, and thus follow the electric processes of the heart step by step as provided in Fig. 14.14. This figure consists of 5 frames, each illustrating the present direction of depolarization as an arrow overlaying a sketched heart (depolarization vector). Also depicted is a dashed line representing the reference line for lead II, onto which the depolarization vector is projected in this measurement. To the left of each frame is the ECG shown as it develops at each stage. The ECG starts at the time when the heart is fully polarized.

The first frame shows the stage when the SA–node has fired (shown as the upper dot on the sketch of the heart) and the depolarization progresses to the two atrial chambers. The depolarization vector points in this stage toward the tip of the heart. This direction is not perpendicular to the direction of lead II and, therefore, the projection of the depolarization vector onto the direction of lead II is needed to quantify the measured potential difference. Due to the polarity of lead II, as shown in Fig. 14.12, a positive potential difference is associated with this stage. The resulting positive peak in the ECG is called the P–peak and represents the atrial depolarization. The peak lasts for about 0.1 seconds.

The second frame contains two features. First, following the P–peak the two atrial chambers are fully depolarized. The depolarization of the AV– node (lower dot in the sketch of the heart) occurs concurrently. Since the AV–node represents a small amount of tissue, no apparent progress of the depolarization occurs during this stage. This leads to a depolarization vector of zero length, and thus no projected length is present along the direction of lead II. As a consequence, the ECG signal is back to the zero potential line, which is called the PQ–interval. The PQ–interval coincides with the depolarization of the AV–node.

The same frame also shows the start of depolarization of the ventricles. The initial depolarization begins on the left side of the septum and progresses initially toward the upper end of the heart. Projecting this direction onto lead II causes a negative potential difference (backwards projection). This stage is called the Q–peak, which corresponds to the depolarization of the upper end of the ventricles.

Once the depolarization of the upper end of the ventricles is complete, the primary direction of the progressing depolarization is toward the tip of the heart. Projecting this depolarization vector in the third frame onto lead II shows that the sign of the measured potential difference switches to a positive value. The resulting peak is particularly strong as a large number of tissue cells are involved in this part of the ventricles. This peak is called the R–peak and represents the major depolarization of the ventricles. Note that the equipotential lines during the R–peak are shown in Fig. 14.10.

Not all parts of the heart are depolarized when the depolarization of the lower part of the ventricles is complete. A small part of the back left side of the heart (posterobasal region) depolarizes after the R–peak is complete, as shown in the fourth frame. Since the respective depolarization vector is associated with a projection onto lead II which has again turned in direction, a second peak with negative potential difference is obtained. This peak is called the S–peak and represents the completion of the ventricle depolarization. The Q– and S–peaks are smaller than the R–peak because a lesser amount of tissue is affected by their respective depolarizations.

The last frame shows the repolarization of the ventricles (note the Ca^{2+} transport related time delay discussed above). The repolarization starts at the tip of the heart and progresses upwards. This constitutes the opposite direction to the R–peak. However, we also have a reversed process: a repolarization instead of a depolarization. Since we define the direction of the vector we project onto lead II as a depolarization vector, an inversion of its direction must be taken into account. Thus, the repolarization leads again to the measurement of a positive potential difference. The corresponding feature in the ECG is the T–peak, which represents the repolarization of the ventricles.

At this stage the repolarization of the heart is complete, and a new cycle can begin. Note that we did not identify a feature in the ECG which corresponds to the repolarization of the atrial chambers. This is due to the fact that the respective signal is overshadowed by the much stronger QRS–peak feature, indicating that the repolarization of the atrial chambers occurs less than 0.2 seconds after the onset of the P–peak.

P–peak: atrial depolarization
PQ–interval: depolarization of the AV–node
Q–peak: depolarization of upper end of ventricles
R–peak: major depolarization of the ventricles
S–peak: completion of the ventricle depolarization
T–peak: repolarization of the ventricles

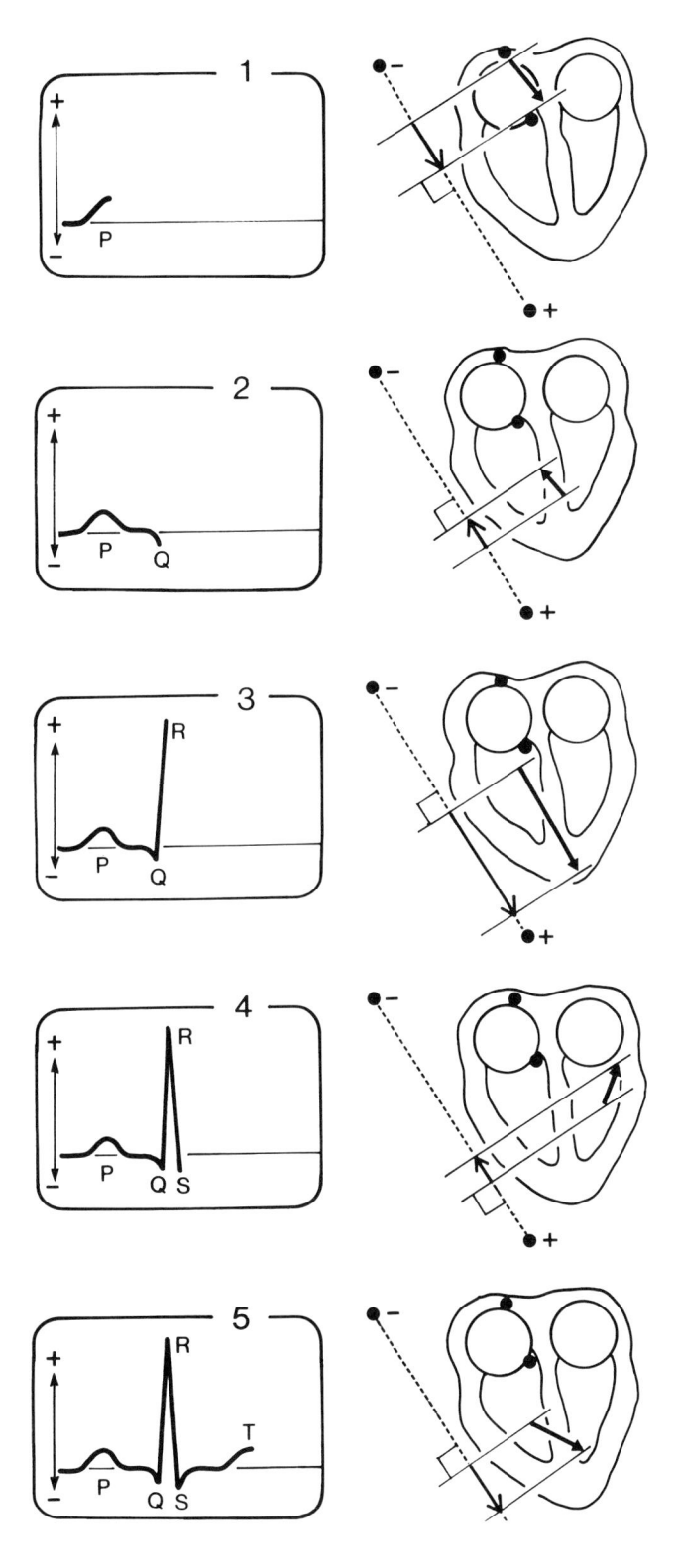

Fig. 14.14: Development of the ECG signal in 5 steps. The oscilloscope image is shown at the left, the depolarization vector in the heart is shown in the sketches at the right. The dashed line represents lead II as defined by Einthoven. The two solid dots on each heart represent the SA– and AV–nodes, respectively.

14.3. Medical use of the ECG

Fig. 14.15 shows typical examples of ECG diagrams for abnormal hearts. The QRS–peak is widened in Fig. 14.15(a), indicating an enlarged heart. In Fig. 14.15(b) the usual relationship between the P–peak and the QRS–peak is lost. This points toward a blockage of the electric

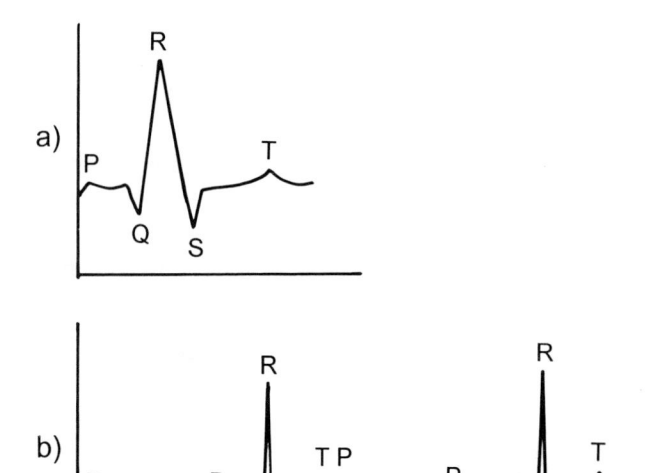

Fig. 14.15: Three cases of ECG signals for an abnormal heart.
(a) The QRS–peak is broadened,
(b) the rhythm of the P– and the QRS–peaks is lost, and
(c) an absence of the P–peak and an irregular spacing of QRS–peaks.

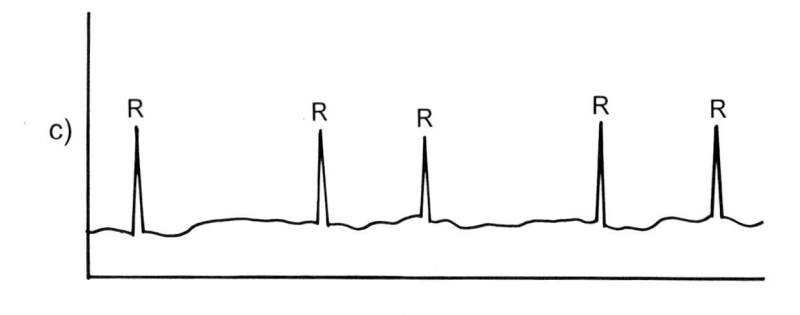

conduction path between the SA–node and the AV–node. Finally, the diagram in Fig. 14.15(c) is characterized by the absence of the P–peak and an irregular spacing between QRS–peaks. This occurs for patients with a condition called fibrillation.

A cardiac pacemaker is an external device, which is electrically attached to the heart (at the right ventricle) to provide a steady state heart beat rate, overriding the natural electric activity of the SA–node. Such a device is introduced when the natural activity of the SA–node is either weakened or irregular, e.g. due to old age or disease. The device itself consists of a capacitor which charges up to a certain potential and then automatically discharges.

If the heart maintains its natural beating rate, the capacitor never charges fully and therefore does not discharge, because the impulse rate of the pacemaker (usually 60 beats/minute) is somewhat slower than the natural heart beat rate.

Chapter XV

Elastic Tissue

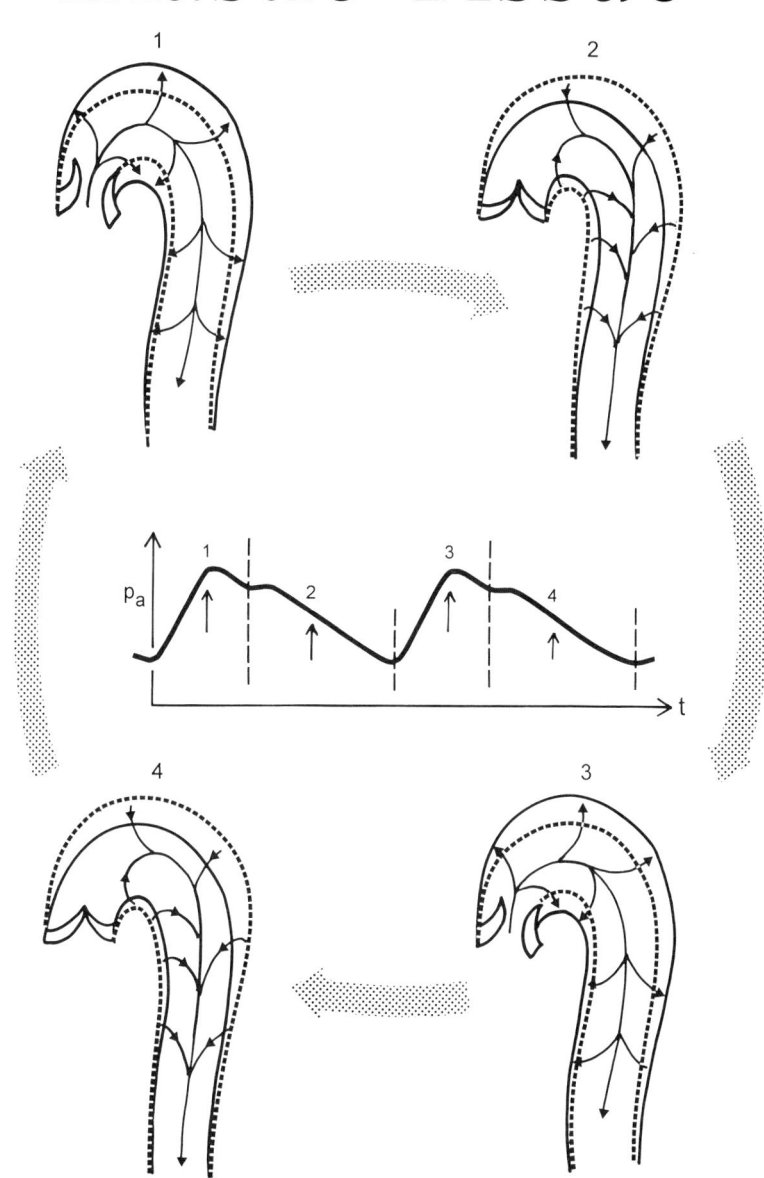

Elasticity and vibrations

ELASTIC TISSUE
ELASTICITY AND VIBRATIONS

The rigid body model we introduced in Chapter 4 is insufficient to describe many fundamental properties of extended objects, such as stretching, twisting, deformation and rupture. In the current chapter a more general model is provided: the elastic object. An elastic object responds to a stress (a force acting on the surface of an extended object) with a strain (a change in size of the object) which is linearly proportional to the stress. This linear relation is called Hooke's law. Examples include elongation in response to tensile stress, twisting as a result of shear stress and compression due to hydraulic stress. Some important physiological systems do not respond elastically but can be discussed qualitatively using the same elasticity concepts.

The most important property of elastic systems is their dynamic behavior when released from a mechanical non–equilibrium state: the system undergoes sinusoidal vibrations about its equilibrium state in response to a restoring force which is linear in the displacement from the equilibrium. A new form of potential energy, the elastic potential energy, is introduced for such systems. It depends quadratically on the displacement from the equilibrium position.

Three examples are discussed: the vibration of an object attached to a spring, which is a useful model for intramolecular vibrations; the pendulum, which is also suitable to model bipedal walking; and a freely moving piston confining a gas. The latter system is a useful starting point for the discussion of acoustic waves in the next chapter.

We introduced in Chapter 4 the rigid body as a model sufficient to describe the rotation of bones about a joint. The rigid body model fails, however, in the description of many other physical processes of extended objects, most notably when we focus on softer materials. We observed this already in a qualitative fashion at the beginning of Chapter 2 when we described muscles and their ability to exert forces on attached bones.

To illustrate this observation in more detail, we return briefly to the microscopic sketch of the sarcomere in Fig. 2.2. This unit can actively contract when the myosin filaments slide toward the two terminal Z discs along the actin filaments. The sarcomere can also be stretched passively by the action of an antagonistic muscle.

The graph in Fig. 15.1 is a conceptual sketch of the dependence of the contractile (active) force the sarcomere unit can exert when stretched to a given length l. The length l of the sarcomere is defined by the distance between two adjacent Z discs. The force is shown as a value relative to the maximum force the sarcomere can exert. The maximum force occurs when the sarcomeres are at their average lengths of $l = 2.1$ μm. The graph allows us to emphasize some important features of the active force: as the sarcomere length varies, the overlap of the myosin and actin filaments varies as well. As shown in the insets along the curve, the variation of overlap of actin and myosin filaments causes a loss of muscle force when stretched far from the average length. When the sarcomere shortens to less than 1.65 μm length, the myosin filaments touch the two adjacent Z discs. This provides a physical limitation as muscle contraction by more than 20 to 25 % is practically not possible. When the sarcomere is passively stretched to lengths around 2.8 μm or more (i.e., when the muscle is stretched to 130 % or more of its average length) its ability to contract is significantly reduced as the overlap of the actin and myosin filaments is reduced. If there were no counteracting process, this would be dangerous for the muscle as its own ability to withstand the stretching through contraction is weakened.

The curves in Fig. 15.2(a) illustrate how the muscle is protected against overstretching. The dash–dotted curve shows again the active force the muscle can exert when stretched to various lengths (shown relative to the average length). This curve corresponds to the curve in Fig. 15.1. Comparing Figs. 15.1 and 15.2 we note the benefit of the conceptual sketch: straight line

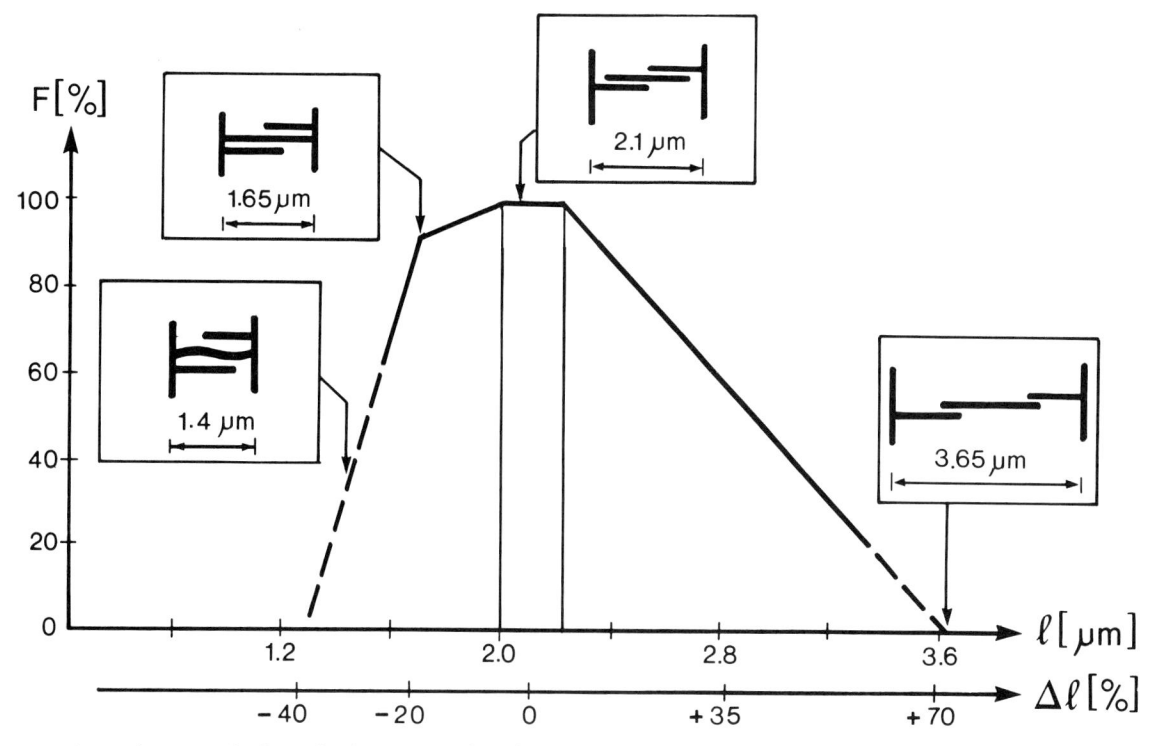

Fig. 15.1: The active muscle force is shown as a function of the sarcomere length. The force is given as a fraction of the maximum force a muscle can exert when it is at its average length of 2.1 μm. The sarcomere length is given as an absolute value l [μm] (top abscissa) and as a length change relative to the average length Δl [%] (bottom abscissa). For several specific sarcomere lengths the overlap of the myosin and actin filaments is illustrated in the inserted boxes. These insets indicate the origin of loss of active muscle force when the muscle is stretched too far (too weak overlap between actin and myosin filaments) and when the muscle tries to contract too far (myosin filaments collide with Z discs).

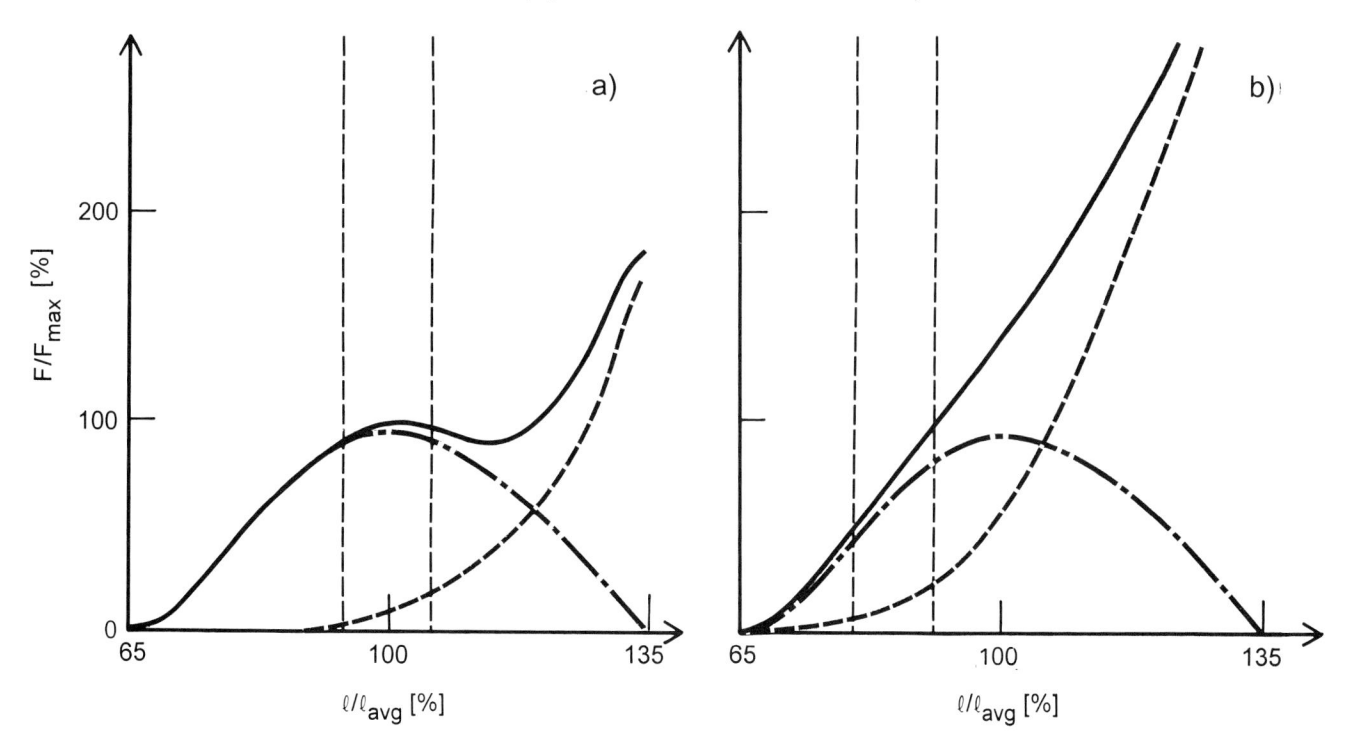

Fig. 15.2: Active (dash–dotted) and passive (dashed) components of the muscle force for (a) skeletal muscles, and (b) the heart muscle. The figures show the force, relative to the maximum force, as a function of the muscle length, relative to the muscle length at the point when the muscle exerts a maximum active force. This length is called the average length. The solid lines show the total force, which is the sum of the active force and the passive stretching force. The two vertical dashed lines indicate the normal operating regime of the muscle. The dash–dotted curve in part (a) is equivalent to the curve shown in Fig. 15.1. Note that the passive stretching force acts as a protection of the muscle, preventing an excessive bending of the tissue.

segments in Fig. 15.1 are easier to quantify than the curved dashed–dotted function in Fig. 15.2. Whether it is sufficient to use the sketch in Fig. 15.1 or whether it is necessary to use the data from the plot in Fig. 15.2 depends on the specific purpose or argument we want to make.

Fig. 15.2 shows a second curve applicable to the same sarcomere (dashed line). While the dash–dotted curve shows the active muscle force, i.e., the force the muscle can exert on the bones to which it is attached, the dashed curve is the passive stretching force, i.e., the force by which the muscle resists being stretched. This passive stretching force is a property of the muscle tissue and is capable to protect the muscle against being extended to a length from which it can no longer contract by its own action. The net force with which a muscle can oppose being stretched is shown in Fig. 15.2 as a solid line. This net force is the sum of the active and passive forces. Muscles cannot be overstretched because the passive force limits the stretching at large values of length l.

Fig. 15.2 illustrates two points. First, a muscle is not a rigid body as it can contract or be stretched. Second, when a muscle is stretched beyond its average length, a force counteracts against further stretching. This force increases with increasing length of the muscle, it tends to restore the original length of the muscle. Thus, it is necessary to extend the rigid body model to allow for deformations as a result of external forces and to allow for restoring forces which are caused by deformations of an extended object.

Fig. 15.2(b) illustrates that the same observations apply to muscles with other functions than the skeletal muscles. For the heart muscles the passive force counteracting its stretching is even more dominant than in the case of the skeletal muscle. The total force acting on the tissue (solid curve) is again a combination of two contributions: an active force (dash–dotted curve) and a passive stretching force (dashed curve).

Thus, we see that the ability of materials to be deformed and the response to the deformation is important to prevent damage to tissues. The response to a deformation is a force which tries to restore the resting state of the tissue. We develop this concept in the present chapter and call it elasticity. Elasticity then allows us to study vibrations as a new type of motion which the more restrictive point mass and rigid body models were not suitable for.

15.1. Elasticity

In this section deformations of tissues are quantitatively related to the forces acting on the extended object, thereby expanding the model of a rigid body introduced in Chapter 4, in which shape changes were excluded. The cause of a deformation of an extended object is called *stress*, which is a force exerted per unit area of surface of the extended object. The stress leads to a *strain* which is the relative change in the size of the object. We distinguish three types of deformations based on the type of strain: a change in the length of an object is called a stretching, a change of an angle of the extended object is called twisting, and a change in the volume of an object is called an expansion or a compression. Each of these strain types is associated with a different form of stress, with the tensile stress leading to stretching, the shearing stress leading to twisting, and the hydraulic stress leading to expansion or compression. These types of stress are discussed in turn in the next three sections.

15.1.1. Tensile stress and stretching

Stretching of an extended object is illustrated in Fig. 15.3. The stretching in the vertical direction is achieved by two opposite normal forces, $\mathbf{F}_1$ and $\mathbf{F}_2$. The volume of the object (and, therefore, also its density) is conserved in this process since the width and depth of the object are reduced simultaneously. Such a stretching is possible for solids and liquids.

We define the terms stress and strain for Fig. 15.3. Strain is the relative change in size, in the case of stretching expressed as $\Delta l/l$. Δl is the absolute change in length, $\Delta l = l_{\text{final}} - l_{\text{initial}}$. The strain is a dimensionless quantity since two lengths are divided in the term $\Delta l/l$. The stress leading to this stretching, i.e., the tensile stress, is given by F/A with F the magnitude of force $\mathbf{F}_1$. The parameter A represents the surface area of the object on which the force $\mathbf{F}_1$ acts. F/A has unit [Pa], analogous to the quantity pressure which we introduced in Chapter 5. The two forces in Fig. 15.3 are connected by Newton's first law due to the condition of mechanical equilibrium: $\mathbf{F}_2 = -\mathbf{F}_1$. This is not an application of Newton's third law as both forces act on the same object!

We expect an elongation of the object when a tensile stress acts on it. The object stretches to a certain length at which the restoring forces within the object balance the external forces, establishing a new mechanical equilibrium for the system. We call the response of the object *elastic* if the strain and stress are proportional to each other, i.e., when the length change of the object increases linearly with the stress:

$$\frac{F}{A} = Y \frac{\Delta l}{l} \qquad (1)$$

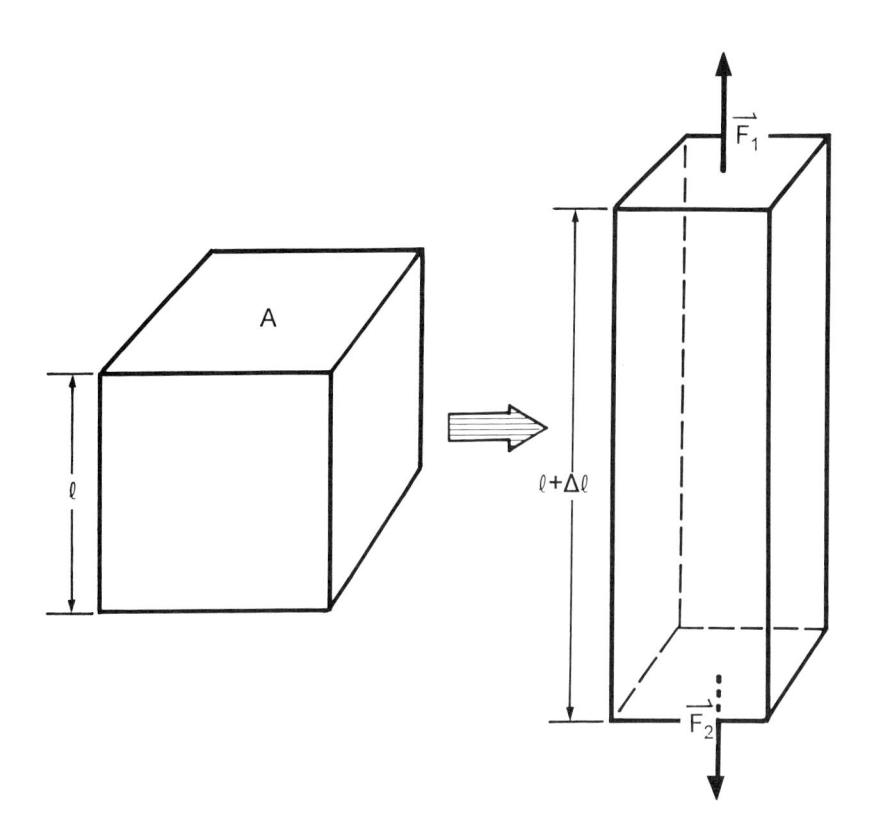

Fig. 15.3: Sketch of a stretching deformation of an extended object, chosen to be initially a cube. Two equal but opposite forces pull on opposing surfaces of area A. The stress $|\mathbf{F}|/A$ leads to a strain in the form of a length increase from l to $l + \Delta l$.

The proportionality factor Y is called *Young's modulus* (named for Thomas Young) with unit [Pa]. Therefore, Young's modulus is the quotient of stress to strain. Since this formula is used frequently in the description of mechanical properties of solids and liquids, new variables are introduced: σ for the stress, with $\sigma = F/A$; and ϵ for the strain, with $\epsilon = \Delta l/l$. These definitions allow us to rewrite Eq. (1) in the form:

$$\sigma = Y \epsilon \quad (2)$$

A large value of Young's modulus, for example for steel, means that even a large force acting on the material leads only to a small length increase. In turn, small values of Young's modulus, e.g. for a blood vessel, mean that even small forces cause a large length variation. We call materials with large Young's moduli "strong materials" and materials with small Young's moduli "soft materials". Table 15.1 lists several values for Young's moduli, primarily comparing biological materials.

Extensive stretching deformations usually don't obey Eq. (2). Thus, an elastic limit for the strain is introduced which describes the threshold of the relative length change beyond which Eq. (2) is no longer applicable. For a larger strain the object encounters permanent deformations (plastic deformations). The elastic limit is discussed in section 15.1.4 in which we generalize Eq. (2) to include also the cases discussed in the next two sections.

Table 15.1: Young's modulus for various materials.

Material	Y [Pa]
Steel	2×10^{11}
Douglas Fir wood	1.3×10^{10}
Compact bone (e.g. femur)	$1 - 2 \times 10^{10}$
Teeth	$7 \times 10^9 - 1.5 \times 10^{10}$
Cartilage	$1 - 4 \times 10^7$
Tendon	$2 \times 10^7 - 1 \times 10^6$
Rubber	$7 \times 10^6 - 2 \times 10^7$
Blood vessels	$1.2 - 4.0 \times 10^5$

15.1.2. Shearing stress and twisting

A second type of deformation is illustrated in Fig. 15.4: two equal but opposite forces, $\mathbf{F}_1$ and $\mathbf{F}_2$, are applied tangentially to two opposite faces of an extended object, i.e., the force vectors lie parallel to the surface they act on, as shown in the figure. To maintain a mechanical equilibrium, i.e., to avoid a torque acting on the object, additional forces must be applied to hold the object stationary. This type of deformation can only occur in solids because liquids and gases cannot sustain tangential forces. The two forces shown, $\mathbf{F}_1$ and $\mathbf{F}_2$, lead to a deformation of the extended object which we quantify by measuring the change of the angle θ. In the case of Fig. 15.4, where we began with a rectangular prism, we use geometry to rewrite the change of the angle:

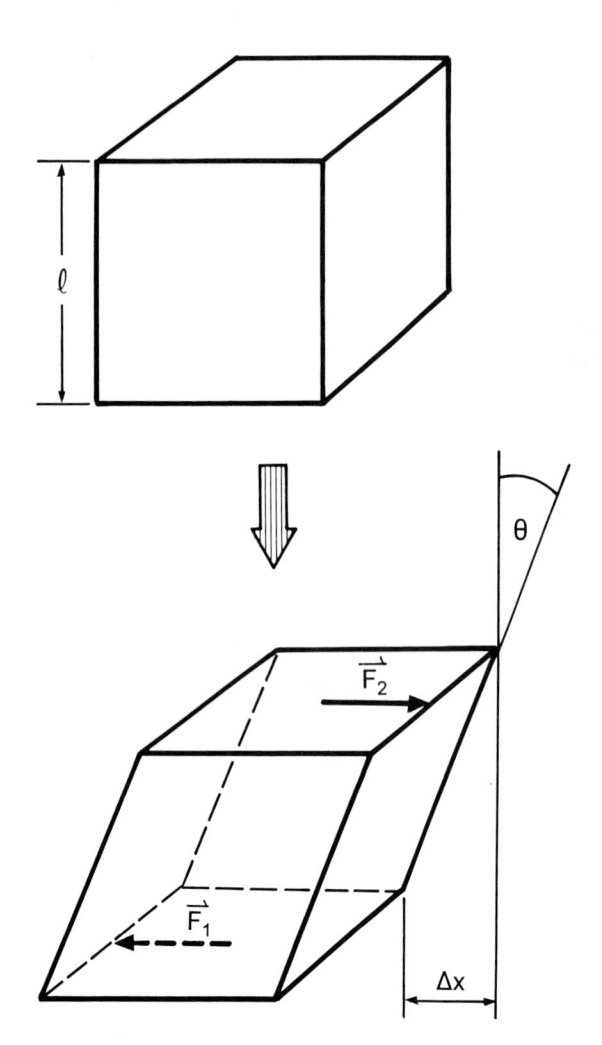

Fig. 15.4: Sketch of a twisting deformation of an extended object, chosen to be initially a cube. Two tangential forces act on opposing surfaces of the object to change θ. This change is expressed as a function of the lengths Δx and l.

$$\theta \simeq \tan\theta = \frac{\Delta x}{l} \qquad (3)$$

In analogy to the stretching case, we define the twisting as an elastic twisting deformation when the stress and strain are proportional to each other:

$$\frac{F}{A} = G \frac{\Delta x}{l} \qquad (4)$$

Eq. (4) defines G, the *shear modulus*, with unit [Pa]. A large value of G means that even a large tangential force leads to only a small twisting. An example is steel, which has a value of $G = 8 \times 10^{10}$ Pa. In turn, a material with a small G value is easily twisted by small forces. An example is cartilage with $G = 2.5 \times 10^7$ Pa.

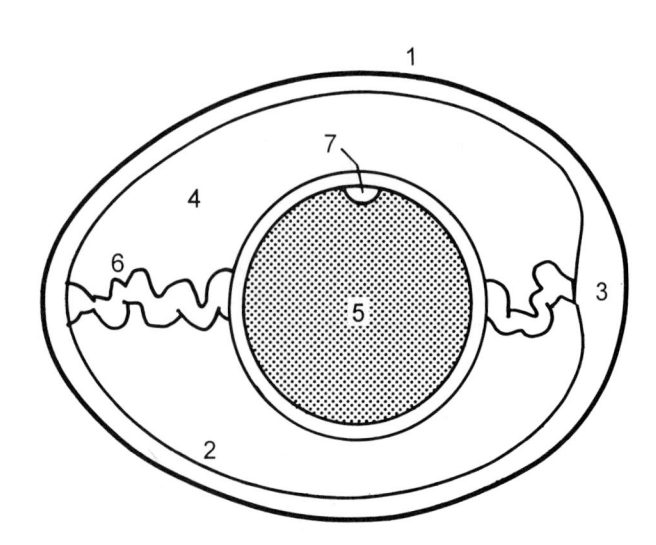

Fig. 15.5: Twisting motion in a chicken egg. The yolk (5) and the germ disk (7) are attached to the inner shell membrane (2) with a pair of elastic cords (6). These allow the germ disk to remain at the top of the yolk at all times because the center–of–mass of the yolk/germ disk–unit lies off–center away from the germ disk. This allows for a small net torque due to gravity when the germ disk is rotated sideways. Other components of the egg are shown: (1) shell, (3) air sac, and (4) egg white.

An interesting application of the twisting motion is illustrated in Fig. 15.5 for the chicken egg. The yolk of the egg is connected to the germ disk, from which the chicken develops. It is beneficial for the developing chicken to have the germ disk at all times directed upwards because the warmth of the object of the breeding hen flows into the egg from above. Rotation of the egg in the nest should not allow the germ disk to turn to the side or facing downwards.

To stabilize the germ disk in the upwards position, the yolk is connected to the inside of the egg shell as shown. The spiral–shaped cords have a very small shear (or torsion) modulus, allowing the yolk to turn easily about the longitudinal axis of the egg. The germ disk has a lower density than the yolk. Therefore, the center–of–mass of the suspended yolk/germ disk–unit, floating in the egg white, lies off–center away from the germ disk. This provides a small net torque due to the gravitational force, enough to rotate the germ disk always to the top.

15.1.3. Hydraulic stress and compression

A third type of deformation is possible for solids, liquids and confined gases: a compression or expansion is obtained by applying a force of magnitude |**F**| perpendicu-

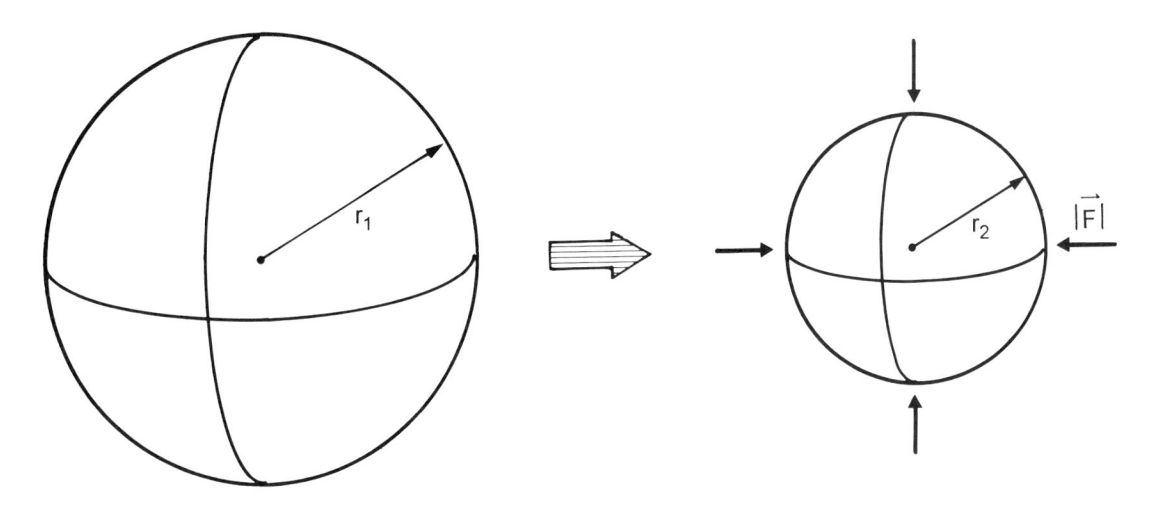

Fig. 15.6: Sketch of a compression of a spherical extended object due to uniformly applied external forces of magnitude **F**|. The volume change is expressed as a change in the radius of the sphere.

lar to the surface of an extended object from all sides, as illustrated in Fig. 15.6. In this case the stress not only carries the unit of pressure, [Pa], but is identical to the pressure as defined in Eq. (5.13). The strain is defined as the relative volume change, $\Delta V/V$.

An elastic deformation is given when the stress and strain are related linearly to each other:

$$p = -B \frac{\Delta V}{V} \quad (5)$$

The negative sign is introduced in Eq. (5) to ensure that the coefficient B is a positive number. It is needed since an increasing external pressure leads to a decreasing volume. The coefficient B is called the *bulk modulus* and has unit [Pa]. A typical value for the bulk modulus of a solid material is $B = 1.6 \times 10^{11}$ Pa, which is the value for steel. Liquids have only slightly lower values, e.g. for water we find $B = 2.1 \times 10^9$ Pa. Gases in turn have significantly lower values as they are easily compressed. It is important to distinguish that the bulk modulus describes the change in volume of a material while Young's modulus describes the change in length of a material.

The bulk modulus is used to define the *compressibility* of a material. The compressibility is 1/B, i.e., a material with a large bulk modulus has a small value.

15.1.4. Inelastic (plastic) deformations

The three elastic relations we introduced in Eqs. (1), (4) and (5) can be generalized in the form of Eq. (2). The deformation is reversible when Eq. (2) applies because the object returns to its original shape when the stress is removed.

We know from experience that Eq. (2) does not always hold. Only minor forces have to be applied to deform play dough permanently. This deformation is irreversible because the strain does not return to zero when the stress on the material is removed.

Stronger materials also respond to a large stress in an irreversible fashion, e.g. when a steel girder of a suspension bridge rips. Fig. 15.7 shows the entire range of the stress/strain relation for a medium–strength steel. For low stress values a linear relation is observed (this elastic part of the curve is extended in a dashed line). As the stress is increased beyond the linear regime, microscopic structural alterations in the steel take place leading to a significant strain increase, often occurring in sudden bursts. In this regime a permanent, plastic deformation of the material takes place. Eventually the material can no longer withstand the stress, passing through its ultimate strength point. Beyond this point the material approaches the rupture point quickly without need for a further increase of the stress.

> *Near the mechanical equilibrium, a linear relation applies between the cause of a deformation (stress) and the response by the extended object (strain). The material is called elastic when a linear stress/strain behavior is observed.*

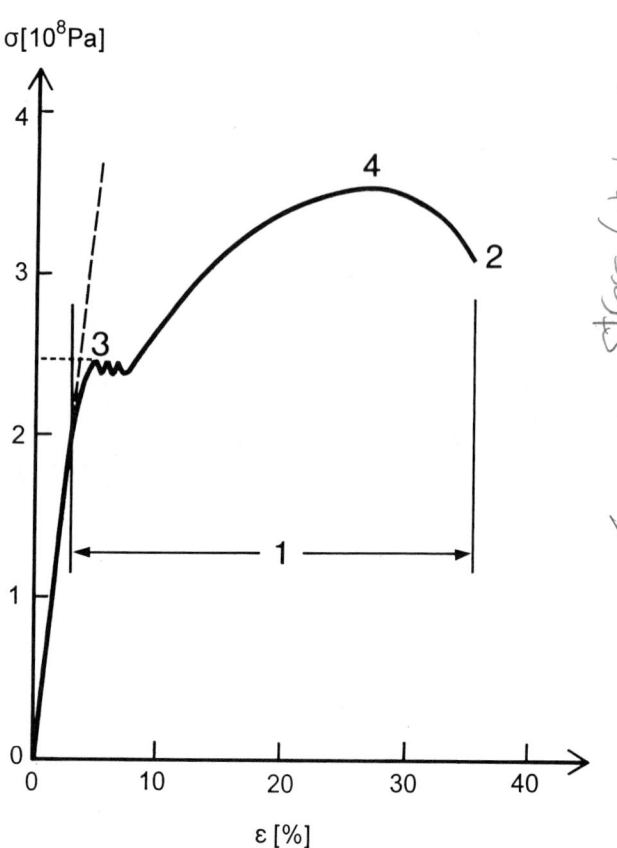

Fig. 15.7: Stress–strain relation of medium–strength steel. The stress is linearly proportional to the strain for strain values up to about 3 %. This linear regime is indicated by the dashed line. The plastic deformation regime (1) is more complex. Sudden bursts of strain increase indicate that structural changes occur within the material (3). The maximum strength is reached at a strain of about 28 % (4). The ultimate strength is reached near a strain value of 40 %, at which value the material ruptures (2).

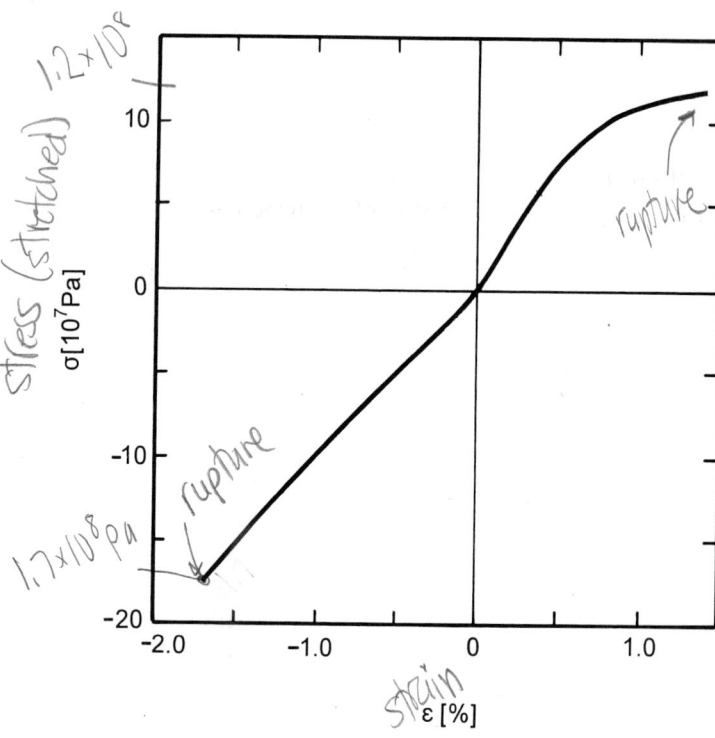

Fig. 15.8: Stress–strain relation for compact bone material. The graph includes both tensile stress (when the bone is stretched) and compressive stress (when the bone is compressed in one direction).

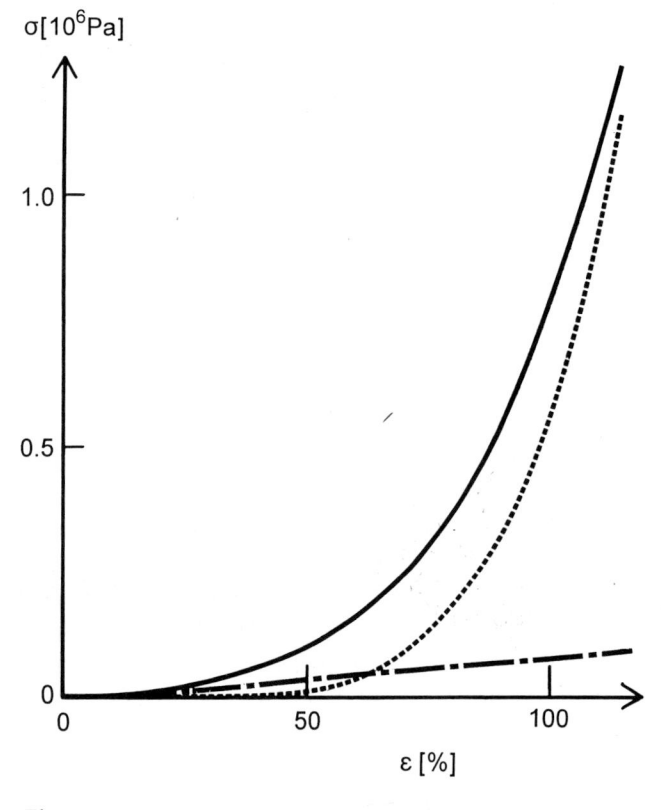

Fig. 15.9: Stress–strain relation for the elastic tissue of blood vessels. The blood vessel contains two components which play a role in its elastic properties: elastin (dash–dotted curve) and collagen with a bulk modulus increasing with strain (dashed curve). These contributions are combined (solid curve) for an actual blood vessel.

Example 15.1
Fig. 15.8 shows the stress–strain relation of compact bone. Positive values of the strain correspond to a stretching of the bone and negative values correspond to a compression of the bone.

In an adult male the femur has a minimum diameter of about 2.8 cm. At what force will the femur break?

Solution: We read the maximum stress for the compressive and the tensile case from Fig. 15.8. Rupturing occurs where the curves end at each side. For bone this occurs at strain values below 2 %, which means that bones can be stretched safely only very little. The maximum compressive stress is -1.7×10^8 Pa and the maximum tensile stress is 1.2×10^8 Pa. The corresponding forces are obtained from the definition of the stress, i.e., $\sigma = F/A$, when rewritten as $F = \sigma A$. In this formula the cross–sectional area of the bone is identified as the area onto which the force acts. The area A is calculated by assuming a cylindrical shape of the bone with a circular cross–section of radius r. With r = 1.4 cm we find $A = r^2\pi = 6.2 \times 10^{-4}$ m². Thus, the compressive force is:

$$F_{comp} = 1.7 \times 10^8 [Pa]\ 6.2 \times 10^{-4}[m^2]$$
$$\Rightarrow F_{comp} = 1.05 \times 10^5\ N \quad (6)$$

and the tensile force is:

$$F_{tensile} = 1.2 \times 10^8 [Pa]\ 6.2 \times 10^{-4}[m^2]$$
$$\Rightarrow F_{tensile} = 7.4 \times 10^4\ N \quad (7)$$

To obtain an idea what the compressive force implies we convert it into a corresponding weight (using $F = mg$): the femur can withstand the pull of a mass of more than 10 tons (10,700 kg). Even though this is a large value, the corresponding forces do indeed occur, even though only for a fraction of a second, e.g. during a fall onto a hard surface.

Fig. 15.10: The windkessel effect of the aorta. Shown at the center is a plot of the blood pressure in the aorta p_a as a function of time for two heart beats. When blood is ejected from the heart (1 and 3) the blood vessel tissue responds to the pressure increase (stress) by widening (strain). As the heart valve closes (shown at the left end of the aortic bend) and blood flows forward the pressure is lowered (2 and 4). This reduction of the stress leads to a contraction of the vessel (strain reduction) which helps to push the blood downstream.

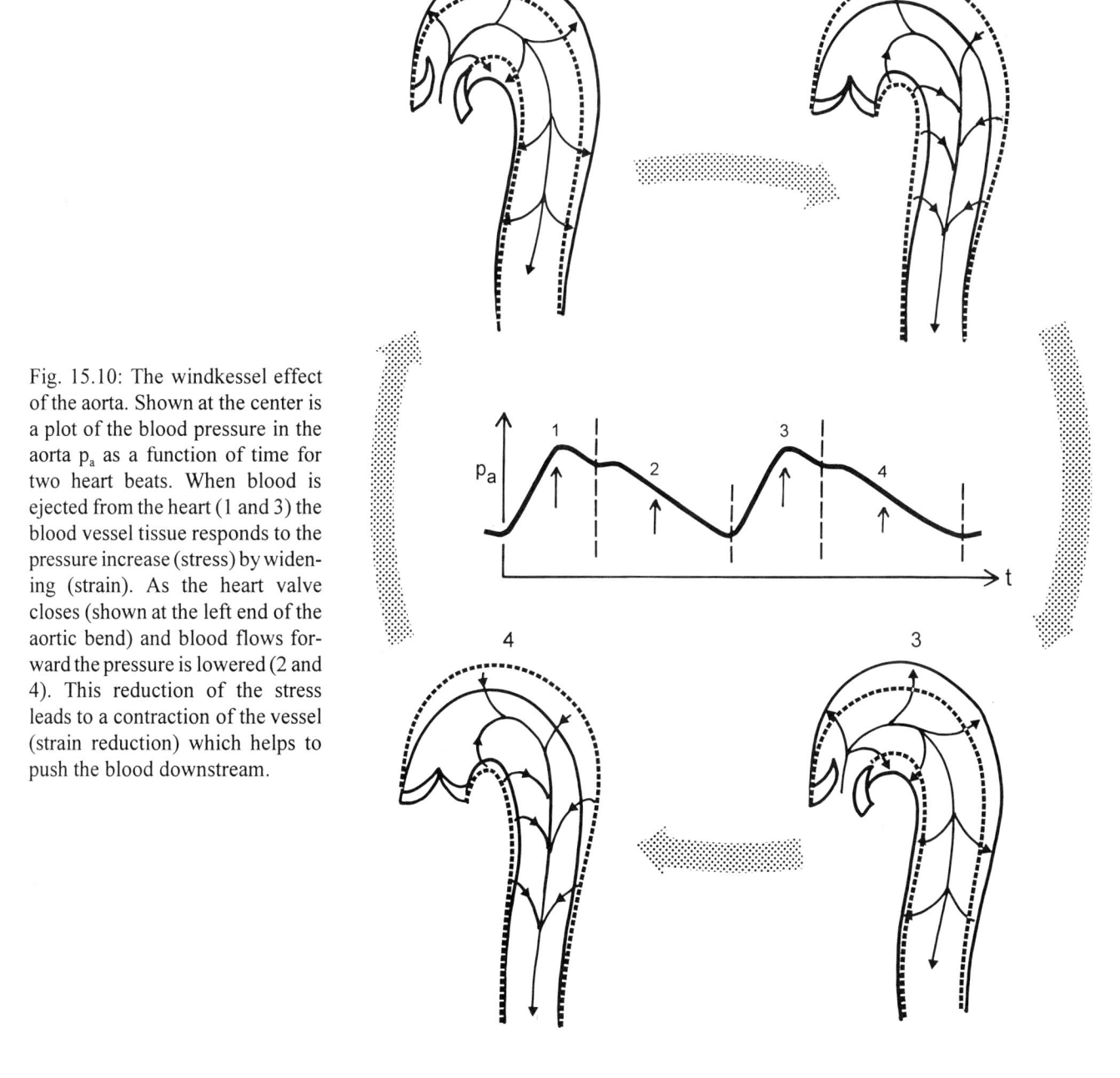

Some systems don't display a linear stress–strain regime at all. The most prominent case is the elastic tissue of the aorta. Note that the term "elastic" used for this case in the biological literature is misleading since it has been reserved for the linear regime. It is used by biologists to indicate that only reversible deformations of the tissue are considered. Fig. 15.9 shows the stress–strain curve for the tissue material of large arteries. The blood vessel tissue contains two main structural materials, the protein elastin and collagen. Their elastic properties are additive, leading to a continuously curved dependence of the stress on the strain. The third component of the blood vessel wall, which is the contractile smooth muscle cell, does not contribute to the mechanical properties of the vessel.

Elastin determines the deformation properties of the artery at small stress values due to its small bulk modulus B. Collagen fibrils with a larger bulk modulus play an increasing role as the strain increases beyond 25 %. The collagen is slack while the artery is narrow, but stiffens notably when the artery widens.

We consider two physiological applications of this type of response to deforming forces in arteries: the Windkessel effect of the aorta and the development of aneurysms.

Windkessel effect of the aorta
The ability of a blood vessel to deform under stress is used in the aorta to buffer the pressure variations due to the pulsatile operation of the heart. By smoothening the ventricular pressure variations a more continuous blood flow is achieved in the arteries.

The Windkessel effect is illustrated in Fig. 15.10. The aorta is bent by almost 180^0 just beyond the heart. This bend must therefore accommodate the largest fraction of the rush of blood ejected by the heart during each heart beat. When the blood rushes into the aorta, the blood pressure increases as shown in the blood pressure plot at the center of Fig. 15.10. The pressure increases at 1 and 3 represent an increased stress on the aorta wall. The aorta wall responds, according to Fig. 15.9 by widening, which effectively lowers the blood pressure locally to accommodate the blood volume increase. The increased strain in the aorta wall serves in turn as an additional component pushing the blood forward through the blood vessel against the flow resistance, as illustrated in sketches 2 and 4 of Fig. 15.10. The blood vessel contracts in response to the lowering of the stress, which is indicated at points 2 and 4 in the blood pressure curve at the center of Fig. 15.10. Blood cannot flow back to the heart in this stage as the heart valve is closed as shown at the left end of the blood vessels in the figure.

The elasticity of the blood vessel tissue reduces with age, causing the aorta to stiffen. This process is called arteriosclerosis. The age–related change in the elasticity leads also to changes of the average blood pressure as indicated in Table 10.1.

Aneurysms
The stress–strain curve shown in Fig. 15.9 applies to healthy blood vessel tissue. If a blood vessel is weakened, the tissue responds to the same blood pressure with a larger strain, as shown by the dash–dotted curve in Fig. 15.11. The weakening may lead to strain values twice as large as for the healthy vessel.

We can predict the consequences of such a weakened spot in the cardiovascular system based on the discussions in Chapter 11: at the weakened spot, the blood vessel becomes wider than in adjacent sections. As a result of the equation of continuity, the blood flow slows in the weakened section. This slowing of the blood flow causes a local increase in the blood pressure as described by Bernoulli's equation. With the blood pressure rising locally, an increase of the stress on the blood vessel occurs. We see from Fig. 15.11 that this leads yet again to a larger strain, i.e., a further widening of the vessel. This is called a positive feedback loop, which has a negative effect on the health of the individual patient. The blood vessel widens significantly at the weakened spot, causing a ballooning which is called

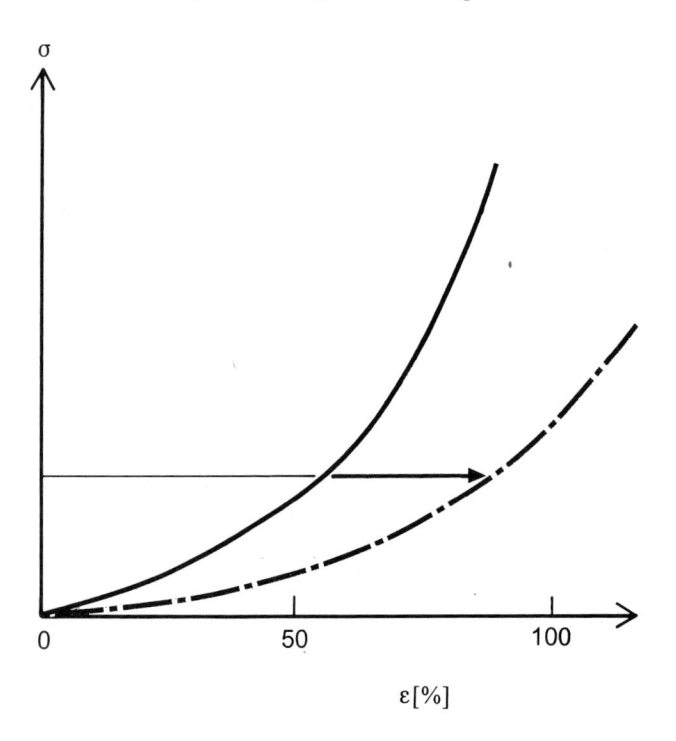

Fig. 15.11: Stress–strain curves for healthy (solid curve) and weakened blood vessel tissue (dash–dotted curve). The healthy tissue curve corresponds to the solid curve shown in Fig. 15.9. The horizontal arrow indicates the excess strain for the weakened tissue in comparison to the adjacent healthy tissue at a given stress.

an aneurysm. Such aneurysms may eventually rupture, releasing blood into the adjacent tissue. Depending on where in the object this happens the result may be fatal, e.g. in the brain. Modern non–surgical treatment techniques include insertion of a curling platinum wire through a 0.7 mm thick catheter into the expanded section to prevent further blood flow and stress built–up in the aneurysm. The procedure is illustrated in Fig. 15.12. The wire is transported through a cannula along a blood vessel, e.g. from the thigh to the brain, as a surgical opening in the skull would be more dangerous for the patient.

Example 15.2
In 1934, Charles William Beebe of the New York Zoological Society made a record descent into the ocean off Bermuda to a depth of 923 m. He and a second researcher used for this descent a steel sphere of 1.5 m diameter with a wall thickness of 5 cm (bathysphere). The weight of passengers and instruments was 4900 N. The bathysphere was suspended from a steel rope with a diameter of 3 cm (density of steel is $\rho = 7.5$ g/cm³). What would have been the maximum depth to which the bathysphere could have been lowered before rupturing? Use for the tensile stress at the ultimate strength point of the steel rope $\sigma = 6.87 \times 10^8$ Pa, which is about 5 times the value of bone material.

Solution: We calculate first the total weight suspended from the steel rope. This includes the instruments, the passengers and the bathysphere. The weight of the bathysphere is due to its steel wall of thickness d. With the surface of a sphere, $A = 4\pi r^2$, the volume of the steel wall was $V = 4\pi r^2 d$ and its weight:

$$W_{bathy} = 4\pi r^2 d\, \rho\, g =$$
$$4\pi (0.75 [m])^2\, 0.05 [m]\, 9.8 \left[\frac{m}{s^2}\right] 7.5 \times 10^3 \left[\frac{kg}{m^3}\right] \quad (8)$$

This leads to:

$$W_{bathy} = 25980\ N \quad (9)$$

Thus, the total weight of the fully equipped bathysphere was 30880 N. Due to buoyancy, the steel rope did not need to support this entire weight. The weight is reduced by the weight of the displaced water (Eq. (10.24)):

$$F_{buoy} = \frac{4}{3}\pi r^3\, \rho_{H_2O}\, g =$$
$$\frac{4}{3}\pi (0.75[m])^3\, 9.8 \left[\frac{m}{s^2}\right] 1.0 \times 10^3 \left[\frac{kg}{m^3}\right] \quad (10)$$

which leads to:

$$F_{buoy} = 17320\ N \quad (11)$$

Thus, only 30,880 N – 17,320 N = 13,560 N have to be supported by the rope. A rope of 3 cm diameter can carry a maximum weight of:

$$W_{max} = \sigma A = \sigma r^2 \pi =$$
$$6.87 \times 10^8 [Pa]\, (1.5 \times 10^{-2}[m])^2\, \pi \quad (12)$$

which yields:

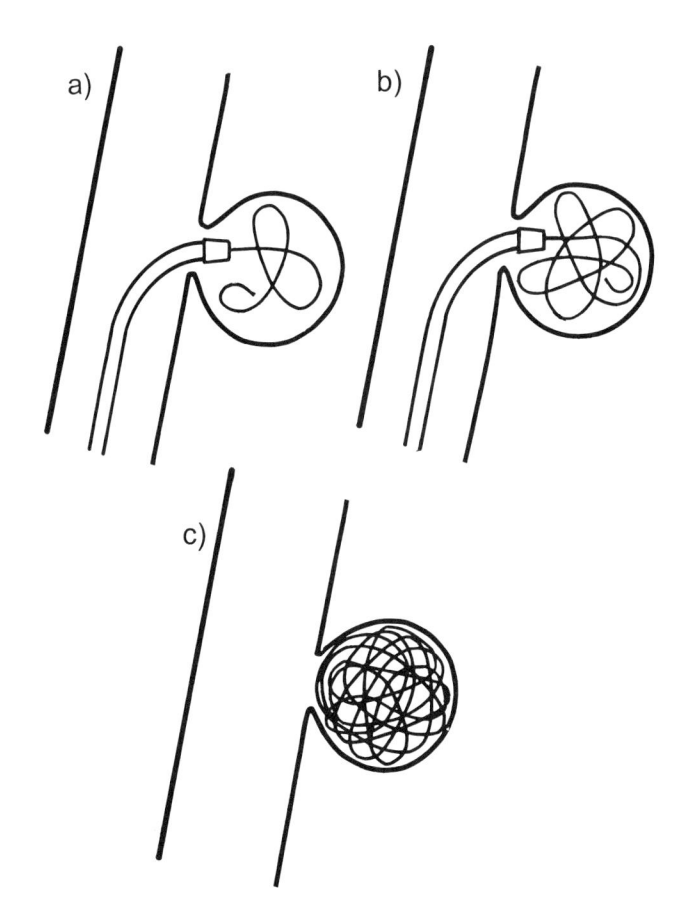

Fig. 15.12: Non–surgical treatment of an aneurysm in the brain. A 0.7 mm wide catheter is inserted through an artery in the thigh. A platinum wire is pushed through the catheter and fills the aneurysm like a skein of wool.

$$W_{max} = 4.86 \times 10^5 \, N \qquad (13)$$

This allows for an additional weight of the rope under water of 4.72×10^5 N. The length l of a rope with this weight (again including a correction for buoyancy) is calculated by using a cylindrical shape of the rope:

$$W_{rope} = \pi r^2 l \, (\rho_{steel} - \rho_{H_2O}) \, g \qquad (14)$$

from which we obtain for the length l:

$$l = \frac{W_{rope}}{\pi r^2 (\rho_{steel} - \rho_{H_2O}) \, g} \qquad (15)$$

Using the values of the Example text this corresponds to:

$$l = \frac{4.72 \times 10^5 [N]}{\pi (1.5 \times 10^{-2} [m])^2 \, 6.5 \times 10^3 \left[\frac{kg}{m^3}\right] 9.8 \left[\frac{m}{s^2}\right]} \qquad (16)$$

$$\Rightarrow \quad l = 10480 \, m$$

Beebe and his partner had to allow for a significant safety margin, thus they had to choose a more shallow maximum depth. Nylon would have been a better choice for the rope material because it has almost the same tensile stress at the ultimate strength point (85 % of the value of steel) but a much lesser weight.

15.2. Linear regime of stress–strain curves

The stress–strain curves of most materials are similar to the curves shown in Figs. 15.7 and 15.8 in that there is a linear regime for small strain values where the stress F/A and the strain are related in the form:

$$\frac{F}{A} \propto \frac{\Delta l}{l} \quad \text{or} \quad \frac{F}{A} \propto \frac{\Delta V}{V} \qquad (17)$$

The linear relation between stress and strain in this regime is called *Hooke's law*. It is named after Robert Hooke, who discovered this relation in the late 17th century.

Hooke's law applies in the elastic regime of a material and states that the stress and the strain of the material are linearly proportional.

Confining our discussion in this chapter to systems in the regime where Hooke's law is applicable, we study vibrations of the system as a new mechanical property resulting from this law. While all three types of deformation can lead to vibrations in the system, we focus only on two cases:

(I) the vibration of an ideal gas confined by a piston. The vibration is the result of compressions and expansions under hydraulic stress.

(II) The vibration of an object attached to a spring. The vibration is the result of a stretching of the spring under tensile stress. The latter case is closely related to the motion of an object on a string (pendulum motion), which is briefly discussed in analogy to the motion of an object attached to a spring.

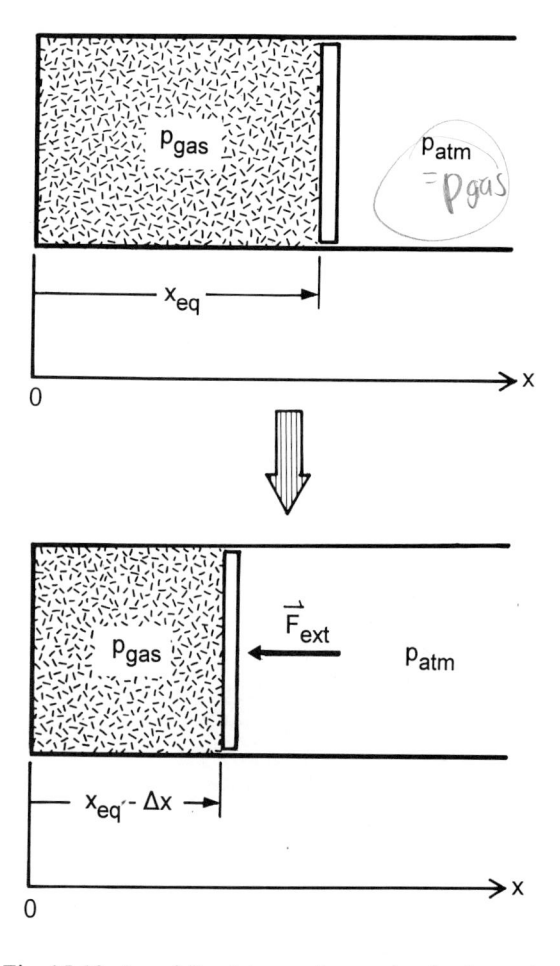

Fig. 15.13: A mobile piston seals a gas in a horizontal cylinder. The piston is in mechanical equilibrium at position x_{eq} when the gas pressure p_{gas} is equal to the external atmospheric pressure p_{atm}. An external force allows us to move the piston to a new position at $x_{eq} - \Delta x$. The origin of the x–axis is chosen at the left end of the gas cylinder.

In this section we first establish the specific form of Eq. (17) for these cases. The resulting motion of the system is then discussed in detail.

15.2.1. Piston–confined gas with hydraulic stress

Fig. 15.13 illustrates the system we want to study. An ideal gas is confined in a container by a mobile piston sealing the container at the right side. Choosing a horizontal arrangement allows us to neglect any gravitational effects on the gas or on the piston. The piston is in mechanical equilibrium when the pressure of the ideal gas inside and the atmospheric pressure outside are equal. We call this position the equilibrium position of the piston, x_{eq}, with the x–axis extending toward the right and the origin chosen at the fixed left wall of the cylindrical container, as shown in Fig. 15.13.

By exerting an external force on the piston we displace the piston by a small distance Δx to a new position at $x = x_{eq} - \Delta x$. To achieve this displacement, an external force of magnitude $|\mathbf{F}_{ext}|$ is applied toward the left, i.e., the x–component of the external force is negative, $F_x = -F_{ext} < 0$.

A mechanical equilibrium is established as long as we hold the piston at this new position. Quantifying Newton's first law for this case allows us to determine the specific form of Hooke's law for the piston–confined ideal gas. Defining the area of the piston as A we find:

$$\sum_i F_{i,x} = -p_{atm} A - F_{ext} + p_{gas} A = 0 \quad (18)$$

which leads to:

$$F_{ext} = A(p_{gas} - p_{atm}) \quad (19)$$

In the next step Eq. (19) is modified by using the ideal gas law. For the atmospheric pressure we write the gas pressure at the equilibrium position of the piston since these two pressures were initially equal:

$$F_{ext} = nRTA \left(\frac{1}{V_{gas}} - \frac{1}{V_{gas,eq}} \right) \quad (20)$$

The volumes of the cylinders in Eq. (20) are expressed as the product of the cross–sectional area A and the varying length of the tube between the left wall and the piston:

$$F_{ext} = nRTA \left(\frac{1}{A[x_{eq} - \Delta x]} - \frac{1}{A x_{eq}} \right) \quad (21)$$

To cancel the cross–sectional area A simplifies Eq. (21):

$$F_{ext} = nRT \left(\frac{1}{x_{eq} - \Delta x} - \frac{1}{x_{eq}} \right) \quad (22)$$

Next, the bracket in Eq. (22) is simplified for the limiting case $\Delta x \ll x_{eq}$ by using:

$$\frac{1}{x_{eq} - \Delta x} - \frac{1}{x_{eq}} = \frac{x_{eq} - [x_{eq} - \Delta x]}{x_{eq}[x_{eq} - \Delta x]} \quad (23)$$

Δx is sufficiently small that it can be neglected in the denominator on the right hand side. This yields:

$$\frac{1}{x_{eq} - \Delta x} - \frac{1}{x_{eq}} \cong \frac{\Delta x}{x_{eq}^2} \quad (24)$$

Inserting Eq. (24) in (22) then leads to:

$$F_{ext} = \frac{nRT}{x_{eq}^2} \Delta x \quad (25)$$

Dividing both sides of Eq. (25) by A gives a stress term of the form F/A on the left hand side and converts one of the factors x_{eq} in the denominator to the equilibrium volume of the gas, V_{eq}. Further multiplying the right hand side of Eq. (25) with a factor A/A converts the other factor x_{eq} in the denominator into V_{eq} and converts the Δx term in the numerator into a volume change, $-\Delta V$:

$$\frac{F_{ext}}{A} = -\frac{nRT}{V_{eq}} \frac{\Delta V}{V_{eq}} \quad (26)$$

Comparing Eq. (26) with Eq. (5) yields for the bulk modulus of the ideal gas:

$$B_{ideal\ gas} = \frac{nRT}{V_{eq}} = p_{eq} \quad (27)$$

Thus, the bulk modulus for an ideal gas is equal to its equilibrium pressure at the given temperature. Note that Eq. (26) contains a linear proportionality between the stress and the volume strain. Therefore, a small displacement of a piston is a valid case of Hooke's law.

The system discussed above is in mechanical equilibrium since the external force is balanced by an equal but opposite force exerted by the gas on the piston. If we remove the external force by releasing the piston, a mechanical non–equilibrium situation is created, i.e., a case which we have to treat with Newton's second law. The only force acting on the piston is the force exerted by the gas on the piston. We call this force a *restoring force* since it points in the direction toward the equilibrium position of the piston.

The unbalanced restoring force accelerates the piston toward the right in Fig. 15.13. We predict qualitatively what happens next. As the piston moves toward the right it will reach the equilibrium position. At that instant no force acts on the piston, i.e., it will no longer accelerate. However, the inertia of the piston due to Newton's first law prevents it from suddenly coming to rest. Thus, the piston moves even further to the right. Once the piston has moved beyond the equilibrium position the confined ideal gas has a lower pressure than the external atmospheric pressure. Therefore, a restoring force acts on the piston pushing it back toward the equilibrium position again. This force slows the piston down to rest, which occurs at $x_{eq} + \Delta x$ if the piston is moving frictionless in the cylindrical container. Thereafter the piston continues to move back and forth. We discuss this motion in greater detail in section 15.3.

15.2.2. An object attached to a spring

In Chapter 2 we studied single isolated objects and found that they display uniform motion along a straight line when left alone. We now attach such an object to a spring, as shown in Fig. 15.14. This establishes a continuous interaction resulting in a different type of motion.

A spring is a device that causes an object to move towards its equilibrium position in response to a displacement, very similar to the motion we observe for the released piston in Fig. 15.13. Before quantifying the spring force further, we note that a horizontal arrangement is chosen in Fig. 15.14. An object could also be attached to a spring in a vertical arrangement. In such an arrangement the gravitational force needs to be included in the discussion as an additional force. We want to avoid this as the gravitational force plays a negligible role at microscopic length scales to which we ultimately want to apply the spring force concept. Thus, we confine ourselves to the horizontal arrangement of Fig. 15.14.

Before the object is released, it is held in mechanical equilibrium by an external force at the position shown in Fig. 15.14. For a sufficiently small displacement $\Delta x = x - x_{eq}$ the external force is linearly proportional to the displacement from the equilibrium position:

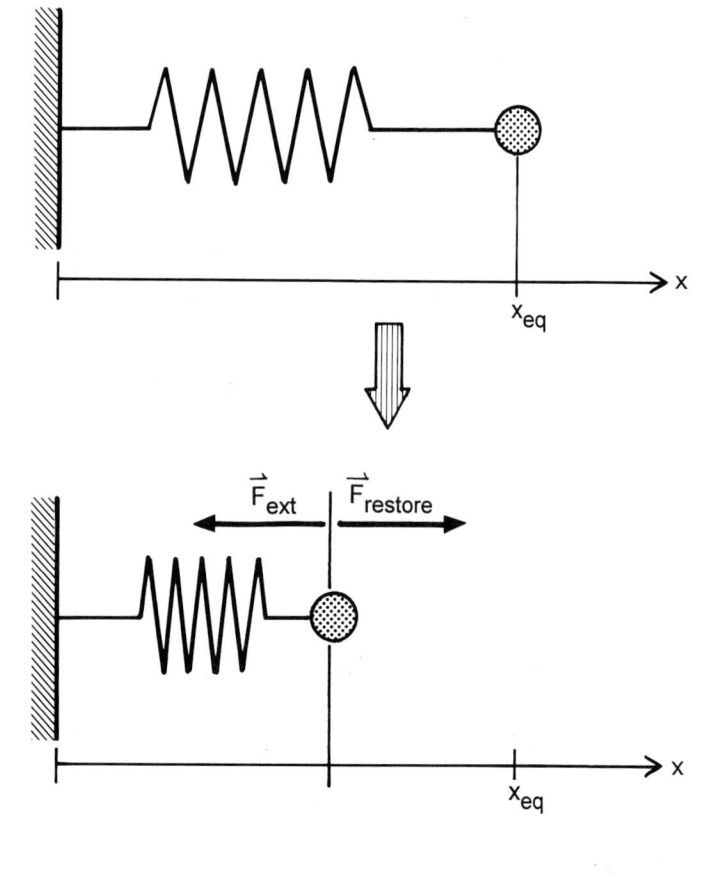

$$F_{ext} = k\left(x - x_{eq}\right) \qquad (28)$$

Fig. 15.14: An object is attached to a spring which in turn is attached horizontally to a rigid wall at the left. The equilibrium position of the object is at x_{eq} where no external forces act on it. With an external force applied toward the left, the object is moved to a new equilibrium position in which the external force and the restoring force, exerted by the spring, are balanced.

Eq. (28) is again written in the form of Hooke's law, and is given for a displacement along the x–axis as shown in Fig. 15.14. k is called the *spring constant* and has unit [N/m]. A large spring constant means a stiffer spring.

The mechanical equilibrium in Fig. 15.14 is due to a force exerted on the object by the spring. We call this force the elastic spring force. It is a restoring force as it causes the object to accelerate toward the equilibrium position once the external force is removed:

$$F_{elast} = -k\left(x - x_{eq}\right) \quad (29)$$

The restoring character of the force is represented by the negative sign in Eq. (29): for positions $x > x_{eq}$ the force $\mathbf{F}_{elast}$ is negative, i.e., the force pulls the object back to smaller values of x. For positions $x < x_{eq}$ the force $\mathbf{F}_{elast}$ is positive, pushing the object toward larger values of x.

The spring described by Eq. (29) is called an ideal spring as real springs need not to follow this law. In general, springs do not follow Hooke's law if the displacement is too far from the equilibrium position. Most springs, however, are well described by Hooke's law near the equilibrium position of the object, and this is the reason why the applications of Eq. (29) are widespread, including the description of intra–molecular forces.

15.2.3. Simple Pendulum

Fig. 15.15 illustrates a simple pendulum. An object of mass m is attached to a taut string of length L which in turn is connected to a pivot point at the ceiling. The equilibrium position of the object is reached when the string is vertical, i.e., the angle θ between the vertical and the string is $\theta = 0^0$. After applying an external force, which is chosen to be tangential to the path of the object in Fig. 15.15, the object comes to rest at a new position shown in the figure. At this point, a mechanical equilibrium exists between three forces acting on the object: the tension in the string, the weight of the object and the external force.

When the external force is removed, a mechanically unbalanced system results, as shown in Fig. 15.16. Two forces act on the object: the tension and the weight. Since these two forces are neither parallel nor perpendicular to each other, we choose the x– and y–axes as

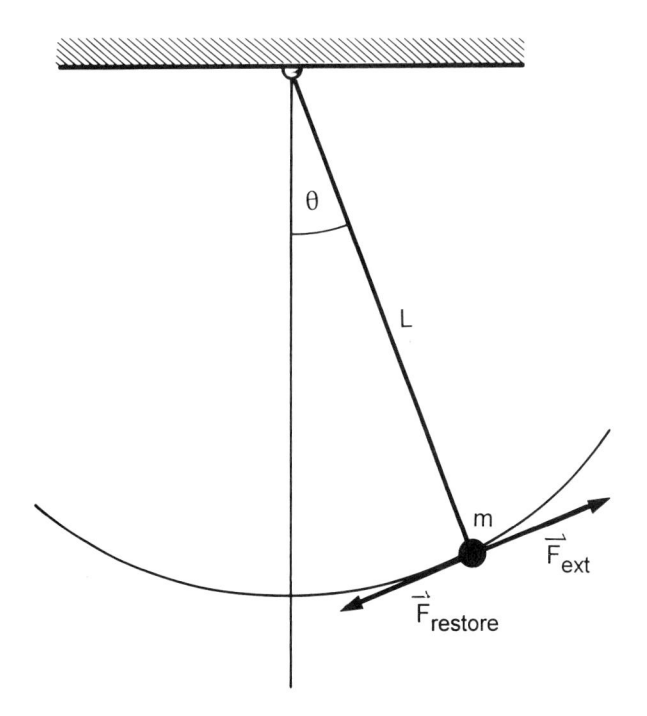

Fig. 15.15: An object of mass m is attached to a string of length L which forms an angle θ with the vertical. We can model the object with two forces while it is held in mechanical equilibrium: a restoring force $\mathbf{F}_{restore}$ (which is a combination of the gravitational force and the tension in the string) and an external force $\mathbf{F}_{ext}$.

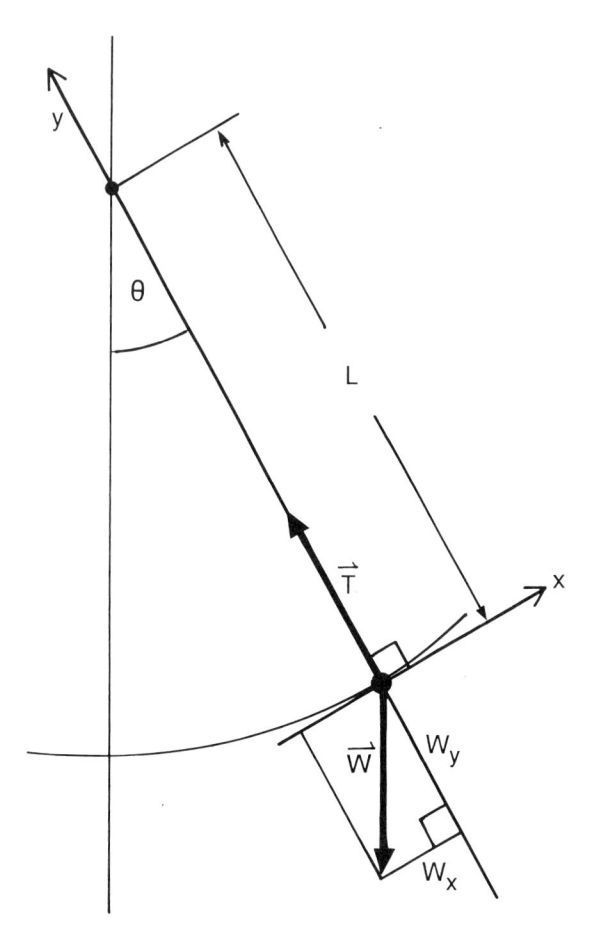

Fig. 15.16: A simple pendulum which is not in mechanical equilibrium. The tension and the y–component of the weight compensate each other in the y–direction. The x–component of the weight leads to an acceleration toward the equilibrium position of the object.

shown in Fig. 15.16 and determine the x– and y–components of the weight from the figure, leading to the components W_y and W_x, respectively. We note that the forces in the y-direction are balanced while the x-component of the weight leads to an acceleration. The x-component of the weight represents a restoring force because the acceleration of the object is toward its equilibrium position. Based on Fig. 15.16, the restoring force is written as:

$$F_{restore} = W_x = -mg\sin\theta \qquad (30)$$

This restoring force is not linear in the angle θ, i.e., Eq. (30) is not a formula conforming to the formulation of Hooke's law in Eq. (17). Instead of dismissing the pendulum case as leading to a different type of motion, however, we study Eq. (30) with an additional assumption that θ is a small angle.

What changes when the angle θ is small? For a small angle we can use the approximation $\sin\theta = \theta$. You can test this approximation with your pocket calculator, for example for an angle of $10°$. Note, however, that angles must be expressed in unit [rad], not degree [°]. How both units for angles are related is illustrated in the Appendix of this chapter. Based on that discussion, $10°$ is indeed a small angle because $10° = 0.1745$ [rad] and $\sin 10° = 0.1736$, i.e., both values vary only by 0.5 %.

If θ is a small angle and $\sin\theta = \theta$ applies, we can rewrite Eq. (30) in the form:

$$F_{restore} = -mg\theta \qquad (31)$$

In this form, the restoring force in the case of a pendulum is a force linear in the variable θ, thus the pendulum is an application of Hooke's law if the object is not too far from the equilibrium position. We still want to rewrite Eq. (31) such that the variable is not the angle θ but the distance of the object from the equilibrium position. This distance is defined in Fig. 15.17 as the path segment s. If θ is small, the position of the object along the x-axis in Fig. 15.16 and the length of the path segment s are essentially the same, i.e., $s \approx x$. Thus, the angle θ is replaced by the distance x as $\theta = s/L \approx x/L$. With this result, Eq. (31) is rewritten in the form:

$$F_{restore} = -mg\theta = -\frac{mg}{L}x \qquad (32)$$

This equation is mathematically equivalent to Eq. (29). Both forces must lead to the same motion since we can replace the spring constant k in Eq. (29) with the term mg/L. Thus, a simple pendulum and an object attached to an ideal spring need not to be treated separately.

15.3. Vibrations

We will use each of the three cases discussed in section 15.2 to describe the motion of a system on which a restoring force acts:
(I) For simplicity, we start the discussion of vibrations in section 15.3.1 with a single object attached to a horizontal ideal spring. The spring in turn is attached to a rigid, immobile wall. This case will also allow us to describe molecular vibrations in section 15.3.2.
(II) In section 15.3.3 we illustrate the point made at the end of the previous section that the pendulum case can be treated in full analogy to the case of the object on a spring.
(III) The case of a mobile piston sealing an ideal gas is then used to discuss acoustic phenomena in the next chapter.

15.3.1. Objects on an ideal spring

The only object of interest in the system of an object on a spring is the object itself since the spring is not a separate object but the origin of a force of the type de-

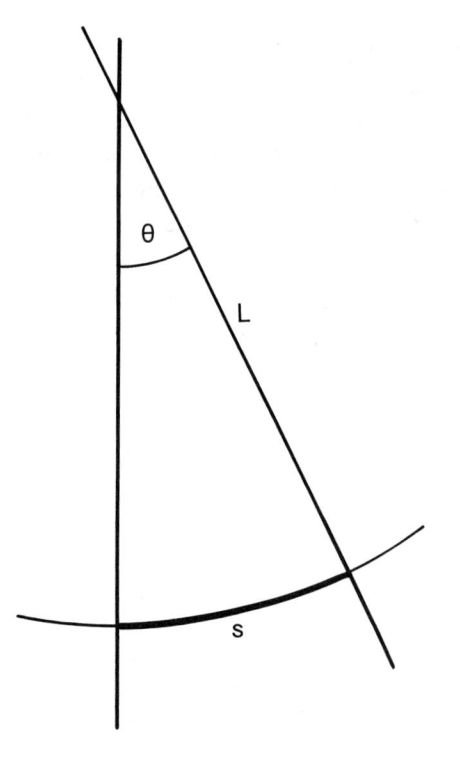

Fig. 15.17: Sketch defining the path segment s which corresponds to the displacement from the equilibrium position for the object on the string of length L at an angle θ with the vertical.

scribed by Eq. (29). Newton's second law of mechanics applies to an object which is attached to a spring and is allowed to perform horizontal motion with small displacements around the equilibrium position. Choosing the horizontal axis as the x–axis, the equilibrium position is written as x_{eq} and Newton's second law reads:

$$\sum_i F_i = -k(x - x_{eq}) = m\,a \qquad (33)$$

To derive the formula for the position of the object as a function of time from Eq. (33) is mathematically more complicated than solving previously discussed cases of Newton's second law. The reason is that Eq. (33) contains both the position x and the acceleration a, which in turn is linked to the change of the position with time via the velocity. Thus, we cannot simply isolate the position in Eq. (33) as the independent variable.

Based on our discussion in Chapter 5, we have an alternative way to approach Eq. (33). In this approach we take an intermediate step by first calculating the potential energy of the object on the spring. We call this energy the *elastic potential energy* to distinguish it from the gravitational potential energy we introduced in Chapter 5. Both are potential energies as defined in Chapter 5: they are energy forms dependent on the relative position of objects, here the object relative to its equilibrium position.

As before in Chapter 5, the potential energy is derived from the work associated with displacing the object. Let's assume that we move the object from the equilibrium position, for which we assume $x_{eq} = 0$, to a final position x_f, holding it at that point in a mechanical equilibrium with an external force $\mathbf{F}_{ext}$. From the discussion in section 15.2.2 we know that $\mathbf{F}_{ext} = -\mathbf{F}_{elast}$. We recall that the work results as the area under the curve of the force as a function of position. For the current case this is illustrated in Fig. 15.18. With the force linearly proportional to the displacement, $F_{ext} = kx$, the area under the curve between $x = 0$ and $x = x_f$ is a triangle with:

$$W = \frac{1}{2} F_{ext}\, x_f = \frac{1}{2}(kx_f)x_f = \frac{1}{2}k x_f^2 \qquad (34)$$

Thus, we define the elastic potential energy of an object attached to a spring:

$$E_{elast} = \frac{1}{2} k\, x^2 \qquad (35)$$

for $x_{eq} = 0$, i.e., when the equilibrium position of the spring is chosen as the origin, or:

$$E_{elast} = \frac{1}{2} k\,(x - x_{eq})^2 \qquad (36)$$

for $x_{eq} \neq 0$, i.e., when the origin is chosen arbitrarily.

> *A system with a linear restoring force (Hooke's law) has an elastic potential energy which is proportional to the square of the displacement from the equilibrium position of the system.*

Fig. 15.19 compares the potential energies, shown as solid lines, (a) for gravity acting on an object and (b) for an object attached to a spring, i.e., an object on which an elastic force acts. The parabolic shape of the elastic potential energy in (b) defines a minimum in the elastic energy at the equilibrium position. There is no well–defined point of minimum potential energy in the case of gravity (a) as the gravitational force is given as $\mathbf{F} = m\mathbf{g}$.

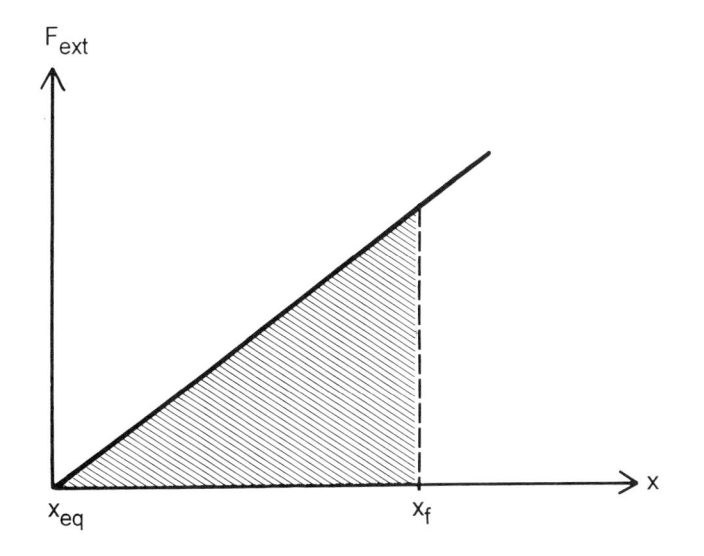

Fig. 15.18: The external force as a function of displacement for an object attached to a spring. The work is given by the area under the curve. The elastic potential energy is related to this work because the external force is the force which establishes the mechanical equilibrium for the system.

positions for which the potential energy exceeds the total energy are not allowed for the object. Thus, the gravitational system in sketch (a) is not confined, it can move toward the left indefinitely. An object which travels toward the left (physically travelling upwards) will turn around at the point where the kinetic energy becomes zero, but then never returns to this point. In contrast, the system in sketch (b) is spatially confined, i.e., an object moves back and forth between the two points at which the kinetic energy is zero.

Example 15.3

The elastic force and the elastic energy are sufficient to determine the spring constant if that parameter is not given. To illustrate this we consider the spring in Fig. 15.20. The top figure shows the case when the spring is relaxed and the bottom figure shows the case when the spring is extended by a distance $\Delta x = 0.15$ m. To pull the spring this distance, a total work of 20 J is needed (typi-cal workout equipment). What force do you need to hold the stretched spring at that point?

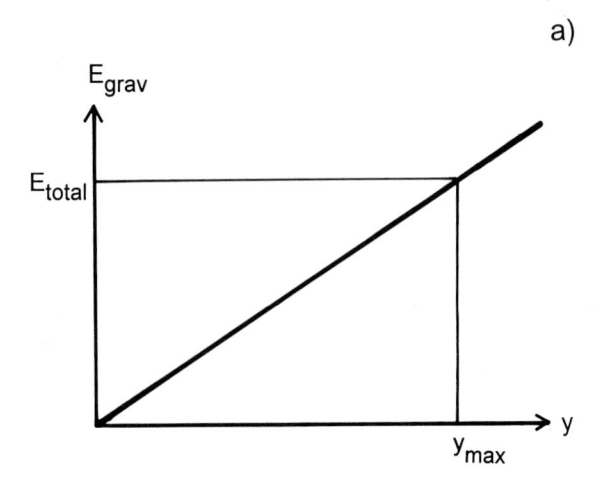

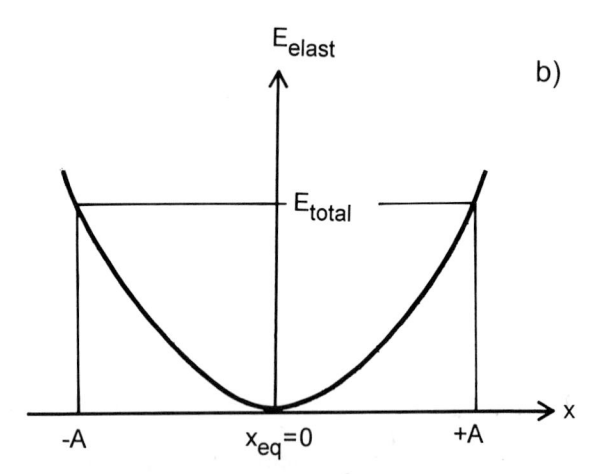

Fig. 15.19: Comparison between the potential energy (a) due to gravity and (b) due to an elastic spring force. The potential energy is shown as the solid curve. The thin horizontal lines indicate an arbitrarily chosen total energy for the system. The curve for the elastic spring force allows us to define the amplitude $\pm A$ for the motion of an object.

With the definition of the elastic potential energy in Eq. (35), the conservation of energy for an object on a horizontal spring is written as:

$$E_{total} = E_{kin} + E_{elast} = \frac{1}{2}mv^2 + \frac{1}{2}kx^2 \quad (37)$$

where we have chosen the x–axis such that $x_{eq} = 0$.

The interpretation of Eq. (37) is best done with Fig. 15.19. The two thin horizontal lines represent an arbitrarily chosen total energy. The difference between the total energy (dashed line) and the potential energy (solid line) corresponds to the kinetic energy. Obviously,

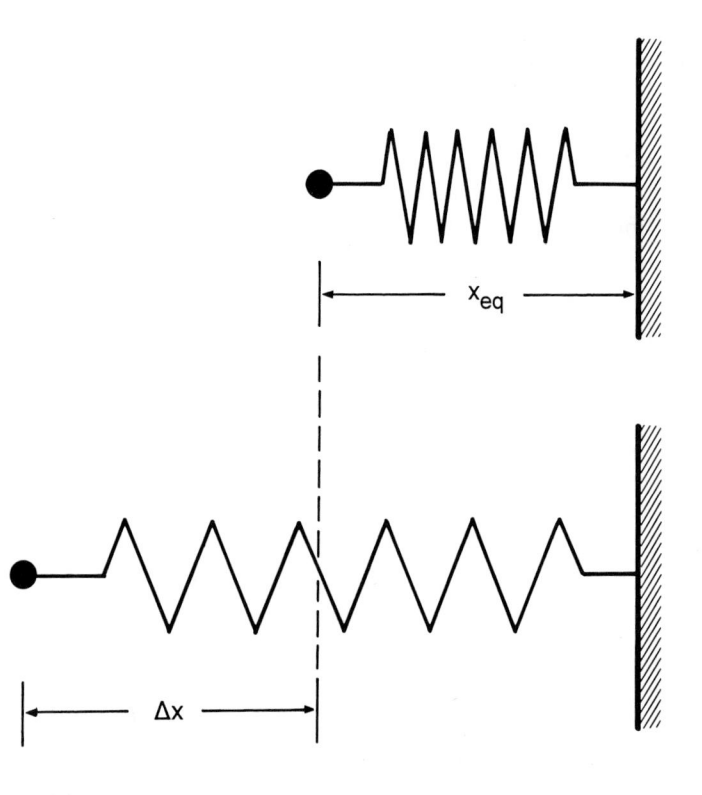

Fig. 15.20: Sketches of a relaxed and an expanded horizontal spring. The spring in the bottom panel is extended by a length Δx.

Solution: We use $x_{initial} = x_{eq} = 0$ and $x_{final} = \Delta x$. The work needed to pull the spring to the final position is given by:

$$W = \frac{1}{2} k \left(x_{final}^2 - x_{initial}^2 \right) = \frac{k}{2} \Delta x^2 \quad \textbf{(38)}$$

which allows us to calculate the spring constant k:

$$k = \frac{2W}{\Delta x^2} = \frac{2 \cdot 20[J]}{(0.15[m])^2} = 1780 \frac{N}{m} \quad \textbf{(39)}$$

The spring constant is then used in Hooke's law:

$$F_{elast} = -k(x - x_{eq}) = -k \Delta x =$$
$$-1780 \left[\frac{N}{m} \right] 0.15[m] = -267 \, N \quad \textbf{(40)}$$

A force $F_{ext} = F_{elast} = 267$ N is needed to hold the spring.

Example 15.4
An object of mass 1.0 kg is attached to a spring with spring constant k = 1000 N/m. If the object is displaced by 30 cm from the equilibrium position and is released, with what speed does the object pass through the equilibrium position during its motion?

Supplementary physical information: We first define the *amplitude* of the motion of the object using Fig. 15.19. The amplitude A is the maximum distance to which a vibrating object moves from the equilibrium position. At that point its kinetic energy is zero and $E_{total} = E_{elast}$:

$$E_{total} = \frac{1}{2} k A^2 \quad \textbf{(41)}$$

which leads to:

$$A = \sqrt{\frac{2 E_{total}}{k}} \quad \textbf{(42)}$$

Solution: From Eq. (42) we calculate the total energy:

$$E_{total} = \frac{1}{2} 1000 \left[\frac{N}{m} \right] (0.3[m])^2 = 45 \, J \quad \textbf{(43)}$$

Now we study the instant when $x = x_{eq} = 0$. At that point the elastic energy is zero, and the conservation of energy leads to:

$$E_{total} = \frac{1}{2} m v_{max}^2 \quad \textbf{(44)}$$

which yields:

$$v_{max} = \sqrt{\frac{2 E_{total}}{m}} = \sqrt{\frac{2 \cdot 45[J]}{1.0[kg]}} = 9.5 \frac{m}{s} \quad \textbf{(45)}$$

A general relation between the amplitude, as defined in Eq. (41), and the maximum speed of an object attached to a spring is derived from Eqs. (42) and (45):

$$E_{total} = \frac{1}{2} k A^2 = \frac{1}{2} m v_{max}^2$$
$$\Rightarrow v_{max} = \pm \sqrt{\frac{k}{m}} A \quad \textbf{(46)}$$

Using Eq. (46), we continue the derivation of the algebraic formula describing the position of the object as a function of time, x = f(t). Starting with Eq. (37), we choose the initial state to be the instant when the object is at its amplitude point x = A. With the final state at any other instant, Eq. (37) is written as:

$$E_{total} = \frac{1}{2} k A^2 = \frac{1}{2} k x^2 + \frac{1}{2} m v^2 \quad \textbf{(47)}$$

This equation contains the position and the velocity, i.e., the change of the position with time. It is mathematically simpler than Eq. (33) since it does not contain the acceleration. However, Eq. (47) is still not simple to solve because it is a non–linear equation. Therefore, we don't discuss the required mathematical operations but just note the result, which is an equation for the position of the object as a function of time:

$$x(t) = A \cos(\omega t + \phi) \quad \textbf{(48)}$$

This formula describes the cyclic motion of an object, called *simple harmonic motion*. In simple harmonic motion, an object oscillates about a point of mechanical equilibrium. The object is subject to a restoring force which depends linearly on the displacement. The harmonic motion of an object obeying Eq. (48) is illustrated in Fig. 15.21. To discuss the figure in detail, the two constants ω and ϕ in Eq. (48) have to be defined.

ω is called the *angular frequency* and has unit [1/s]. It depends on the mass of the object and the spring constant:

$$\omega = \sqrt{\frac{k}{m}} \qquad (49)$$

ω expresses the fraction of a complete cycle (2π) through which a vibrating object moves per unit time. It is important to keep in mind that ω should not be used in unit of degree per second [°/s] but in unit of radians per second [rad/s]. See the Appendix of this chapter for the relation of the units degree and radians.

Closely related to ω is the *period* T. The period is the time the object requires to complete one full cycle of its motion. Mathematically, a full cycle of a cosine or sine function is a change of 2π in the cosine-argument. Thus, $t = 0$ and $t = T$ correspond in Eq. (48) to a cosine-argument change from ϕ to $\omega T + \phi$. This yields the relation $2\pi = \omega T$ or $T = 2\pi/\omega$.

ϕ in Eq. (48) is called the *phase angle*. Its role is best seen from the curves in Fig. 15.21. If $\phi = 0$, the object starts at position $x = A$ and time $t = 0$ s and reaches its second amplitude point at $x = -A$ at time $t = T/2$. Then the object returns to position $x = A$ at time $t = T$. For an object starting at another stage of its cyclic motion, we need a phase shift $\phi \neq 0$. As an example, the phase shift $\phi = \pi/2$ is used to obtain the bottom curve in Fig. 15.21. In this case the object starts at position $x = 0$ and initially moves towards negative x-values until it reaches the point $x = -A$ at $t = T/4$. A complete cycle still takes the same time T.

The frequency f is often used in the literature instead of the angular frequency ω. It is defined by:

$$f = \frac{1}{T} = \frac{\omega}{2\pi} \qquad (50)$$

The unit of frequency is Hertz [Hz] (named after Heinrich Hertz) with $1 \text{ Hz} = 1 \text{ s}^{-1}$. Eq. (48) contains all the terms needed to describe the periodic motion of an object attached to a spring.

Example 15.5
The vibration of the tympanic membrane in the human ear (eardrum) can be described as a harmonic motion. Assuming a mass of 24 mg and a natural vibration frequency of 550 Hz, calculate
(a) the spring constant of the eardrum, and
(b) the angular frequency and the period of the vibration.

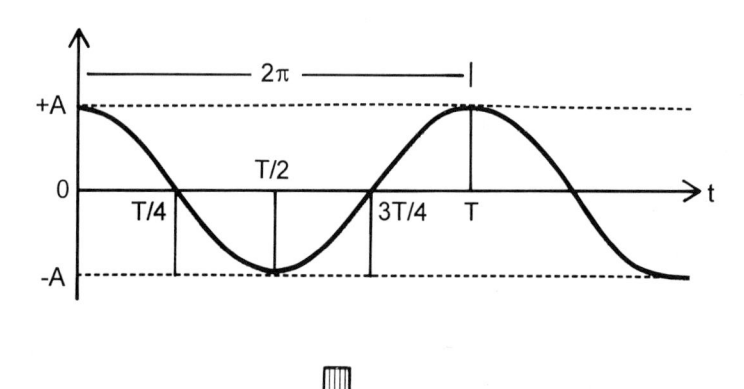

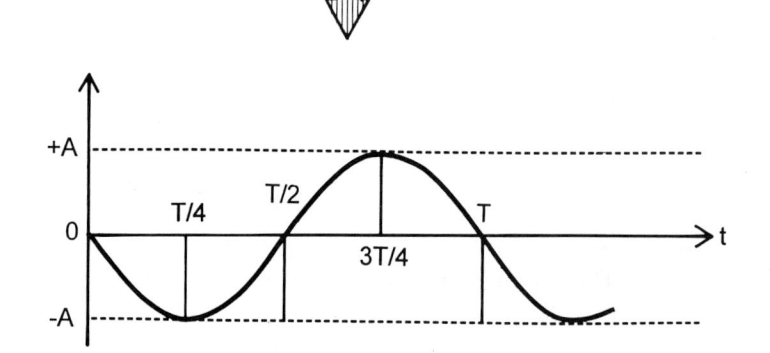

Fig. 15.21: Position as a function of time for a harmonic oscillator for two different values of the phase angle ϕ: (top) $\phi = 0°$ and (bottom) $\phi = \pi/2$.

Solution part (a): We note that it is the frequency and not the angular frequency which is given in the example text. We use Eq. (50) to relate the two frequencies and we use Eq. (49) to relate the frequency to the spring constant k:

$$f = \frac{\omega}{2\pi} = \frac{1}{2\pi}\sqrt{\frac{k}{m}} \qquad (51)$$

$$\Rightarrow k = 4\pi^2 f^2 m$$

Substituting in Eq. (51) the values given in the example, we find:

$$k = 4\pi^2 (550[Hz])^2 \, 2.4 \times 10^{-5}[kg]$$

$$\Rightarrow k = 290 \, \frac{N}{m} \qquad (52)$$

Solution part (b): The angular frequency ω is obtained from Eq. (50):

$$\omega = 2\pi f = 2\pi \, 550[Hz] = 3455 \left[\frac{rad}{s}\right] \qquad (53)$$

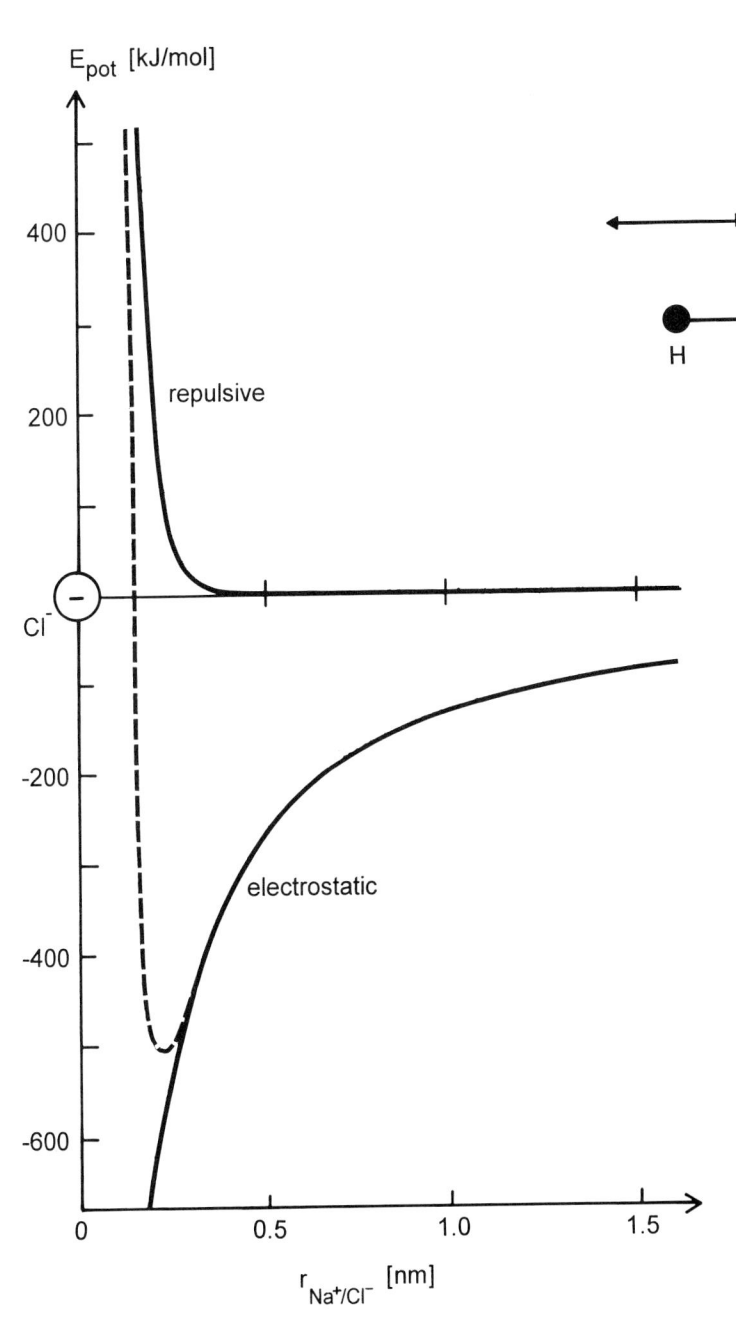

Fig. 15.22: Simplified model of the HCl molecule. The Cl atom is considered immobile. The spring allows the hydrogen atom to undergo simple harmonic oscillations.

Fig. 15.23: Potential energy as a function of distance between Na$^+$ and Cl$^-$ ions in rock salt (NaCl). The electrostatic attraction between the ions (solid curve at negative energies) is overcompensated by a repulsive term (solid curve at positive energies) at closer proximity. The combined potential energy curve for the Na–Cl bond is shown as an asymmetric dashed curve.

Eq. (50) also relates the period and the frequency. With the frequency given in the Example text, we find:

$$T = \frac{1}{f} = \frac{1}{550[Hz]} = 1.8 \times 10^{-3} \, s \quad (54)$$

15.3.2. Chemical bonds in molecules

The relative motion of atoms in a molecule is the most important application of simple harmonic motion. This is illustrated for the HCl molecule and a NaCl bond in a rock salt crystal. HCl is a binary molecule in which the chlorine atom is about 35 times heavier than the hydrogen atom. This allows us to simplify the model for the HCl molecule as shown in Fig. 15.22, where the chlorine atom is considered to be immobile like the wall to which the spring is attached on the left side in Fig. 15.14. The hydrogen atom is modelled as an object attached to the Cl atom by an ideal spring. In comparison, the description of a chemical bond with atoms of similar masses, e.g. NaCl, requires a formalism allowing both atoms to vibrate simultaneously relative to their center–of–mass.

We test whether the model proposed in Fig. 15.22 is useful for describing real chemical bonds. For this we analyse the interaction between the sodium and chlorine ions in NaCl, as well as the interaction between the hydrogen atom and the chlorine atom in HCl. These interactions have two contributions as illustrated in Fig. 15.23 for NaCl:

(I) an attractive component shown at negative energies. In the case of an electrostatic interaction, the attractive component is due to the electrostatic force:

$$E_{attract} = - \frac{1}{4\pi\epsilon_0} \frac{e^2}{r} \quad (55)$$

ϵ_0 is the permittivity of vacuum and e is the elementary charge. If this attraction were the only interaction in the Na–Cl system, then the sodium atom would crash into the chlorine atom as if it was swallowed up by a black hole.

(II) This doesn't happen because the attraction is shielded when the two ions penetrate each other and negative electrons and positive nuclei come very close to each other, adding a repulsive term (solid curve at positive energy values). Max Born determined a semi–empirical formula for the repulsive contribution:

$$E_{repulsive} = b \, e^{-ar} \quad (56)$$

in which a and b are constants which have to be determined experimentally for each chemical bond. The exponential function in Eq. (56) is steeper than the 1/r dependence in Eq. (55). Therefore, the repulsive term dominates at shorter distances of the two atoms and the attractive term dominates at longer distances.

Both contributions were combined by Heitler and London in 1927, describing the complete potential function as shown as the dashed line in Fig. 15.23 for a NaCl bond, and as shown as the solid line in Fig. 15.24 for an HCl molecule. In the case of HCl, a minimum energy is

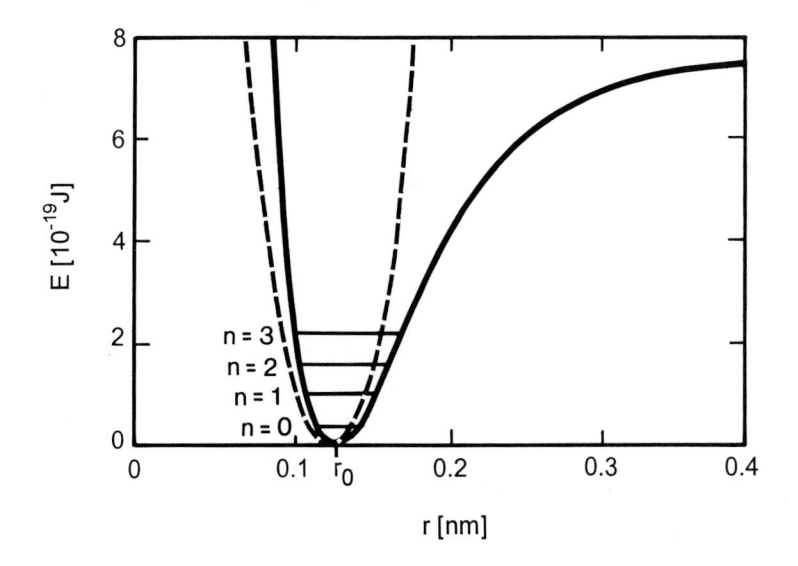

Fig. 15.24: Intra–molecular potential curve (solid line) and harmonic oscillator model (dashed curve) as a function of the separation distance between the atoms in the HCl molecule. Horizontal lines represent the allowed total energy levels of the molecule.

reached when the H atom is separated by a distance r_0 of about 0.13 nm from the Cl atom.

The combination of the potential energies in Eqs. (55) and (56) doesn't produce the potential curve for an object on an ideal spring. This is highlighted in Fig. 15.24, where the energy curve for the model of an object attached to a spring (dashed line) is overlapped with the actual potential energy curve for the HCl molecule. Recall that the model of an object on a spring in Fig. 15.22 predicts that the potential energy of the hydrogen atom in the HCl molecule is described by the function $E_{elast} = \frac{1}{2}k(x-x_{eq})^2$. The disagreement between the two potential energy curves is particularly obvious at higher total energies.

Do we therefore dismiss the harmonic oscillator as a model for a molecular bond? Not necessarily: at typical temperatures, such as room temperature or temperatures which molecules reach during most chemical reactions in solutions, almost all of the HCl molecules have a total energy corresponding to the ground state, which is indicated in Fig. 15.24 by the horizontal line labelled $n = 0$. Note that the energy of this ground state is higher than the minimum of the potential energy curve due to quantum-mechanical reasons (Heisenberg's uncertainty relation, see Chapter 21). Only a negligible fraction of the HCl molecules has an energy corresponding to one of the excited states of the molecule (labelled $n = 1, 2, ...$). The reason for this small fraction of molecules at an energy other than the ground state is the fact that the molecules cannot have any other total energy than the ones indicated by the horizontal lines in Fig. 15.24, which are labelled n. Thus, for a molecule to reach an excited state from the ground state, a significantly higher amount of energy is needed than available due to the thermal energy, which is of the order of $kT \approx 4 \times 10^{-21}$ J at room temperature.

Table 15.2: Spring constants for various chemical bonds. R stands for "rest", i.e., an organic extension of the functional group.

Bond	Molecule	k [N/m]
H–Cl	HCl	484
H–O	H_2O	780
H–C	CH_3R	470 – 500
C–C		450 – 560
C=C		950 – 990
C≡C		1560 – 1700
N–N		350 – 550
C–O		500 – 580
C=O		1180 – 1340

For HCl molecules in the ground state, Fig. 15.24 indicates that the potential energy formula of a simple harmonic oscillator (dashed line) is a quite reasonable approximation of the actual interaction potential (solid line). Remember that the hydrogen atom cannot travel beyond the two points at which its potential energy is equal to its total energy. The range accessible to the confined atom coincides with the range in which the potential energy of the harmonic oscillator (dashed line) and the actual potential energy curve (solid line) match quite well. Thus, we accept the simple harmonic oscillator as a model for chemical molecules.

Example 15.6

We quantify some key properties of the HCl molecule by treating the molecule as a simple harmonic oscillator. The mass of a hydrogen atom is $m = 1.67 \times 10^{-27}$ kg and the spring constant of the molecule is $k = 484$ N/m, which is a value obtained from spectroscopic data listed in Table 15.2. Calculate
(a) the angular frequency,
(b) the frequency, and
(c) the period for the vibration of the hydrogen atom in the HCl molecule.

Solution part (a): We use Eq. (49) to determine the angular frequency:

$$\omega = \sqrt{\frac{k}{m}} = 5.38 \times 10^{14} \frac{rad}{s} \quad (57)$$

Solution part (b): Using Eqs. (50) and (57) we find for the frequency:

$$f = \frac{\omega}{2\pi} = 8.6 \times 10^{13} \ Hz \quad (58)$$

Solution part (c): Eq. (50) also connects the frequency and the period:

$$T = \frac{1}{f} = 1.2 \times 10^{-14} \ s \quad (59)$$

The hydrogen atom in the HCl molecule vibrates with an extremely short period.

The short period of vibration of molecules is very important for their chemical properties. The hydrogen atom moves away from the chlorine atom once during each vibration cycle. If another molecule is close to the HCl molecule, this represents the opportunity for the hydrogen atom to engage in a chemical reaction with the neighboring atom. f is therefore the frequency with which the hydrogen atom tries to escape from the molecule by moving toward the outer limit of the potential energy barrier in Fig. 15.24. While no neighboring molecule is present, a dissociation of the HCl molecule does not take place (which would require that the hydrogen atom moves all the way beyond the right end of Fig. 15.24). However, when a neighboring molecule is close enough for there to be a strong interaction, then an escape attempt may result in a regrouping of atoms, i.e., in a successful completion of a chemical reaction. Since the period of closest proximity between molecules in a reaction volume is very short, a high attempt frequency is vital to obtain an appreciable rate at which chemical reactions take place. Due to the relevance of the vibrational frequency for chemical kinetics, some f values are summarized in Table 15.3.

Table 15.3: Vibration frequencies for organic molecules.

Bond	f [Hz]
H–O	$1.05 \times 10^{14} - 1.11 \times 10^{14}$
H–N	$9.9 \times 10^{13} - 1.05 \times 10^{14}$
H–C	$8.64 \times 10^{13} - 9.09 \times 10^{13}$
C=C	$4.8 \times 10^{13} - 5.04 \times 10^{13}$
C≡C	$6.6 \times 10^{13} - 6.78 \times 10^{13}$
C=O	$4.98 \times 10^{13} - 5.61 \times 10^{13}$

15.3.3. Simple and physical pendulum

We noted in section 15.2.3 that the mathematical form of the restoring force of a simple pendulum (an object on a taut string) and the restoring force for an object attached to an ideal spring are equivalent. All what is needed for us to do when switching from the spring to the pendulum is to replace the spring constant k by the factor mg/L, in which m is the mass of the object and L is the length of the string. Thus, we need not to repeat the discussion of section 15.3.1 for the pendulum motion. We illustrate this procedure for the potential energy in Eq. (35). Replacing k in Eq. (35) leads to:

$$E_{pot} = \frac{1}{2} \frac{mg}{L} x^2 \qquad (61)$$

To validate Eq. (61) we start with Fig. 15.16, for which we know that the potential energy of the object is equal to $E_{pot} = mgh$, where h is the height of the object above the equilibrium position. Fig. 15.25 shows how the various geometric parameters are related for the simple pendulum. We use the Pythagorean theorem for the triangle in Fig. 15.25 to derive Eq. (61) from $E_{pot} = mgh$. From Fig. 15.25 we find:

$$(L - h)^2 + x^2 = L^2$$
$$\Rightarrow -2Lh + h^2 + x^2 = 0 \qquad (62)$$

For small displacements from the equilibrium position we know that $h \ll L$ and thus $h^2 \ll hL$ in the last formula of Eq. (62). With this result we rewrite Eq. (62):

$$0 = -2Lh + h^2 + x^2 \approx -2Lh + x^2$$
$$\Rightarrow h = \frac{x^2}{2L} \qquad (63)$$

Example 15.7
Read the total energy of the HCl molecule in the ground state off Fig. 15.24 and calculate the amplitude and the maximum speed of the hydrogen atom in HCl.

Solution: The total energy of the molecule in the ground state is $E_{total} = 2.87 \times 10^{-20}$ J. With this value we use Eqs. (42) and (46) to obtain the amplitude and the maximum speed of the vibrating hydrogen atom:

$$A = \sqrt{\frac{2 E_{total}}{k}} = 1.09 \times 10^{-11} \, m \qquad (60)$$

$$v_{max} = \sqrt{\frac{k}{m}} A = 5860 \, \frac{m}{s}$$

The amplitude is 0.011 nm or about 10 % of the distance to the chlorine atom. The maximum speed of the hydrogen atom is not too fast. Human spacecrafts, benefiting at launch from the speed of the Earth around the sun at 30 km/s, exceed this maximum speed of the hydrogen atom. Note that spacecraft designed to leave the solar system require a minimum speed of 42 km/s.

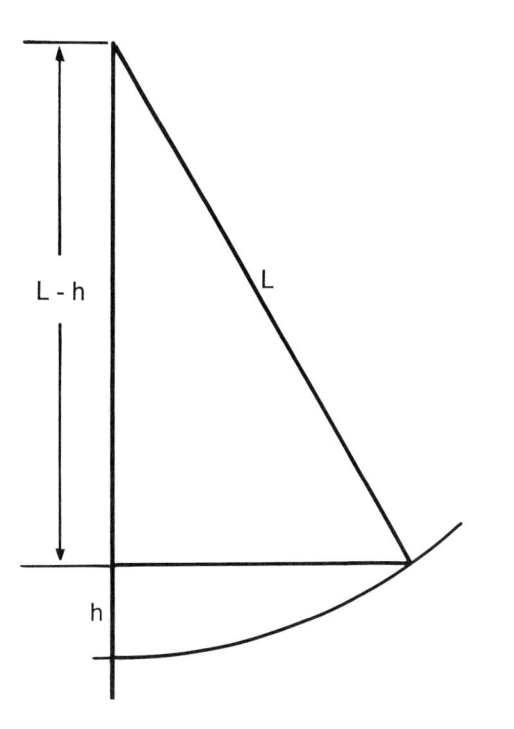

Fig. 15.25: Sketch relating the geometric parameters of an object attached to a taut string and displaced toward the right of the vertical equilibrium position.

Substituting h from Eq. (63) in $E_{pot} = mgh$ confirms the validity of Eq. (61).

Other relations for the simple pendulum are obtained by substituting mg/L in spring–system equations:
(I) The amplitude of the simple pendulum is:

$$A = \sqrt{\frac{2E_{total}L}{mg}} \quad (64)$$

(II) The maximum speed of the object on the string is:

$$v_{max} = \sqrt{\frac{g}{L}}\, A \quad (65)$$

(III) The angular frequency of the pendulum motion is:

$$\omega = \sqrt{\frac{g}{L}} \quad (66)$$

and (IV) the period of the pendulum motion is:

$$T = 2\pi \sqrt{\frac{L}{g}} \quad (67)$$

The period T does not depend on the object's mass m.

A pendulum motion of special interest in biomechanics is the natural motion of a person's leg during walking, as illustrated with four consecutive snapshots in Fig. 15.26. In the figure the right leg describes half a period corresponding to the forward motion (the front outline of the right leg is highlighted) while the left leg describes the other half of a full period.

The simple pendulum is not a suitable model for quantifying the walking process as the mass of the leg is not centred in the foot, but distributed along the entire leg (with a larger fraction in the thigh). We therefore extend the model of the simple pendulum to a *physical pendulum*. A physical pendulum is defined as an extended rigid body with a rotation axis which is not located at the center–of–mass. The easiest physical pendulum consists of a uniform rod of length L, pivoted at one end. The pendulum motion of such a physical pendulum is illustrated in Fig. 15.27.

The motion of a physical pendulum is closely related to the motion of a simple pendulum as both are derived from Hooke's law. The different mass distribution of the physical pendulum leads, however, to a different formula for the natural period:

$$T = 2\pi \sqrt{\frac{2L}{3g}} \quad (68)$$

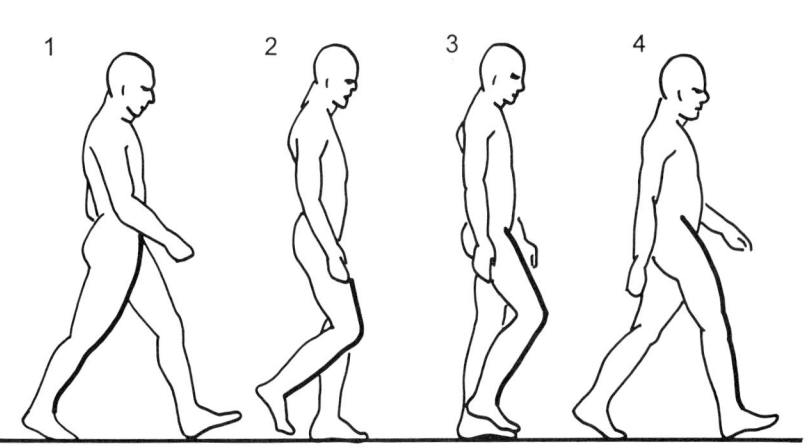

Fig. 15.26: Four frames showing a person walking. The time elapsed from the first to the last frame corresponds to half a period. The front of the right leg is highlighted to demonstrate the harmonic pendulum motion of the leg.

433

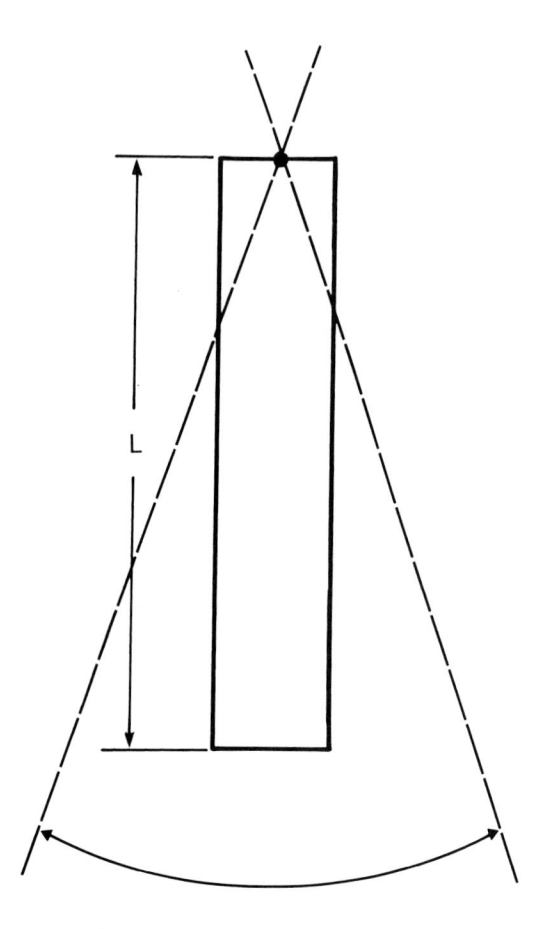

Fig. 15.27: A physical pendulum of length L with uniform mass distribution and the pivot point at the upper end of the rigid body.

Example 15.8
A comfortable walking pace for a human requires the least effort because the legs move with the natural period. We model the leg as a uniform rod, pivoted at the hip joint, and use a length L = 95 cm for the leg. What is the period of this average human's leg during walking?

Solution: We substitute the given values in Eq. (68):

$$T = 2\pi \sqrt{\frac{2L}{3g}} = 2\pi \sqrt{\frac{2 \cdot 0.95 [m]}{3 \cdot 9.8 \left[\frac{m}{s^2}\right]}} \quad (69)$$

$$\Rightarrow T = 1.6 \ s$$

Example 15.9
One of the best known dinosaurs is Tyrannosaurus rex, which lived during the Cretaceous period ending about 65 million years ago. This large carnivore walked on two legs like we do, although it was anatomically different in that it balanced the weight of the upper body with a massive tail (compare with the human and chimpanzee hip joints in section 4.5). We can derive the following data from the fossil record and petrified footsteps: the average length of T. rex's leg from the hip joint to the sole was L = 3.1 m. Its stride length, which is the distance between two foot prints of the same foot, was *l* = 4.0 m. Estimate the natural walking speed of the dinosaur.

Solution: We can solve this problem by using Eq. (68) if we assume a uniform mass distribution along the dinosaur's leg:

$$T = 2\pi \sqrt{\frac{2L}{3g}} = 2\pi \sqrt{\frac{2 \cdot 3.1 [m]}{3 \cdot 9.8 \left[\frac{m}{s^2}\right]}} \quad (70)$$

$$\Rightarrow T = 2.9 \ s$$

This leads to a walking speed for T. rex of:

$$v = \frac{l}{T} = \frac{4.0[m]}{2.9[s]} = 1.38 \ \frac{m}{s} \cong 5.0 \ \frac{km}{h} \quad (71)$$

Note that both the human leg and the leg of T. rex are not uniform. This leads to corrections which are more significant for the dinosaur with a more massive upper leg. The actual value is v = 3.6 km/h for the average human with a stride length of 1.6 m. For T. rex, v = 8 km/h and a period of 1.8 s are more appropriate values.

Note that this does not imply that T. rex was slow. Comparison between walking and running is not straight forward as additional parameters play a role in the ability to run which do not matter when walking. As an example of such a parameter, Fig. 15.28 shows the correlation between the femur length and the femur circumference. The solid circles are the data for various living mammals which hop and/or run fast, the open circles are data for the dinosaur subgroup ornithomimids, including the various tyrannosaurus species (T. rex is represented by the upmost circle), and the open triangles are from humans and hominid species. The straight lines (representing power law relations for each subgroup) illustrate that the robustness of the dinosaur legs matches

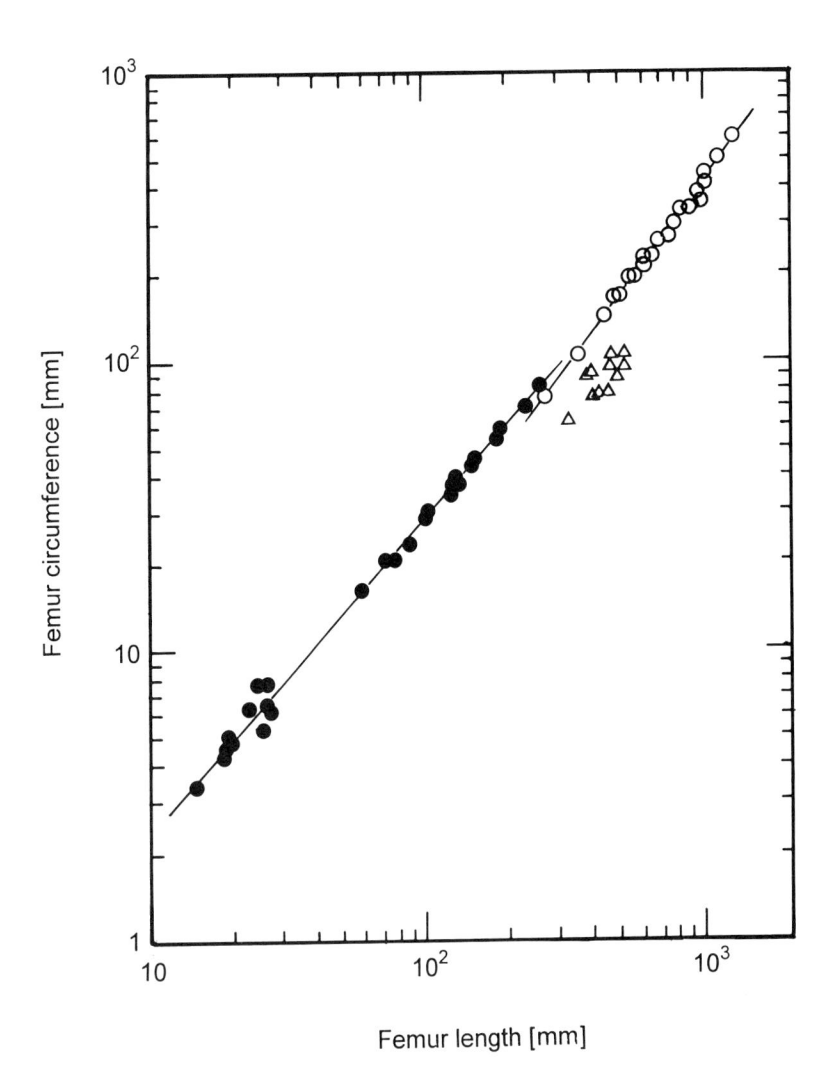

Fig. 15.28: Double–logarithmic plot of the correlation between the femur length and the femur circumference for various mammals and dinosaurs. The solid circles represent living mammals which hop and/or run fast. The open circles represent various species of the dinosaur subgroup ornithomimids, including several Tyrannosaurus species (T. rex is represented by the upmost circle). The open triangles represent humans and hominid species. The straight lines are power law relations for each subgroup and illustrate that the robustness of the dinosaur legs matches that of fast–running mammals, while humans have rather slender legs.

that of the various fast–running mammals, while humans have rather slender legs. Robustness of the femur in particular is important when running as this bone has to accommodate major forces. The conclusion of Fig. 15.28 is that the ornithomimids were designed for fast motion, while the human anatomy is based on other principles.

We complete our discussion of the pendulum with a comparison between two frequently studied systems, the object on a horizontal spring and the object on a vertical string. Table 15.4 summarizes the relevant formulas for both cases.

Table 15.4: Comparison between the various parameters of motion for a point mass on a horizontal spring and a point mass attached to a vertical string.

Property	Symbol	Spring system	Pendulum
Force constant		spring constant k	mg/L
Angular frequency	ω	$(k/m)^{1/2}$	$(g/L)^{1/2}$
Frequency	f	$1/T = \omega/2\pi$	$1/T = \omega/2\pi$
Period	T	$2\pi (m/k)^{1/2}$	$2\pi (L/g)^{1/2}$
Kinetic energy	E_{kin}	$\frac{1}{2}mv^2$	$\frac{1}{2}mv^2$
Potential energy	E_{pot}	$\frac{1}{2}kx^2$	mgh

15.4. Appendix

Radians and degrees

Radians are a mathematical unit for angles, but they do not show up in the units of a physical quantity. The unit radians must be used instead of other units for angles, such as degree or revolutions, in order to obtain proper quantitative results. It is worthwhile to study your pocket calculator to figure out how it calculates values for functions such as sine or cosine. In the degree–mode (DEG) it provides you with the following results:

$$\begin{array}{ll} \sin(0^0) = 0.0 & \cos(0^0) = 1.0 \\ \sin(90^0) = 1.0 & \cos(90^0) = 0.0 \\ \sin(180^0) = 0.0 & \cos(180^0) = -1.0 \\ \sin(270^0) = -1.0 & \cos(270^0) = 0.0 \end{array} \quad (72)$$

In the radians–mode (RAD) it provides you instead with the following results:

$$\begin{array}{ll} \sin(0) = 0.0 & \cos(0) = 1.0 \\ \sin(\pi/2) = 1.0 & \cos(\pi/2) = 0.0 \\ \sin(\pi) = 0.0 & \cos(\pi) = -1.0 \\ \sin(3\pi/2) = -1.0 & \cos(3\pi/2) = 0.0 \end{array} \quad (73)$$

in which the conversion is given as π [rad] = 180^0, and 1 rad = 57.3^0.

15.5. Problems

P–15.1
For the graph in Fig. 15.1, express the force (in % of the maximum force) as a mathematical function of the sarcomere length (in μm) for the linear segments
(a) in the interval 2.2 μm ≤ l ≤ 3.2 μm,
(b) in the interval 2.0 μm ≤ l ≤ 2.2 μm, and
(c) in the interval 1.4 μm ≤ l ≤ 1.65 μm.

P–15.2
Assume a leg contains a 1.2 m long bone with an average cross–sectional area of 3 cm². By how much does the bone shorten when the entire body weight of the person (use 700 N) is supported by the leg? Use for Young's modulus of the bone $Y = 1.8 \times 10^{10}$ Pa.

P–15.3
We determine an upper limit of the maximum height of building construction on Earth. This limit is due to the maximum stress in the building material prior to rupture. For steel of density ρ = 7.9 g/cm³ the maximum stress is σ = 2.0×10^8 Pa.

Hint: The pressure in the steel at the ground level may not exceed the maximum stress.

P–15.4
We suspend a uniform rod of length L and let it swing as a physical pendulum.
(a) What is the period of the pendulum if the length L = 2.0 m?
(b) If we want a simple pendulum with an object at the end of a massless string of length *l* to have the same period as the pendulum in part (a), what must the length *l* be?

P–15.5
If you have no meter stick but a precise clock, you can measure the height of structures by attaching an object to the end of a massless string, with the string pivoted at the top of the structure of which you want to measure the height and the object at the bottom of the structure.
(a) If the object swings 10 times back and forth in 110 s, what is the height of the structure?
(b) If you change the object on the string to one with double the mass, how does the answer given in part (a) change?

P–15.6
An object has a mass of m = 0.7 kg. It is attached to a spring which has a spring constant of value k = 80 N/m. At time t = 0 the object is pulled to a distance of 10 cm from its equilibrium position (which you may choose conveniently at x = 0). The surface on which the object moves is frictionless.
(a) What force does the spring exert on the object just before it is released?
(b) What are the angular frequency, the frequency and the period of the oscillation?
(c) What is the amplitude of the oscillation?
(d) What is the maximum speed of the object?
(e) What is the phase angle ϕ of the motion?

P–15.7
(a) What is the total energy of the system in P–15.6?
(b) What is the elastic potential energy of this system when the object is halfway between the equilibrium position and its turning point?

P–15.8
An object undergoes a simple harmonic motion. During that motion the object needs 0.4 s to reach one point of zero velocity from the previous such point. If the distance between those points is 50 cm, calculate
(a) the period,
(b) the frequency, and
(c) the amplitude of the motion.

P–15.9

An object has a mass of 250 g. It undergoes a simple harmonic motion. The amplitude of that motion is 10 cm and the period is 0.5 s.
(a) What is the spring constant (assuming that the spring obeys Hooke's law)?
(b) What is the maximum magnitude of the force which acts on the object?

P–15.10

An object is attached to an ideal spring. It undergoes a simple harmonic motion with a total energy of E = 1.0 J. The amplitude of the motion is 15.0 cm and the maximum speed of the object is 1.2 m/s. Find
(a) the spring constant,
(b) the mass of the object, and
(c) the frequency of the oscillation.

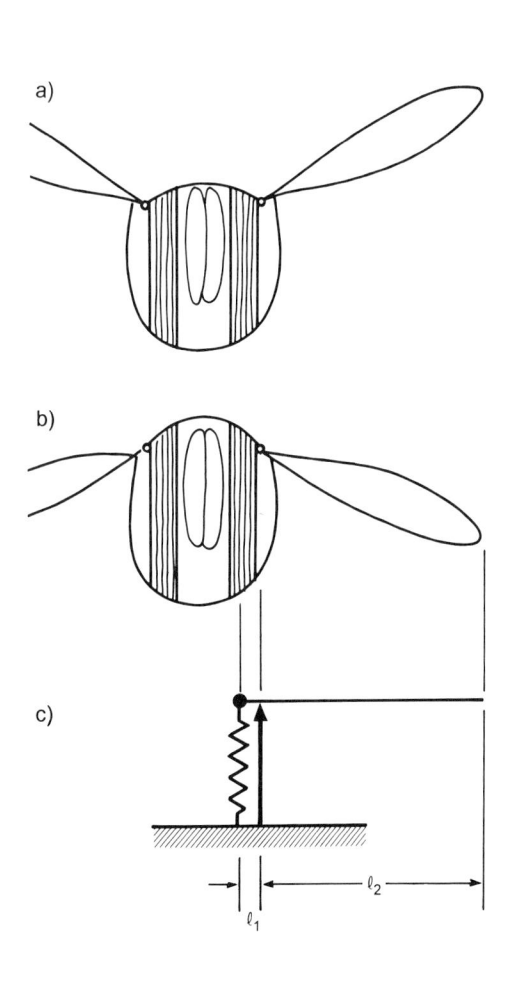

Fig. 15.29 for problem P–15.11

P–15.11

Fig. 15.29 shows a simplified model of an insect moving its wings during flight. The wing is pivoted about the outer chitin capsule. The end of the wing lies 0.5 mm inside the insect's body and moves up and down by a distance of 0.3 mm from its position of equilibrium. We use an effective spring constant of k = 0.74 N/m for the elastic tissue in the insect's body surrounding the end of the wing, and we use m = 0.3 mg as the effective mass of the wing which is moved up and down. The motion of the wing corresponds in this model to the vibration of the end of the wing attached to a spring (elastic tissue).
(a) With what frequency flap the wings of the insect during flight?
(b) What is the maximum speed of the inner end of the wing?
(c) What is the maximum speed of the outer tip of the wing if the wing is treated as a rigid body?
Use l_2 = 1.4 cm.

P–15.12

The vibration frequencies of atoms in solids at room temperature are of the order of 10^{13} Hz, similar to the values shown in Table 15.3. Using a simplified model for a solid in which the atoms are connected by ideal springs we want to study how a single atom in a piece of copper vibrates with this frequency relative to surrounding atoms, which we assume are at rest.
(a) Calculate the (effective) spring constant, using the weight of 1 mol of copper from the General Appendix (Chapter 24).
(b) What is the ratio of the (effective) spring constant of a gold atom in a piece of gold and the (effective) spring constant of the copper atom of part (a)?

Summary

Definitions:
- Stress: σ [N/m² = Pa] = F/A
- Strain: ε = Δl/l
- Amplitude: A [m] is maximum displacement during a vibration.
- Period: T [s] is the time to complete a full cycle during a vibration.
- Frequency: f [1/s = Hz] = 1/T
- Angular frequency: ω [rad/s] = 2πf = 2π/T

Laws:
- Elastic deformation (Hooke's law):
(i) for tensile stress (stretching):

$$\sigma = Y\epsilon$$

Y [Pa] is Young's modulus.
(ii) for hydraulic stress (volume compression):

$$p = -B\frac{\Delta V}{V}$$

B [Pa] is bulk modulus.

(iii) form used for elastic spring:

$$F_{elast} = -k(x - x_{eq})$$

k [N/m] is the spring constant, x_{eq} is the equilibrium position of the spring.
(iv) form used for simple pendulum:

$$F_{restore} = -mg\theta = -\frac{mg}{L}x$$

θ is the angle of deviation from the vertical equilibrium position, L is the length of string, x is the horizontal displacement from the vertical position.

- Elastic energy for an object attached to a spring:

$$E_{elast} = \frac{1}{2}kx^2 \quad \text{for } x_{eq} = 0$$

or:

$$E_{elast} = \frac{1}{2}k(x - x_{eq})^2 \quad \text{for } x_{eq} \neq 0$$

- Simple harmonic oscillation:

$$x(t) = A\cos(\omega t + \phi)$$

ϕ is phase angle, ω is angular frequency; ω for an object attached to a spring (k is spring constant):

$$\omega = \sqrt{\frac{k}{m}}$$

Chapter XVI

Ear and Communication

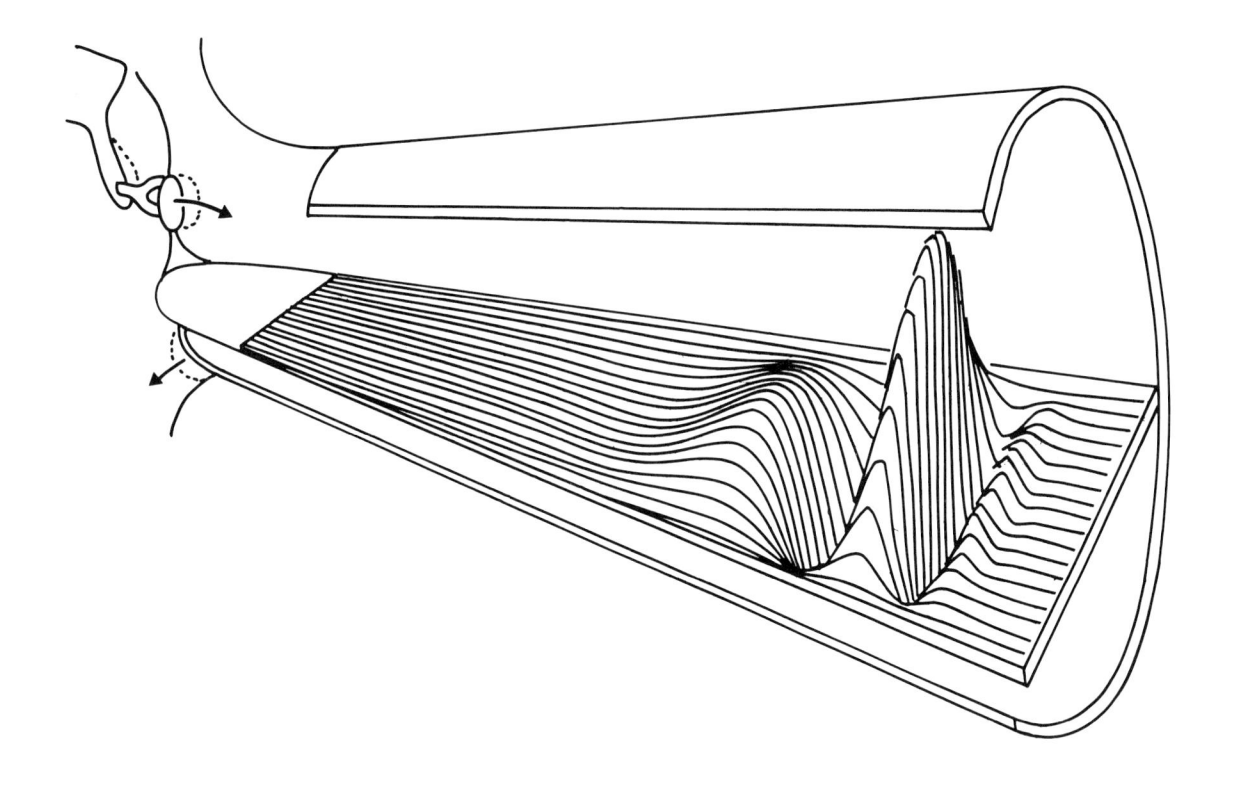

Longitudinal waves

EAR AND COMMUNICATION
LONGITUDINAL WAVES

When we cause a deformation within a medium, the perturbation is not confined to the excitation source but propagates through the medium. The perturbation travels away from the source with a fixed speed. The mathematical formula expressing its dependence on time and position is called a wave. This definition of waves covers a wide range of phenomena in the natural sciences, with acoustic waves (sound) and light the two physiologically most important cases. These two types of waves also represent the two fundamental categories of waves: transverse waves are waves for which the propagation direction is perpendicular to the direction in which the deformation oscillates (e.g., the electric field vector is perpendicular to the direction of a light ray). Longitudinal waves are waves for which the propagation direction is collinear with the direction in which the deformation oscillates (e.g., air elements in sound vibrate back and forth in the direction in which the sound travels). Light is discussed in Chapters 17 to 19, here we establish the basic properties of acoustics.

The perturbation in a gas carrying sound is an oscillating variation of the density and pressure of small gas elements. This local variation of the gas element's position relative to its equilibrium position represents a total energy contained in the wave. This energy travels with the speed of sound. The product of energy and speed defines the sound intensity. The intensity of a point sound source attenuates with the inverse square of the distance from the source (geometric effect). It further diminishes exponentially when energy is absorbed by the medium (Beer's law).

In confined media, such as closed or half–closed tubes, the wave is described by a sinusoidal function if it is caused by an elastic vibration obeying Hooke's law; such waves are called harmonic waves. When harmonic waves reflect off the closed end of the tube and superimpose on themselves, standing waves emerge if the length of the tube and the wavelength of the wave are related in a certain way. Such standing waves are called harmonics. Harmonics result from an external excitation which couples into the confined system resonantly. An example is the vibration of the vocal cord causing the human voice in the vocal tract. The inverse process causes the vibrations of the eardrum when sound enters the outer ear.

Beats result when two waves of similar frequency overlap. The Doppler effect describes the received sound frequency when either the source or the receiver are in motion relative to the medium.

Psychophysics is the term invented more than 120 years ago by Gustav Fechner to describe the physics and physiology of the human senses. This term combines the scientific physical approach with the more interpretative concepts of psychology. We will indeed find in this and the next chapters that the stimulus detection and signal processing of our senses is quite complex and that the naïve assumption of objectivity is often not applicable. Whether we hear a symphony, see a painting, taste a sweet dessert or smell the freshness of a crisp winter morning, we have to understand that the beauty of these things does not exist anywhere but in our mind. It is the interpretation our brain attaches to the tremendous flow of stimuli arriving from the environment which we perceive as reality, while the physical and chemical reality is a much more profane maze of electromagnetic frequencies, acoustic waves, and chemical reactions in our mucous membranes.

Of the human senses, we have already discussed two simpler ones: the equilibrium sense and the sense of touch. Our two most powerful senses are vision and hearing. Both are discussed in detail in this textbook, hearing in the present chapter and vision in Chapters 17 to 19. Comparing both senses we note a number of similarities. Both are sufficiently developed to analyze a wide range of different external stimuli (light in vision and sound in hearing). These stimuli originate in the environment and reach the eye or the ear across appreciable distances, which usually allows for sufficient time to react.

To understand the physical properties of the stimuli and the physiological principles of stimulus detection, the concept of waves is introduced in the present chapter. Hidden in the details of the respective wave models for light and sound lies the reason why we discuss them in separate chapters: sound is carried by air while light needs no medium. We have discussed in detail the properties of gases and are therefore well prepared to expand on these concepts to develop a model for sound propagation. On the other hand, to understand the wave nature of light magnetism has to be introduced.

16.1. The acoustic environment

Acoustic stimuli are generated by sound sources which use mechanical vibrations. Mechanical vibrations have been studied in the previous chapter. We discussed in particular a gas confined by a mobile piston in a cylinder. In this model the piston represents the mechanical component of the system which we can set in motion by displacing the piston from its equilibrium position.

The moving piston causes adjacent air to move back and forth. This air movement is linked to pressure variations in the gas. We will use the ideal gas law to study the consequences of air being compressed and expanded by a piston which undergoes harmonic motion. Such compressions and expansions can be described as non–equilibrium processes allowing us to develop the concept of an acoustic wave based on a mechanical vibration of a source placed in the gas medium.

There is almost an infinite number of different sound sources. Humans can distinguish about 400,000 different sounds. On one end are the various forms of noise, ranging from the crackling of wood in a fireplace to a jet engine, and on the other end are the harmonic sounds of musical instruments and the characteristic patterns of the human voice. All of these sources create different sound patterns, causing a highly complex sound environment for our ear. Yet we can distinguish all of these sounds; we are as confident in picking out a familiar voice as we are in recognizing a person's face. To be able to distinguish so many sounds a range of parameters must exist to characterize sound. This is illustrated in Fig. 16.1, which provides a first glimpse at the complexity of the human voice. Shown is the time dependence of the sound amplitude in the upper graph (as recorded with a microphone) and the frequency range for each sound in the lower graph for the word "acoustic". The word has seven different sounds as distinguished at the bottom of the figure, each displaying different amplitudes, different frequency bands and time

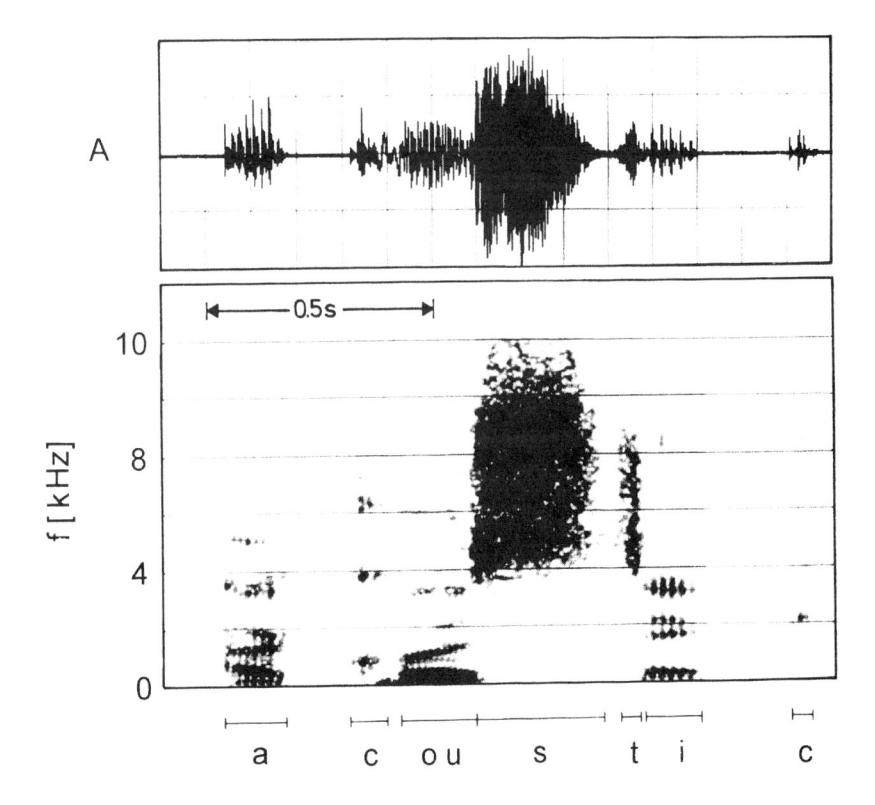

Fig. 16.1: Acoustic analysis of the word "acoustic". Recorded as a function of time are (I) in the upper panel, the acoustic vibration amplitude as measured by a microphone, and (II) in the lower panel, the range of frequencies associated with each separate sound in the word. The higher the sound energy at each frequency, the darker the graph.

lengths. To appreciate the formation of voice and to develop a model how our ear can detect voices, the concepts of frequency and amplitude have to be established for sound waves, and their relation to pitch, timbre and loudness have to be developed.

Once we understand acoustic waves in open space, we need to study various cases of spatial confinement arising from the phenomena of sound reflection and sound absorption at walls. We establish the unique properties of sound in closed tubes and tubes open at one end. This allows us to develop concepts of resonant sound amplification applicable to the outer ear canal and the vocal tract.

The physiological functions of the ear are discussed once all the fundamental concepts of sound have been established. The outer ear is shown to act as a half–open tube with arriving sound waves causing the eardrum to vibrate. These vibrations are mechanically amplified in the middle ear and then propagate as a wave through the fluids in the inner ear (cochlea). There, the wave is analyzed for its frequency profile.

With the function of the ear established we conclude the chapter with three special features: stereoscopic hearing (i.e., detection of the direction of the sound source due to hearing with two ears), acoustic illusions (illustrated with the concept of beats) and an application of moving sound sources and sound detectors. The latter phenomena lead to the Doppler effect and are important for medical applications.

16.2. Waves in an unconfined medium

Since the particles in any homogeneous medium (e.g. solids, liquids and gases) interact with each other, local vibrations of atoms or molecules around their equilibrium position affect other particles in the close vicinity. The interaction of a local vibration with adjacent areas in a medium leads to a propagating wave.

16.2.1. General properties of waves

The easiest way to illustrate the connection between a local vibration and the resulting wave is to swing a rope attached to a wall up and down at the free end. The formation of a wave along the rope is shown in Fig. 16.2. Assume that the rope is initially stretched horizontally from the wall to your hand (solid dot at the origin). At time t = 0 you start to move your hand up and down with the position of your hand oscillating vertically with amplitude A. At time t = T/4, i.e., when your hand has completed a quarter period, your hand is at position +A.

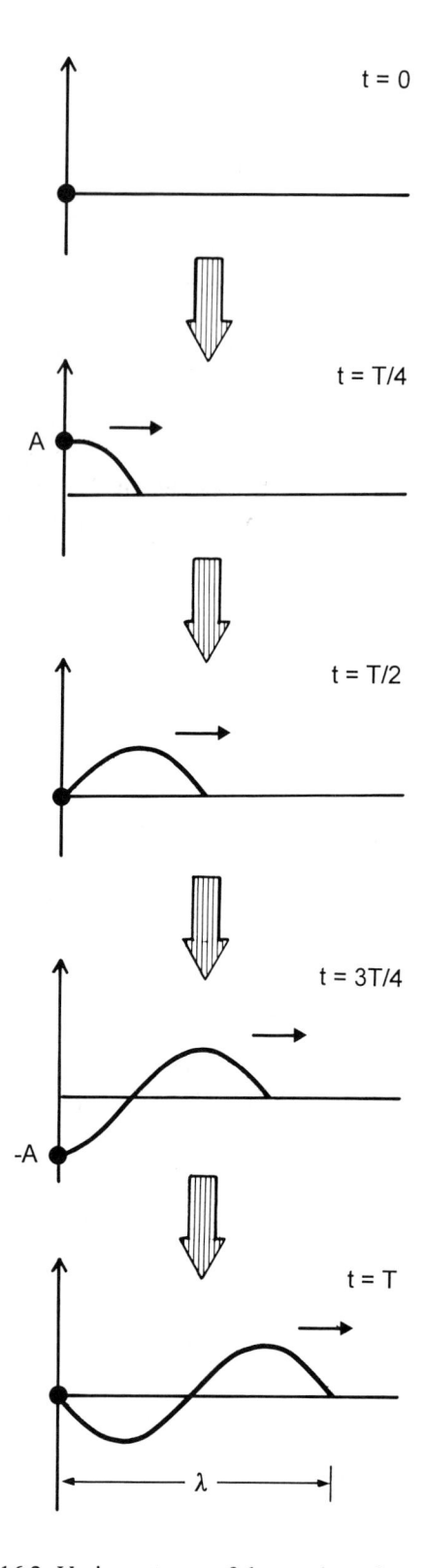

Fig. 16.2: Various stages of the motion of a rope when the free end at the origin oscillates up and down with period T. Once a full period of the vibration is completed (bottom panel), the rope is displaced by the vibration to a distance λ, called the wavelength.

Since the rope is a continuous string, the parts of the rope adjacent to your hand must have been pulled up as well. This is shown in the second frame of Fig. 16.2. Later, at time t = T/2, your hand has returned to the origin. However, since the rest of the rope has been following your hand, it is not stretched as it was initially, but contains a bulge (see the third frame of Fig. 16.2). In the next two frames your hand completes another half period by moving to the position – A and back to the origin. Again, the adjacent part of the rope follows and a downward bulge results. The initial, upward directed bulge did not disappear, but has moved further to the right. Thus, at time t = T, the local oscillation of your hand has been transformed into a full sinusoidal curve along the rope, reaching a point at distance λ in front of your hand. The curve the rope describes is called a wave and λ is its wavelength. The speed of the perturbation along the rope, resulting from the vibration caused by your hand, can then be expressed as a function of the wavelength and the period:

$$v_{wave} = \frac{\lambda}{T} = \lambda f \qquad (1)$$

in which f is the frequency, which we defined as f = 1/T.

> *The speed of a wave is equal to the product of its wavelength and its frequency.*

Example 16.1
(a) The musical note C_4 (Middle C) on a piano is caused by a string vibrating with a frequency of 261.6 Hz. The vibration of the string interacts with the adjacent air, as discussed in more detail below, causing a sound wave to propagate away from the piano with a wavelength of 1.31 m. What is the speed of sound in air?
(b) An FM station broadcasts at f = 100 MHz with radio waves of wavelength λ = 3 m. Find the speed of the radio wave.

Solution part (a): The speed of waves is given by Eq. (1) as v = λf = 1.31[m] 261.6[Hz] = 342.7 m/s. Thus, the speed of the wave, which we call the speed of sound in this case, is about 340 m/s.

Solution part (b): We use Eq. (1) to find for the speed of the wave: v = λf = 3[m] 100[MHz] = 3 × 10^8 m/s. Thus, the speed of a radio wave is significantly higher than the speed of a sound wave.

Example 16.2
Bats use ultrasound echo–location to detect small insects in flight. To do so, the wavelength used by bats must be smaller or equal to the size of their prey. Bats therefore use frequencies of about 80 kHz. Dolphins and porpoises also use ultrasound echo–location for hunting.
(a) If a dolphin's prey were as small as the insects eaten by bats, what frequency would the dolphins have to use?
(b) Dolphins actually use frequencies up to 225 kHz. How much bigger is their smallest prey when compared to the insects which bats hunt?
Hint: Use for the speed of sound in air c_{air} = 340 m/s and c_{sea} = 1530 m/s for the speed of sound in sea water.

Solution part (a): We use Eq. (1), written once for the medium air and once written for the medium sea water. In both cases, the wavelength is specified by the smallest length required for each predator, $\lambda = L_{insect}$ for the bat and $\lambda = L_{squid}$ (assuming that squid is the smallest prey a dolphin hunts). In part (a) we assume that $L_{insect} = L_{squid}$. This leads to:

$$\frac{c_{air}}{f_{bat}} = \frac{c_{sea}}{f_{dolphin}} \qquad (2)$$

which provides for the frequency of the dolphins:

$$f_{dolphin} = \frac{c_{sea}}{c_{air}} f_{bat} = \qquad (3)$$

$$\frac{1530[m/s]}{340[m/s]} 80 \times 10^3 [Hz] = 360 \; kHz$$

Solution part (b): The result in Eq. (3) of part (a) shows that dolphins cannot hunt prey as small as the insects which are hunted by bats. To answer part (b) we allow for the size of a squid and the size of an insect to differ and use $c_{air} = L_{insect} f_{bat}$ and $c_{sea} = L_{squid} f_{dolphin}$ to calculate the ratio L_{squid}/L_{insect}:

$$\frac{L_{squid}}{L_{insect}} = \frac{c_{sea}}{c_{air}} \frac{f_{bat}}{f_{dolphin}} = \qquad (4)$$

$$\frac{1530[m/s]}{340[m/s]} \frac{80 \times 10^3[Hz]}{225 \times 10^3[Hz]} = 1.6$$

Thus, among those hunting in a three–dimensional

space, dolphins are probably the most versatile. Given the typical size of an insect hunted by bats with a size just over 4 mm, the much larger dolphin can detect objects as small as 7 mm in size under water. The smallest adult squid are 2 to 3 cm long. In addition, the dolphin can detect objects of that size over a much longer distance because the sound absorption in water is much less than in air.

It is worthwhile to analyse the results of Example 16.1 in more detail. The wave propagation speed in part (a) is consistent with the range of speeds we calculated for air molecules at room temperature using the kinetic gas theory in Eq. (6.58). Thus, we propose that air is the medium which carries sound waves. We will see that the vibration of a sound source creates a periodic variation in the density of the adjacent air, and this density perturbation travels through the medium, superimposed on the random motion of the gas particles. It is the speed of individual air molecules which limits the propagation speed of sound since they collide with gas molecules in neighboring gas elements.

Accepting this reasoning requires us to identify a different medium for the propagation of radio waves as studied in part (b) of the Example. We recognize the speed found in that case to be the speed of light. Thus, we expect that radio waves and light are similar. Indeed, we know that both types of waves do not need a medium as both are transmitted through outer space.

Waves are not just distinguished by different wavelengths, frequencies and wave propagation speeds. We illustrate another major difference by studying Fig. 16.2 once more. Note that the vibration which causes the wave, is based on an up–down motion of the left end of the rope. The propagating wave in turn moves toward the right, i.e., in a direction perpendicular to the vibration. We call such a wave a *transverse wave*. Important examples of this type of wave are surface waves on water as well as radio and light waves, which we discuss in Chapter 19.

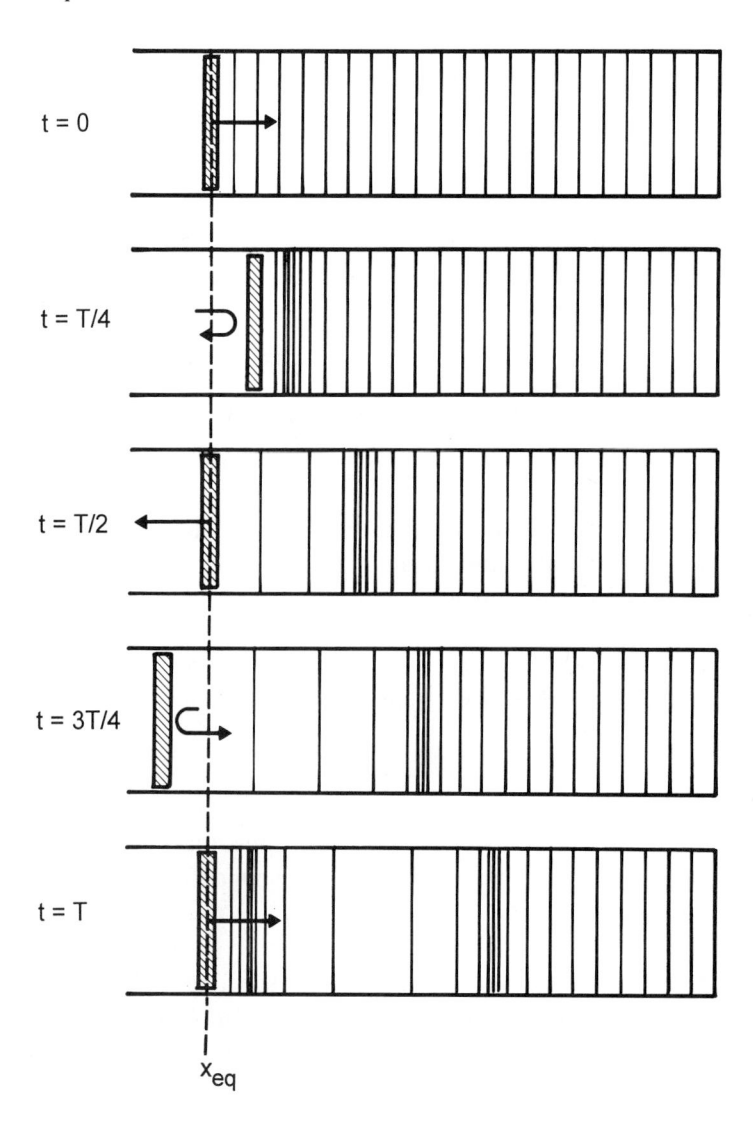

Fig. 16.3: Five snapshots illustrating the development of an acoustic wave in a gas–filled cylinder due to the vibrational motion of a piston about its equilibrium position x_{eq}. The piston reaches the amplitude point toward the right at time $T/4$ and the amplitude point toward the left at time $3T/4$. When the piston moves toward the right the air pocket adjacent to the piston is compressed (indicated by an increased density of thin lines). When the piston moves toward the left the air pocket adjacent to the piston is expanded (indicated by a decreased density of thin lines).

Other wave forms, in particular the sound waves that we are primarily interested in this chapter, differ from the transverse wave type. This is illustrated with the five sketches in Fig. 16.3, showing a gas in which an acoustic wave is generated. In the first frame at time t = 0 the gas on the right hand side of the piston has a uniform density. The equilibrium position of the piston is indicated by a vertical dashed line. The gas density is indicated graphically by the density of thin lines in the gas volume. At time t = 0 the piston is set into motion toward the right as indicated by an arrow. At t > 0 the piston will undergo a harmonic oscillation as discussed in Chapter 15. During this oscillation, we focus on the air in front of the piston.

The four lower frames in Fig. 16.3 correspond to the frames (b) to (e) in Fig. 16.2 for the formation of a wave on a rope. When the piston reaches its amplitude toward the right at t = T/4, a locally compressed pocket of air is created in front of the piston (indicated by the high density of thin lines). The gas molecules in this area of increased density have also been given an additional velocity component toward the right. When the piston then moves back to its equilibrium position (reached at time t = T/2), the gas molecules in front of the piston are pulled back toward the left, causing an area of decreased air density (indicated by a low density of thin lines).

By moving beyond the equilibrium position to the amplitude point at the left (reached at time t = 3T/4), the piston increases the volume of the gas pocket directly in front of it at the right. Thus, the volume with decreased air density is further enlarged. In the meantime, the initially created zone of increased air density has travelled toward the right and remains present in the system (illustrated as a zone of denser thin lines). Note that it is the density variations which travel, not the individual molecules in the gas. The absolute density of the gas is very high and thus individual gas molecules encounter frequent collisions which essentially keep them near their original position.

In the last frame of Fig. 16.3 we notice that the piston, turning toward the right after t = 3T/4, compresses the air in front of it once more while completing a full period of motion. Thus, at the final time t = T, a second regime of increased air density is generated which subsequently travels toward the right following the initial high density regime at a constant distance.

What distinguishes the case in Fig. 16.3 from the case in Fig. 16.2 is the fact that the direction of the vibration of the piston and the direction of the propagating sound wave are collinear. Such waves are called *longitudinal waves*.

> *The direction of the exciting oscillation and the direction of the propagating wave are collinear for longitudinal waves.*

There are important differences between longitudinal and transverse waves. We will discuss one such difference in detail in Chapter 19 when introducing the linear polarization of light. Acoustic waves do not have this feature because longitudinal waves cannot be polarized. Other forms of waves occurring in nature are often a combination of longitudinal and transverse waves. A typical example are the seismic waves caused by an earthquake. Both the longitudinal and transverse components are detected with the seismograph.

16.2.2. Longitudinal waves in a gas

We look at Fig. 16.4 for a quantitative approach to the propagation of waves in a gas. The figure shows a small gas element of length Δx between the dashed lines in a cylindrical tube. The gas to the left of the element causes a local pressure $p(x)$ and the gas to the right causes a local pressure $p(x+\Delta x)$. The small gas element is not in mechanical equilibrium if we assume that somewhere to the left a piston vibrates like in Fig. 16.3. This means that the two local pressure values differ and cause an acceleration of the small gas element due to Newton's second law. This law connects the pressure change along the x–axis with the change of speed with time, which is the acceleration.

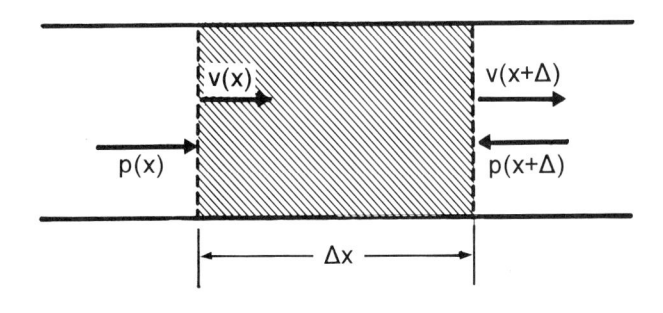

Fig. 16.4: A small gas element in a cylindrical tube with a one–dimensional sound wave generated by a vibrating piston far to the left. The vertical dashed lines define the gas element of length Δx. We distinguish the gas pressure and the speed of the gas at both interfaces confining the gas element.

Secondly, we also expect the speed of the two interfaces which separate the gas element and the gas outside to vary, with values v(x) and v(x+Δx). This difference leads to a change in the volume of the small gas element. The volume change is connected to a change in pressure due to Eq. (15.5) for the compressibility of the gas. This second argument then connects the change of the speed along the x–axis with the change of the pressure with time.

Both of these arguments can be quantified and combined. This leads to the *wave equation*, which is an equation that relates the time dependence and the position dependence of the parameters of a wave which each other. The specific dependence of the displacement, the pressure variations and the density variations on position and time (called the *wave function*) can obviously not be specified based on Fig. 16.4 alone as any change in the vibrations, which cause the wave, will lead to different wave forms. Thus, additional information is needed to specify the wave function. We will study the most important case, in which the vibration of the piston is a simple harmonic oscillation, in the next section.

However, there are a few general properties of waves which apply regardless of the specific form of vibration causing the wave. We discuss two issues:
(I) the fact that the position and the time dependences of a wave are not independent of each other, and
(II) the value of the speed of sound.

Position and time dependence in a wave
We define the displacement of a small element of the gas in Fig. 16.4 as ξ with $\xi = x - x_{eq}$. Looking at a sound wave, the displacement varies from point to point in space and also in time. Thus, the most general mathematical form in which a formula could be written for the displacement is $\xi = f(x,t)$. This means that the right hand side of the equation is any function which contains the independent variables time and position. There are restrictions on the possibilities of how x and t occur in the wave function: if a certain displacement of the gas element is given at one particular time, the displacement of the neighboring element shortly after (that is, after the speed of sound allows the perturbation to move there) is predetermined. Thus, we can write:

$$\xi = f(x \pm ct) \quad (5)$$

which states that the displacement depends on a single variable x ± ct. This variable is called the *phase of the wave*. The constant c in Eq. (5) is the speed of sound.

The speed of sound
We want to discuss the speed of sound using Eq. (5). For this we study two different times t_1 and t_2. At the earlier time t_1 the wave function has the form $\xi = f(x \pm ct_1)$, i.e., is only a function of the position. An arbitrary example is shown in the top sketch of Fig. 16.5. Studying the wave function at a later time t_2 leads to $\xi = f(x \pm ct_2)$, as illustrated in the lower sketch of Fig. 16.5. The function differs at the later time t_2 only in that the wave pattern has shifted along the x–axis. This is illustrated in Fig. 16.5 by identifying the position of a specific feature of the wave, which is initially at position x_1 and later at position x_2. The wave function is in both cases identical if the appropriate combination of position shift and elapsed time between an initial and final snapshot is taken into account:

$$x_1 - ct_1 = x_2 - ct_2$$

$$\Rightarrow \quad c = \frac{x_2 - x_1}{t_2 - t_1} \quad (6)$$

c is, therefore, called the phase velocity of the wave. This quantity should not be mixed up with the speed of a particular gas particle or the root–mean–square speed introduced in Chapter 6.

Sound propagation does not only occur in gases. Fig. 16.4 illustrates that the occurrence of a travelling sound wave in a gas is due to the compressibility of the gas. In Chapter 15 we discussed that real solids and liquids are also compressible. Thus, wave phenomena

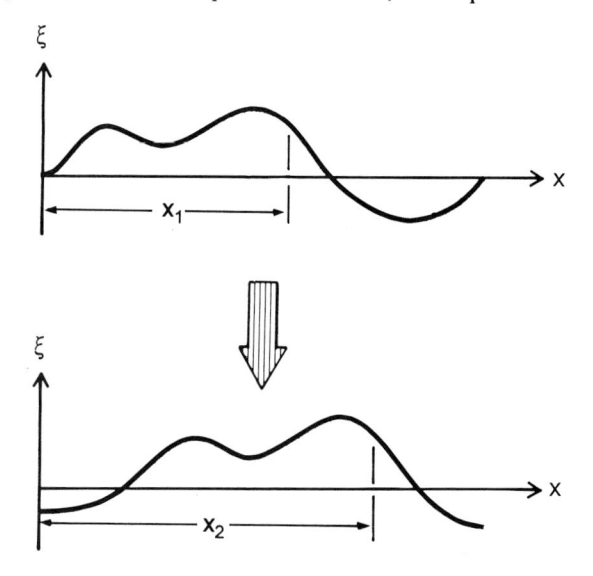

Fig. 16.5: A displacement of a gas element from its equilibrium position, $\xi = x - x_{eq}$, due to a perturbation moving through the medium. The figure shows the wave twice, at time t_1 (top) and at time t_2 (bottom). During the time interval $\Delta t = t_2 - t_1$ the wave travels a distance $\Delta x = x_2 - x_1$ towards the right. The speed of the wave is $c = \Delta x/\Delta t$.

occur in these two states of matter as well. We can describe the sound phenomena in solids, liquids and gases by writing the speeds of sound of Eqs. (5) and (6) as a function of the elastic moduli of section 15.1:

$$(I) \quad c_{liquid} = \sqrt{\frac{B}{\rho}}$$

$$(II) \quad c_{solid} = \sqrt{\frac{Y}{\rho}} \quad (7)$$

$$(III) \quad c_{gas} = \sqrt{\frac{C_p}{C_V} \frac{p}{\rho}}$$

in which B is the bulk modulus, Y is Young's modulus, C_p is the molar heat capacity of the gas at constant pressure, and C_V the molar heat capacity at constant volume.

> *Wave equations describe the wave as a function of position and time. They contain the speed of sound, which is linked to the elastic properties of the medium.*

The speed of sound in a gas (formula (III) in Eq. (7)) is derived from formula (I) as that formula applies to fluids in general. Note that we calculated the bulk modulus for an ideal gas in Eq. (15.27) but do not use that result to derive the third formula in Eq. (7). The reason is that Eq. (15.27) is derived with the assumption of a constant temperature (T = const). For an expansion to occur isothermally, the expansion must be done slowly. This does not apply to the fast vibrations of air in a travelling sound wave. The vibrations of air are better described by an adiabatic compression since the time during which the compression occurs is too short to allow a heat exchange with the adjacent air. Using an adiabatic process to calculate the bulk modulus of an ideal gas leads to the third formula in Eq. (7), which is called *Laplace's equation* for the speed of sound. Table 16.1 summarizes the speeds of sound in various solids, liquids and gases.

Example 16.3
The ratio of the two heat capacity values in the third formula in Eq. (7) is usually labelled κ. For a typical real gas κ = C_p/C_v = 1.4. Use for the density of air at 0°C as ρ = 1.293 kg/m³. Confirm the speed of sound at 0°C and for air pressure 1 atm, as shown in Table 16.1.

Table 16.1: Speed of sound in various materials.

Material	Speed of sound [m/s]	Temperature [K]
Gases:		
Air	331	273
Air	343	293
Air	386	373
Liquids:		
Water	1400	273
Water	1490	298
Seawater (3.5% salt)	1530	298
Solids and soft matter:		
Steel	5940	
Human body tissue	1540	310
Vulcanized rubber	55	

Solution: Substituting the values in the third formula of Eq. (7) we find:

$$c_{air} = \sqrt{1.4 \frac{1.013 \times 10^5 [Pa]}{1.293 [kg/m^3]}} = 331.3 \frac{m}{s} \quad (8)$$

As Table 16.1 shows, the speed of sound in gases and liquids depends strongly on the temperature. We know from Charles' law that the ideal gas expands linearly when the temperature is increased (see Eqs. (6.17) and (6.18)). We rewrite Charles' law with a reference volume V_0 at 0°C: $V = V_0 (1 + \alpha T)$. In this formula, α is the linear *expansion coefficient* for an ideal gas with α = 1/273.2 K^{-1}. This means that the expansion is by a fraction of 1/273.2 per degree of temperature increase. With this volume formula, the definition of the density, ρ = m/V, is written in the form:

$$\rho = \frac{\rho_0}{1 + \alpha T} \quad (9)$$

in which ρ_0 is the reference density at 0°C temperature. Eq. (9) is substituted into the last formula in Eq. (7) to determine the temperature dependence of the speed of sound at constant gas pressure:

$$c = c_0 \sqrt{1 + \alpha T} \quad (10)$$

Example 16.4
Using the data for air at 0°C from Table 16.1, find at a pressure of 1 atm and at T = 20°C (room temperature)
(a) the density, and
(b) the speed of sound of air.
Hint: use an ideal gas approximation for the linear expansion coefficient for air.

Solution part (a): We calculate the density of air at room temperature from Eq. (9) first, using $\Delta T = 20$ K:

$$\rho = \frac{1.293 [kg/m^3]}{1 + \frac{1}{273.2}\left[\frac{1}{K}\right] 20[K]} = 1.205 \frac{kg}{m^3} \quad (11)$$

Solution part (b): Eq. (10) allows us to calculate in the same fashion the speed of sound at 20°C:

$$c = 331.3 \left[\frac{m}{s}\right]\sqrt{1 + \frac{20[K]}{273.2[K]}} = 343.2 \frac{m}{s} \quad (12)$$

16.2.3. Harmonic waves

In our discussion of vibrations we identified a unique role for the harmonic vibrations because they are the result of a mechanical system that obeys Hooke's law with a linear restoring force.

> *The waves caused by harmonic vibrations are called harmonic waves. This name is justified since sinusoidal functions describe the waves.*

With harmonic vibrations causing the wave, the general wave function of Eq. (5) takes a specific form for the displacement of the gas element ξ:

$$\xi = A \sin\left(2\pi f \left(t - \frac{x}{c}\right)\right) =$$
$$= A \sin\left(2\pi (f \cdot t - \frac{x}{\lambda})\right) \quad (13)$$

where A is the amplitude, f the frequency, λ the wavelength and c the speed of sound. Eq. (13) applies for a wave travelling in the x–direction (plane wave). Other interesting wave forms include spherical waves travelling outwards from a point source. For spherical waves the position parameter in the wave equation is the radius r, replacing x in Eq. (13). Note that Eq. (13) is consistent with the general form given in Eq. (5).

The harmonic wave function is shown in Fig. 16.6. The top curve shows the harmonic wave function at time t = 0 and the bottom curve shows it at time t = T/4 when the wave has travelled a quarter of a wavelength, i.e., the wave function has shifted by $\lambda/4$.

The harmonic wave function is often written in a slightly different form in the literature, using the angular frequency $\omega = 2\pi f$ and the wave number $\kappa = 2\pi/\lambda$. This leads to an equation that is equivalent to Eq. (13):

$$\xi = A \sin(\omega t - \kappa x) \quad (14)$$

Fig. 16.4 indicates that the pressure in the gas element varies in the same fashion as the displacement of the gas element. This remains true for harmonic waves, leading to another way in which the wave function can be written:

$$\Delta p = \Delta p_{max} \sin(\omega t - \kappa x) \quad (15)$$

in which the maximum pressure variation, Δp_{max}, is linearly related to the maximum displacement (amplitude A) in Eq. (14) in the form:

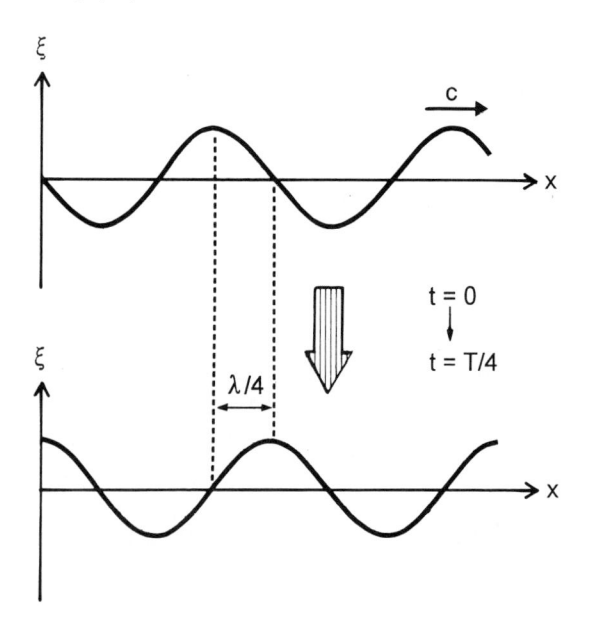

Fig. 16.6: Two harmonic waves. The top curve shows the harmonic wave at time t = 0 and the bottom curve shows the harmonic wave a quarter of a period later (t = T/4). During this time the wave has travelled toward the right by a quarter of a wavelength, $\lambda/4$ (dashed interval).

$$\Delta p_{max} = (c\rho\omega) A \qquad (16)$$

in which c is the speed of sound and ρ is the density of the medium. It is always useful to check the units for new equations, particularly when we do not derive them in the text. In Eq. (16), the units on the right hand side are: [m/s] for the speed of sound, [kg/m³] for the density of the medium, [rad/s] for the angular frequency and [m] for the amplitude. Neglecting the unit [rad], these units combine to [kg/ms²] = [N/m²] = [Pa], the unit of pressure. This unit is consistent wit the unit of the term on the left hand side of Eq. (16).

Example 16.5
The equation of a wave along the x–axis is given as:

$$\xi \, [cm] = 2.0 \, \sin(1.0t - 1.5x) \qquad (17)$$

in which ξ is the displacement. Units on the right hand side are: $\kappa = 1.5$ [cm^{-1}] and $\omega = 1.0$ [s^{-1}]. Determine: (a) the amplitude, (b) the wavelength, (c) the angular frequency, (d) the period, (e) the frequency, and (f) the travelling speed of the wave. (g) Draw two sketches for the wave: ξ versus x at time t = 0, and ξ versus t at x = 0.

Solution part (a): We compare the specific case in Eq. (17) with the harmonic wave equation in Eq. (13). The amplitude is the pre–factor of the *sine* function, i.e., A = 2.0 cm. The unit of A is [cm] since the only factor on the right hand side of Eq. (17) is A. This factor must therefore have the same unit as the displacement ξ.

Solution part (b): Eq. (17) identifies the wave number as the value $\kappa = 1.5$ [cm^{-1}]. Using the definition of the wave number, $\kappa = 2\pi/\lambda$ we find for the wavelength:

$$\lambda = \frac{2\pi}{\kappa} = \frac{2\pi}{1.5[1/cm]} = 4.2 \, cm \qquad (18)$$

Solution part (c): The angular frequency is read directly from Eq. (17): $\omega = 1.0$ rad/s.

Solution part (d): The period follows from the result in part (c), using Eq. (15.50):

$$T = \frac{2\pi}{\omega} = \frac{2\pi}{1.0[rad/s]} = 6.3 \, s \qquad (19)$$

Solution part (e): The frequency also follows from Eq. (15.50), either in combination with the result in part (c) or the result in part (d):

$$f = \frac{1}{T} = \frac{\omega}{2\pi} = \frac{1}{6.3[s]} = 0.16 \, Hz \qquad (20)$$

Solution part (f): From Eq. (1) we find:

$$v_{wave} = \lambda f = 0.042[m] \, 0.16[Hz] =$$
$$6.7 \times 10^{-3} \frac{m}{s} = 0.67 \frac{cm}{s} \qquad (21)$$

Due to the negative sign in Eq. (17), the wave travels with 0.67 cm/s in the positive x–direction.

Solution part (g): The two sketches are shown in Fig. 16.7. Note from trigonometry that the following identity holds: $\sin(-1.5x) = -\sin(1.5x)$.

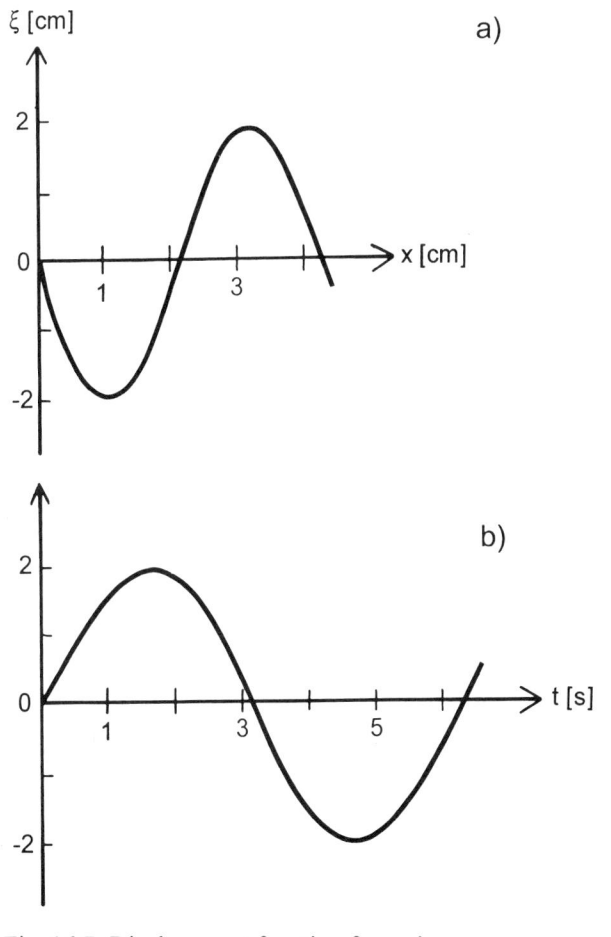

Fig. 16.7: Displacement function for a given wave.
(a) The displacement as a function of position along the x–axis at time t = 0.
(b) the displacement as a function of time at the origin, i.e., the position x = 0.

Example 16.6
The maximum pressure variation that is acceptable for the human ear is about 30 Pa. What is the amplitude of a gas element in this case at 20°C when the sound source emits a frequency of 3.0 kHz (i.e., in the range where the ear is the most sensitive)?

Solution: We use the air density which we calculated in Example 16.4. From Eq. (16) we find:

$$A = \frac{\Delta p_{max}}{c\rho\omega} = \frac{30[Pa]}{343.2\left[\frac{m}{s}\right]1.205\left[\frac{kg}{m^3}\right](2\pi\ 3000[Hz])} \quad (22)$$

which leads to A = 3.85 μm. Note that both the pressure variations and the amplitude are comparably small values. The maximum pressure variation used in this example corresponds to less than 0.03 % of the normal air pressure (1 atm) and the amplitude of 3.85 μm is a distance we cannot see with the naked eye (size range of large bacteria is 1 to 2 μm).

16.2.4. Sound intensity

The intensity is a measure of the amount of energy transported by a wave per time interval Δt through a plane of unit area which is placed perpendicular to the wave's propagation direction. To evaluate the intensity of a sound wave, we first have to establish the total energy carried in a wave. The total energy is the sum of the kinetic and potential energies of the local vibration of its small gas elements:

$$E_{tot} = \frac{1}{2}mv^2 + \frac{1}{2}k\xi^2 \quad (23)$$

in which v is the speed with which the gas element moves. We quantify the total energy in analogy to the calculation we used in Eq. (15.47) to determine the total energy of a vibrating system. We found that the total energy can be expressed as the spring potential energy at the point of maximum displacement (amplitude) or, alternatively, as the kinetic energy at the maximum speed, i.e., when the object passes through its equilibrium position. The same applies to a vibrating air element. We use the instant when the gas element passes through its equilibrium position and express the total energy as the kinetic energy at that instant. From Eqs. (15.46) and (15.49) we find for a vibrating system that $v_{max} = \omega A$ and therefore the kinetic energy $E_{kin,\ max} = \frac{1}{2}m\omega^2A^2$. As this formula applies to each single vibrating molecule in a gas, we multiply this energy with the number of molecules in the gas element, N_{elem} to obtain an expression for the total energy of the gas element. The product mN_{elem} equals to the mass of the element, i.e., the density of the gas, ρ, multiplied with the volume of the gas element, ΔV. Thus:

$$E_{tot} = \frac{1}{2}\rho\Delta V A^2\omega^2$$
$$\frac{E_{tot}}{\Delta V} \equiv \epsilon_{tot} = \frac{1}{2}\rho A^2\omega^2 \quad (24)$$

In the second formula of Eq. (24) both sides have been divided by the volume of the gas element, with ϵ_{tot} representing the energy density. The energy density has units of [J/m³]. Eq. (24) therefore shows that the energy density of a sound wave is proportional to the square of the amplitude, $\epsilon_{tot} \propto A^2$.

The energy density of the wave travels with speed c in a medium carrying the sound. Thus, the intensity I is given as:

$$I = c\epsilon_{tot} = \frac{1}{2}c\rho A^2\omega^2 \quad (25)$$

with the unit for the intensity [J/(m²s)].

> *The intensity of a wave is the amount of energy passing through a unit area perpendicular to the propagation direction of the wave. It is proportional to the square of the amplitude.*

The pressure variation and the density variation in the gas are closely linked. This led to a proportionality between the pressure difference encountered by a gas element and the amplitude of the motion of the gas element. Thus, the intensity of the sound wave is also proportional to the square of the maximum pressure variation, i.e., $I \propto (\Delta p_{max})^2$. This result is useful later when we quantify the sound intensity as judged by the human ear. This relation also allows us to convert between sound intensities and sound pressure variations as quantitative values are frequently reported as one or the other.

The most commonly used unit–system for sound pressure and intensity variations is based on a logarithmic scale since both parameters vary widely, e.g. between a whisper and a jet engine by about 7 orders of magnitude (a factor of 10^7). The pressure variation in a sound wave is defined as *sound pressure level* (SPL):

$$SPL = 20 \log_{10} \frac{p}{p_0} \quad (26)$$

with: $p_0 = 2 \times 10^{-5} \, Pa$

in which $\log_{10}$ indicates the logarithm with the base 10 (not the natural logarithm with the base e). p_0 in Eq. (26) is a reference pressure, chosen near the faintest detectable sound for the human ear. The unit of SPL is called the *decibel* [dB]. The prefactor 20 is chosen arbitrarily, except that a factor 2 is included to accommodate the difference to the *intensity level* (IL). The relation $I \propto \Delta p^2$ leads to $2 \log_{10}(p/p_0) = \log_{10}(I/I_0)$. Thus:

$$IL = 10 \log_{10} \frac{I}{I_0} \quad (27)$$

with: $I_0 = 1 \times 10^{-12} \, \frac{J}{m^2 s}$

We do not provide a table of IL values because such values could be misleading. The human ear judges sounds of equal IL values as quite different depending on the frequency of the sound (you do not hear a loud dog's whistle at all). Thus, we introduce later a second unit to measure loudness, the unit [phon].

Example 16.7
A sound has an intensity of $I = 5.0 \times 10^{-7}$ J/sm². What is the intensity level IL of this sound?

Solution: The intensity level IL is defined in Eq. (27). Substituting the given intensity value in Eq. (27) yields:

$$IL = 10 \log_{10} \frac{5.0 \times 10^{-7} [J/sm^2]}{1.0 \times 10^{-12} [J/sm^2]} \quad (28)$$

$$\Rightarrow IL = 57 \, dB$$

Example 16.8
How does the sound intensity change with distance from a point sound source?

Solution: Fig. 16.8 shows a point sound source. Two concentric spherical surfaces with areas A_1 and A_2 are drawn with the point source at the center. We know that the same amount of energy must flow through each of these surfaces per time unit to satisfy energy conservation, $\Delta E/\Delta t$ = const. Sound would have to pile up or disappear between the two spheres were this not the case. Thus, we write specifically for Fig. 16.8:

$$\left(\frac{\Delta E}{\Delta t}\right)_{A_1} = \left(\frac{\Delta E}{\Delta t}\right)_{A_2} \quad (29)$$

We use Eq. (29) to relate the intensity to this change of total energy with time:

$$I = c\epsilon_{tot} = c\frac{\Delta E}{\Delta V} = \frac{\Delta r}{\Delta t}\frac{\Delta E}{A \Delta r} = \frac{\Delta E/\Delta t}{A} \quad (30)$$

in which the speed of sound is expressed as the change of the radial position with time, $c = \Delta r/\Delta t$, and in which the volume containing the sound energy is calculated as

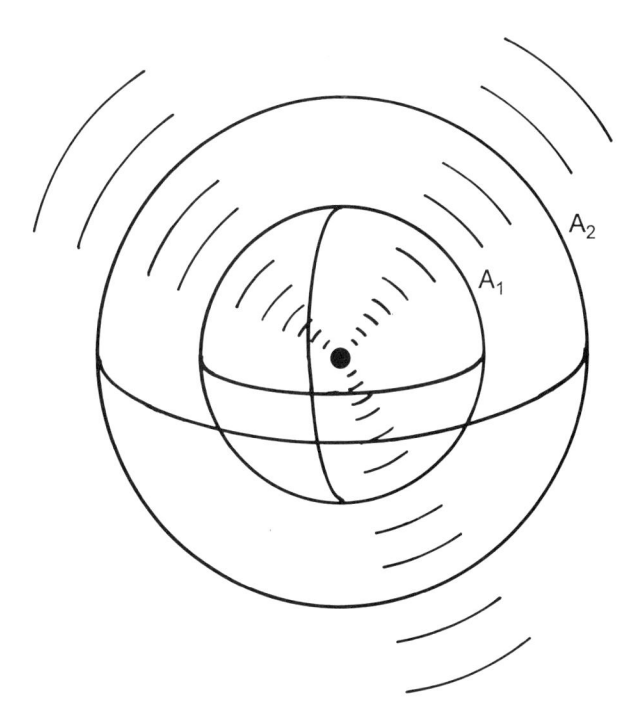

Fig. 16.8: A point sound source (dot) shown at the center of two concentric spherical surfaces with areas A_1 and A_2. The sound intensity per unit area, travelling past the two areas, diminishes as the area increases.

the area multiplied with the width, $\Delta V = A\Delta r$. This volume is the volume of a spherical shell of thickness Δr. In Eq. (30) we found that the intensity is the rate of change in the total energy per unit area. Thus, Eq. (29) yields:

$$I_1 A_1 = I_2 A_2$$

$$\Rightarrow \quad \frac{I_2}{I_1} = \frac{A_1}{A_2} = \frac{4\pi r_1^2}{4\pi r_2^2} \qquad (31)$$

After cancelling the term 4π on the right hand side of the last formula in Eq. (31), we find $I \propto 1/r^2$, i.e., the intensity diminishes proportional to the square of the distance from the sound source.

===

This sound intensity reduction is a purely geometric effect. The sound travelling through a medium can further diminish due to energy loss to the medium when the vibrations of the gas elements are not perfectly harmonic.

16.2.5. Sound absorption

The sound intensity diminishes when sound energy is absorbed by the medium. This absorption is caused by vibrations of air molecules which are not perfectly adiabatic. Thermal energy loss occurs, which slightly heats up the gas element. We choose to study a one–dimensional wave, e.g. a wave travelling in a tube. This eliminates the geometric sound intensity loss we discussed in the previous section and allows us therefore to isolate the absorption effect called *Beer's law*. Beer's law states that the loss of intensity per unit length of distance travelled is proportional to the absolute intensity of the sound wave:

$$\lim_{\Delta x \to 0} \frac{\Delta I}{\Delta x} = -\beta I \qquad (32)$$

The limit $\Delta x \to 0$ is needed for Eq. (32) to be mathematically exact since the intensity I on the right hand side of the equation varies continuously. Thus, Eq. (32) states that the slope of the intensity variation with position (gradient) is proportional to the intensity at the respective position. The constant β is the *absorption co-*

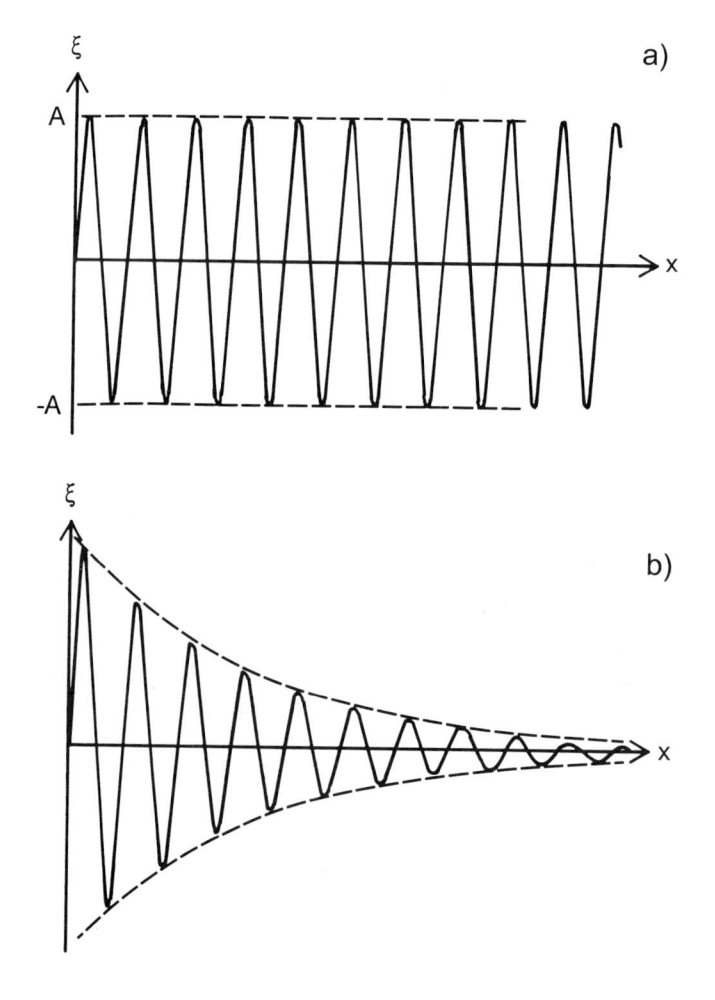

Fig. 16.9: Two harmonic waves with amplitude A.
(a) The sound carrying medium is (ideally) non–absorbing, and
(b) the sound carrying medium absorbs sound energy with an absorption coefficient $\alpha > 0$.

efficient and has unit [m⁻¹]. It is a materials constant but also depends on the frequency and type of wave (visible light and X–rays are also absorbed). We discussed formulas such as Eq. (32) in the context of the signal decay time in a resting nerve in Chapter 13. Therefore we know that it leads to an exponential decay function:

$$I = I_0 \, e^{-\beta x} \qquad (33)$$

Eq. (33) is the solution to Eq. (32) since the exponential function is the only function for which the function and the slope of the function are the same (except for a constant factor). In Eq. (33), I_0 is the intensity emitted by the source, i.e., at x = 0.

We want to investigate the implications of Eq. (33) a little bit further. For this we rewrite the equation by introducing the length $x_{abs} = 1/\beta$, which is called the *absorption length*. This yields:

$$\frac{I}{I_0} = \exp\left[-\frac{x}{x_{abs}}\right] \qquad (34)$$

At the origin, which is the location of the sound source, the intensity is $I = I_0$. When we move from the source to a distance equal to the absorption length, i.e., to $x = x_{abs}$, then Eq. (34) yields $I/I_0 = 1/e \cong 0.37$. Moving further to a distance twice the absorption length, $x = 2x_{abs}$, we find $I/I_0 = 1/e^2 \cong 0.14$ and finally at a distance of three times the absorption length, $x = 3x_{abs}$, we obtain $I/I_0 = 1/e^3 \cong 0.05$. Thus, the sound intensity drops to about 1/3 of the initial intensity at the absorption length and drops to 5 % at three times the absorption length. Therefore, the absorption length is a good measure of the distance at which the sound intensity is significantly reduced due to absorption.

We saw in the previous section that the intensity is proportional to the square of the amplitude of the vibration of the small gas element, $I \propto A^2$. Thus, we can extend Eq. (14) by using Eq. (33) for an absorbing medium in the form:

$$\xi = A \, e^{-\alpha x} \sin(\omega t - \kappa x) \qquad (35)$$

in which α is the decay coefficient for the sound amplitude. Fig. 16.9 presents a comparison between a one–dimensional sound wave in an idealized, absorption–free medium obeying Eq. (14) in part (a) of the figure, and a one–dimensional wave in an absorbing medium obeying Eq. (35) in part (b). The dashed line is called the *envelope* and corresponds to the first two factors in Eq. (35), $A_0 e^{-\alpha x}$.

16.3. Waves in a confined medium

The previous two sections allow us to understand how sound travels from a sound source through air. However, the introduced concepts are not sufficient to understand either how the human voice operates nor do they allow us to understand how the human ear detects sound. The most important issue not included up to now is a spatial confinement of the sound wave. Sound waves are confined during the hearing process as illustrated by the anatomic overview of the ear in Fig. 16.10. The auditory canal (1) resembles a cylindrical tube, allowing one–di-

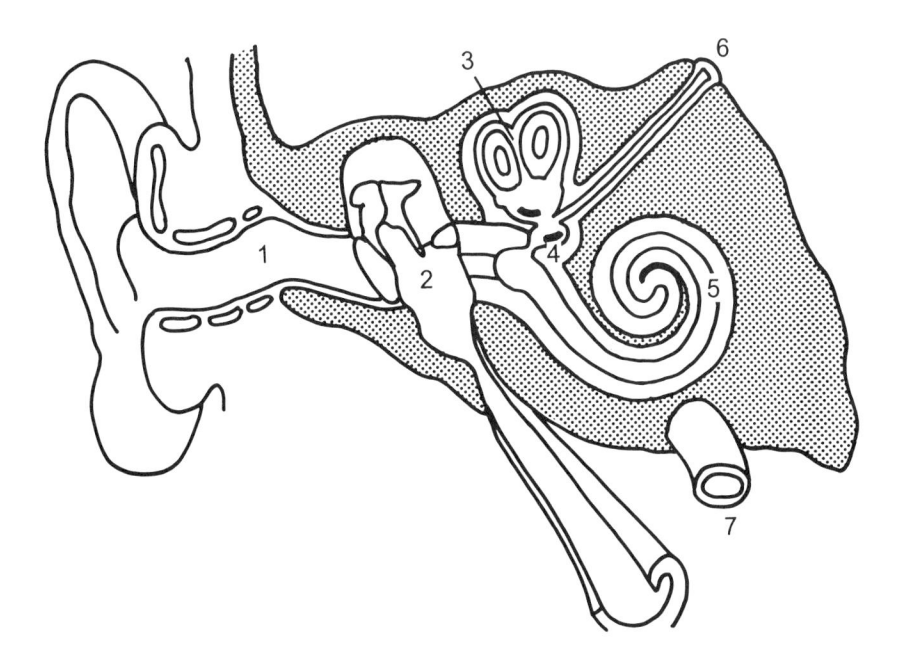

Fig. 16.10: Overview of the human ear. We can distinguish three main sections of the ear: the outer ear with the auditory canal (1) ending at the ear drum, the middle ear with the three ossicles, hammer, anvil and stirrup (from left, 2), and the inner ear with the vestibular organ. The vestibular organ includes the semi-circular canals (3) which we discuss in the context of acceleration detection in the head, and the macula (4) which we discuss in the context of gravity detection. Other highlighted components of the inner ear are the cochlea (5), the endolymphatic canal (6) and the cerebral artery (7).

mensional waves to travel inside. However, the auditory canal is a semi–closed tube and sound cannot travel further than the eardrum, which separates the outer ear from the middle ear. The current section focusses on waves which are confined in either closed or semi–closed tubes. We assume that the absorption of sound by the medium in the tube is negligible. Thus, we use Eq. (14) and not Eq. (35) for the subsequent discussion.

The study of a longitudinal wave in a confined space begins with a simple model system: a cylindrical tube filled with an ideal gas and closed at both ends. Inside, the gas may move back and forth. We use closed tubes to introduce the most important features of confined waves: standing waves, harmonics, and resonance.

16.3.1. Standing waves

Eq. (15.48) quantifies the harmonic vibration of a piston attached at the end of a tube. That formula already contains the time dependence of the harmonic wave we developed later, in form of the term ωt, but it also contains the phase angle ϕ. The phase angle is needed to allow Eq. (15.48) to describe any harmonic vibration, including those in which the piston does not start at the amplitude point $x = +A$ at time $t = 0$.

During our discussion of the wave properties in the previous section, the phase angle was neglected. We assumed $\phi = 0$, which is a convenient simplification while studying a single wave. We can no longer make this simplification when studying waves in a confined tube because waves interact with the walls and, as our experience with echos shows, at least some of the sound energy bounces back. To simplify the required formalism only cases are considered in which the wave reflects off the wall perpendicularly.

The inclusion of a reflected wave means that at least two waves are present in the tube at the same time. To see what consequences this has, let us consider two waves travelling in a tube in the same direction. To study how these waves interact with each other, each of the waves has to be described by a more complete formula than given in Eq. (14) to allow a phase angle difference, $\Delta\phi = \phi_2 - \phi_1$, between both waves:

$$\begin{aligned}\xi_1 &= A\,\sin(\omega t - \kappa x + \phi_1) \\ \xi_2 &= A\,\sin(\omega t - \kappa x + \phi_2)\end{aligned} \quad (36)$$

Since we want to focus on the role of the phase angle, we wrote Eq. (36) for the special case in which both waves have the same amplitude, A, the same angular frequency, ω, and the same wave number, κ. The more general case with different values for these parameters is discussed later.

As long as the amplitudes are not too large, the principle of additive superposition of the two waves from Eq. (36) is valid. This leads to two limiting cases:

(I) when the two waves are shifted relative to each other by half a wavelength, i.e., when the phase angle difference is $\phi_2 - \phi_1 = (2n + 1)\pi$, destructive superposition occurs and the resulting wave has a vanishing amplitude, $A_{sup} = 0$. This is illustrated in Fig. 16.11 where the two initial waves are indicated by a dashed and a dash–dotted line. The superpositioned wave is coincident with the x–axis (no wave).

(II) The second case occurs when the two waves are shifted by a multiple of a full wavelength, which corresponds to $\phi_2 - \phi_1 = n\,2\pi$. This case is called constructive superposition and is shown in Fig. 16.12. Again, the

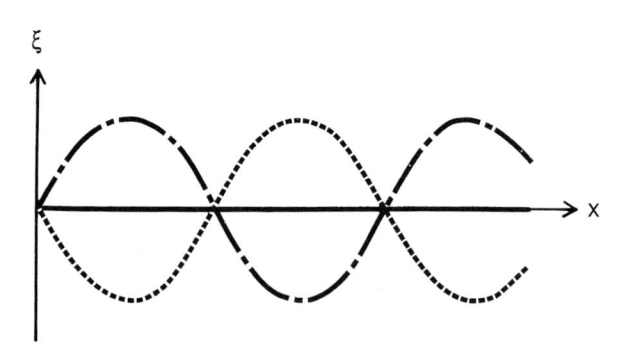

Fig. 16.11: Destructive superposition of two harmonic waves with same angular frequency, wave number and amplitude. This occurs when there is a half wavelength phase shift between the two waves. The two original waves are shown as dashed and dash–dotted curves. The resulting wave coincides with the x–axis.

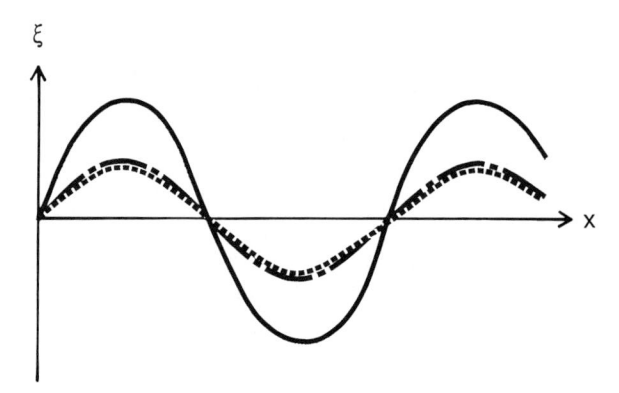

Fig. 16.12: Constructive superposition of two harmonic waves with same angular frequency, wave number and amplitude. This occurs when there is a phase shift equal to a multiple of a full wavelength between the two waves. The two original waves are shown as dashed and dash–dotted curves. The resulting wave is shown as a solid curve with double the amplitude.

dashed and dash–dotted curves are the original waves, drawn besides each other only to allow them to be distinguished. The superposition of both waves yields a wave with double the amplitude (solid curve).

Harmonic waves travelling back and forth in a closed tube are a special application of the superposition principle since the reflection at the end of the tube guarantees automatically that both waves have the same amplitude (assuming no sound absorption), angular frequency and wave number since the initial and the reflected wave are caused by the same vibration. In this case, the two waves are written as:

$$\xi_1 = A \sin(\omega t - \kappa x)$$
$$\xi_2 = -A \sin(\omega t + \kappa x) \quad (37)$$

Note that the reflected wave has a negative sign. This results because the wave has a phase shift $\Delta\phi = \pi$ when reflected off a wall. Fig. 16.13 illustrates how this arrangement can lead to a *standing wave*. Fig. 16.13(a) shows a sound source at the right end of an enclosed tube, filled with a gas. The sound waves, moving back and forth, coincide such that the amplitude of the local vibration of a small gas element become time independent. A standing wave is generated if the distance between the sound source and the wall of the tube at the left end is a multiple of half a wave length.

We can derive this result also mathematically from Eq. (37). Adding the two waves leads to:

$$\xi_{sup} = A \left(\sin(\omega t - \kappa x) - \sin(\omega t + \kappa x)\right) \quad (38)$$

We use a trigonometric relation, $\sin(\alpha-\beta) - \sin(\alpha+\beta) = -2\cos\alpha \sin\beta$, to simplify Eq. (38):

$$\xi_{sup} = -\{2A \cos(\omega t)\} \sin(\kappa x) \quad (39)$$

Eq. (39) is a wave with a fixed wavelength which is given by $\lambda = 2\pi/\kappa$, and an amplitude which varies with time as given in the {...}–bracket in the equation. The maximum amplitude is 2A.

We want to interpret Eq. (39) with a microscopic picture. Fig. 16.13(b) shows a section of the tube and the respective motion of the gas elements. In a standing wave, certain points have a zero amplitude all

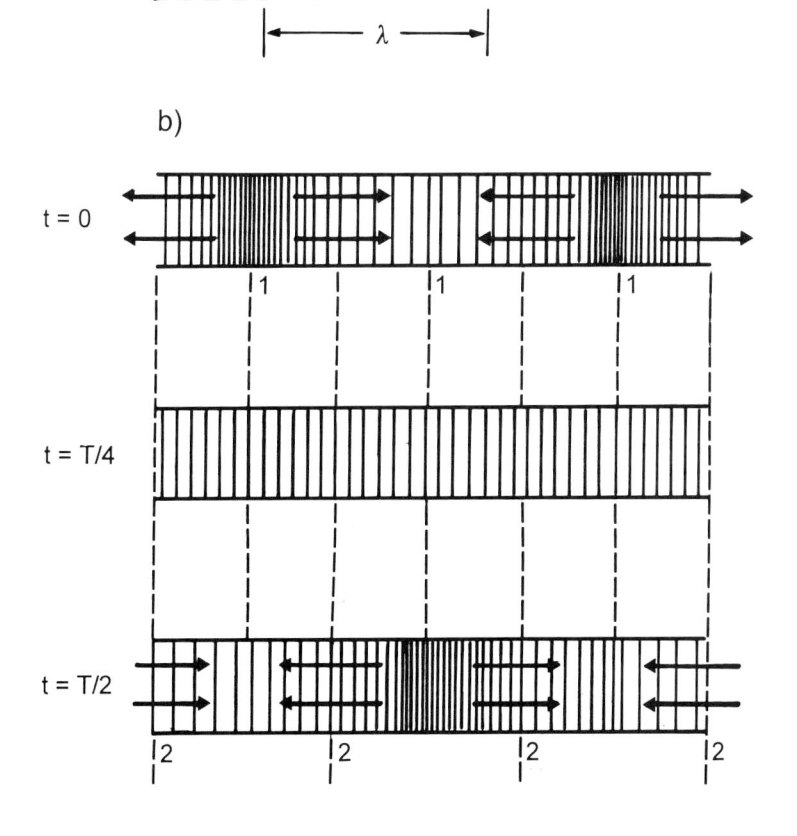

Fig. 16.13: Standing wave in a closed, air–filled tube.
(a) A mobile piston varies the length of the tube. A standing wave is possible when the distance between the piston and the end of the tube is a multiple of half the wavelength of the standing sound wave.
(b) The air density profile in the tube at three different times. Note that a standing wave does not travel toward the left or the right. Amplitude nodes (1) and pressure or density nodes (2) remain stationary.

455

the time. These points are labelled (2) in the three snapshots of the gas in the tube, i.e., at times t = 0, t = T/4 and t = T/2. They are called *pressure nodes*. Between two pressure nodes the gas pressure and density oscillate between an increased value, indicated by a higher density of lines, and a decreased value, indicated by a less dense zone of lines.

The points labelled (1) in Fig. 16.13(b) are *velocity nodes* since the gas element at those points does not move (motion of gas is indicated by arrows). Such a velocity node must be located at the end of the tube in Fig. 16.13(a) since the gas cannot move into the wall.

> *A standing wave forms in a closed tube when the wavelength of the sound and the distance to the end wall in the tube allow for a velocity node at that wall.*

Example 16.9
We consider again the wave travelling along the x–axis as described by Eq. (17). Assume that this wave reflects off a rigid surface.

(a) What is the equation for the reflected wave?
(b) What is the equation of a resulting standing wave?
(c) Sketch the standing wave at t = 0 and t = T/2 with T the period.

Solution part (a) : The reflected wave has exactly the same properties as the incoming wave, except (i) that it travels in the opposite direction and (ii) that it is phase–shifted by half a wave length (i.e., a phase shift of π radians). This is achieved in Eq. (17) by (i) switching the sign of the position–dependent term and by (ii) switching the sign of the amplitude term in the same fashion as in Eq. (37):

$$\xi_{reflect} = -2.0 \sin(1.0t + 1.5x) \qquad (40)$$

Solution part (b): The standing wave is the superposition of the wave in Eq. (17) and the wave in Eq. (40). We need not to repeat the mathematical steps leading to the resulting standing wave as the calculation has already been done in the text, leading from Eq. (37) to (39). Inserting the specific values from Eq. (17) or from Eq. (40) we find:

$$\xi_{sup} = -4.0 \cos(1.0t) \sin(1.5x) \qquad (41)$$

Solution part (c): The two sketches are shown in Fig. 16.14 with the solid curve for t = 0 and the dashed curve for t = T/2.

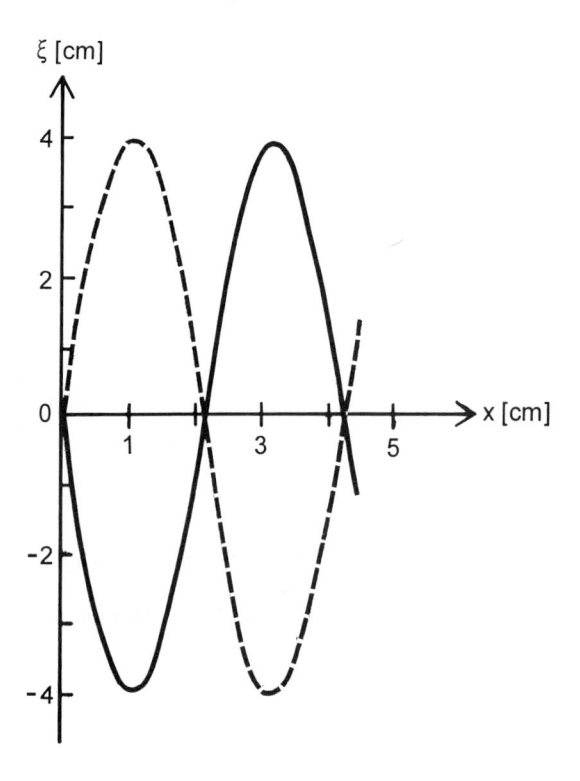

Fig. 16.14: Sketch of a standing wave. The solid curve represents the standing wave at time t = 0; the dashed curve represents the same wave at time t = T/2, i.e., one half of a period later.

16.3.2. Harmonics

In free space, waves with any combination of wavelengths and angular frequencies consistent with the speed of sound in the medium may occur. In a confined space, only certain waves, the standing waves, can be sustained. Their selection rule is based on the size and type of the confining space: for longitudinal waves in a closed tube a multiple of half wavelengths must fit into the space of the tube. However, any integer number of half–wavelengths is acceptable, and thus, several standing waves with different wavelengths can form in the same closed tube.

Fig. 16.15 shows the three longitudinal waves with the longest wavelengths between the ends of the tube. The standing wave in part (a) is called *first harmonic*, which has the lowest frequency that the tube can support. The standing waves in parts (b) and (c) are the second and third harmonics, respectively. Note that the harmonic of n–th order has two amplitude nodes at the fixed ends of the tube and n − 1 amplitude nodes between the ends at equal distances. The name "harmonic" is derived from the use of the term in music. It is applied in the current context in spite of the fact that we are not studying a string on a guitar because a string on a music instrument must be set into transverse motion.

Table 16.2 lists the wavelengths and frequencies for the various longitudinal harmonics for a one-dimensional closed tube. The frequencies and the wavelengths are related to each other by the speed of sound, $c = \lambda_n f_n = (Y/\rho)^{1/2}$ (see Eq. (15.1) and Eq. (7)). As the table illustrates, higher harmonics have shorter wavelengths and higher frequencies but the same wave speed.

For applications, we have to supplement the discussion of closed tubes with a second system in which a confined gas can sustain a longitudinal wave: a half-open tube. The half-open tube is a model for the outer ear in Fig. 16.10. The waves sustained in a half-open tube differ from the harmonic waves of the closed tube because the air can move back and forth at the open end of the tube. Indeed, a half-open tube has an anti-node at its open end, that is, a standing wave forms such that a

Table 16.2: Wavelengths and frequencies for various harmonics of air in a tube closed at both ends. n is an integer number.

Mode	wavelength	frequency
1st harmonic	$\lambda_1 = 2L$	$f_1 = c/2L$
2nd harmonic	$\lambda_2 = L$	$f_2 = c/L = 2 f_1$
3rd harmonic	$\lambda_3 = 2L/3$	$f_3 = 3c/2L = 3 f_1$
n-th harmonic	$\lambda_n = 2L/n$	$f_n = nc/2L = n f_1$

pressure node instead of an amplitude node lies in the open end. The pressure node is associated with a maximum amplitude of the standing wave as shown in Fig. 16.16. Part (a) shows the first harmonic and parts (b–d) illustrate the next three lowest harmonics. For the half-closed tube the frequencies of allowed harmonics are:

$$f = \frac{nc}{4L} \quad \text{with } n = 1, 3, 5, 7, \ldots \quad (42)$$

i.e., only odd numbered harmonics are possible.

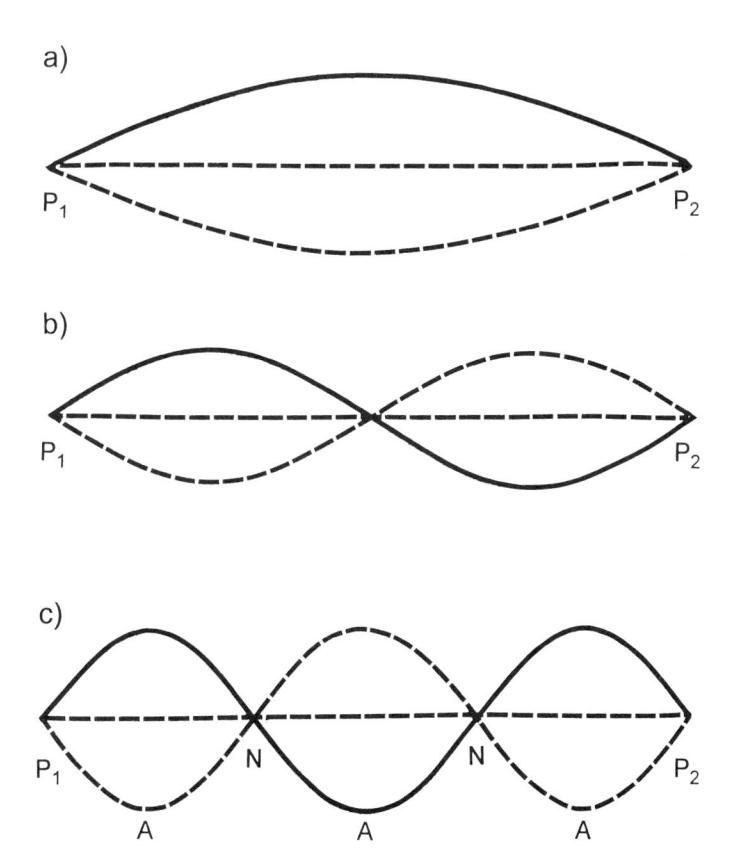

Fig. 16.15: (a) The first harmonic, (b) the second harmonic, and (c) the third harmonic for a standing longitudinal wave in a closed tube. N identifies nodes and A antinodes. The vertical deviation from the horizontal line in the figure is a measure of the longitudinal displacement of the gas element in the tube.

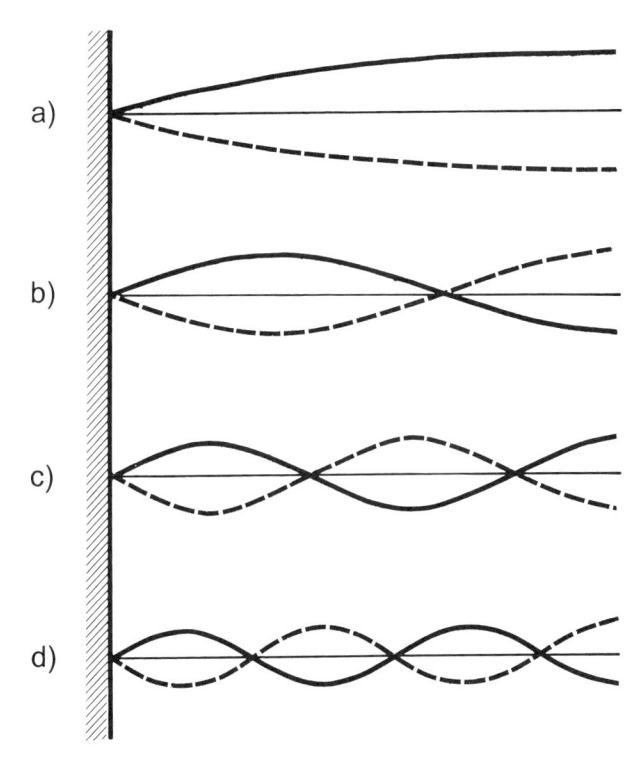

Fig. 16.16: (a) The first harmonic and (b–d) the corresponding higher harmonics of a tube open at one end. Note that an amplitude anti-node (a pressure node) forms at the open end. The vertical deviation from the horizontal line in the figure indicates the longitudinal displacement of a gas element in the tube.

> *Closed and half–closed tubes can sustain standing waves which we call harmonics.*

Higher harmonics play an essential role in the human voice. Human voices are characterized by the number and relative amplitude (or intensity) of higher harmonics generated. The first harmonic in a human voice is defined as the pitch and the higher harmonics define the timbre. When these data are plotted, e.g. in the lower part of Fig. 16.1, the resulting graph is called a frequency spectrum. In a spectrum, a independent variable, such as the intensity, is shown as a function of frequency.

Example 16.10

Fig. 16.17 shows the frequency spectrum of the moan of a Blue whale.
(a) What model would you use to describe the technique of sound generation by the Blue whale, an air column closed at both sides, or a half–open air column?
(b) What is the first harmonic of the Blue whale? What is the highest harmonic shown in Fig. 16.17?

Biological information: Blue whales generate two types of sound. The low–frequency moans shown in Fig. 16.17 and high–frequency click–sounds in the range between 21 kHz and 31 kHz. The moans occur in the range of 12.5 Hz to 200 Hz with the greatest intensities between 20 Hz to 32 Hz. The sound duration lies usually between 15 seconds and 40 seconds; however, with more careful measurements further detailed features can be identified than revealed in Fig. 16.17, including amplitude modulations at 0.26 second repetition cycles, and, later during the sound, with 0.13 second repetition cycles.

Solution part (a): Table 16.2 and Fig. 16.15 show that the frequencies of the various harmonics of a closed tube are all equally spaced:

$$\Delta f = f_{n+1} - f_n = \frac{c}{2L} = const \qquad (43)$$

which applies for all values $n \geq 1$. This frequency spacing is equal to the absolute frequency of the first harmonic:

$$closed: \quad f_1 = \Delta f \qquad (44)$$

On the other hand, Eq. (42) and Fig. 16.16 show that the frequencies of the various harmonics of a half–

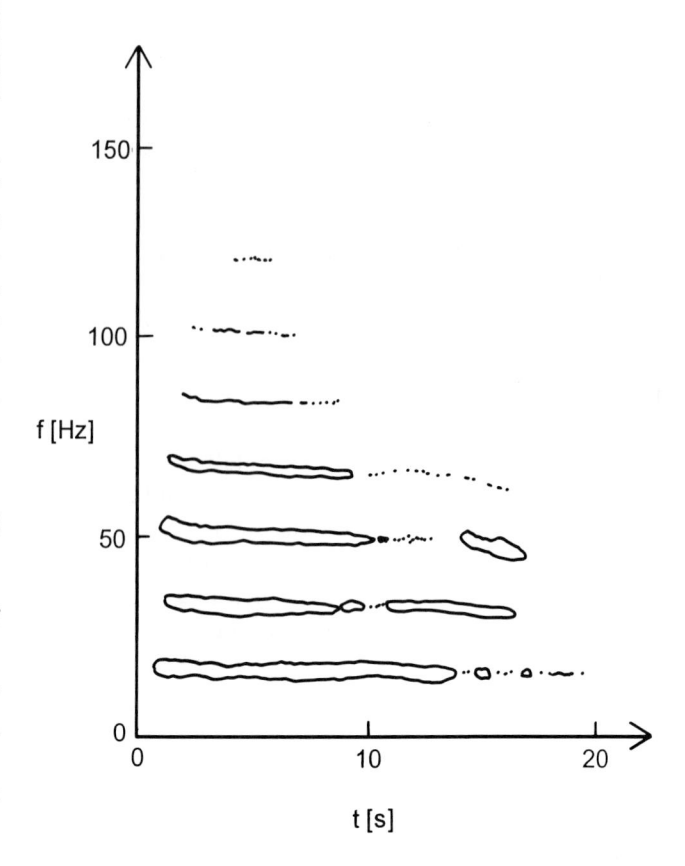

Fig. 16.17: Frequency spectrum of the sound emitted by a Blue whale. Bands represent frequency ranges of high sound intensity. These low–frequency moans last for 15 to 40 seconds.

closed tube, while also spaced as shown in Eq. (43), are twice as wide spaced than the value of the first harmonic:

$$half\text{--}closed: \quad 2f_1 = \Delta f \qquad (45)$$

The frequencies shown in Fig. 16.17 are: 17 Hz, 34 Hz, 51 Hz, 68 Hz, 85 Hz, 102 Hz, and 119 Hz. Thus, from comparison with Eqs. (44) and (45) we conclude that a closed tube model describes the moans of the Blue whale best, because the lowest frequency measured is equal to the frequency spacing between the harmonics shown in Fig. 16.17.

Solution part (b): The first harmonic is the lowest frequency emitted. In the case of the moan of the Blue whale shown in Fig. 16.17 this frequency is 17 Hz. Every higher frequency band shown indicates the next higher harmonic according to Table 16.2. Thus, the highest harmonic shown at 119 Hz is the 7th harmonic.

16.3.3. Resonance

In the first two parts of section 16.3 we deviated from our earlier approach and derived the concepts of sound in a confined space from the wave model and not from the vibrations which cause the wave. For the description of resonances it is useful now to return to our original approach and link the vibration of an object to the sound phenomenon.

If you look at the human voice, or, more simply, at a musical instrument such as a flute, you notice that none of these generate a sound unless a mechanical excitation is applied. In the case of the human voice, you sense the effort involved in speaking. In both cases, the flute or the voice, the external excitation is usually not a vibration with a frequency perfectly matching the frequency of a standing wave in the adjacent air column. This is obvious for the flute when you just blow for a short moment into the mouth–piece. In this case, you obviously do not provide a harmonic vibration at all. But even if you tried to vibrate the piston in Fig. 15.13, it is unlikely that you would do so with the right frequency for the standing wave. Still, the flute responds to the blowing with a sound, representing the first and several higher harmonics characteristic of the length of the flute's barrel. In the same fashion, the human voice has a characteristic frequency pattern, as shown in Fig. 16.1.

To understand the response of a flute or of the vocal tract, we need to study two phenomena:
(I) the sound amplitude for a system responding to an externally forced resonance, and
(II) the reason why a sudden excitation instead of a harmonic excitation causes harmonic waves.

Resonance formation
We start with Fig. 15.13 and assume that an external force is used to move the piston harmonically back and forth with the maximum force F_{max}, and an angular frequency ω_{ext}. Note that we need not consider the vector character of the force as the entire experiment is done one–dimensionally along the x–axis:

$$|F_{ext}| = F_{max} \cos(\omega_{ext} t) \quad (46)$$

We will find that such an externally caused vibration can lead to high sound intensities under certain conditions.

We further extend Eq. (15.33) to describe the displacement of the gas in a closed tube in response to the external force:

$$-kx + F_{max}\cos(\omega_{ext} t) = ma \quad (47)$$

The second term on the left hand side is a newly introduced force acting on the piston. Solving Eq. (47) is obviously more complicated that solving Eq. (15.33). Instead of trying this, we use an experimental test. It consists of an object attached to a horizontal spring, as shown in Fig. 15.14. In addition to the arrangement in Fig. 15.14, a string is attached to the point mass which allows us to exert a force of the type given in Eq. (46) on the point mass by moving the string continuously back and forth. The moving string sets the object in motion. Depending on the frequency with which we move the string back and forth, the object will respond little or very strongly. We express this response of the object to the motion of the string by the amplitude of the vibrations of the object.

The observed amplitude is illustrated in Fig. 16.18. If you move the string very slowly back and forth, the object follows the motion with exactly the same amplitude as the external motion. We define this amplitude as A_0. The plot shows values near $A/A_0 = 1$ for angular frequencies near $\omega_{ext} = 0$, where ω_{ext} describes the angu-

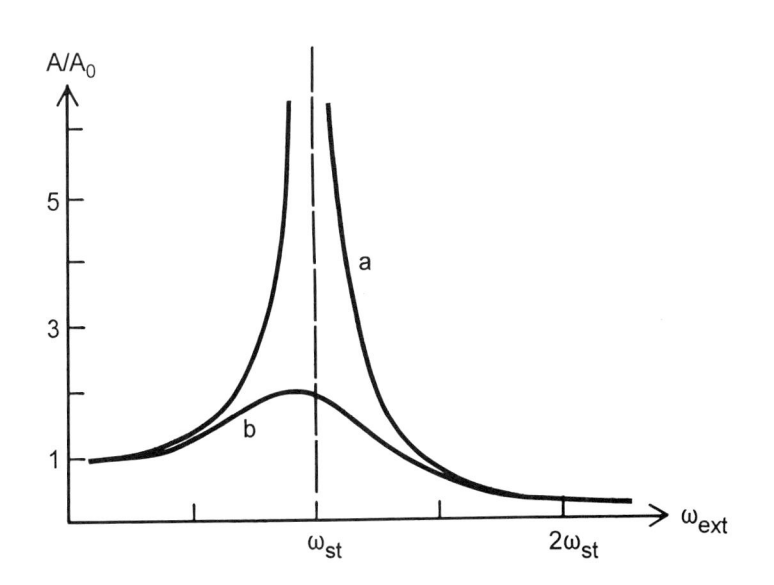

Fig. 16.18: The amplitude in a resonant system, shown as a value relative to the amplitude A_0 for small external angular frequencies, ω_{ext}. The system follows the sinusoidal variation of the external force when $\omega_{ext} \ll \omega_{st}$, with ω_{st} the natural angular frequency. When ω_{ext} reaches ω_{st}, an amplification of the amplitude occurs, which is called a resonant amplification. For $\omega_{ext} \gg \omega_{st}$ the inertia of the system prevents it from following the external angular frequency.

lar frequency of the motion of the externally driven string. In this case, the motion of the object is not altered by the spring to which it is attached.

As we increase the frequency with which we move the object back and forth, we get closer and closer to the natural angular frequency of the object on the spring. This is the angular frequency we calculated in Eq. (15.49), $\omega_{natural} = (k/m)^{1/2}$. Equally, if we consider the case of a piston moving back and forth at the end of an air column, moving the piston faster means that we are getting closer to the angular frequency of the first harmonic of the standing wave forming in the closed gas tube, ω_{st} (where the subscript "st" stands for standing wave). As Fig. 16.18 shows, this leads to an increasing amplitude because the external push transfers energy to the vibrating object (or piston) more and more effectively.

Following curve (a) in Fig. 16.18, an infinite amplitude occurs when the natural frequency of the object or the first harmonic of a closed tube is reached. This is called a *resonance*. An infinite amplitude is not a physically possible result. Real systems follow curves like the one shown in Fig. 16.18(b), with a finite amplitude at the resonance. The change from curve (a) to curve (b) is called damping. Damping is the result of non–ideal behavior, for example friction between the edge of the piston and the inside wall of the tube. In an energy–based picture, damping represents the absorption of mechanical energy and its conversion into non–mechanical forms of energy, such as heat. Curve (b) assumes a moderate damping which results in a finite amplitude oscillation at the resonance. The shock absorbers in your car, for example, have a significantly stronger damping as you do not want an increased vertical amplitude for the car's cabin when you are driving through potholes.

The resonance is reached when the external angular frequency equals the natural angular frequency or the angular frequency of the first harmonic of the system. Fig. 16.18 shows that the confined system responds to an external excitation with an enhanced amplitude in the vicinity of the resonance, and therefore with an enhanced intensity, since we saw earlier that the intensity is proportional to the square of the amplitude.

If we increase the frequency of the external vibration beyond the resonance frequency, a decrease of the amplitude of the object is observed. Once the external frequency is much larger than the natural frequency of the object, the amplitude of the object ceases and the object does not respond to the external force at all. This is due to the inertia of the system. In order to follow the motion of the string, the object must constantly accelerate back or forth. Every object requires some time for that: the heavier the object, the slower the response to a force. You can redirect a tennis ball in a short instant; redirecting a shot put thrown to you takes longer. With the change of direction of the external force occurring faster and faster, eventually the inertia of the object no longer allows enough time for the object to follow.

The curve labelled (a) in Fig. 16.18 is described quantitatively in the form:

$$A = \frac{F_{max}}{m(\omega_{st}^2 - \omega_{ext}^2)} \qquad (48)$$

in which F_{max} is the magnitude of the maximum force exerted on the system of mass m, ω_{ext} is the angular frequency of the harmonic oscillation of the external force, and ω_{st} is the angular frequency of the lowest harmonic standing wave of the system. The difference of quadratic terms in the denominator causes the steep increase close to the resonance. This formula is useful for systems with negligible damping.

> *A system is in resonance when an external harmonic excitation causes it to respond with a maximum harmonic amplitude. This occurs at the first harmonic of a closed or half–closed tube.*

Example 16.11
Calculate the size of a room in which a person singing in one of the major opera categories listed in Table 16.3 obtains a maximum intensity amplification of the sound.

Solution: From Eq. (48) we know that the condition for maximum resonance is:

$$\omega_{ext} = \omega_{st} \qquad (49)$$

This holds independent of the degree of damping as illustrated in Fig. 16.18. Thus, the frequencies in Table

Table 16.3: Frequency range of opera voices

Opera voice	Frequency range
Bass	66 – 350 Hz
Tenor	100 – 520 Hz
Alto	130 – 700 Hz
Soprano	200 – 1050 Hz

Table 16.4: Frequency range and spatial dimensions for Example 16.11.

Opera voice	Frequency range [Hz]	L dimension [m]
Bass	66 – 350	0.5 – 2.6
Tenor	100 – 520	0.33 – 1.7
Alto	130 – 700	0.25 – 1.3
Soprano	200 – 1050	0.16 – 0.85

16.3 must be equal to the first harmonic of an air column in a closed tube, in which the length of the tube equals the dimensions of the room. We use the formula for n = 1 in Table 16.2 to calculate the room dimension L, using the speed of sound at room temperature from Table 16.1:

$$L = \frac{c}{2f} = \frac{343 \ [m/s]}{2f} \quad (50)$$

The resulting length intervals are summarized in Table 16.4. Table 16.4 shows that the singer with the higher frequency voice sets the air in a smaller room into resonance. For a real opera singer on stage, such resonances are undesirable. Indeed, opera houses are much larger than the dimensions we calculated in Table 16.4 and therefore none of these effects do occur. However, such resonance–enhanced sounds might be perceived as satisfactory by a person singing aloud. Loosely spoken, women get the best effect in a washroom and men in a bathroom.

Non–harmonic excitation
The second phenomenon we want to study in this section is the observation that a non–harmonic external excitation, such as a brief blowing into a flute, can also excite a standing wave in a closed tube. To illustrate this effect we consider a piano, even though generating a sound with this instrument leads to a transverse standing wave on a string in the instrument. However, the concepts are the same for a flute, except it is easier to do the following experiment on a piano, as originally proposed by Hermann von Helmholtz.

We consider the keys shown in Fig. 16.19, which represent the second to tenth harmonics of a string when C_3 is the first harmonic. For the notation of musical notes note that C_4 is the C–key in the middle of a piano. In the first step of the experiment you push a key for one of the higher harmonics soundlessly, i.e., very slowly down. This lifts the damper off the string inside the piano. Now you hit hard and short the C_3 key. You hear a resonance at the pitch of the higher harmonic which corresponds to the held–down key. If the key you hold down is not one of the higher harmonics of the C_3 key, no resonance is heard. Confirm that the resonance indeed corresponds to the key you are holding down by hitting this key afterwards.

The reason why a short, non–harmonic hit can excite many different frequencies in a free medium or many harmonics of a standing wave in a closed or half–open tube was first described by Jean Baptiste Fourier. He took a non–sinusoidal function like the triangular function shown in Fig. 16.20(a). Note that this is a periodic function; we will consider non–periodic functions a little bit later. Since the function in Fig. 16.20(a) is periodic with period T, there is a lowest angular frequency $\omega = 2\pi/T$ which is consistent with the periodicity of the function. Starting with the lowest angular frequency, Fourier constructed a function of time, f(t), which represents a superposition of all higher harmonics:

$$f(t) = A_0 + A_1 \cos\omega t + A_2 \cos 2\omega t + ...$$
$$... + B_1 \sin\omega t + B_2 \sin 2\omega t + ...$$
$$f(t) = A_0 + \sum_{n=1}^{\infty} A_n \cos n\omega t + \sum_{n=1}^{\infty} B_n \sin n\omega t \quad (51)$$

in which A_n and B_n are constant coefficients. The second formula in Eq. (51) is a condensed notation of the two infinite sums in the first formula. Fig. 16.20(b) shows a plot of the values of these coefficients which cause Eq. (51) to match the triangular function of Fig. 16.20(a) for the specific case of f = 10 Hz. To do so, all B – coeffi-

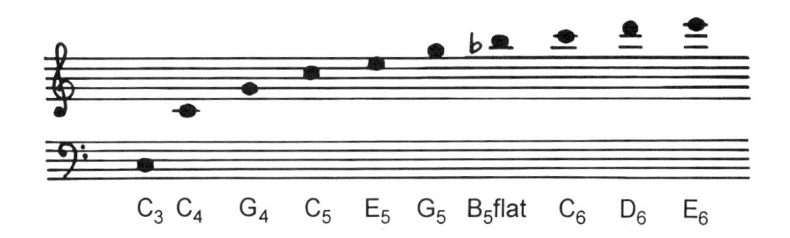

Fig. 16.19: The first harmonic of the C_3 key on a piano and its second to tenth harmonics. The higher the harmonic, the weaker the resonance when conducting Helmholtz's experiment described in the text.

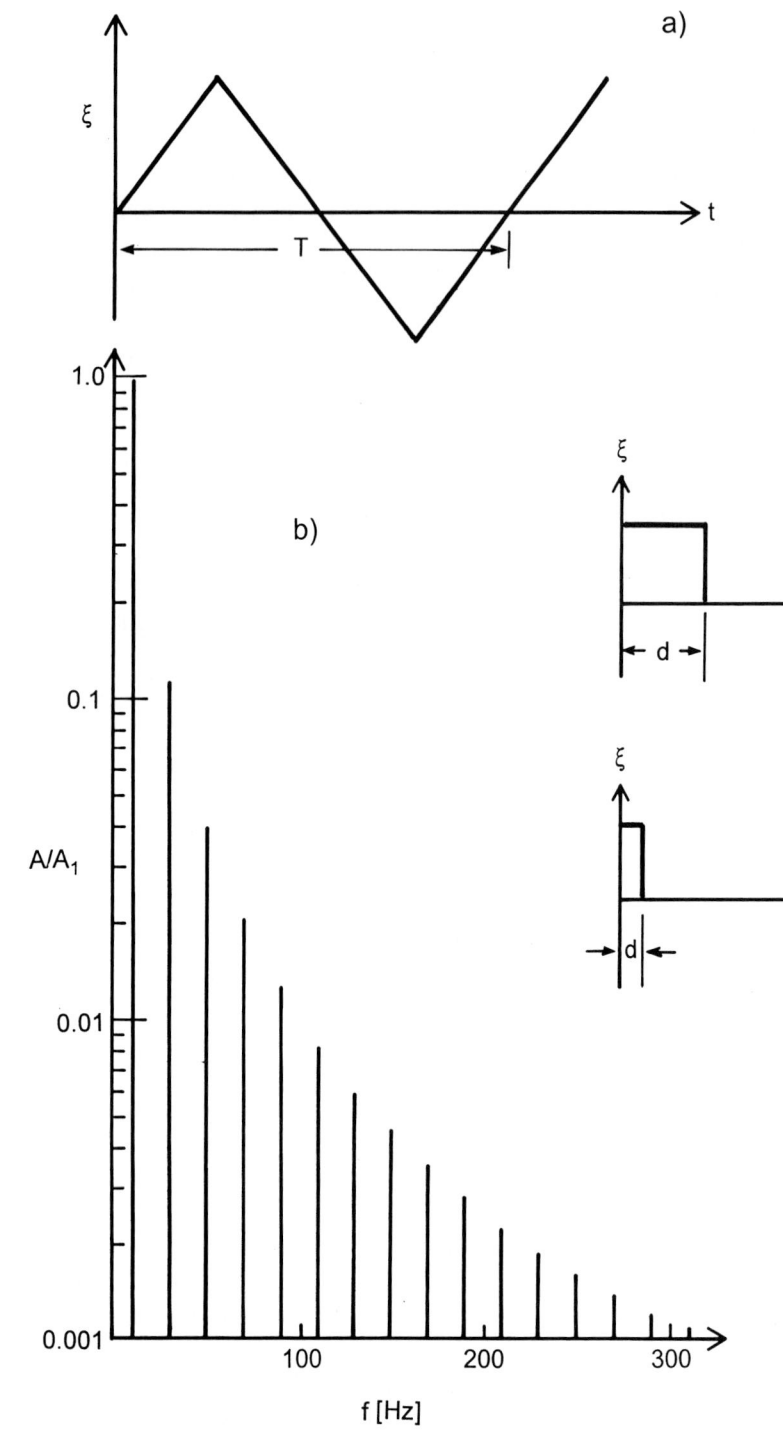

Fig. 16.20: The Fourier series (based on Eq. (51)) for the periodic triangular function shown in part (a). The curve represents the displacement as a function of time with the period T. The relative amplitudes in part (b) form a discrete spectrum (i.e., there are only specific frequencies which contribute as shown). The particular case is based on a frequency of $1/T = 10$ Hz for the function in part (a).

Fig. 16.21: If a function is not periodic, like the two box–shaped functions shown at the left in parts (a) and (b), Fourier analysis provides spectra of the amplitude as a function of frequency assuming a superposition of an infinite number of harmonic waves. The spectra, shown at right, are continuous, not discrete. Comparison between parts (a) and (b) shows how the respective amplitude spectra are related for a longer (a) and a shorter (b) box–shaped function, representing a longer or shorter hit of a string in a piano or blow into a flute.

cients are zero and the A – coefficients follow the relation $A_n \propto 1/n^2$.

If the function f(t) is not periodic, a more general approach is needed as no discrete frequency spectrum, such as the one given in Fig. 16.20(b) with integer multiples of the fundamental frequency ω, can be found. It is, however, possible to determine continuous frequency spectra for non–periodic functions, as illustrated in Fig. 16.21. In that figure, two box–shaped functions are shown in the left column, describing a constant excitation which lasts for a time $t = d$. Such a function corresponds to a hitting of a string in a piano or a blow of air into a flute. The corresponding amplitudes are shown in the right column as a function of frequency. These are obtained from a mathematical procedure which is closely related to Eq. (51) and is called the *Fourier analysis*. Comparing the spectra at the right for the two cases in Fig. 16.21, it is evident that a shorter hit (bottom) is capable of exciting more frequencies than a longer hit (top). For this reason we need a short hit of the C_3 key in Helmholtz's experiment to excite the resonances at higher frequencies.

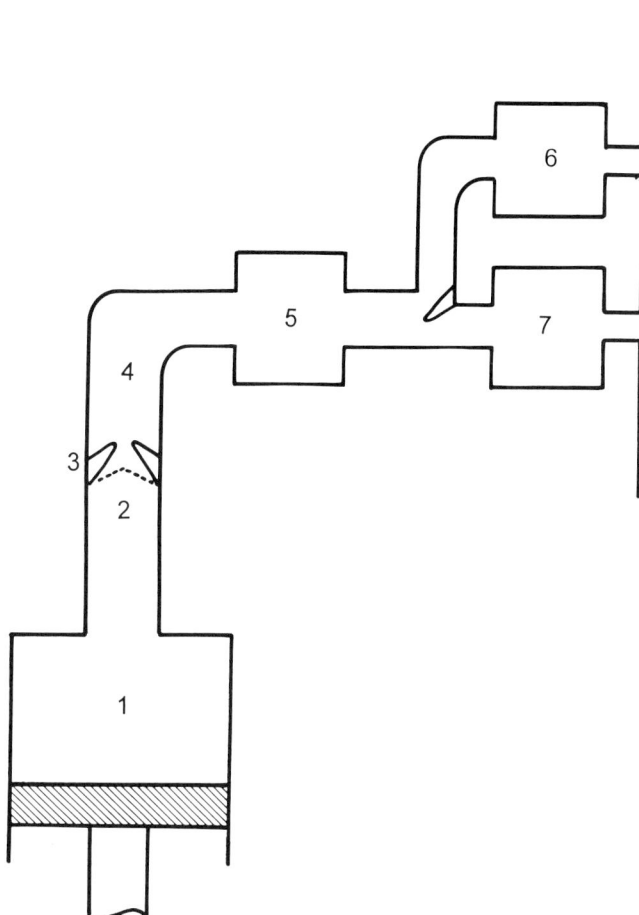

Fig. 16.22: Conceptual sketch of the vocal tract, which consists of the larynx (4), the pharynx (5), the nasal cavity (6) and the mouth (7). Air is supplied from the lungs (drawn as a piston, 1) through the trachea (2). The vocal tract is a semi–closed gas system. The vocal cord (3) closes the vocal tract. The vocal fold allows us to generate a forced vibration which causes in turn a resonance in the vocal tract.

16.4. The acoustic systems of humans

In this section we apply the concepts introduced above to the formation of sounds in the human voice tract and to the hearing with the human ear.

16.4.1. The voice

Fig. 16.22 shows a schematic overview of the human vocal tract. It includes the pharynx (5) above the larynx (4). The pharynx splits into the nasal cavity (6) and the mouth (7). This system of cavities is confined by the vocal cords (3) with a variable opening, the rima glottidis. This opening connects with the lungs (1) which force air up through the trachea (2). Most of the upper components of the human vocal tract are shown in an anatomically correct cross–section of the head in Fig. 4.7.

The larynx contains the vocal folds, which are elastic bands set in vibrational motion by the air flowing from the lung when the rima glottidis is almost closed.

The high frequency vibration of the vocal folds is a result of the equation of continuity and Bernoulli's equation, both of them discussed in Chapter 11: the air arriving from the lung must accelerate to a higher speed when passing through the narrow vocal fold to satisfy the equation of continuity. The higher air speed leads to a reduction in air pressure in the vocal fold relative to the pressure in the trachea, due to Bernoulli's equation. The reduced pressure leads to a temporary closing of the vocal fold. In the next instant the air flow from the lung pushes the vocal fold open again.

The repetitive closing and opening of the vocal fold leads to a vibration analogous to the forced vibration of a piston in a semi–closed gas system. A half–closed gas system is a good model for the vocal tract since the vocal cords represent the closed end, and the nose and the lips represent the open end. As a result, resonances occur in the vocal tract.

The variation in the speed of the air flowing from the lungs contributes to the variations in loudness of the voice. But why does every voice sound different? The basic difference between male and female is associated with the design of the larynx and the first harmonic it generates: males have a range of 100 to 170 Hz and females have a range of 220 to 330 Hz.

A more detailed analysis is necessary when analysing speech characteristics. We can modify the resonances in the vocal tract by varying the relative positions of three components of the system: (a) the tongue, (b) the lips, and (c) the soft palate (which is the ceiling of the mouth). We distinguish four basic forms of sounds: (I) the labial sounds made by the lips and teeth alone (examples: p in part, b in brain, v in van, w in water, f in five, m in mouth); (II) the dental sounds formed by the teeth and the tongue (examples: d in done, t in table, s in sand, c in face, n in never); (III) the lingual sounds for which the tongue is close to the front end of

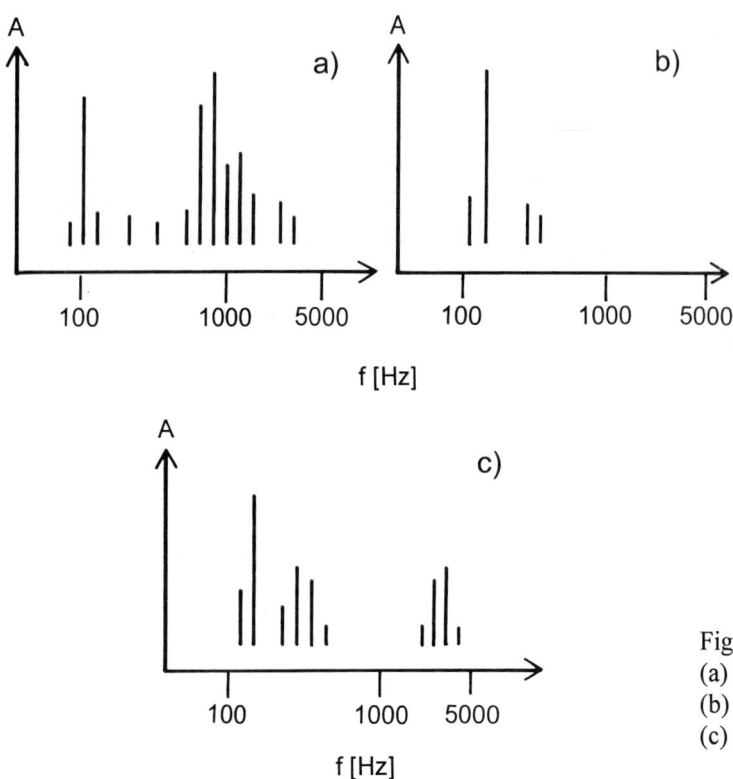

Fig. 16.23: Frequency spectra for three vowels:
(a) the vowel–sound in the word hunt,
(b) the vowel–sound in the word hood,
(c) the vowel–sound in the word heat.

the soft palate (examples: *l* in language, *sh* in ship); and (IV) the guttural sounds for which the tongue is farther back along the soft palate (examples are: *g* in good, *k* in kite, *c* in carrot).

The different vowels have the same first harmonic but differ in the higher harmonics. Three frequency spectra are shown in Fig. 16.23, with (a) higher amplitudes around 1000 Hz for the vowel–sound in the word *hunt*, (b) a lack of harmonics other than the first harmonic for the vowel–sound in the word *hood*, and (c) higher amplitudes in the range near 1400 Hz for the vowel–sound in the word *heat*.

16.4.2. The outer ear

The human ear is an extremely sensitive sound detection system. It can analyse sound intensities ranging over 12 orders of magnitude and is able to distinguish frequencies between 16 Hz and 16 kHz.

To achieve this performance all three components of the ear of Fig. 16.10, the outer ear, the middle ear and the inner ear, are essential. The outer ear is a half–closed tube with a first harmonic which generates a resonant amplification across most of the range of audible frequencies. The mechanical mechanism in the middle ear circumvents a major loss in intensity which would occur if the external medium air would directly couple across a single membrane to the inner ear's liquid medium. The inner ear provides the frequency analysis, which is encoded in electric signals sent to the brain.

Example 16.12
What is the first harmonic of the human auditory canal?

Supplementary anatomical information: The outer ear consists of the auditory canal and ends at the eardrum. The auditory canal is about 2.5 cm long.

Solution: We use Eq. (42) to calculate the first harmonic, assuming that a semi–closed tube is the appropriate model for the auditory canal. We find for the outer ear for n = 1:

$$f_1 = \frac{c}{4L} = \frac{343 [m/s]}{4 \cdot 2.5 \times 10^{-2} [m]} = 3.4 \; kHz \quad (52)$$

This frequency is close to the frequency of the maximum sensitivity of the ear.

Due to the width of the peak of the resonance curves in Fig. 16.18 (the range where $A/A_0 > 1$), an appreciable range of frequencies around the first harmonic is amplified. This range and the amplification factor depend on the damping of the resonance curve. The human ear amplifies the arriving sound by about a factor of two, i.e., the curve in Fig. 16.18(b) is a good representation of the resonance behavior of the auditory canal. We benefit from the resonant amplification of the outer ear in the frequency interval from about 2 kHz to 7 kHz.

16.4.3. The middle ear

The middle ear transports the sound signal from the eardrum to the oval window. The anatomical set–up is shown in Fig. 1.3. The vibrations of the oval window (5) cause waves in the perilymph (6), which is the liquid in the inner ear. The perilymph is a fluid similar to highly filtered blood plasma, comparable to the extracellular fluid. Like other body fluids, the perilymph is an electrolyte with a concentration of 14 mmol/l Na$^+$, but it has only a low concentration of proteins.

The middle ear is physiologically necessary because the sound travels toward the denser medium (air to perilymph). It consists of the hammer (2) which is attached to the eardrum (1), the anvil (3) and the stirrup (4) which is attached to the oval window of the cochlea (7).

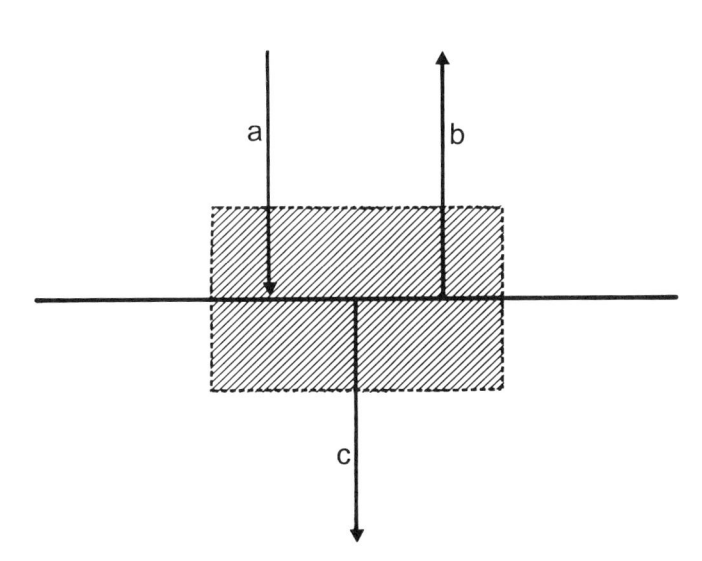

Fig. 16.24: Conceptual sketch of a wave passing through an interface. At the interface section (dashed box) three wave components have to be considered: (a) an incoming wave, (b) a reflected wave and (c) a transmitted wave. The transfer of sound intensity is particularly ineffective when the densities of the media on both sides of the interface differ significantly.

To illustrate the purpose of the middle ear we assume for a moment that it does not exist. In this case the eardrum and the oval window would be the same membrane and the sound would have to be coupled across this membrane from the medium air of the outer ear to the denser medium perilymph of the inner ear. The interface between both media (hypothetical combined membrane) is schematically shown in Fig. 16.24. At this interface an incoming wave (a) is partially reflected (b) and partially transmitted (c). To quantify the efficiency of sound transmission across the membrane we determine the ratio of the reflected to the transmitted wave intensity. For the ear, we find that the transmitted intensity would be significantly less than the incoming intensity if the eardrum and the oval window were merged into a single interface. This justifies the complex middle ear as a necessary sound amplification component.

To quantify the model of Fig. 16.24, a small section of the interface is studied (dashed box). On the incoming side, a superposition of the incoming and reflected wave occurs. Two conditions must apply in the dashed section:

(I) to satisfy the continuity of physical properties across the interface, the maximum speed of vibration due to the incoming wave, v_i, and the maximum speed due to the reflected wave, v_r, must match the maximum speed due to the transmitted wave, v_t:

$$v_i + v_r = v_t \qquad (53)$$

(II) Further, the energy passing through the interface must be conserved. The transported energy is given in Eq. (25). In that equation we rewrite the angular frequency in the form $v_{max} = \omega A$ by using Eqs. (15.46) and (15.49). Thus:

$$\frac{1}{2}\rho_1 c_1 v_i^2 = \frac{1}{2}\rho_1 c_1 v_r^2 + \frac{1}{2}\rho_2 c_2 v_t^2 \qquad (54)$$

in which the index 1 represents the medium in which the incoming wave travels and the index 2 represents the medium in which the transmitted wave travels.

We use Eq. (53) to eliminate v_r in Eq. (54):

$$\begin{aligned}\rho_1 c_1 v_i^2 &= \rho_1 c_1 (v_t - v_i)^2 + \rho_2 c_2 v_t^2 = \\ &\rho_1 c_1 v_t^2 - 2\rho_1 c_1 v_t v_i + \rho_1 c_1 v_i^2 + \rho_2 c_2 v_t^2\end{aligned} \qquad (55)$$

Note that the third term in the last line of Eq. (55) cancels with the term on the left hand side of the equation. We divide Eq. (55) by v_t on both sides to obtain:

$$2\rho_1 c_1 v_i = (\rho_1 c_1 + \rho_2 c_2) v_t \quad (56)$$

This yields a relation between the transmitted speed v_t and the incoming speed v_i of the wave:

$$v_t = \frac{2\rho_1 c_1}{\rho_1 c_1 + \rho_2 c_2} v_i \quad (57)$$

Substituting Eq. (57) in the equation for the intensity of a wave (Eq. (25)), $I = \frac{1}{2}c\rho v^2$, the ratio of incoming and transmitted intensity is determined:

$$\frac{I_t}{I_i} = \frac{\frac{1}{2}c_2\rho_2 v_t^2}{\frac{1}{2}c_1\rho_1 v_i^2} = \frac{c_2 \rho_2}{c_1 \rho_1} \left(\frac{2\rho_1 c_1}{\rho_1 c_1 + \rho_2 c_2} \right)^2$$

$$= \frac{4\rho_1 \rho_2 c_1 c_2}{(\rho_1 c_1 + \rho_2 c_2)^2} \quad (58)$$

This formula can be simplified in the case of a significant difference between medium 1 and medium 2, i.e., when $\rho_2 c_2 \gg \rho_1 c_1$. In this case we get:

$$\frac{I_t}{I_i} = 4 \frac{\rho_1 c_1}{\rho_2 c_2} \quad (59)$$

First, we test the condition $\rho_2 c_2 \gg \rho_1 c_1$ for our hypothetical membrane between outer and inner ear. For this calculation we approximate the properties of the perilymph by those of water. Taking the ambient temperature to be 20°C we find:

$$\begin{aligned} 1: \rho_{air} &= 1.205 \frac{kg}{m^3} \; ; \; c_{air} = 343.2 \frac{m}{s} \\ 2: \rho_{H_2O} &= 1000 \frac{kg}{m^3} \; ; \; c_{H_2O} = 1485 \frac{m}{s} \end{aligned} \quad (60)$$

thus, $\rho_2 c_2 \gg \rho_1 c_1$ is satisfied. Eq. (59) allows us then to calculate the ratio of sound intensities between air and water:

$$\frac{I_{perilymph}}{I_{air}} = 4 \frac{1.205 \cdot 343.2}{1000 \cdot 1485} = 1.1 \times 10^{-3} \quad (61)$$

Eq. (61) illustrates a general result: sound transfer between media of significantly different density is very ineffective. In particular, this means that nature could not construct our ear with a single membrane between the outer ear and the inner ear, as a sound intensity transfer

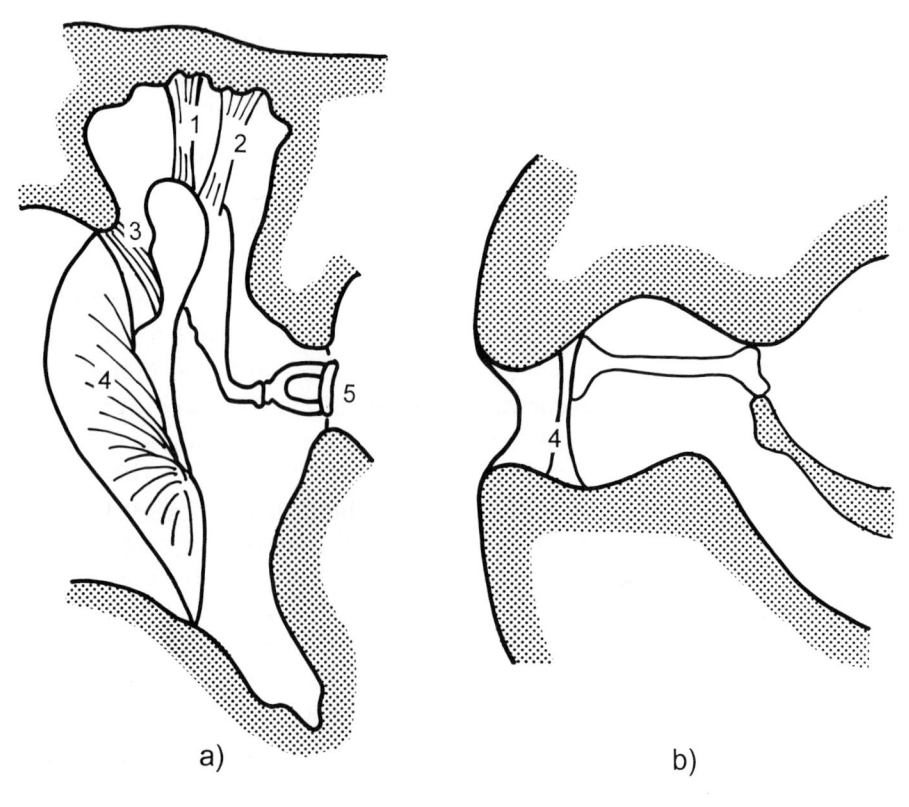

Fig. 16.25: (a) Human middle ear anatomy, highlighting the ligaments which stabilize the three ossicles between the eardrum (4) and the oval window (5). Ligamentum mallei superius (1) and Ligamentum incudis superius (2) hold the hammer and the anvil in position. Ligamentum mallei laterale (3) acts as a fulcrum for the rotation of the hammer. (b) Middle ear anatomy of reptiles. Note that only one bone bridges the middle ear section.

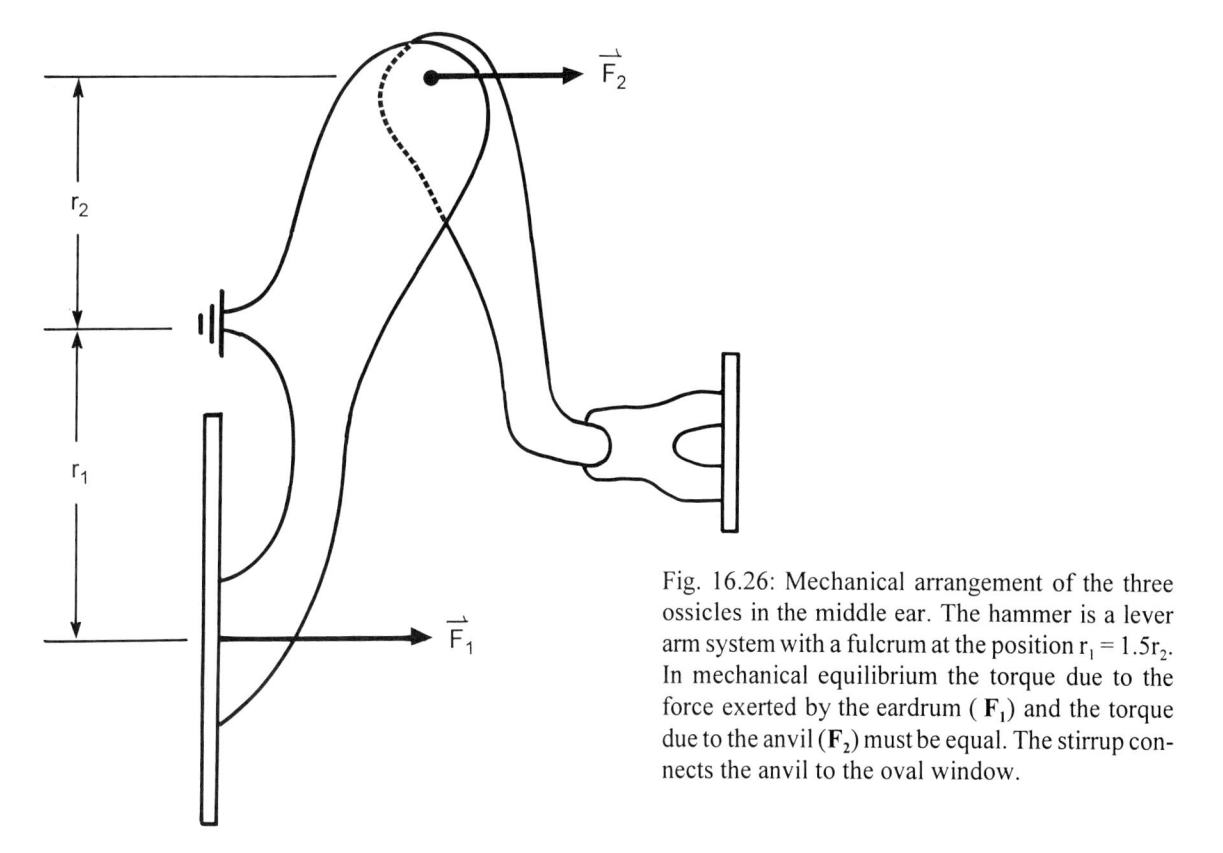

Fig. 16.26: Mechanical arrangement of the three ossicles in the middle ear. The hammer is a lever arm system with a fulcrum at the position $r_1 = 1.5 r_2$. In mechanical equilibrium the torque due to the force exerted by the eardrum ($\mathbf{F_1}$) and the torque due to the anvil ($\mathbf{F_2}$) must be equal. The stirrup connects the anvil to the oval window.

of only about 0.1 % would leave us essentially deaf.

So, how does the middle ear circumvent this problem? The middle ear transports the vibration of the eardrum as a mechanical vibration to the oval window. This eliminates the intensity loss discussed above. Beyond that, the middle ear provides a moderate amplification of the vibration due to the specific design of the interacting mechanical components. This amplification has two components, a force amplification and a pressure amplification. We calculate each component separately and then combine them to arrive at the overall amplification of the middle ear.

The force amplification of the middle ear
Fig. 16.25 shows a comparison of the anatomy of the middle ear of (a) humans and (b) reptiles. The figure illustrates the more recent evolution of the complex arrangement in the mammalian ear. Reptiles and birds have a single bone connecting the eardrum (4) to the inner ear. Some of these bones were quite heavy in dinosaurs, allowing them at best to hear very low frequencies. For humans, sound transmission between the eardrum (4) and the oval window of the inner ear (5) is accomplished by three ossicles. The ligaments in Fig. 16.25(a) identify the mechanical mobility of the ossicles. The ligamentum mallei superius (1) and the ligamentum incudis superius (2) hold the hammer and the anvil in position. The ligamentum mallei laterale (3) is responsible for allowing a rotation of the hammer. We identify this last ligament as the fulcrum. Fig. 16.26 is a sketch of the hammer as a mechanical lever arm system. The eardrum can exert a force $\mathbf{F_1}$ and the anvil can exert a force $\mathbf{F_2}$ on the lever arms at distances r_1 and r_2 from the fulcrum, respectively. The hammer is in mechanical equilibrium when a torque equilibrium is established:

$$\sum_i \tau_i = r_1 F_1 - r_2 F_2 = 0$$

$$\Rightarrow \quad F_2 = \frac{r_1}{r_2} F_1$$

(62)

With the fulcrum located above the half–way point of the lever arm, $r_1 = 1.5\, r_2$, the force on the oval window is 1.5 times larger than the force exerted by the eardrum.

The pressure amplification of the middle ear
The pressure amplification is the result of the difference in area of eardrum and oval window. The pressure on the eardrum equals the force acting on the eardrum divided by the area of the eardrum. Equally, the pressure on the oval window equals the force on the oval window divided by the area of the oval window. Anatomically we find an area for the eardrum of 65 mm² (of which, however, as little as 45 mm² might be mechanically active), and an area of 3.2 mm² for the oval window. Thus the pressure amplification accounts for a factor 15 to 20.

We combine the force and the pressure amplifications:

$$\Delta p_{oval} = \frac{F_{oval}}{A_{oval}} = \frac{1.5 F_{eardrum}}{A_{oval}}$$

$$= 1.5 \frac{A_{eardrum}}{A_{oval}} \Delta p_{air} \quad (63)$$

which yields:

$$\frac{\Delta p_{oval}}{\Delta p_{air}} = 1.5 \frac{65 [mm^2]}{3.2 [mm^2]} \cong 30 \quad (64)$$

The middle ear provides an 30 fold amplification of the incoming pressure difference, instead of diminishing the signal to less than 1 % as shown for a single membrane separating the outer and inner ear!

16.4.4. The inner ear

The acoustic components of the inner ear are located in the cochlea, shown in its characteristically curled shape in Fig. 16.10. This shape is also the origin of the name cochlea which means snail in Latin. The cochlea is cut open in Fig. 1.3, illustrating the arrangement of its internal structure. The same cross–section is shown in more detail in Fig. 16.27. The cochlea consists of three separate channels. The vestibular chamber (1) starts at the oval window and runs along the cochlea to its far end, called the apex or helicotrema. The vestibular chamber is open to the tympanic chamber at the apex, with the tympanic chamber (2) running back along the cochlea to the round window at the end of the inner ear. Both chambers are filled with perilymph and are separated by the basilar membrane. The third channel, called the cochlear duct (4), contains the organ of Corti (named for Alfonso de Corti, highlighted in a box at the right end of the cochlear duct). The cochlear duct is separated from the other two channels by the basilar membrane and by Reissner's membrane (5, named for Ernst Reißner) and is filled with endolymph, a liquid solution similar to the perilymph but which contains 145 mmol/l K$^+$. This different ionic content of both liquids leads to an electric potential of the endolymph relative to the perilymph of +80 mV. In the present discussion we neglect electric phenomena.

Dendrites emerge from the organ of Corti and run through the basilar membrane toward the brain. The organ of Corti is shown separately in Fig. 16.28. The basilar membrane (3) is located at the bottom of the sketch. It carries an array of support cells (6) in which three external (at left) and one internal auditory hair cells (dotted) are embedded. Each auditory hair cell carries about 80 hair–like extensions, called stereovilli. The stereovilli extend into the cochlear duct, which forms a narrow gap between the basilar membrane and the tectorial membrane above the auditory hair cells.

Fig. 16.27: Cross–section of the cochlea. Three liquid–filled channels are shown: (1) the vestibular chamber, and (2) the tympanic chamber containing perilymph; (4) the cochlear duct containing endolymph. The vestibular and tympanic chambers on one side and the tympanic chamber and the cochlear duct on the other side are separated by the basilar membrane (3). The vestibular chamber and the cochlear duct are separated by Reissner's membrane (5). The organ of Corti is supported by the basilar membrane in the cochlear duct. Dendrites extend through the basilar membrane to the organ of Corti.

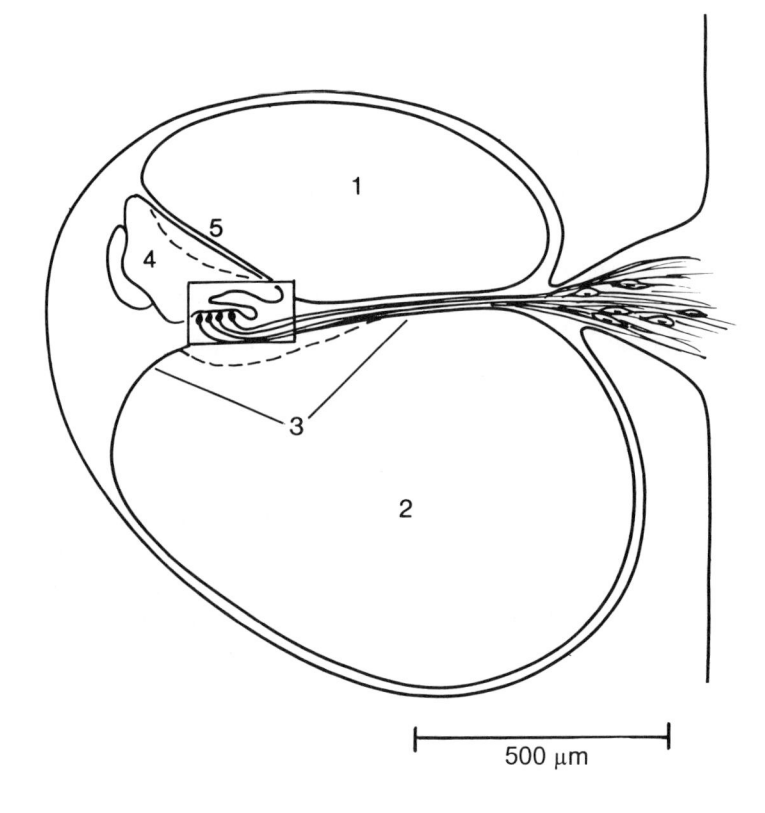

Fig. 16.28: Detail of the organ of Corti (indicated by the rectangular box in Fig. 16.27). The basilar membrane (3) supports a layer of supportive cells (6) in which three external and one internal auditory hair cells (dotted) are embedded. The auditory hair cells have hair–like extensions (stereovilli) which extend into a gap between the basilar membrane and the tectorial membrane (7) in the cochlear duct.

Fig. 16.29: A travelling wave in the vestibular chamber, caused by a vibration of the stirrup at the oval window (upper arrow). The basilar membrane vibrates at a point determined by the frequency of the travelling wave. This vibration causes the wave to be transferred to the perilymph in the tympanic chamber in which the wave travels towards the round window (lower arrow).

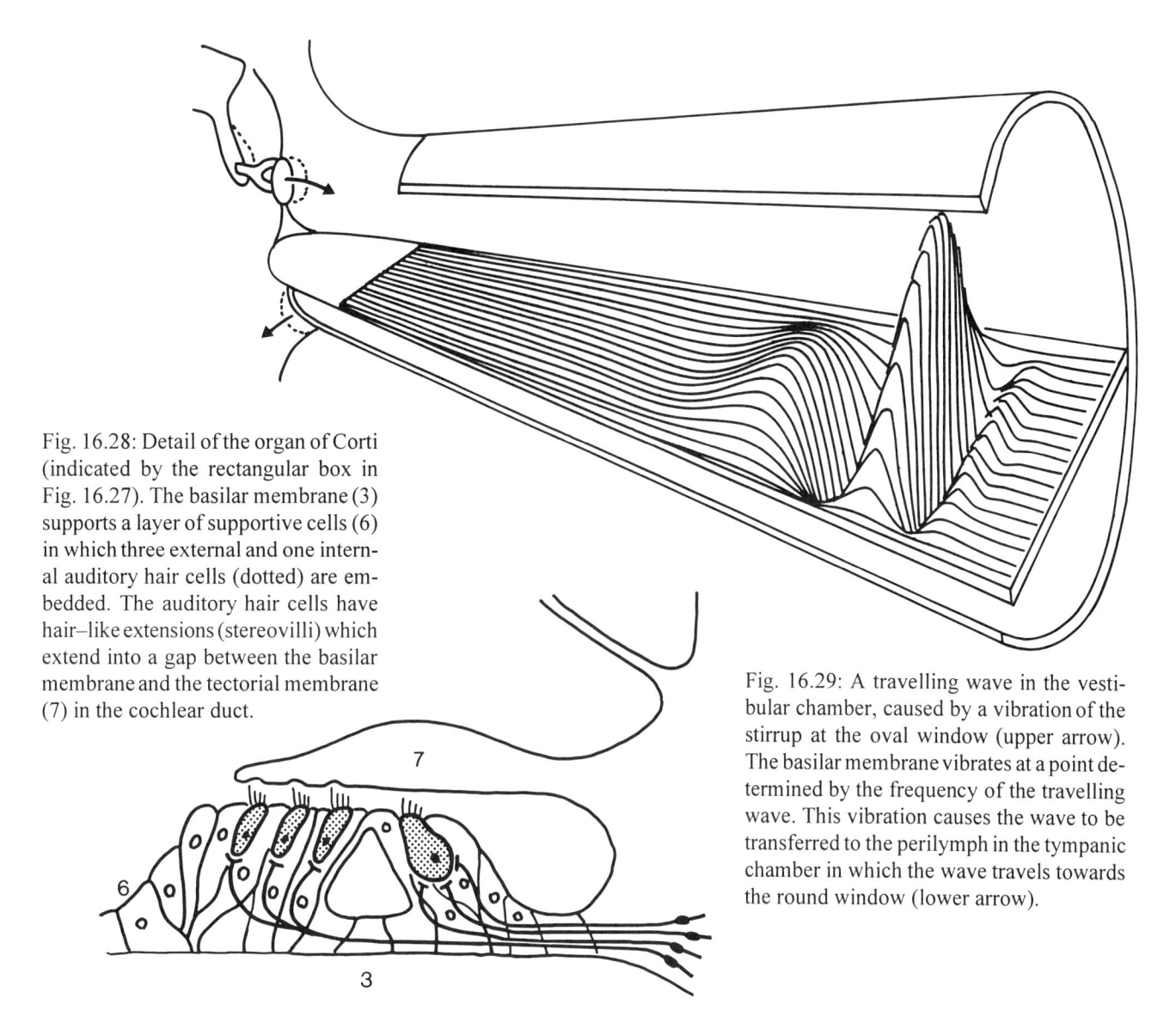

These components allow for sound detection and sound frequency analysis in the following fashion. The inner ear represents a closed tube (both confining windows are elastic membranes). Thus, the excitation at the oval window cannot form resonances along the tube as this would confine the frequencies we hear to a set of harmonics as discussed in section 16.3. Instead, the excitation at the oval window leads to a travelling wave, similar to a single bulge you form on a rope stretched between your hand and the wall if you briefly swing your hand up and down. Such a travelling wave is shown in Fig. 16.29 which indicates the amplitude of a wave in the perilymph as a function of position along the vestibular chamber. The two arrows indicate the initial excitation at the oval window and the later mechanical response at the round window below. For each sound frequency, there is a specific point between the oval window and the apex where the travelling wave amplifies in the perilymph and causes the basilar membrane to vibrate. This process is controlled by the stiffness of the basilar membrane which reduces by a factor of 10^4 along its entire length. This is achieved by a thickness variation of the basilar membrane. It starts with a thickness of 0.04 mm at the oval window and ends with a thickness of 0.5 mm at the apex.

Two figures are provided to illustrate the position dependence of the point at which a certain frequency causes the basilar membrane to vibrate: Fig. 16.30(a) shows a conceptual sketch in which the cochlea is shown as if stretched–out. The oval window is excited by the stirrup (1). The wave then travels along the perilymph (2). The frequency properties are shown in Fig. 16.30(b). For higher frequencies, e.g. 1.6 kHz, the wave causes the basilar membrane (3) to vibrate near the oval window. This causes the wave to transfer to the tympanic chamber (4) where it travels back to the round window (6). At an intermediate frequency, e.g. 200 Hz, the wave travels to an intermediate point along the basilar membrane, and at low frequencies, e.g. 50 Hz, the wave travels all the way to the apex.

Fig. 16.30: Schematic sketch of the path taken in the inner ear by a wave of specific frequency. (a) Overview of the cochlea with the stirrup and the oval window (1), the vestibular chamber (2), the basilar membrane (3), the tympanic chamber (4), the apex (5), and the round window (6). (b) Waves of higher frequencies travel a shorter distance along the cochlea.

Fig. 16.31: Plot of the position of the vibration of the basilar membrane as a function of the travelling wave frequency along the cochlea. Frequencies near 20 kHz are detected near the oval window (pointed end at the bottom right) while frequencies at 200 Hz (0.2 kHz) and below travel close to the apex (shown as the wide end).

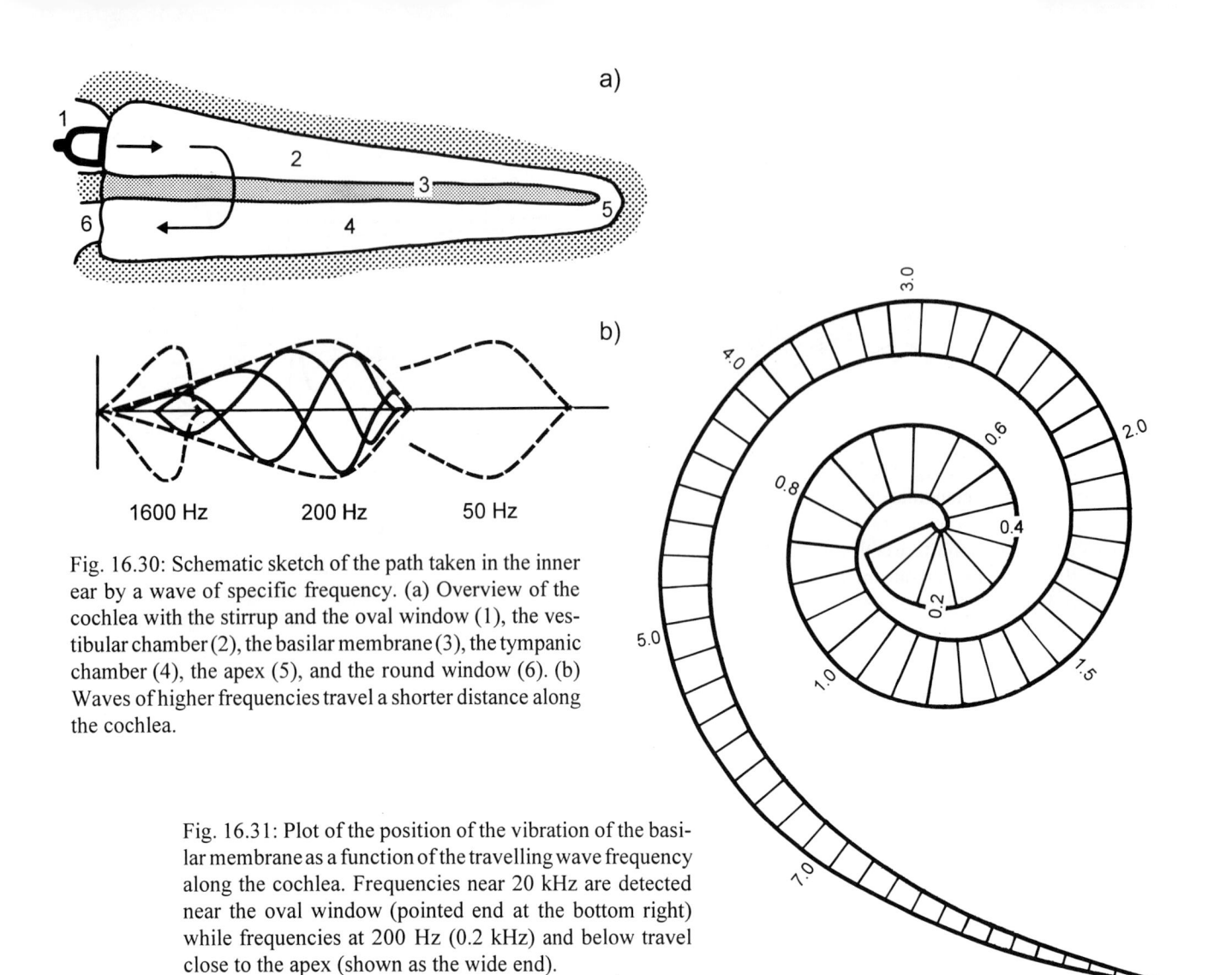

Fig. 16.31 illustrates the connection between frequency and distance from the oval window (in the figure at the pointed end at the bottom) with the numbers representing frequencies in unit [kHz].

The vibration of the basilar membrane also causes the tectorial membrane to vibrate in synchrony. The mechanism by which this leads to an excitation of the dendrites in the organ of Corti is illustrated in Fig. 16.32, which shows the two membranes in their equilibrium position in the upper sketch and when moved upwards by an angle ϕ in the lower sketch. The narrowness of the gap between both membranes causes the stereovilli to bend sideways during the vibration. Only the internal auditory hair cell is connected to dendrites, thus, the stereovilli of the internal auditory cell must be bent before a signal is sent to the brain.

What is reported to the brain? Two components of the vibrational motion of the basilar membrane are encoded in the sequence of the nerve impulses leaving the organ of Corti through the dendrites:
(I) the information which dendrite along the cochlea responds provides a frequency information pretty much in the same way the Fourier series is developed mathematically (see section 16.3). This property of the cochlea was already proposed by Georg Ohm and Hermann von Helmholtz more than 100 years ago.
(II) The frequency at which signals are sent by the dendrite to the brain is also proportional to the original frequency of the sound wave (periodicity analysis). This is illustrated in Fig. 16.33 for a frequency shown as a harmonic wave in the lower part of the figure. The nerve impulses shown in the upper part of the figure are clearly tuned into the periodicity of the sinusoidal sound wave.

The human ear is extremely sensitive to sounds ranging from between 15 and 20 Hz to about 16 to 20 kHz (dogs hear up to 40 kHz while elephants communicate sub–sonically as these frequencies carry much farther in air). However, the sensitivity of human hearing varies across this frequency interval, primarily due to the resonance properties we discussed above for the outer ear. This is illustrated quantitatively in Fig. 16.34. The figure shows

Fig. 16.32: Mechanism of dendrite excitation in the organ of Corti. The basilar membrane and the tectorial membrane vibrate in synchrony in response to a travelling wave. The upper sketch shows the equilibrium position and the lower sketch shows the position at the instant when both membranes moved upwards by an angle ϕ. The stereovilli of the auditory hair cells are bent sideways in this process due to the narrowness of the gap between the two membranes. A signal is sent to the brain only from the internal auditory hair cell.

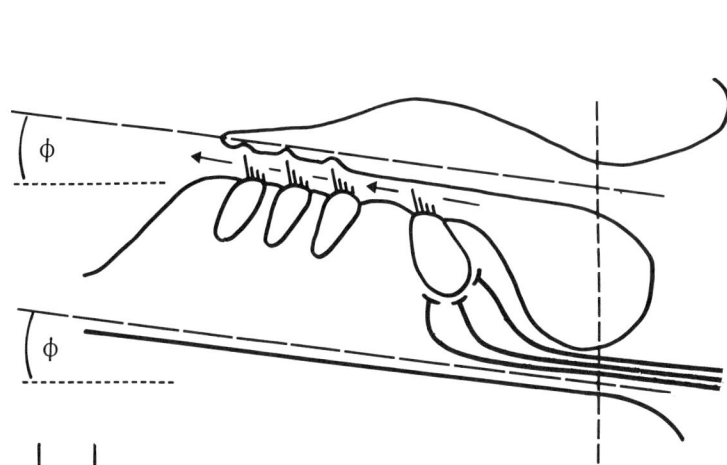

Fig. 16.33: Frequency of nerve impulses in response to a sinusoidal sound wave. The sinusoidal sound wave is shown as the lower curve in the figure. The nerve impulse response is shown in the upper curve.

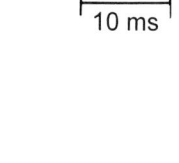

Fig. 16.34: The hearing range of the human ear, shown as a function of the frequency of the sound f (horizontal axis) and as a function of the sound pressure level (SPL) in decibel (vertical axis). Each line in the plot represents sounds which are judged as equally loud. The lowest curve is the acoustic reflex threshold and the highest curve is the pain threshold. The dotted area corresponds to the normal range of conversations. The unit [phon] is defined by the decibel scale of SPL at 1 kHz.

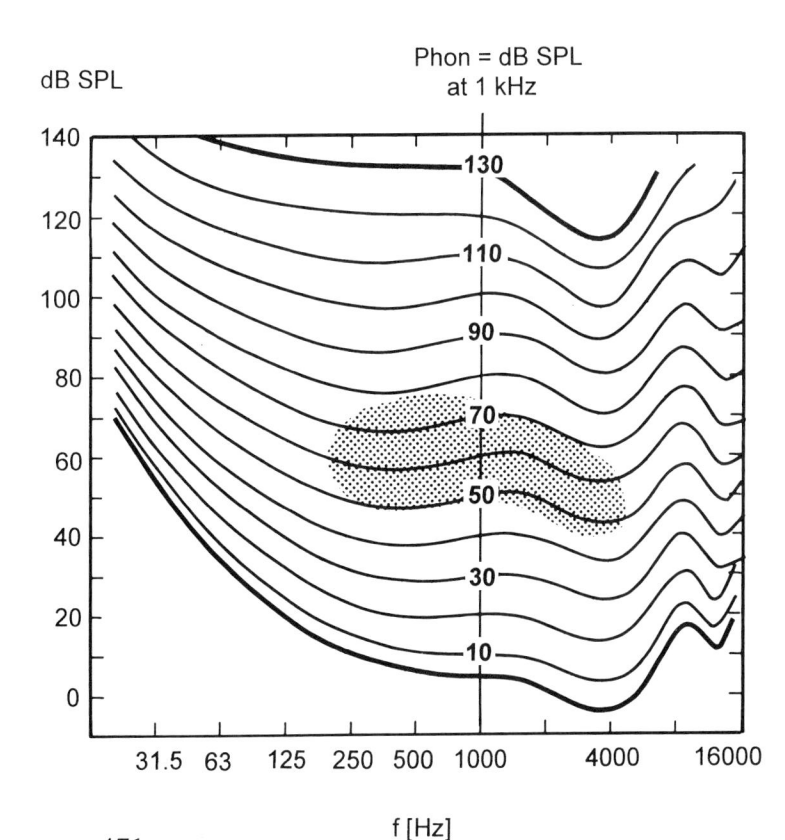

the frequency range from about 10 Hz to 16 kHz and sound pressure levels from 0 dB to 140 dB (for the definition of the sound pressure level scale see Eq. (26)). Each curve in the plot represents the pressure levels as a function of frequency which are judged by a person as being equally loud. The thicker lowest line corresponds to the normal acoustic reflex threshold and the thicker highest line corresponds to the pain limit. The range of normal conversations is shown as a dotted area near the center of the plot.

A maximum sensitivity near 3 kHz in agreement with Example 16.12 is clearly demonstrated. As frequencies are lower or higher, the sensitivity diminishes until it ceases at the lower or higher frequency limit of the ear. This variation of perceived loudness as a function of frequency causes some trouble for the physical scales to measure the pressure or intensity levels of sound (the SPL and IL scales discussed in section 16.2) as we would disagree that a 100 dB sound at 40 Hz is equally loud as a 100 dB sound at 3000 Hz.

For this reason, a new scale is introduced based on Fig. 16.34 and is recorded in unit [phon]. The convention is to set the decibel scale and the phon scale equal at a sound frequency of 1 kHz: 100 dB = 100 phon at 1 kHz. The phon scale deviates from the SPL or IL scales at all other frequencies, with the same phon value representing the same perceived loudness of a sound. Table 16.5 provides several examples for sounds, with sound levels recorded in [phon]. The maximum sound pressure level produced by an animal is 188 dB for the low–frequency moans of the Blue whale. These sounds can be heard by other whales as far away as hundreds of kilometers.

Table 16.5: Sound perception in [phon].

Sound level	Example
4 phon	threshold of normal hearing
20 phon	quiet countryside
40 phon	whispering, talking with a low voice
60 phon	normal conversation
80 phon	city traffic noise
100 phon	industrial plant
110 phon	comfortableness limit
120 phon	thunder
130 phon	pain threshold
140 phon	jet engine

16.5. Special properties of the auditory system

16.5.1. Stereoscopic hearing

The human head has two ears. As we all know from listening to music, this allows us to detect the direction from which a sound approaches us. We distinguish deviations as small as 4^0 between two sound sources. This is based on the two phenomena illustrated in Fig. 16.35:
(I) The sound travels of the order of 10^{-5} s longer to the farther ear, and
(II) the sound pressure level at the farther ear is slightly lower due to the reduction of intensity with distance, as discussed in section 16.2. A lower pressure level is associated with a longer latency time, which is the time

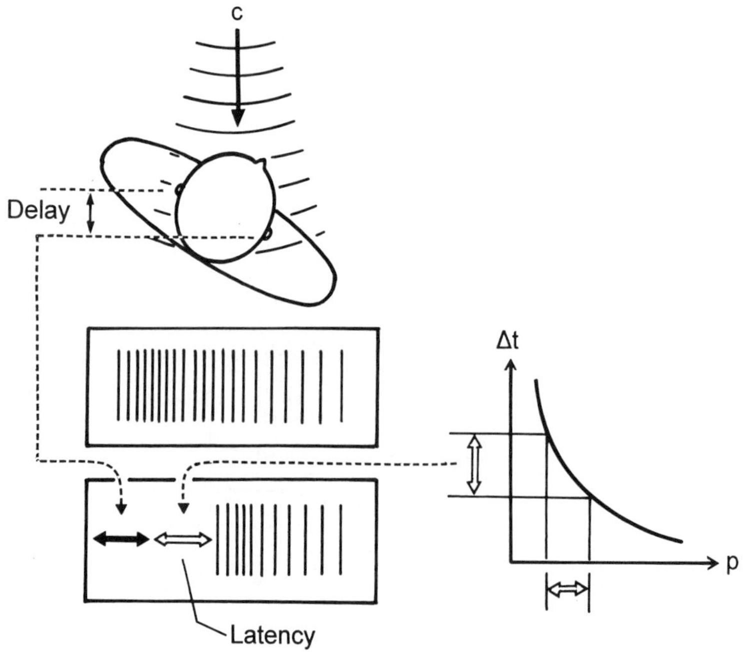

Fig. 16.35: Mechanism of stereoscopic hearing. Two delay mechanisms contri-bute to the ability to detect the direction of a sound source: A delay due to the longer distance from the sound source to the farther ear, and a latency delay due to the slightly lower sound pressure level of the sound at the farther ear (indicated by the inverse proportionality between the delay time Δt and the sound pressure p in the plot at the right). The two boxes below the sketched person show the time dependence of the nerve impulses sent to the brain for the closer ear (upper box) and the farther ear (lower box).

between the arrival of a sound wave at the ear and the instant the dendrites at the auditory hair cells send signals to the brain. The sum of both these delays enhances the perception of the delay at the farther ear.

16.5.2. The role of the brain: beats

The brain does not necessarily interpret the signals received from the ears in an objective fashion, i.e., like a physical instrument. We discuss illusions in greater detail in the context of vision, where these phenomena are even more surprising. Illusions are associated with various effects, for example the preferential absorption of higher frequencies in air, which causes us to believe that a lower frequency sound comes from a farther distance. This effect is used in movies to create anxiety when the sound pitch is raised toward a climactic event.

We discuss in more detail the formation of beats in this section and the Doppler effect in the next section.

Our ear is able to distinguish several sounds arriving at the ear at the same time. The ear can even tune into a specific pattern of a first harmonic and the corresponding higher harmonics, enabling us to listen to a specific person in spite of high background noise at a party. However, when two first harmonics are too close (below a difference of $\Delta f = 15$ Hz), they are no longer interpreted as two separate sounds. The origin of this effect is illustrated with the superposition of two waves. We use for simplicity two waves with equal amplitudes:

$$\xi_{sup} = A\sin\omega_1 t + A\sin\omega_2 t =$$
$$= 2A \sin\left(\frac{\omega_1+\omega_2}{2}t\right)\cos\left(\frac{\omega_1-\omega_2}{2}t\right) \quad (65)$$

in which the last line was obtained with the trigonometric identity:

$$\sin\alpha + \sin\beta = 2\sin\frac{\alpha+\beta}{2}\cos\frac{\alpha-\beta}{2} \quad (66)$$

The function in Eq. (65) is shown in Fig. 16.36. The two separate wave functions are shown as the two upper curves. The superposition is shown in the lower sketch. The higher frequency of the sine–term in the last line of Eq. (65) is very similar to the two frequencies of the original waves. The lower frequency of the cosine–term in the last line of Eq. (65) leads to the frequency causing an envelope in Fig. 16.36 with wavelength Δx. If the frequency due to this term is less than or equal to 7.5 Hz, the brain does not interpret the pattern in Fig. 16.36 as two distinct sounds, but as one sound with the average frequency and with a time dependent amplitude, which we can write as:

$$A_{sup}(t) = 2A\cos\left(\frac{\omega_1-\omega_2}{2}t\right) \quad (67)$$

Example 16.13
Two sounds are originally generated with equal amplitudes and frequencies of values $f_1 = 1000$ Hz and $f_2 = 1010$ Hz. What does a person hear?

Solution: Eq. (65) leads to a superposition frequency in the Example of $f_{sup} = \frac{1}{2}(f_1 + f_2) = 1005$ Hz for the pitch we hear. Played separately, the sounds with f_1, f_2 and f_{sup}

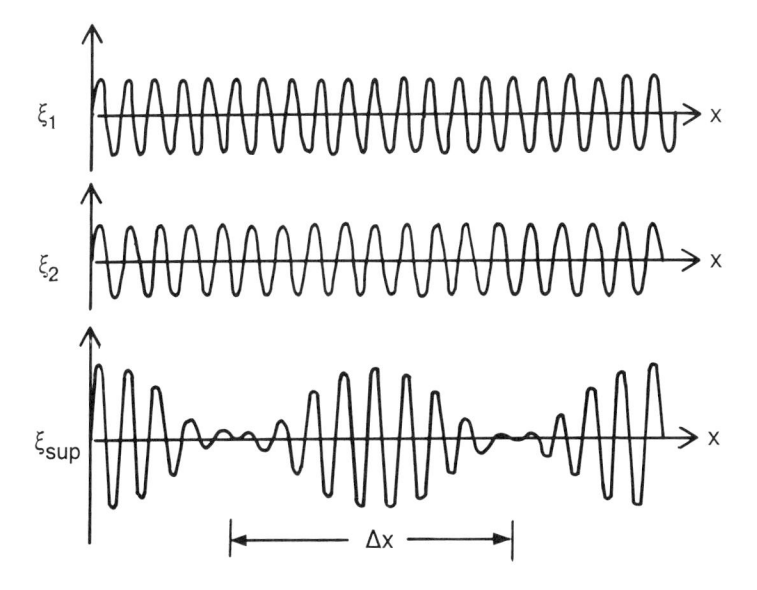

Fig. 16.36: Superposition of two waves (two top curves) with the same amplitude but slightly different frequencies. The result of the superposition is shown in the lower curve. The ear can either interpret this wave as two separate waves or, if the frequency difference is less than 15 Hz, as a single wave with a time dependent amplitude (beat).

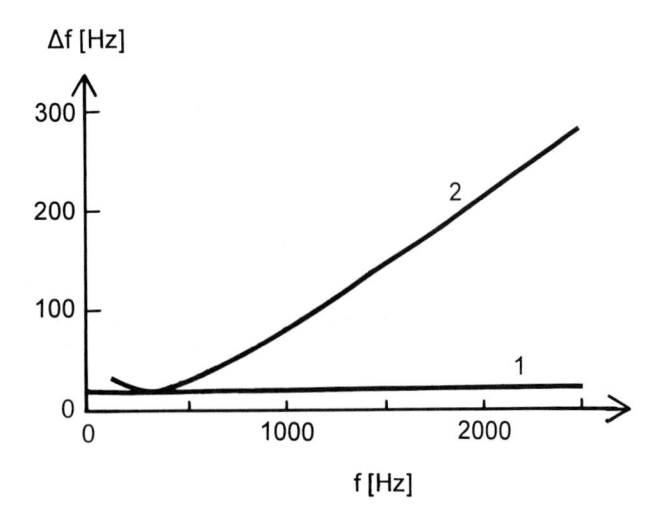

Fig. 16.37: There are two threshold curves for the perception of the human ear for two waves of different frequencies: if the frequency difference is less than 15 Hz (curve 1), we hear a beat, and if the frequency difference lies between curve 1 and curve 2, we perceive the sound as uncomfortably harsh.

frequency difference of 15 Hz and less. Hit any two of these keys together and listen to the sound.

Fig. 16.37 illustrates two frequency difference thresholds for which our hearing is deceived. Shown as curve (1) is the frequency difference $\Delta f = 15$ Hz below which we hear beats. The figure illustrates that this threshold is independent of the frequency of the sound. The figure shows also a second curve labelled (2). This curve indicates the threshold of frequency difference Δf below which we perceive two sounds as uncomfortably harsh. The cause for this phenomenon is again the beat given in Eq. (65). However, above a difference of 15 Hz our ear is no longer able to resolve the timing of the beat frequency $f_1 - f_2$. The threshold curve (2) is over a wide range proportional to the original sound frequency.

could barely be distinguished. However, when the sounds with f_1 and f_2 are received at the same time, the sound amplitude varies (beat) with a sound frequency of $\frac{1}{2}(f_1 - f_2) = 5$ Hz, which is heard as an up– and down–swelling of the sound.

You can easily verify the phenomenon with a piano. All neighboring keys from A_0 to about C_4 have a

16.5.3. Doppler effect and Doppler Ultrasound

An altered sound frequency is detected when the sound source or the receiver (e.g. the human ear) moves relative to the medium. Two cases are distinguished, (I) the sound source at rest and the receiver moving with speed v_R, and (II) the sound source moving with speed v_S while the receiver is at rest. The latter case is well known from

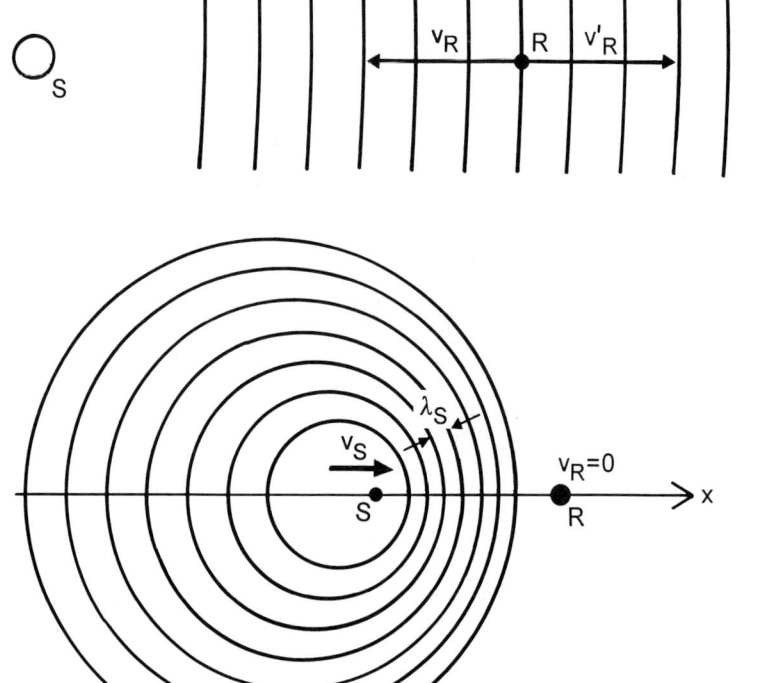

Fig. 16.38: Sketch of the motion of a receiver R moving with speed v_R towards the sound source S or moving with speed v_R' away from the sound source S. The nearly vertical lines indicate the waves emitted by the source, the distance between the lines corresponds to the wavelength.

Fig. 16.39: Sketch of the motion of a sound source S moving with speed v_S toward a receiver R at rest, $v_R = 0$. The large circles represent spherical sound waves emitted from the point sound source. The motion of the source along the x–axis leads to a change in the wavelength λ_S of the emitted sound as received by the receiver.

474

police car sirens when they approach us or move away from us. Both cases are called Doppler effect, named for Christian Doppler.

The receiver moves, the sound source is at rest
The first case is illustrated in Fig. 16.38. The source (S) emits waves which travel outwards. Between every two lines indicating the waves lies a full wavelength of the sound; the lines are separated by equal distances as long as the frequency of the source does not change. When the receiver (R) moves toward the source, the receiver receives more waves per time unit than if R were at rest. Correspondingly, when the receiver moves away from the sound source a lesser number of waves is received per time unit.

We quantify this effect for a source of frequency f_0. We consider a time interval Δt in which a receiver at rest receives $f_0 \Delta t$ wavelength cycles. During the same time interval the receiver moves by a distance $v_R \Delta t$. This distance corresponds to $v_R \Delta t / \lambda$ wavelength cycles. Thus, the total number of wavelength cycles is the sum, and the frequency is obtained after dividing by Δt:

$$f_R = f_0 \pm \frac{v_R}{\lambda} = f_0 \left(1 \pm \frac{v_R}{c}\right) \quad (68)$$

The ± sign in Eq. (68) has been introduced to allow the formula to describe both possibilities, the receiver moving toward (+) or away (−) from the source.

The sound source moves, the receiver is at rest
The second case is illustrated in Fig. 16.39. The source emits waves of wavelength λ. The concurrent motion of the source leads to an apparent wavelength λ_S. Using for the speed of the source v_S, we calculate an audible wavelength of $\lambda_S = \lambda_0 \pm v_S/f_0$ if the source moves straight toward or straight away from the receiver. We obtain the audible frequency from $c = \lambda_S f_S$:

$$f_S = \frac{c}{\lambda_S} = \frac{c}{\lambda_0 \pm \frac{v_S}{f_0}} = f_0 \frac{c}{c \pm v_S} \quad (69)$$

which leads to:

$$f_S = f_0 \frac{1}{1 \pm \frac{v_S}{c}} \quad (70)$$

The (+) sign applies when the source moves away from the receiver and the (−) sign applies when the source moves toward the receiver.

Doppler ultrasound diagnosis
A combination of both effects leads to an interesting application in the field of medicine: Doppler ultrasound. Ultrasound is sound at frequencies beyond the limit of human hearing, usually between 20 kHz and 10 GHz. It is widely used as a diagnostic tool in medicine, where it is best known for studying the unborn child.

The ultrasound technique is also used to detect the speed of moving components in the human body, such as blood cells. The principle is illustrated in Fig. 16.40. A standard transducer (shown at right) is brought into air–free contact with skin. A typical transducer frequency in this technique lies between 2 and 8 MHz. At the same time, the transducer serves as a receiver. The rate of switching between the two functions is 1 kHz.

Three steps are included in the Doppler ultrasound technique:
(I) the sound wave emitted by the resting transducer is received by the moving blood cell (receiver). The blood cell moves with speed v, e.g. in Fig. 16.40 toward the transducer, but possibly at an angle for which further corrections are needed that we do not discuss here.
(II) At the same instant it receives the ultrasound, the erythrocyte becomes a passive source by reflecting the

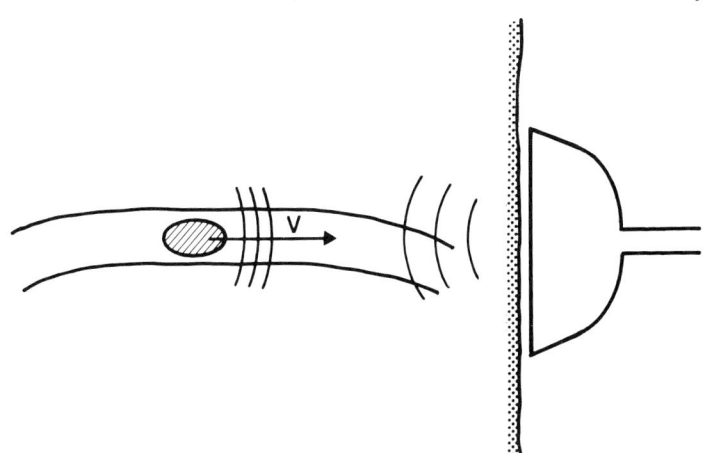

Fig. 16.40: Sketch of the Doppler ultrasound method. A transducer at right, in contact with the skin, sends an ultrasound signal which is reflected by an object moving with speed v, e.g. an erythrocyte.

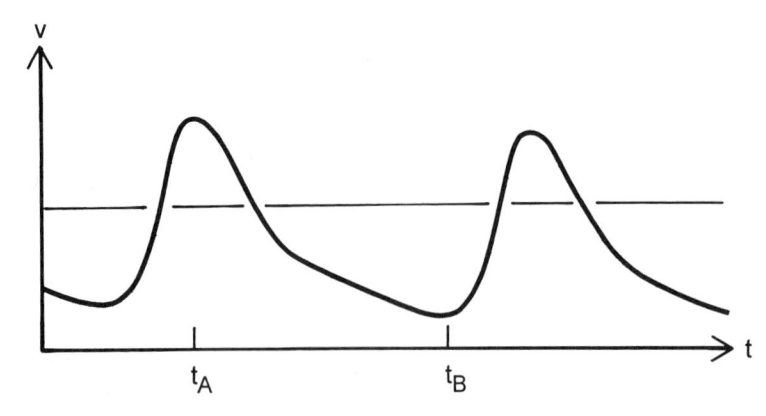

Fig. 16.41: Typical Doppler shift pattern for erythrocytes in an artery. The Doppler shift is converted to a speed of the blood using Eq. (74). The periodic speed variation of blood cells between times t_A and t_B is due to the rhythmic action of the heart.

sound wave (echo).
(III) The transducer receives the sound wave emitted from a moving source.

To describe the overall effect of all three steps, the two cases of the Doppler effect discussed above must be combined. Using the subscript "erythro" for erythrocyte and "trans" for transducer, we write for step (I) and step (III) above:

$$(step\ I) \quad f_{erythro} = f_0 \left(1 + \frac{v}{c}\right)$$

$$(step\ III) \quad f_{trans} = f_{erythro} \left(\frac{1}{1 - v/c}\right) \quad (71)$$

The sign in step (I) is chosen positive because the receiver moves toward the sound source in Fig. 16.40, and the sign in step (III) is chosen negative because, as a source, the erythrocyte moves toward the receiver. The velocity parameter v has no subscript because it is the velocity of the erythrocyte in both cases. Eq. (71) leads to:

$$f_{trans} = f_0 \left(\frac{1 + v/c}{1 - v/c}\right) \quad (72)$$

Note that Eq. (72) also confirms that the measured frequency would remain f_0 if both receiver and source move with the same velocity in the same direction. In this case, both the signs in step (I) and step (III) would be the same and the bracket in Eq. (72) would become equal to 1.

The difference between the frequency emitted and received by the transducer is called the Doppler shift Δf. Eq. (72) can be simplified in the limiting case that the speed of the blood cell is much slower than the speed of sound in the tissue, $v \ll c$. Since this is always the case, the Doppler shift can be shown to be linearly dependent on the speed of the blood cell:

$$\Delta f = f_{trans} - f_0 = f_0 \left(\frac{1 + v/c}{1 - v/c} - 1\right)$$

$$= f_0 \left(\frac{1 + v/c - (1 - v/c)}{1 - v/c}\right) \quad (73)$$

which leads to:

$$\Delta f = 2 f_0 \frac{v}{c} \quad for\ v \ll c \quad (74)$$

Example 16.14
How does a Doppler ultrasound measurement change for a blood vessel with a stenosis, i.e., with a constriction?

Solution: We first describe the result of a Doppler ultrasound measurement for a healthy blood vessel. The average speed of the erythrocytes in the aorta is $v \approx 0.16$ m/s while the speed of sound in body tissue is 1540 m/s. Thus, the assumption $v \ll c$ is satisfied and Eq. (74) applies. Assuming a transducer frequency of 5 MHz, an average Doppler shift of about 1 kHz is expected:

$$\Delta f = \frac{2f_0 v}{c} = \frac{2 \cdot 5 \times 10^6 [s^{-1}]\ 0.16 [m/s]}{1540 [m/s]} \quad (75)$$

$$\Rightarrow \quad \Delta f = 1040\ Hz = 1.04\ kHz$$

Since the blood pressure varies, variations in the speed of the erythrocytes during the pumping cycle of the heart are expected. This is illustrated in Fig. 16.41, in which the Doppler shift is plotted as a function of time.

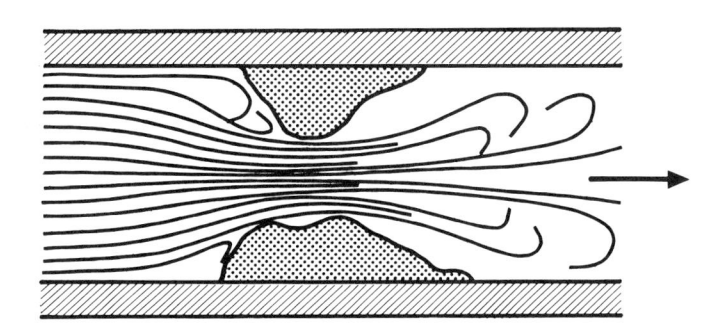

Fig. 16.42: Illustration of the origin of a broadening of the Doppler shift for blood cells passing through a blood vessel with a stenosis.

For a stenosis, a different blood speed pattern is expected. This is indicated in Fig. 16.42. As discussed in Chapter 11, a constriction in a blood vessel causes the flow speed to increase and even to reverse due to turbulence. A range of different erythrocyte speeds exists in each blood vessel section near a stenosis, thus a broadening of the speed versus time curves of a Doppler ultrasound measurement is observed.

16.6. Problems

P–16.1
A wave with frequency 5.0 Hz and amplitude 40 mm moves in the positive x–direction with speed 6.5 m/s. What are
(a) the wavelength,
(b) the period,
(c) the angular frequency?
(d) Write a formula for the wave.

P–16.2
The best way to measure the compressibility of liquids or solids is to measure the speed of sound in the material. If such a measurement for water yields c = 1.4 km/s (which is about four times the value in air!), what is the compressibility of water?

P–16.3
The range of frequencies heard by the healthy human ear stretches from about 16 Hz to 16 kHz. What are the corresponding wavelengths of sound waves at these frequencies?

P–16.4
Bats can detect small insects whose size is about equal to the wavelength of the sound the bat makes with its echo–location system. A bat emits a chirp at a frequency of 60 kHz. Using the speed of sound in air as 340 m/s, what is the smallest insect this bat can detect?

P–16.5
The sound intensity of 1.0×10^{-12} J/(sm²) is the threshold of hearing for human beings. What is the amplitude of the motion of the air molecules? Use c = 340 m/s and the density of air as 1.2 kg/m³.

P–16.6
(a) During a 5 s time period a microphone with an area of 3 cm² receives a sound energy of 1.5×10^{-11} J. What is the intensity of the sound?
(b) Using the sound intensity from part (a), what is the variation in pressure in the sound wave, Δp?
Use T = 293 K and ρ_{air} = 1.2 kg/m³.

P–16.7
A jet airplane has a sound intensity I = 100 J/(sm²) when heard at a distance of 30 m.
(a) What is the maximum sound intensity heard by a person on the ground when the airplane cruises 5000 m above the ground?
(b) What is the intensity level IL heard?

P–16.8
A certain sound has an intensity which is four times the intensity of a reference sound at the same frequency.
(a) What is the difference in the intensity level of the two sounds?
(b) If the reference sound causes a sound perception of 60 phon, what is the sound perception value of the more intense sound?

P–16.9
Why is it not possible for two divers to communicate by talking under water?

P–16.10
Ultrasound echo–location is used by bats to enable them to fly and hunt in the dark. The ultrasound used by bats has frequencies in the range from 60 kHz to 100 kHz. We consider a bat which uses an ultrasound frequency of 90 kHz and flies with a speed of 10 m/s. What is the frequency of the echo the bat hears which is reflected off an insect which moves towards the bat with a speed of 3 m/s?

P–16.11
Table 16.6 presents the frequencies of the eight C keys and the neighboring D keys on a well–tuned piano. When you hit the C and D keys together, for which cases do you expect to hear a beat and what is its frequency?

Table 16.6: Frequencies of piano keys

Octave n	f [Hz]: C_n	f [Hz]: D_n
0	16.35	18.35
1	32.70	36.71
2	65.41	73.42
3	130.8	146.8
4	261.6	293.7
5	523.3	587.3
6	1046	1175
7	2093	2349
8	4186	4699

P–16.12
There is a hypothesis saying that the upper limit in frequency a human ear can hear can be determined by the diameter of the eardrum, which should have approximately the same diameter as the wavelength at the upper limit. If we use this hypothesis, what would be the radius of the eardrum for a person able to hear frequencies up to 18.5 kHz?

P–16.13
Neglecting the additional delay due to the difference in sound pressure levels, we want to verify the statement made in section 16.5.1 that stereoscopic hearing is based on a delay in the time the sound travels to the farther ear. Using Fig. 16.43 for a sound source far from the person, we define d as the distance between both ears and θ as the angle between the direction of the sound source and the direction perpendicular to the line connecting both ears.
(a) Find the formula for the time delay Δt of the sound from the source at very large distance as a function of d and θ.
(b) Calculate the delay for the same sound source at θ = 45° for d = 16 cm.

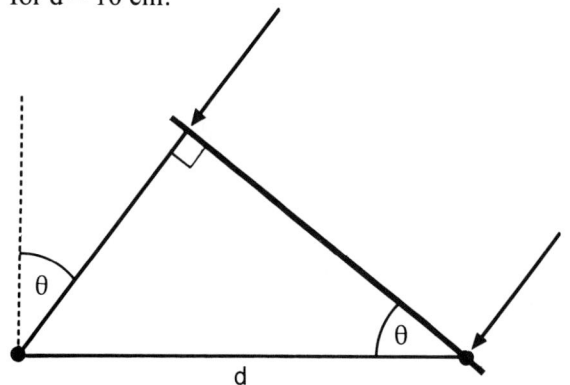

Fig. 16.43 for problem P–16.13

Summary

Definitions:
● One–dimensional harmonic wave function:

$$\xi = A \sin(\omega t - \kappa x)$$

κ [1/m] is the wave number with $\kappa = 2\pi/\lambda$, λ [m] is the wavelength.
● Speed of wave: $c = \lambda f$, with f the frequency in [Hz].
● Energy density ϵ [J/m³] of a sound wave:

$$\epsilon_{tot} = \frac{1}{2}\rho A^2 \omega^2$$

A is amplitude, ρ is density and ω is angular frequency.
● Intensity I [J/(m²s)] of a sound wave, defined as energy passing area A per time unit Δt:

$$I = c\epsilon_{tot} = \frac{1}{2}c\rho A^2 \omega^2$$

c is speed of sound.
● Sound pressure level SPL [dB]:

$$SPL = 20 \log_{10}\frac{p}{p_0}$$

with: $p_0 = 2 \times 10^{-5}$ Pa

● Sound absorption:
(i) for intensity (Beer's law):

$$I = I_0 \, e^{-\beta x} = I_0 \, e^{-x/x_{abs}}$$

I_0 is the source intensity at x = 0, β [1/m] is absorption coefficient, x_{abs} [m] is the absorption length.
(ii) for amplitude:

$$\xi = A_0 \, e^{-\alpha x} \sin(\omega t - \kappa x)$$

ξ is displacement, α [1/m] is decay coefficient for the sound amplitude.

Laws:
● Speed of sound (formula for gases is called Laplace's equation):

$$liquid: \quad c = \sqrt{\frac{B}{\rho}}$$

$$solid: \quad c = \sqrt{\frac{Y}{\rho}}$$

$$gas: \quad c = \sqrt{\frac{C_p\, p}{C_V\, \rho}}$$

- Standing waves for a reflected wave:

$$\xi_{sup} = -\{2A\, \cos(\omega t)\}\, \sin(\kappa x)$$

ξ_{sup} is the displacement in the wave which results from the superposition.
- Harmonics:
(i) allowed frequencies for a closed tube:

	wavelength	frequency
n–th harmonic	$\lambda_n = 2L/n$	$f_n = nc/2L = nf_1$

(ii) allowed frequencies for a half–open tube:

$$f_n = \frac{nc}{4L} \quad \text{with } n = 1, 3, 5, 7, \ldots$$

- Amplitude for resonant coupling of system with negligible damping:

$$A = \frac{F_{max}}{m(\omega_{st}^2 - \omega_{ext}^2)}$$

F_{max} is maximum of periodic force applied to the system, ω_{ext} is angular frequency of external force, ω_{st} is angular frequency of standing wave of system.
- Beats: displacement function for superposition of two waves with same amplitude A:

$$\xi_{sup} = 2A\, \sin\left(\frac{\omega_1+\omega_2}{2}\, t\right) \cos\left(\frac{\omega_1-\omega_2}{2}\, t\right)$$

which defines the superposition amplitude:

$$A_{sup}(t) = 2A\, \cos\left(\frac{\omega_1-\omega_2}{2}\, t\right)$$

- Doppler effect:
(i) for moving receiver (index R), (ii) for moving source (index S), (iii) for receiver and source moving relative to medium:

$$(i) \quad f_R = f_0\left(1 \pm \frac{v_R}{c}\right)$$

$$(ii) \quad f_S = f_0\left(\frac{1}{1 \pm v_S/c}\right)$$

$$(iii) \quad f_{combined} = f_0\left(\frac{1 \pm v_R/c}{1 \pm v_S/c}\right)$$

Chapter XVII

The Eye

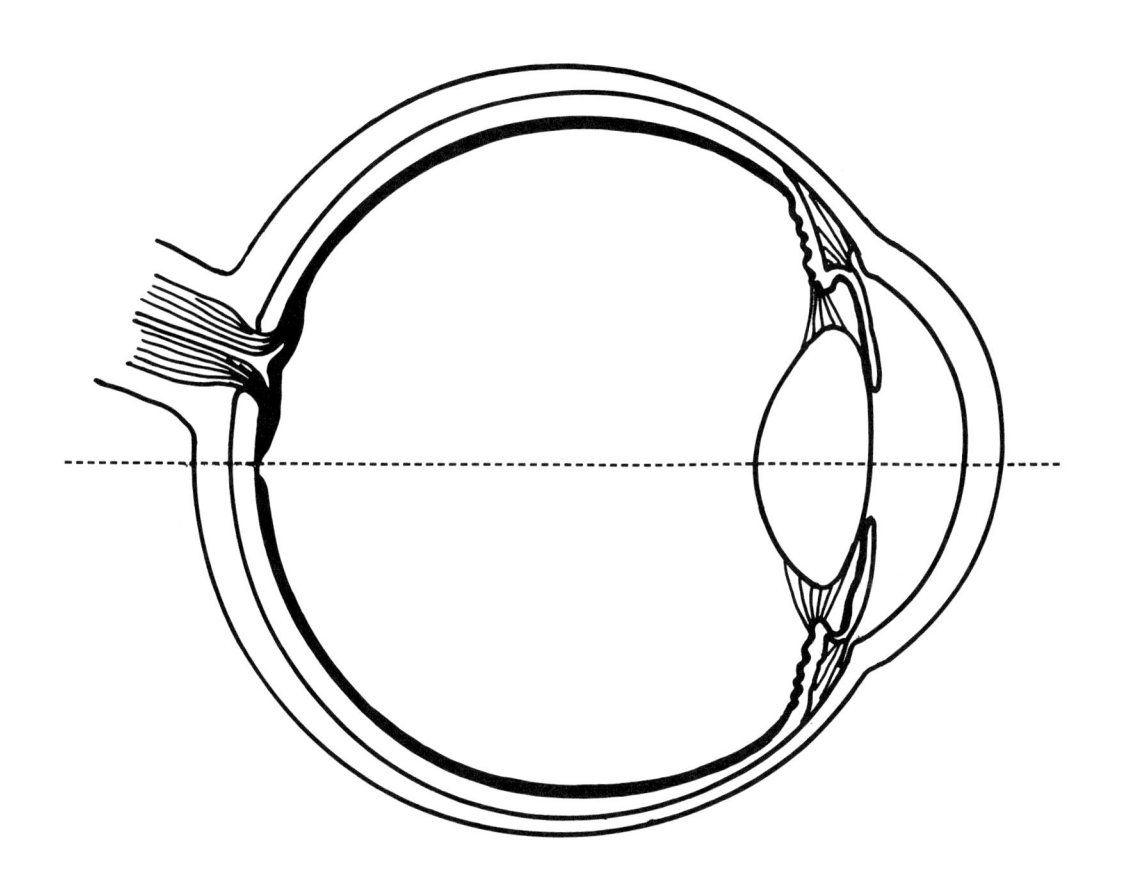

Ray model of light (Geometric optics)

THE EYE
RAY MODEL OF LIGHT (GEOMETRIC OPTICS)

Depending on the experiment, light either behaves like a wave or like a corpuscle (photon). Its basic properties are described with the simpler ray model in which light is assumed to travel along straight lines until it reaches an interface between two different media. At such an interface it will be reflected and/or pass the interface and travel in a new direction (refraction).

Reflection is studied with mirrors. The angle between the incoming and the reflected light rays with the normal direction of the mirror surface are equal. For a spherical mirror, clear images of objects in front of the mirror can form when the mirror has a focal point. The mirror equation relates the inverse focal length to the sum of the inverse object and image distances. The image is magnified if the object is closer to the mirror than the radius of curvature.

When a light ray passes through an interface it travels closer to the normal direction of the interface in the medium with the higher index of refraction (usually the denser medium). If the interface is spherical, an object in front of the interface forms a clear image if the interface has a focal point. Lenses are combinations of two spherical interfaces. The thin lens formula and the equation for the magnification of the lens are identical to the respective equations for the spherical mirror. The inverse focal length of a lens defined as the refractive power of the lens, measured in diopters.

One of the three necessary conditions of life is the recognition of external stimuli and the ability to respond. Arguably one of the most astonishing achievements of the evolutionary process in satisfying this condition is vision. The human eye's complexity in design and versatility in function is extraordinary. The anatomy of the human eye, shown as a side–view cross–section in Fig. 17.1, identifies at least eight individual components required for us to see: light reaches the eye at the cornea (3), then passes through the anterior chamber (2). Its intensity is adjusted by the iris (4) and it is focussed by the lens (1). To accomplish the focussing the lens must be adjusted, which is achieved by the ciliary muscles (6). Before forming an image on the retina (7) the light still

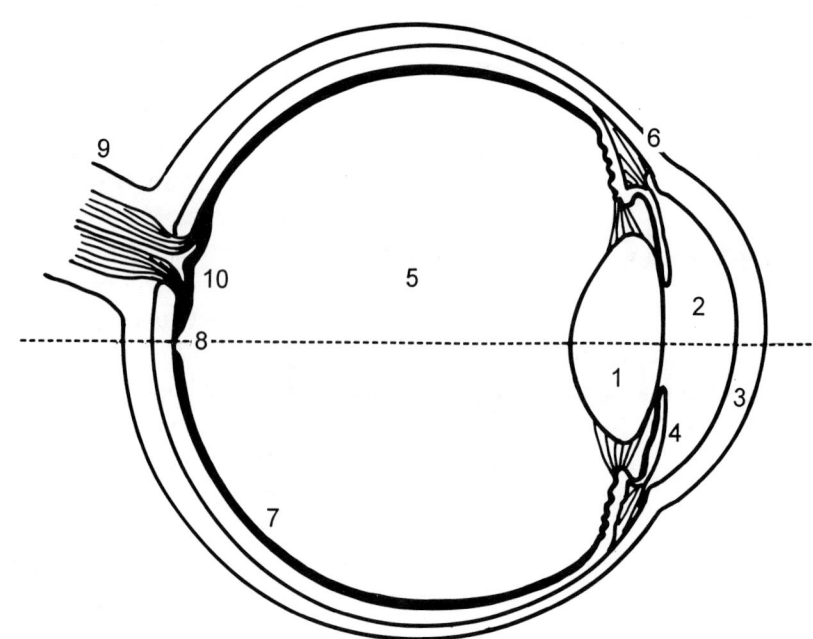

Fig. 17.1: Cross–section of human eye. (1) lens, (2) anterior chamber, (3) cornea, (4) iris, (5) vitreous body, (6) ciliary muscle, (7) retina, (8) fovea centralis and (9) optic nerve. (10) is the blind spot, which is due to the optic nerve passing through the retina to the brain.

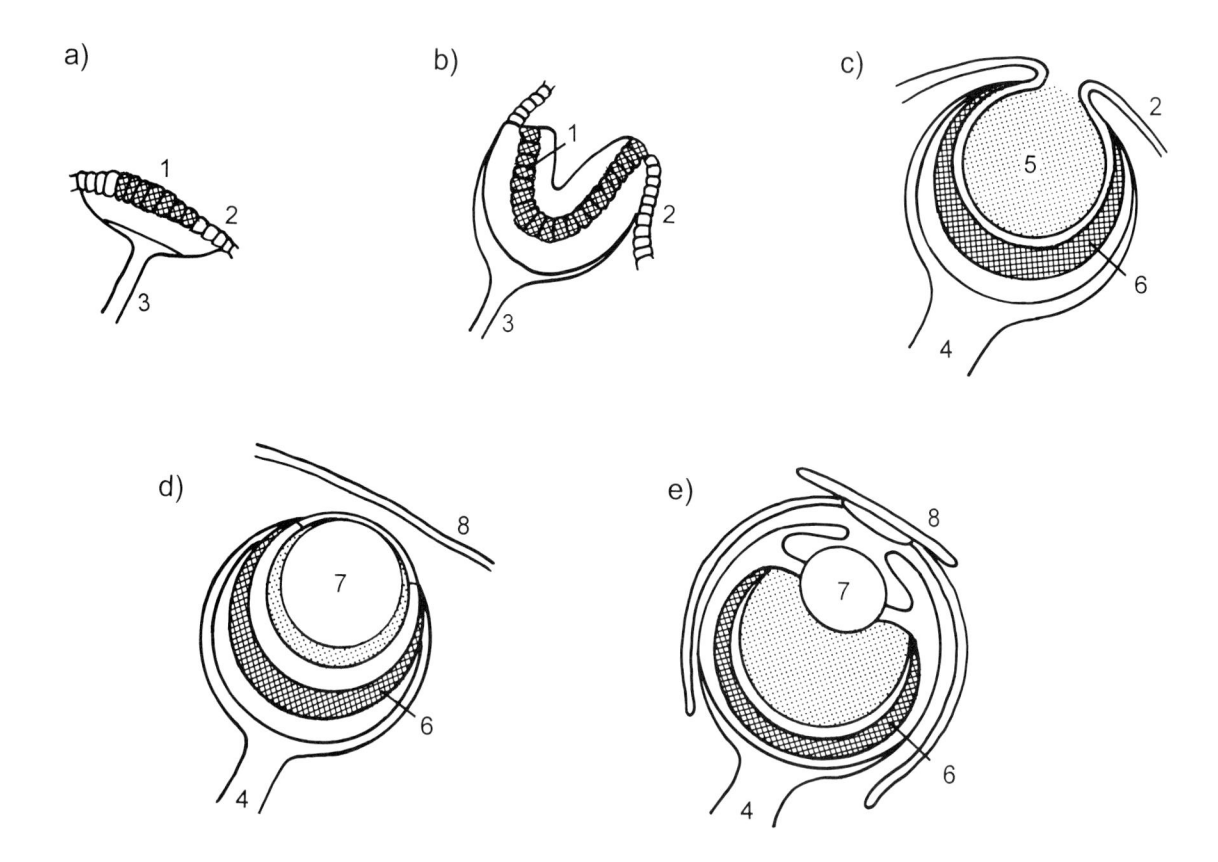

Fig. 17.2: Increasing complexity of the eye of mollusks. (a) The simplest form of a light detector is found for the limpet Parella. A group of pigmented cells (1) act as photoreceptors. These cells are embedded in a patch of regular epithelium cells (2) and are connected with nerve fibers (3) to the nerve center. (b) The same cell arrangement is formed into an eye–cup for protection for the slit shell mollusk Pleurotomaria. (c) The eye of the nautilus functions like a pinhole camera, i.e., a camera without a lens. The cavity is filled with fluid (5) in front of the pigmented layer, which we now call a retina (6). The nerve has evolved in complexity and is labelled an optic nerve (4). (d) Murex is a marine snail that possesses a primitive lens made of cellular fluid (7) and separated from the outside by a transparent epithelium layer, called cornea (8). (e) An eye fully developed like the human eye is found for the squid Loligo.

passes through the vitreous body (5). The retina converts the image into electric signals which are sent to the brain through the optic nerve (9). The interplay of these components allows us to see clearly structures on an object as far away as the moon or to read small letters in a book at just twenty centimeters in front of the eye.

The eye's complex design and its perfect adaption to the purpose of vision had been presented during Darwin's times as strong proof of supernatural creation. Yet, we know of the many improvements light–sensitive organs have undergone during evolution. Fig. 17.2 shows an example for various mollusks. Starting with simple pigmented cells, which serve as photoreceptors, successive steps of cup formation and closure of the cups with a transparent cornea led to the camera–style eye of the squid. These developments took place independent of the development of the human eye, which becomes evident when comparing the approach toward focussing: humans use the ciliary muscles to change the shape of a pliable lens while the octopus moves its lens back and forth.

But does the complex human eye work indeed as precise as an instrument? What does it measure, and how does it measure? Even though we return with these questions to the psychophysical boundary between the exact physical sciences and the subjective psychological perception we discussed before for the hearing process, it is necessary to investigate our vision to understand its limitations.

An interesting hint toward the imperfections of the human vision are the many optical illusions we easily fall victim to. The most stunning examples in-volve color vision and are discussed in Chapter 19. We will then see that optical illusions are never only psychological deceptions, but are linked to an attempt to correct an adverse physical effect. A well–known example is shown in Fig. 17.3. Close your left eye and look at the cross with your right eye. Now bring the textbook slowly towards you. You will notice that the black spot disappears when the distance from your eye to the book is about 30 cm! Continue to bring the textbook closer to your eye. When you come closer than 20 cm the spot reappears. This self–experiment clearly illustrates that part of the image we see is the result of perception rather than fact.

Let's briefly explain the effect of Fig. 17.3. The position of the blind spot in our field of vision is shown in Fig. 17.4. The plot applies to the left eye. Each concentric circle represents an angle increment of 10^0 with the outmost circle corresponding to 90^0. The solid line encloses the field of vision for black–white vision, the other lines enclose the field of vision for various colors. The solid dot at about 15^0 on the temporal side is the blind spot we noticed in the experiment of Fig. 17.3.

You can easily verify Fig. 17.4: close the right eye and look with the left eye straight. Stretch your left arm, bending it slightly behind your shoulder line. Now make fast finger movements as you move the arm in an

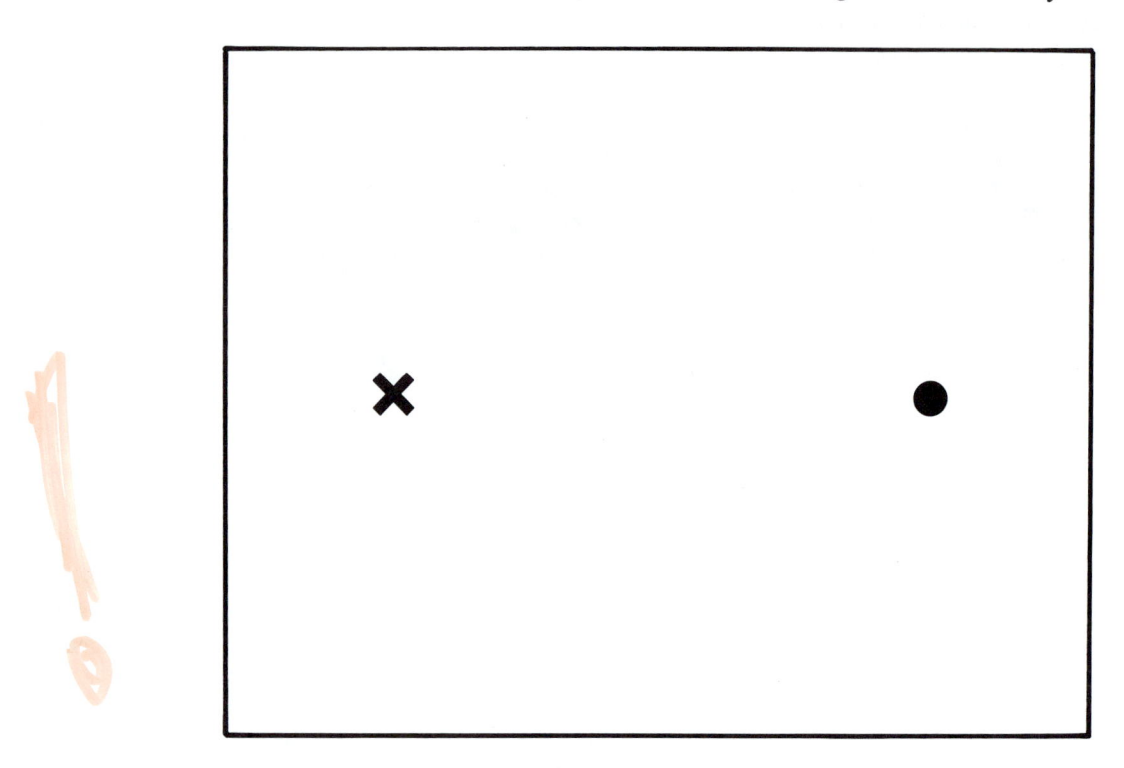

Fig. 17.3: Self–test to illustrate the existence of the blind spot in the field of vision. With the left eye closed look at the cross with the right eye. Move the textbook from about a meter (arm's length) toward you. When the image is at a distance between 20 cm and 30 cm in front of your eye the black dot disappears.

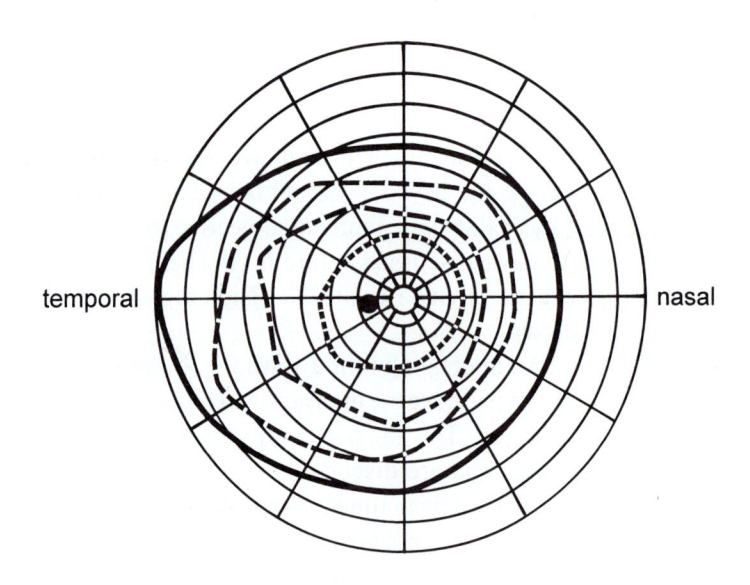

Fig. 17.4: A polar plot illustrating the field of vision for the left eye. The field of vision depends on the color: the largest field applies to black/white vision (solid line), the long–dashed line is for blue vision, the dash–dotted line is for red vision and the short–dashed line is for green vision. The concentric circles correspond to angle increments of 10^0 with the center as the direction in which the person looks and the outmost circle at 90^0 to that direction.

arc slowly forward. You should see the finger movement at the periphery of your field of vision when the arm reaches an angle of about 80^0 to 90^0 with the direction of vision. Now repeat the same experiment with the right arm. This time you have to bring it much further forward before the finger movement is noticed, to about 60^0 with the direction of vision. The asymmetry of the field of vision of the left eye is due to the nose. The combined field of vision of both eyes compensates for this asymmetry.

Leaving the issue of colors raised by Fig. 17.4 to Chapter 19, we want to understand the physical origin of the blind spot, which must be located near the middle of our field of vision. For this we look at the anatomy of the human eye in Fig. 17.1. The area on the retina the light reaches when travelling straight through the center is called the fovea centralis (8) and is the most light sensitive area of the eye. This point is located at the center in Fig. 17.4. The blind spot (10) is the point at which the optic nerve is bundled and leaves the eye. This leads to an area with no vision because the optic nerve has to interrupt the retina to pass through it to the brain.

Like in other cases of optical illusions, our brain corrects for otherwise confusing signals from the eye. In this case, the brain does not allow us to have a black spot near the middle of our field of view. Instead, the brain modifies the image received from the eye by filling in the blind spot based on a best guess before allowing the image to reach our conscience. Usually this works without problems as we move our head and eyes constantly. However, in the case of Fig. 17.3, the uniform white area around the spot is too tempting to not correct for the blind spot by adding a uniform white!

Observations like these motivate us to investigate the fundamental concepts of vision. The benefit of studying these effects, however, surpasses the primary purpose by far: we will learn in Chapters 17 to 19 how to visualize objects too small to see and we will find that the electric concepts we have established in Chapter 9 are part of the fundamental nature of light.

17.1. What is optics?

There are three different models which have been developed to describe various aspects of the physics of light: the ray model, the wave model, and the corpuscle model.

All three models were considered early on. The initial development of the field came in the 17th century when Réne Descartes, Christiaan Huygens and Sir Isaac Newton tried to understand their observations when experimenting with visible light. Already the ancient Greeks thought of light to consist of corpuscles, an idea further developed by Newton. Newton looked at light to consist of a stream of small particles which interact with matter like mechanical objects. At the same time, Huygens promoted a wave model for light, treating light as a propagating wave similar to surface waves on water. In spite of initial problems with that model, such as the fact that light, other than sound, does not need a medium to travel, Huygens' theory was widely adopted from about 1800 to 1905, in particular, after James Clerk Maxwell derived in 1865 the properties of visible light from electromagnetic wave equations.

The corpuscle theory was revived in the early 1900s when Albert Einstein used a corpuscle model (light particles are called photons) to describe the photoelectric effect, which is the ability of light to knock electrons out of solid matter. Our modern view of light is that it has a dual wave and corpuscle character. Therefore, it may be better described by one or the other model depending on the specific experiment. At the same time we have to be aware that neither model grasps all aspects of light by itself!

In this chapter we start our discussion of optics however with a simpler model, called the ray model. This is a greatly simplified model that is applicable as long as the objects involved in the study are not smaller than the wavelength of light which is about 500 nm. The physical laws we derive with the ray model are summarized by the term "geometric optics" because we can construct these features of light with geometrical methods.

> *In the ray model, the assumption is made that light moves along straight lines while travelling within a homogeneous medium. It may change its direction when reflecting and/or passing through an interface to another medium.*

The important features of geometrical optics are established in the current chapter. These include reflection off a mirror and refraction when light passes through a transparent interface. Geometrical optics fails to describe many other light related phenomena, e.g. the existence of colors. Thus, we replace the ray model with the wave model in Chapter 19 to provide a more complete description of light. The wave model of light must be introduced carefully as it differs from the wave concepts we developed for sound in Chapter 16. We consider the corpuscle theory of light in this textbook only later when we discuss light absorption and light emission by atoms and molecules (see Chapter 21).

17.2. Reflection

17.2.1. Flat mirrors

Fig. 17.5 shows the main features of a light ray which is reflected off a planar mirror. The direction of the traveling light ray is shown by arrows. The two features we will use frequently are:

(I) The incoming ray and the reflected ray are in the same plane as the vector directed perpendicular to the mirror surface. This vector is called the normal vector in which the word "normal" is synonymous for perpendicular (in the same fashion as we used the term when we defined the normal force in Chapter 2).

(II) The angle between the incoming ray and the normal vector, α_{in}, is equal to the angle between the reflected ray and the normal vector, α_{out}.

These two conditions constitute the *law of reflection*. It is quantitatively written in the form:

$$\alpha_{in} = \alpha_{out} \quad (1)$$

> *The law of reflection states that the angles between the incoming and reflected light rays with the normal to the mirror surface are equal.*

We use Fig. 17.6 to illustrate how we can use the law of reflection to form an image, as we are used to see it in a flat mirror. We start with a point light source (solid dot at top right). The light source emits light rays which travel along straight lines in all directions. When such a straight line reaches the mirror surface (shown for three rays in the figure), the law of reflection is applied, as illustrated for the center ray in Fig. 17.6. After the reflection, the rays continue to travel along straight lines, until they reach the eye of the observer. Observers can interpret the light rays reaching the eye in two ways. Either they are aware of the presence of the mirror and draws the lines as shown on the right side of the mirror, or they are not aware of the mirror and extrapolates the rays straight to the dashed point source at the left of the mirror, i.e., behind the mirror. At the point where these lines cross each other forms the image of the point light source. The position of the light source (object) and its image are both at a distance d from the mirror. This is a direct consequence of the law of reflection.

We call an image *real* when light rays actually pass through the point at which the image appears. In Fig. 17.6, light cannot physically reach the point where

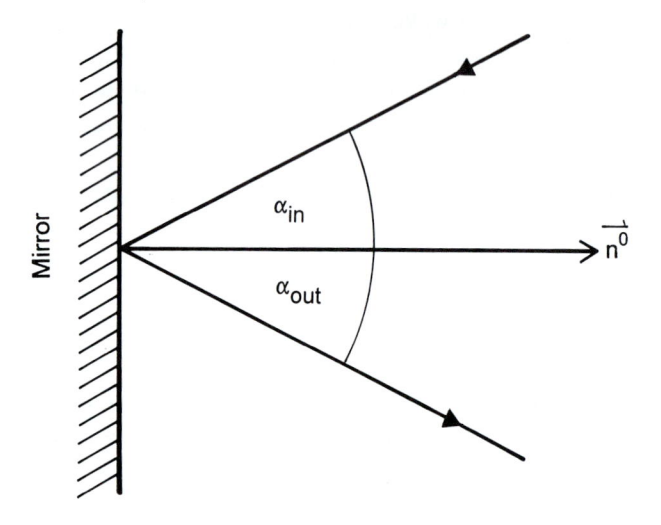

Fig. 17.5: A light ray reflects off a flat mirror. $\mathbf{n}^0$ indicates the direction perpendicular to the mirror surface (normal vector), α_{in} is the angle of the incoming lightray with the normal, and α_{out} is the angle of the reflected light ray with the normal. The two angles are related by the law of reflection.

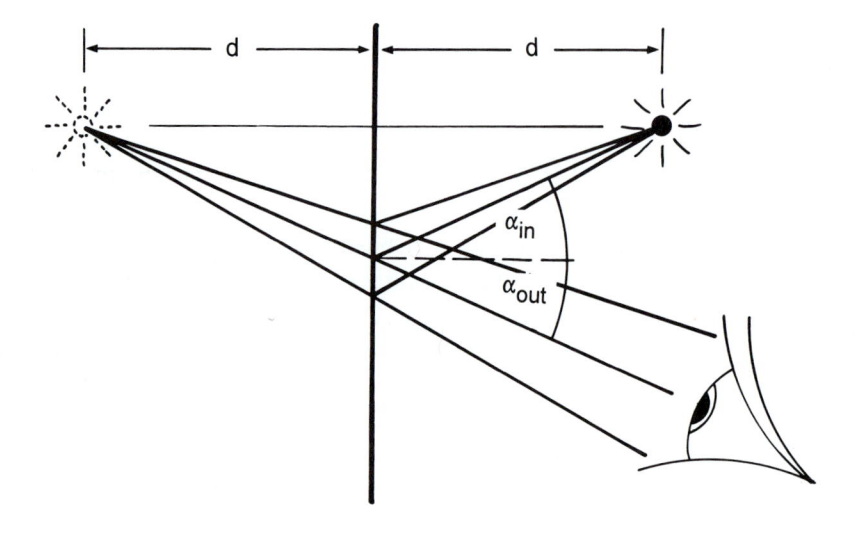

Fig. 17.6: When a person observes a point light source in a flat mirror, a virtual image of the point light source is seen at the same distance d behind the mirror surface. The image of the light source is constructed using the law of reflection, as indicated for the middle light ray.

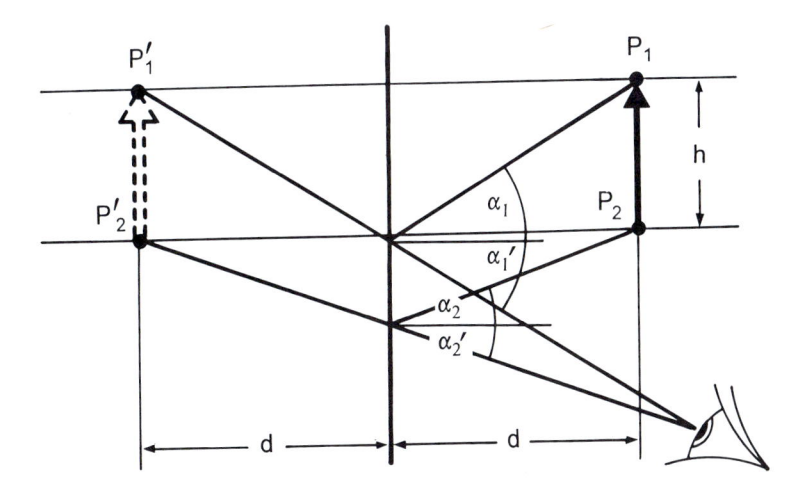

Fig. 17.7: Formation of the image of an extended object in a flat mirror. Light rays from both the top and the bottom end of the object are used to construct the virtual image.

the image appears since a mirror contains a metallic layer which prevents light from passing through. In this case, the image is called a *virtual image*.

In Fig. 17.7 we generalize our choice of object, replacing the point light source of Fig. 17.6 with an extended object of height h (reaching from P_2 to point P_1). The object is still a distance d from the mirror. Using the law of reflection for light rays coming separately from points P_2 and P_1, i.e., $\alpha_1 = \alpha_1'$ and $\alpha_2 = \alpha_2'$, we find that the image in Fig. 17.7 is a virtual image. It appears at distance d behind the mirror. For comparison with later cases, note also that the image is upright, i.e., the corresponding image points P_2' and P_1' are at positions y = 0 and y = h, respectively.

17.2.2. Spherical mirror

Fig. 17.7 also illustrates why a flat mirror is scientifically of limited interest. Unless observers want to look at themselves, for which a mirror is clearly needed, there is little benefit in observing an image which is identical in size to the object itself. This changes, however, when the mirror is no longer flat. Of the many possible shapes of mirrors, we focus in this textbook on the only case of practical importance: the spherical mirror. A spherical mirror is a reflecting surface shaped as a partial sphere. A spherical mirror can be arranged in two ways:

(I) the light rays approach from the side where the center of curvature of the mirror lies, as shown in Fig. 17.8. In this case the mirror is called a *concave mirror*.
(II) The light rays approach from the opposite side of the mirror. In this case the mirror is called a *convex mirror*.

For simplicity, we always use concave mirrors for the discussions in this chapter. This is done with no loss of generality as every relation we introduce applies to convex mirrors in an analogous fashion.

In addition to the center of curvature (point C) and the radius of the mirror (distance R), Fig. 17.8 allows us to introduce the *optical axis*: an incoming light ray defines the optical axis if it passes through C.

We follow several parallel light rays in Fig. 17.8 and use the law of reflection at the point where they hit

Fig. 17.8: Replacing a flat mirror with a spherical mirror does not yield a useful image if light rays reach the mirror which are far from the optical axis compared to the radius of curvature of the mirror. The figure illustrates that the light from an object at infinite distance (parallel incoming light) does not allow us to define a focal point for the mirror.

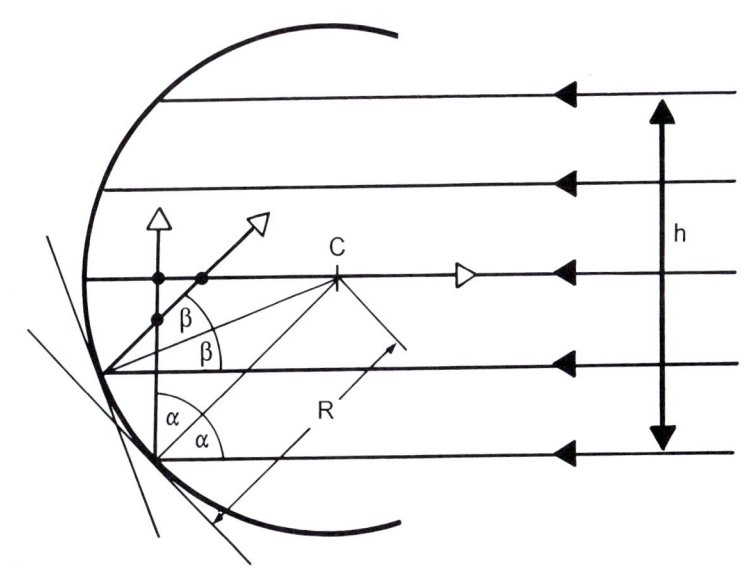

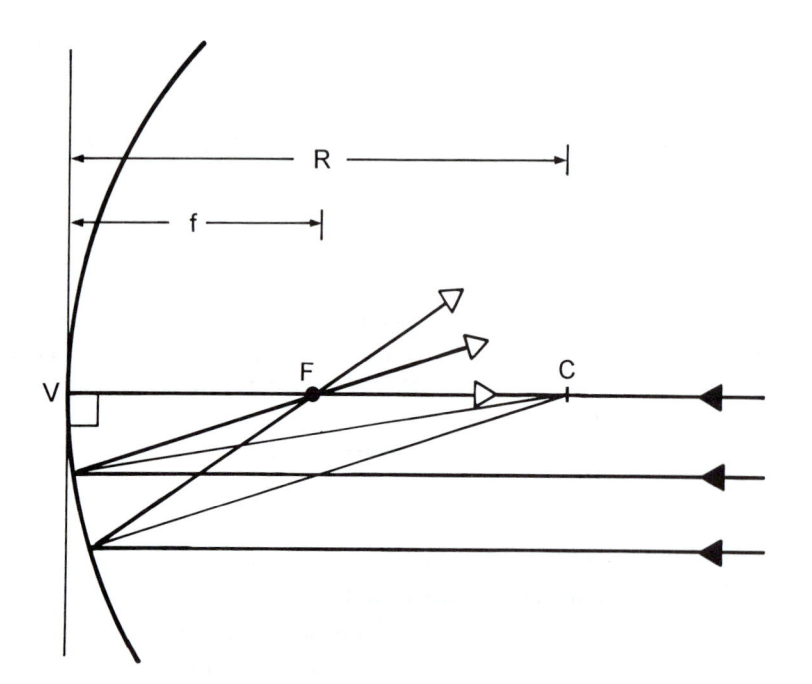

Fig. 17.9: Spherical mirrors can be used to form images if the incoming light rays travel close to the optical axis, i.e., at a distance which is small compared to the radius of curvature of the mirror. Light from an object at infinite distance (parallel light) allows us to define a focal point at the position on the optical axis where all reflected light rays cross.

the mirror. We notice that the reflected rays as shown do not intersect at a common point. We will find such an intersection point very useful in developing the concepts of geometrical optics and dismiss, therefore, the set–up of Fig. 17.8 as not sufficient for the purpose of studying non–flat mirror arrangements. To correct for this problem we need to introduce a further restriction on the mirrors we use.

The additional restriction follows from comparing Fig. 17.8 and Fig. 17.9. The two figures vary only in the distance of the incoming light rays to the optical axis relative to the radius of curvature of the mirror. In both cases we assume that the object is at a very large distance from the mirror (an infinite distance) and that, therefore, the light rays from the object approach the mirror parallel to each other. The three incoming light rays in Fig. 17.9 are all close to the optical axis, while the spread of incoming rays in Fig. 17.8 is almost as wide as the mirror's diameter. As a result, the light rays intersect at a common point in Fig. 17.9. This point is called the *focal point* F and the focal length is the distance from the mirror to the focal point (labelled f).

If in practice the problem of Fig. 17.8 occurs, i.e., when no single focal point exists for a mirror, we call this a *spherical aberration*. To avoid such cases we assume for the remainder of this chapter that the radius of curvature of the mirror is much larger than the spread of the incoming light rays. In experimental set–ups this is usually guaranteed by using apertures. Another way to state this restriction is to say that a focal point must exist, i.e., that all incoming parallel light rays must intersect at a single point F after reflection.

Where is the focal point located for a given mirror? Firstly, the focal point lies on the optical axis. Secondly, the focal point of a spherical mirror is at half distance between the center of curvature and the point V at which the optical axis intersects with the mirror:

$$f = \frac{R}{2} \qquad (2)$$

That this statement is generally true for a spherical mirror is proven with Fig. 17.10, which shows a geometrical derivation of the relation between f and R. The two horizontal lines in the figure are the optical axis and an incoming light ray which is reflected at point P, then passing through point F. The law of reflection gives $\alpha_1 = \alpha_2$.

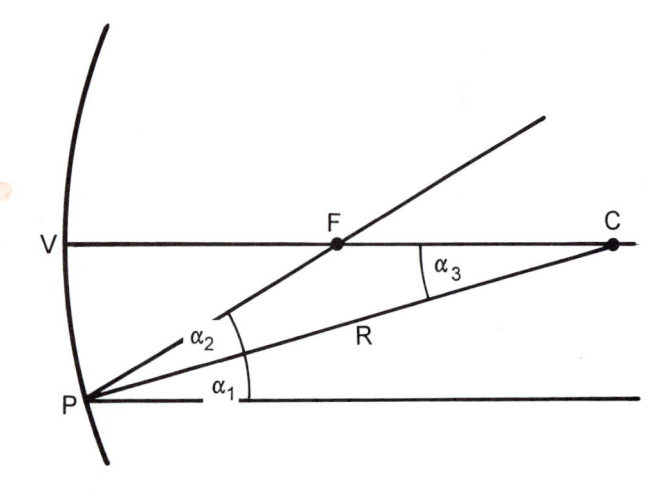

Fig. 17.10: Geometrical construction of the relation between the focal length (length VF) and the radius of curvature (R is the length VC) for a spherical mirror with C the center of curvature of the mirror.

Further we know from geometry that $\alpha_3 = \alpha_1$ because the line PC intersects two parallel lines to form these two angles. Thus, the triangle PFC is isosceles, i.e., the lines PF and FC are equally long. If we now bring the incoming light ray closer and closer to the optical axis, then all three angles α approach 0^0 and VF = FC = R/2. Since VF is the focal length f, we have shown that f = R/2. The need to look at very small angles α reinforces once more the point made for Figs. 17.8 and 17.9 that a focal point exists only when we limit our considerations to light rays that move very close to the optical axis.

Comparing Figs. 17.5 and 17.9 we note that the concave mirror can form an image at a distance different from the object distance. In the particular case of Fig. 17.9, a point light source at infinite distance has generated an image at the focal distance. To develop the properties of a concave mirror further, we consider in Fig. 17.11 an object at finite distance p from the mirror. To find the image in this or similar cases geometrically, three different light rays must be followed, one along the optical axis from the lower end of the object (which is always placed on the optical axis) and two from the upper end of the object. The optical axis is used for convenience to reduce the amount of graphic construction needed. We need two rays from the upper end of the object as the position of the corresponding upper end of the image does not lie on the optical axis. The upper end of the image is then defined as the point at which the two light rays from the upper end of the object intersect.

The two light rays emerging from the upper end of the object are chosen such that one reaches the mirror parallel to the optical axis and the other reaches the mirror after passing through the focal point F. Using these two light rays we can easily construct their path after reflection with the observations we made in Fig. 17.9: the light ray moving parallel to the optical axis passes through the focal point after reflection and, vice versa, the light ray passing through the focal point become rays which moves parallel to the optical axis.

Using these principles, we find that the image in Fig. 17.11 is inverted (upside–down) and real. Defining the distance between the image and the mirror as q we are now able to develop a general relation between the object distance p, the image distance q and the focal length f. This formula is called the *mirror equation* and was derived geometrically by Newton, using h_O as the height of the object and h_I as the height of the image. The argument is based on the geometrical similarity of two pairs of triangles in Fig. 17.11, Δ_1, Δ_2 and Δ_3, Δ_4, respectively, leading to:

$$\begin{array}{ll} \Delta_1 \ \& \ \Delta_2 & f : (p - f) = h_I : h_O \\ \Delta_3 \ \& \ \Delta_4 & f : (q - f) = h_O : h_I \end{array} \quad (3)$$

Eq. (3) contains two relations for h_I/h_O:

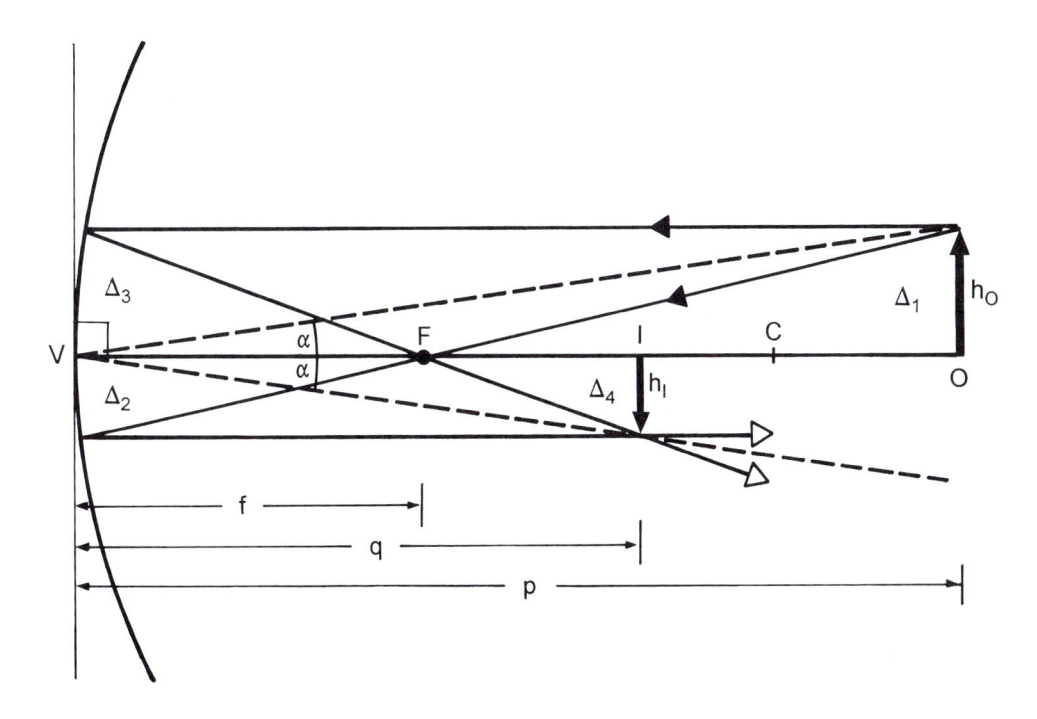

Fig. 17.11: Formation of an image I for an object O at finite distance p from a concave mirror. Three light rays are used to construct the image: one along the optical axis (line CFV) since the bottom end of the object is placed on the optical axis. The second and third rays come from the top of the object of size h_O, with one ray travelling parallel to the optical axis and one ray passing through the focal point F. The image has a size h_I, is inverted and located at the image distance q from the mirror. The various triangles labelled in the figure are used for geometrical constructions in the text.

$$\frac{h_I}{h_O} = \frac{f}{p-f} = \frac{q-f}{f} \quad (4)$$

The second formula in Eq. (4) leads to:

$$f^2 = (p-f)(q-f) = f^2 - (p+q)f + pq \quad (5)$$

where the f^2 term is dropped on both sides to arrive at:

$$pq = (p+q)f \quad (6)$$

Eq. (6) is further rewritten with $1/f$ as the independent variable:

$$\frac{1}{f} = \frac{p+q}{pq} \quad (7)$$

in which the right hand side is further developed into the final form of the *mirror equation*:

$$\frac{1}{f} = \frac{1}{p} + \frac{1}{q} \quad (8)$$

> *The mirror equation connects the focal length of a mirror with the object and image distances.*

An interesting feature of the concave mirror, which is not a feature of the flat mirror, is the possibility of obtaining a magnified image. This is not the result of Fig. 17.11 since $h_I < h_O$. However, if the object in Fig. 17.11 is removed and instead placed where the figure shows the image, then object and image switch places as all light rays can travel along the same path in the opposite direction.

Eq. (4) allows us to quantify the magnification M, which is defined as the ratio of the size of the image to the size of the object:

$$M = \frac{h_I}{h_O} = -\frac{f}{p-f} \quad (9)$$

in which the negative sign originates from the fact that the image in Fig. 17.11 is inverted. The second formula in Eq. (9) follows from Eq. (4). The magnification can alternatively be expressed in terms of the object distance p and the image distance q using Fig. 17.11. Due to the law of reflection, the two angles α_{in} and α_{out}, which are formed by the dashed line in the figure, are equal. From geometry we find:

$$\tan(\alpha_{in}) = \frac{h_O}{p}$$
$$\tan(\alpha_{out}) = -\frac{h_I}{q} \quad (10)$$

which leads to:

$$M = \frac{h_I}{h_O} = -\frac{q}{p} \quad (11)$$

Eq. (11) allows us to establish the cases for which the magnification is larger than one, which are the cases for which the image is larger than the object: $M > 1$ follows for $p - f < f$, which is equivalent to $p < 2f = R$. Thus, the image is larger than the object if the object is placed closer to the mirror than the center of curvature.

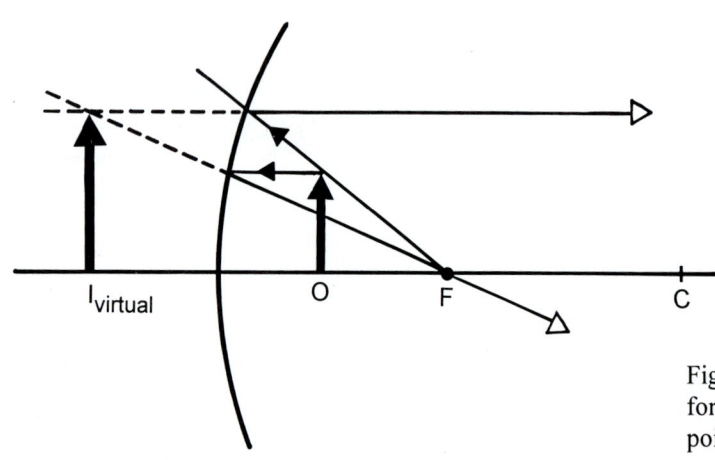

Fig. 17.12: Formation of an upright virtual image for an object closer to the mirror than the focal point. C is the center of curvature of the mirror.

> *A spherical mirror produces a magnified image when the object distance is smaller than the image distance. This requires the object distance to be smaller than twice the focal length.*

If the object is closer to the mirror than the focal point, a magnified but virtual image is formed which is no longer inverted. This case is illustrated in Fig. 17.12. Again, to construct the image, two rays are followed as they emerge from the upper end of the object, one which travels parallel to the optical axis and then reflected through the focal point, and one which travels in the direction away from the focal point and becomes parallel to the optical axis after reflection. These two light rays do not intersect anywhere on the right (real) side of the mirror, but they do intersect on the left (virtual) side of the mirror.

To use the mirror equation consistently in all such cases, Table 17.1 summarizes the sign conventions for mirrors. In this table, as throughout this chapter, p is the object distance, q is the image distance, f is the focal length, R is the radius of curvature of the mirror and M is the magnification as defined in Eq. (11).

You can verify qualitatively several of the possible combinations of parameters in Table 17.1 by using a well–polished table spoon and a small object such as the tip of a pencil. Move the pencil closer and closer to the spoon while observing the changes to the image: its magnification, whether it is inverted or upright, and whether it is real or virtual. By using either the back or front side of the spoon as a mirror you can switch between concave and convex mirrors.

Example 17.1
A dentist uses a mirror to examine a tooth. The tooth is 1.0 cm in front of the mirror, and the image is formed 10.0 cm behind the mirror. Determine

(a) the radius of curvature of the mirror, and
(b) the magnification of the image.

Solution part (a): The focal length of the mirror is found from the mirror equation in Eq. (8) with p = +1.0 cm and q = − 10.0 cm. The image length is negative due to the sign conventions defined in Table 17.1. Thus:

$$\frac{1}{f} = \frac{1}{p} + \frac{1}{q} = \frac{1}{0.01\,[m]} - \frac{1}{0.1\,[m]} \quad (12)$$
$$\Rightarrow f = + 1.11\ cm$$

Thus, the radius of curvature of the mirror is R = 2f = 2.22 cm.

Solution part (b): We obtain the magnification from Eq. (11):

$$M = -\frac{q}{p} = -\frac{-10.0\,[cm]}{1.0\,[cm]} = +10.0 \quad (13)$$

The image is upright because the magnification is positive. This is convenient since this is the way the dentist prefers to look at the image.

17.2.3. Fermat's principle

While the law of reflection is simple and in agreement with experimental observations, it does not reveal any fundamental property of nature. The reason is that it is a descriptive law, only connecting two angles but not relating them to any other physical quantity. It also does not allow us to predict any other property of light rays, e.g. what happens when light passes an interface between two media (e.g. an air–glass interface) as discussed in the next section.

Table 17.1: Sign conventions for mirrors. These conventions are used when the mirror equation is applied.

p is positive	Object is in front of mirror (real object)
p is negative	Object is in back of the mirror (virtual object)
q is positive	Image is in front of mirror (real image)
q is negative	Image is in back of the mirror (virtual image)
f and R are positive	Center of curvature is in front of mirror (concave mirror)
f and R are negative	Center of curvature is in back of mirror (convex mirror)
M is positive	Image is upright
M is negative	Image is inverted

For this reason, a more fundamental justification for the law of reflection was sought. Pierre de Fermat postulated the *Fermat principle of least time*: the actual path of light rays between two points (in the same or different media) is such that it takes less time for the light to traverse this path than it would to traverse any other path. This principle provides a fundamental characterization of light and allows us to derive the law of reflection. It is also intriguingly different from an analogous principle in classical mechanics, which states that any physical object free of external forces travels along the path between two points which is the shortest in length.

17.3. Refraction

17.3.1. Flat interface

Light can pass through transparent media, e.g. visible light passes through window glass. Except for vacuum, the intensity of light attenuates as it passes through any medium, leading to the definition of *optical depth* of the medium. As an example, you have no problem seeing an object at the bottom of a beaker filled with water, but you do not see the ground of a deep lake. Also, you can see the ground through Earth's atmosphere from outer space (e.g. from the Space Shuttle) but you cannot see the surface of Jupiter during a fly–by mission. Still, for short distances, the gases in Jupiter's atmosphere (helium and hydrogen) are transparent to visible light. In the remainder of this chapter we refer to transparent materials with the assumption that the thickness is chosen such that light travels through the material without noticeable loss in intensity.

When light is incident on an interface between two transparent media under a not too steep angle, we observe that a fraction of the light is reflected and a fraction of the light passes through the interface into the second medium. This is illustrated in Fig. 17.13 for a light ray approaching a glass surface from vacuum. The reflected ray obeys the law of reflection of Eq. (1): $\alpha_{in} = \alpha_{out}$. The angle between the direction of the normal vector of the glass surface (along the thin vertical line) and the light ray which has passed through the interface, labelled β in Fig. 17.13, depends on the material forming the interface with vacuum. The relation of this angle to the incoming ray's angle is *Snell's law* (named for Willebrord Snell):

$$\frac{\sin\alpha_{in}}{\sin\beta} = n \qquad (14)$$

where **n** is the *index of refraction*, which is a dimensionless materials constant. Table 17.2 lists indices of refraction for a range of materials. Note that gases have indi-

Table 17.2: Index of refraction for various materials. (The data are measured with light rays of vacuum wavelength 589 nm)

Material	Index of refraction
Solids at 20 °C	
Diamond (C)	2.42
Sapphire (Al_2O_3)	1.77
Fluorite (CaF_2)	1.43
Fused quartz (SiO_2)	1.46
Crown Glass	1.52
Flint Glass	1.61
Ice (H_2O, at 0°C)	1.31
Sodium chloride (NaCl)	1.54
Liquids at 20 °C	
Benzene (C_6H_6)	1.50
Carbon tetrachloride (CCl_4)	1.46
Ethanol (C_2H_5OH)	1.36
Glycerine	1.47
Water (H_2O)	1.33
Sugar solution (30%)	1.38
Sugar solution (80%)	1.49
Gases at 20 °C and 1 atm	
Air	1.00027
Carbon dioxide (CO_2, at 0°C)	1.00045
Vacuum	1.0

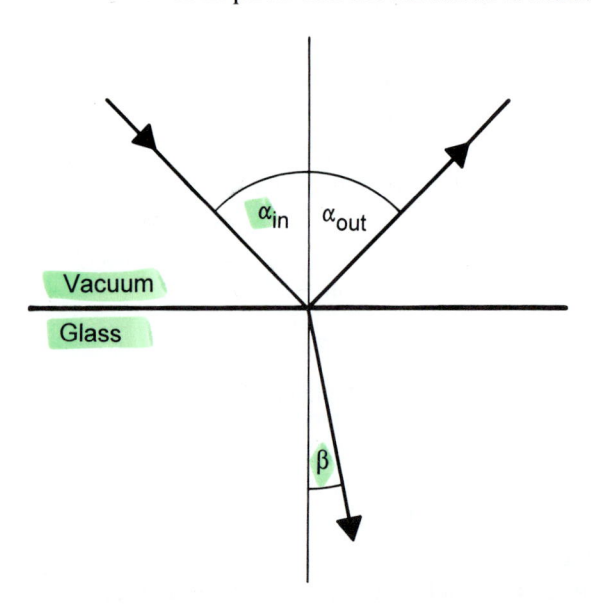

Fig. 17.13: A light ray arriving through vacuum reflects off a transparent glass surface. Part of the light passes through the interface and forms a refracted light ray in the glass. The angles α_{in} and β are related by Snell's law.

ces of refraction very close to the value of vacuum. This is convenient from a practical point of view: we need not to distinguish whether we do the experiment in air or in vacuum, with the latter very expensive to establish and often restrictive to the experimental conditions (e.g., biological systems deteriorate instantaneously in vacuum). The reason for the wavelength restriction in the table caption of Table 17.2 is discussed in Chapter 19 when the effect of dispersion is studied. We can omit this issue from the further discussions in the present chapter.

As Fig. 17.13 indicates, refraction causes light to travel closer to the normal direction in denser materials. Since the path of a light ray is reversible, light can of course also be sent across an interface approaching from the denser medium. Fig. 17.13 shows that in this case the light is refracted away from the normal direction. This allows us to choose an angle β^* such that the angle on the vacuum side becomes 90^0. This is called the threshold angle for *total reflection* since light approaching the interface from the denser side at angles larger than β^* cannot leave into the lighter medium. The threshold angle for total reflection is calculated from Eq. (14). Total reflection is used in fiber–optics to guide light over longer distances without intensity loss.

Note that Snell's law is not the simplest possible mathematical relation, which would be $n = \alpha_{in}/\beta$. The actual law is of course the result of experimental observations when varying the angle α_{in} for a given interface. But we want to know why nature chooses the relation as given in Eq. (14).

The underlying effect is a variation of the speed of light. The speed of light in vacuum is $c = 3 \times 10^8$ m/s. However, when light rays pass through a medium, the light interacts with the medium and that slows it down. With the assumption that light is slower in a dense medium, Fermat's principle applied across an interface from vacuum to a denser medium, in which the speed of light is $v_{light} < c$, yields:

$$\frac{\sin\alpha}{\sin\beta} = \frac{c}{v_{light}} \quad (15)$$

In comparison to Eq. (14) the index "in" of the angle α has been dropped in Eq. (15) since the reversibility of the light ray means that we do not need to specify whether α or β is associated with an incoming beam. Eq. (15) shows that the ratio of the two sine–terms is constant since c and v_{light} are both constant at a given interface. Due to Eq. (14), the index of refraction represents the factor by which the speed of light is lowered in a medium in comparison to vacuum. This index is never smaller than 1 as light cannot be faster in any medium than in vacuum. It can be slowed down considerably, e.g. in diamond by more than a factor of two!

If we replace the vacuum in Fig. 17.13 with a medium with another index of refraction of value $n_2 > 1$, Snell's law is generalized as the *law of refraction*:

$$n_1 \sin\alpha_1 = n_2 \sin\alpha_2 \quad (16)$$

> *A light ray passing through an interface is refracted. The law of refraction connects the angle of the light ray with the normal on both sides of the interface to the two indices of refraction. Snell's law is a special case with one medium being vacuum (or air).*

The conceptual difference between Fermat's principle and Newton's first law of mechanics is particularly obvious when refraction effects are involved. Inuit hunting fish with spears, for example, must aim their spear at a point closer to themselves than where the fish appear which they are hunting. The hunter sees the fish along a light path similar to that in Fig. 17.13 while the spear travels along a straight line once released.

Example 17.2
As shown in Fig. 17.14, a light beam travels through a transparent medium of index of refraction n_1 and then passes through a thick transparent slab with parallel faces and index of refraction n_2. Show that the emerging light ray is parallel to the incident ray.

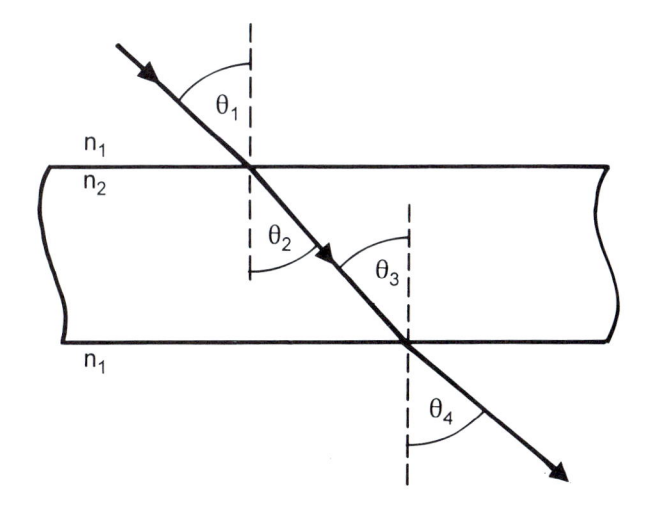

Fig. 17.14: A light ray passes through a sheet of transparent material with index of refraction n_2. The sheet forms two parallel interfaces with an external medium of index of refraction n_1. The four angles shown are used to determine the angle θ_4 at which the light ray leaves the sheet.

Solution: We apply Snell's law in Eq. (14) twice, once at the upper interface and once at the lower interface. Since both interfaces are parallel and the light ray travels along a straight line inside the slab, we know from geometry that $\theta_2 = \theta_3$. Snell's law at the upper interface reads:

$$n_2 \sin\theta_2 = n_1 \sin\theta_1 \quad (17)$$

At the lower interface it reads:

$$n_2 \sin\theta_3 = n_1 \sin\theta_4 \quad (18)$$

Combining Eqs. (17) and (18) and using $\theta_2 = \theta_3$ we get:

$$n_1 \sin\theta_1 = n_1 \sin\theta_4 \;\Rightarrow\; \theta_1 = \theta_4 \quad (19)$$

Eq. (19) confirms the expected result.

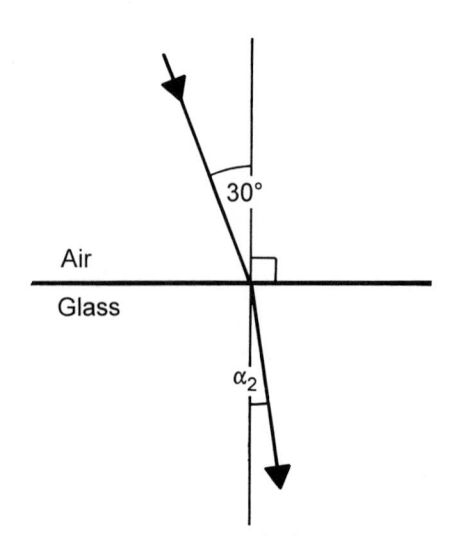

Fig. 17.15: A light ray is refracted at an air–glass interface.

===

Example 17.3
A light ray travelling through air is incident on a flat slab of transparent material. The incident beam makes an angle of 40^0 with the normal, and the refracted beam makes an angle of 26^0 with the normal. Find the index of refraction.

Solution: We use the law of refraction to solve for the unknown index of refraction of the transparent material with the given data and the index of refraction of air of approximately n = 1 (see Table 17.2):

$$n_{slab} = n_{air} \frac{\sin\alpha_{air}}{\sin\alpha_{slab}} = 1.00 \frac{\sin 40^0}{\sin 26^0} \quad (20)$$

$$\Rightarrow n_{slab} = 1.47$$

Would we have to identify the material in this experiment, we would suggest fused quartz from Table 17.2 since glycerine is a liquid.

===

Example 17.4
A light ray travelling through air is incident on a flat slab of Crown Glass at an angle of 30^0 to the normal, as illustrated in Fig. 17.15. Find the angle of refraction.

Solution: The index of refraction for Crown Glass is found in Table 17.2. Using the law of refraction we get:

$$\sin\alpha_{glass} = \frac{n_{air}}{n_{glass}} \sin\alpha_{air} = \frac{1.00}{1.52} \sin 30^0 \quad (21)$$

which leads to:

$$\sin\alpha_{glass} = 0.329 \;\Rightarrow\; \alpha_{glass} = 19.2^0 \quad (22)$$

===

Example 17.5
Find the speed of light in fused quartz.

Solution: We use Snell's law and Eq. (15):

$$\frac{c}{v_{fused\ quartz}} = n_{fused\ quartz} \quad (23)$$

Thus:

$$v_{fused\ quartz} = \frac{c}{n_{fused\ quartz}} = \frac{3 \times 10^8\ [m/s]}{1.46} \quad (24)$$

$$\Rightarrow v_{fused\ quartz} = 2.05 \times 10^8\ \frac{m}{s}$$

This is about 70 % of the speed of light in vacuum.

17.3.2. Single spherical interface

Like in the case of the law of reflection, the more interesting applications of the law of refraction result for spherical interfaces. Spherical interfaces of transparent materials include all types of lenses, e.g. in optical instruments and corrective eye glasses.

Before studying lenses, which have two glass–air interfaces, we first establish the basic relations for a single, spherical interface between air and a transparent medium. We start with Fig. 17.16, showing a spherical slab of material with radius R. The indices of refraction are n_2 at the right side and n_1 at the left side. We choose $n_1 < n_2$. When introducing a point light source O at a distance p from the interface, we automatically define the optical axis as the line passing through O and C, the center of curvature of the spherical slab.

Following the path of light rays from O which are incident on the interface, we observe that they pass through a common point on the optical axis as long as the incident angle α_1 is not too large. This point defines the image I. We calculate the distance q between this point and the interface by using the law of refraction for the spherical interface:

$$\frac{n_1}{p} + \frac{n_2}{q} = \frac{n_2 - n_1}{R} \qquad (25)$$

This equation is derived in the first appendix of this chapter. It allows us to determine one variable parameter in the formula: either the index of refraction, the radius of the spherical slab or the object or image distance from the interface. Based on Eq. (25) the refractive effect of the interface is determined by the term $\Delta n/R$ on the right hand side. This term is the *refractive power* of a single interface and has unit diopter $[dpt] = [m^{-1}]$. We will use this term when single interfaces play a role in an optical set–up, such as the surface of the cornea in the human eye.

> *The refractive power of a single interface is equal to the difference in indices of refraction divided by the radius of curvature of the spherical interface.*

When using Eq. (25), a new set of sign conventions for p, q and R is required, analogous to those for mirrors in Table 17.1. The sign conventions for refracting surfaces are given in Table 17.3.

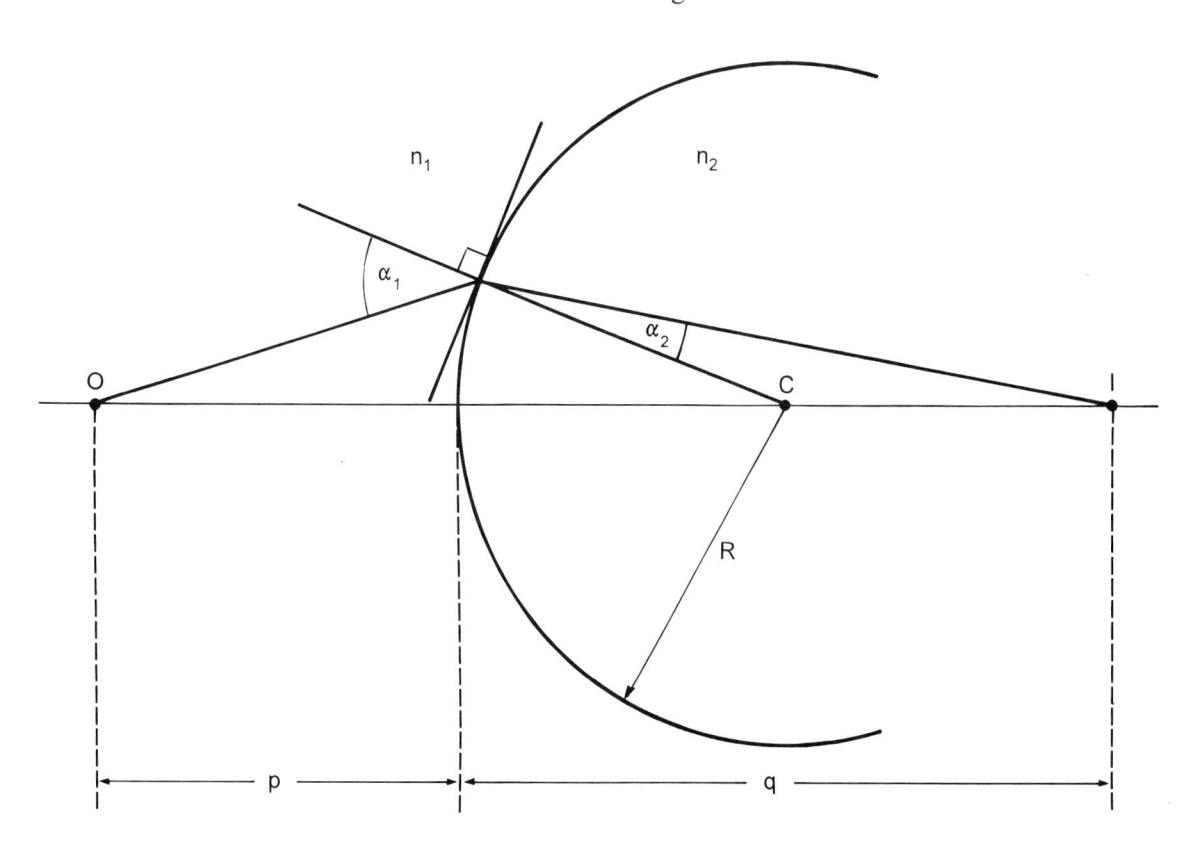

Fig. 17.16: Refraction of the light of a point source O at object distance p from a spherical interface separating two media of indices of refraction n_1 and n_2. C is the center of curvature of the interface of radius R. An image I is formed on the optical axis at the image distance q from the interface.

Table 17.3: Sign conventions for single refracting surfaces.

p is positive	Object is in front of the surface (real object)
p is negative	Object is in back of the surface (virtual object)
q is positive	Image is in back of the surface (real image)
q is negative	Image is in front of the surface (virtual image)
R is positive	Center of curvature is in back of the surface
R is negative	Center of curvature is in front of the surface

Eq. (25) can also be applied to a flat refracting surface by extrapolating in the formulas $R \to \infty$. We find for the relation of object and image distances:

$$\frac{n_1}{p} + \frac{n_2}{q} = 0 \qquad (26)$$

which leads to:

$$q = -\frac{n_2}{n_1} p \qquad (27)$$

Following the sign conventions in Table 17.3, the image and the object are on the same side of the refracting surface as shown in Fig. 17.17. Their respective distance to the interface depends on the difference of the two indices of refraction with the case $n_1 > n_2$ illustrated in (a) and the case $n_1 < n_2$ illustrated in (b).

Example 17.6
A small fish is swimming at a depth d below the surface of a fish–bowl, as shown in Fig. 17.18. What is the apparent depth of the fish as viewed directly from above?

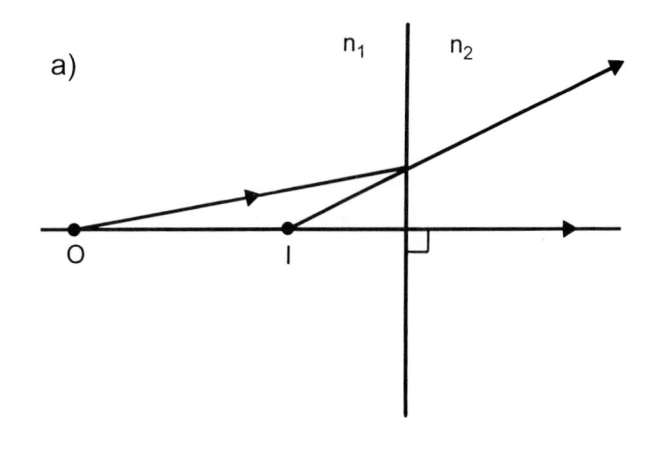

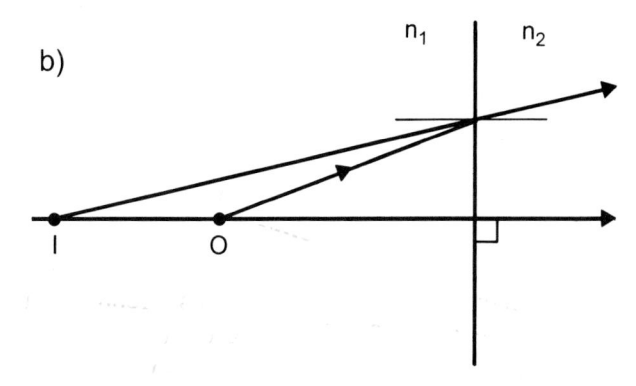

Fig. 17.17: Formation of image I for a point object O for a flat refracting surface. (a) $n_1 > n_2$, (b) $n_1 < n_2$.

Solution: In this problem the refracting interface is flat and the object is in the denser medium, which is the medium with the higher index of refraction. This case corresponds to Fig. 17.17(a). We apply Eq. (27) with the indices of refraction $n_2 = 1$ (for air) and $n_1 = 1.33$ (for water) to find the image distance:

$$q = -\frac{n_2}{n_1} p = -\frac{1}{1.33} d = -0.75\, d \qquad (28)$$

The apparent depth of the fish is 3/4 of the real depth.

The index of refraction may also change gradually rather than abruptly. Based on the same refraction principles we discussed above a curved path of the light is derived. A well–known phenomenon of this type is the apparent wetness of the asphalt ahead of your car when driving in the hot summer sun. What you actually see is an image of the sky as the heat radiating from the asphalt increases the temperature of the air immediately above the road surface, which causes a reduction in the index of refraction. Thus, for light to require a minimum time from the sky to your eye it travels first toward the asphalt and then along the road surface, although this is the longer path (Fermat's principle).

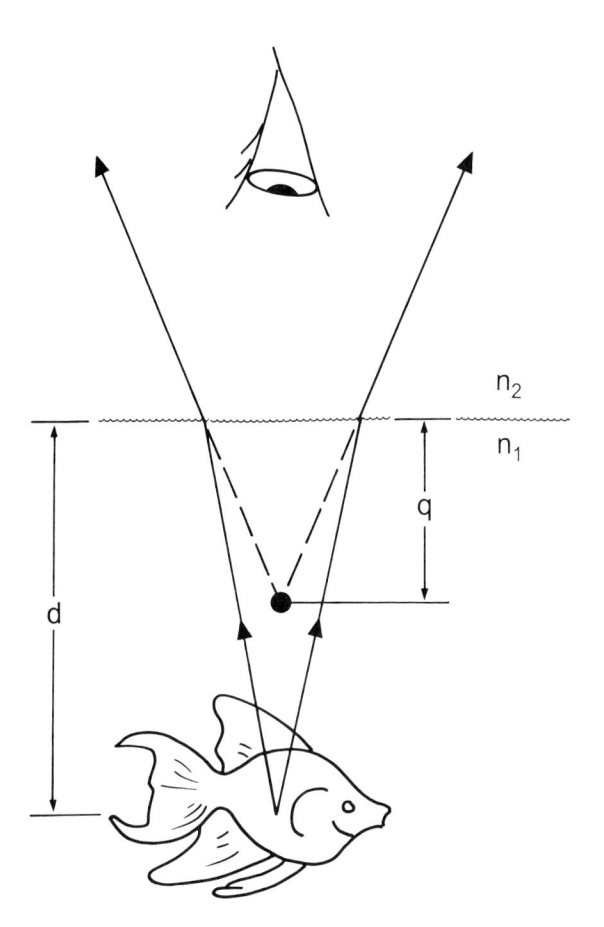

Fig. 17.18: A fish is observed from a position vertically overhead.

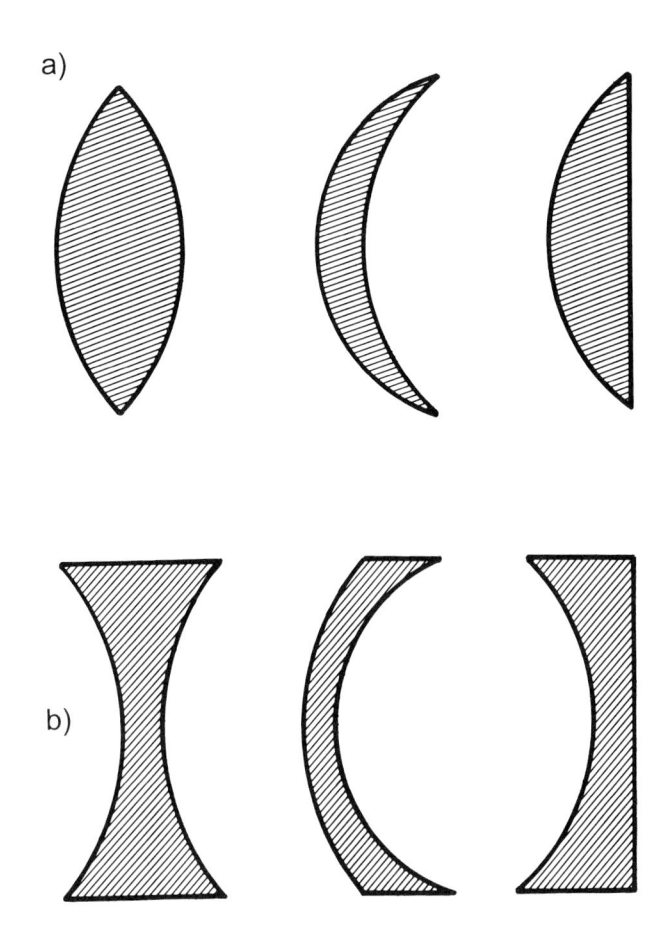

Fig. 17.19: Various types of commonly used lenses.
(a) Converging lenses which are thicker at the optical axis than toward the edges.
(b) Diverging lenses which are thinner at the optical axis.

17.3.3. Lenses

We now turn our attention to lenses. Lenses represent a combination of two refracting surfaces. Light passes through both surfaces before an image is formed. Lenses come in many shapes, as illustrated in Fig. 17.19. All lenses have in common partially spherical or flat refracting surfaces. They are characterized by two physical parameters:
(I) lenses are grouped as either converging lenses (Fig. 17.19(a)) or diverging lenses (Fig. 17.19(b)), based on their effect on incoming light rays, and
(II) lenses are distinguished as thick lenses or thin lenses, based on their thickness in relation to other lengths, such as the object and image distances.

In this textbook, we limit our discussion to thin lenses and choose mostly converging lenses for the examples. The discussion of diverging lenses is entirely analogous though, and therefore a duplication of the presentation is omitted without loss of generality. The discussion of thick lenses would lead to mathematically complicated

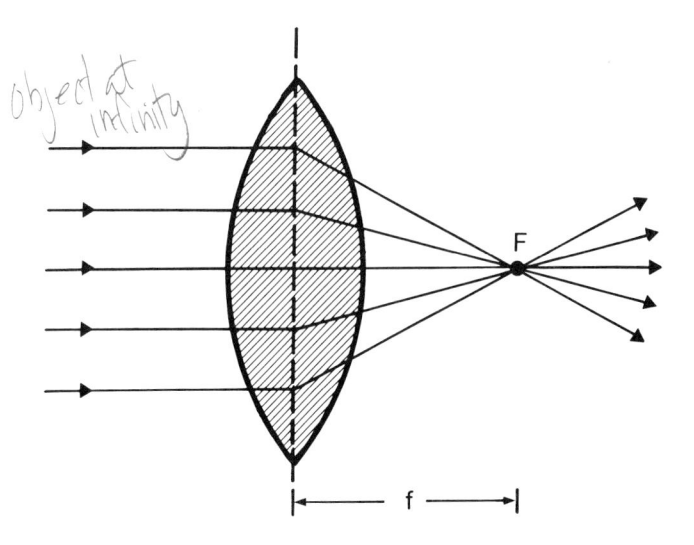

Fig. 17.20: Definition of the focal point for a converging lens. As in the case of the mirror, parallel incoming light rays are used, such as light rays from an object at infinite distance. F is the focal point and f is the focal length. The lens is a thin lens which is indicated by the dashed vertical line at which the refraction is drawn in a single step.

formulas, but does not provide any further fundamental insights. Also, most applications of lenses in the life sciences are based on thin lenses.

We first reintroduce the concept of a focal point for the lens. Fig. 17.20 shows several parallel incoming light rays, as in Fig. 17.9, in which we defined the focal point for a mirror. Incoming parallel light rays correspond to a light source (object) at infinite distance. The focal point is the point (if it exists) at which all these light rays intersect, i.e., where they form a point image of the light source. This approach allows us to define a focal point F and a focal length f for a lens since light rays not too far from the optical axis do indeed intersect at a single point on the optical axis in Fig. 17.20.

Fig. 17.20 also illustrates an important simplification for thin lenses: instead of treating each interface individually, a dashed line is drawn perpendicular to the optical axis at the center of the lens. In the geometrical construction, the direction of any light ray incident on the lens is changed only once at this line.

We use three light rays to determine the position and size of images, like we did in the case of mirrors:
(I) a light ray travelling along the optical axis,
(II) a ray incident on the lens along a path parallel to the optical axis, and
(III) a ray incident on the lens after passing through the focal point.

How this approach allows us to construct the image of an object at finite distance from the lens is shown in Fig. 17.21. The object O of height h_o is placed at distance p to the left of a thin converging lens. The image is constructed by placing one end of the object on the optical axis. Two light rays are followed from the upper end of the object. The ray parallel to the optical axis is refracted through the focal point on the right side of the set-up, i.e., the side of the lens opposite to the object, passing through the optical axis at that point with an angle θ. A second ray emerging from the upper end of the object passes through the focal point at an angle φ on the left side, which is the same side of the lens on which the object is located. This ray becomes a light ray travelling parallel to the optical axis beyond the lens. Both light rays emerging from the upper end of the object intersect at a distance q from the lens, defining the upper point of the image I. This point determines the height of the image, h_I.

We first derive the magnification of a thin lens from Fig. 17.21. To allow for a simple geometric derivation, a light ray is drawn from the top of the object to the top of the image (dashed line), crossing the optical axis at the center of the lens and defining an angle α on both sides. We find $\tan \alpha = h_o/p$ for the triangle on the left side of the lens and $\tan \alpha = -h_I/q$ for the triangle on the right side of the lens. Thus, using the definition of the magnification from Eq. (26), we get:

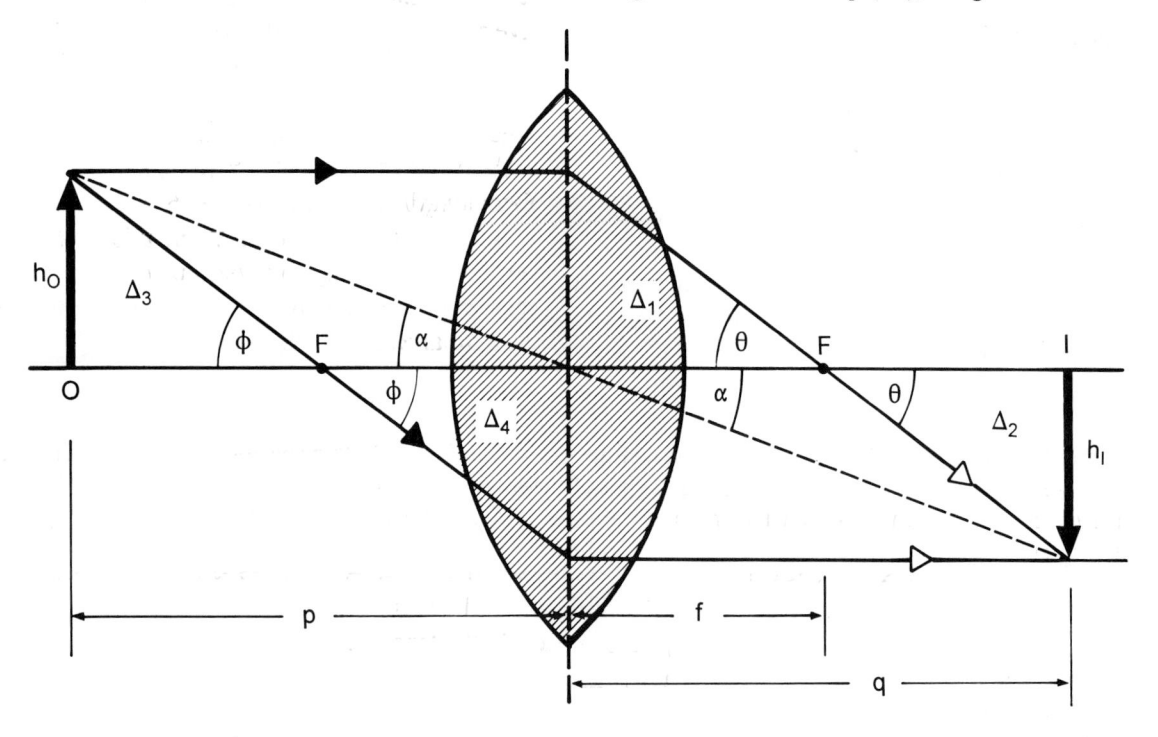

Fig. 17.21: Construction of the image I at image distance q for an object O at object distance p from a converging lens. The lens is a thin lens with the refraction drawn at the dashed vertical line. F indicates the focal point. Note that only three rays are needed to find the image size h_I: (I) a light ray along the optical axis from the bottom end of the object, (II) a light ray travelling from the top of the object parallel to the optical axis, then refracting through the focal point, and (III) a light ray travelling through the focal point and proceeding parallel to the optical axis after refraction.

$$M = \frac{h_I}{h_O} = \frac{-q\,\tan\alpha}{p\,\tan\alpha} = -\frac{q}{p} \qquad (29)$$

which is the magnification of the lens, and, conveniently, is the same formula that we obtained for the concave mirror in Eq. (11).

Using Fig. 17.21 further, we also develop a relation between the various distances relevant for the refraction of a lens, i.e., p, q and f. To do this, we start with the two triangles labelled Δ_1 and Δ_2 in the figure. Δ_1 and Δ_2 are similar, since both contain the angle θ. From the geometrical relations for the triangles we find:

$$\Delta_1: \quad \tan\theta = \frac{h_O}{f}$$
$$\Delta_2: \quad \tan\theta = \frac{-h_I}{q-f} \qquad (30)$$

which leads to:

$$\frac{h_I}{h_O} = -\frac{q-f}{f} \qquad (31)$$

Using Eqs. (29) and (31), we find:

$$-\frac{q}{p} = -\frac{q-f}{f} \qquad (32)$$

which is rewritten as:

$$\frac{q}{p} = \frac{q}{f} - 1 \qquad (33)$$

and finally leads to:

$$\frac{1}{p} + \frac{1}{q} = \frac{1}{f} \qquad (34)$$

Eq. (34) is called the *thin lens formula* and, again, is the same formula we found earlier for the spherical concave mirror in Eq. (8).

> *The formulas for the magnification and for the relation between focal, object and image lengths are the same for spherical mirrors and lenses.*

The thin lens formula is also closely related to the *lens maker's equation* which is discussed in the second appendix of this chapter. Note that the left hand side of Eq. (34) connects the object and image distances of a lens; the right hand side is therefore a measure of the ability of the lens to refract the light. Using this observation, the *refractive power of a lens* $\Re$ is defined in the form:

$$\Re = \frac{1}{f} \qquad (35)$$

Note that Eq. (35) combines the effect of two refractive interfaces. For each single interface the refractive power had been defined in section 17.3.2 as $\Delta n/R$ with R the radius of curvature of a spherical interface. Eq. (35) is consistent with that definition, i.e., the combined refractive power of two spherical interfaces, which is the sum of two $\Delta n/R$ – terms, is equal to the inverse focal length of the lens formed by the two interfaces.

All formulas derived in this section for converging lenses apply to diverging lenses as well. In both cases a set of sign conventions must be followed which is summarized in Table 17.4.

Table 17.4: Sign conventions for thin lenses. These conventions are used when the thin lens formula and related relations for thin lenses are applied. Note two radii: R_1 is the radius of curvature of the front surface of the lens and R_2 is the radius of curvature of the back surface of the lens. These are used when the Lens maker's equation (introduced in the Appendix of the chapter) is applied.

p is positive	Object is in front of the lens
p is negative	Object is in back of the lens
q is positive	Image is in back of the lens
q is negative	Image is in front of the lens
R_1 and R_2 are positive	Center of curvature for each surface is in back of the lens
R_1 and R_2 are negative	Center of curvature for each surface is in front of the lens
f is positive	Converging lens
f is negative	Diverging lens

> *The refractive power of a lens $\Re$, in unit [dpt] (diopters), is equal to the inverse of the focal length of a thin lens.*

Example 17.7
A converging lens of focal length f = 10 cm forms images of objects at (a) 30 cm, (b) 10 cm, and (c) 5 cm from the lens. In each case, find the image distance and describe the image.

Solution part (a): Substituting the given values in the thin lens formula in Eq. (34) and the magnification formula in Eq. (29) we find:

$$\frac{1}{10[cm]} = \frac{1}{30[cm]} + \frac{1}{q} \Rightarrow q = 15\ cm$$

$$M = -\frac{q}{p} = -\frac{15[cm]}{30[cm]} = -0.5$$

(36)

A positive q value means that a real image is formed on the side of the lens opposite to the object. The image is half the height of the object and is inverted (due to the negative sign of M). This case is shown in Fig. 17.22(a).

Solution part (b): Replacing p = 30 cm with p = 10 cm in Eq. (36) leads to q = ∞. Note that this case is equivalent to the situation in Fig. 17.20, where an object at the focal length has an image at infinite distance.

Solution part (c): In the third case the object lies inside the focal length. Replacing p = 30 cm with p = 5 cm in Eq. (36) leads to:

$$\frac{1}{10[cm]} = \frac{1}{5[cm]} + \frac{1}{q} \Rightarrow q = -10\ cm$$

$$M = -\frac{q}{p} = \frac{10[cm]}{5[cm]} = 2.0$$

(37)

This result is illustrated in Fig. 17.22(b). The negative image distance represents an image on the same side of the lens as the object (virtual image). A positive magnification M > 1 means that the image is enlarged and upright.

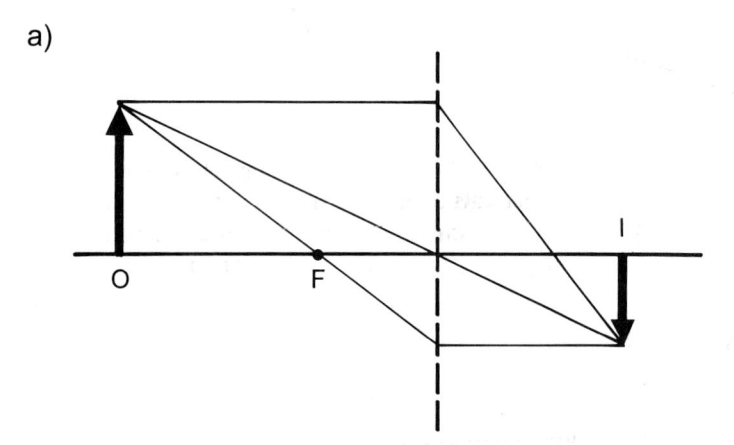

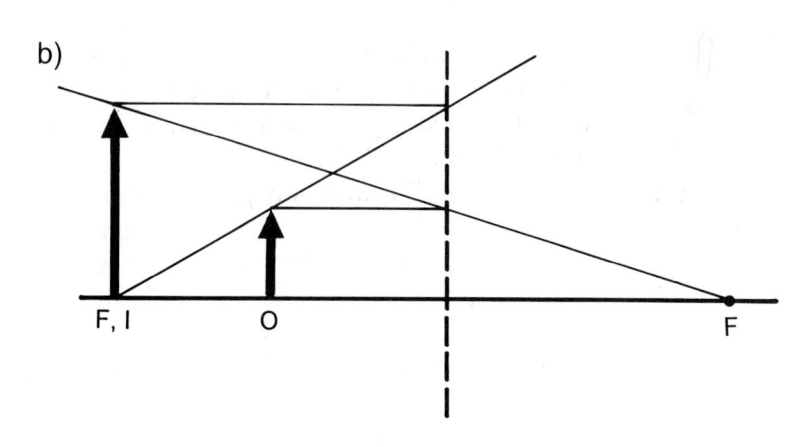

Fig. 17.22: (a) Sketch of an image I formed for an object O located at a distance larger than the focal length from the lens. Note that, for convenience, the thin lens is not drawn but represented by a dashed vertical line. Note that the three rays shown allow us to construct the image. (b) Sketch of an image I formed for an object O located at a distance closer than the focal length from the lens. Like in part (a), the thin lens is only drawn as a dashed vertical line. Again, three rays allow us to construct the image.

17.4. Applications in the life sciences

There are two main areas of application of the ray model of optics in physiology: vision and microscopy. We discuss both in this textbook, beginning with the healthy eye in this section. We then proceed to the most common eye defects and their corrections. The discussion of light and electron microscopes, which allow us to see objects too small to observe with the naked eye, follows in Chapter 18.

17.4.1. The eye

Fig. 17.1 is a sketch of the side–view cross–section of a human eyeball. The optically active parts of the eye are the cornea and the lens. The cornea contains a convex external interface (facies externa) and a concave internal interface (facies interna). It has a small radius of curvature of about 7.8 mm and bridges the biggest difference in indices of refraction, from n = 1.0 of air to n ≅ 1.33, with the latter close to the index for water. Thus, the cornea provides the biggest fraction of the refractive power of the eye with $\Delta n/R \cong 40$ dpt.

The lens is suspended by fibers (suspensory ligament of the lens or zonula ciliaris) which in turn are stretched or loosened by the ciliary muscle. The iris controls the opening of the lens around the optical axis, allowing light to pass only through the visible area of the lens, called the pupil. The iris can vary the diameter of the pupil to adjust the total light intensity reaching the retina.

The lens is a transparent, pliable, biconvex body with an index of refraction of n = 1.41. The elastic variation of the lens is illustrated in Fig. 17.23, which allows for a refractive power change between $\Re = 18$ dpt and $\Re = 32$ dpt. When the ciliary muscle is relaxed (lower part of Fig. 17.23) the suspension fibers of the lens are stretched and the lens is elongated. This leads to a flatter surface with increased radius of curvature and reduced refractive power $\Re$. When the relaxed eye looks at an object at an infinite distance (p ≥ 60 m) its focal length is calculated from the two contributions to the refractive power of the eye:

$$\Re_{eye} = \Re_{lens} + \left(\frac{\Delta n}{R}\right)_{cornea} = \quad (38)$$

$$40[dpt] + 18[dpt] = 58 \; dpt$$

which results in f = 1.7 cm.

While focussing up close, as is illustrated in the

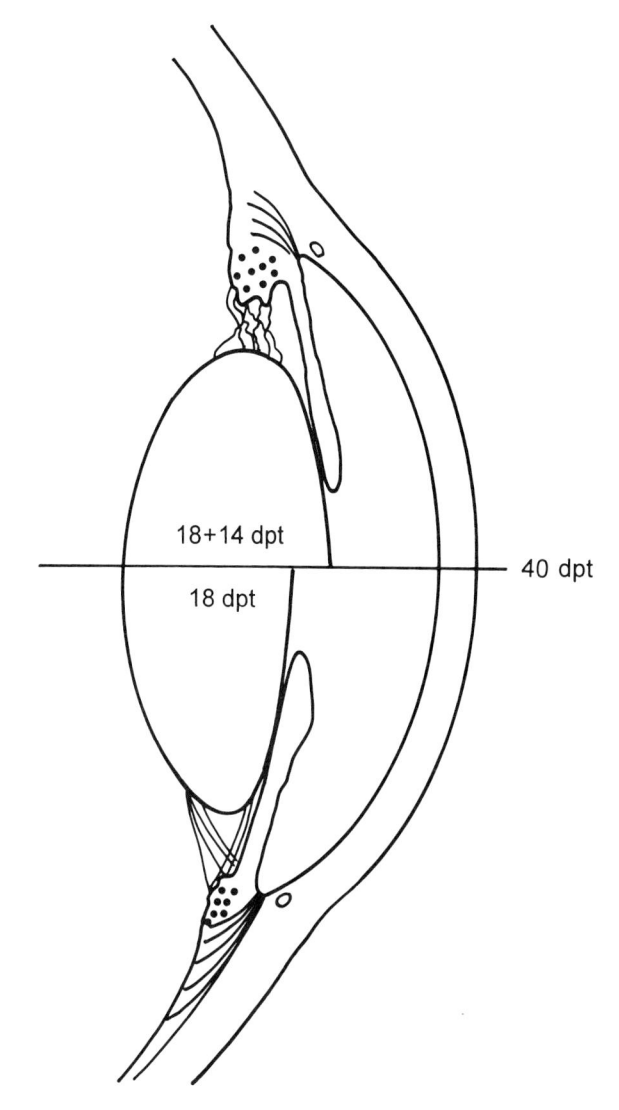

Fig. 17.23: Anatomy of the lens, the ciliary muscles and ligaments of the human eye: note the changes of these three components between close vision (top half of figure) and far vision (bottom half of figure). The cornea has a fixed refractive power of 40 dpt to which the lens adds a refractive power between 18 dpt and 32 dpt.

upper part of Fig. 17.23, the ciliary muscle is contracted, relaxing the suspension fibers and allowing the lens to contract in response to its elasticity. The surfaces of the contracted lens have smaller radii of curvature, and thus, a larger refractive power. The process of changing the refractive power of the lens due to ciliary muscle action is called accommodation.

The ability to view objects close up deteriorates with age due to the sclerosing effects of the lens. Physiologically, this is quantified by defining the *near point*. The near point is the shortest object distance p for which the human eye produces a sharp image on the retina. Table 17.5 shows how the near point distance changes as a function of age.

Table 17.5: Near point as a function of age.

Age	Near point
10 years	7 cm
20 years	9 cm
30 years	12 cm
40 years	22 cm
50 years	40 cm
60 years	100 cm
70 years	400 cm
> 75 years	∞

17.4.2. Eye defects and diseases

There are six commonly occurring deviations from a healthy eye listed below. Two are discussed in greater detail as examples of how prescription eyeglasses are used to correct vision deficiencies.

Astigmatism
A point light source (object) leads to an elongated image on the retina, as sketched in Fig. 17.24. This is usually caused by a difference between the horizontal and vertical radius of curvature of the cornea. Astigmatism is often inborn and inherited. Some exceptions are due to cornea injury. Glasses with asymmetric lenses correct this deficiency.

Example 17.8
An art historian has claimed that Domenikos Theotokopoulos, famous under the name El Greco, must have been highly astigmatic since he painted people and their faces unnaturally elongated. Does this argument make sense?

Solution: No. Assume that El Greco (1541 – 1614) intended to paint his models as he saw them. In this case he would only have been satisfied with his work once the painted image looked exactly like the model. Thus, he would have painted the image without distortions no matter whether he suffered from an astigmatism. If he suffered from astigmatism, he might have seen the model elongated, but his painting would only have looked right to him when it would have shown to him the same elongation. The same elongation requires that the actual image (as we see it) is perfect in proportions.

El Greco was a Crete born painter, living in Toledo, Spain (thus his name). The elongated distortions of humans and human faces in his paintings were intentional and are associated with his association with the school of Mannerism, a style developed by Raphael's students in Rome after 1520, reflecting on a highly cultivated religious spirituality.

Cataracts
The lens becomes cloudy and eventually opaque. This condition is usually inborn or caused by traumatic injury, diabetes, old age, or as a side effect of diseases. It requires surgical removal or exchange of the lens.

Glaucoma
Glaucoma is a collective term for various eye diseases associated with an increase in the fluid gauge pressure in the eye from an average normal value of 2.0 kPa to values between 6.7 kPa and 10.7 kPa (acute case). Glaucoma is often treatable with drugs.

Graves' disease
The eyeball is pushed forward usually due to thyroiditis, which is a thyroid inflammation.

Hyperopia
Hyperopia is an eye defect associated with an insufficient elasticity of the lens, leading to an incomplete reshaping when the suspension fibers of the lens are relaxed. As a result, the refractive power of the lens, $\Re$ = 32 dpt in Fig. 17.23, is not reached and the eye cannot form an image on the retina of nearby objects.

Hyperopia is illustrated in Fig. 17.25. Part (a) shows the optical properties of a hyperopic eye when observing an object at great distance. The ciliary muscle is relaxed, the suspension fibers and the lens are stretch-

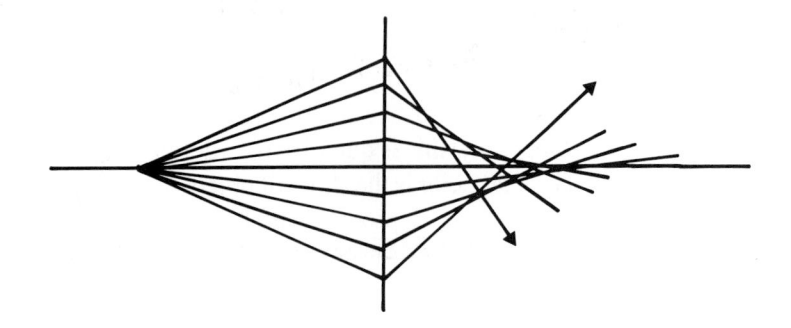

Fig. 17.24: Sketch to illustrate the effect of astigmatism on the focussing of light which arrives at the eye from a point light source.

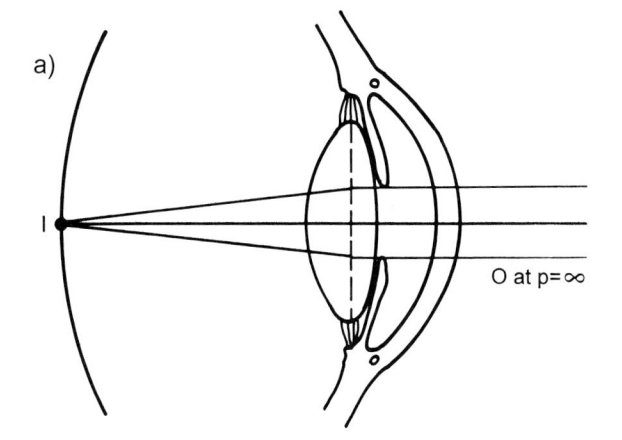

Fig. 17.25: Hyperopia.
(a) Far vision,
(b) close vision,
(c) correction with prescription glasses.

ed and an image of the object is formed properly on the retina. Thus, the person is called farsighted. Part (b) illustrates the problem of the patient when focussing on a nearby object, i.e., when the ciliary muscle contracts and the lens should relax toward its most spherical shape. If the object is closer than the near point, the image is formed behind the retina. If this near point is too far from the eye, there is a problem for the patient, for example, when reading. This is a typical effect of old age, but may also occur when the eyeball is too short. The correction is done with prescription glasses, as illustrated in Fig. 17.25(c). The corrective lens is a convex lens with a positive refractive power $\Re$ to add to the too small refractive power of the eye. As indicated in the figure, the glasses cause an apparent shift of the object to greater distance, a distance at which the defective eye is able to see it clearly.

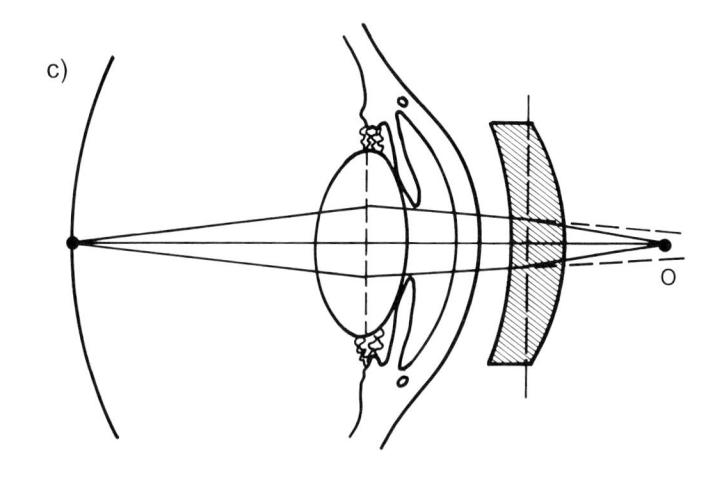

Example 17.9

The near point of a particular person is at 50 cm. What focal length must a corrective lens have to enable the eye to see an object 25 cm away clearly?

Solution: We use the thin lens formula with an object distance of p = 25 cm. The lens we want to prescribe must form an image on the same side of the lens as the object, but at a distance of 50 cm. Then the eye of the person looks at that image and sees it clearly. Thus, using the sign convention from Table 17.4, q = – 50 cm. This leads to a focal length of:

$$\frac{1}{f} = \frac{1}{p} + \frac{1}{q} = \frac{1}{0.25\ m} + \frac{1}{-0.5\ m} \quad (39)$$

$$\Rightarrow f = 0.5\ m$$

$\Re = 1/f = +2.0$ dpt is the refractive power of the prescribed glasses.

Myopia

Myopia is an eye defect due to an insufficient stretching of the lens when a person tries to obtain a lower refractive power of $\Re = 18$ dpt. Myopia is illustrated in Fig. 17.26. Part (a) shows the eye trying to observe an object at great distance. The lens is not sufficiently elongated, and thus, the image is formed in front of the retina. The same person can see an object at the near point without any problem as the elasticity of the lens is sufficient to reshape the lens to form an image on the retina (illustrated in 17.26(b)). Fig. 17.26(c) shows how myopia is corrected with prescription glasses: the parallel light rays reaching the eye from an object at great distance are refracted away from the optical axis such that they form an image I' at a point closer to the eye. This image is observed with the myopic lens, forming the final image on the retina.

Typical causes of myopia are elongated eyeballs or weakened ligaments and muscles, e.g. due to diabetes mellitus. The prescription glasses are concave to lower the too high refractive power $\Re$ of the eye.

Example 17.10
A certain person cannot see objects clearly when they are beyond a distance of 50 cm. What focal length should the prescribed lens have to correct this problem?

Solution: The object distance is infinite, $p = \infty$, since we want to enable the eye to see anything beyond 50 cm, including objects very far away. The image of the prescription lens must be on the same side of the lens as the object, and cannot be further than 50 cm, that means $q = -50$ cm (the negative sign results from the sign conventions in Table 17.4). If the lens accomplishes this, then the eye can look at the image of the lens and see it properly. The thin lens formula reads:

$$\frac{1}{f} = \frac{1}{p} + \frac{1}{q} = \frac{1}{\infty} + \frac{1}{-0.5\,m} \quad (40)$$

$$\Rightarrow f = -0.5\,m$$

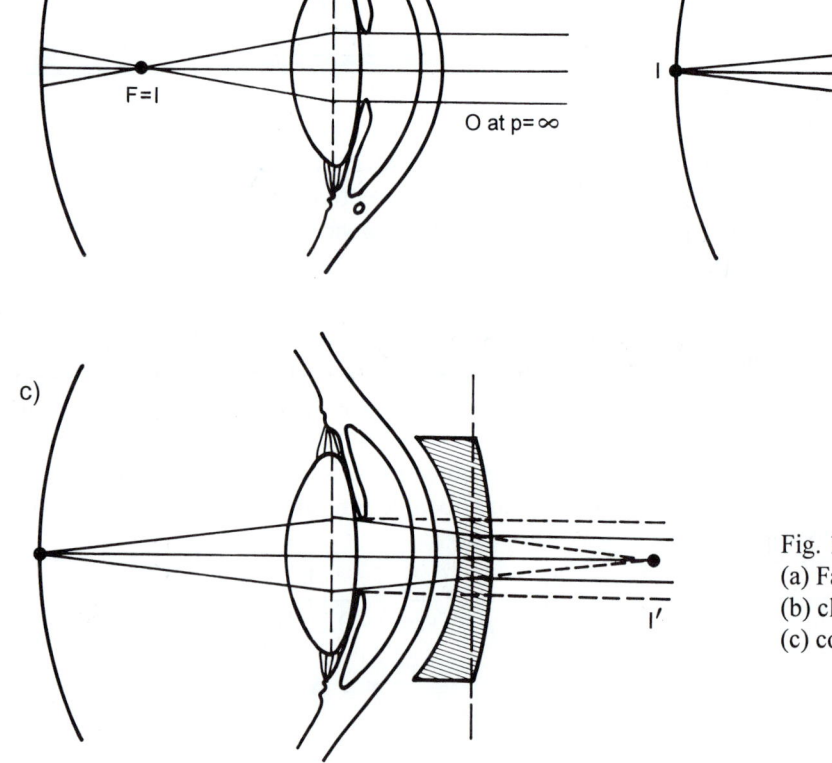

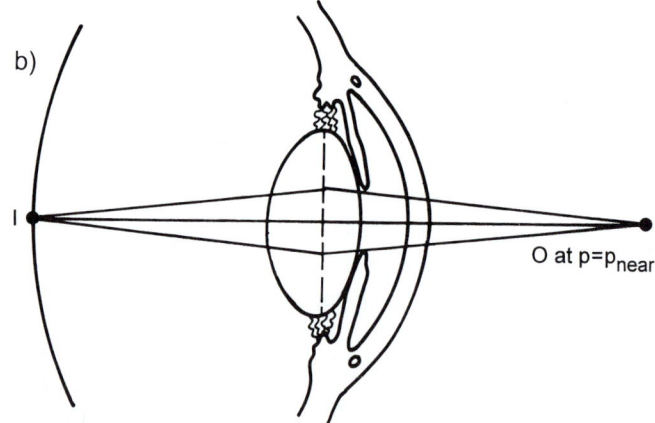

Fig. 17.26: Myopia.
(a) Far vision,
(b) close vision,
(c) correction with prescription glasses.

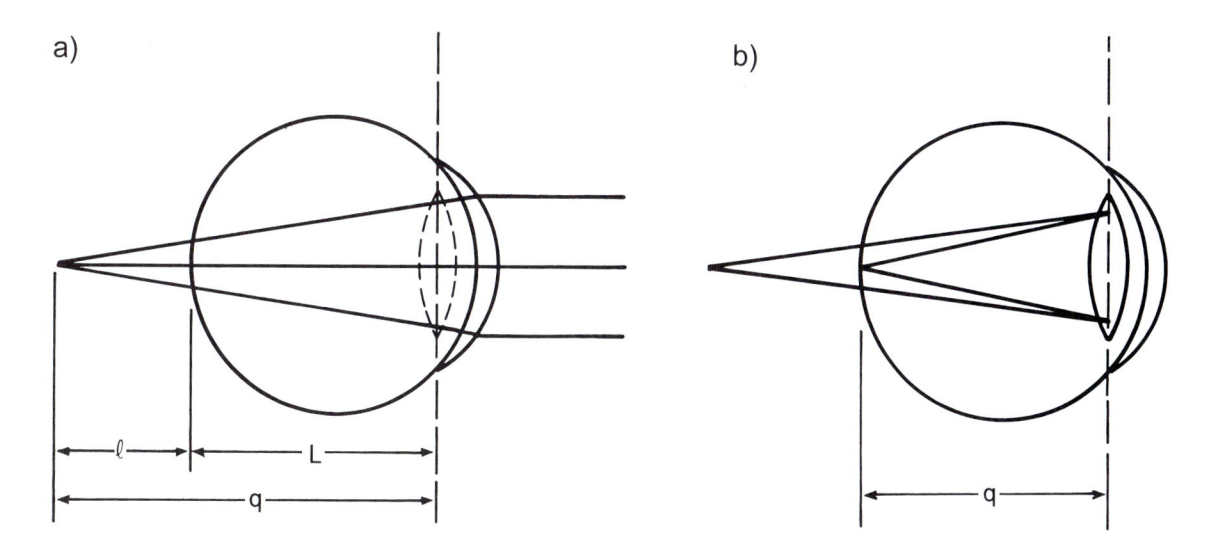

Fig. 17.27: (a) Eye with a surgically removed lens (dashed lines indicate the missing lens). The cornea is the only focussing component of this eye but does not have a sufficient refractive power to focus light from a source at infinite distance. Thus, the image forms behind the retina. The person would only see a very blurred image. (b) The artificial lens implanted into the eye of part (a) must correct the position of the image such that the image is formed on the retina.

A negative focal length means that a concave lens must be prescribed (see again the sign conventions in Table 17.4). The lens has a refractive power $\Re = -2.0$ dpt.

Example 17.11

An artificial lens is implanted in a patient's eye to replace a diseased lens. The distance between the artificial lens and the retina is 2.8 cm. In the absence of the lens, the image of a very distant object (formed by the refraction of the cornea) is formed 2.53 cm behind the retina. The lens is designed to put the image of the distant object on the retina. What is the refractive power $\Re$ of the implanted lens?

Hint: Consider the image formed by the cornea as a virtual object.

Solution: Following the hint, we consider the image formed by the eye without the implanted lens as a virtual object for the implanted lens. To use later the thin lens formula to determine the focal length of the implanted lens, we need to determine the object distance for the implanted lens from the image distance of the cornea without a lens. Thus, the image distance has a value $q = (2.53 \text{ cm} + 2.8 \text{ cm}) = 5.33$ cm, as shown in Fig. 17.27(a). The two lengths in the bracket are added since the original image is formed behind the retina, i.e., further away from the location of the missing lens.

When the new lens is implanted, the image distance calculated above becomes the object distance for the implanted lens. The value of the object distance is $p = -5.33$ cm, where the negative sign indicates that this is a virtual object, i.e., an object which appears behind the lens. The implanted lens must now form a final image on the retina as indicated in Fig. 17.27(b), i.e., at a distance $q = +2.8$ cm behind the lens. The thin lens formula yields in this case:

$$\frac{1}{f} = \frac{1}{p} + \frac{1}{q} = \frac{1}{-5.33 [cm]} + \frac{1}{2.8 [cm]} \quad (41)$$

$$\Rightarrow f = +5.9 \text{ cm}$$

Using Eq. (35) we find the refractive power of the implanted lens to be $\Re = +17.0$ dpt. Note that this is a much larger value than a typical refractive power for a prescription lens.

17.5 Appendix

Single spherical interface

Eq. (25) connects the image and object distances with the two indices of refraction and the curvature for a single spherical interface. To find this formula, we copy Fig. 17.16 to Fig. 17.28 and add relevant geometrical terms. We find at point P_1:

$$\alpha_1 + (90^0 - \phi_1) + (90^0 - \beta) = 180^0$$
$$\Rightarrow \alpha_1 - \phi_1 = \beta \quad (42)$$

and for triangle Δ_1:

$$\alpha_2 + \phi_2 + (180^0 - \beta) = 180^0$$
$$\Rightarrow \alpha_2 + \phi_2 = \beta \quad (43)$$

Further, the following trigonometric relations hold for ϕ_1, ϕ_2 and $\beta \ll 1$:

$$\tan\phi_1 \cong \phi_1 \cong \frac{y}{p}$$
$$\tan\phi_2 \cong \phi_2 \cong \frac{y}{q} \quad (44)$$
$$\tan\beta \cong \beta \cong \frac{y}{R}$$

We also apply Snell's law for small angles of refraction since we assume that $\alpha_1, \alpha_2 \ll 1$:

$$\frac{n_2}{n_1} = \frac{\sin\alpha_1}{\sin\alpha_2} \cong \frac{\alpha_1}{\alpha_2} \quad (45)$$

With the preliminary steps in Eqs. (42) to (45), we now combine the two geometric relations of Eqs. (42) and (43) and replace the angles ϕ_1 and ϕ_2 using the trigonometric relations in Eq. (44):

$$\alpha_1 - \phi_1 = \alpha_2 + \phi_2 = \beta$$
$$\Rightarrow \alpha_1 - \frac{y}{p} = \alpha_2 + \frac{y}{q} = \frac{y}{R} \quad (46)$$

In the next step, α_2 in Eq. (46) is replaced using Eq. (45):

$$\alpha_1 - \frac{y}{p} = \frac{n_1}{n_2}\alpha_1 + \frac{y}{q} = \frac{y}{R} \quad (47)$$

Eq. (47) is now used twice. First, we use the equation between the first and last terms in Eq. (47) to isolate α_1 as the independent variable:

$$\alpha_1 = \frac{y}{R} + \frac{y}{p} \quad (48)$$

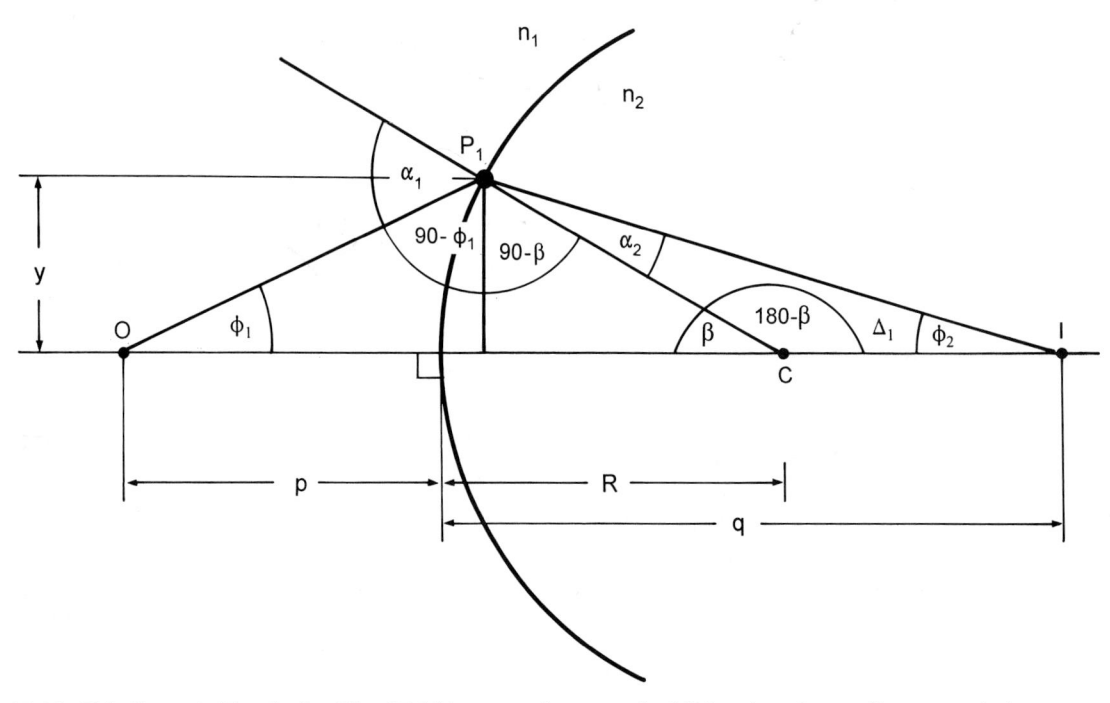

Fig. 17.28: This figure is identical to Fig. 17.16 but contains several additional angles to allow us to derive Eq. (25), which is the relation connecting the various distances and the two indices of refraction.

Next we use the equation between the first and second terms in Eq. (47) to substitute the result in Eq. (48) for α_1:

$$\frac{n_1}{n_2}\left(\frac{y}{R}+\frac{y}{p}\right)+\frac{y}{q}=\frac{y}{R} \qquad (49)$$

This is rewritten in the form:

$$\frac{n_1}{R}+\frac{n_1}{p}+\frac{n_2}{q}=\frac{n_2}{R}$$

$$\Rightarrow \frac{n_1}{p}+\frac{n_2}{q}=\frac{n_2-n_1}{R} \qquad (50)$$

This is Eq. (25).

A second formula, not derived in this textbook, allows us to calculate the magnification for the image size h_I of an object of height h_O:

$$M=\frac{h_I}{h_O}=-\frac{n_1\,q}{n_2\,p} \qquad (51)$$

There is a nice way to illustrate that Eq. (51) indeed allows for a magnification of objects seen across a single spherical interface. Cut off the bottom and top lid of a food can. Then cover one side with a transparent plastic foil. Push the can below the surface of a shallow pond with the foil covered side down. The water pressure forces the foil upwards, which creates a spherically shaped interface. If you now observe objects in the pond through the can you see them magnified.

Lens maker's equation, derived for two spherical refracting interfaces

The properties of two consecutive refracting surfaces are discussed using Fig. 17.29. The first interface separates material 1 with an index of refraction n_1 and material 2 with an index of refraction n_2. The two materials are chosen such that this interface alone does not allow the formation of a real image on the right side. This means that the change in the index of refraction is not sufficiently large to cause the diverging light rays from the object O at object distance p to converge after passing the interface. A second interface, from material 2 to material 3 with index of refraction n_3, is added so that an image I at distance q is formed. Note that the distance q is defined with reference to the same point along the optical axis as the distances p, p' and $-q'$. This is a good approximation for the case of a thin lens where the thickness of material 2 is negligible when compared with p, q, and R_1 or R_2.

A formula describing the relation between all the relevant parameters in Fig. 17.29 is developed. For this, we apply Eq. (25) at the first interface:

$$(I)\quad \frac{n_1}{p}+\frac{n_2}{q'}=\frac{n_2-n_1}{R_1} \qquad (52)$$

where q' is the image distance, which is negative as shown in Fig. 17.29. R_1 is the radius of the first interface, i.e., the interface that light coming from the object hits first. For the second interface, the same equation applies, except that the image distance of the first interface becomes the object distance for the second interface, $p'=-q'$:

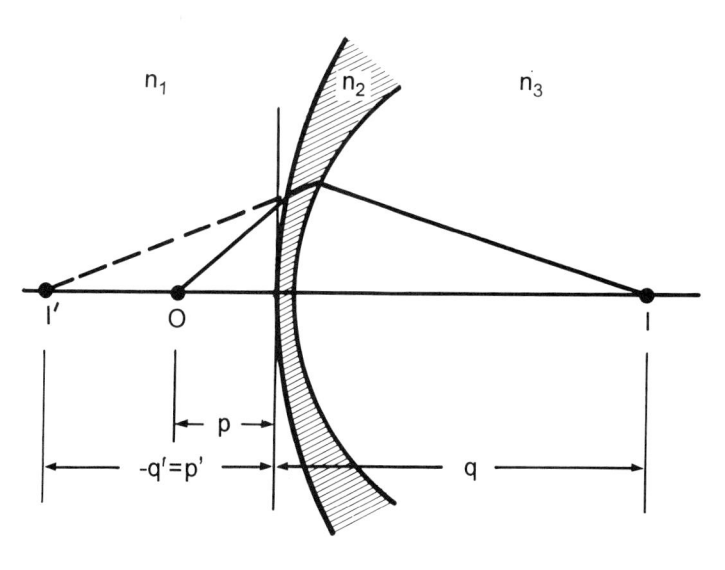

Fig. 17.29: Formation of an image I for a point light source O located on the optical axis with the light passing two refracting surfaces, travelling through three media with indices of refraction n_1, n_2 and n_3. Note that the two interfaces are located very close to each other to allow us to develop relations applicable to thin devices.

$$(II) \quad \frac{n_2}{p'} + \frac{n_3}{q} = \frac{n_3 - n_2}{R_2}$$

$$-\frac{n_2}{q'} + \frac{n_3}{q} = \frac{n_3 - n_2}{R_2} \quad (53)$$

The intermediate term n_2/q' is eliminated by combining Eq. (52) with the second formula in Eq. (53), yielding:

$$\frac{n_1}{p} + \frac{n_3}{q} = \frac{n_2 - n_1}{R_1} + \frac{n_3 - n_2}{R_2} \quad (54)$$

The terms on the left hand sides in Eqs. (54) and (25) are the same, containing the parameters of the medium left of the sequence of interfaces, and of the medium at right of the sequence of interfaces. Thus, sequential interfaces do not change the left hand side of the equation. The effect of additional interfaces is evident from the right hand sides of Eqs. (25) and (54): A term of the form $\Delta n/R$ is added for each interface. The term $\Delta n/R$ we defined in the text as the refractive power of a single interface.

═══════════════════════════════════════

Example 17.12
Can you see clearly under water without diving goggles? For the discussion, simplify the combination of cornea and lens of the human eye by using Eq. (54) for a single symmetric lens with n = 1.5, and take n = 1.3 for the vitreous body of the eye.

Solution: Eq. (54) connects the object distance, the image distance and the radii of curvature for two consecutive refractive interfaces (both spherical). The set–up is shown in Fig. 17.29, illustrating that the light travels from a medium with refractive index n_1, through a medium of refractive index n_2, and finally into a medium of refractive index n_3.

In the current example we want to compare a bathing tourist, first looking at other people at the beach and then looking at an approaching shark under water. When looking at the beach, medium 1 is air, medium 2 is the lens of the eye and medium 3 is the vitreous body behind the eye's lens, with $n_1 = 1.0$, $n_2 = 1.5$ and $n_3 = 1.3$. With these values Eq. (54) yields for a symmetric lens, i.e., when $-R_1 = R_2 \equiv R$:

$$\frac{1}{p} + \frac{1.3}{q} = \frac{2 \cdot 1.5 - 1.0 - 1.3}{R} \cong \frac{0.7}{R} \quad (55)$$

If people at the beach are practically at infinite distance, $p = \infty$, they generate a focussed image on the tourist's retina (using q = 2.8 cm for a typical distance between lens and retina) if the effective radius of curvature of the lens is R = 1.5 cm. This is a value well within the range of accommodations of the human eye, which can reach a maximum effective accommodation of R = 1.0 cm.

Once underneath the surface of the water the index of refraction of the medium containing the object, now the shark, changes to $n_1 = 1.33$. This changes Eq. (55) to:

$$\frac{1.33}{p} + \frac{1.3}{q} = \frac{2 \cdot 1.5 - 1.33 - 1.3}{R} \cong \frac{0.37}{R} \quad (56)$$

and a shark at infinite distance ($p = \infty$) leads to an image distance of q = 3.5 cm for the maximum effective accommodation of the eye with R = 1.0 cm. Thus, even an object at infinite distance creates a significantly blurred image on the retina, which we said is only about 2.8 cm behind the eye's lens.

The situation does not improve when the object is closer instead. If we choose, for example, p = 25 cm we find q = 4.1 cm at the maximum effective accommodation of the eye. Thus, the image of a near object under water is even more blurred on the retina. This is an interesting scientific observation which will, however, likely escape the tourist's attention. It is further interesting to note that most fish suffer from a similar problem and are indeed nearsighted.

═══════════════════════════════════════

Eq. (54) simplifies greatly when medium 1 and 3 are identical. This is also the most common case as it applies specifically to lenses, where medium 1 and 3 are either air or vacuum ($n_1 = n_3 = 1$) and medium 2 is a transparent material with $n_2 = n$. In this case, Eq. (54) becomes the *lens maker's equation* for thin lenses:

$$\frac{1}{p} + \frac{1}{q} = (n-1)\left(\frac{1}{R_1} - \frac{1}{R_2}\right) \quad (57)$$

Again, note that p and q are measured to the same point along the optical axis, i.e., the transparent material 2 is of negligible thickness.

Example 17.13

The lens in Fig. 17.30 has an index of refraction of 1.5. The radius of the front surface is $R_1 = 10$ cm and the radius of the back surface is $R_2 = -15$ cm. Find the focal length f.

Solution: Note that the positive and negative signs in the Example text are chosen accordingly to Table 17.4: the center of curvature for R_1 is on the side of the lens opposite to the object and the center of curvature for R_2 is on the same side of the lens as the object.

We combine the lens maker's equation in Eq. (57) with the thin lens formula in Eq. (34):

$$\frac{1}{f} = (n-1)\left(\frac{1}{R_1} - \frac{1}{R_2}\right) \qquad (58)$$

which yields:

$$\frac{1}{f} = (1.5 - 1)\left(\frac{1}{10[cm]} - \frac{1}{-15[cm]}\right) \qquad (59)$$

$$\Rightarrow f = 12 \ cm$$

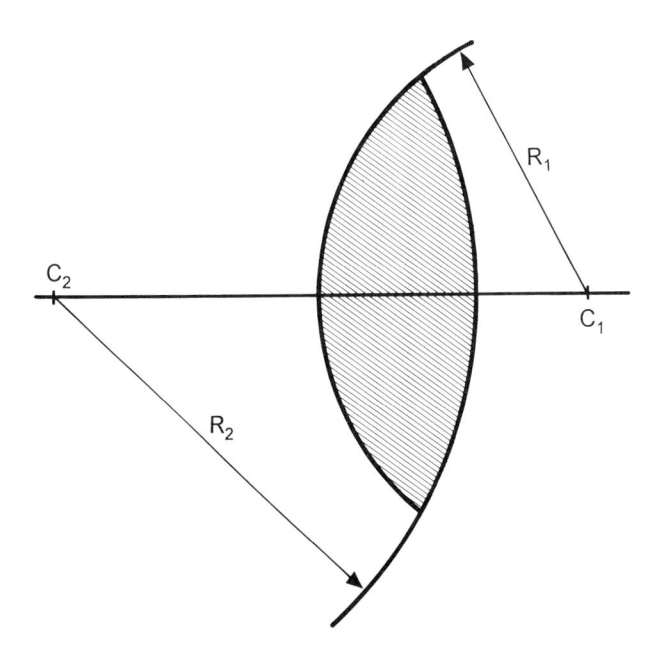

Fig. 17.30: A lens with two different radii of curvature, R_1 and R_2.

17.6. Problems

P–17.1
When you look at your face in a small bathroom mirror from a distance of 40 cm, the upright image is twice as tall as your face. What is the focal length of the mirror?

P–17.2
Optometrists use the *Snellen test* to evaluate the vision of their patients. The Snellen test consists of letters of different sizes which a person with healthy eyes can read at particular distances. The patient is 20 feet (6.1 m) from the chart and has to read the letters. If the patient's eyes are healthy, he/she will read the same line without errors, which the healthy reference group was able to read at that distance. We call this therefore 20/20 vision. A juvenile may have 20/10 vision, which means that he/she can read a line a healthy adult can only read at a distance of 10 feet (3.05 m). Vision impaired patients may score as low as 20/200, which corresponds to the single, largest letter at the top of the Snellen test. A person with healthy eyes can read that letter as far away as 200 feet (61 m) which coincides with the distance at which the eye is accommodated for vision of objects at infinite distance.

Many optometrists have offices in a mall with high rent. To keep the cost down, the examination room may only have a length of 4 meters with the patient siting at the examination instruments near the center of the room. Suggest an appropriate set–up for the Snellen test in this room.

P–17.3
A concave spherical mirror has a radius of curvature of 20 cm. Locate the images for object distances as given below. In each case, state whether the image is real or virtual and upright or inverted, and find the magnification.
(a) p = 10 cm
(b) p = 20 cm
(c) p = 40 cm

P–17.4
Find the images for the three objects in Fig. 17.31.

P–17.5
When you look at yourself in a flat mirror, you see yourself with left and right sides switched, but not upside down. How come?
Hint: Remember that you are a three–dimensional body. Study the image of the following three vectors: (I) head to foot, (II) left to right hand and (III) nose to back of head. The remainder of the puzzle is perception of the brain!

a)

b)

c)

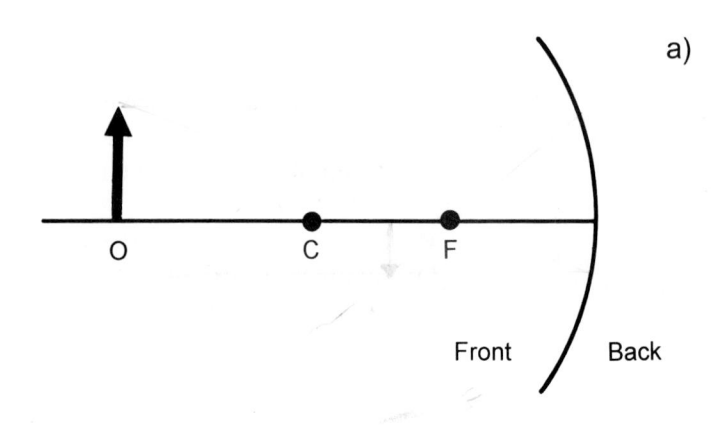

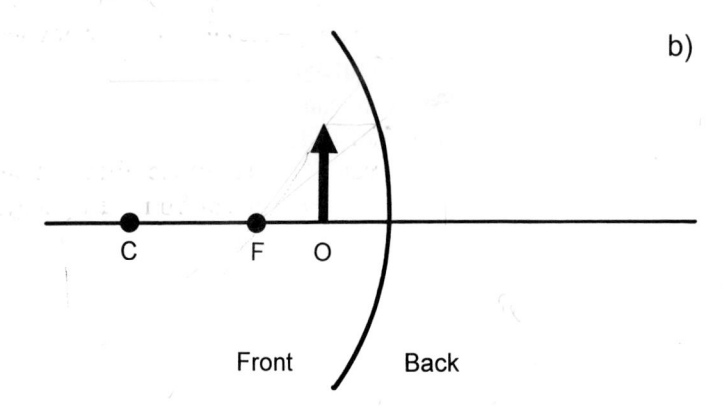

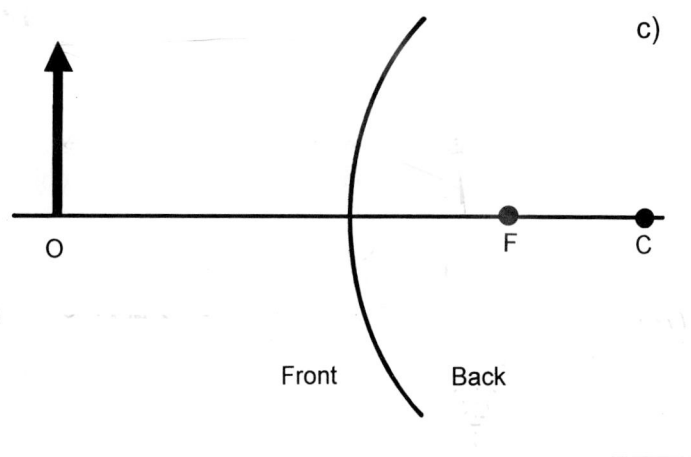

Fig. 17.31 for problem P–17.4

P–17.6
A light ray enters a layer of water at an angle of 36° with the vertical. What is the angle between the refracted light ray and the vertical?

P–17.7
A light ray strikes the flat, L = 2.0 cm thick block of glass (n = 1.5) in Fig. 17.32 at an angle of θ = 30° with the normal.
(a) Find the angles of incidence and refraction at each surface.
(b) Calculate the lateral shift of the light ray, d.

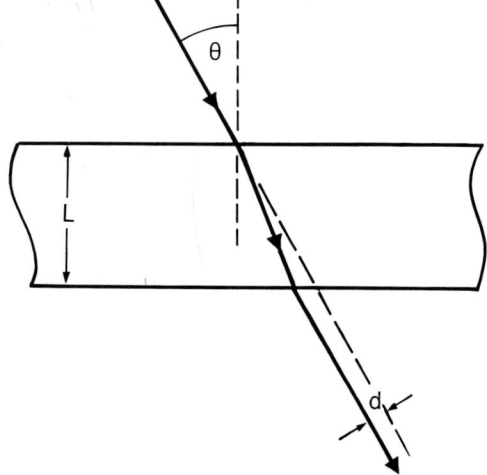

Fig. 17.32 for problem P–17.7

P–17.8

In Fig. 17.33, an ultrasonic beam reflects off a tumor (dotted) in an organ (shaded) at $\theta = 50^0$ with a shift L = 12 cm. If the speed of the wave is 10 % less in the organ than in the medium above, determine the depth of the tumor below the organ's surface.

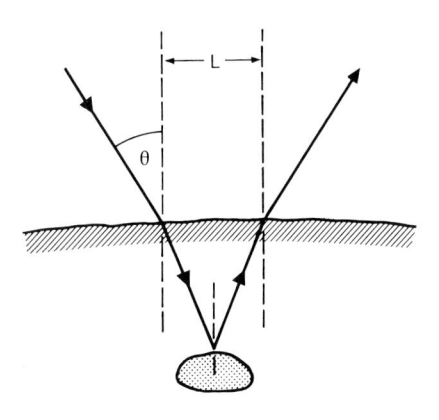

Fig. 17.33 for problem P–17.8

Fig. 17.34 for problem P–17.9

P–17.9

Construct the images for the three lenses shown in Fig. 17.34. Note that the third case is a diverging lens.

P–17.10

A converging lens has a focal length f = 20.0 cm. Locate the images for the object distances given below. For each case state whether the image is real or virtual and upright or inverted, and find the magnification.
(a) 40 cm
(b) 20 cm
(c) 10 cm

P–17.11

Where must an object be placed to have no magnification (|M| = 1.0) for a converging lens of focal length f = 12.0 cm?

P–17.12

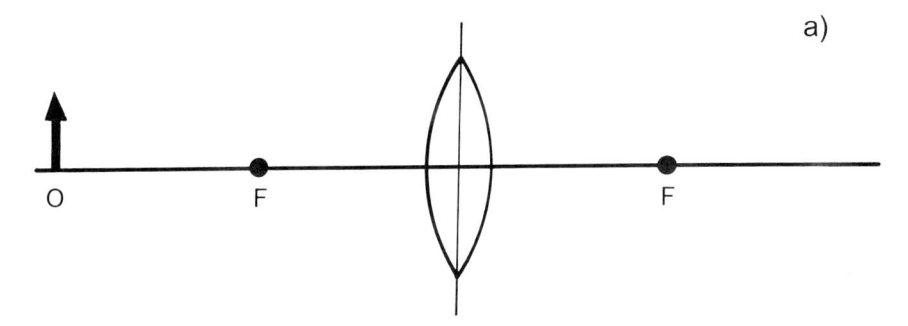

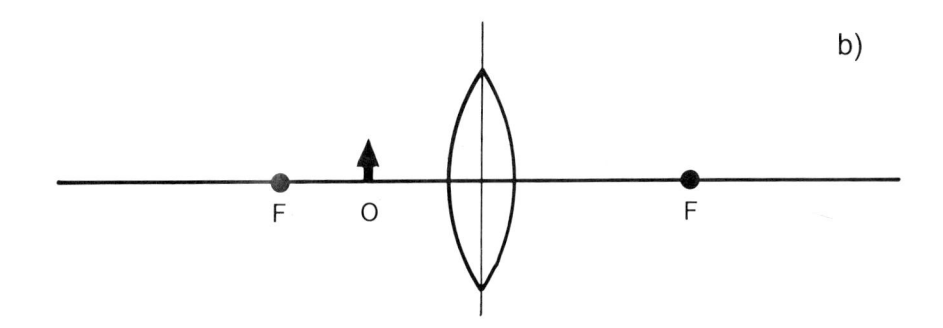

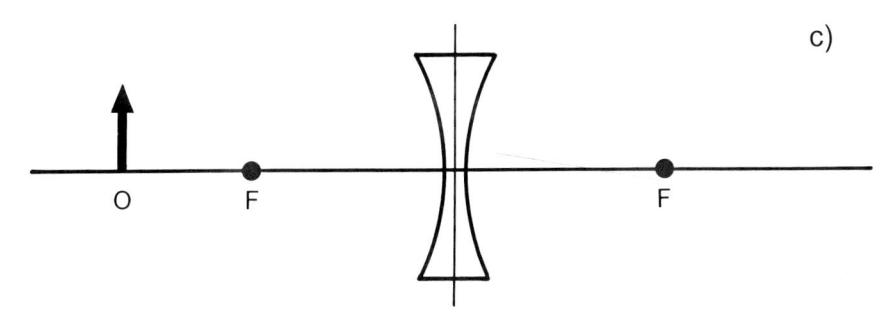

A person can see an object focussed only if the object is no further than 30 cm from the right eye and 50 cm from the left eye. Write a prescription for the refractive powers $\Re$ (in diopters) for the corrective lenses.

P–17.13
The near point of an eye is 100 cm. A corrective lens is to be used to allow this eye to focus clearly on objects 25 cm in front of it.
(a) What should be the focal length of the lens?
(b) What is the refractive power $\Re$ of the lens?

P–17.14
A person, who can see clearly when objects are between 30 cm and 1.5 m from the eye, is to be fitted with bifocals.
(a) The upper portion of the corrective glasses are designed such that the person can see distant objects clearly. What refractive power $\Re$ does that part of the glasses have?
(b) The lower portions of the glasses has to enable the person to see objects comfortably at 25 cm. What refractive power $\Re$ does that part of the glasses have?

P–17.15
The near point of an eye is 75.0 cm.
(a) What should be the refractive power $\Re$ of a corrective lens prescribed to enable the patient to see an object clearly at 25.0 cm?
(b) If, using these corrective glasses, the patient can see an object clearly at 26.0 cm but not at 25.0 cm, by how many diopters did the lens grinder miss the prescription?

P–17.16
(a) Some gardeners advice against watering flowers in full sun shine to avoid burns to leaves due to the focusing effect of water droplets. Is this advice reasonable? Hint: Treat the water droplet as a sphere placed on the leaf and use the thin lens formula.
(b) For the plant scientists: do you know why it is still not a good idea to water the flowers in full sun light?

P–17.17
A contact lens is made of plastic with an index of refraction of n = 1.58. The lens has a focal length of f = +25.0 cm, and its inner surface has a radius of curvature of +18.0 mm. What is the radius of curvature of the outer surface?

Summary

Definitions:
- Focal length of a spherical mirror: f = R/2, R is radius of curvature of mirror.
- Magnification of spherical mirror or lens:

$$M = \frac{h_I}{h_O}$$

h_I is the height of the image and h_O the object height.
- Index of refraction n (Snell's law where the incoming ray is in vacuum or air):

$$\frac{\sin\alpha_{in}}{\sin\beta} = n$$

α_{in} and β are the angles of the light ray with the normal.
- Refractive power:
(I) for a single interface: $\Re = \Delta n/R$
(II) for a symmetric lens: $\Re = 1/f$

Units:
- Refractive power $\Re$ [dpt] (diopters): [dpt] = [1/m]

Laws:
- Reflection, flat mirror:

$$\alpha_{in} = \alpha_{out}$$

- Law of refraction at the interface of media 1 and 2:

$$n_1 \sin\alpha_1 = n_2 \sin\alpha_2$$

- Mirror equation, and thin lens formula:

$$\frac{1}{f} = \frac{1}{p} + \frac{1}{q}$$

p is the object distance and q is the image distance.
- Magnification of spherical mirror or lens:

$$M = -\frac{q}{p} = \frac{f}{f-p} = \frac{f-q}{f}$$

- Law of refraction for a spherical interface between medium 1 and medium 2:

$$\frac{n_1}{p} + \frac{n_2}{q} = \frac{n_2 - n_1}{R}$$

- Magnification at spherical interface of media 1 and 2:

$$M = \frac{h_I}{h_O} = -\frac{n_1 q}{n_2 p}$$

Chapter XVIII

The Microbial World

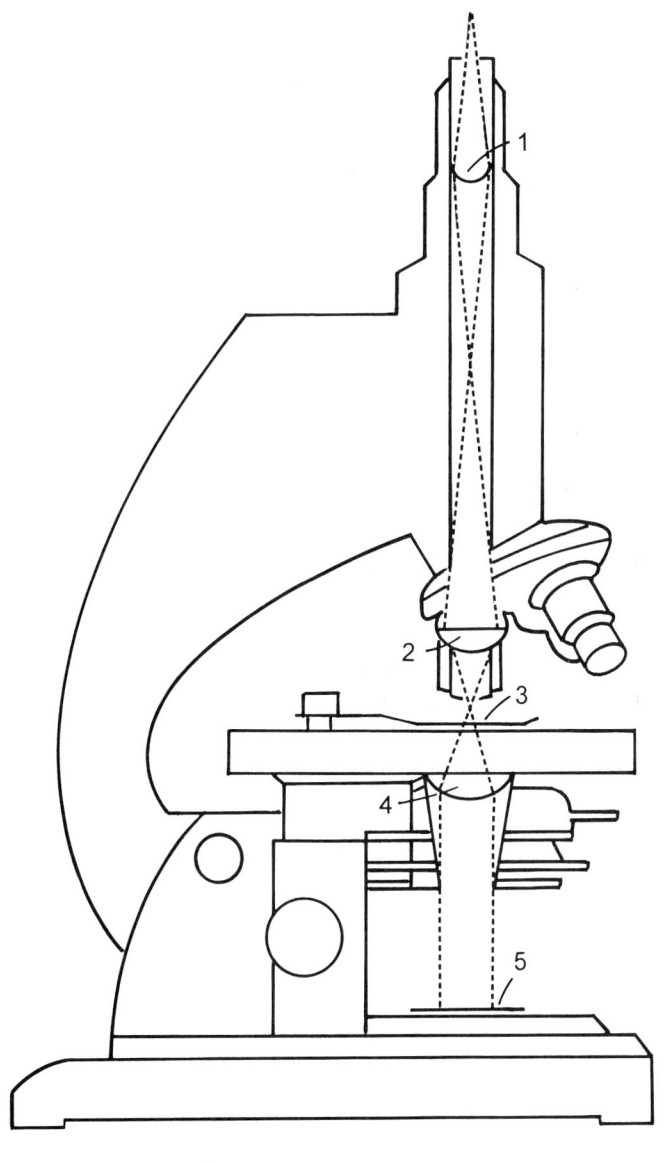

Microscopy

THE MICROBIAL WORLD
MICROSCOPY

The geometric optics concepts introduced in the previous chapter are applied to the compound microscope. To quantify the magnification of a microscope properly the eye of the observer has to be included as part of the optical set–up. This leads to the definition of the angular magnification of a magnifying glass (eyepiece). Variable combinations of eyepieces and objective lenses are studied for their total angular magnification, which is the product of the angular magnification of the eyepiece and the magnification of the objective lens.

The electron microscope is introduced as an alternative method to avoid the resolution limitations of the optical microscopes at about 200 nm. With an electron microscope structures smaller than 1 nm can be distinguished.

No other technological development has influenced the early history of biology and medicine as much as the development of microscopes. The first light microscopes were introduced by Antoni van Leeuwenhoek in the late 1600's. With light microscopes, such as the one shown in Fig. 18.1, we can see small cells such as human erythrocytes and bacteria. Later in the chapter we discuss electron microscopes, which allow us to overcome the limits of the light microscope and enable us to see objects as small as 1 nm. The first electron microscope was developed by Ernst August Ruska in 1932. The range of the electron microscope includes viruses, proteins and even amino acids. We need even more powerful instruments, such as the scanning tunnelling microscope, to see single atoms.

For biologist or medical researchers microscopes like the one depicted in Fig. 18.1 are a tool used on a daily basis. Many of you will develop that level of familiarity with this instrument. It is dangerous to confuse familiarity and a good grasp on the technical specifications and limitations: microscopes can easily deceive you, as many examples of faulty publications attest to. Particularly in the 19th century, there were quite interesting things "discovered" which later turned out to be artifacts of the optical set–up of the microscope used. While modern instruments are designed to minimize such mistakes, it is the user's proper knowledge of the

Fig. 18.1: In a light microscope, visible light from a light source (5) is focussed on a sample (3) by a condenser lens (4). This light is used to form an image that is magnified by an objective lens (2) and an eyepiece (1).

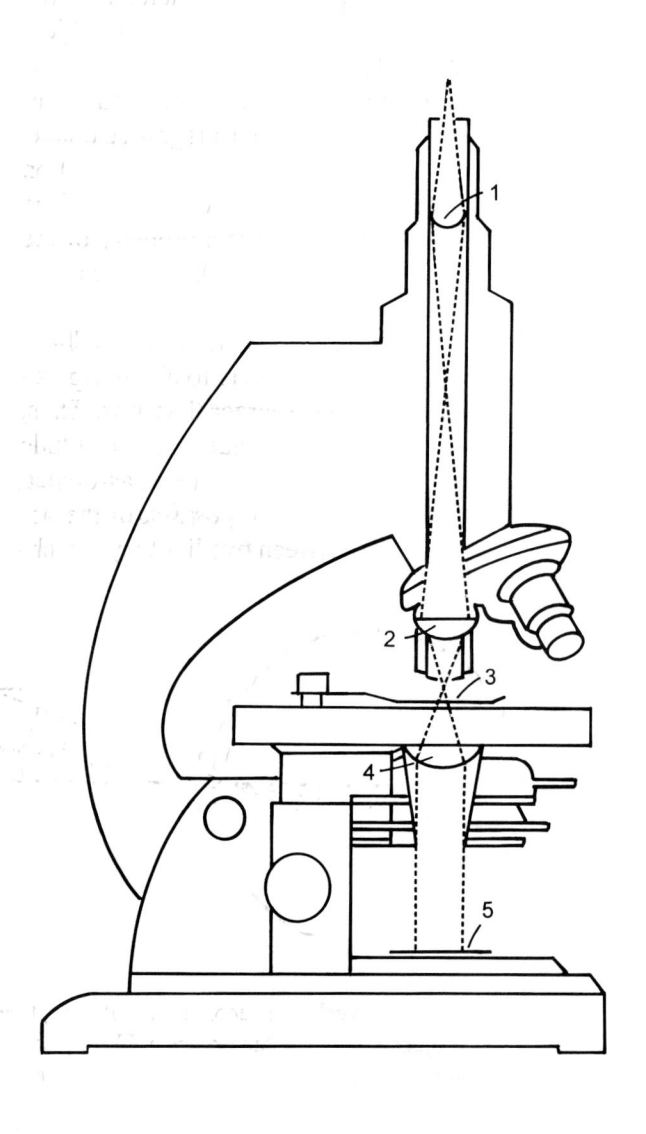

physical properties of the instrument which ultimately has to prevent unwarranted embarrassment. We built a solid foundation of the basic properties of the light microscope in this chapter, using the optics concepts developed in Chapter 17. Some issues, such as diffraction effects, spectral resolution and Abbe's theory of the resolving power of a microscope are not included as their discussion requires more advanced concepts from wave optics. The reader may wish to consult advanced texts on optics for information on these issues.

18.1. From lenses to microscopes

In the previous chapter we saw that a single lens allows us to obtain magnified images. The formula describing the magnification of a single lens reads:

$$M = -\frac{q}{p} = \frac{f}{f-p} = \frac{f-q}{f} \quad (1)$$

with p the object distance, q the image distance and f the focal length. To obtain a magnified image, the object must be closer to the lens than the image, which is possible when $p - f < f$ or $p < 2f$: an object placed closer than twice the focal length generates a magnified image. Note that the magnification in Eq. (1) is only a function of f, p and q; it does not depend on the position of the observer! Thus, the magnification is a property of the physical lens but does not tell us what an observer actually sees.

A microscope, in turn, is not just a device, but it is a process which allows the observer to obtain a particular outcome: to see an object larger than it is. Thus, the step from lens to microscope requires us to include the observer to quantify the apparent size of an object. This is illustrated in Fig. 18.2. The position of the observer defines the angle θ between two light rays reaching the eye from opposite ends of the object. The figure compares the size of the image on the retina for two identical objects, one at object distance p_1 and the other one at object distance p_2. The figure defines the *angular magnification m*:

$$m = \frac{\theta}{\theta_0} \quad (2)$$

in which θ_0 is the angle subtended by the object when placed at p = 25 cm, which we define as s_0, the standard near point of a healthy adult eye. Thus, an object you hold at a distance of 25 cm from your eye has an angular magnification of m = 1. An object further away appears smaller (m < 1) and an object closer is bigger (m > 1).

The justification for defining a new parameter with the angular magnification is that this is the quantity in which we are ultimately interested. However, it also illustrates the limitations of our ability to see things larger than they are with the naked eye. Even the juvenile eye cannot focus on an object closer than about 10 cm before the eye (touch your nose with the ball of the thumb and try to see the palm of your hand focussed). Using a small object of size h_O in the sketch of Fig. 18.3, e.g. a human hair, we determine the maximum angular magnification a juvenile eye can achieve:

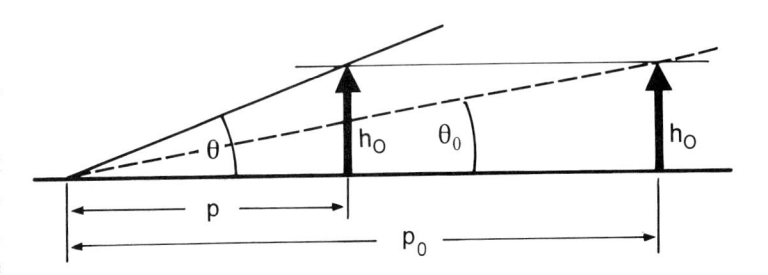

Fig. 18.3: Sketch illustrating the maximum angular magnification of the human eye.

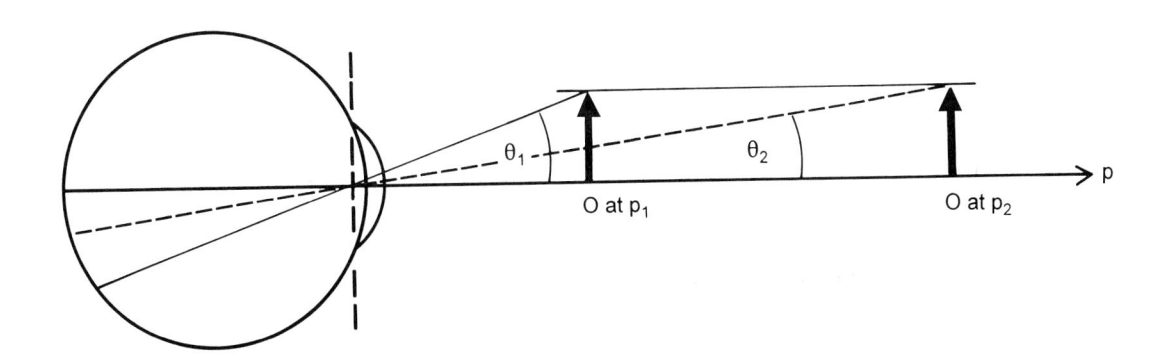

Fig. 18.2: When the observer's eye becomes part of the optical system we define an angular magnification based on the angle under which an object appears to the observer. The figure shows a geometrical sketch to illustrate that the apparent size of an object O varies with its distance from the observing eye.

$$m = \frac{\theta}{\theta_0} \cong \frac{\tan\theta}{\tan\theta_0} = \frac{p_0}{p} = \frac{25[cm]}{10[cm]} = 2.5 \quad (3)$$

We are, of course, not satisfied with this limitation, particularly not for research in the life sciences. There is an entire world at microscopic length scales we cannot see, as illustrated in Fig. 18.4. The lower limit of objects we can see without optical instruments is about 100 μm (e.g., a human oocyte). Below, we discuss first a simple magnifying glass (with angular magnification of m = 20 – 30) and then the light microscope. These allow us to see objects as small as 200 nm, near the wavelengths of visible light.

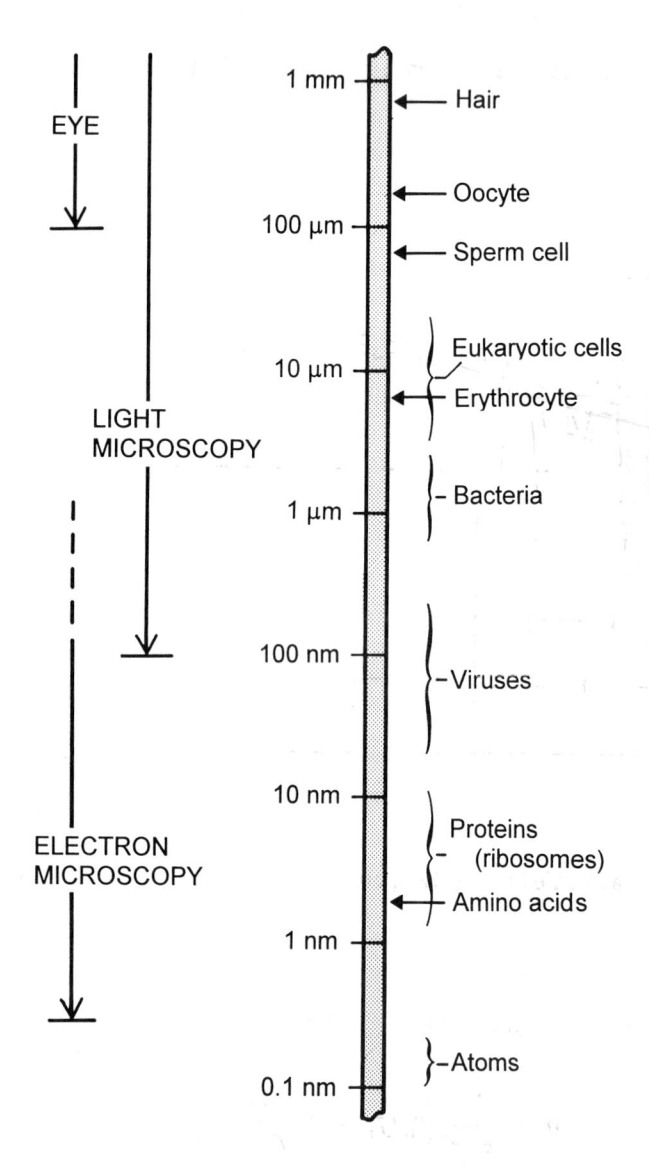

Fig. 18.4: Size range of typical objects of biological interest. The vertical range indicators at the left hand side illustrate what is visible with the eye, the light microscope and the electron microscope.

18.2. The magnifying glass

A lens produces an image larger than the object size if the object is placed closer than twice the focal length to the lens. Using Eq. (1), which applies to specific lenses such as magnifying glasses, we see that the object has to be moved very close to the focal point to obtain a large magnification M. Thus, we arrange the set-up of the lens such that p ≅ f. We determine the angular magnification m for such an arrangement. We do this twice, the first time assuming that the observer wants to look at the object as if it is at infinite distance, and the second time assuming that the observer is prepared to focus the eye on an object apparently at the near point.

18.2.1. Magnifying glass case I: observer with relaxed eye

In Fig. 18.5 an object O of size h_o is placed at the focal point F of a lens, allowing the observer to look at the image I with relaxed eyes. Remember that an image which appears at infinite distance produces parallel light rays incident on the eye. In this case the angular magnification is determined from the angle θ, which is the angle under which the object appears at the observer's eye at a distance f behind the lens. With $\theta \cong \tan\theta = h_o/f$ and with s_0 the distance to the near point of 25 cm, we find:

$$m = \frac{\theta}{\theta_0} = \frac{h_o/f}{h_o/s_0} = \frac{s_0}{f} \quad (4)$$

i.e., the shorter the focal length f of the magnifying lens the larger the angular magnification.

18.2.2. Magnifying glass case II: observer focussing at near point

In Fig. 18.6, the shaded lens forms a virtual image at a convenient distance for the observer, most effectively at the near point for which the observer's eye is accommodated. To achieve a magnification with the lens, the object must be placed within the focal length in front of the lens (see Example 17.7(c)). For the observer, the object appears then under an angle $\theta \cong h_o/p$, which leads to an angular magnification of $m = (h_o/p) / (h_o/s_0) = s_0/p$. The object distance p is determined using the thin lens formula (with $q = -s_0$):

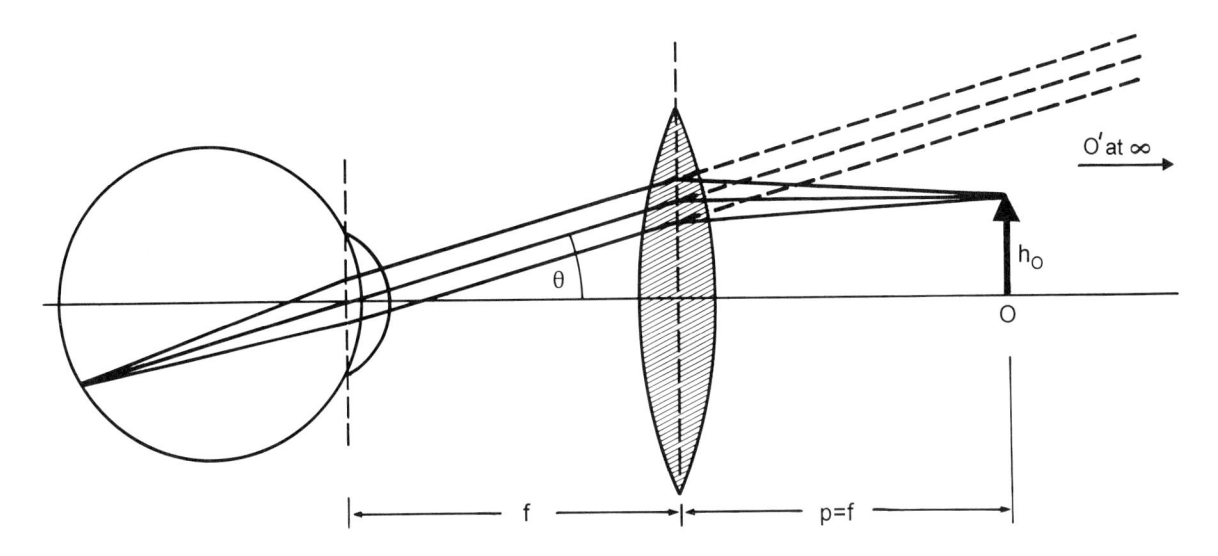

Fig. 18.5: A magnifying glass is used to observe an object O with relaxed eyes. The lens simulates an object O′ at infinite distance.

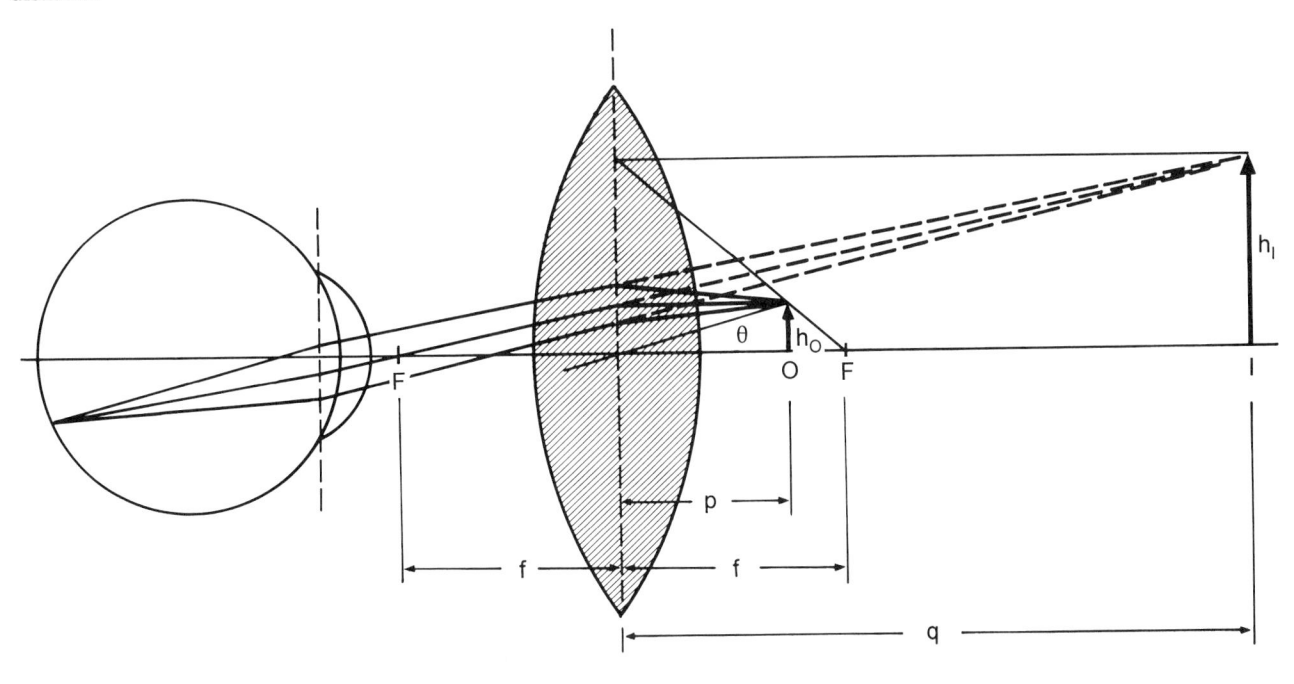

Fig. 18.6: A magnifying glass is used to observe the same object as studied in Fig. 18.5, but the eye is focussed on an image I of the object O at the near point of the observer.

$$\frac{1}{f} = \frac{1}{p} + \frac{1}{q} = \frac{1}{p} + \frac{1}{-s_0} \quad (5)$$

$$\Rightarrow \quad p = \frac{s_0 f}{s_0 + f}$$

Substituting p from Eq. (5) into the formula for the angular magnification m we find:

$$m = \frac{s_0}{s_0 f}(s_0 + f) = \frac{(s_0 + f)}{f} = 1 + \frac{s_0}{f} \quad (6)$$

This is a larger value than we found in section 18.2.1 for case I. Therefore, the result in Eq. (6) is called the maximum angular magnification for a given lens.

Example 18.1
What is the maximum angular magnification of a lens with focal length f = 10 cm, and what is the angular magnification of the same lens when a relaxed eye observes the object?

Solution: For the maximum angular magnification we use Eq. (6): m = 1 + (25 cm)/(10 cm) = 3.5. Thus, the magnifying glass works less effectively for the relaxed eye as we find from Eq. (4) that m = (25 cm)/(10 cm) = 2.5.

18.3. Optical compound microscope

To achieve angular magnifications larger than a value of m = 20 – 30, a single magnifying lens is no longer sufficient. Using Eq. (6) we find that an angular magnification of m ≥ 26 requires a lens with a focal length with a value f ≤ 1 cm. To significantly exceed this angular magnification, compound microscopes are used with two or more lenses. An instrument with two lenses is sketched in Fig. 18.7. It combines an *objective lens*, which has a very short focal length of f_O < 1 cm, and an *eyepiece* (ocular lens), which has a focal length f_E of a few centimeters. The two lenses are separated by a distance L with L ≫ f_O, f_E. The instrument allows the observer to look with the eyepiece at the image of the objective lens, i.e., $I_O = O_E$. The small object, which is to be viewed, is positioned just outside the focal length of the objective lens. This generates a real, enlarged image I_O far from the lens. This image lies within the focal distance of the eyepiece. Therefore, treating the image of the objective lens as the object for the eyepiece leads to a virtual image I_E. To obtain a maximum overall angular magnification, the eye has to focus on the image I_E. Note that Fig. 18.7 also shows several other lines which help constructing the two images, I_O and I_E. As for the single lens that we discussed before, these constructions include a light ray which is incident on the lens parallel to the optical axis and a second ray which is incident on the lens through the focal point of the lens. Fig. 18.7 illustrates the compound microscope conceptually; in a real instrument the intermediate image lies much further to the right, beyond the objective lens.

We can determine the total angular magnification achieved by the arrangement of lenses shown in Fig. 18.7. Two contributions have to be combined: the magnification of the objective lens, M_O, and the angular magnification of the eyepiece, m_E. We use the magnification for the objective lens because the size of the

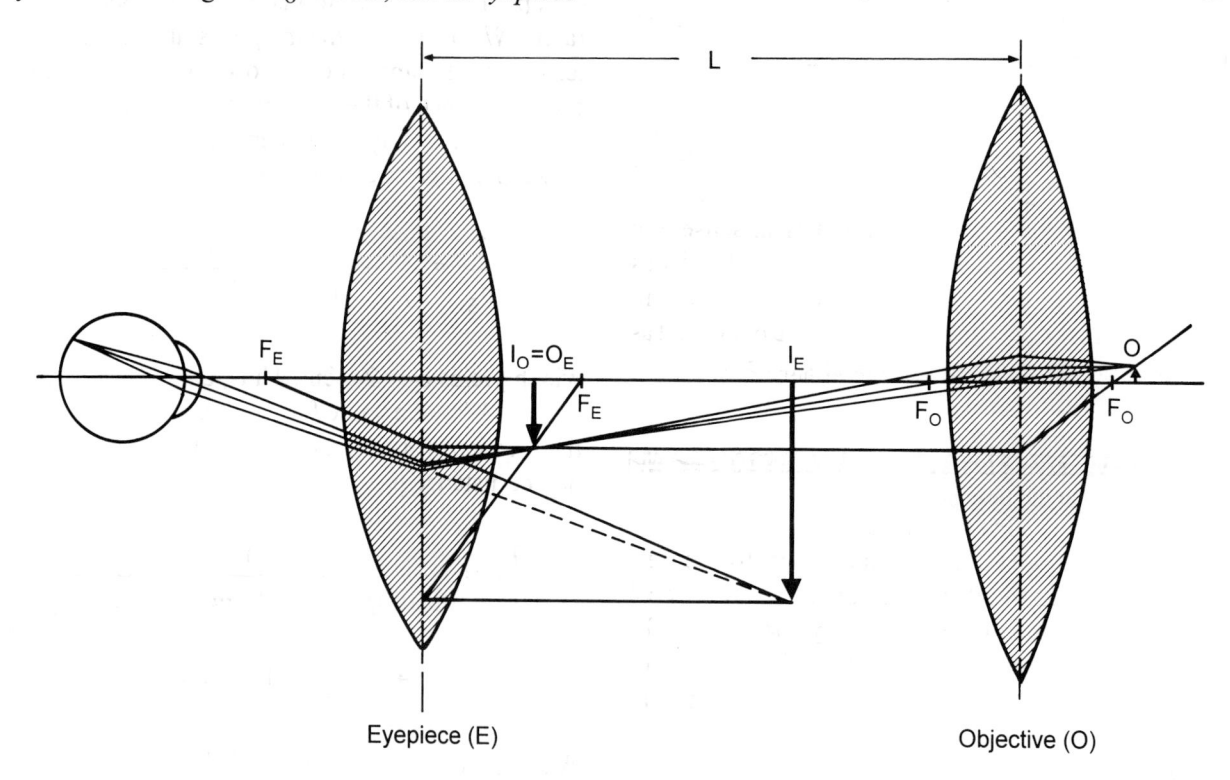

Fig. 18.7: A typical compound microscope with objective lens O and eyepiece E at a distance L which coincides with the length of the tube of the microscope. The final image I_E is constructed with the same three light rays we used for single lenses and mirrors before.

image I_O does not depend on the position of the observer. In turn, the angular magnification of the eyepiece is used since we want to know the total angular magnification seen by the observer. For a relaxed eye of the observer, we find from the definitions above (Eqs. (1) and (4)):

$$(I) \quad M_O = -\frac{q_O}{p_O} \cong -\frac{L}{f_O}$$
$$(II) \quad m_E = \frac{s_0}{f_E} \quad (7)$$

with $s_0 = 25$ cm for the near point of the observer. The second part of formula (I) is obtained from Eq. (1) and the approximation $q_O - f_O \cong L$. M_O is negative since the image of the objective lens is inverted. The total angular magnification of the two–lens arrangement is the product of both contributions,

$$m_{total} = M_O \, m_E \cong -\frac{L}{f_O}\frac{s_0}{f_E} \quad (8)$$

in which the term $M_O m_E$ is the exact formula and the last term provides an approximate result. Both relations in Eq. (8) can be used to calculate the total angular magnification of a compound microscope with two lenses. As illustrated in Example 18.3, the approximate formula in Eq. (8) is much easier to apply.

Note that we did not use Eq. (6) to express the angular magnification, assuming that the observer's eye is focussed at the near point. Two reasons allow us to use Eq. (4) instead of Eq. (6): in a practical sense, the observer's eyes tire much faster when required to focus on the near point all the time. Also, the additional term +1 in the last bracket of Eq. (6) can often be neglected as the firm term is much larger than one: $s_0 f_E \gg 1$.

Example 18.2
A microscope has two interchangeable objective lenses. One has a focal length 20 mm and the other has a focal length 2 mm. Also available are two eyepieces with focal lengths 2.5 cm and 5 cm. If the length of the microscope is 18 cm, what range of total angular magnifications is available?

Solution: We substitute $f_O = 2.0$ cm or $f_O = 0.2$ cm, L = 18.0 cm, and $f_E = 2.5$ cm or $f_E = 5.0$ cm in the approximate form of Eq. (8), using $s_0 = 25.0$ cm. We obtain four angular magnifications, $m_{total} = -54, -99, -540$ and -990, i.e., the microscope offers total angular magnifications between 50 and 1000.

Example 18.3
The length of a microscope tube is given as 15.0 cm. The focal length of the objective lens is 1.0 cm and the focal length of the eyepiece is 2.5 cm. What is the total angular magnification of the microscope if the eye of the observer is relaxed?
(a) Calculate the exact result using Eq. (8), and
(b) calculate the approximate result using Eq. (8).

Solution part (a): To apply the exact formula in Eq. (8), we need to determine the angular magnification of the eyepiece, m_E, and the magnification of the objective lens, M_O.

m_E is obtained from the focal length of the eyepiece, f_E, directly:

$$m_E = \frac{s_0}{f_E} = \frac{25.0 \, [cm]}{2.5 \, [cm]} = 10.0 \quad (9)$$

The magnification of the objective lens is defined by the object distance and the image distance of the lens, $M_O = -q_O/p_O$. Both of these terms have to be calculated separately. We begin with the image distance of the objective lens. For the compound microscope, q_O is related to the object distance of the eyepiece via $q_O = L - p_E$, in which L is still the distance between the two lenses in the microscope. p_E can be determined with the given data:

$$\frac{1}{p_E} = \frac{1}{f} - \frac{1}{q_E} = \frac{1}{2.5\,[cm]} - \frac{1}{\infty} \quad (10)$$

which yields $p_E = 2.5$ cm. Thus, $q_O = L - p_E = 12.5$ cm.

With the value for the image distance, we apply the thin lens formula to the objective lens to obtain its object distance p_O:

$$\frac{1}{p_O} = \frac{1}{f_O} - \frac{1}{q_O} = \frac{1}{1.0\,[cm]} - \frac{1}{12.5\,[cm]}$$
$$\Rightarrow \quad p_O = 1.09 \; cm \quad (11)$$

We know now all the data needed to determine the magnification of the objective lens. Note that we do not calculate the angular magnification of the objective lens as the observer is not involved in the process of image formation at the objective lens. We find with Eq. (1):

$$M_O = -\frac{q_O}{p_O} = -\frac{12.5[cm]}{1.09[cm]} = -11.5 \quad (12)$$

Thus, the total angular magnification of the microscope is given by:

$$m_{total} = M_O \, m_E = -11.5 \cdot 10.0$$
$$\Rightarrow m_{total} = -115 \quad (13)$$

Solution part (b): The problem becomes a simple substitution problem when applying Eq. (8) in its approximate form:

$$m_{total} = -\frac{L}{f_O}\frac{s_0}{f_E} = -\frac{0.15[m]\,0.25[m]}{0.01[m]\,0.025[m]} \quad (14)$$
$$\Rightarrow m_{total} = -150$$

The difference between Eqs. (13) and (14) illustrates the extend to which the second approach yields an approximate result. For most applications, the result in Eq. (14) is sufficient.

18.4. Electron microscope

The light microscope discussed in the previous section becomes useless when the object size is of the order of the wavelength of visible light, i.e., $h_O \le 200$ nm. To observe even smaller objects, a microscope would be needed which uses light of smaller wavelength than visible light, e.g. X–rays. This is not a practical solution. A significant improvement is, however, achieved when using electron beams. We discuss in Chapter 21 that electrons can not only be treated as particles, but under certain conditions act also as if they are waves. The electron microscope is a set–up which exploits the wave properties of electrons. Louis de Broglie determined a formula for the corresponding wavelength of electrons; for electrons of energy 300 eV this wavelength is only 0.07 nm, and even shorter when the energy of the electrons is further increased.

Before describing the optic properties of the electron microscope, the methods of generating and manipulating electron beams are briefly discussed as these differ significantly from those of visible light.

Generation of free electrons

When electrons behave like particles they obey the gas laws we derived in Chapter 6. They are also scattered easily due to their low mass. Therefore, to use electrons, they have to be generated in an evacuated system (e.g. the tube of a standard TV set). In a vacuum, free electrons are generated by evaporation from a hot metallic filament (*Richardson effect*, named after Sir Owen Williams Richardson). The work associated with removing an electron from a metal is called the *work function* and typically lies between 1 eV and 5 eV (which corresponds

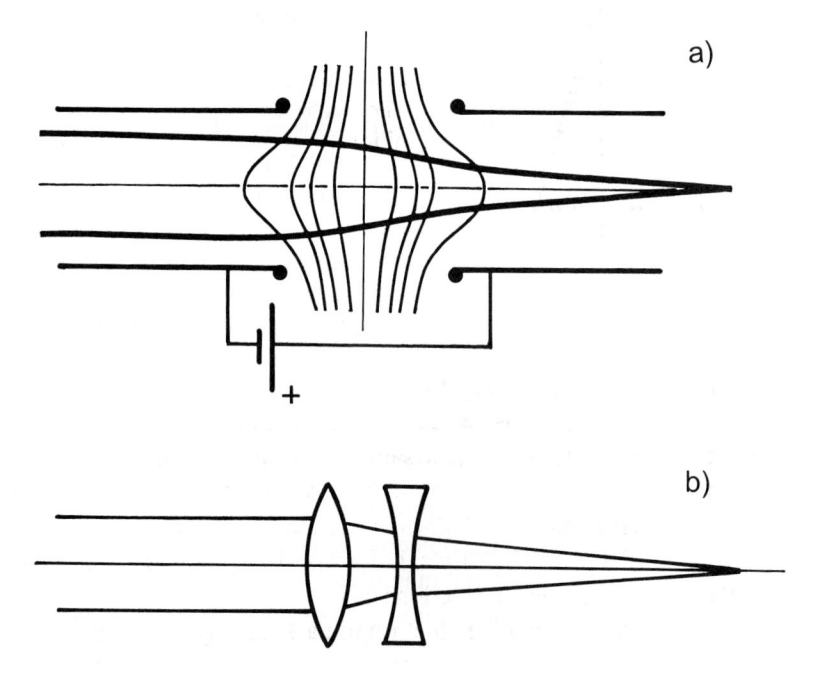

Fig. 18.8: (a) An electron lens, based on two cylindrical conducting tubes with a gap. A potential difference is applied between the two tubes, causing an electric field similar to a parallel plate arrangement but with the lines of equal potential reaching into the tube on both sides. The solid lines show how a wide beam of parallel electrons is focussed in the device.
(b) The net effect of the device in part (a) on the electron beam corresponds to the sequential combination of a converging and a diverging lens for light rays.

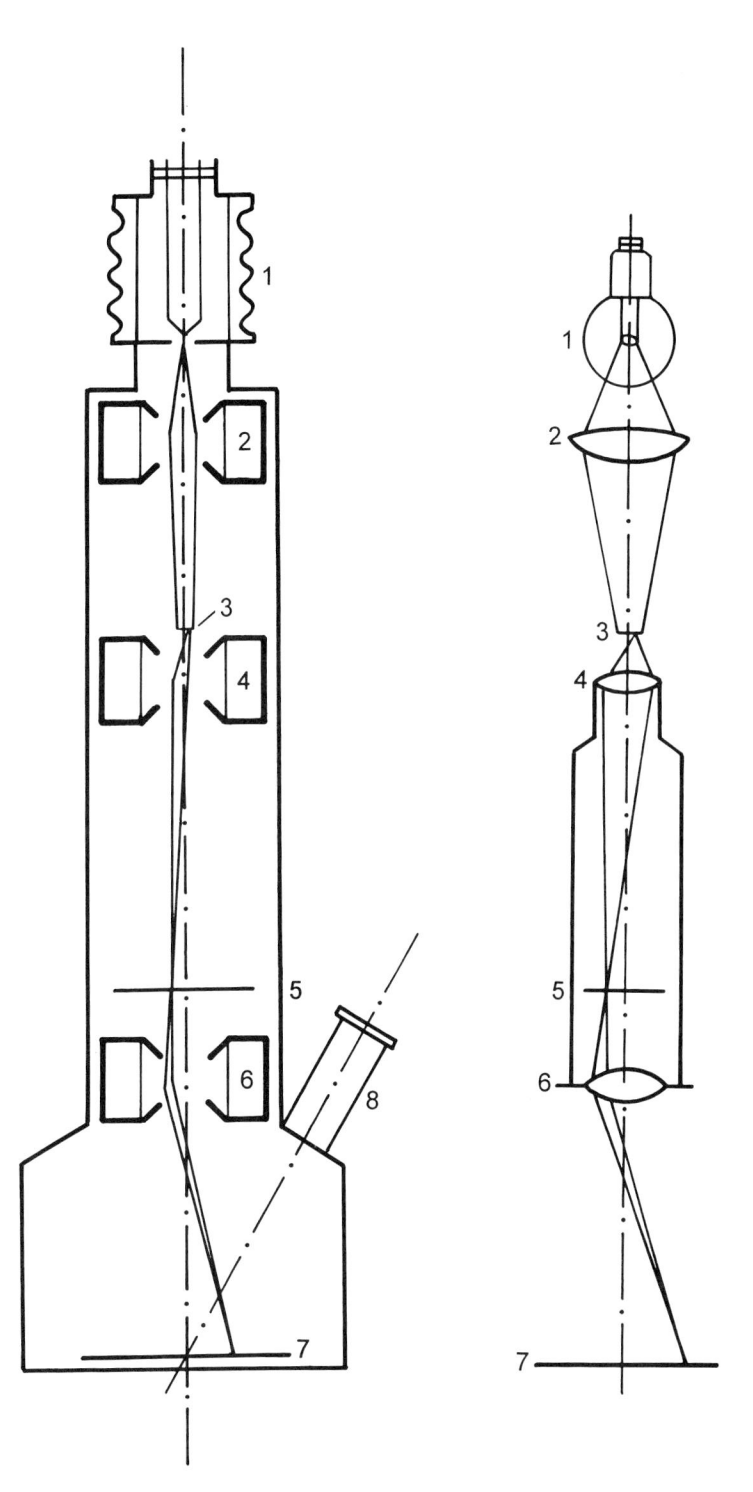

Fig. 18.9: Comparison of an electron microscope (left) and an optical microscope (right). The numbers indicate corresponding components in both systems:
(1) the radiation source,
(2) a lens to focus the beam on the object for maximum illumination,
(3) the object,
(4) the objective lens,
(5) the intermediate image, labelled I_0 in Fig. 18.7,
(6) the eyepiece (ocular lens), and
(7) the recording film or the fluorescent screen.
The electron microscope has an additional magnifying glass (8) for observation of the screen.

to 1.6×10^{-19} J and 8.0×10^{-19} J). At room temperature, electrons have an energy of 1/40 eV, i.e., about 1 % of the energy needed to escape from a metal. The fraction of electrons with sufficient energy increases significantly when the temperature of the metal is increased to temperatures close to its melting point. Alternatively, electrons can be pulled out of a metal with a high electric field (*field emission microscope*).

Manipulation of free electrons

In order to use electrons in an analogous fashion to light in a microscope, the same type of manipulations must be possible, i.e., we must be able to vary the trajectory of electrons (like light is reflected on mirrors) and focus electrons (like light is focussed in a converging lens). Small angle reflections of an electron beam are obtained by allowing the electron to pass through a parallel plate capacitor with the electron beam directed parallel to the plates. The electrons accelerate toward the positive plate while they pass through the device, leading to a deflection of the electron beam by an angle, which is a function of the voltage across the plates and the initial speed of the electron.

Electron lenses are either magnetic devices or consist of two metallic tubes which the electrons pass through in sequence, as shown in Fig. 18.8. When a potential difference is established between the two tubes, an electric field forms in the gap. This focuses the electron beam, as illustrated in the figure.

With these components introduced, we can compare the electron microscope and the optical microscope in Fig. 18.9. In the electron microscope, an electron beam is generated in the electron source, then electrically extracted from the source and focussed onto the objective plane. After passing through the object, which must be very thin, the electron beam forms an initial image which is then focussed onto a fluorescent screen to produce the final image of the electron microscope. The observer uses a standard light microscope to look at the fluorescent screen. This is possible because the electrons striking the ZnS or ZnSe coating of the screen cause visible light emission in the same fashion light is emitted from a TV screen.

18.5. Problems

P–18.1
Two converging lenses which have focal lengths of $f_1 = 10.0$ cm and $f_2 = 20.0$ cm are placed $L = 50$ cm apart. The final image is shown in Fig. 18.10.
(a) How far to the left of the first lens is the object placed if $l = 31$ cm?
(b) What is the combined magnification (not the total angular magnification in this case!) of the two lenses using the same data as in part (a)?

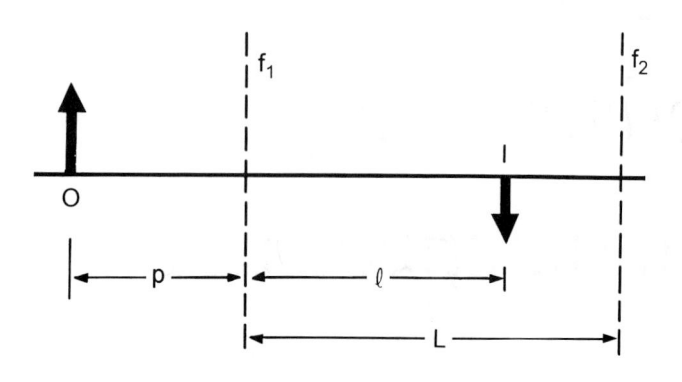

Fig. 18.10 for problem P–18.1

P–18.2
A magnifying glass is used to examine the structural details of a human hair. The hair is held 3.5 cm in front of the magnifying glass, and the image is 25.0 cm from the eye.
(a) What is the focal length of the magnifying glass?
(b) What angular magnification is achieved?

P–18.3
A microscope has an objective lens with $f = 16.22$ mm and an eyepiece with $f = 9.5$ mm. With the length of the microscope's barrel set at 29.0 cm, the diameter of an erythrocyte's image subtends an angle of 1.43 mrad with the eye. If the final image distance is 29.0 cm from the eyepiece, what is the actual diameter of the erythrocyte? Hint: Start with the size of the final image. Then use the thin lens formula for each lens to find their combined magnification. Use this magnification to calculate the object size in the final step.

Summary

Definitions:
- Near point $s_0 = 25$ cm for standard healthy eye.
- Angular magnification: $m = \theta/\theta_0$, with θ the angle subtended by the object and θ_0 the angle subtended by the same object placed at the near point.

Laws:
- Angular magnification m of a lens:
(I) for relaxed eye:

$$m = \frac{s_0}{f}$$

(II) for eye focussed at near point:

$$m = 1 + \frac{s_0}{f}$$

- Total angular magnification of a compound microscope:

$$m_{total} = M_O\, m_E \cong -\frac{L}{f_O}\left(\frac{s_0}{f_E} + 1\right)$$

in which the index O stands for objective lens and the index E stands for eyepiece. L is the distance between both lenses.

Chapter XIX

Color Vision

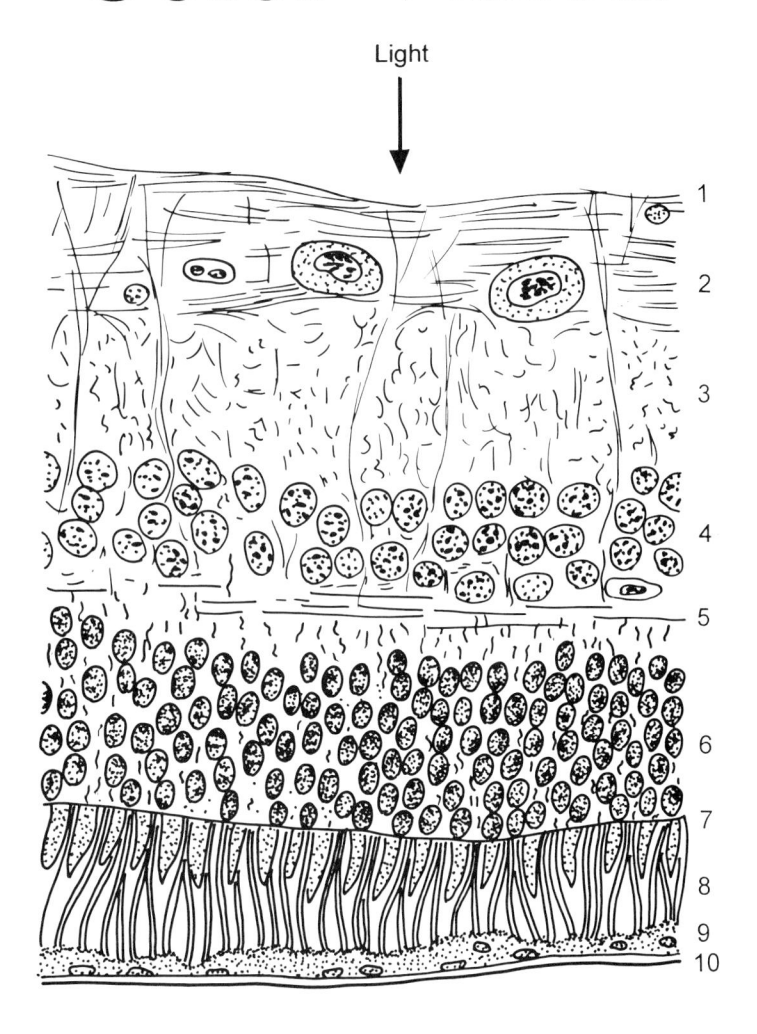

Light
↓

Magnetism and electromagnetic spectrum

COLOR VISION
MAGNETISM AND ELECTROMAGNETIC SPECTRUM

Colors are a physiological measure of the various wavelengths in the visible part of the electromagnetic spectrum. This spectrum consists of all waves which travel in vacuum with the speed of light carried by their own electric and magnetic fields.

The magnetic force is observed when moving electric charges interact. It is proportional to the two currents for a set of parallel conductors. The force is also inversely proportional to the distance between the conductors. The magnetic field is obtained from the magnetic force by redefining one of the currents as a test current; thus, a single conductor carrying an electric current possesses a magnetic field. The magnetic field resumes its simplest possible form (constant direction and magnitude) inside a solenoid.

When charges oscillate along an antenna, alternating magnetic fields (when the charges move) and electric fields (when the charges are separated like in a dipole) cause electromagnetic waves which allow energy to propagate radially away from the antenna.

Electromagnetic waves are transverse waves as the propagation direction is perpendicular to both electric and magnetic fields. The electric field vector cannot oscillate across an interface, allowing light to be polarized during refraction.

The visible part of the electromagnetic spectrum constitutes the major fraction of the light reaching the surface of the Earth from the sun. This is due to the black body radiation emitted by the sun and the absorption occurring in Earth's atmosphere.

We have learned a great deal about the manipulation of light in the two previous chapters. We saw how it travels to the observer, either as a straight light ray or modified with reflecting mirrors or refracting surfaces and lenses. The simple concepts of ray optics allowed us also to follow light through the eye of the observer, from entering the cornea to forming an image at the back on the retina. At no point in the whole discussion did we need to refer to the concept of color, nor did we find any concept which would allow us access to defining colors. Yet, colors matter to us as much as a focussed vision.

A famous example of a human struggling with problems of color vision is the impairment of vision of the French impressionist Claude Monet (1840 – 1926). He reported the first signs of cataracts in 1908 suffering thereafter from a steady deterioration of his eye sight. He was operated twice in 1923 with only partial success. During the later period of his life he chose a narrow number of motives, painting since 1906 repeatedly water lilies and the Japanese bridge across the pond in his garden in Giverny near Paris, France. He also kept a diary. It is interesting to correlate his late paintings with his progressive ailment and the changes due to the operations.

The following are two excerpts from Monet's diary. He wrote in 1918: "I can no longer perceive colors with the same intensity, I do not paint light with the old accuracy. Red appears muddy, pink appears insipid. The intermediate tones escape me. Initially I tried to pretend all this doesn't happen to me. How often did I try to ... recapture the freshness that has disappeared from my palette! It's a wasted effort. What I paint is more and more dark, like an old picture. When I compare my paintings now with my former work, I am seized by a frantic rage. I have slashed all my canvases with a knife." By about that time his eyesight had deteriorated to the point where the cataracts had discolored his lenses in a yellow–brownish tint. Several dominantly yellowish paintings date from that period.

Cataract surgery was done in early 1923 on his right eye only. However, his cataract glasses were of poor quality. Now he observed: "I see blue, but I no longer see red or yellow. This bothers me very much since I know that these colors exist. I know that there is red and yellow, a special green and a particular shade of violet on my palette, but I do not see them anymore as I saw them before. I only recall the color impressions they gave me". Paintings dating from that period are predominantly blue.

There are two reasons why the concept of color

has not yet entered the physical discussion:

(I) The concept of color can only be developed with the wave model of light. Chapter 17, in which we studied the properties of light with the simplified ray model, allowed us to describe how light travels between different points in space. In the current chapter we will use the wave model to separate the various color components of white light and discuss the properties of these components.

(II) The formation and detection of light were assumed in Chapter 17 but not discussed. The concept of color based on the wave model is a necessary prerequisite for the discussion of light formation and detection. However, we also need the corpuscle model of light and the atomic model of matter for a thorough discussion of this issue. Thus, the emission and absorption of light by matter will be discussed in Chapter 21.

We devote an entire chapter to the issue of color because proceeding beyond the concepts of Chapters 17 and 18 in developing the field of optics meets with several challenges: first, the wave model of light is based on two fundamental physical disciplines, electricity and magnetism. Of these, we have only discussed electricity in Chapters 9 and 13. Thus, an introduction to magnetism and the combination of electric and magnetic phenomena as electromagnetic waves has to proceed our discussion of the wave properties of light. Secondly, in no other area of biophysics must we distinguish between the objective laws of physics and our subjective perception as carefully as in the case of interpreting the color images formed on the retina. This is due to the experimentally inseparable physicochemical processes of image formation and light detection and the psychological process of interpretation by the brain.

This second point is illustrated with three self–test examples on the back–covers of the textbook and the solutions manual. There you find a pudding on a dish (Fig. 19.1), (II) a thunderbolt striking the ground from a cloud (Fig. 19.2), and (III) a single red fish in one of two adjacent fish–bowls (Fig. 19.3). If you follow carefully the instructions below, you will become aware how each of these three simple images can irritate the interplay of physical vision and psychological seeing of the picture.

We begin with Fig. 19.1, which shows a pudding on the back–cover of the solutions manual. As kids, most of us liked pudding, not just for its taste but also for the funny way in which it wobbles on a plate. Obviously, the ability to wobble on the plate should be limited to the real thing; a pudding on a picture cannot do the same, or can it? The following works best in dimmed light. Hold Fig. 19.1 at arms length and slowly move it left and right (back and forth somewhere between 5 cm and 20 cm, about once every half-second to a second). You should now see the pudding wobble.

Of course, the pudding on the picture did not really wobble. This is an optical illusion based on the difference in colors, with the pudding a reddish–brown and the background a bluish–green. It works because our vision for different colors in not equal, in particular, our vision of red differs significantly from our vision of blue and green in that the eye needs much longer to switch to the next color impression where it was seeing red. This is usually not a handicap because the brain processes the signals for red different than for the other basic colors. The pudding allows us to exploit this timing issue.

That red vision is different from blue and green vision is further illustrated with Fig. 19.2, which shows a lightning bolt in the top frame on the back of the textbook. Again, we need dimmed light. Hold Fig. 19.2 at usual reading distance and focus for a while on the blue sky left of the lightning bolt. Now let your eyes jump fast back and forth looking at the blue sky right and left of the lightning bolt. Do this with a few jumps per second. You should see the lightning bolt flash each time as if it were a real lightning bolt.

What happens? Again, the eye adjusts fast to seeing blue where ever there is blue in your field of vision. However, it takes the areas on the retina a little longer to notice that there is no longer red where there was red just before. Thus, for a split second the retina sends a signal for red and blue to the brain at the area where the image of the lightning bolt was formed just a moment ago. The brain adds the blue and red, which makes almost white, thus the flash. Its a flash since our color vision is highly developed, optical illusions of this type work only for a very short instant until the eye and the brain have sorted out what image to communicate to your consciousness.

In an attempt to dismiss such irritating observations, one may blame the dimming of the light. But sure enough, such illusions work also in bright daylight. To convince you, let us look at Fig. 19.3 which shows a fish and two fish–bowls in the bottom frame on the back of the textbook. There is one fish, and the right fish–bowl is empty, right? Maybe not: hold Fig. 19.3 at usual reading distance from your eyes and focus on the fish in the bowl at the left. You need to do this for a while, a minute is recommended for the best effect. Then suddenly look at the black dot in the empty fish–bowl. Sure enough there is a red fish, you see it for a split second. Even more amazing is the fact that the bowl around the fish turns from the unnatural white to a proper bluish–green.

Again, everything is gone very fast. But the observations are valuable in trying to understand how the brain struggles with the information arriving from the eye: at first, the brain accepts the information of the eye at face value. Since the retina encounters the delay in erasing a red impression as discussed above, looking at a red surface for a longer time saturates the impression, to the point where the brain turns the signal from those areas of the retina off. When the sudden change in image occurs, the brain continues to interpret as red the same area as before. But your brain also realizes that your eyes moved to the right bowl and it remembers that the right bowl is plain white. Rather than waiting for the red impression to fade away, the brain has the means to correct the problem even faster: internally it adds blue and green impressions to the image from the retina and, thus, is able to communicate a white impression to your consciousness. Unfortunately, this adding isn't limited to the exact boundaries of the fish, therefore occur the bluish–green water impression around the fish; this is an impression created without any involvement of the eye!

Should we worry, therefore, which of all the things we think we see are in reality made up by our brain? Experience tells us no. After all, vision has been developed in a long evolutionary process to exploit the light which reaches us from our environment to give us an edge in the struggle for survival. Thus, we can safely assume that the glitches in the vision system are minimized. Indeed, the illusion in Fig. 19.3 works only because the picture contains a second, identical fish–bowl and a black dot to define where to focus. Usually our eyes move a lot autonomously to prevent such an effect from fooling us.

Still, the three illusions in Figs. 19.1, 19.2 and 19.3 should motivate us to investigate the issue of color. After all, only once we have developed the concept color can we truly claim that we understand our vision.

19.1. The anatomy of color vision

We begin with the micro–anatomy of the retina to identify the detection systems of light. As shown in Fig. 19.4, light arriving at the retina passes through three layers of tissue to reach about 120 million retinal rods and 3 – 6 million retinal cones. These light receptors are embedded in the neuroepithelium just inside of Bruch's membrane, which is the barrier between the eye and the brain. The fact that two different types of light detectors exist hints that there must be various parameters characterizing the incoming light which the eye measures.

The rods are only sensitive to the brightness of the light, thus, they produce a black and white picture. The cones in turn are color–sensitive. In 1807, Thomas

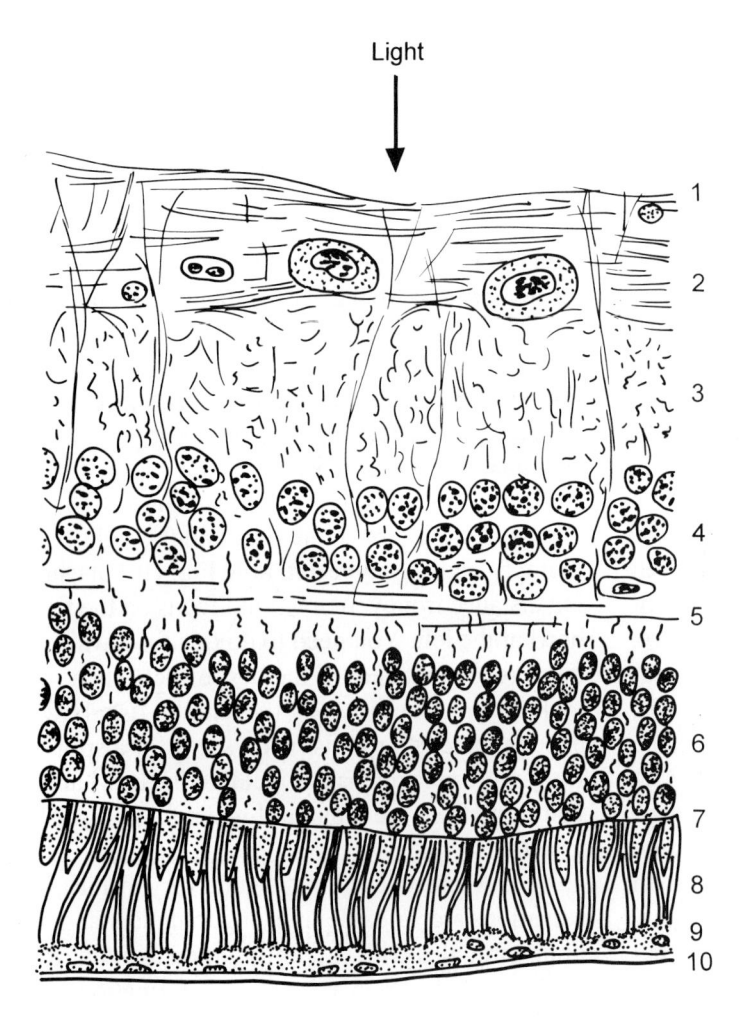

Fig. 19.4: Cross–section of the retina. (1) Bruch's membrane, which is the boundary layer to the brain. The first neuron consists of: (2) the retinal pigmented epithelium, (3) the neuroepithelium with the light sensitive rods and cones, (4) the membrana limitans externa, (5) the external granular layer and (6) the external reticular layer. The second neuron consists of: (7) the internal granular layer and (8) the internal reticular layer. The third neuron consists of: (9) the optic nerve's ganglion cells and (10) the membrana limitans interna, which forms the interface to the vitreous body.

Young postulated that the retina must contain at least three independent color receptors to enable us to see colors the way we do. While there is still some debate about the exact details of the mechanism, Young's receptors have indeed been identified as the retinal cones; the chemical properties of these cones vary to allow for sensitivity in three different color intervals.

Have a second look at Fig. 19.4. It is certainly surprising that the cones and the rods are embedded so deep in the retina. But even if we accept that they are located at the end close to Bruch's membrane, why does the remaining retinal layer consist of so many different layers as indicated in the figure? This has to do with a complex switching pattern of the signal paths between the cones and the rods at one end and the visual center of the brain on the other. Fig. 19.5 illustrates that a significant fraction of that data reduction is already achieved before the signal leaves the eye. The retina consists of three layers of neurons. The three neuron levels form an interconnected hierarchy of nerves as indicated in Fig. 19.5, where the signal of several receptors is combined. This indicates that there is a tremendous amount of information sent from the eyes to the brain.

But what is color? Do they exist as a real physical quantity, or does our brain make them up, assigning colors to objects to highlight them like we do when applying false–color enhancement in computer graphics? The latter is not necessarily unrealistic; after all, people with a red–green defect can as confidently drive on roads with traffic lights as people can who have no color–vision impediment. However, we can easily prove that colors are a real physical phenomenon. Foreign flags consist for most of us of arbitrarily chosen colors. For example, the flag of Italy has three vertical bars which are green, white and red, the flag of France has three vertical bars which are blue, white and red, and the bars of the flag of Nigeria are green, white and green. Would our brain assign such colors based on independent knowledge, it would often not know what to do with an isolated flag.

Thus, we start the current chapter with a description of what colors are and how light carries a particular color. The aim of that part of the chapter is to enable us to understand the experiment shown in Fig. 19.6. White light, arriving from the sun, is guided through a transparent slab of glass, which is cut in the shape of a prism. The light leaving the prism consists of many colors (rainbow effect) and the rays for the various colors do no longer travel parallel to each other. Developing the physical explanation of the phenomenon seen in Fig. 19.6 will take us a little while because we need to develop the wave model for light, which, in turn, requires concepts from electricity and magnetism. Thus, in the early part of this chapter fundamental properties of magnetism are introduced. In order to turn this chapter not into a chapter on magnetism though, only the components of magnetism necessary for the discussion of light waves are considered. Other important aspects of magnetism are postponed until Chapter 21 where they

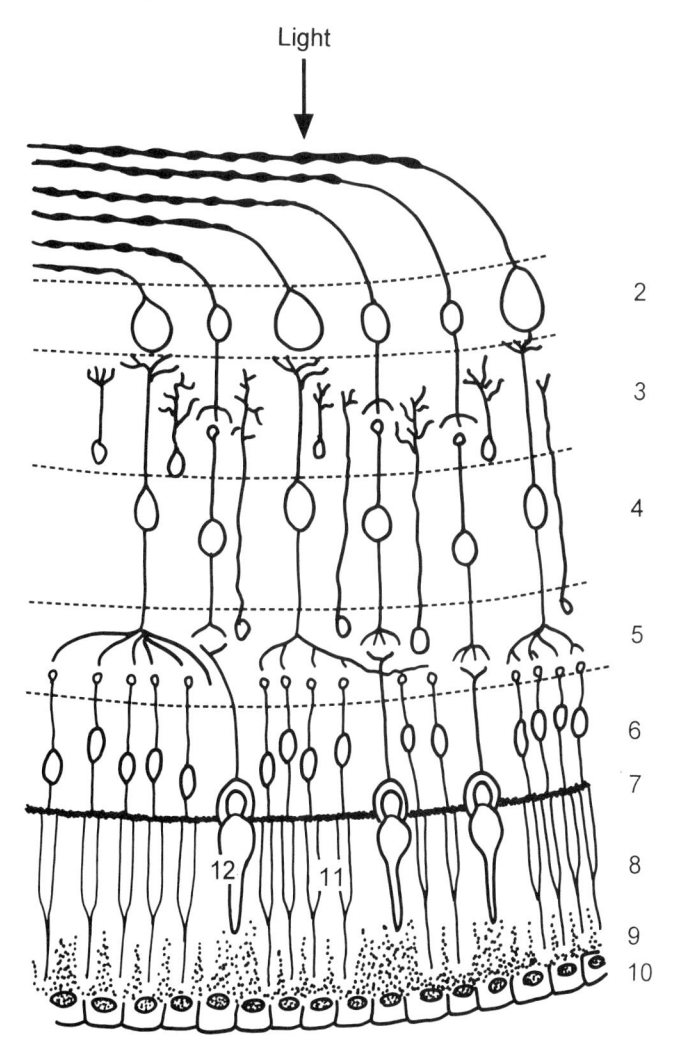

Fig. 19.5: Hierarchy of retinal nerves. The numbers on the side of the figure correspond to the same layers shown in Fig. 19.4. The sketch distinguishes rods (11) with a more extensive network of neurons, and cones (12).

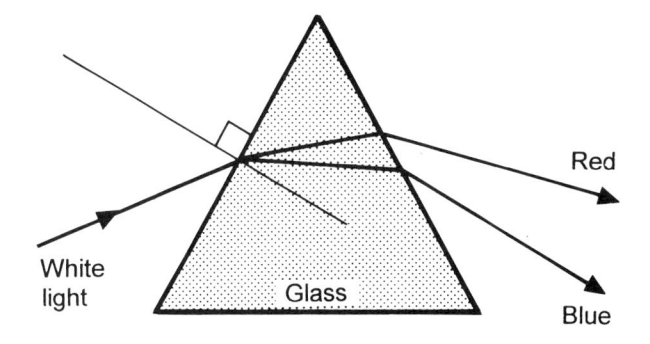

Fig. 19.6: When white light passes through a prism it is split into the colors of the rainbow.

become important in the understanding of atoms and molecules.

Once we have established the wave model of light, we will return to the color vision of humans. At that point this will seem less straight forward than now, because the wave model will after all not tell us that an object is red or green. All it will establish are two parameters, the frequency and the wavelength of light. Thus, the light from an object can be characterized e.g. by $\lambda = 700$ nm or by $f = 4.3 \times 10^{14}$ Hz, and the response of the cones in the retina depends solely on these values. Interestingly, it is in the end indeed only the brain that assigns color perception to the objects we see, except it does it not arbitrarily or based on experience, but based on the measurement of wavelengths done in the eye.

19.2. Towards a wave model of light: magnetism

The first time we encountered waves in this textbook was in Chapter 16 in the context of the motion of a piston vibrating around its equilibrium position. This vibration leads in a continuous medium to motion of gas elements adjacent to the piston. The interaction of the gas with neighboring gas elements causes the initial perturbation to propagate through the medium as a wave. Note that the medium itself does not travel with the wave but just vibrates locally around its equilibrium position, as we illustrated with a rope that is connected to a wall. The wave concept developed in Chapter 16 connected the parameters frequency, wavelength and velocity with which the wave travels through the medium.

However, we excluded in Chapter 16 explicitly light waves from the discussion due to fundamental differences to sound waves. The most striking difference is that light does not need a medium such as air; we see light from distant stars in spite of the vast empty space separating them from Earth. To apply the wave model to light we have to find some new physical properties which can propagate through space without a medium. We will find the electric field to be part of this mechanism. We have introduced the concept of the electric field in Chapter 9. But electric fields cannot propagate on their own, they need to be coupled with magnetic fields. To show this and how this coupling leads to a propagating wave we have to introduce the concept of magnetism first.

The discussion of magnetism is divided in two parts in this textbook. In the current chapter we introduce its fundamental properties, mostly following an analogy to the introduction of the electric phenomena in Chapter 9. Magnetism is associated with electric currents, for which we consider initially the currents in a wire and later, as a generalization, changing electric fields. Combining electric and magnetic fields allows us to establish the properties of electromagnetic waves, which then includes visible light.

We return for a second discussion of magnetism in Chapter 21, where we abstract from a current to the motion of single charged particles. This enables us to understand such phenomena as the intensive radiation belts around the Earth and their relevance to human space exploration, but also explains applied analytical techniques such as mass spectrometry.

What may appear unusual about these two sections on magnetism is the fact that the most prominent everyday occurence of magnetism, the magnetic materials such as refrigerator magnets, do not form the starting point of the discussion. This has a conceptual and a practical reason:

(I) magnetism is closely related to electricity since the magnetic force is caused by electric currents. This is not obvious when looking at a permanent magnet since the electric current in this case is a peculiar feature of atomic properties and their collective interactions.

(II) Magnetic materials play practically no role in living organisms. The clinical use of magnetic effects in the human body, e.g. magneto–cardiograms of the heart, are based on the interpretation of magnetism as resulting from electric currents during the transport of an impulse in a nerve. Some bacteria synthesize in their cells linear strings of up to 20 magnetite particles (Fe_3O_4, which is also the iron–richest ore found on Earth). Magnetite responds to the Earth's magnetic field (essentially like the needle of a compass) allowing bacteria of the Northern Hemisphere to identify the direction towards north. The benefit to the bacteria is that they are able to identify directions independent of their immediate environment, allowing them to avoid moving in circles as we do when lost in the desert. Magnetic materials are also used by some species in the animal kingdom for orientation purposes. Magnetite particles are found in bees, pigeons (in the dura, which is the outer covering of the brain) and fish (for example the yellowfin tuna). Illustrating their purpose in these cases is complicated as these animals process a range of sensory information. Recent results suggest that migrating birds operate with three types of compasses to adjust to the significant deviation of the magnetic and geographic North Poles on Earth. The Savannah sparrow uses the magnetic compass, a compass associated with the position of stars at night and a visual compass using cues from the sky at sunset.

19.2.1. Magnetic force

In Chapter 9 we introduced the electric force based on Coulomb's experiment with charged spheres. In order to do that we established first that charges exist and that they are a property of particles independent of the mass. Trying to find magnetic monopoles in the same fashion to introduce the magnetic force remained unsuccessful. Thus, the magnetic force must be the result of properties of particles we already introduced.

In 1819, Hans Christian Oersted and André Marie Ampère established the magnetic force as the interaction between two electric currents. Fig. 19.7 shows two metallic wires of length l at a distance d. Varying the distance, the lengths and the electric currents I_1 and I_2 in both conductors, Ampère found that the magnitude of the magnetic force is proportional to the two currents and the length, and inversely proportional to the distance between the conductors:

$$|F_{mag}| \propto \frac{I_1 I_2}{d} l \quad \Rightarrow \quad \frac{|F_{mag}|}{l} \propto \frac{I_1 I_2}{d} \quad (1)$$

in which the second formulation represents the force per unit length of the conductor. Note that the two forces shown in Fig. 19.7, $\mathbf{F}_{1\,on\,2}$ and $\mathbf{F}_{2\,on\,1}$, are an action–reaction pair as defined by Newton's third law.

> *The magnetic force between two currents is proportional to each current and inversely proportional to the distance between the conductors.*

Because the electric force is a field force (i.e., not a contact force) we rewrote Coulomb's law by eliminating the mobile test charge from the system of fixed charges, thereby introducing the electric field due to the stationary charges. As we see from Fig. 19.7 the magnetic force

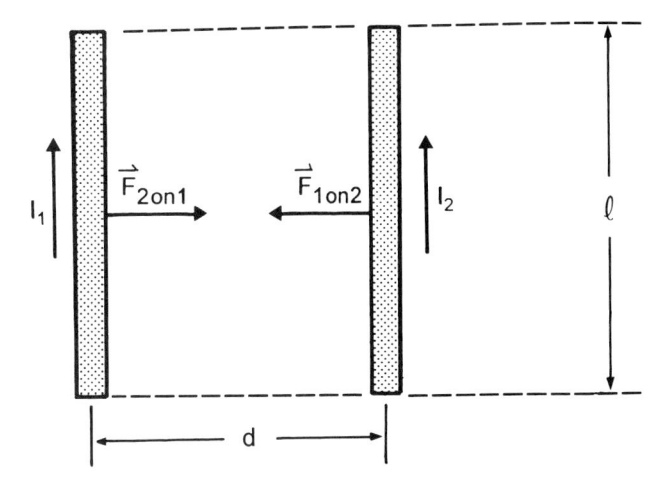

Fig. 19.7: Two parallel conductors of length l and distance d carry currents I_1 and I_2. As a result a magnetic force is observed, $\mathbf{F}_{2\,on\,1}$ acting on conductor 1 and $\mathbf{F}_{1\,on\,2}$ acting on conductor 2. The two forces shown are an action/reaction pair as defined by Newton's third law.

is also a field force. Therefore, we want to take the same approach and assign a magnetic field to a single current. That this is a reasonable approach is evident when considering how Oersted discovered the magnetic force between two currents in the first place: he accidentally noted that a compass needle responded when he sent an electric current through a wire nearby.

The definition of the magnitude of the magnetic field $|\mathbf{B}|$ follows from Eq. (1) with one of the currents identified as a test current and removed from the system:

$$|B| = \frac{\mu_0}{2\pi} \frac{I}{d} \quad (2)$$

> *The magnitude of the magnetic field of a conductor is proportional to the current and inversely proportional to the distance from the conductor.*

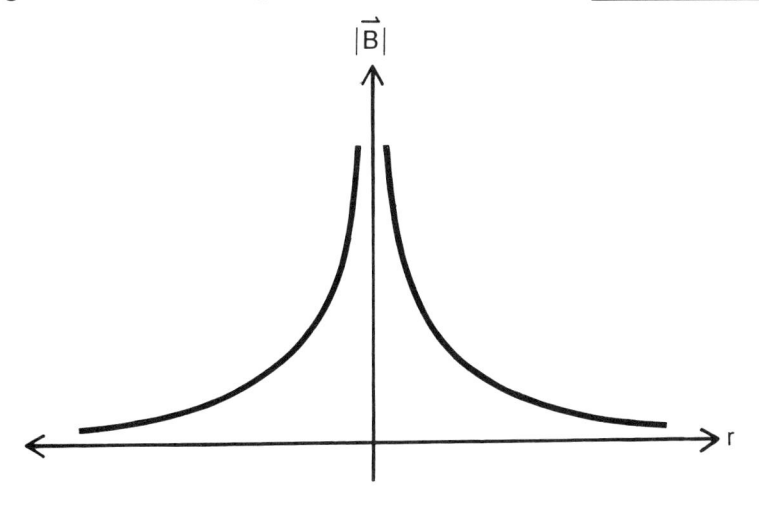

Fig. 19.8: Sketch of the magnitude of the magnetic field $|\mathbf{B}|$ as a function of distance r from a straight wire carrying an electric current.

Several comments are necessary for Eqs. (1) and (2):

(I) The magnitude of the magnetic field of a straight conductor is shown in Fig. 19.8. It has a cylindrical symmetry, i.e., the absolute value of the field is the same in all directions at a given distance from the conductor.

(II) The magnetic field is connected to the force per unit length of the conductors in Eq. (1), therefore, the length of the conductor is not a parameter in the definition of the magnetic field.

(III) We wrote Eq. (2) as an equation, which required the introduction of a proportionality constant, $\mu_0/2\pi$. This constant is introduced in an analogous fashion as the permittivity of vacuum in Chapter 9: the factor 2π takes the cylindrical symmetry of the magnetic field around a straight wire into account. μ_0 is called the *permeability of vacuum*, and has a value of $\mu_0 = 1.26 \times 10^{-6}$ N/A².

(IV) The unit of the permeability of vacuum and the unit of the magnetic field are derived from Eqs. (1) and (2): For μ_0 we relate the force in Eq. (1) with unit [N], the current with unit [A] and the length and distance with units [m] each. The unit of the magnetic field $|\mathbf{B}|$ follows from Eq. (2):

$$\left[\frac{N}{A^2}\frac{A}{m}\right] = \left[\frac{N}{Am}\right] = \left[\frac{N}{Cb\frac{m}{s}}\right] = [T] \quad (3)$$

The new unit is called *Tesla* [T], in honor of Nikola Tesla. You find several non–standard units still in use in the literature, including the unit Gauss [G] (named after Carl Friedrich Gauß) with the conversion 1 G = 1 × 10⁻⁴ T, and the unit Oersted [Oe] for $|\mathbf{B}|/\mu_0$ for which 1.0 Oe = 79.59 A/m. Typical values include the Earth's magnetic field at the surface, with the magnitude $|\mathbf{B}| = 5 \times 10^{-5}$ T, a standard bar magnet with $|\mathbf{B}| \approx 1 \times 10^{-2}$ T and the largest superconducting magnets with fields of up to 20 T.

(V) The direction of the magnetic field has to be treated carefully. We note from Fig. 19.7 that the magnetic force is directed perpendicular to the direction in which the current flows through the wires. Since the force is a vector, we have to be able to write the right hand side of Eq. (1) also as a vector. If the right hand side of Eq. (1) would contain only one quantity with vector character, that vector must point in the same direction as the force for mathematical reasons. However, none of the parameters on the right hand side can be written as a vector in that form. This leads to a vector product notation for Eq. (1).

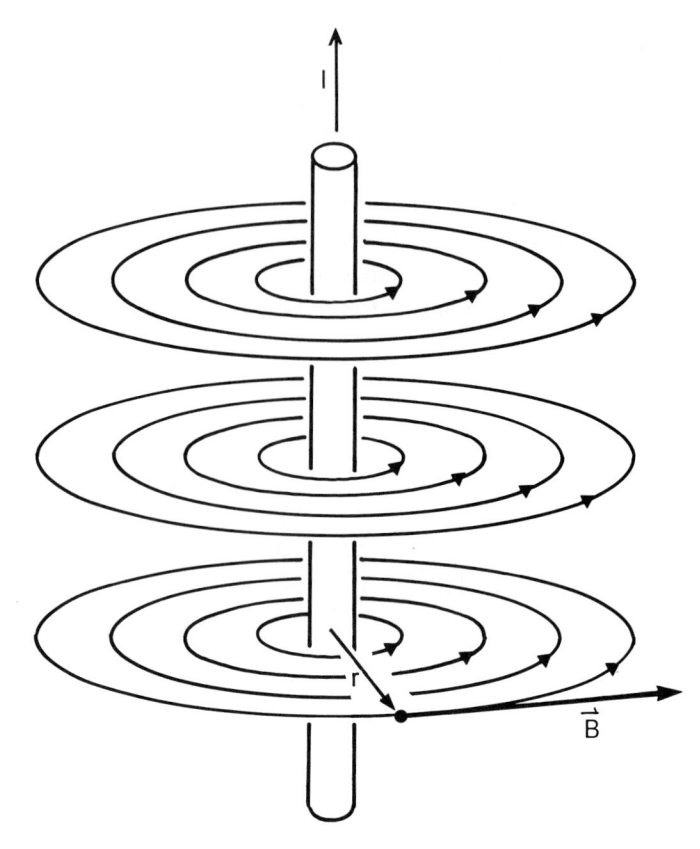

Fig. 19.9: The magnetic field is perpendicular to the direction of the current at any point in space near a current carrying conductor. The field is also perpendicular to the radius vector from the conductor to the point in space. Instead of drawing each magnetic field vector separately, the figure illustrates the direction of the magnetic field with thin lines connecting all points in a plane perpendicular to the conductor which have equal magnitude of the magnetic field.

The best way to see this is to consider Eq. (2). The magnetic field of a long straight wire is illustrated in Fig. 19.9: the magnetic field is perpendicular to the direction of the conductor carrying the current and is also perpendicular to the radial direction pointing away from the conductor. The circular lines in the figure connect positions of equal magnitude of the magnetic field. The direction of the magnetic field vector is at every point tangential to the field lines, as illustrated at one point in the figure. The direction of the magnetic field can be determined with a (modified) right hand rule: when the thumb points in the direction of the current (direction of flow of positive charges in the conductor) the remaining fingers of the right hand curl in the same fashion as the magnetic field.

Thus, Eq. (1) contains three vectors which are perpendicular to each other, The force, the direction of the flow of the current in the test wire, and the magnetic field of the original wire. This is the second time we encounter the need of the vector product notation to fully describe a physical phenomenon, the first time occurred when we discussed torque in Chapter 4. Like then, we circumvent the need to perform vector product operations: in the discussions in this textbook, we use the magnitude of the magnetic field in Eq. (2) for quantitative calculations. The directional information contained in the vector **B** is only referred to in a qualitative fashion based on Fig. 19.9. This restriction means in turn that we will not calculate components of the magnetic field vector in Cartesian coordinates.

Example 19.1

A straight wire is placed between the poles of a permanent horseshoe magnet. The magnet produces a uniform magnetic field of 2.0 T. The wire runs through the gap between the poles of the magnet, perpendicular to the direction of the magnetic field. The length of the wire is 0.3 m in the gap of the magnet. When the wire is connected to a battery, it carries a current. What current must flow to obtain a force of 0.98 N?

Solution: The horseshoe magnet provides the magnetic field acting on the wire. We combine Eqs. (1) and (2) for the force acting on the wire:

$$|F_{on\ wire}| = |B|\ I\ l \quad (4)$$

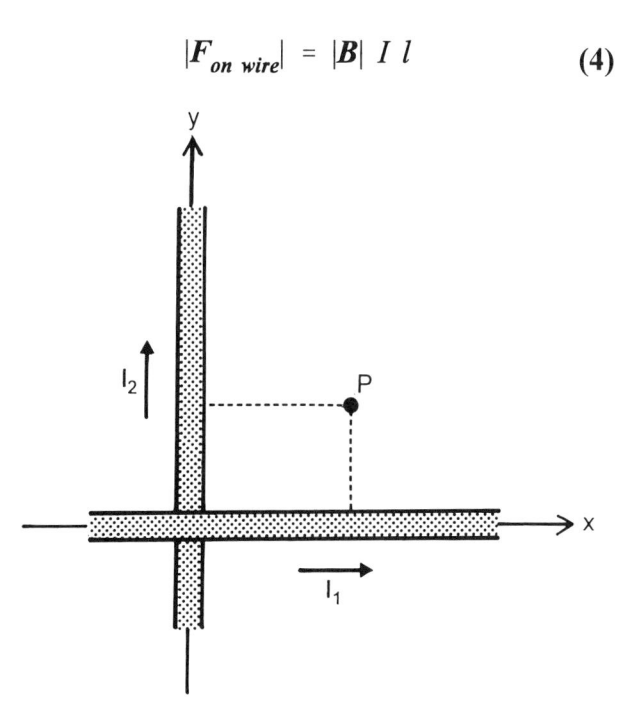

Fig. 19.10: Two straight conducting wires are positioned perpendicular to each other, each carrying a current as indicated. The magnetic field at point P is calculated in the text.

this leads to:

$$I = \frac{F}{l\ B} = \frac{0.98[N]}{0.3[m]\ 2.0[T]} = 1.63\ A \quad (5)$$

Note that the wire runs perpendicular to the direction of the magnetic field in this example. If the wire and the magnetic field have any other relative orientation, Eq. (4) is corrected in the form:

$$|F_{on\ wire}| = |B|\ I\ l\ \sin\theta \quad (6)$$

in which θ is the angle between the direction of the magnetic field and the direction normal to the cross–sectional area through which the current passes. In the current example, $\theta = 90^0$ or $\sin\theta = 1$, i.e., Eq. (6) becomes Eq. (4).

Example 19.2

Two long wires cross at the origin, as shown in Fig. 19.10. One wire runs along the x–axis and carries a current of $I_1 = 2$ A. The other wire runs along the y–axis and carries a current of $I_2 = 3$ A. What are the magnitude and direction of the magnetic field at the point P, which is located 4 cm from the x–axis and 6 cm from the y–axis?

Solution: If several currents are present in a system their magnetic fields are added at each point in space. Thus, we use Eq. (2) to calculate the magnitude of the magnetic field at point P for each of the two wires. For wire one:

$$|B_1| = \frac{\mu_0 I_1}{2\pi d_1} = \frac{1.26 \times 10^{-6} \left[\frac{N}{A^2}\right] 2[A]}{2\pi\ 0.04[m]} \quad (7)$$

$$\Rightarrow\quad |B_1| = 1.0 \times 10^{-5}\ T$$

and for wire 2:

$$|B_2| = \frac{\mu_0 I_2}{2\pi d_2} = \frac{1.26 \times 10^{-6} \left[\frac{N}{A^2}\right] 3[A]}{2\pi\ 0.06[m]} \quad (8)$$

$$\Rightarrow\quad |B_2| = 1.0 \times 10^{-5}\ T$$

The respective directions of the two contributions to the magnetic field at point P are determined with the right hand rule: for the current along the x–axis the magnetic field at P is directed out of the plane of the paper and for the current running along the y–axis the magnetic field at point P is directed into the plane of the paper. Thus, the two contributions have to be subtracted from each other. The net magnetic field at point P is therefore $\mathbf{B}_{net} = 0$ T.

When we developed the concept of electric field in Chapter 9 we noted that one benefit of the approach is to allow us to calculate the electric field for systems with large numbers of charges prior to studying the properties of the test charge in the field. While the calculation of the field may be a difficult mathematical task, once a formula for the field has been obtained it can be used in many contexts. This has proven particularly valuable for the parallel plate arrangement in Chapters 9 and 13: it allowed us to describe many experimental capacitor arrangements (including the nerve membrane) with a very simple formula for the electric field.

We proceed with the magnetic field concept again in analogy to the electric case. Instead of a straight wire, many other arrangements of one or several wires of practical interest have been studied. One particular arrangement was found which has a magnetic field with a simpler formula than Eq. (2). Like in the electric case, we study this arrangement in more detail as it provides us with a convenient model system for applications of magnetism.

The arrangement is called a *solenoid*, which is a single conductor that is curled as shown in Fig. 19.11.

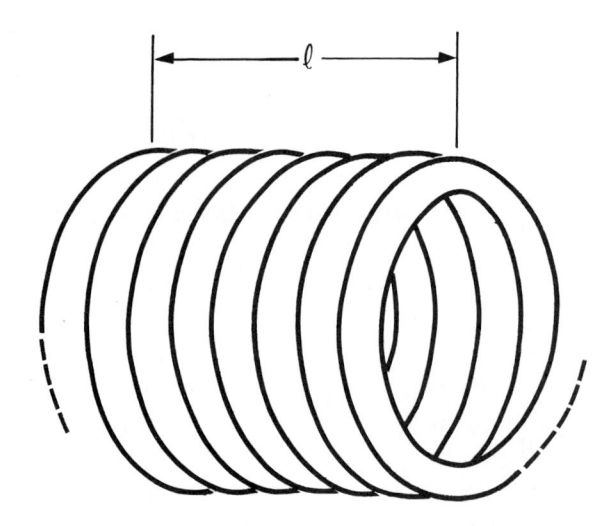

Fig. 19.11: A solenoid is a coiled conductor with a fixed radius of the coils and a constant number N of coils per length *l*.

The radius of the cross–sectional area of the cylindrical shape of the solenoid is constant, as is the number of windings N per length *l* of the solenoid. When a current is sent through the wire, a magnetic field develops outside of the wire in the same fashion we discussed before for the straight wire (Fig. 19.9). Both the magnitude and the direction of the magnetic field within a solenoid take particularly simple forms. The magnitude is given by:

$$|\mathbf{B}_{solenoid}| = \mu_0 \frac{N}{l} I \qquad (9)$$

i.e., the magnitude of the magnetic field in a solenoid has a constant value. The direction of the magnetic field is shown by the thin lines in Fig. 19.12: the direction of the field does not vary and runs parallel to the axis of the solenoid.

Eq. (9) describes indeed a much simpler case than Eq. (2) since in Eq. (2) the magnitude of the magnetic field varies with distance from the wire, i.e., the magnetic field in Eq. (2) is not position independent.

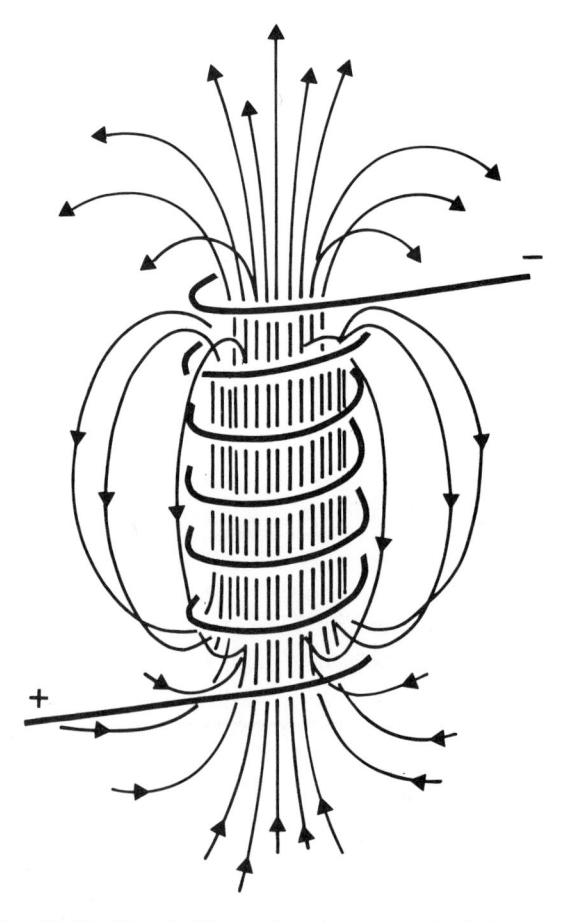

Fig. 19.12: Sketch illustrating the magnetic field of a solenoid. Inside the coil exists a magnetic field that is position–independent both in direction and magnitude. The direction of the magnetic field inside the solenoid is parallel to the axis of the solenoid.

Also, the magnetic field in the vicinity of a straight wire changes its direction from point to point as illustrated in Fig. 19.9, while the magnetic field in a solenoid is always directed along its axis.

Due to these simple properties, solenoids are widely used as electromagnets (i.e., devices which act as magnets when an electric current passes through). The lenses used in state–of–the–art electron microscopes are no longer electric devices, as discussed in the previous chapter, but are magnetic devices based on solenoids.

19.2.2. Electromagnetic waves

When magnetism was discovered, it was initially considered an entirely separate natural phenomenon. However, in many experiments it became clear that magnetic effects and electric effects are very similar. Magnetism causes electric effects and vice versa. In 1865, James Clerk Maxwell combined the electric theory and the theory of magnetism in four equations connecting electric and magnetic fields. When he applied these formulas to a region without charges (e.g., to outer space), differences between the electric fields and the magnetic fields vanish. Thus, Maxwell concluded that magnetism and electricity are essentially the same and it is only a matter of perspective whether we interpret a phenomenon as electric or magnetic. We call fields electric which are due to resting charges and we call fields magnetic which are due to moving charges.

Maxwell's equations allow us further to describe how a combination of electric or magnetic fields leads to a travelling wave, called an *electromagnetic wave*. Maxwell's equations tell us the speed at which these electromagnetic waves move, the speed of light, and they do not rely on a medium. Therefore, the origin and the propagation mechanism of electromagnetic waves are physically very different from sound waves.

Maxwell's equations are mathematically rather complex. Instead of deriving them, a qualitative approach using experimental observations is chosen to illustrate how electromagnetic waves are generated.

Our discussion of sound waves illustrated two principles we need to follow: waves are generated by vibrations and harmonic waves are obtained when the vibration is a harmonic vibration. Due to Ampère's and Oersted's observations, we want to use the harmonic vibration of electric charges instead of a mechanical vibration, since magnetic fields are generated by a current, which are moving charges. The device in which we set charges in vibrational motion is called an antenna.

We use a straight wire as a model for an antenna. Fig. 19.13 illustrates the harmonic motion of charges. At time t = 0 the antenna is charged like a di-

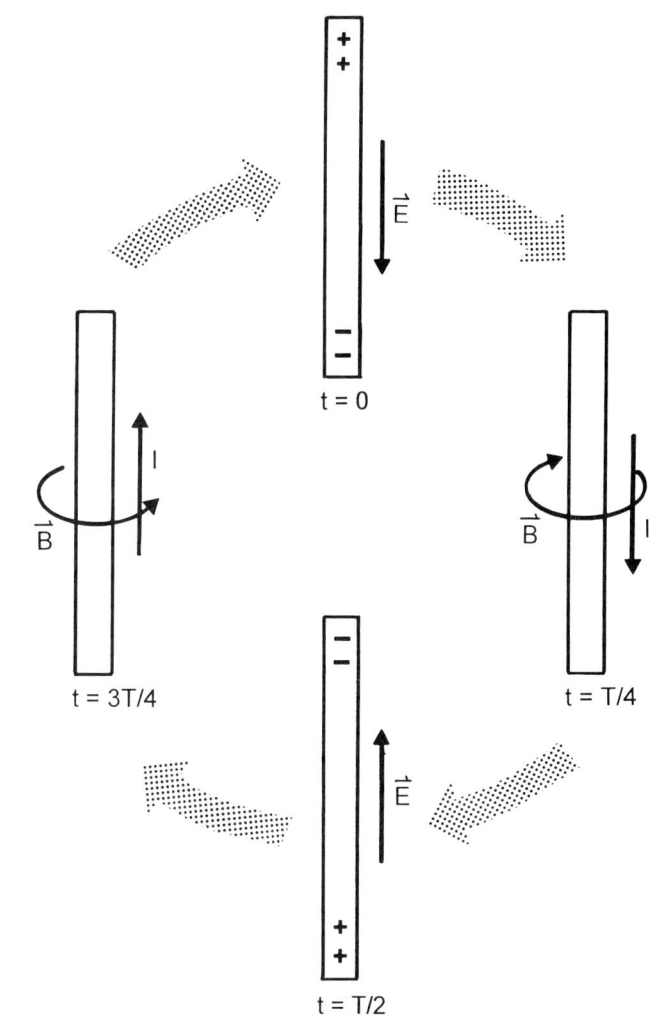

Fig. 19.13: Four frames at fixed time intervals $\Delta t = T/4$ illustrating the concept of an antenna. Positive and negative charges are separated along the antenna in a periodic fashion. When the charges move along the conductor, a magnetic field forms.

pole, with the positive charges at the upper end and the same number of negative charges at the lower end. Associated with the separated charges is an electric field. At time t = T/4, we allow the charges to recombine (the antenna is a conductor) which requires the motion of charges along the wire, which yields a current. Associated with the current is a magnetic field as illustrated in Fig. 19.9. The current continues to flow until, at t = T/2, the charges are again separated, however, this time the negative charges are at the top and the positive charges are at the bottom. Therefore, the electric field points now in the opposite direction. At the next time frame (at t = 3T/4) the charges are once more recombining. The current flows now upwards, causing a magnetic field opposite to the one observed at time t = T/4. A harmonic oscillation of charges in the antenna follows if we force the charges to move as shown in Fig. 19.13 in a periodic fashion with period T.

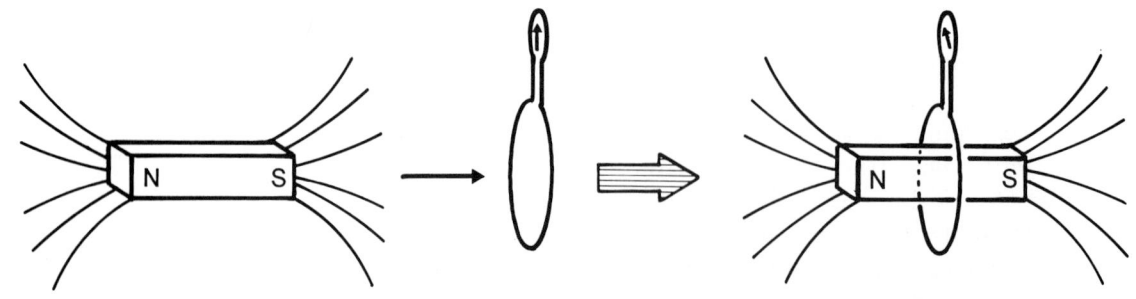

Fig. 19.14: Michael Faraday's experiment: A bar magnet is moved into a single loop of a conductor which is connected to a galvanometer (measuring the electric current which flows through the loop). In this experiment the magnetic field in the wire changes as the magnet is moved. While the magnetic field changes a current is detected.

The magnetic field near the antenna itself changes periodically with time. In 1831, Michael Faraday illustrated the effect of such a changing magnetic field. His experiment is shown in Fig. 19.14: a bar magnet is moved through the loop of a conductor which is connected to an Ampère–meter (galvanometer). The galvanometer shows a flowing current while the magnetic field changes. We conclude that the changing magnetic field must cause an electric field at the position of the wire since we identified in Chapter 13 electric fields as the only way to set charges in motion in a wire. This effect is called *induction*.

The direction of the current in the loop is such that the magnetic field of the current is directed against the external magnetic field. This is called Lenz's rule: The resulting current in the wire loop tries to minimize the external effect. Instead of moving the magnet through the conductor's loop, you can also move the conductor loop in the magnetic field. The magnetic break is an example that Lenz's rule applies in this case as well. When the conducting metal plate in Fig. 19.15 swings through the magnetic field of the horseshoe magnet, the changing magnetic field causes electric currents in the metal plate (called eddy currents). These currents cause in turn a magnetic field which opposes the external field. The opposing magnetic field interacts with the magnetic field of the horseshoe magnet and causes the metal plate to slow down. The slowing represents a loss of mechanical energy into work done against the magnetic interaction.

In Ampère's and Faraday's experiments we allowed the magnetic field to develop in the free space outside a conductor, but we restricted the electric field to the conducting wire since we wanted an observable current. What happens in the vicinity of a changing magnetic field where no conductor loop is present? Maxwell postulated that the changing magnetic field causes a changing electric field in free space instead of a current. The vector direction of this electric field is perpendicular to the vector direction of the magnetic field. This addition to the list of electric and magnetic interactions by Maxwell is illustrated in Fig. 19.16: A changing magnetic field, $\Delta \mathbf{B}_1/\Delta t$ causes an electric field $\mathbf{E}$, which in

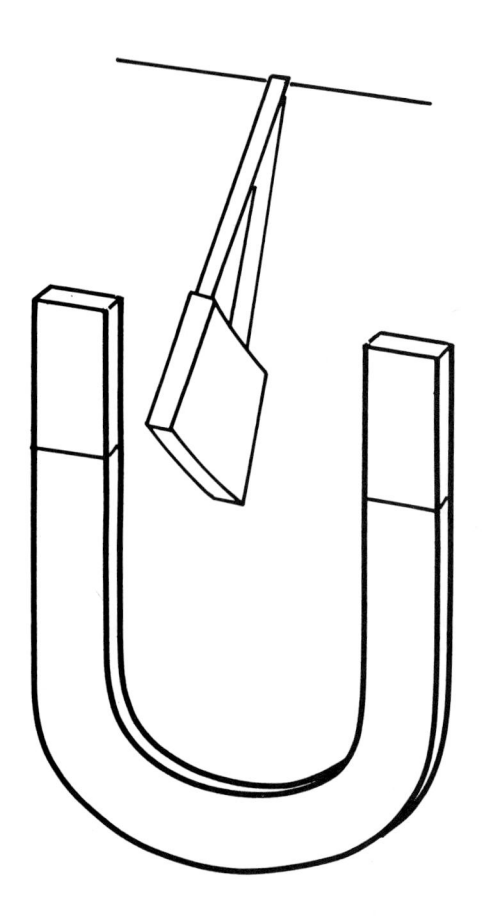

Fig. 19.15: The magnetic break is an experiment closely related to Faraday's experiment in Fig. 19.14: A metal plate swings into the magnetic field of a horseshoe magnet. This causes a changing magnetic field in the conducting plate. Eddy currents flow in small circles within the metal plate in response to the changing magnetic field. The eddy currents develop their own magnetic field which is directed in the direction opposite to the magnetic field of the horseshoe magnet.

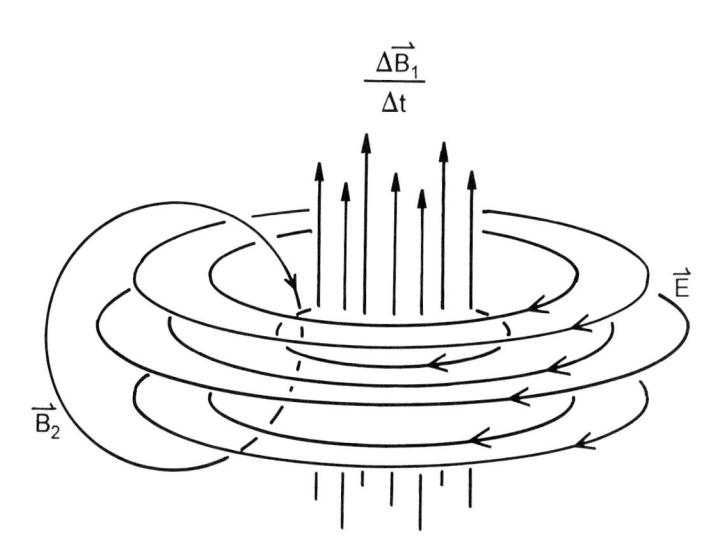

Fig. 19.16: Maxwell discovered that a changing magnetic field $\Delta \vec{B}_1/\Delta t$ can not only cause a current in a conductor, but can also cause a changing electric field **E** outside a metallic medium. The changing magnetic and electric fields stipulate each other as illustrated with the secondary magnetic field $\vec{B}_2$.

fields maintain each other. This is illustrated in Fig. 19.17, where the perpendicular magnetic and electric fields are indicated by arrows. The perturbation travels in the direction perpendicular to both the electric and magnetic fields (transverse wave) with a speed which can be derived from Maxwell's theory as $c = (\epsilon_0 \mu_0)^{1/2}$, in which ϵ_0 is the permittivity of vacuum from Coulomb's law and μ_0 is the permeability of vacuum from Eq. (2). c is the speed of light in vacuum.

> *Visible light is an electromagnetic wave which propagates in vacuum with the speed of light.*

turn causes a magnetic field **B**$_2$ which is opposed to the original magnetic field.

Now we return to the harmonic vibration of charges in the antenna of Fig. 19.13. The changing magnetic field shown in the figure causes a changing electric field, which in turn causes a changing magnetic field, as illustrated in Fig. 19.16. These interacting electric and magnetic fields travel outwards from the antenna like the sound waves we discussed in Chapter 16. In the current case no medium is needed as the electric and magnetic

19.3. Polarization of light

The first wave property of light we discuss is due to its transverse character. We define the polarization of light based on the orientation of its electric field vector in Fig. 19.17: if the orientation of the vector **E** of a light ray is time–independent (e.g. always along the y–axis) then we call the light *linearly polarized light*. Usually, visible light is not polarized since it emerges from a very large number of independent atomic transitions, as discussed in detail in Chapter 21. Each atomic transition contributes a random orientation of the electric field vector.

> *The electric vector of linearly polarized light points in a fixed direction relative to the propagation direction of the electromagnetic wave.*

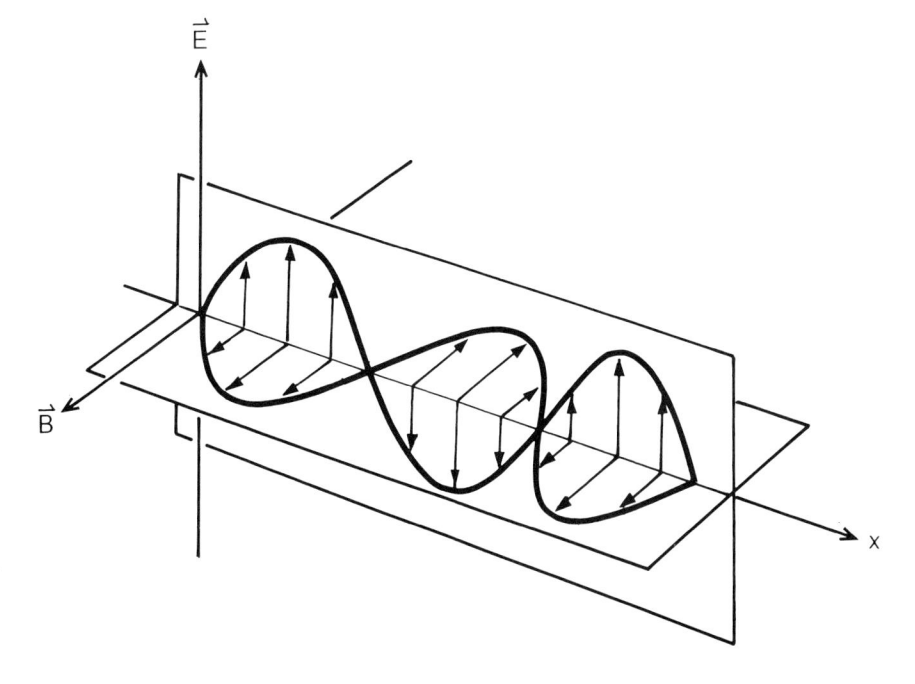

Fig. 19.17: Maxwell's theory allows changing magnetic and electric fields to sustain each other as they travel outwards from the vibrating charges of an antenna. The resulting electromagnetic waves are characterized by magnetic and electric field vectors which are perpendicular to each other and to the direction of wave propagation. The speed of the wave is identical to the speed of light.

Even though light does not require a medium to carry it, when it travels through matter interactions between matter and light occur. We noted this already in the previous chapter when we found that light slows down while passing through a transparent material. Remembering the discussion of the interaction between water mole-cules and an external electric field in Chapter 9, we can understand the nature of the interaction between light and matter: the electric field of the light ray interacts with the electric fields within the molecules of the material the light is passing through. This interaction allows us to control the properties of a light ray. There are two types of materials which interfere with the polarization of light:

Light polarizing crystals
Some materials allow only a fraction of the incident light to pass through, which is the light with a particular electric field component. Light with an electric field component perpendicular to that orientation is blocked. This property is common among many crystals which are not too symmetric. A frequently used material is $CaCO_3$ which forms transparent crystals which are highly symmetric only about one direction. These materials are used for polarizers and analyzers as illustrated in the top sketch of Fig. 19.18: randomly oriented light enter the polarizer (P) from the left. Only light with the electric field pointing in the up–down direction is allowed to pass through due to the orientation of the crystal in the polarizer. The light then passes through a second crystal of the same type, but turned 90^0 relative to the first crystal. As a result the light is fully blocked and the screen behind the second crystal is dark (indicated by a heavy shading). A mechanical rotary dial is connected to the second crystal to allow a fine tuning for complete shielding of the polarized light.

There are several other methods to generate polarized light. Reflection leads under certain conditions to polarization. This is illustrated in Fig. 19.19. In the figure we study the two perpendicular components of an incoming, randomly oriented light ray: in part (a) the electric field vector $\mathbf{E}_1$ is directed in and out of the plane of the paper, and in part (b) the electric field vector $\mathbf{E}_2$ is directed perpendicular to the ray but lies in the plane of the paper (indicated by an arrow with two opposite arrowheads). If the light is incident at an angle of 45^0, we know from the law of reflection in Eq. (17.1), that the reflected ray travels at a 45^0 angle with the vertical, i.e., at an angle of 90^0 with respect to the incoming beam. Thus, only light with the electric field component shown in part (a) is reflected. For the ray in part (b) the electric field vector would be directed in the direction of the reflected light ray which is inconsistent with the transverse character of electromagnetic waves.

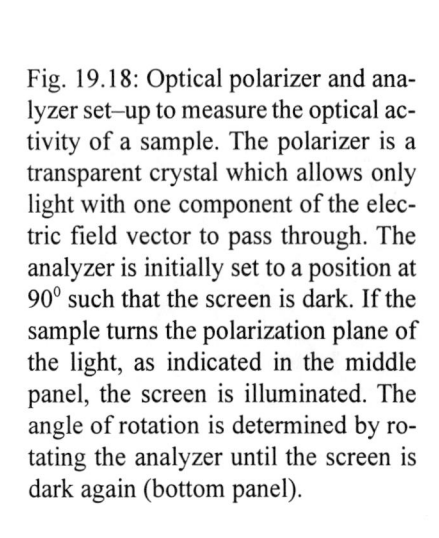

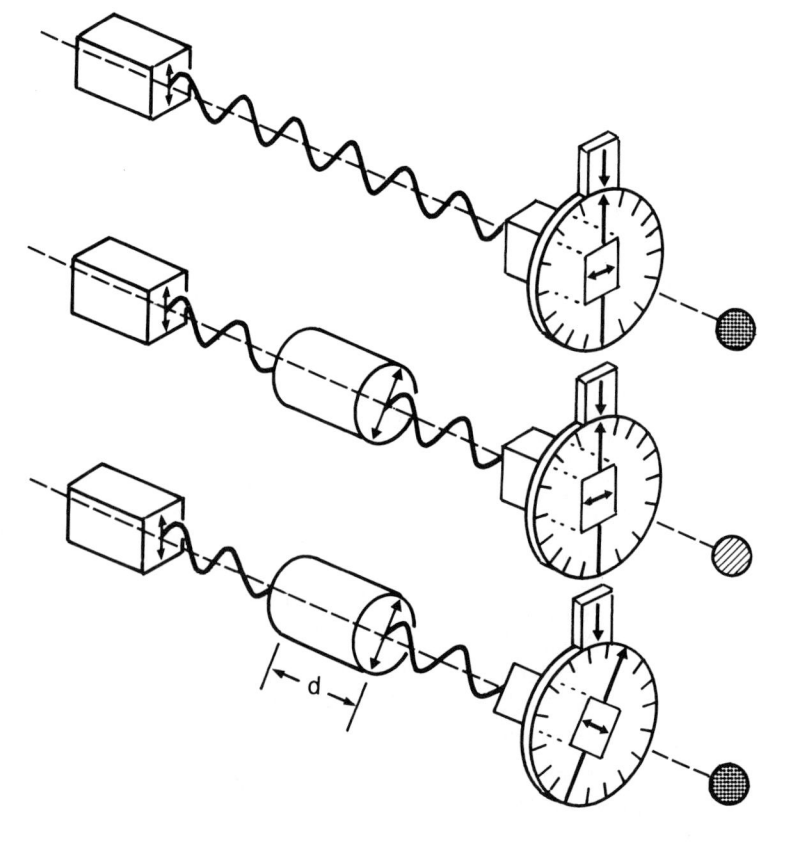

Fig. 19.18: Optical polarizer and analyzer set–up to measure the optical activity of a sample. The polarizer is a transparent crystal which allows only light with one component of the electric field vector to pass through. The analyzer is initially set to a position at 90^0 such that the screen is dark. If the sample turns the polarization plane of the light, as indicated in the middle panel, the screen is illuminated. The angle of rotation is determined by rotating the analyzer until the screen is dark again (bottom panel).

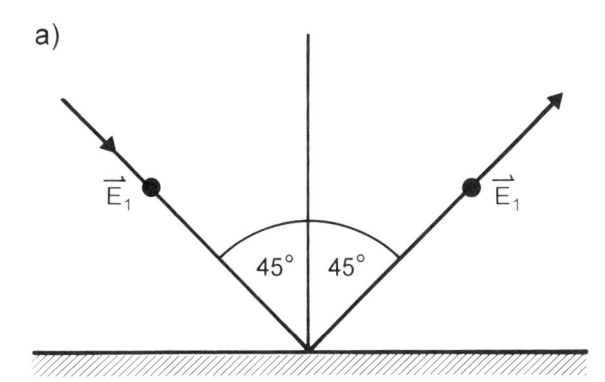

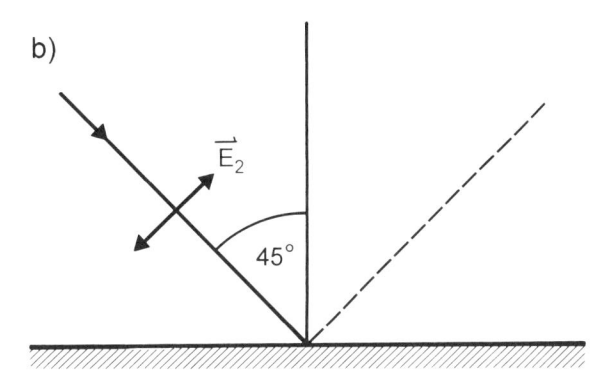

Fig. 19.19: Light can be polarized when it reflects at a planar surface with the incoming light ray at 45° with the normal. This is due to the fact that the light with the component of the electric field directed as shown in (b) would require the electric field vector to point in the direction of the reflected beam after reflection. This is inconsistent with the transverse nature of electromagnetic waves. Thus, only light with the electric field component shown in (a) is reflected.

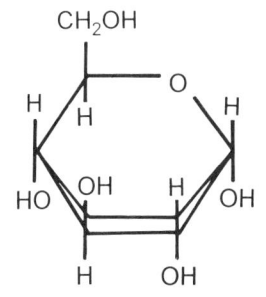

Fig. 19.20: Glucose molecule. This molecule is optically active. Its presence in a urine sample is an indication for diabetes mellitus.

Optically active materials
In 1815, Jean Baptiste Biot discovered that some organic molecules actively turn the polarization direction of light. These materials are called optically active materials. As an example, the glucose molecule shown in Fig. 19.20 is optically active. A detectable level of glucose in the urine is an indication for diabetes mellitus. Thus, a simple (contact–free) analysis technique for the glucose concentration in urine is clinically desirable. The second and third sketch in Fig. 19.18 illustrate how glucose is detected in a urine sample with polarized light. After the polarizer and analyzer are placed such that the light is completely blocked (top sketch in the figure) the urine sample of given length d is inserted between the two crystals. If there is no optically active component in the sample, the screen behind the analyzer remains dark. However, if an optically active component is contained in the sample, light will reach the screen. By turning the rotary dial of the analyzer (bottom sketch in Fig. 19.18), an angle is found at which the light is fully blocked. The angle through which the analyzer had to be turned, α, is read off the instrument.

The information obtained about the sample can be analyzed qualitatively by determining whether the light has been turned toward the right or toward the left, which corresponds to a clockwise or a counter–clockwise turn of the analyzer, respectively. This may not be sufficient if there is one of several possible optically active components in a sample, or when the absolute concentration of the optically active component is sought. To quantify a light polarization measurement to obtain the concentration of the optically active component in the sample, c, we need to know the specific rotation α_{spec}, which is a characteristic property of the molecule, like the melting point. Obtaining the specific rotation from a tabulation of such values, we quantify the con-centration by:

$$c = \frac{\alpha}{d\,\alpha_{spec}} \qquad (10)$$

Note that α_{spec} depends on the temperature and the wavelength of the light. Standard values are reported, therefore, for room temperature and for a particular wavelength obtained from a sodium lamp ($\lambda = 589$ nm).

How can irregularly moving molecules in a solution turn the polarization of the light in this fashion?

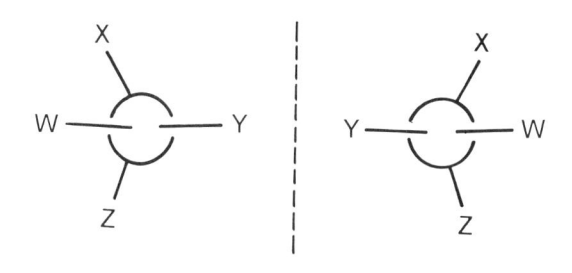

Fig. 19.21: Optically active organic isomers (enantiomers) require four different ligand groups attached to a carbon atom. The dashed line indicates the mirror symmetry of the isomers.

At the molecular level the answer is the same as for the polarizer and analyzer crystals: the intra–molecular electric fields interact with the electric field of the light ray passing through the molecule. But this would only lead to a back and forth wobbling of the direction of the electric field vector of the light ray as the ray passes through a very large number of randomly oriented molecules before leaving the sample. This is indeed the case, and therefore, most chemical solutions do not turn the polarization of light in a detectable fashion.

Exceptions are solutions in which only one type of enantiomers is present. Enantiomers are optically active structural isomers, i.e., chemical compounds with the same chemical formula which exist in more than one structural variation. An organic molecule is an enantiomer, or has one or more enantiomer groups, if it contains a carbon atom with four different ligands, C–WXYZ, as illustrated in Fig. 19.21. Note that the tetrahedral structure shown at the left of the dashed line and the tetrahedral structure shown at the right of the dashed line are mirror symmetric to each other (e.g. with the dashed line as a mirror). Neither molecule can be transferred into the other molecule by rotations. A solution containing 50 % of molecules of the left type and 50 % of the right type is optically inactive. However, a solution which contains only one type of molecules shown in Fig. 19.21 is optically active as any small turn of the polarization of light in one molecule cannot be compensated by the light ray passing through a second molecule with its intra–molecular electric field turning light the opposite way.

Living systems often rely on only one of two enantiomers. Two examples are illustrated in Fig. 19.22, part (a) shows lactic acid, of which (+)–lactic acid can be extracted from human muscle tissue, and part (b) shows a byproduct of the fermentation of starch to ethanol, of which only (–)–2–methyl–1–butanol is naturally synthesized. The notation in the bracket preceding the chemical name is defined as follows: a molecule which turns the polarization of light to the right (i.e., the analyzer in the set–up in Fig. 19.18 is turned clockwise) is labelled (+).

Not all organic molecules are optically active. An example of an optically inactive molecule is shown in Fig. 19.23. Note that the isopropyl molecules on both sides of the mirror plane can be transferred into each other by rotation.

Polarized light is also applied in modern medicine for diagnosing skin ailments. Light, which is reflected from the skin, is a combination of two components: (I) light reflected from the skin surface according to the law of reflection (Eq. (17.1), this component is called glare), and (II) light which initially penetrated the skin surface but is backscattered from deeper layers. A technique allowing for a separation of these two components enables us to study the skin surface and the tissue below the skin surface, e.g. pigmentation, infiltrates and other intra–cutaneous components, independently. This separation is possible when using polarized incident light and a polarizer to study the skin, because the glare does not affect the polarization of the light while the backscattered component no longer maintains the polarization. Thus, depending on the rotation of the polarizer used by the health practitioner, either the skin surface or intra–cutaneous structures are highlighted. It is noteworthy in this context that, contrary to our intuition, only 4 % to 7 % of the incident light is indeed reflected off the surface while 93 % to 96 % penetrate the outmost layer. This reminds us of another novel by H. G. Wells: The Invisible Man, written in 1897. We are not invisible, but it would be fair to characterize the outmost layer of our skin as almost transparent!

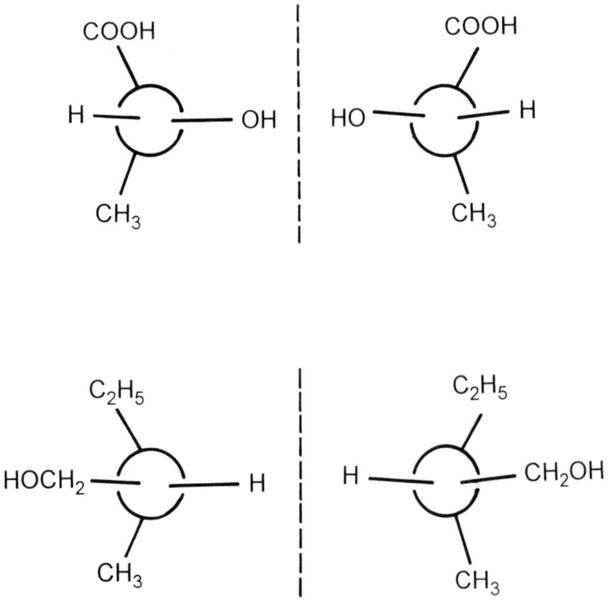

Fig. 19.22: Two examples of optically active molecules: (a) lactic acid and (b) 2–methyl–1–butanol.

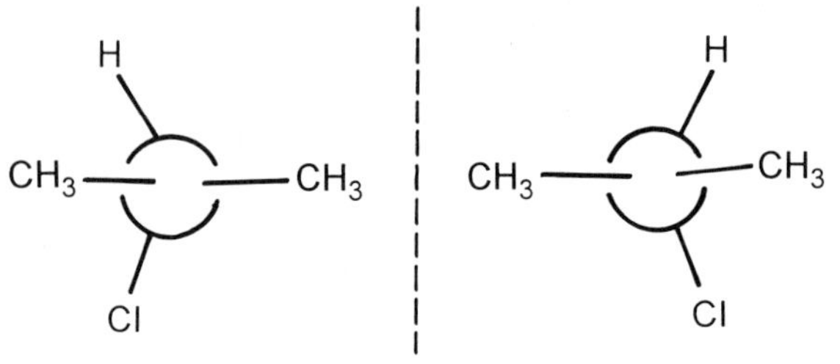

Fig. 19.23: Isopropyl chloride is an example of an organic molecule that is not optically active.

19.4. The physics and physiology of color

19.4.1. Dispersion

What other effects does the medium have on a propagating electromagnetic wave? Since the speed of light is affected, we know that at least one of the quantities wavelength λ and frequency f must vary as light passes across an interface between two media, because these three quantities are related to each other in the form:

$$v_{light} = \lambda f \quad (11)$$

Which one of these quantities varies from medium to medium is determined from Fig. 19.24. Shown in the figure are two media with different indices of refraction n_1 (in the top region) and n_2 (in the bottom region). We assume that $n_2 > n_1$. Light of wavelength λ_1 and frequency f_1 approaches the interface from the top, as indicated by a wave. From Eq. (17.15) we know that light travels slower in medium 2, $v_{light, 2} < v_{light, 1}$.

Let's assume that two observers, at positions A and B, count the number of wave maxima passing through their respective dashed observation planes. If the observer at A were to count a smaller number of wave maxima passing through per time interval than the observer at B, then eventually there would be no wave maxima left in the range between the two observers and the whole experiment would somehow collapse. If, in turn, the observer at A were to count a larger number of wave maxima passing through per time interval than the observer at B, then wave maxima would pile up near the interface. Since neither case makes sense, we conclude that the same number of wave maxima must pass observers at A and B in any time interval, i.e.,

$$f_1 = f_2 \quad \Rightarrow \quad \lambda_2 < \lambda_1 \quad (12)$$

Thus, the speed of light and the wavelength of light change when light passes through an interface (as illustrated for the wavelength in Fig. 19.24), but the frequency of the light remains unaltered. From this we conclude that the frequency of the light is the most fundamental of the three quantities, frequency, wavelength and speed of light in a medium, as nature conserves it for light travelling through different media.

To find the frequency to be more fundamental than the wavelength or the speed of light in a particular medium is consistent with the corpuscle theory for light. The light corpuscles are called *photons*. The energy of a photon is given by the relation E = hf in which h is the Planck constant h = 6.6×10^{-34} [Js]. Since energy is conserved the corpuscle theory illustrates why the frequency of light is not easily altered.

A further conclusion is that n, the index of refraction, must depend on the wavelength of light, λ. This follows from the fact that both n and λ change from one medium to another while the frequency f remains constant.

> *The dependence of the index of refraction on the wavelength, n = f(λ), is called dispersion.*

Typical dispersion curves for three different types of glass are shown in Fig. 19.25.

Dispersion also explains the observation illustrated in Fig. 19.6 that white light incident on a prism is split into several different light rays of different colors. White light is composed of light rays of different wavelengths, and since the index of refraction of the glass depends on the wavelength, some light rays are refracted more strongly and others more weakly. Specifically, the light component which looks red to us is refracted less than the light component which looks blue to us.

Dispersion affects the lens in our eye in the same fashion. This leads to several color-related illusions. An example is the perception that the red and blue bars of the French flag have different widths. For a red and a blue field at same distance, the lens must be bent

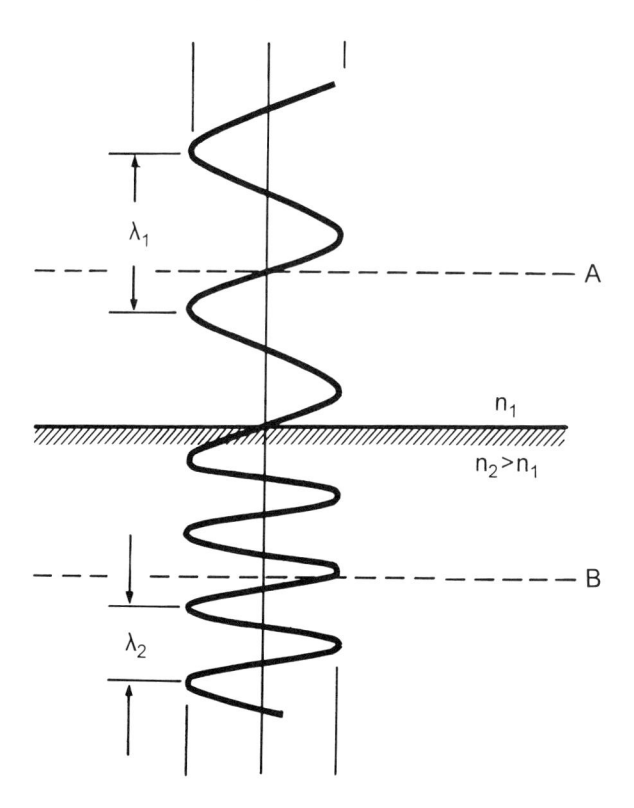

Fig. 19.24: Light wave passing through an interface. The wavelength varies, the frequency remains unaltered.

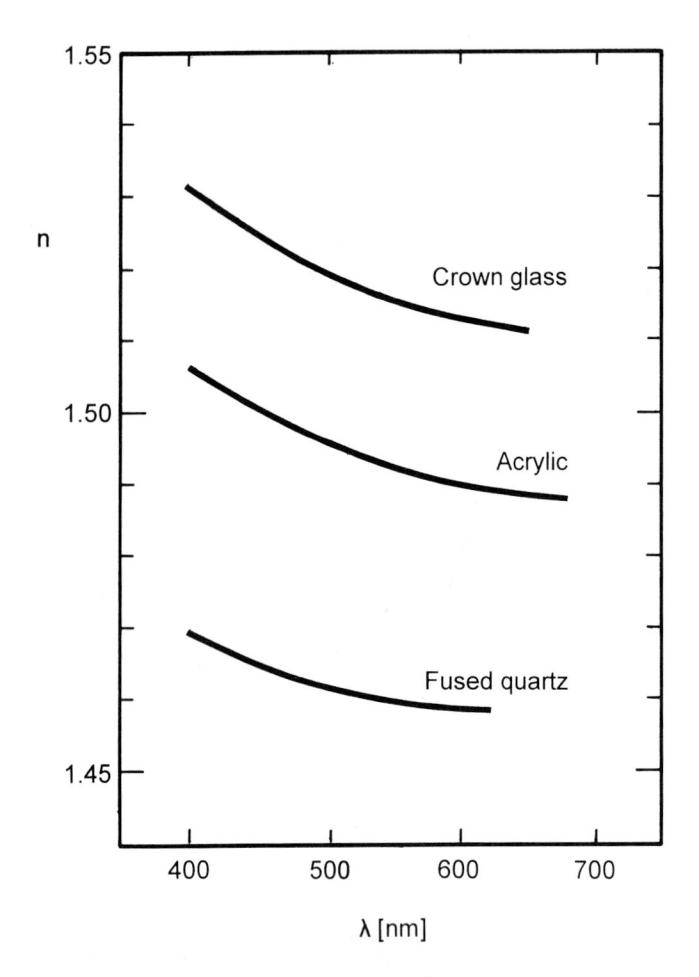

Fig. 19.25: Dispersion relation n(λ) in the visible part of the electromagnetic spectrum for three types of glass: crown glass, acrylic and fused quartz.

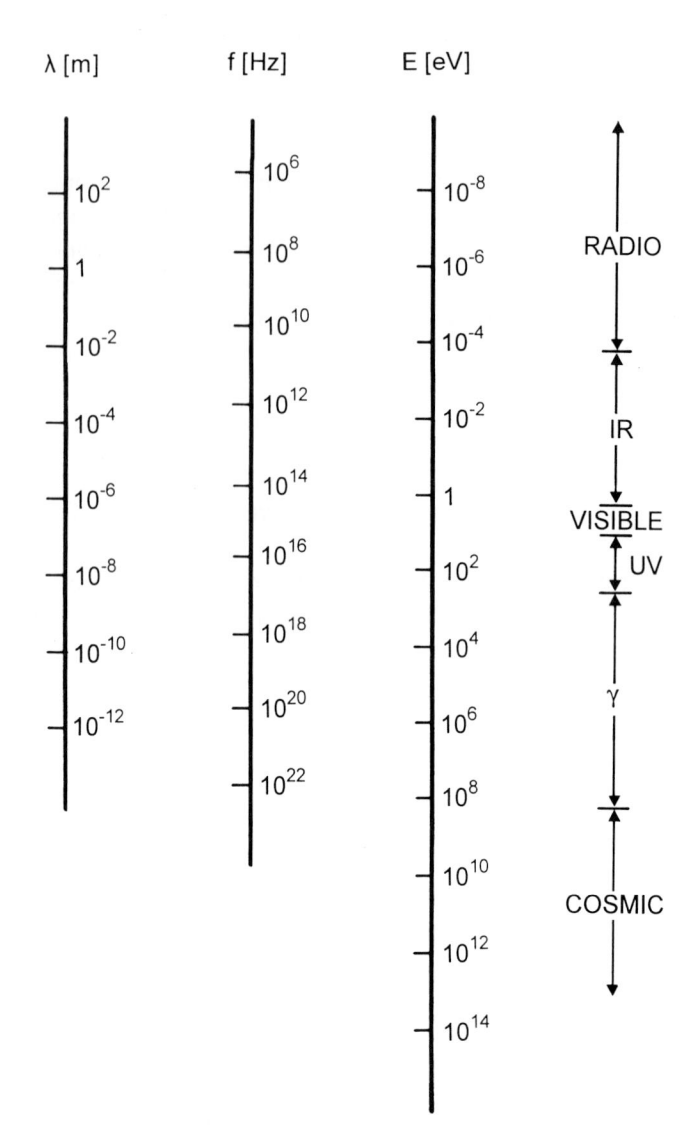

Fig. 19.26: Electromagnetic spectrum showing the relation between the frequency f, the wavelength λ and the photon energy E = hf.

more to focus the red light as it is refracted less by a given lens. The focussing of the eye is associated with adjustments of the lens caused by action of the ciliary muscle. The brain notices the degree of work the ciliary muscle is doing and interprets this information as a measure of distance to the observed object. Thus, while you focus on the red area of the flag your brain thinks "nearer" and while you focus on the blue area of the flag your brain thinks "further away". There is indeed a lot of motion of your eyes while looking at an object such as the French flag in order to get the picture right (see the earlier discussion about the blind spot). The apparent difference in width of the two bars is an illusion, which results when your brain tries to correct for the obviously inconsistent depth information; you know that the three bars of the flag are at the same distance since they are woven together.

19.4.2. Color as a physical concept

The fact that electromagnetic waves have variable wavelengths and frequencies is not sufficient to explain why we see colors. To understand color vision, two additional phenomena must be discussed. The first is the range of visible wavelengths of the electromagnetic spectrum. This also explains why we see white light emerging from the sun and why white light is a mixture of all colors of the rainbow.

The other necessary ingredient in understanding color vision is the mechanism by which our eye and our brain convert wavelengths into color impressions. This second issue requires us to study the interplay of physics and physiology, which we do in the last section of this chapter.

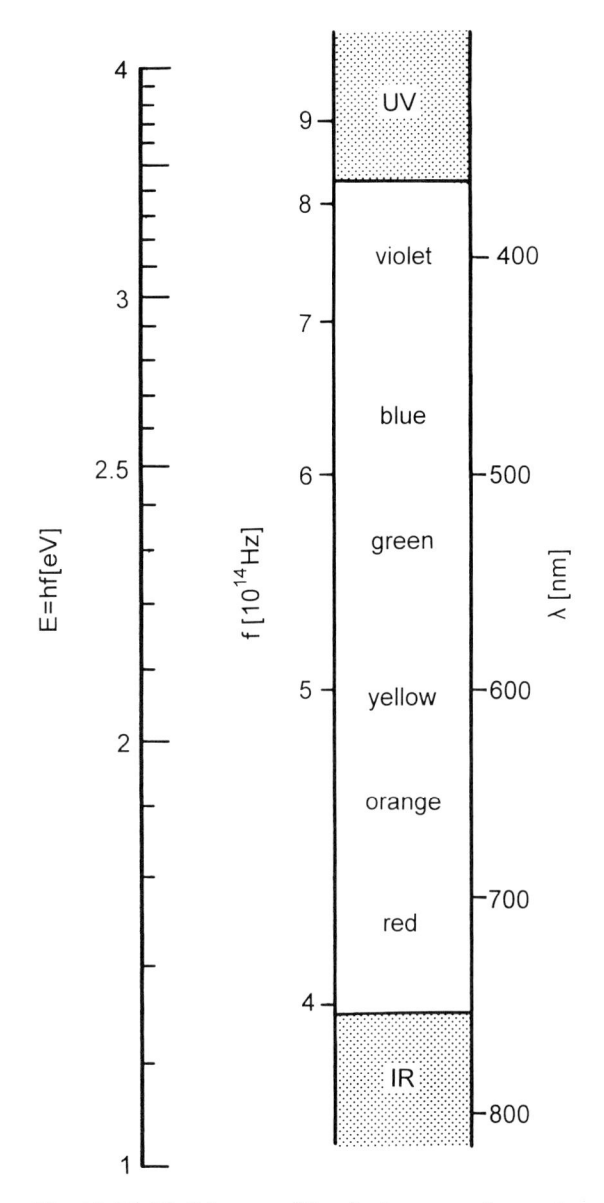

Fig. 19.27: Visible part of the electromagnetic spectrum. The indicated colors correspond to the respective wavelengths.

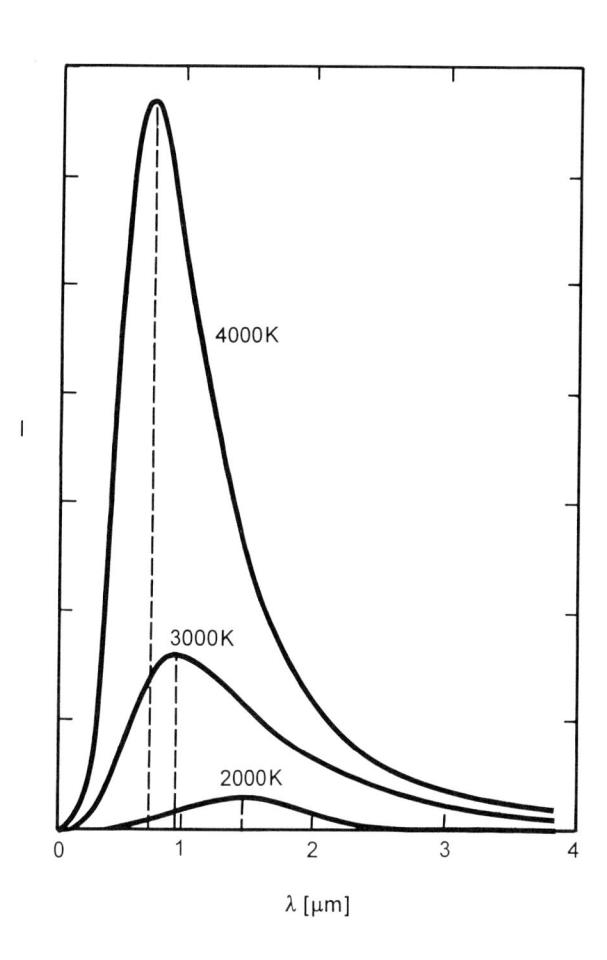

Fig. 19.28: Radiation intensity I from a black body at three different temperatures. The vertical dashed lines indicate the wavelengths of the respective maximum intensity.

The complete spectrum of electromagnetic waves is shown in Fig. 19.26. It reaches from radiowaves with wavelengths in the centimeter and meter regime, to microwave and infrared radiation in the micrometer to centimeter wavelength regime, to visible and ultraviolet light in the nanometer wavelengths regime and then to gamma–rays and cosmic rays at the shortest wavelengths. The fraction of this spectrum which is visible is very small, reaching from about 370 nm (violet) to about 760 nm (red). This visible part of the electromagnetic spectrum is highlighted in Fig. 19.27, which correlates the names of various colors to the respective wavelengths, frequencies and energies of the light. Note that the reason we can give an energy scale in Figs. 19.26 and 19.27 is due to the corpuscle theory of light which defines the energy of light photons of frequency f as $E = hf$. That E is indeed an energy is evident when you let sunlight shine on your skin. The warmth you feel is the energy of the photons deposited in your skin, retained due to light absorption.

Do we have to conclude from Figs. 19.26 and 19.27 that our vision is rather ill–adapted to the real world around us because it cannot detect most of the electromagnetic spectrum? No, because only a small fraction of the entire electromagnetic spectrum reaches our eye. To understand why, we need to introduce the concept of *black–body radiation*.

A black body is defined as a body that perfectly absorbs all the light which reaches it, and thus, does not reflect any of that light. As a black body absorbs the incoming light, the light's energy is converted into thermal energy, raising the temperature of the black body. If light shines on the black body continuously, it is not in thermal equilibrium but becomes hotter and hotter. When a body becomes hotter, however, we know that it starts to emit light. Examples include the tungsten filament in a light bulb emitting light due to electric heating. By balancing light absorption, this light emission establishes a thermal equilibrium for a black body immersed in a constant light radiation field.

Fig. 19.28 illustrates the intensity of light of various wavelengths emitted from a black body at three different temperatures. Both the overall intensity (area under the curve) and the wavelength of the maximum intensity vary with temperature. The curve in Fig. 19.28 was correctly described by Max Planck using the quantum theory of light. This was the first evidence that quantum mechanics and not classical mechanics is the valid theory for objects at atomic length scales.

Let us assume that the sun is a black body. Due to its high temperature it radiates light with a spectrum like those shown in Fig. 19.28. The actual spectrum (total intensity and wavelength of radiation peak) depends on the sun's surface temperature. While the interior of the sun reaches temperatures as high as 1×10^7 K, the electromagnetic spectrum is determined by the surface temperature of the sun which is 5800 K. Light from greater depths does not leave the sun (the sun's surface layer is not transparent to that light). Using Fig. 19.28 we predict a maximum intensity of the radiation reaching Earth from the sun in the visible wavelength range. As a consequence, many processes on Earth are tuned into this maximum, including the photosynthesis process, but also our vision.

Fig. 19.28 shows also that the total intensity of light emission from a black body depends strongly on the temperature of the black body. This was quantified in 1879 by Josef Stefan (Stefan's law):

$$\frac{\Delta Q}{\Delta t} = -\sigma \epsilon A T^4 \quad (13)$$

in which $\Delta Q/\Delta t$ is the total energy emitted in unit [J/s], A is the surface area of the emitting object, ϵ is the emissivity of the surface, which is a material constant for which $0 \leq \epsilon \leq 1$, and σ is the *Stefan–Boltzmann constant*, $\sigma = 5.67 \times 10^{-8}$ [J/(sm²K⁴)]. Note that Eq. (13) contains a negative sign on the right hand side following our convention that energy lost by the body of interest is negative. Stefan's law allows us to quantify radiative energy loss. Energy loss by radiation is also significant for objects near room temperature, as shown in Table 7.2 for the energy loss from the human body.

Example 19.3
A person with a skin temperature of 37 °C is in a room with the temperature of 20°C. How much heat does the person's body lose in 10 minutes if the human body has a surface area of 1.5 m² and is modelled as a black body with emissivity $\epsilon = 0.9$?

Solution: Modelling the human body as a black body means that the human body is in a radiative equilibrium when placed in an environment of the same temperature. As a consequence, the emissivity ϵ for radiative loss and radiative gain must be the same, otherwise the body's temperature would eventually differ from the 37°C temperature of the environment.

Placing the human body in an environment with a different temperature means that no radiative equilibrium is established and the warmer body loses energy to the colder body. In the given case, we determine the radiative energy loss and radiative energy gain using Stefan's law:

$$\left(\frac{\Delta Q}{\Delta t}\right)_{loss} = -\sigma \epsilon A T^4_{body}$$

$$\left(\frac{\Delta Q}{\Delta t}\right)_{gain} = +\sigma \epsilon A T^4_{environment} \quad (14)$$

which leads to a net heat balance of:

$$\Delta Q_{net} = \sigma \epsilon \Delta t A \left(-T^4_{body} + T^4_{en}\right) \quad (15)$$

in which environment has been abbreviated as "en." Inserting the numerical values in Eq. (15) leads to:

$$\Delta Q = 5.67 \times 10^{-8} \left[\frac{J}{sm^2 K^4}\right] 0.9 \; 600[s] \cdot \ldots$$
$$\ldots \cdot 1.5[m^2]\left(293^4[K^4] - 310^4[K^4]\right) \quad (16)$$

which yields:

$$\Delta Q = -8.6 \times 10^4 \; J \quad (17)$$

Note that the heat loss discussed in Example 19.3 is due to radiation at electromagnetic wavelengths, and thus, is not dependent on a medium to carry the heat. However, heat cannot pass through opaque interfaces radiatively. This is the reason for the greenhouse effect. In a greenhouse, incoming energy from the sun passes through the glass surfaces in the visible range. The radiation of the plants in the greenhouse occurs at much longer wavelengths (infrared) since the temperature of the plants is much lower than the surface temperature of the sun. For infrared wavelengths the glass is opaque, i.e., the radiation cannot escape from the greenhouse, thus, increasing the temperature in the greenhouse beyond the temperatures outside.

This explains also why our vision is limited to a narrow range of wavelengths. The assumption that the sun is a black body for wavelengths above 300 nm agrees very well with the actual irradiance measured on Earth. Fig. 19.29 shows three intensity curves as a function of wavelength: the solid curve is the intensity at sea level, the long-dashed curve is the intensity above the atmosphere and the short-dashed curve is the intensity for a black body at 5800 K. Oxygen, ozone, water and carbon-dioxide molecules in the atmosphere attenuate the sun's irradiance across the entire spectrum but the wavelength interval present at sea level clearly resembles the curve derived from the black body radiation model.

The sun does not behave like a black body for wavelengths $\lambda \leq 300$ nm where significant UV radiation is due to non-thermal activities of the sun, such as sun flares. We discuss these types of radiation in Chapter 21, where we also show that none of that radiation reaches the sea level on Earth.

19.4.3. Color as a physiological concept

As complex and subjective as the interpretation process of wavelengths in our brain may be, there is interesting physics included in the physiological aspects of color vision. These we want to establish in this section.

Once the light from an object reaches the retina, the color you see depends on the relative excitation of the three color-sensitive receptor types at each point in your retina. We mentioned already that Young postulated that three different receptors are needed. Their respective sensitivity as a function of the wavelength of the incoming light is shown in Fig. 19.30. Corresponding to the range of greatest sensitivity, the three receptors are labelled R, G and B for red receptor, green receptor and blue receptor. The strong overlap of sensitivities in Fig. 19.30 rules out any simple color composition concept. Instead, each color we perceive in our brain is associated with light that has excited at least two different cones, and most color impressions result from an excitation of all three types of cones.

How we use Fig. 19.30 to predict a color impression is illustrated next. We start with the definition of the color triangle. For any object with a defined color, let the absolute excitation intensity of the red receptor be R, the absolute excitation intensity of the green receptor be G and the absolute excitation intensity of the blue receptor be B. Then the total excitation intensity is then R + G + B. The total excitation intensity determines whether the object appears bright or dim and duplicates the information the brain receives from the retinal rods. Using the total excitation intensity, we define a relative excitation intensity for each of the three receptor types:

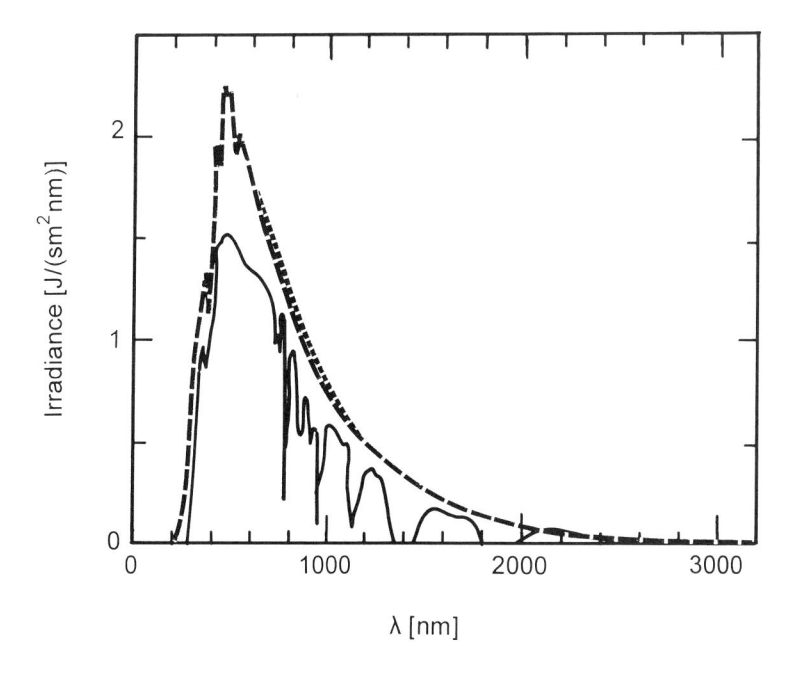

Fig. 19.29: Comparison of the solar irradiance on Earth with the radiation of a black body at 5800 K (short-dashed curve). The agreement in the shown wavelength interval is very good above the atmosphere (long-dashed curve). At sea level (solid curve) attenuation occurs due to absorption of radiation by various molecular components of the atmosphere.

Fig. 19.30: Sensitivity of the three types of cones as a function of the wavelength in the visible range of the electromagnetic spectrum. The cones are labeled R (red), G (green) and B (blue), according to the color (from Fig. 19.27) at the wavelength of the maximum of each curve. ⇒

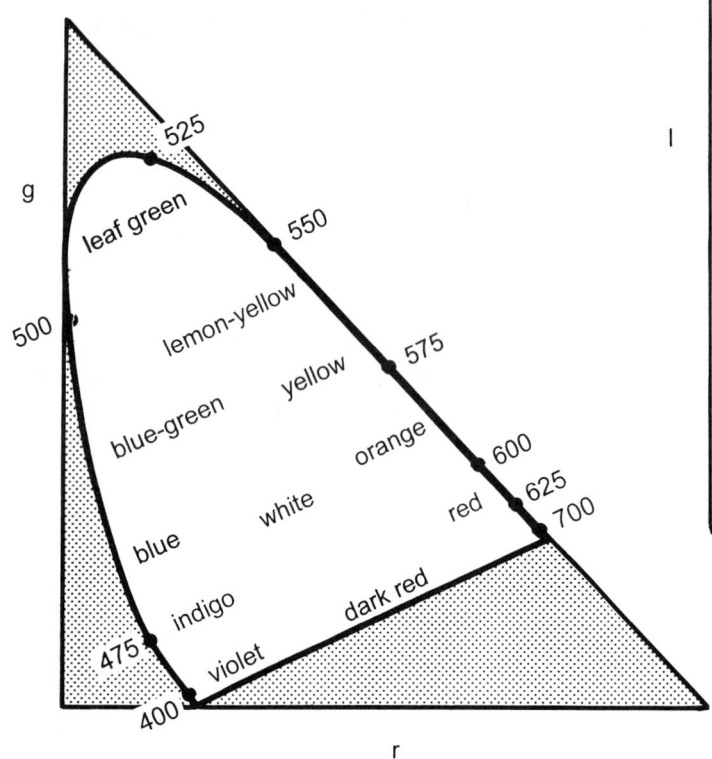

$$r = \frac{R}{R + G + B} \quad \text{with} \quad 0 \leq r \leq 1$$

$$g = \frac{G}{R + G + B} \quad \text{with} \quad 0 \leq g \leq 1 \tag{18}$$

$$b = \frac{B}{R + G + B} \quad \text{with} \quad 0 \leq b \leq 1$$

$$\text{and} \quad r + g + b = 1$$

The red and the green relative excitation intensities, r and g, are used to form the two perpendicular sides of the color triangle in Fig. 19.31. With r and g given in the figure, the value of b is derived from $b = 1 - g - r$.

Not all relative intensity combinations represented in the color triangle are accessible. For example, the point $g = 1$ and $r = b = 0$ is inaccessible due to the overlap of the three receptors in Fig. 19.30, which shows that there is no wavelength of light which excites only the green receptor. In Fig. 19.31 the accessible part of the color triangle is identified, with various color impressions connected to points along the outer perimeter of the accessible area. In the center of the triangle lies the point which is perceived as white (color addition).

The use of the color triangle is illustrated for the color pink. Pink is located in the color triangle as shown in Fig. 19.32. We can read the values for r and g directly off the figure: $r = 0.44$ and $g = 0.27$. Thus, $b = 0.29$.

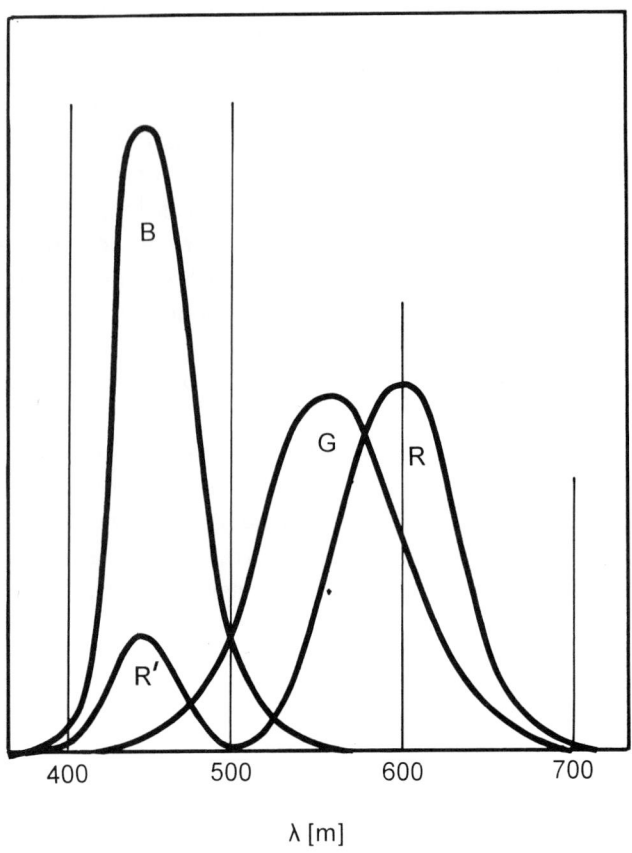

⇐ Fig. 19.31: Visible part of the color triangle and respective color impressions. No color impressions are possible in the shaded areas due to the overlap of the sensitivity curves in Fig. 19.30.

Example 19.4

Do all humans see colors the same way? More specifically, did Homer, who lived around 750 BC to 700 BC, see colors as we do? Homer wrote a sizable amount of literature, including the *Iliad* and the *Odyssey*. He often described the Aegean Sea (part of Mediterranean Sea) as "a sea colored like violets" or "wine–colored sea", color descriptions most of us would disagree with. So, did he see colors differently?

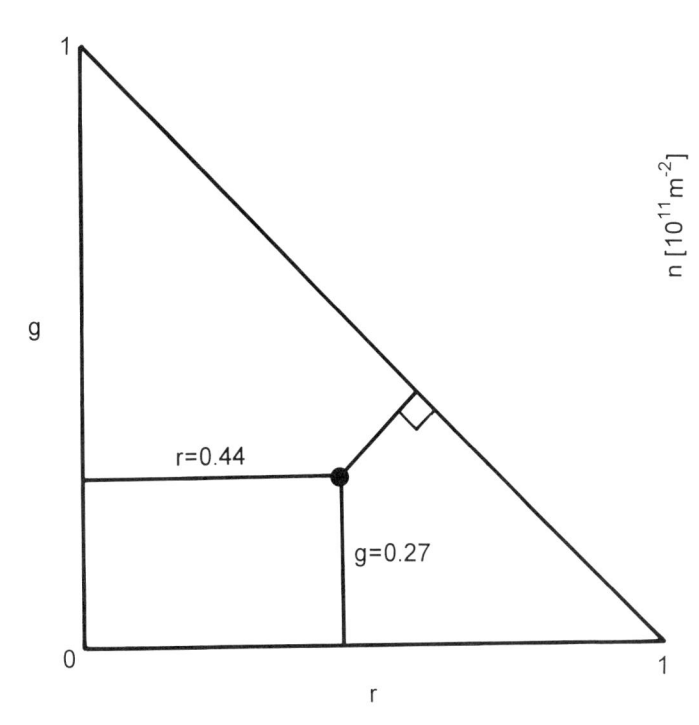

Fig. 19.32: The position of pink in the color triangle.

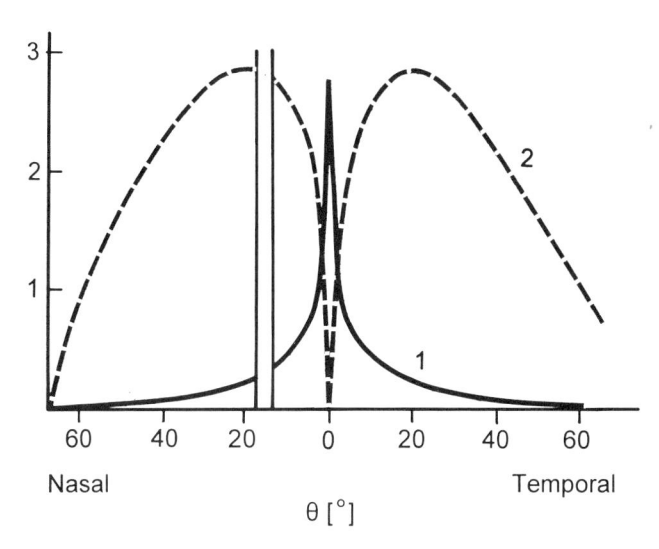

Fig. 19.33: Density of cones (1) and rods (2) in the retina as a function of distance from the fovea centralis.

Supplementary biological information: It is not impossible to assume that one creature sees a different part of the electromagnetic spectrum than another. For example, bees see well into the UV part of the spectrum where the eyes of modern humans are insensitive.

Solution: We cannot say for sure:
(I) The sensitivity of the eyes of the ancient Greek people stretched slightly further toward shorter wavelengths (into what we call today ultraviolet). To allow for this, Figs. 19.30 and 19.31 must be modified for Homer.
(Ia) A first possibility for Homer's vision is to shift the sensitivity peak of the blue receptor toward the left in Fig. 19.30, and shift the minor maximum of the red receptor accordingly. Using Fig. 19.31, we find that Homer would have seen near–UV as we see blue today. The only difference would be that he might have per-ceived the color of the Aegean sea as being more intense due to the high reflection of UV light on water.
(Ib) A second possibility for Homer's eye would be to again shift the sensitivity peak of the blue receptor toward the left in Fig. 19.30, but leave the minor maximum of the red receptor where it is in our eye. In this case we simply cannot say what Homer would have seen. When looking at the Aegean sea, his brain would have received signals corresponding to a point in the shaded area close to b = 1 in Fig. 19.31. We do not know what the brain would do with such a signal as none of our brains had ever to deal with that. The only thing we know is that the physiological rule of specific sensory perception applies, i.e., that the retina responds even to inadequate stimuli (e.g. electrical or mechanical stimulation) with a vision perception.
(II) Of course, Homer, being a poet, might just have chosen to exercise his poetic freedom when describing the sea beloved by the Greeks!

Example 19.5
(a) Why look all cats grey at night?
(b) Why are we more prone to believe in seeing ghosts at night?

Solution part (a): Our eye contains retinal cones for color vision and retinal rods for black and white vision. As the intensity of light diminishes at night time, a lower threshold for color vision is passed and the color vision is shut off. Once the light intensity has fallen below this threshold, only the black and white vision remains active and everything we see looks grey (somewhere between black and white). Since cats are active at night, they are typical objects for this observation.

Solution part (b): The retinal rods and cones are not equally distributed across our retina. The density of the black and white–sensitive rods is much larger further away from the fovea centralis ((8) in Fig. 17.1), while the color–sensitive cones are concentrated near the fovea, as illustrated in Fig. 19.33. This is an artifact of our evolutionary past: during a long span of time while the dinosaurs ruled the world at day, mammals had been relegated to nocturnal life. Most mammals still show very effective adjustments to nocturnal life, such as well developed olfaction and limited color vision. Humans are, in that sense, exceptional mammals in that we have fully developed color vision.

Our brains are used during daylight to process primarily information transmitted from near the fovea centralis, defining our normal field of vision. At night, with only the retinal rods operational due to low light intensities, the brain now receives a higher fraction of information from far outside the color field of vision, as identified in Fig. 17.4. Thus, we respond more sensitively to motions near the edge of our field of vision, emphasizing objects at the fringes. This is perceived as unusual or frightening since we are used to daytime vision. Thus, ghostly impressions are night time phenomena and always try to creep in on us from the edge of our field of vision.

The fact that three independent color receptors are associated with our color vision leads to several interesting optical illusions, including those we discussed at the beginning of this chapter based on the three pictures on the back–cover of the textbook. These are usually associated with two effects:

(I) The retinal cones sensitive to the red part of the spectrum have a larger decay time than the cones sensitive to the blue and green parts of the spectrum. As a result, a red impression lasts a little longer when an object moves. The cones sensitive to red are saturated more quickly and become insensitive after focussing on a red surface for a while.

(II) The human eye also participates in judging distances. The degree of focussing required to see an object is correlated to the degree of contraction of the ciliary muscle. The muscle work is used in turn by the brain to interpret how far an object is from the eye. For objects with clearly separated areas of various colors, such as church windows or the French flag we discussed already earlier, this distance measurement can be deceived when red and blue are involved.

19.5. Problems

P–19.1
Two long, parallel wires are separated by a distance of $l_2 = 5$ cm, as shown in Fig. 19.34. The wires carry currents $I_1 = 4$ A and $I_2 = 3$ A in opposite directions. Find the direction and magnitude of the net magnetic field (a) at point P_1 that is a distance $l_1 = 6$ cm to the left of the wire carrying current I_1,
(b) at point P_2 that is a distance $l_3 = 5$ cm to the right of the wire carrying current I_2.
(c) At what point is the magnitude of the magnetic field zero, $|\mathbf{B}| = 0$?

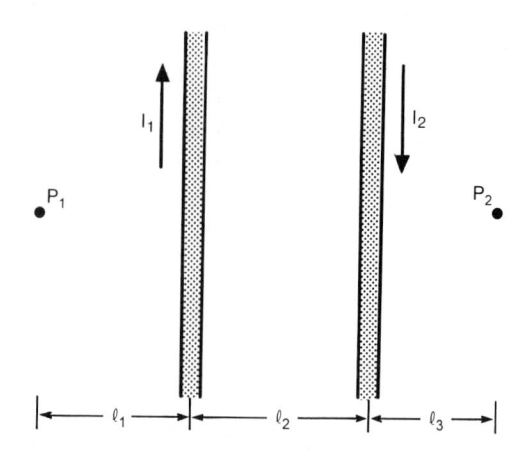

Fig. 19.34 for problem P–19.1

P–19.2
At what distance from a long straight conductor which carries a current of 1 A is the magnitude of the magnetic field due to the wire equal to the magnitude of the Earth's magnetic field at the surface of the Earth, which is $|\mathbf{B}| = 50$ µT?

P–19.3
A conducting wire has a mass of 10 g per meter length. The wire carries a current of 20 A and is suspended directly above a second wire of the same type which carries a current of 35 A. How long do you have to chose the separation distance between the wires so that the upper wire is balanced at rest by magnetic repulsion?

P–19.4
Two parallel conductors carry each a current of 2 A and are 6 cm apart.
(a) If the currents flow in the opposite direction, find the force per unit length exerted on either of the two conductors. Is the force attractive or repulsive?
(b) How do the results in part (a) change if the currents flow parallel to each other?

P–19.5
Fig. 19.35 shows two parallel wires which carry currents $I_1 = 100$ A and I_2. The top wire is held in position, the bottom wire is prevented from moving sideways but can slide up and down without friction. If the wires have a mass of 10 g per meter of length calculate current I_2 such that the lower wire levitates at a position 4 cm below the top wire.

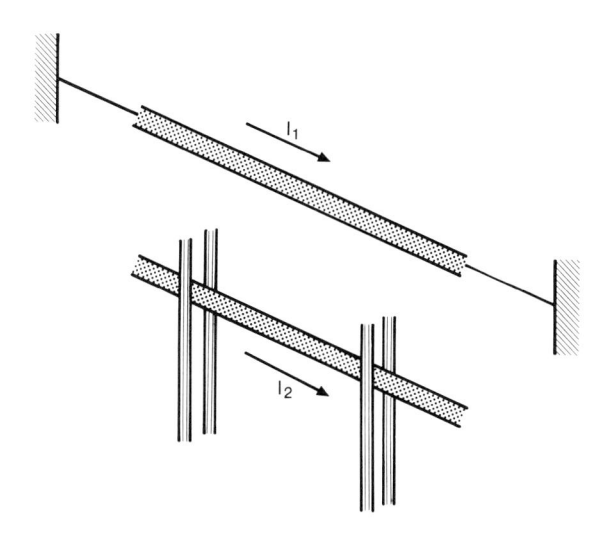

Fig. 19.35 for problem P–19.5

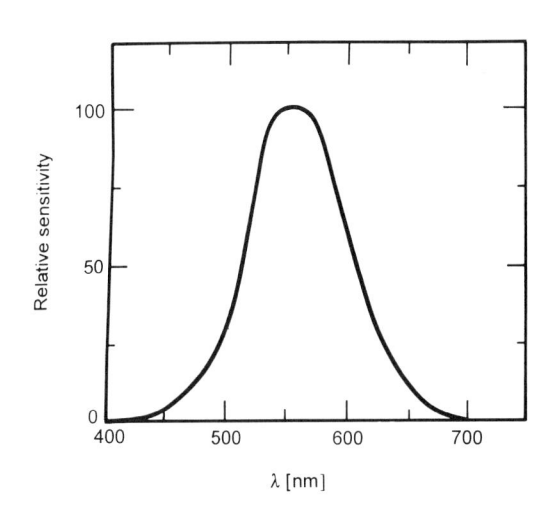

Fig. 19.37 for problem P–19.8

P–19.6
The index of refraction for violet light in silica flint glass is 1.66, and that for red light is 1.62. What is the angular dispersion of visible light (expressed as the angle ϕ) passing through the equilateral prism shown in Fig. 19.36, if the angle of incidence is 50^0?

P–19.9
Describe the color vision of an alien if the sensitivity of the three color receptors in the eye of the alien were as shown in Fig. 19.38.

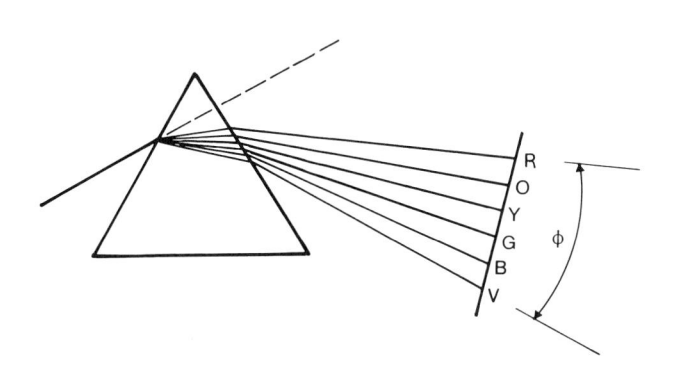

Fig. 19.36 for problem P–19.6

P–19.7
Light of wavelength λ_0 in vacuum has a wavelength of $\lambda_w = 438$ nm in water and it has a wavelength of $\lambda_b = 390$ nm in benzene.
(a) What is the wavelength λ_0 in vacuum?
(b) Using only the given information, determine the ratio of the index of refraction of benzene to that of water.

P–19.8
Fig. 19.37 shows that our eye is much more sensitive to absolute intensities of green light in comparison to absolute intensities of red light. Why are the green and red lights of a traffic light still looking roughly equally bright?

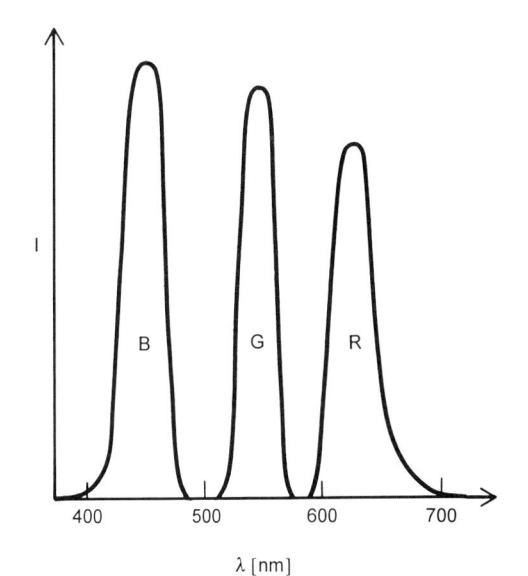

Fig. 19.38 for problem P–19.9

547

Summary

Definitions:
- Permeability of vacuum: $\mu_0 = 1.26 \times 10^{-6}$ N/A².
- σ is Stefan–Boltzmann constant:
$\sigma = 5.67 \times 10^{-8}$ [J/(sm²K⁴)]

Units:
- Magnetic field $|\mathbf{B}|$: [T] = [N/Am]

Laws:
- Magnetic force between two parallel currents in wires of length l and distance d:

$$|\mathbf{F}_{mag}| \propto \frac{I_1 I_2}{d} l \quad \Rightarrow \quad \frac{|\mathbf{F}_{mag}|}{l} \propto \frac{I_1 I_2}{d}$$

- Magnetic field:
(i) of a current in a straight wire:

$$|\mathbf{B}| = \frac{\mu_0}{2\pi} \frac{I}{d}$$

(ii) in a solenoid:

$$|\mathbf{B}_{solenoid}| = \mu_0 \frac{N}{l} I$$

N is number of windings.
- Stefan's law for black body radiation:

$$\frac{\Delta Q}{\Delta t} = - \sigma \, \epsilon \, A \, T^4$$

$\Delta Q/\Delta t$ [J/s] is the total energy emitted, A is the surface area, ϵ is the emissivity of the surface ($0 \leq \epsilon \leq 1$) and σ is Stefan–Boltzmann constant.

Chapter XX

The Human Body in Space

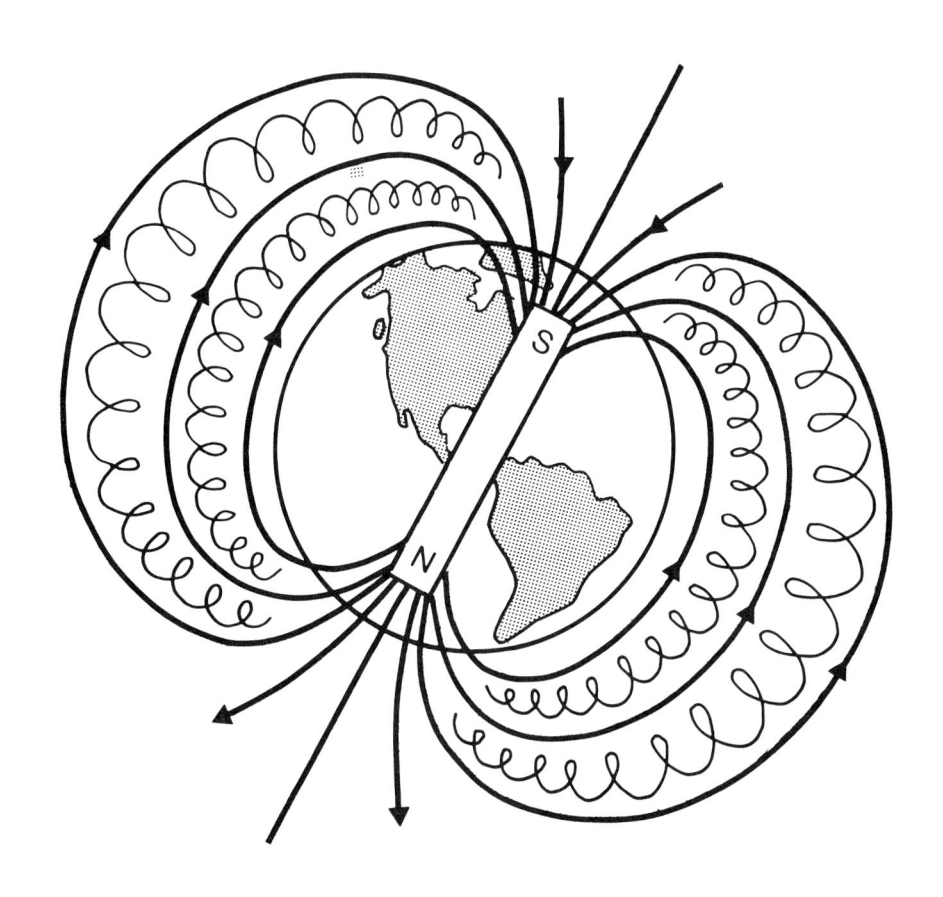

Circular motion

THE HUMAN BODY IN SPACE
CIRCULAR MOTION

Two phenomena unique to low–orbit space flight, weightlessness and the occurrence of radiation belts, are linked to the concept of uniform circular motion. This type of motion results when an object has constant centripetal acceleration. Gravity provides such an acceleration for objects in the vicinity of a planet or star; a uniform magnetic field exerts such a force on a moving charged particle. The radius of the circular motion of the object also depends on its speed. The centripetal acceleration is used in Newton's second law to calculate the various parameters of the motion of the system.

When we think of life on Earth we imagine an abundant diversity of life forms which have developed over the past four billion years, conquering every corner of the vast seas and huge continents. However, when we include the third–dimension, we realize that the biosphere is limited to a very thin, almost two–dimensional layer sandwiched between the solid lithosphere and the sterile tranquillity of outer space. With the deepest trenches in the oceans reaching about 10 km below sea level and our ability to breathe limited to altitudes of less than 10 km above sea level, life has only adapted to a layer 0.3 % as thick as the distance to the center of the Earth.

Challenging these limitations has been a human dream for centuries. The idea of reaching into the lithosphere remains a topic for science–fiction (such as "A journey to the center of the Earth" by Jules Verne, written in 1864). On the other hand, expanding our reach into outer space has during the past 50 years become an option for human civilization.

20.1. Outer space: the challenges

The environment at heights above 15 km above sea level becomes extremely hostile. A whole range of physical parameters take values beyond those tolerable by any known form of life, including the human body. Fig. 20.1 illustrates the most important changes. The axis at the left shows the altitude above sea level. Note that this is a logarithmic scale, ranging from 1 km to 100,000 km. The average distance of the moon is about 384,000 km, thus, the moon is off the scale, but not by much.

The first parameter that changes significantly with height is air pressure. Gravity prevents the gases of the atmosphere from escaping into outer space and holds most of the gas components near the surface of the Earth. The pressure already drops noticeably below altitudes of 13 km (the limit of oxygen breathing), with an air pressure decrease by about a factor of 10, as shown on the first axis on the right side of Fig. 20.1. The pressure diminishes faster at higher altitudes, to about 0.1 % at 50 km and to about 1 billionth of the pressure at ground at the altitude where the International Space Station (ISS) orbits Earth (between 370 km and 460 km). Exposure to such low pressures causes instant death. The human body must be protected with a pressurized suit at altitudes above 19 km.

The planet Mars has a much thinner atmosphere than Earth. This is due to the mass of Mars which is only about 10 % of the mass of the planet Earth. The gravitational pull of Mars is not sufficient to prevent light molecules such as oxygen and nitrogen from escaping over a period of millions or billions of years.

The second parameter that changes notably with altitude is temperature. The temperature profile of the atmosphere is shown as the solid curve at the center of Fig. 20.1. There are several zones with varying temperature changes due to complex composition variations and dynamic processes in the atmosphere. The human body cannot withstand temperatures outside the interval from 0^0C to $+ 50^0C$ for extended periods. This intolerance is based on the physiology of the human body temperature that we discussed in Chapter 7. Thus, temperature becomes a problem within a few kilometers from the ground, as we already know from mountain climbing.

Since the effects of temperature and pressure variations on the human body have already been discussed in previous chapters, we focus in this chapter on changes of two other parameters: the reduction of gravity and the exposure to energetic particles and X–rays. These factors play a unique role at high altitudes; this is evident

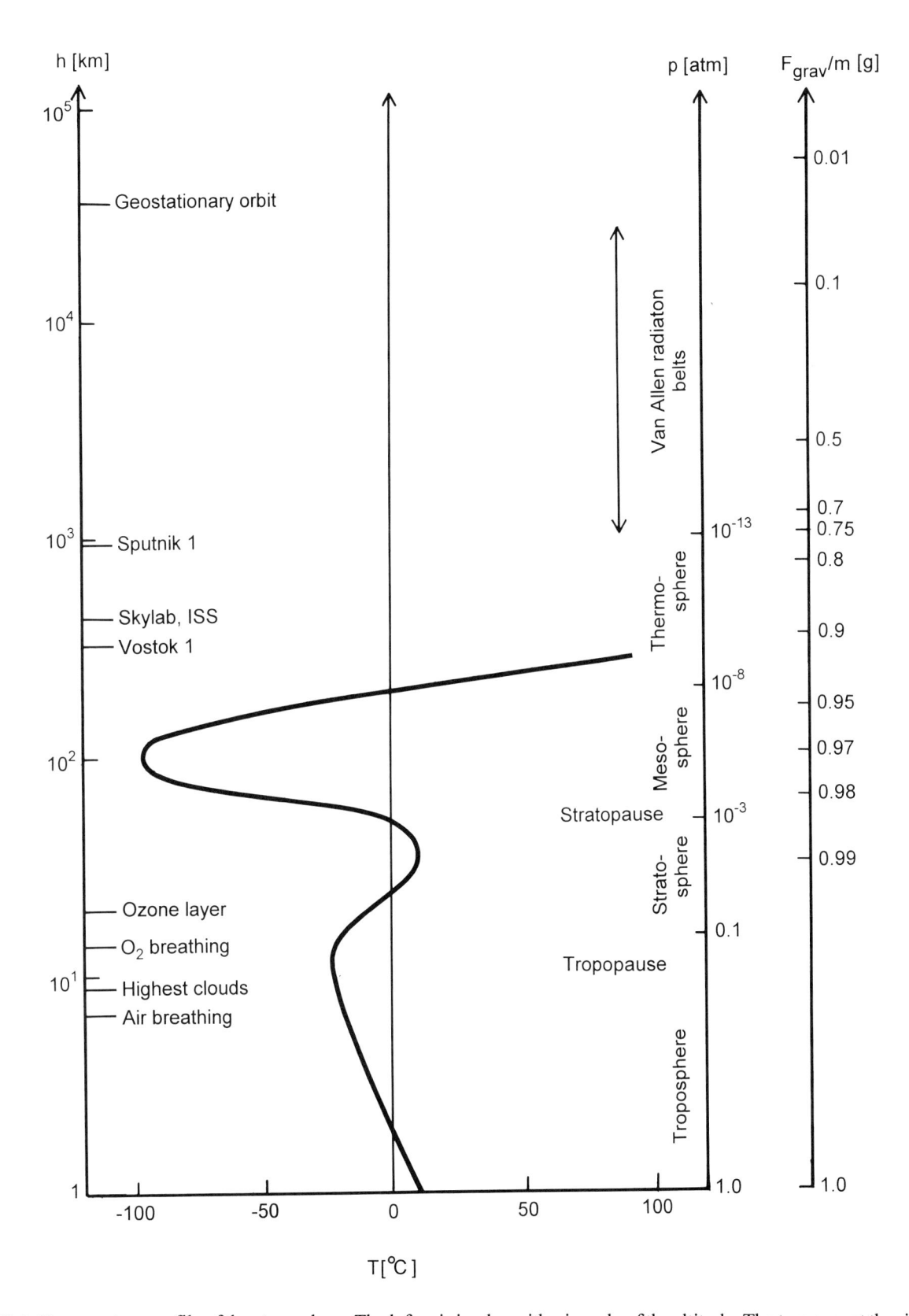

Fig. 20.1: Temperature profile of the atmosphere. The left axis is a logarithmic scale of the altitude. The two axes at the right indicate the pressure profile in [atm] and the gravitational acceleration relative to the gravitational acceleration at sea level as a function of altitude.

from the fact that the field of their study, Aerospace Medicine, is a distinctive discipline within medicine. It emerged as an extension of Aviation Medicine, which started about 1784 when physiological experiments were made on the newly developed hot–air balloons (first manned ascent in November 1783 by Joseph Michel Montgolfier). This type of research yielded the oxygen mask in 1894 and the pressurized suit in 1934. Space Medicine began in 1948 with animal testing on rockets. In 1957, Russia sent a dog into orbit, followed by a monkey launched in 1958 by the USA. The first human in space was Yury Gagarin on Vostok I orbiting the Earth once on April 12, 1961, during a 1 hour and 48 minute flight (Gagarin was killed seven years later in a test–airplane crash).

The early space explorations eliminated some space travel concerns; for example, the 21 day quarantine of the early Apollo missions to the moon were scrapped during later missions as no extraterrestrial microbes were detected, and the worries about emotional stress due to close confinement proved unfounded thanks to intensive training of the astronauts.

However, with later longer missions, two serious health issues moved into the forefront of aerospace medical research: weightlessness was found to severely diminish bone development and muscle strength, and radiation levels were found to be more critical than anticipated.

Since the physics associated with both these issues has not been discussed yet in this textbook, we will focus on them in detail in this and the next chapter. Before we do so, we take another look at Fig. 20.1 to see what implications these issues have for our modern, space station–based exploration of outer space.

First we focus on the axis at the far right of the figure. It shows the gravitational force divided by the mass of the object. What does this axis mean? We start with Newton's law of gravity:

$$F_{gravity} = G * \frac{m\, M}{r^2} \quad (1)$$

in which M is the mass of the Earth. Note that the radius in the denominator is kept variable (not set equal to r_{Earth}) because we want to describe the distance to the center of the planet from any point, not just points on the surface of the Earth. This way we don't limit our considerations to the gravitational effect at the surface of the Earth as we did in Chapter 2, where we found that we can rewrite the gravitational force as the weight W = mg at sea level. Dividing Eq. (1) by the mass m of the object attracted by the Earth we find for the gravitational acceleration (in unit [m/s²]):

$$\frac{F_{gravity}}{m} = G * \frac{M_{Earth}}{r^2} \quad (2)$$

i.e., the gravitational pull on the object decreases with the square of the distance of the object from the center of the Earth. The right axis in Fig. 20.1 does not provide the gravitational acceleration in absolute units but as a multiple of g, which is the gravitational acceleration at sea level introduced in Chapter 2 as:

$$g = \frac{G * M_{Earth}}{r_{Earth}^2} = 9.8\, \frac{m}{s^2} \quad (3)$$

To quantify values on the right axis of Fig. 20.1 we divide Eq. (1) by g:

$$\frac{F_{gravity}/m}{g} = \left(\frac{R_{Earth}}{r}\right)^2 \quad (4)$$

which now provides us with the relative gravitational acceleration, which diminishes as the factor on the right hand side of Eq. (4).

Inspecting the axis of the relative gravitational acceleration in Fig. 20.1 more closely we notice that the ISS, like its US forerunner Skylab, orbits at a height where the gravitational acceleration is still about 90 % of the value at sea level. That means that people at that height should weigh about 90 % of what they weigh down here on the surface of the Earth. Why then do astronauts float weightlessly in the ISS? The first section of this chapter will answer that question.

All the original plans for manned space exploration were dashed when Explorer I, a US satellite sent into space in February 1958, discovered a belt of high intensity ionizing radiation starting at an altitude of about 1000 km above the Earth. The belt was named in honor of the mission chief as the *van Allen belt*. By now we know of three such belts, reaching out into space as far as 25,000 km. The radiation exposure in the inner belt can exceed in an hour the annual limit allowed for professionals exposed to radioactive materials by a factor of 10! This limits the possible altitudes for orbiting space stations, such as the ISS, to a narrow gap above the point where the atmosphere is still too dense and would slow the station down too much, and the lower end of the van Allen radiation belt.

The radiation belts are not too dangerous for interplanetary travel because astronauts in a spaceship pass through them in a relatively short time, as did 27

Americans twice when flying on the Apollo 8 to Apollo 17 missions to the moon. However, for space travel exceeding a few days (like the Apollo missions) other sources of radiation become a concern. During periods of solar flares dangerous levels of gamma radiation are emitted by the sun. We want to understand what types of radiation there are, how they are generated and what biological impact they have. For this reason, atomic and nuclear physics concepts are discussed in the next chapter.

20.2. The physical concept of weightlessness

The major focus of human exploration of space during the past 50 years has been the direct vicinity of Earth. Once the moon landing programs were completed by the end of 1972 (with a total of 80 hours spent walking and driving rovers on its surface) the attention turned to the development of space stations. Russia maintained seven Salyut stations in orbit between 1971 and 1991 and operated the Mir station from 1986 to 2001. The USA started with the Skylab program, active from 1973 to 1979, but NASA then turned its attention to the space shuttle program, for which the longest stay was just over 16 days in orbit. Since 2000, an international group of space agencies is operating the International Space Station (ISS). To date, the longest period a single astronaut stayed in space in the Skylab mission was 84 days, and the longest stay of a cosmonaut on Mir was 437 days.

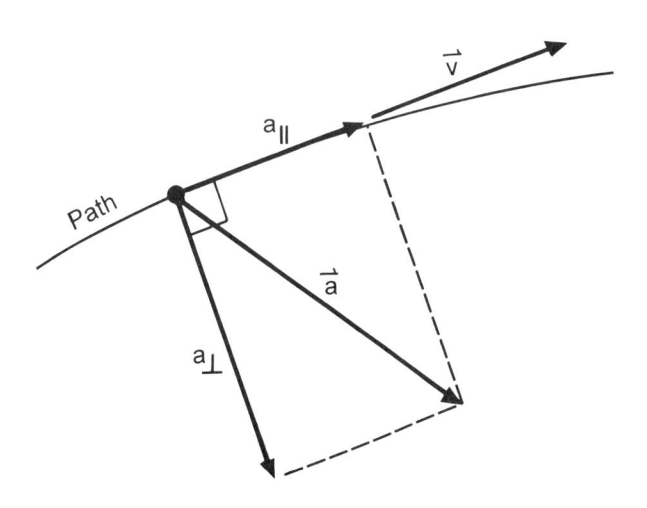

Fig. 20.2: An object (solid dot) moving along a curved path. The indicated velocity and acceleration components are derived for an object centred coordinate system. The index ∥ indicates components tangential to the path and the index ⊥ indicates components perpendicular to the path.

While no adverse effects due to weightlessness were observed during earlier missions, which were always completed within a few days, extended periods of time spent under conditions of weightlessness were found to lead to serious structural decay of the human bones with a calcium loss of 1 % to 2 % per month. Recovery after the space flight is partially possible, but the recovery time is very long. How do we know this? Doesn't Fig. 20.1 imply that the gravitational force at the height where the ISS flies is about 90 % of the gravitational force that we are subject to on the ground? To clarify this apparent discrepancy in the argument we must study the concept of circular motion first.

20.2.1. Uniform circular motion

When we studied Newton's laws in Chapters 2 and 3 we focussed on the motion of an object along a straight line, even when applying the second law to situations in which an acceleration changes the velocity of the object. While we found the restriction of linear motion to be a useful simplification for many mechanical problems, it must ultimately be lifted when we want to study the motion of an object along a curved path.

Such a motion and its physical origin are illustrated in Fig. 20.2. For convenience, we continue to confine our considerations to cases of motion in a two–dimensional plane as we did for most of the discussion in Chapters 2 and 3. The object, shown as a dot, follows the line labelled *path*. At any instant, the velocity vector of the object must be tangential to the path. This is due to the definition of the velocity in two dimensions in component form:

$$\lim_{\Delta t \to 0} \frac{\Delta x}{\Delta t} = v_x$$

$$\lim_{\Delta t \to 0} \frac{\Delta y}{\Delta t} = v_y \tag{5}$$

The change of the position of an object, which is the combination of the terms $\Delta x/\Delta t$ and $\Delta y/\Delta t$, constitutes the path of the object. The vector components of the changing path are equal to the vector components of the velocity of the object. Consequently, the path is described by the tangent to the curve describing the position as a function of time.

We now show that we obtain a motion other than a motion along a straight line in a two–dimensional plane, when the object is accelerated with the vector direction of the acceleration different from the direction of the velocity vector. We verify this statement by studying

Fig. 20.2 in more detail. If the magnitude of the acceleration were zero, $|\mathbf{a}| = 0$, Newton's first law would apply. This law states that motion with constant speed along a straight line results, i.e., no curved path is possible.

We need the second law of mechanics where the acceleration does not vanish. But even if the magnitude of the acceleration is not zero we found many cases before in which the acceleration is parallel to the motion, i.e., again no curved path results. To establish the condition which leads to a curved path, we study the definition of the acceleration in component form:

$$\lim_{\Delta t \to 0} \frac{\Delta v_x}{\Delta t} = a_x$$

$$\lim_{\Delta t \to 0} \frac{\Delta v_y}{\Delta t} = a_y \quad (6)$$

In order to change the direction of the path of an object, we know from Eq. (5) that we need to change the values of the two velocity vector components relative to each other. Eq. (6) shows that such a change of the velocity components requires a ratio of the two components of the acceleration which is different from the respective ratio of the two current components of the velocity. In other words, the acceleration vector has to point into another direction than the velocity vector.

Looking at Eqs. (5) and (6) we notice that describing the motion along a curved path using Cartesian coordinates is not the most convenient approach: all six acceleration, velocity and position coordinates continuously change during the motion. It is, therefore, useful to substitute the Cartesian coordinates with a *coordinate system which is attached to the object*. The two directions which replace the fixed x– and y–axes are an axis along the direction tangential to the path of the object and an axis perpendicular to the tangential direction. There are two reasons why this coordinate system leads to simpler physical descriptions of the motion:
(I) The velocity has only one component in the new system with $\mathbf{v} = (v_\parallel, 0)$.
(II) In principle, the acceleration has two components, written as $\mathbf{a} = (a_\parallel, a_\perp)$. However, the motion associated with the tangential acceleration component, $a_\parallel$, has already been described fully in Chapters 2 and 3: the object accelerates in the direction of the velocity vector, which results in motion along a straight line. Thus, we expect new physical phenomena in this section only due to the perpendicular acceleration component, $a_\perp$.

This allows us to simplify the discussion without loss of generality by eliminating the part of the process we considered already. We do this by choosing a case where the acceleration tangential to the path is zero, i.e., $a_\parallel = 0$. If further $a_\perp = const$, we call the motion a *uniform circular motion*. Uniform refers to the fact that the magnitude of the velocity of the object does not change, i.e.,

$$a_\parallel = 0 \quad \Rightarrow \quad v_\parallel = |\mathbf{v}| = const \quad (7)$$

For writing the result as given in Eq. (7) we recall that $v_\perp$ is always zero. The term *circular* indicates that the path becomes a circular path when the condition $a_\perp = const$ is considered. This is the only case we consider. That this case indeed results in circular motion can be illustrated with an object attached to a string. When you swing the mass horizontally, the fixed length of the string forces the object onto a circular path around your hand. Throughout the swing you need the same magnitude of force to keep the object on its path; the constant magnitude of force is associated with a constant magnitude of acceleration due to Newton's second law. Note, however, that neither the acceleration nor the needed force are constant as both are vectors which continuously change their directions.

We want to further quantify the relations between the various parameters describing the uniform circular motion. To do so, we specify several parameters in Fig. 20.3. Part (a) shows two points, P_1 and P_2, along the circular path with center C. The two points are characterized by the position vectors $\mathbf{r}_1$ and $\mathbf{r}_2$ which enclose an angle θ. The two points on the path are separated by a distance $\Delta \mathbf{s}$. An object at point P_1 has the velocity $\mathbf{v}_1$, and at point P_2 it has the velocity $\mathbf{v}_2$. Sketch 20.3(b) illustrates the corresponding relation between the two velocity vectors; they also describe an angle θ due to the geometrical fact that both $\mathbf{r}_1 \perp \mathbf{v}_1$ and $\mathbf{r}_2 \perp \mathbf{v}_2$. The difference vector between $\mathbf{v}_1$ and $\mathbf{v}_2$ is defined as $\Delta \mathbf{v}$.

The magnitude of the perpendicular acceleration component $a_\perp$ is related to the other parameters of the motion, i.e., the velocity and the radius of the path by using the two sketches in Fig. 20.3. For this we assume that only a very short time Δt has elapsed between the time when the object passes through point P_1 and the time the object passes through point P_2. That means that both $\Delta \mathbf{s}$ and $\Delta \mathbf{v}$ are very short vectors and θ is a small angle. Using trigonometry we find from the two parts of Fig. 20.3, respectively:

$$\sin\theta = \frac{|\Delta \mathbf{s}|}{|\mathbf{r}|}$$

$$\sin\theta = \frac{|\Delta \mathbf{v}|}{|\mathbf{v}|} \quad (8)$$

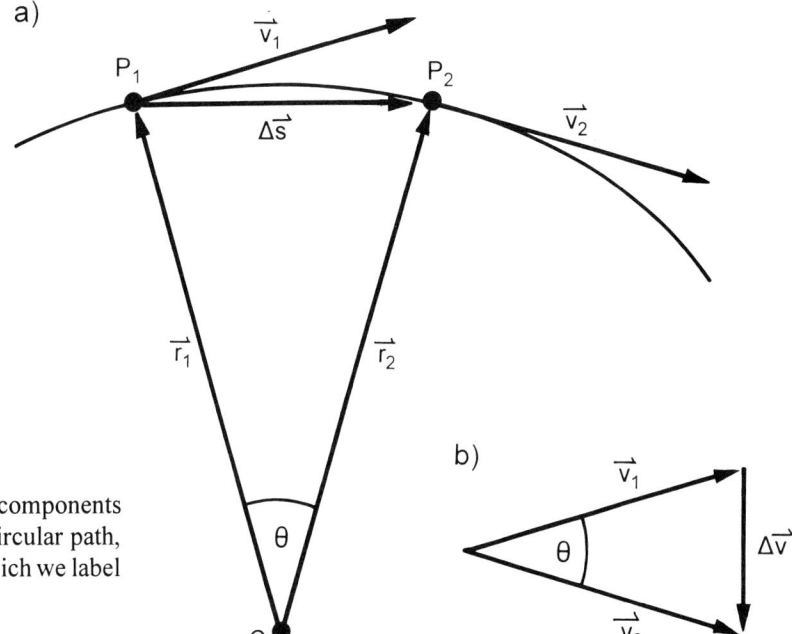

Fig. 20.3: Position and velocity components for an object moving along a circular path, shown at two different times which we label with indices 1 and 2.

In Eq. (8), we simplified the notation to $r_1 \cong r_2 \equiv r$ and $v_1 \cong v_2 \equiv v$ since both position vectors and both velocity vectors are essentially the same for a very small angle θ. We combine both formulas in Eq. (8):

$$|\Delta \mathbf{v}| = \frac{|\mathbf{v}|}{|\mathbf{r}|} |\Delta s| \qquad (9)$$

Next we divide Eq. (9) on both sides by the elapsed time interval Δt:

$$a_\perp = \frac{\Delta v}{\Delta t} = \frac{v}{r} \frac{\Delta s}{\Delta t} = \frac{v^2}{r} \qquad (10)$$

in which $\Delta s / \Delta t = v_\parallel = |\mathbf{v}|$. This acceleration is called the *centripetal acceleration* because it is a constant acceleration towards the center of the circular path. It is important to note again that the acceleration in Eq. (10) is not an x– or a y–component in the xy–plane of the circular motion; in respect to fixed x– and y–axes the components of the centripetal acceleration continuously change.

Uniform circular motion results when the velocity along the path is constant and a constant acceleration toward the center of the circular path occurs. This is called the centripetal acceleration.

In Chapter 15 we defined the period T as the time to complete a full cycle. Since the circumference of a circle has the length $2\pi r$ the definition allows us to rewrite the velocity as $2\pi r/T$. Substituting this in Eq. (10) leads to a second formula for the acceleration perpendicular to the direction of motion:

$$a_\perp = \frac{4\pi^2 r}{T^2} \qquad (11)$$

The centripetal acceleration is larger for an object moving around the center with a shorter period, and the centripetal acceleration is larger for an object at a greater distance from the center of the path. In Chapter 15 we also defined the angular frequency as the angle (in unit radians) through which an object on a cyclic path passes in one second: $\omega = 2\pi/T$. This allows us to rewrite the acceleration perpendicular to the path in Eq. (10) in a third form:

$$a_\perp = \omega^2 r \qquad (12)$$

Example 20.1

Calculate the acceleration due to the rotation of the Earth of a person in New York.
Hint: New York is located at 40.8^0 northern geographical latitude. Use $R_{Earth} = 6370$ km for the value of the radius of the Earth.

Solution: The period of the Earth is 1 day, which corresponds to 86,400 s. A person in New York does not move around the Earth's axis on a circle of radius R_{Earth} since the Earth rotates about an axis connecting its geo-

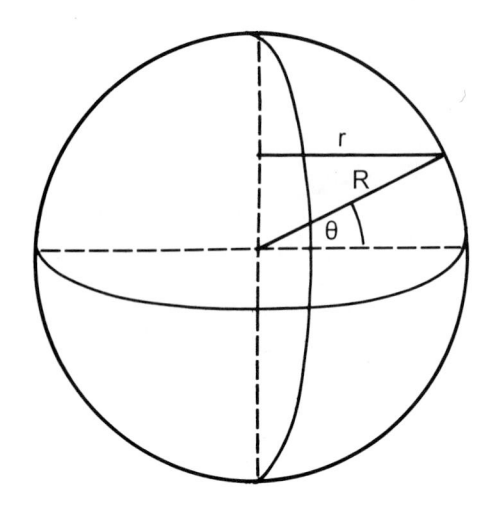

Fig. 20.4: Illustration of the position of New York, at latitude $\theta = 40.8^0$. Note that the distance to the axis, r, is not equal to the Earth's radius, R.

graphical North and South Poles. Thus, a point at $\theta = 40.8^0$ above the equator moves on a circle with a radius $r = R_{Earth} \cos\theta$ as illustrated in Fig. 20.4. This allows us to calculate the centripetal acceleration required to keep a person in New York on the ground:

$$a = \frac{4\pi^2 R_{Earth} \cos\theta}{T_{Earth}^2} \quad (13)$$

which leads with the specific values of the Example text to:

$$a = \frac{4\pi^2 \; 6.37 \times 10^6 [m] \; \cos 40.8^0}{(8.64 \times 10^4 [s])^2}$$
$$\Rightarrow \quad a = 0.026 \; \frac{m}{s^2} \quad (14)$$

Comparing the result in Eq. (14) with the gravitational acceleration g shows that gravity provides a more than sufficient acceleration to keep us from floating off the ground.

Example 20.2

How fast would the Earth have to spin to have the person in Example 20.1 float apparently weightlessly across the room?

Solution: This would happen if the centripetal acceleration were equal to the gravitational acceleration. In this case the entire gravitational pull would be needed to keep us on a circular path as the Earth spins and no fraction of the gravitational acceleration would be left to pull us down on the ground. We rewrite Eq. (11) to determine the period of the Earth required for this case:

$$T = 2\pi \sqrt{\frac{r}{a_\perp}} = 2\pi \sqrt{\frac{R_{Earth} \cos\theta}{g}} \quad (15)$$

in which we can substitute the specific values given in the Example text:

$$T = 2\pi \sqrt{\frac{6.37 \times 10^6 [m] \cos 40.8^0}{9.8 [m/s^2]}} \quad (16)$$
$$\Rightarrow \quad T = 4410 \; s$$

This result means that the Earth would have to spin around once every 1 hour and 13.5 minutes, which would be the length of a day in this case.

20.2.2. Centripetal and centrifugal accelerations

What causes the centripetal acceleration? As before, we consider Newton's laws when trying to identify forces. However, we have to be careful as we do not want to return to the Cartesian coordinates used for Newton's second law in component form in Eq. (3.19). Trying to do this here would require us to determine the x– and y–components of the acceleration in Eq. (10).

For circular motion, we have to rewrite Eq. (3.19) with a different set of three perpendicular axes, two representing the plane in which the circular motion occurs and one which we call the z–component, which is perpendicular to the plane of the circular motion. In this textbook, we will only consider cases in which the velocity component in this z–direction is constant or zero, i.e., cases where Newton's first law applies in the z–direction. It would be possible to consider other cases, however, they lead to complicated mathematical formulas.

In the plane of circular motion (the xy–plane) we use the directions parallel and perpendicular to the object's path as our coordinates. Continuing to use the simplification of a vanishing acceleration in the direction parallel to the path, $a_\parallel = 0$, we write Newton's laws for the case of a uniform circular motion in the form:

$$(I) \quad \sum_i F_{i,\perp} = m\frac{v^2}{r}$$

$$(II) \quad \sum_i F_{i,\parallel} = 0 \tag{17}$$

$$(III) \quad \sum_i F_{i,z} = 0$$

The formulas in Eq. (17) replace Eq. (3.19) in the case of circular motion. Without the simplifying assumptions we made, the right hand side of the second and third formulas in Eq. (17) would be written as $ma_\parallel$ and ma_z, respectively.

> *Newton's second law applies to circular motion with the acceleration identified as the centripetal acceleration.*

Newton's laws, written in the form of Eq. (17), reveal the direction in which the net force acts in a circular motion: perpendicular to the path within the plane in which the circular motion occurs. It is interesting to note that there is no identifiable force that we can call the centripetal force, i.e., there is no additional force in a system with a circular motion. The sum of forces (i.e., the net force) on the left hand side of the first formula in Eq. (17) is sometimes unfortunately referred to as *centripetal force*.

An important assumption of Newton's mechanics is that we must be able to find a physical object causing each force. In turn, we should not find any object causing a force if the force is not individually identified in Newton's laws. Although it is always hard to prove that something doesn't exist (since there is an infinite number of possibilities one may have to test) it is instructive to try and fail to find an object causing the centripetal force in the examples that we discuss below.

We also saw in Chapters 2 and 3 that we can always find action–reaction pairs of forces obeying Newton's third law. This may or may not be the case for the interactions causing the centripetal acceleration. If the net force in the first formula in Eq. (17) is due to a single force, then we can use Newton's third law to identify a reaction force exerted by the system on a particular object in the environment. In this case, and only in this case, can we identify this reaction force as a *centrifugal force*. If, on the other hand, the net force in the first formula of Eq. (17) is due to more than one force then no meaningful definition of a reaction force exists, i.e., no force constitutes a centrifugal force!

The centrifuge is an example of a biologically important device for which the definition of a centrifugal force is meaningful. Centrifuges are used to separate particles suspended in solutions, such as in blood, urine or milk. A centrifuge is an electrically driven device which sets test tubes in circular motion with typically 3000 rotations per minute. During rotation, the solvent exerts a contact force on the heavier particles suspended in the solution to keep them on a circular path (gravity plays no role in this technique). A sedimentation of the heavier components in the solution occurs due to the reaction force, exerted by the heavier particle on the solvent. This force is directed outwards and causes the liquid solvent to move out of the way of the heavier particles.

Example 20.3

An object of mass m is placed at the end of a string of length L. It swings along a horizontal circle with constant speed $|v|$ at angle β with the vertical direction as illustrated in Fig. 20.5. How does the time T for a single revolution depend on the angle β?

Note: this arrangement is called a *conical pendulum*.

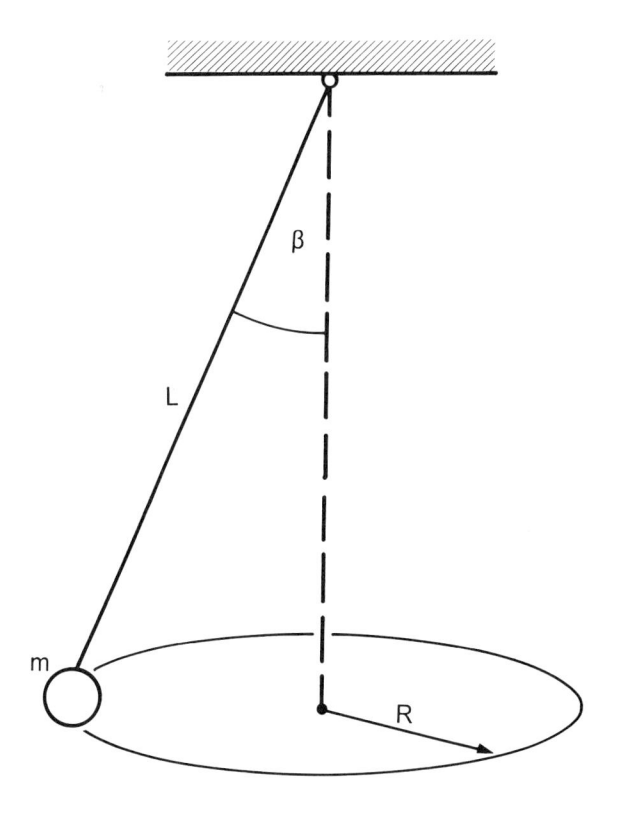

Fig. 20.5: An object of mass m is attached to a string of length L and moves along a circular path of radius R. The string forms an angle β with the vertical.

Solution: Although it is undesirable, we use in this example the same letter for two different quantities, the period and the tension. This is possible since one is a scalar (the period) and the other is a vector (the tension). By maintaining the notation $|\mathbf{T}|$ for the magnitude of the tension no confusion should occur.

We first identify the object as the system and the forces acting on the system. These are the tension, caused by the string, and the weight, caused by the Earth. Note that we do *not* identify a separate centripetal force as there is no further force acting on the system in Fig. 20.5! Next the free–body–diagram is drawn. In agreement with the discussion earlier in this section, we identify the vertical direction as the z–direction because this direction is perpendicular to the xy–plane of the circular motion. In the xy–plane, the directions perpendicular and tangential to the path are identified. To draw a two–dimensional free–body–diagram we neglect the direction tangential to the path as we know that the second formula of Eq. (17) applies in the given form. The resulting free–body–diagram is illustrated in Fig. 20.6. Using this figure we write the two non–trivial formulas from Eq. (17) for the specific case of the present Example:

$$\sum_i F_{i,\perp} = |T|\sin\beta = m\frac{v^2}{R}$$
$$\sum_i F_{i,z} = |T|\cos\beta - mg = 0 \tag{18}$$

In the first formula of Eq. (18) the net force directed toward the center of the circular path is identified as the horizontal component of the tension $\mathbf{T}$ in the string. The second formula in Eq. (18) states that a mechanical equilibrium exists in the vertical direction, which is the direction perpendicular to the plane of the circular motion of the object. As discussed earlier, we limit our discussion in this chapter to cases in which the velocity component in the z–direction remains constant or zero. Eq. (18) is such a case.

It is very useful in this example to carefully identify the known and unknown variables in Eq. (18) and compare with the parameters we are asked to quantify in the Example text. The text refers to four quantities, the mass m, the length L, the speed v and the angle β. Of these the mass and the length are fixed and the angle is variable. Further, the period of the motion varies which implies that also the speed is a variable.

Now we check Eq. (18). The two formulas in the equation contain a total of four variables: the magnitude of the tension, $|\mathbf{T}|$, the angle β, the speed of the object, v, and the radius of the circular path, R. From geometrical considerations based on Fig. 20.6, one additional formula can be written which connects some of the unknown variables: the radius of the circular path R is related to the length of the string and β by $R = L\sin\beta$.

The two formulas in Eq. (18) and the geometrical relation do not introduce the period of the motion. Since the Example text asks about this quantity, we need to introduce a fourth formula relating the speed, the circumference of the circular path and the period: $v = 2\pi R/T$. This formula allows us to change the variable speed to the variable period. Thus, the four formulas we have written for this Example contain five unknown variable, (I) tension $|\mathbf{T}|$, (II) period T, (III) velocity $|\mathbf{v}|$, (IV) radius R, and (V) angle β. Thus, we can not calculate any of these unknown parameters, but we can write as a result how any one of these variables depends on any of the others.

The Example text asks us specifically to calculate $T = f(\beta)$, i.e., the tension, velocity and radius have to be eliminated. We use the two formulas in Eq. (18) to eliminate the tension, we use $R = L\sin\beta$ to eliminate the radius, and we eliminate the velocity with $v = 2\pi R/T$. How this is done is shown step by step below.

We first combine the two formulas in Eq. (18) by dividing the first formula by the second formula:

$$\tan\beta = \frac{v^2}{gR} \tag{19}$$

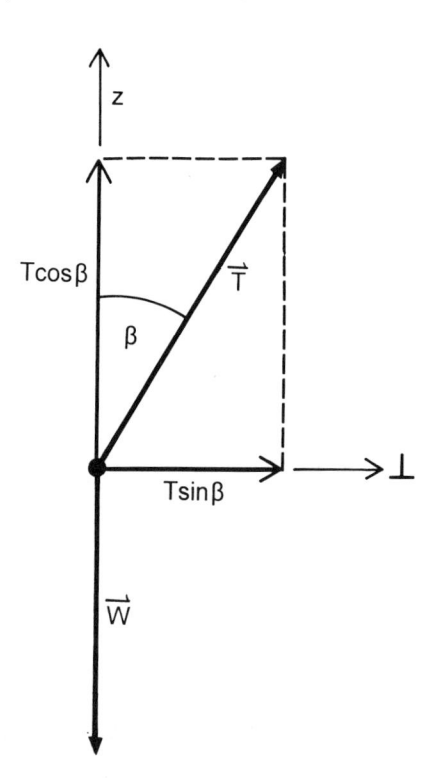

Fig. 20.6: Free–body–diagram for the object shown in Fig. 20.5. Note that an object centred coordinate system is used with the horizontal axis labelled ⊥, i.e., pointing in a direction perpendicular to the path of the object.

Then we eliminate the radius in the equation for the velocity:

$$v = \frac{2\pi R}{T} = \frac{2\pi L \sin\beta}{T} \quad (20)$$

In the next step, Eq. (20) is used to substitute the velocity in Eq. (19):

$$\tan\beta = \frac{\left(\frac{2\pi L \sin\beta}{T}\right)^2}{gL\sin\beta} = \frac{4\pi^2 L \sin\beta}{gT^2} \quad (21)$$

which leads with $\tan\beta = \sin\beta/\cos\beta$ to:

$$\cos\beta = \frac{gT^2}{4\pi^2 L} \quad (22)$$

and after solving for the period:

$$T = 2\pi\sqrt{\frac{L\cos\beta}{g}} \quad (23)$$

This is the formula sought in the problem text.

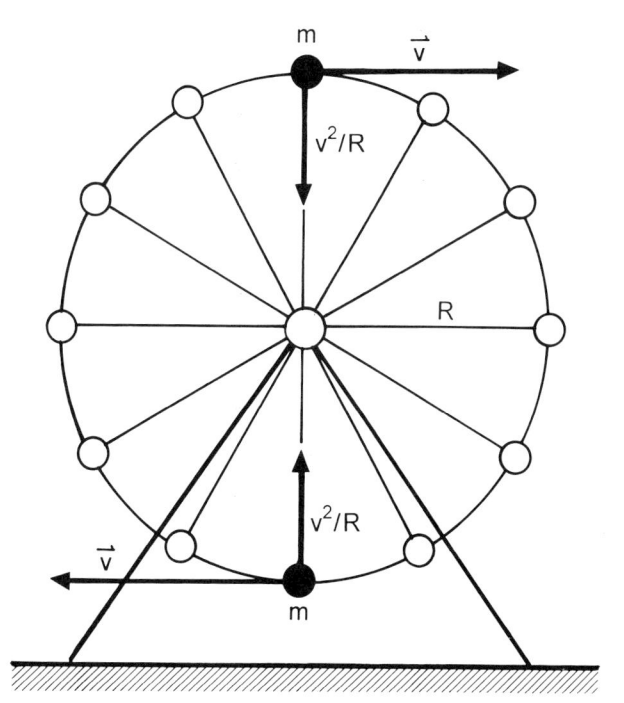

Fig. 20.7: A Ferris wheel with two persons (solid dots) in the seats at top and at bottom. The Ferris wheel has a radius R and rotates such that both persons move with a speed |v|.

We can test this relation with an object attached to a string. Hold the string and vary the speed with which you let the object move in a horizontal circle. If it moves slowly (long period) the object is at a small angle β (which corresponds to a large cosβ). When you let the object move faster, the angle β becomes larger.

Example 20.4
The Ferris wheel provides another instructive example. In a Ferris wheel, one person is at the top and one at the bottom, as shown in Fig. 20.7. The Ferris wheel rotates such that the magnitude of the tangential velocity of each person is equal, $|\mathbf{v}|_{top} = |\mathbf{v}|_{bottom}$. Determine for each person separately the force with which the seat pushes the person up.

Solution: Two forces act on each person, the weight and the normal force exerted by the seat. This leads to the two free–body–diagrams shown in Fig. 20.8. Since there are no forces acting perpendicular to the plane or in the tangential direction, only the first formula in Eq. (17) is used. For the person at the top it reads:

$$\sum_i F_{i,\perp} = N_{top} - mg = -m\frac{v^2}{r} \quad (24)$$

in which the negative sign on the right hand side reflects the fact that the centripetal acceleration is directed downwards, as shown in Fig. 20.8. Eq. (24) allows us to calculate the force exerted by the seat:

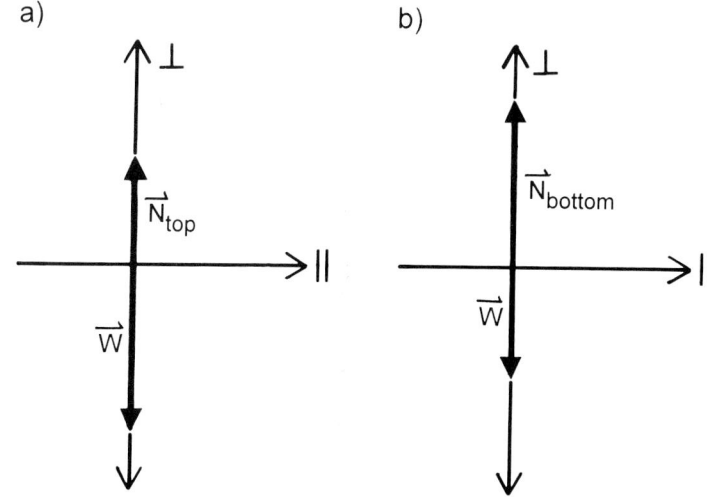

Fig. 20.8: Free–body–diagram for the person in the top seat (a) and the person in the bottom seat (b) of the Ferris wheel shown in Fig. 20.7. Note that the coordinate system is attached to the person and is not fixed in space.

$$N_{top} = m\left(g - \frac{v^2}{r}\right) < mg \qquad (25)$$

Thus, the person at the top feels lighter, which is an effect that is obviously felt more strongly at higher speeds, e.g. on a roller coaster ride.

The corresponding Newtonian equation for the person at the bottom reads:

$$\sum_i F_{i,\perp} = N_{bottom} - mg = +m\frac{v^2}{r} \qquad (26)$$

with the direction of the centripetal acceleration the only difference in Eq. (26), as seen in Fig. 20.8. This leads to the following form for the force exerted by the seat:

$$N_{bottom} = m\left(g + \frac{v^2}{r}\right) > mg \qquad (27)$$

i.e., the person feels heavier than on steady ground.

Example 20.5
Explain the Windkessel effect illustrated in Fig. 15.10 with the concept of circular motion.

Solution: The Windkessel effect is the result of the blood ejected from the heart moving through a 180^0 bend in the aorta. Like the person at the top of the Ferris wheel, the blood has to be accelerated toward the center of the bend (centripetal acceleration). The necessary force is exerted on the blood by the wall of the aorta. In a system with just two objects interacting, an equal but opposite force must act on the wall of the aorta (centrifugal force). Since the wall of the aorta is elastic, it responds to this apparent force by stretching outwards.

20.2.3. Centripetal acceleration for field forces

Field forces and contact forces cause the same effect with respect to circular motion. We have seen this already in Example 20.4 where the gravitational force was used in the form of the weight of the person. Thus, Eq. (17) remains applicable when studying circular motion at larger scales, be it the motion of satellites, including the moon or man–made structures, the motion of planets around the central star, or even the rotation of galaxies. Such applications also allow us to explain why astronauts in the ISS appear weightless. However, the consequences are much more far reaching when electric forces are included, where circular motion concepts will allow us in the next chapter to develop a model for the atom.

Example 20.6
How fast would the Earth have to spin so that we could tread as lightly at the equator as the Apollo astronauts did on the moon?
Hint: Neglect the rotation of the moon around its own axis.

Solution: We first determine the gravitational acceleration the astronauts felt on the surface of the moon. For that we need the following data for the moon:

$$m_{moon} = 7.35 \times 10^{22}\ kg \cong 1.2\%\ m_{Earth}$$
$$r_{moon} = 1.74 \times 10^6\ m = 27\%\ r_{Earth} \qquad (28)$$

Note that these values allow us to calculate a density for the moon which is significantly different from that of Earth (the average density of the Earth is $\rho = 5.52$ g/cm³ and the average density of the moon is $\rho = 3.33$ g/cm³), implying differences in the geophysical development of the moon and the Earth.

Next we use Eq. (3) to determine the gravitational acceleration on the moon:

$$g_{moon} = G * \frac{m_{moon}}{r_{moon}^2} =$$
$$6.67 \times 10^{-11}\left[\frac{m^3}{kgs^2}\right]\frac{7.35\times 10^{22}[kg]}{(1.74\times 10^6[m])^2} \qquad (29)$$

which leads to:

$$g_{moon} = 1.62\ \frac{m}{s^2} = 16.5\%\ g_{Earth} \qquad (30)$$

In the second step the required rotational speed of the Earth is calculated to obtain the gravitational acceleration from Eq. (29) on Earth as well. The free–

body–diagram for a person standing on ground is very simple, and exactly the same as for the person sitting in the seat at the top of the Ferris wheel in Example 20.4. Using Eq. (25), the normal force becomes $N_{top} = mg_{moon}$ in the present Example. Thus:

$$mg_{moon} = m\left(g_{Earth} - \frac{v^2}{R_{Earth}}\right) \quad (31)$$

in which we used R_{Earth} since the person is assumed to stand on the equator. Using $v = 2\pi r/T$ to replace the term speed with the period in Eq. (31), we find:

$$g_{Earth} - g_{moon} = \frac{v^2}{R_{Earth}} = \frac{4\pi^2 R_{Earth}}{T^2} \quad (32)$$

which is solved for the period T:

$$T = 2\pi \sqrt{\frac{R_{Earth}}{g_{Earth} - g_{moon}}} \quad (33)$$

Thus, T = 5544 s = 92 min = 1 hour 32 min.

You may wonder why substituting the actual value of the gravitational acceleration on Earth in Eq. (33) does not lead to a period of 24 hours. This is due to the assumptions we made when formulating Eq. (31). The terms with the g values on both sides of the equation imply an infinite period as explicitly noted for the moon, i.e., we also assume that the Earth does not rotate when $g = g_{Earth}$. In Example 20.2 we determined that the correction to g due to the rotation of the Earth is only a value of about 0.026 m/s², i.e., a value we can indeed neglect.

Example 20.7
(a) The International Space Station orbits at an average altitude of h = 430 km. How long does the ISS need to complete one full orbit?
(b) At what distance above Earth must a satellite be positioned to be in *geostationary orbit*? A satellite in geostationary orbit remains located above the same longitude on Earth all the time.

Solution part (a): For the ISS to neither crash like the Mir station did in 2001, nor float to higher altitudes where the intensive radiation of the van Allen belt would force its occupants to abandon ship, the net force acting on the station perpendicular to the circular path around the Earth (gravitational force) must be equal to the centripetal acceleration multiplied by the station's mass. We find from the first formula in Eq. (17) with gravity the only force contributing to the net force perpendicular to the station's motion:

$$G^* \frac{m_{Earth} m_{ISS}}{(R_{Earth} + h)^2} = m_{ISS} \frac{v_{ISS}^2}{(R_{Earth} + h)} \quad (34)$$

From Eq. (34) we obtain a formula for the speed of the ISS, in which $R_{earth} + h$ is the distance of the satellite to the center of the Earth:

$$v_{ISS} = \sqrt{G^* \frac{m_{Earth}}{R_{Earth} + h}} \quad (35)$$

and with the specific values from the Example text:

$$v_{ISS} = \sqrt{6.67 \times 10^{-11} \left[\frac{m^3}{kgs^2}\right] \frac{5.98 \times 10^{24} [kg]}{6800 [km]}} \quad (36)$$

$$\Rightarrow v_{ISS} = 7660 \frac{m}{s}$$

This high speed is not apparent from the TV images we are used to seeing from the station because the TV camera moves with the station! Using the relation $v = 2\pi r/T$ we connect the speed to the period for a full orbit:

$$v_{ISS} = \frac{2\pi r_{orbit}}{T} \quad (37)$$

the period for the ISS station can be calculated as:

$$T = \frac{2\pi (R_{Earth} + h)}{v_{ISS}} = \frac{2\pi \; 6800 [km]}{7660 [m/s]} \quad (38)$$

$$\Rightarrow T = 5580 \; s$$

i.e., the ISS moves around Earth once every 93 minutes!

Solution part (b): For a geostationary orbit, the altitude h in Eq. (34) must be chosen such that T = 24 hours. For this calculation, we use again Eq. (34) but rewrite the right hand side with Eq. (37) in order to replace the unknown speed of the geostationary satellite with its period and radius:

$$G * \frac{m_{Earth} m_{sat}}{(R_{Earth}+h_{sat})^2} = m_{sat} \frac{4\pi^2 (R_{Earth}+h_{sat})}{T^2} \quad (39)$$

Eq. (39) allows us to express the height above ground for the geostationary satellite:

$$h_{sat} = \left(G * \frac{m_{Earth} T^2}{4\pi^2} \right)^{1/3} - R_{Earth} \quad (40)$$

With the given numerical values we find from Eq. (40):

$$h_{sat} = \left(\frac{1}{4\pi^2} 6.67 \times 10^{-11} \left[\frac{m^3}{kgs^2} \right] \right)^{1/3} \dots$$
$$\dots \left(5.98 \times 10^{24} [kg] \, (8.64 \times 10^4 [s])^2 \right)^{1/3} \dots \quad (41)$$
$$\dots - 6.37 \times 10^6 [m] = 3.588 \times 10^7 \, m$$

The geostationary orbit lies at an altitude of 35,880 km, as indicated in Fig. 20.1. This orbit is used for TV and telephone transmission satellites which have to stay continuously in contact with the ground station.

20.3. Physiological effect of weightlessness

Example 20.7(a) indicates that the weightlessness of astronauts on board the ISS is not due to the value of the gravitational force at the altitude at which the ISS orbits Earth. The ISS and the astronauts aboard are in perpetual free fall toward Earth, but don't come closer to the surface as they are moving with a high speed sideways.

The issues of weightlessness during a long–distance space flight, e.g. during a Mars mission when the gravitational pull of Earth or Mars is negligible for practically the entire trip, are equivalent to the problems with weightlessness encountered in the ISS. For this reason, endurance tests on the space station are of interest in aerospace medicine to determine preventive measures for future mission.

To date the longest stay on a space station was recorded for Valery Polyakov in 1995, who stayed on the Russian station Mir for 437 days. His program included 2 hours per day of intensive exercise to counterbalance the lack of use of his bones and muscles. Polyakov was able to walk away from the landing site under his own power.

Polyakov's record still falls short of the anticipated time that a trip to Mars would take. This is illustrated in Fig. 20.9, which shows the relative constellation of Earth and Mars at the two respective launch dates. Note that the space ship does not travel straight outwards in (b) or straight inwards in (d) as it does have

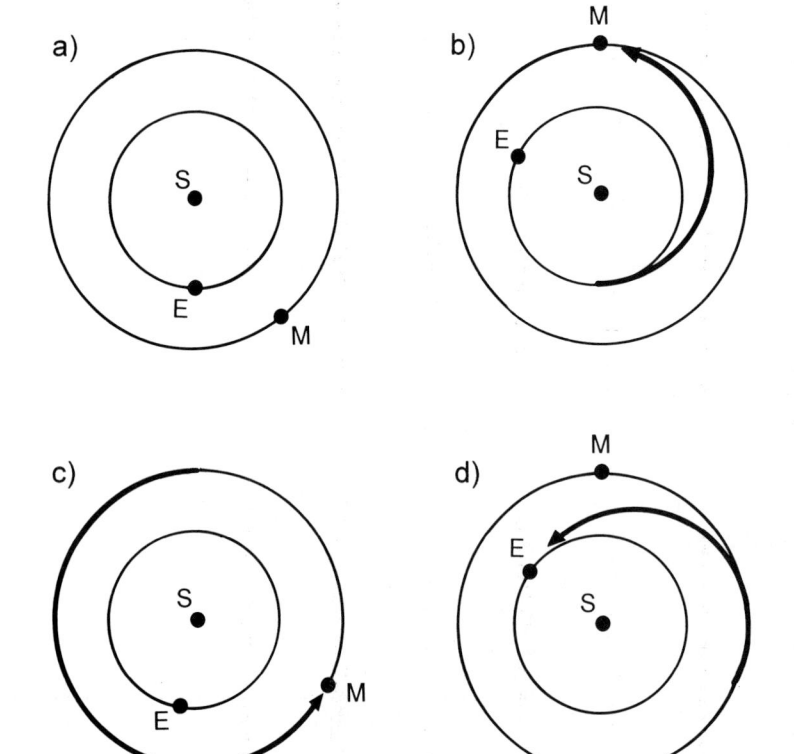

Fig. 20.9: The relative positions of Earth (E) and Mars (M) in their respective orbits around the sun (S) during (a) launch time of a Mars mission (day 0), (b) arrival time of the mission at Mars (day 257), (c) launch time for the return trip to Earth (day 714), and (d) the arrival time at the completion of the mission (day 972).

a tangential velocity component at launch due to the motion of each planet. Since only certain relative constellations of Earth and Mars at each launch lead to a safe passage, there is a minimum stay of 455 days for the mission on Mars (which is still less than a Mars–year) until a return time–window opens. Thus, the entire mission will last 972 days, assuming currently available technology, with a total of about 520 days under weightless conditions while travelling between the two planets.

Those 520 days of weightlessness have a major effect on the human body, as illustrated in Fig. 20.10. Curve (1) shows the change in the density of human bones as a function of age for the average healthy person. The density peaks at age 30 with $\rho = 2.0$ g/cm^3 and then decreases steadily. The two horizontal lines indicate two critical thresholds: below the upper dashed line we speak clinically of osteopenia, a state of reduced bone tissue density which is considered normal in older people. Below the lower dash–dotted line we speak clinically of osteoporosis, which causes pain in the part of the body where the bones are affected, causes general back pain and leads to a characteristic bent–over posture due to the collapse of vertebrae.

Using data from previous endurance stays under weightlessness, we know that there is a 1 % to 2 % loss of calcium in human bones per month. Thus, we anticipate a loss of bone strength due to a loss of about 15 % to 30 % of the Ca in the bones during the Mars trip. This is illustrated in curve (2) of Fig. 20.10. The curve starts at a somewhat higher density, assuming that intensive training precedes the mission. The steep reduction in bone density is due to weightlessness during the Mars mission for astronauts in their early 40s. The individual will return with a bone structure close to that of a fragile 80 year old person! Note the question mark shown with the anticipated recovery curve. We simply don't know whether there would be a recovery, but even if there is one, it must be a very slow process.

Note also that the program that the astronauts would be able to perform on Mars would be limited as they would arrive with already weakened bones, resembling those of a person in their mid 60s.

What causes the loss of calcium in bones? Bones are not a static structure in our body, nor are they inorganic or lifeless. Bones are refurbished in very much the same fashion as other body tissues. In the bones there is a continuous process of adding and removing calcium minerals to a frame–like template of collagen. Collagen, a rubber–like protein, allows bones to bend slightly without breaking. The large, calcium containing phosphate molecules filling the structure are called hydroxyapatite. These make the entire structure almost as strong as concrete. Further components of the bone structure are (I) osteoblasts, which are bone growing cells secreting minerals that eventually entomb the cell. In spite of being immobilized in this fashion, they stay alive and contribute to the porous, spongy nature of the bones. (II) A second type of cells are the osteoclasts, which are bone removing cells that tear down the bone structure for replacement or for scavenging calcium if it is needed elsewhere in the body.

Heavy use of certain bones can lead to significantly thicker bones, e.g. the arm that a professional player uses to play tennis may have bones that are 30 % thicker than in the other arm.

Fig. 20.10: Density of human bones as a function of age (curve 1). A trained astronaut may have a slightly denser bone structure (curve 2), however, encounters a significant bone density loss during a Mars mission as scheduled in Fig. 20.9. The dashed line indicates the threshold for osteopenia and the dash–dotted line indicates the threshold for osteoporosis.

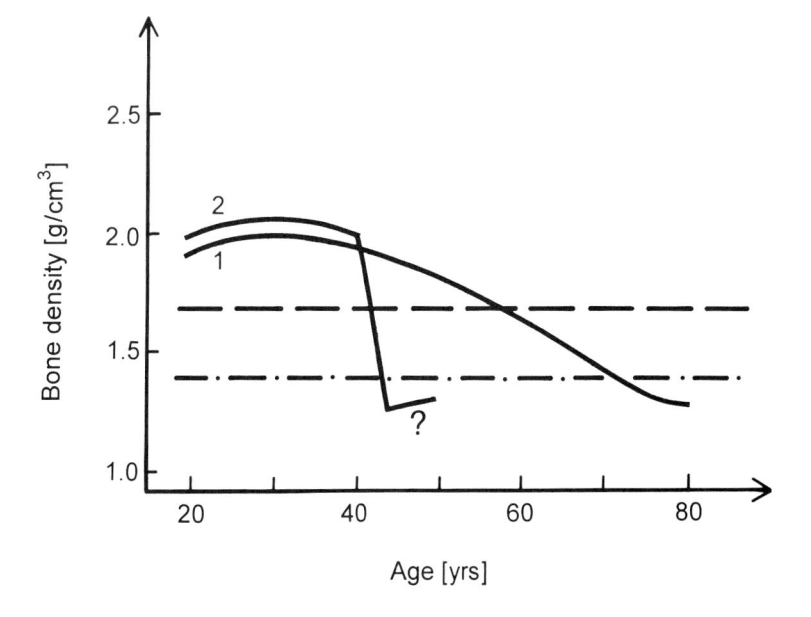

20.4. Radiation exposure

20.4.1. Cosmic rays

The first indication of intensive radiation outside of the Earth's atmosphere was found in 1910 when Viktor Hess noted that the environmental radiation increases with altitude. He correctly concluded that the radiation must come from outer space, and therefore, called it *cosmic rays*.

The intensity of cosmic rays reaching sea level is rather low at about 1 particle/cm²min. What arrives at sea level is secondary radiation, caused by reactions between the primary radiation and the molecules in the atmosphere at about 20 km altitude. The primary radiation consists of 85 % protons, 14 % helium nuclei (α–particles) and about 1 % nuclei of heavier elements, ranging from lithium to iron. This distribution corresponds well to the composition of stars, hinting at the radiation's origin in exploding supernovae.

The next important discovery was that the cosmic radiation is not reaching Earth uniformly from all directions. Instead, the intensity varies with geographic latitude as shown in Fig. 20.11. At sea level the variation is weaker (indicated by the curve labelled with the pressure value of 760 torr), but at greater altitudes, where the atmospheric pressure is reduced to 600 torr (center curve) and 450 torr (top curve), the intensity of the radiation is not only increased, as originally found by Hess, but a profound latitude dependence is observed, with higher levels of radiation close to the poles. That this effect is not the result of unevenly distributed events in the deep universe, but is an Earth–bound effect was recognized when the US satellite Explorer I discovered the radiation belts in 1958. These belts span the outer parts of the atmosphere, between 1000 and 25,000 km altitude. There are three distinct belts, with the innermost belt containing high electron densities with particle energies of 0.8 MeV and protons of extremely high energy, reaching beyond 150 MeV. The outer belts are populated only by electrons.

Another source of radiation is the sun. Particularly during its active periods or when solar flares occur, energetic radiation reaches the Earth. While this radiation again contains particles, the more noteworthy component is energetic electromagnetic radiation.

Fig. 20.12 shows the electromagnetic spectrum of the sun for wavelengths from the infrared region ($\lambda = 10^4 - 10^5$ nm) to wavelengths of less than 1 nm. We compare this spectrum with the spectrum in Fig. 19.29. Note that the data are represented in Fig. 20.12 in a double–logarithmic plot, while Fig. 19.29 is a linear plot. The double–logarithmic plot emphasizes smaller irradi-

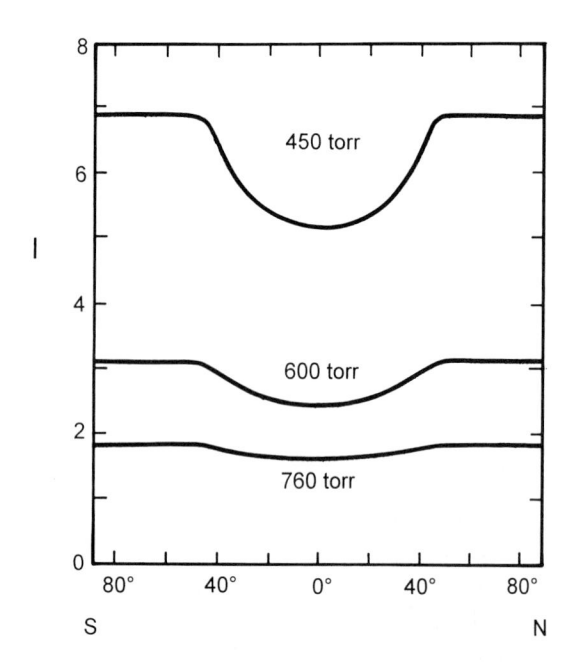

Fig. 20.11: The intensity of cosmic rays as a function of altitude (expressed in unit pressure, which can be correlated to altitudes in Fig. 20.1) and as a function of geographic latitude.

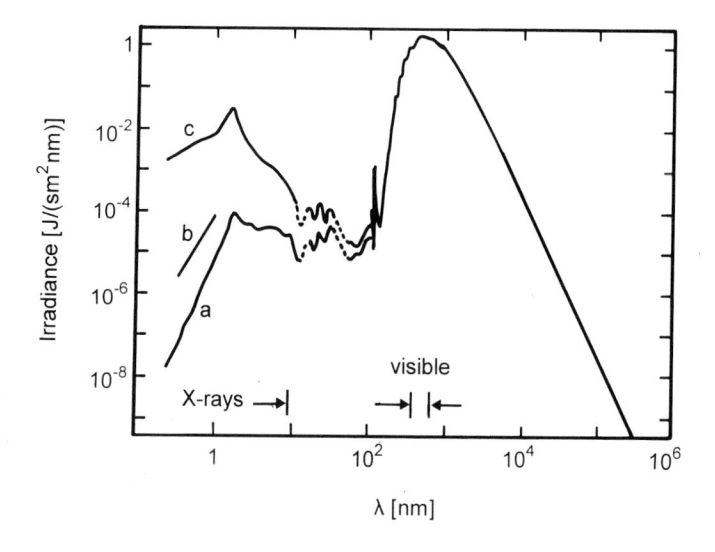

Fig. 20.12: Irradiance of electromagnetic radiation above the atmosphere as a function of wavelength. In the double–logarithmic plot the irradiance is given in unit [J/m²s] and further per nanometer interval of the electromagnetic spectrum. The irradiance is primarily caused by the sun, with the major peak at the longer wavelengths due to the black body radiation of the sun from its surface at 5800 K. The short wavelengths radiation depends on the sun's activity levels: (a) quiet sun, (b) active sun, and (c) during sun flares.

ances. The irradiance in both figures is the amount of energy deposited per square meter and second [J/m²s] as a function of wavelength. Each irradiance value corresponds to the amount reaching in a wavelength interval of a width of 1 nm, which contributes an additional unit [nm⁻¹] to the unit of the irradiance as shown.

In Figs. 19.29 and 20.12, the peak of irradiance lies in the visible range of the electromagnetic spectrum due to the black body model of the sun, as discussed in the previous chapter. However, Fig. 20.12 shows additional radiation at wavelengths which are clearly not explained by the black body model. Attention is drawn to two features which we will explain in the next chapter: the sharp peak close to 100 nm and the radiation between 0.1 nm and 100 nm, i.e. stretching across the entire ultraviolet range, from 10 nm to 100 nm, and the X–ray range at shorter wavelengths. It is useful to remind yourself once more that the radiation in Fig. 20.12 is electromagnetic radiation, while Fig. 20.11 represents particle radiation.

The origin of both particle and electromagnetic radiation, such as X–rays, will be discussed in the next chapter. Here, we want to emphasize the effect that these different forms of radiation have on astronauts. From war– and peace–time testing of atomic and hydrogen bombs, as well from medical applications, we know that these effects may be severe. A first example is given by Fig. 20.13, which shows the fraction of surviving cells after various doses of radiation. The unit Gray [Gy] quantifies the *dose*, which is defined as the total amount of energy deposited by the radiation in the tissue. The figure shows that essentially all cell types in the human body resist lower doses, but get damaged beyond repair at higher doses.

Luckily, higher doses are rare, as shown in Fig. 20.14. In this figure, a different type of dose, called *equivalent dose*, is used. The equivalent dose includes a correction factor for the biological effect of the radiation. This correction factor for the biological effects of radiation is quantified in the next chapter, where we will define a new unit, the Sievert [Sv] for the equivalent dose. Fig. 20.14 compares various activities and the corresponding risk of exposure to biologically damaging radiation. Again, it is important to recognize that Fig. 20.14 has a logarithmic ordinate. Compared to the natural background to which we are all exposed and which corresponds to an equivalent dose of 1 mSv/year, even relatively short space missions represent a significant increase in exposure. This brings us back to the risks of space travel. The longest stay on the US Skylab station was 84 days. The radiation exposure of those astronauts was equivalent to what they would be exposed to over 70 years on the surface of our planet, i.e., equivalent to the radiation dose received during an average life span. Polyakov, the cosmonaut with the current record for endurance stay in space, was exposed to more radiation

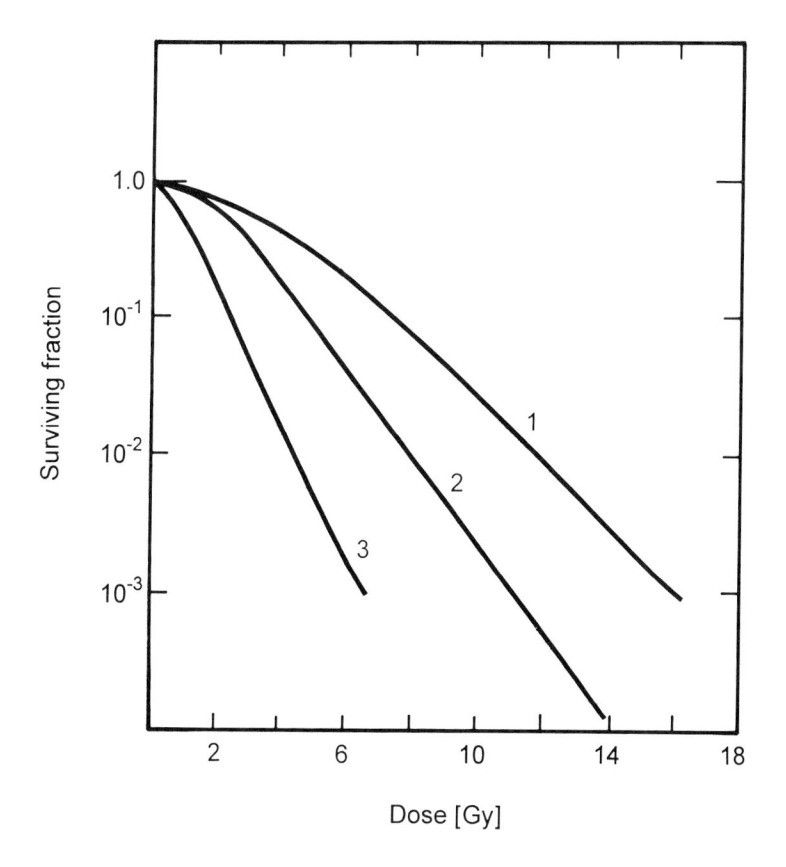

Fig. 20.13: The surviving fraction of three types of human cells as a function of energy dose in unit [Gy]. The energy dose is the energy deposited by the radiation per kilogram of tissue. Note the lower steepness at doses below 1 Gy which is due to self–repair mechanisms in living cells. Various cells respond differently sensitive to radiation: (1) thyroid cells, (2) mammary cells, and (3) bone marrow.

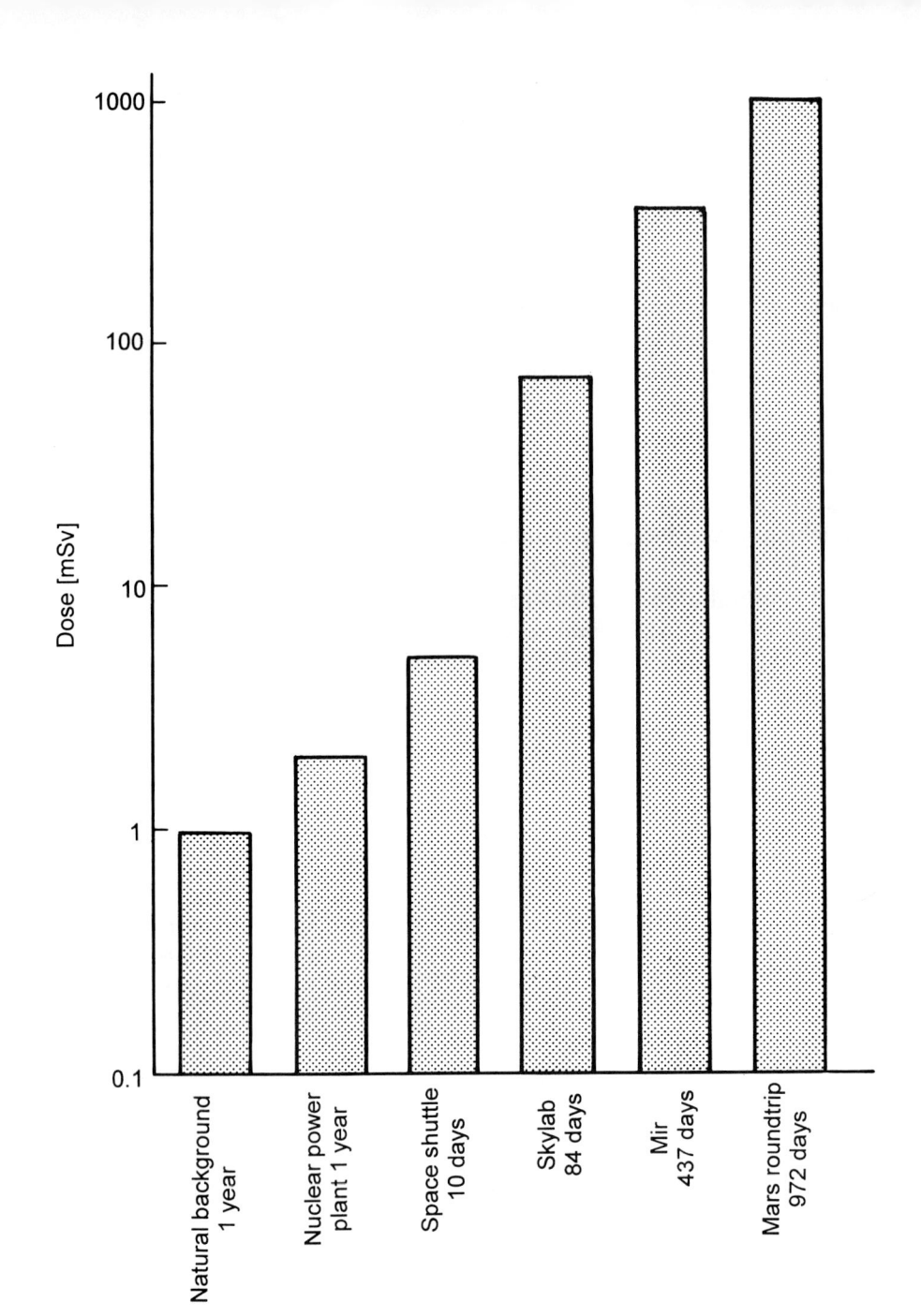

Fig. 20.14: The equivalent full body dose received by a person under various conditions. The lowest full body dose corresponds to the natural background radiation. The full body doses received on the longest Skylab or Mir missions are significantly less than what we have to anticipate during a Mars mission. The equivalent dose, which is closely related to the energy dose but corrected by a biological impact factor, is given in unit milli–Sievert.

than any human has ever received naturally, because a person would have to live 350 years to receive that dose in a natural environment. A Mars mission again will triple the amount. In this section we have so far identified several questions we have to discuss in more detail:
(I) What explains the radiation belts and their non–uniformity with geographic latitude,
(II) how can the sun generate the non–thermal electromagnetic radiation at short wavelengths in Fig. 20.12,
(III) what distinguishes the particle radiation in Fig. 20.11 from the electromagnetic radiation in Fig. 20.12,
(IV) why do we need two units to define the dose of radiation, the Gray and the Sievert?
The answers to these questions come from very different subfields of physics. If we accept that charged particles continuously approach the Earth at high speeds from outer space, then the radiation belts are an issue of magnetism and the motion of charged particles in a magnetic field. This will be illustrated in the next section.

The difference between electromagnetic radiation and cosmic rays is significant in that the former can be explained with an atomic model, while the latter requires nuclear physics models. The next two chapters deal with the atomic model and the formation of X–rays first, followed by nuclear physics concepts as required for biological and medical applications. The biological impact of both types of radiation have to be discussed separate as they differ in several respects, such as penetration depth and energy deposition in tissue.

20.4.2. Origin of the radiation belts

We discussed magnetism in the previous chapter to establish the electromagnetic nature of light, which was needed to explain the phenomena of light polarization and color. We return to the concept of magnetism in the current section to supplement its effect on currents by the effect on moving charged particles. Since the Earth has a magnetic field, charged particles approaching the planet from outer space are subject to magnetic interactions which explain several of the observations discussed above. But we also will see that the interaction of charged particles with magnetic fields allows us to get a step closer to understanding molecular matter.

The magnetic force was defined in section 19.1 as the force acting between two parallel electric currents:

$$|F_{mag}| \propto \frac{I_1 I_2}{d} l \quad \Rightarrow \quad \frac{|F_{mag}|}{l} \propto \frac{I_1 I_2}{d} \quad (42)$$

in which I_1 and I_2 are two parallel currents, d is the distance between the two conductors and l is the length over which the conductors interact.

The definition of the magnitude of the magnetic field **B** followed from Eq. (42) with one of the currents identified as a test current and removed from the system:

$$|B| = \frac{\mu_0}{2\pi} \frac{I}{d} \quad (43)$$

In the present context we want to abstract from the concept of electric current and focus on single charged particles in motion. In a first approach we maintain the two parallel conductors, but use Eq. (13.34) to identify the current as the flow of electrons:

$$I = \frac{\Delta Q}{\Delta t} = n \, e \, v_d \, A \quad (44)$$

in which n is the particle density of mobile charges in the conductor, e is the elementary charge, v_d is the drift velocity and A the cross–sectional area of the conductor.

We substitute Eqs. (43) and (44) into Eq. (42) to remove the currents and replace the magnetic force with the magnetic field. This leads to the following formula for the magnetic force between parallel conductors:

$$\frac{F_{mag}}{l} = B \, I = B \, n_e \, e \, v_d \, A \quad (45)$$

We generalize this formula by replacing the elementary charge e of the electron in a wire with the charge q, which can be then also be the charge of an ion. The product of length l and cross–sectional area A in Eq. (45) equals the volume, V = lA. The volume can be combined with the density of the moving charges, n_e, to yield the total number of charged particles, N_q:

$$l \, A \, n_e = V \, n_e = N_q \quad (46)$$

Thus, Eq. (45) is rewritten for a single particle as:

$$\frac{F_{mag}}{N_q} = B \, q \, v \quad (47)$$

in which the index d for "drift" in Eq. (45) is dropped as the velocity of any moving charged particle obeys this formula, and not only the electrons drifting in a metallic wire. Eq. (47) provides us with the magnitude of the magnetic force per charged particle as the product of the magnitude of the magnetic field, the charge of the particle and the velocity of the particle. We introduce a new parameter for the force per particle in the form $\mathbf{f}_{mag} = \mathbf{F}_{mag}/N_q$. Thus, $\mathbf{F}_{mag}$ represents the total force on a larger number of charged particles while $\mathbf{f}_{mag}$ is the force on a single particle. Note that Eq. (47) is written in scalar form, i.e., all vector quantities are represented by their respective magnitude. If the direction of the magnetic field vector, **B**, and the direction of the velocity of the particle, **v**, are not perpendicular to each other, then Eq. (47) must be modified to take into account the angle between these vectors:

$$\frac{F_{mag}}{N_q} = f_{mag} = q \, v \, B \, \sin\phi \quad (48)$$

in which ϕ is the angle between **B** and **v**. We noted a similar correction before, when discussing the torque in Chapter 4: a product of two vectors leads to a quantity which is again a vector. As stressed in Chapter 4, we do not calculate vector properties based on the vector product in this textbook. Instead, we use Eq. (48) just for the magnitude of the magnetic force on a particle. We will see that Eq. (48) is sufficient to explain a wide range of magnetic phenomena. The directional properties of the magnetic field are discussed qualitatively later in this section.

The standard units of the quantities in Eq. (48) are [Cb] for the charge, [m/s] for the velocity, [T] for the magnetic field and [N] for the force.

> *The magnetic force on a single, moving particle is proportional to its charge, its speed and the magnetic field. It also depends on the angle between the magnetic field and the path of the particle.*

Example 20.8

A 10.0 keV proton beam (i.e., protons extracted from a vacuum ion source with a potential difference of 10 kV) enters a magnetic field of magnitude 2 T perpendicular to the field (2 T is the magnitude of the magnetic field of a strong conventional laboratory magnet).
(a) What is the speed of the protons?
(b) What force acts on each proton in the beam?

Solution part (a): 10 keV is the kinetic energy of each proton. We use for the energy conversion and for the mass of the proton:

$$(I) \quad 10 \; keV = 1.6 \times 10^{-15} \; J$$
$$(II) \quad m_p = 1.67 \times 10^{-27} \; kg \tag{49}$$

With these two values we can calculate the velocity of the protons in the beam:

$$v = \sqrt{\frac{2E}{m}} = \sqrt{\frac{2 \cdot 1.6 \times 10^{-15} [J]}{1.67 \times 10^{-27} [kg]}} \tag{50}$$

$$\Rightarrow \quad v = 1.38 \times 10^6 \; \frac{m}{s}$$

In Eq. (50) we applied the classical formula for the kinetic energy, $E_{kin} = \frac{1}{2}mv^2$. This is justified because the speed of the protons in Eq. (50) is only of the order of 0.5 % of the speed of light.

Solution part (b): We substitute the given values, including the result in Eq. (50), in Eq. (48). The angle between the velocity direction and the magnetic field direction is $\phi = 90°$, thus, $\sin\phi = 1$:

$$f_{mag} = 1.6 \times 10^{-19} [Cb] \; 1.38 \times 10^6 \left[\frac{m}{s}\right] 2.0 [T] \tag{51}$$

$$\Rightarrow \quad f_{mag} = 4.4 \times 10^{-13} \; N$$

It is interesting to compare this force with the forces listed in Table 3.2. While the numerical value of the force is small, we have to keep in mind that this is a force acting on an atomic size particle. It is certainly smaller than the electric force between a proton and an electron in a hydrogen atom; however, it is much stronger than the gravitational force represented by the weight of a hydrogen atom.

When a charged particle enters an area where an electric and a magnetic field are present, the two contributions to the force, electric and magnetic force, are added. The resulting force is called the *Lorentz force*, named for of Hendrik Lorentz. Before we discuss important applications of the Lorentz force, we need to emphasize the difference between the two forces which make up the Lorentz force.

The electric force acts along a straight line drawn between the two interacting charges. In the more general case, in which we consider an electric field which originates from an arrangement of several charges, the test charge is accelerated in a direction parallel or antiparallel to the electric field.

In the case of the magnetic force, there are three directions involved, those of each of the three vector quantities in Eq. (48), $\mathbf{f}_{mag}$, $\mathbf{v}$ and $\mathbf{B}$. These three forces are perpendicular to each other. Based on the right hand rule discussed in the General Appendix in Chapter 24, we note that the direction of the magnetic force for a positive charge results as the direction of the middle finger of your right hand if you point the thumb in the direction of the velocity and the index finger in the direction of the magnetic field.

The directions related to magnetic interactions are illustrated in Fig. 20.15. Note that the sketch is two-dimensional, i.e., shows the plane defined by the force and the velocity. The directional information of the magnetic field in the third dimension is given in a standard notation for vectors pointing into or out of a plane: a circle with a cross ($\otimes$) stands for a vector pointing into the plane and a circle with a dot ($\odot$) stands for a vector pointing out of the plane. This notation is easiest to remember by using the inset in the lower right corner of Fig. 20.15, which shows an arrow as used with a bow in the Middle Ages. When you shoot the arrow, you see the cross of feathers at the end of the arrow moving away (i.e., into the plane of the paper). If you are shot at, you see the sharp tip of the arrow approaching (i.e., coming out of the plane of the paper).

Thus, the magnetic field in Fig. 20.15 is directed into the plane of the figure. On a positively charged par-

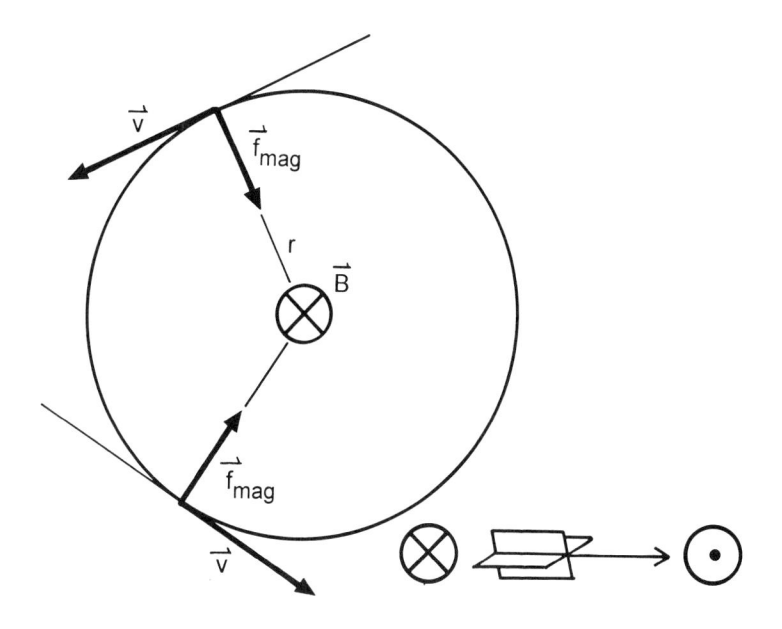

Fig. 20.15: The magnetic force, **f**$_{mag}$, acting on a particle with a positive charge moving on a circle of radius *r* in a magnetic field which is directed into the plane. The arrow at the lower right indicates the standard notation of the vector direction into the plane (⊗) and the direction out off the plane (○).

ticle, moving with a given velocity **v** toward the lower left, a force is exerted toward the lower right, and on a positively charged particle, moving toward the lower right, a force is exerted toward the upper right, as shown in the figure. Confirm these directions by using the right hand rule.

Since the force vector and the velocity vector are perpendicular to each other, we have a situation analogous to that in Fig. 20.3, where a force with constant magnitude and perpendicular to the direction of motion of the object led to uniform circular motion. This type of motion also results when the magnitude of the magnetic field does not change along the path of the particle. Thus, the particle in Fig. 20.15 moves in a circular fashion.

To quantify the circular motion, we can apply Eq. (17). The net force acting in the direction perpendicular to the path of the object is the magnetic force. Thus, the first formula in Eq. (17) reads:

$$\sum_i F_{i,\perp} = q\, v\, B = m\, \frac{v^2}{r} \qquad (52)$$

This equation relates the magnitude of the magnetic field, the mass and charge of the particle, and the radius and speed of the motion of the particle. Eq. (52) must be satisfied to obtain uniform circular motion. The radius of this motion is given by:

$$r = \frac{m\, v}{q\, B} \qquad (53)$$

From Eq. (53) an angular frequency of the circular motion of the charged particle can be calculated. For this we start with the velocity in the form $v = 2\pi r/T$. Dividing by the radius of the circular path, we get:

$$\frac{v}{r} = \frac{2\pi}{T} = \omega \qquad (54)$$

Isolating the term v/r in Eq. (53), therefore, leads to:

$$\omega = \frac{q\, B}{m} \qquad (55)$$

The frequency, $f = \omega/2\pi$, and the period, $T = 2\pi/\omega$, of the circular motion can be obtained from Eq. (55). The angular frequency in Eq. (55) is called the *cyclotron frequency*, because a cyclotron is a set–up which uses the concept of circular motion of charged particles. The synchrotron, a particular example of a cyclotron, is used as a particle accelerator and also to generate intensive and highly focussed X–ray beams. We will discuss in the next chapter why particles moving in circles in a cyclotron emit such radiation.

> *A charged particle moves in a uniform circular motion in a constant magnetic field. The path of the particle curls around the magnetic field lines. Its radius is proportional to the mass and speed of the particle. It is further inversely proportional to the charge of the particle and the magnetic field.*

Example 20.9

Food in a microwave oven gets heated as the water molecules in the food absorb energy from radiation at f = 2450 MHz. What kind of magnet is needed for a microwave oven in which the radiation is obtained from electrons circling in a magnetic field?

Solution: We will discuss the molecular structure in more detail in the next chapter. We already saw in Chapter 16 that electromagnetic radiation of a given frequency f is associated with an energy of E = hf where h is the Planck constant. This energy is carried by a photon. Photons in the microwave region, which lies between radio waves and infrared, cause molecules to rotate. Thus, during microwave cooking, the water molecules in the food are set into fast rotations. As a result of inter–molecular collisions the surrounding molecules slow that rotation down, which turns the rotation energy into heat, i.e., raises the temperature of the food.

To find the magnetic field, we first convert the given frequency into an angular frequency:

$$\omega = 2\pi f = 2\pi \cdot 2.45 \times 10^9 \, s^{-1} \quad (56)$$

$$\Rightarrow \quad \omega = 1.54 \times 10^{10} \, Hz$$

Using Eq. (55) with the electron mass and charge from Table 9.1, this yields:

$$B = \frac{m\omega}{q} = \frac{9.11 \times 10^{-31}[kg] \, 1.54 \times 10^{10}[Hz]}{1.6 \times 10^{-19}[Cb]} \quad (57)$$

$$\Rightarrow \quad B = 0.09 \, T$$

This is a moderate magnetic field, but the magnet still represents a major fraction of the weight of the microwave oven. Note that electrons move in the opposite direction of positive charges in a magnetic field. However, Eq. (55) remains valid as it relates only the *magnitudes* of the vector quantities.

Example 20.10

A proton (positively charged elementary particle) moves along a circular path with radius 20 cm in a uniform magnetic field. The magnitude of the magnetic field is 0.5 T and it is directed perpendicularly to the velocity vector of the proton.
(a) What is the speed of the proton along its path?
(b) If the proton is replaced with an electron moving with the same speed, what is the radius of the circular path of the electron?

Solution part (a): We solve Eq. (53) for the speed and use the mass and charge of the proton from Table 9.1:

$$v = \frac{qBr}{m} = \frac{1.6 \times 10^{-19}[Cb] \, 0.5[T] \, 0.2[m]}{1.67 \times 10^{-27}[kg]} \quad (58)$$

$$v = 9.6 \times 10^6 \, \frac{m}{s}$$

Solution part (b): We could use Eq. (53) directly or, as done here, rewrite it relative for the two cases:

$$\frac{r_{e-}}{r_{p+}} = \frac{m_{e-} v / qB}{m_{p+} v / qB} = \frac{m_{e-}}{m_{p+}} \quad (59)$$

which leads to:

$$r_{e-} = \frac{m_{e-}}{m_{p+}} r_{p+} = 1.1 \times 10^{-4} \, m \quad (60)$$

in which the mass of the electron is taken again from Table 9.1.

Example 20.11

Francis William Aston developed the first mass spectrometer in 1919 by combining two devices, (I) a velocity selector based on a magnetic and an electric field and (II) a mass selector based on a magnetic field. How does this instrument allow us to measure the mass of molecules and fragments of molecules?

Solution: Fig. 20.16 is a conceptual sketch of the mass spectrometer developed by Aston. The instrument consists of an ion source, which is usually a simple hot filament which ionizes molecules as they leave a gas chromatography set–up used to separate gases in the vapor phase of the sample of interest. The ion source is shown at the top of Fig. 20.16. The generated ions travel through a set of slits. These slits serve two purposes: (I) they confine the beam of particles, and (II) they are electrically charged to operate as a parallel plate capacitors to accelerate the ions. Two devices then separate the components of the ion beam on the basis of their masses: (I) a velocity selector (called a Wien filter), and (II) a magnetic mass analyzer.

In Aston's set–up the final mass separation was obtained when the charged ions hit a photographic plate which was developed afterwards. In modern instruments the charged ions are measured as a current with a device called a Faraday cage.

The main components of the instrument are discussed in more detail first, followed by an application of mass spectrometry in chemistry.

(I) *Wien filter* (named for Wilhelm Wien)
The Wien filter serves as a velocity selector. The ionization process of a typical mass spectrometer produces almost exclusively ions with a single positive charge. After these ions pass through the acceleration section, the beam contains a range of ionized molecular fragments, each with a range of different velocities. All of these ions enter the Wien filter parallel to each other. The Wien filter contains a magnetic field and an electric field which are arranged perpendicular to each other and perpendicular to the direction of the motion of the charged particles. This is illustrated in Fig. 20.17(a). The magnetic field points into the plane and the electric field is directed downwards. Fig. 20.17(b) shows the free–body–diagram for a positively charged ion: the electric force acts downwards and the magnetic force acts upwards.

The Wien filter, which includes a narrow slit at its exit (S_3 in Fig. 20.16), allows us to select particles of a single velocity by using Newton's first law based on the free–body–diagram shown in Fig. 20.17(b). Newton's first law defines the condition under which the particle is not accelerated, i.e., the condition under which it moves straight through the Wien filter. Any particle not satisfying Newton's first law is accelerated, moving away from the straight line and blocked at the exit slit. The condition of mechanical equilibrium for the charged particle in Fig. 20.17(a), with the direction upwards labelled the +y–direction, is given in the form:

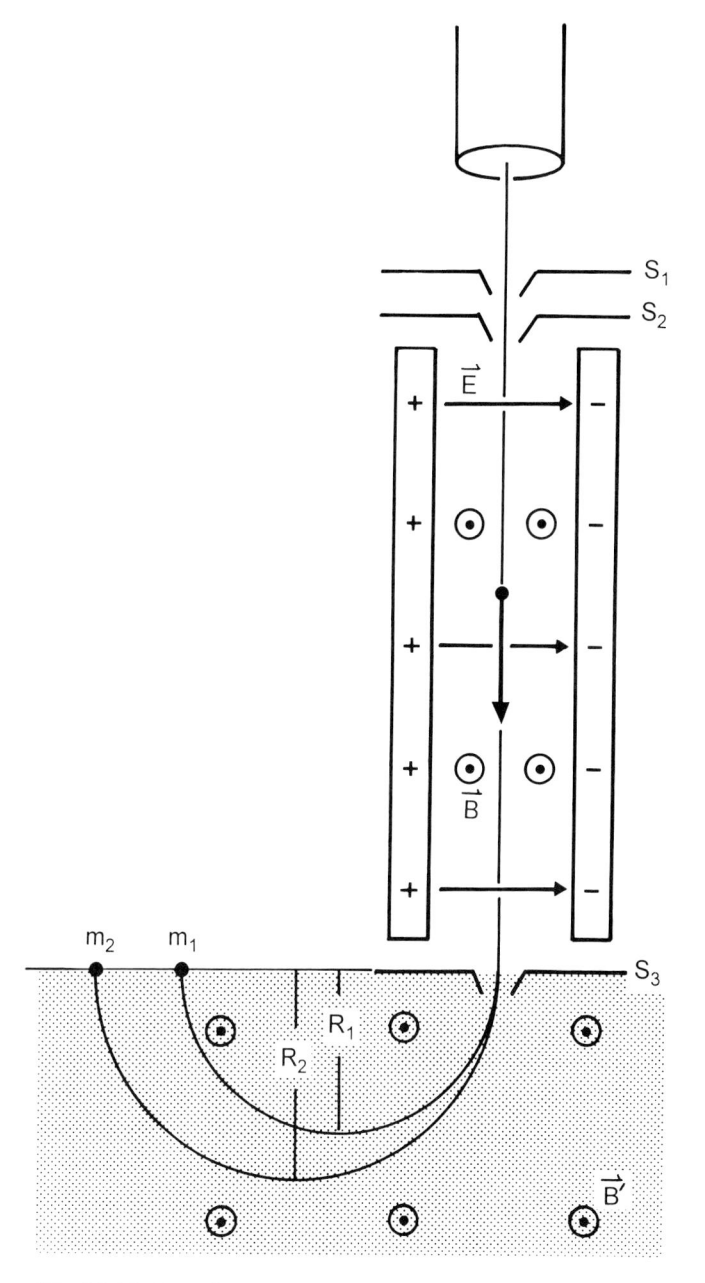

Fig. 20.16: Aston's mass spectrometer. The ions, collimated with slits S_1 and S_2, first pass through a velocity selector (Wien filter) with perpendicular electric and magnetic fields and then enter a mass selector with magnetic field $\vec{B}'$.

$$\sum_i F_{i,y} = -qE + qvB = 0$$

$$\Rightarrow \quad v = \frac{E}{B} \tag{61}$$

Thus, to select a certain velocity with a Wien filter, the ratio of the magnitude of the electric field to the magnitude of the magnetic field must be chosen according to Eq. (61).

(II) 180^0 sector magnet

Once a single velocity is selected with the Wien filter, the beam of particles enters a 180^0 sector magnet in Aston's set–up. The charged particles move in a circular fashion through the magnetic field, with a radius of the path as described by Eq. (53). Because all particles enter the magnet with the same speed, the only variable term on the right hand side of Eq. (53) is the mass of the ions. Thus, the heavier the ion, the farther to the left it hits the photographic plate in Fig. 20.16. The analysis of the obtained data is very simple as the distances along the film are directly proportional to the ion's mass, $R \propto m$.

Applications of the mass spectrometer

Five mass spectra in Fig. 20.18 illustrate typical applications of this technique. Organic molecules usually contain a large number of atoms. A mass spectrometric analysis contains a great amount of information about the molecule as usually not only the positively charged molecule itself, but also a range of its fragments are observed. In modern instruments, the information about the fragments includes not only the mass but also their relative probability as formed in the source.

The study of the mass and formation probability of various fragments is useful since the ionization process in a mass spectrometer is not an indiscriminate process. Weaker chemical bonds in the molecule break more easily, causing characteristic fragments to occur. Figs. 20.18(a–c) compare the mass spectra for three benzene–ring systems: (a) a benzene–ring with a cyano– and a butyl–ligand, (b) a benzene–ring with an amino– and a bromine–ligand and (c) a benzene–ring with an amino– and a chlorine–ligand. Characteristic fragmentation for the first molecule includes the loss of a methyl–group (15 mass units) and a subsequent loss of a C_2H_4–group. The bromine compound prefers to lose the bromine atom (79 and 81 mass units for the two stable bromine isotopes), while the loss of the chlorine and amino–groups are about equally likely for the last molecule.

The second comparison of spectra in Figs. 20.18(d, e) illustrates another strength of the technique. Organic molecules are rather similar to each other as they usually consist of only a few types of atoms, carbon, oxygen, nitrogen and hydrogen. The greater the molecular similarity of two species, the fewer the differences in properties which allow us to distinguish the compounds. An extreme case is steric modification of molecules which have the same composition, such as the two benzene–ring based ether molecules in Figs. 20.18(d, e). In spite of the great similarity of the molecules, the mass spectra shown are quite distinct, with a characteristic loss of 15 mass units of a methyl–group in the lower spectrum which is not observed in the upper spectrum.

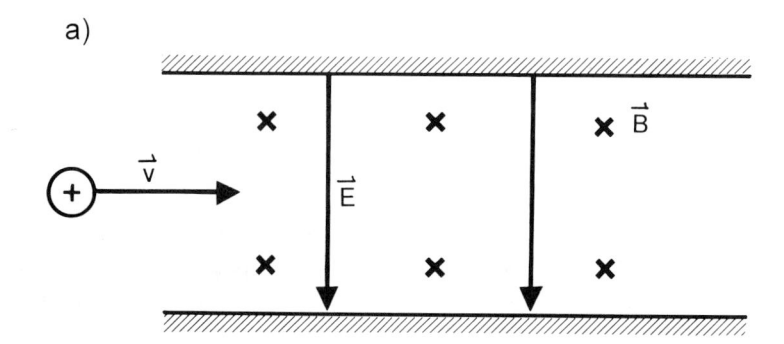

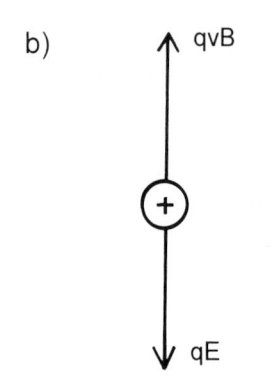

Fig. 20.17: (a) Sketch of a Wien filter. The positively charged ion enters horizontally, with the electric field due to a parallel plate capacitor directed vertically and the magnetic field (usually provided in the gap between two coaxial solenoids) directed perpendicular to the plane of the paper. (b) Free–body–diagram for the particle shown in part (a) after it has entered the Wien filter.

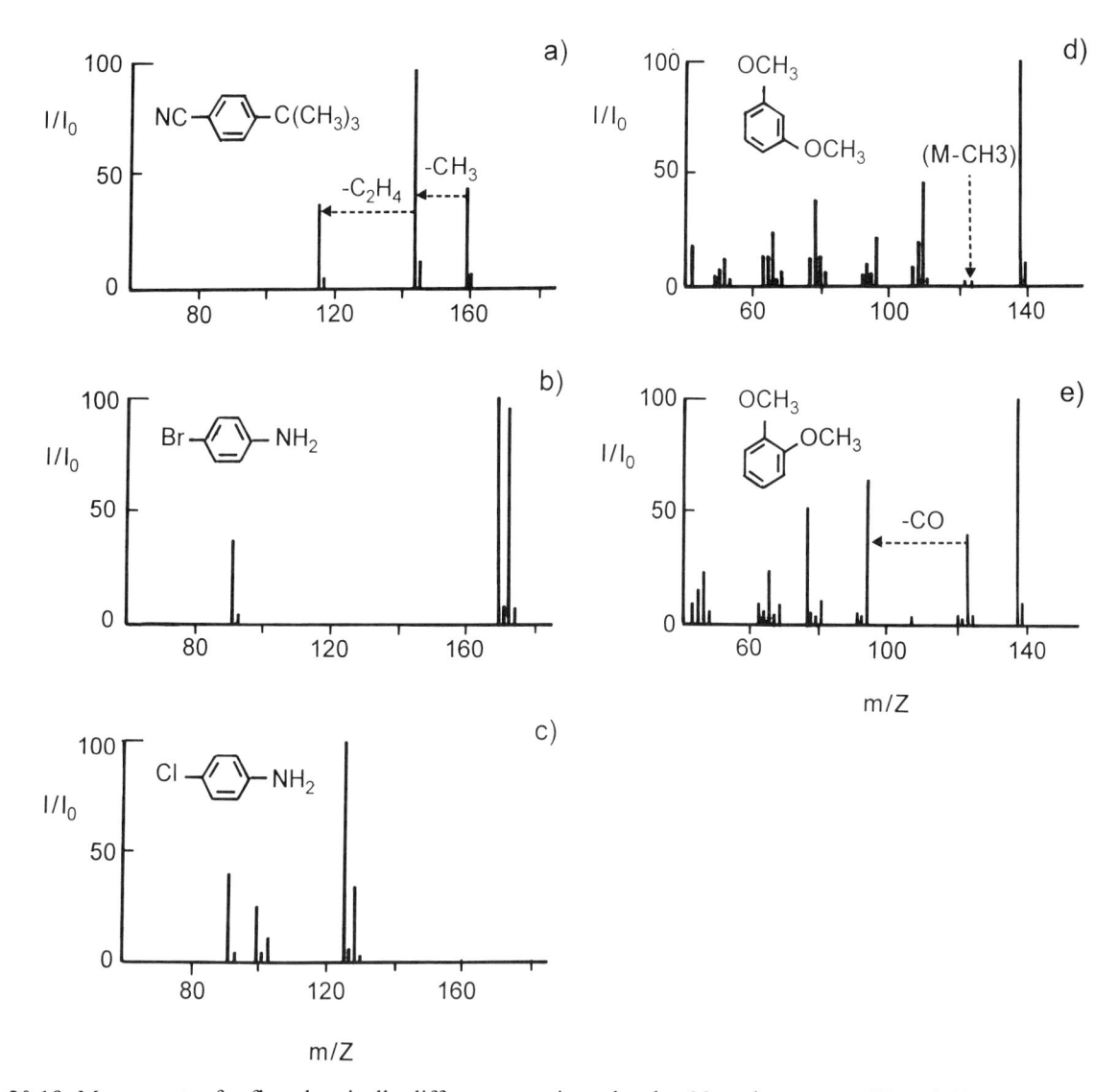

Fig. 20.18: Mass spectra for five chemically different organic molecules. Note that spectra (d) and (e) are given for two different organic molecules with the same chemical formula.

The circular motion of charged particles in a magnetic field also explains the existence of the radiation belts at high altitudes. To understand how, we begin with the Earth's magnetic field. Fig. 20.19 is a sketch of the magnetic field lines which resemble the field lines of a regular bar magnet. The bar magnet's South Pole lies below the surface of the Northern Hemisphere (in the vicinity of Bathurst Island in the Northwest Territories of Canada, 1600 km from the geographic North Pole), and the Earth's North Pole lies below the surface of the Southern Hemisphere near Adélie Coast, Antarctica (2600 km from the geographic South Pole). The magnetic poles of the Earth are not stationary (a phenomenon called polar wandering). At moderate latitudes the magnetic field vector point toward North with a horizontal component for the magnetic field of 50 μT.

In reality, however, the Earth cannot contain a permanent magnet (like a bar magnet) since the material inside the Earth cannot sustain a magnetization beyond temperatures of 540°C, a value which the material in the Earth's core significantly exceeds. The mechanism by which the Earth generates its magnetic field has not yet been fully explained, although the *dynamo theory* is widely accepted. This theory assumes that huge convec-

Table 20.1: Composition of Earth

Structure	Distance from center [km]	Density [g/cm^3]
Solid core*	0 – 1400	13.0
Liquid core	1400 – 3500	10.0
Solid mantle	3500 – 6000	3.3 – 6.0
Crust	6000 – 6300	
Lithosphere	6300 – 6400	2.7

* T ≅ 6650°C

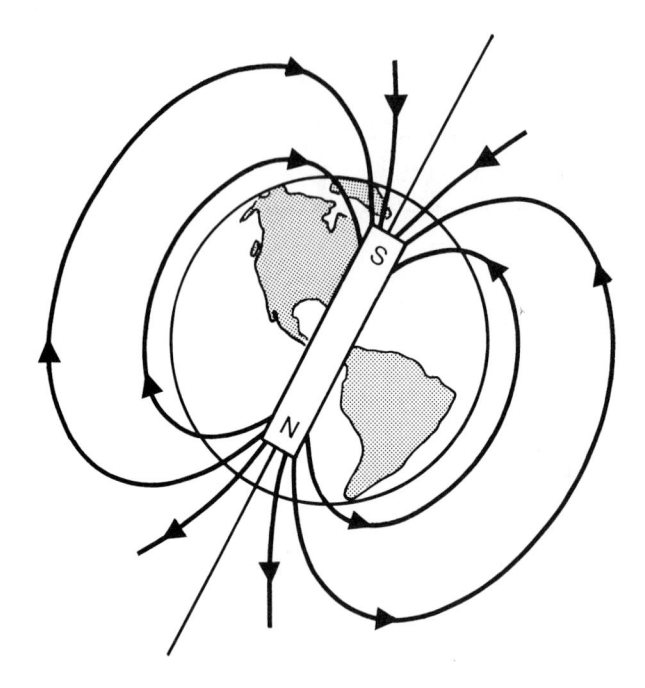

Fig. 20.19: The magnetic field of the Earth, for simplicity indicated as a bar magnet located in the Earth. The real origin of the magnetic field must differ from the sketch as no permanent magnet can exist at the temperatures at the center of the Earth.

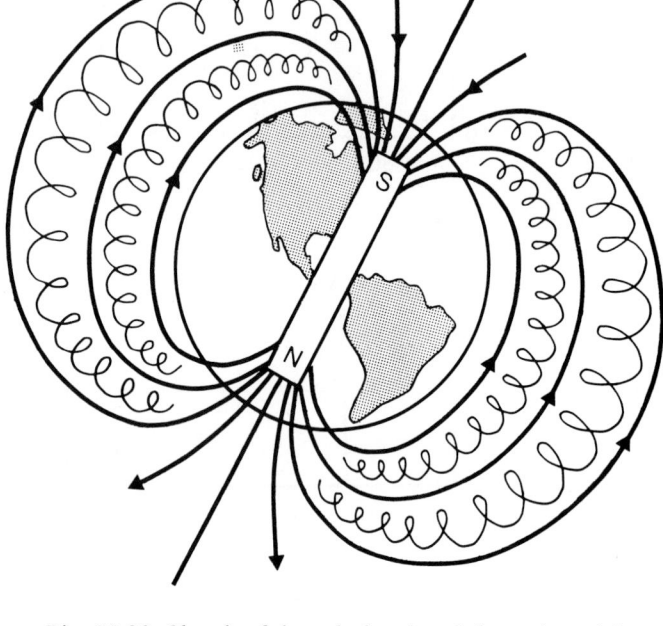

Fig. 20.20: Sketch of the spiral paths of charged particles trapped in the Earth's magnetic field. Trapped electrons and protons cause the innermost belt, which is called the van Allen belt.

tion currents in the liquid outer core carry charges. The moving charges cause in turn the magnetic field. The depth range of this liquid zone is shown in Table 20.1. Note that the central part of the Earth is solid due to extreme pressures.

Fig. 20.20 illustrates the paths that fast charged particles take when approaching the Earth from outer space. The magnetic field lines of Fig. 20.19 act as a trap for the particles, forcing them onto circular paths around the magnetic field lines. The narrowing of the field lines toward the poles causes the particles to bounce back and remain trapped between both poles. This explains the non–uniformity of the radiation belts seen in Fig. 20.11. Only particles with a very high energy or when traveling at an unusually steep angle to the magnetic field lines, e.g. after a collision with the dilute atmospheric molecules in the radiation belts, escape. Thus, the Earth's magnetic field shields us from intensive particle showers from the outer universe by trapping these particles in the belts. However, locating a space mission in the van Allen belt would expose the astronauts to intensive radiation, as high as 4.5 million times the natural radiation exposure at sea level.

20.5. Problems

P–20.1
A roller coaster ride includes a circular loop with radius R = 10 m.
(a) What minimum speed must the car have at the top to stay in contact with the tracks?
(b) What minimum speed must the car have when entering the loop to satisfy the solution in part (a)?

P–20.2
The gravitational constant, G^*, and the gravitational acceleration on the surface of the Earth, g, can be measured in independent laboratory experiments.
(a) What other information do you need about the Earth to determine the Earth's mass?
(b) Finding this information (it is also used in the current chapter), calculate the mass of the Earth.

P–20.3
Calculate the orbital speed for the two Russian missions shown in Fig. 20.1. Use the mass and the radius of the Earth from the Examples in this chapter.

P–20.4

A centrifuge of radius 12 cm is used to separate a blood sample with the result shown in Fig. 12.4. The force needed to obtain sedimentation of red blood cells in a plasma solution is about 4×10^{-11} N, acting on the erythrocyte of average mass of 3×10^{-16} kg. At what number of revolutions per second must the centrifuge be operated?

P–20.5

A proton (mass and charge are given in Table 9.1) moves with a speed of 100 km/s through the magnetic field of the Earth, which has at the particular location a magnitude of 50 µT. What is the ratio of the gravitational force and the magnetic force on the proton when the proton travels perpendicular to the magnetic field?

P–20.6

A long straight wire in a vacuum system carries a current of 1.5 A. A low–density, 20 eV electron beam is directed parallel to the wire at a distance of 0.5 cm. The electron beam travels against the direction of the current in the wire. Find
(a) the magnitude of the magnetic force acting on the electrons in the electron beam, and
(b) find the direction in which the electrons are deflected from their initial direction.

P–20.7

We consider Aston's mass spectrometer as illustrated in Fig. 20.16. The magnitude of the electric field is given as E = 1.0 kV/m and the magnitude of the magnetic fields in both Wien filter and the mass selector is 1.0 T. Calculate the radius of the path in the mass selector for an ion with a single positive charge and with a mass of $m = 2.0 \times 10^{-26}$ kg.

P–20.8

A mass spectrometer as shown in Fig. 20.16 is used to separate isotopes. If the beam emerges with a speed of 250 km/s and the magnetic field in the mass selector is 2 T, what is the distance between the collectors for
(a) ^{235}U and ^{238}U, and
(b) ^{12}C and ^{14}C?

Summary

Definitions:
● Uniform circular motion:
(i) tangential velocity:

$$v_\parallel = \frac{2\pi r}{T}$$

(ii) perpendicular velocity: $v_\perp = 0$
(iii) tangential acceleration: $a_\parallel = 0$
(iv) centripetal acceleration:

$$a_\perp = \frac{v^2}{r} = \omega^2 r = \frac{4\pi^2 r}{T^2}$$

Laws:
● Newton's law for a system with uniform circular motion:

$$(I) \quad \sum_i F_{i,\perp} = m\frac{v^2}{r}$$
$$(II) \quad \sum_i F_{i,\parallel} = 0$$
$$(III) \quad \sum_i F_{i,z} = 0$$

● Magnetic force per particle $\mathbf{f}_{mag}$:

$$\frac{F_{mag}}{N_q} = f_{mag} = q\,v\,B\,\sin\phi$$

F_{mag} is the magnitude of the total magnetic force, N_q is the number of charged particles with charge q, ϕ is the angle between the magnetic field **B** and the velocity vector of the particle **v**.
● Motion of a charged particle in a uniform magnetic field:
(i) radius of circular trajectory:

$$r = \frac{m\,v}{q\,B}$$

(ii) cyclotron frequency:

$$\omega = \frac{q\,B}{m}$$

● Velocity selected in a Wien filter: v = E/B, with E the electric field and B the magnetic field.

Chapter XXI

The Chemical Bond

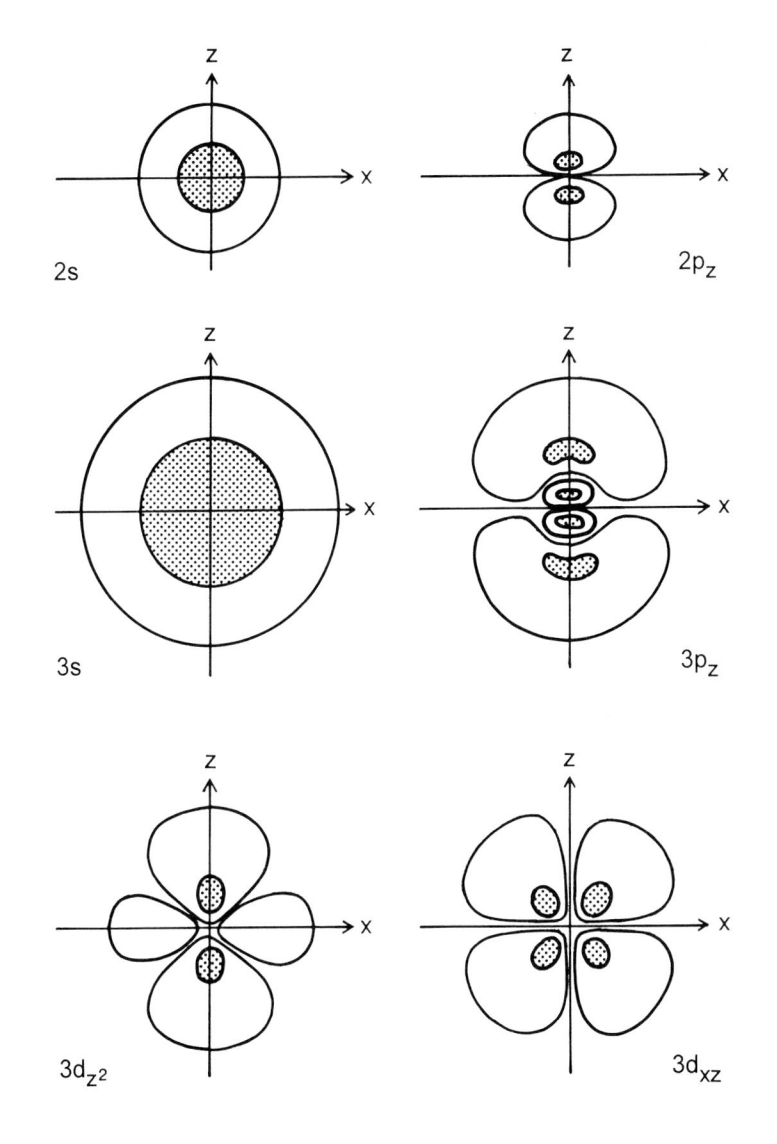

Atomic and molecular physics

THE CHEMICAL BOND
ATOMIC AND MOLECULAR PHYSICS

Matter consists of discrete units called atoms. Each electrically neutral atom has a positively charged nucleus and a shell of negatively charged electrons. Bohr's model of the hydrogen atom is based on two quantum conditions: that electrons in certain orbits do not lose energy through radiation, and that radiation absorbed by or emitted from an atom is due to intra–atomic electron–transfer between two allowed orbits. The second conditions leads to discrete absorption and emission spectra (allowing for spectral analysis of matter). An atom is in its stable ground state when its electrons occupy exclusively the energetically lowest orbitals.

Molecules result when two or more atoms form chemical bonds, i.e., the original atomic orbitals overlap and form new, stationary molecular orbitals. The molecular orbitals can in first approximation be derived from a linear combination of the atomic orbitals (LCAO–method). The molecule is stable if energetically favored binding orbitals are filled with electrons to a larger extend than anti–binding orbitals.

We want to study a little bit further the way light is generated and absorbed. We start with an example from the medical sciences: one of the original applications of amniocentesis was to diagnose fetal erythroblastosis based on a sample of amniotic fluid. Erythroblastosis is a term used for those sicknesses which lead to a presence of immature red blood cells in the blood. In the case of a fetus this occurs usually as an immune system reaction due to the transfer of antibodies across the placenta, triggered by an incompatibility of blood types between mother and fetus.

To diagnose fetal erythroblastosis, a ray of white light (including all wavelengths from 300 nm to 700 nm) is sent through the amniotic fluid and the intensity of the transmitted light is analyzed as a function of wavelength (spectroscopic analysis). Fig. 21.1 shows the intensity of the absorbed light as a fraction of the incident light versus the wavelength. The four spectra correspond, from left to right, to a normal pregnancy, minor, medium and severe cases of fetal erythroblastosis.

Note that the relative light absorption in Fig. 21.1 is shown with a logarithmic scale. This means that the amniotic fluid is quite transparent for red light around 700 nm, where almost 90 % of the incident light passes through the sample, while it is almost opaque for violet light around 350 nm, where only 20 to 25 % of the incident light pass through the sample. In addition to the steady decrease in transparency with decreasing wave-

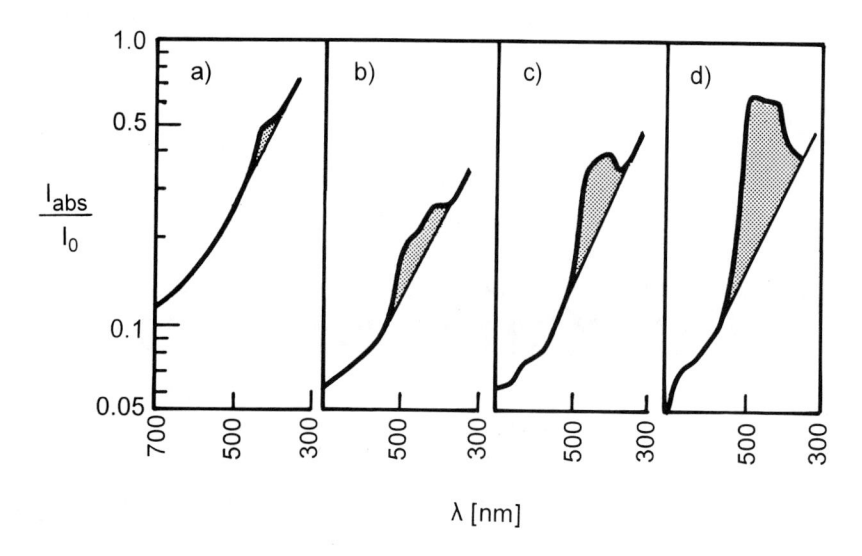

Fig. 21.1: Spectroscopic analysis of amniotic fluid obtained in an amniocentesis for (a) a healthy baby, (b) a light case, (c) a medium case, and (d) a severe case of fetal erythroblastosis. The shaded peak near the wavelength of $\lambda = 450$ nm is a measure of the severeness of the illness. The ordinate is the logarithmic axis of the relative absorbed intensity, I_{abs}/I_0.

length, a characteristic absorption of light occurs in the range between 410 nm and 460 nm if the fetus suffers from fetal erythroblastosis. This additional absorption is quantified by the difference between the peak height and the corresponding level along the extrapolated background at 450 nm (Liley's method). E.g., for the severe case in Fig. 21.1 the peak value is 64.5 % and the corresponding extrapolated base value is 19.8 %, leading to an additional absorption of 64.5 % – 19.8 % = 44.7 %. This value is then used in Fig. 21.2 to determine the severeness of the case: 44.7 % corresponds as a fraction to 0.447 in this plot, which is indeed a severe case at any stage of the pregnancy.

But how is the light absorption of the amniotic fluid linked to fetal erythroblastosis, i.e., why does the above analysis yield a diagnosis? Heme, which is a component of the hemoglobin molecule of the red blood cells, is chemically degraded to bilirubin which the body of the fetus in turn disposes into the amniotic fluid. The higher the bilirubin concentration in this fluid, the higher its absorption of light in the wavelength range around 450 nm. This means that the more severe the fetal erythroblastosis, the higher the absorption in the interval from 410 nm to 460 nm of the electromagnetic spectrum.

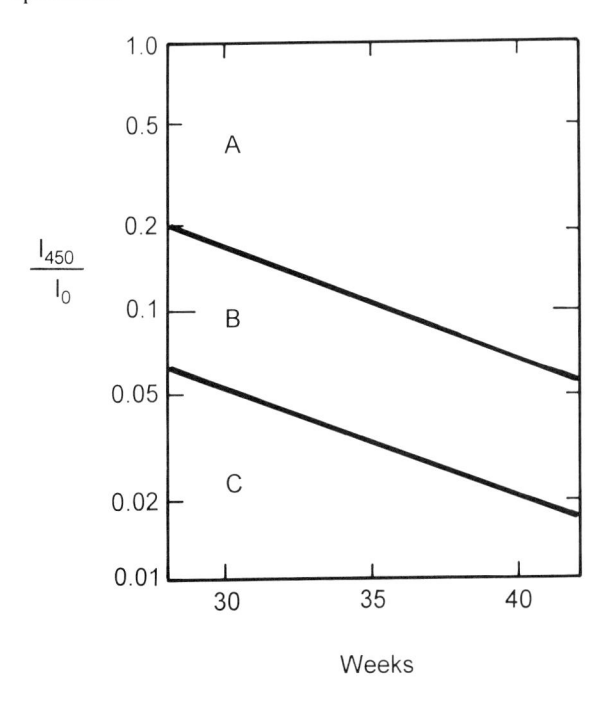

Fig. 21.2: Liley's method to allow a physician to determine the severeness of fetal erythroblastosis as a function of the week in a pregnancy. The ordinate shows the difference between the peak height at $\lambda = 450$ nm from Fig. 21.1 and the corresponding level along the extrapolated background at 450 nm. The chart allows to distinguish light cases (C), medium cases (B) and severe cases (A). During the early years of amniocentesis, a severe case would have led to induction of labor or intra–uterine blood transfusion.

Implicit in the discussion above is the assumption that the bilirubin molecule is capable to pick light of a certain wavelength out of a ray of white light passing through the solution. How does the molecule do this? And can the bilirubin molecule in turn generate light of the same wavelength? Are there other molecules which can do the same in other parts of the electromagnetic spectrum? In order to answer these questions, we must develop a model for the molecule. We can no longer treat them as structureless particles since these effects hint toward an internal structure which must be characteristic for each type of molecules.

21.1. Early atomic models

Before we can interpret molecular spectra such as Fig. 21.1 or the radiation effects we identified in the previous chapter, a quantitative model must be established for the atom and the atomic nucleus. Only with these fundamental building blocks in place can more complex structures, such as molecules, be understood.

The idea that matter is not infinitely divisible was already discussed in antiquity. However, Avogadro's hypothesis introduced in section 6.2 and Dalton's law introduced in section 12.2 were the first serious experimental hints at the atomic or molecular structure of matter. The success of the kinetic gas theory, which we discussed in section 6.3, added credibility to the concept, which was at the end of the nineteenth century, however, still considered only to be a useful mathematical approach rather than a theory describing actual, physical particles.

In 1897, Sir Joseph Thomson discovered the electron with an apparatus in which electric and magnetic fields deflected the rays emerging from a hot metallic wire in a vacuum. He was able to demonstrate that the particles in the ray were negatively charged and had a very small mass. This apparatus was developed further by Aston as the mass spectrometer (see Fig. 20.16).

Thomson's experiment was the first direct evidence of an elementary particle. Since the electron is negatively charged and the matter from which it came is electrically neutral, Thomson concluded that atoms must consist of something positively charged and electrons. His model is shown in Fig. 21.3: electrons oscillate back and forth within an area defined by a diffusely spread positive charge. The positive charge distribution defines the boundaries of the atom, which has a diameter of the order of 0.1 nm. While this model describes a stable state for the electron in Newton's classical framework, it contradicts all experimental evidence about atoms which had been collected in the late 1800s. Thus, it had to be abandoned.

The next model was proposed by Ernest Rutherford in 1911. Bombarding a gold foil with α–particles, which are energetic helium nuclei emitted from natural sources such as thorium or uranium, he found that the mass and the positive charge of an atom is concentrated at its center. Note that we were able to quantify Rutherford's experiment already in Example 9.14 because the α–particle and the gold nucleus in the foil interact electrically. We can illustrate the significant difference between the size of the nucleus and the size of the atom by considering the values obtained from Eq. (13.61). Taking, for example, a carbon atom with an atomic mass of 12.01 u, in which u is the atomic mass unit which is defined in the General Appendix (Chapter 24). For this atom, we find for the radius of the nucleus from Eq. (13.61):

$$r = 1.2 \times 10^{-15} \, A^{1/3}$$
$$\Rightarrow \quad r = 2.75 \times 10^{-15} \, m \tag{1}$$

The atomic radius of carbon atoms is 7.7×10^{-11} m, i.e., 28,000 times the nuclear radius. This tremendous difference in size is also the reason that atomic concepts were developed and understood in the 1920s while our understanding of the internal structure of the nucleus developed only after World War II. We follow this chronological order and develop nuclear concepts in the next chapter after the atomic model has been discussed.

Rutherford tried to explain his findings with an intriguing analogy. The mass of the solar system has a distribution that is very similar to that of an atom: almost the entire mass is centred in the sun while the planets define the size of the solar system by their orbits.

Thus, he proposed that the nucleus carries most of the mass and all the positive charge of the atom and the electrons, which carry the negative charge, orbit the nucleus like planets. This model is sketched in Fig. 21.4. The problem with this model stems, however, from the fact that the particles are charged. We discussed in the previous chapter that circular motion requires a continuous centripetal acceleration of the orbiting object. We saw in Chapter 19 that accelerating electric charges in an antenna emit electromagnetic radiation. Thus, Rutherford's electrons would continuously lose energy through radiation and would, therefore, rapidly plunge into the nucleus.

21.2. The hydrogen atom

In 1913, Niels Bohr concluded that all possible explanations based on classical physics, i.e., the physical ideas derived from Newton's laws and the electromagnetic theory, were failing for the atom. He formulated instead two postulates which contradict classical physics, but describe the atomic structure very well. These postulates and the quantitative description of the possible energy levels of electrons in a hydrogen atom are discussed in this section. In the next section we then review the predictions for the atom based on the theory of quantum mechanics, which was developed in the 1920s and abandons the classical concepts completely. That discussion will lead us to the next step toward biological systems, the step from the atom to the molecule.

In spite of first hints that non–classical concepts were needed, which came from Max Planck's work on

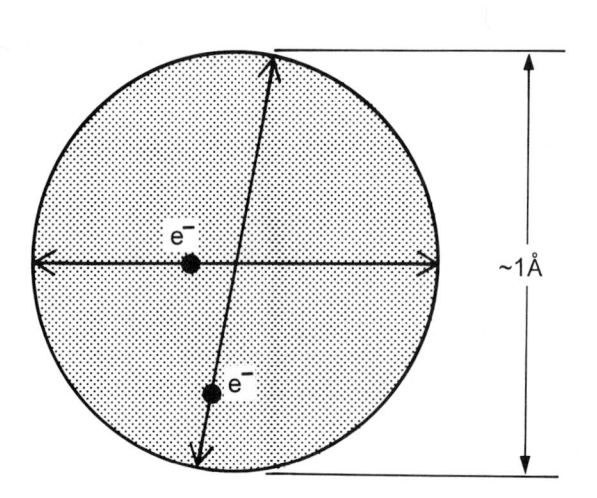

Fig. 21.3: Thomson's atomic model: electrons oscillate in a uniform positive charge distribution.

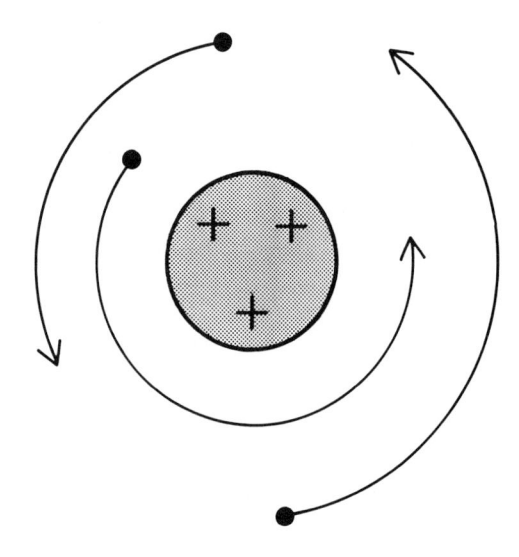

Fig. 21.4: Rutherford's planetary atomic model: the electrons circle around a massive nucleus like planets move around the sun.

the black body radiation (which explained the data in Fig. 19.28), Bohr was hesitant to abandon the classical concepts. This necessitated on one hand the later revisions done in quantum mechanics, but on the other hand led to a model which relates the new concepts in the best way possible to the classical concepts which govern our everyday life (since our everyday life is based on macroscopic processes), and therefore, are easier to accept intuitively.

> *Bohr's two postulates are:*
> *(I) Electrons do not lose energy via radiation while they are in certain orbits around the nucleus. These orbits are called allowed orbits because electrons can only be found in these.*
> *(II) An electron loses or gains energy when it transfers between two allowed orbits. The energy lost or gained is equal to the energy difference of the two orbits (initial and final orbit of the transition).*

Bohr's second condition is quantified in the form:

$$\Delta E = E_{final} - E_{initial} = h f \qquad (2)$$

in which h is Planck's constant and f is the frequency of the electromagnetic radiation absorbed or emitted by the atom during the transition of the electron from one orbit to the other. We want to use Bohr's two postulates to describe the simplest possible atom quantitatively. That atom is the hydrogen atom since it consists of only one electron and a nucleus with only one positive charge.

21.2.1. The angular momentum

We begin with Bohr's postulate that only certain orbits are allowed in which an electron can be placed without losing energy via radiation. No such orbit should exist according to the earlier classical argument that the electron is a particle moving around the nucleus. In 1923, Louis de Broglie provided a useful idea to circumvent this problem. Let us assume that the electron is not a particle but a wave. This is a non–classical idea that we now call particle–wave dualism, since electrons can indeed act like particles or waves; however, they never act as both in the same experiment. Once we accept this assumption, we refer to Chapters 16 and 19 instead of Chapters 2 and 3 to determine the properties of the electron. It proves useful in particular that we studied waves in confined spaces in Chapter 16. We saw that a wave which is confined becomes a standing wave, which is a time–independent state. This distinguishes the standing waves from travelling waves, e.g. in the cochlea. Travelling waves change with time. The atom does not change with time, thus, travelling wave concepts are not suitable for describing atoms. For standing waves, we found a relation between the wavelength and the length of the confined space in Table 16.2. Forcing the electron onto a circular path around the nucleus confines the length of the wave to the length of the circumference of the path. Allowing n wavelengths to be fit on the circumference in the fashion illustrated for two complete wavelengths in Fig. 21.5, we find the condition:

$$2\pi r = n\lambda \qquad (3)$$

in which n is a positive integer: n = 1, 2, 3, ... Up to this point we can accept this argument without hesitation as we already saw electrons act like light waves when we examined the electron microscope in Chapter 18. However, Eq. (3) is not yet sufficient to characterize the allowed orbits because we could find any radius of the orbit if we were able to continuously vary the wavelengths. This possibility is excluded by de Broglie's theory as we see below. The possibility that a given electron can act as either a particle or as a wave requires that the parameters describing the electron as one or the other need to be related to each other. This leads to de Broglie's wavelength equation for the electron:

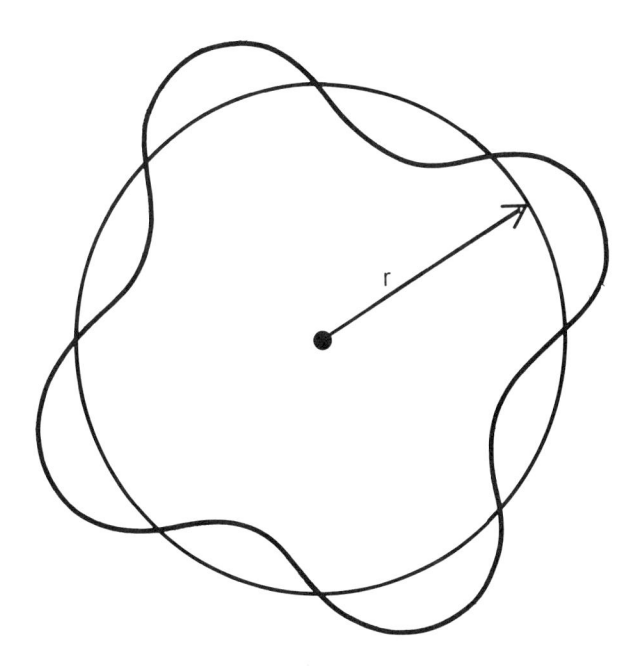

Fig. 21.5: An electron forming a standing wave in an orbit of radius r around the nucleus.

$$\lambda = \frac{h}{p} = \frac{h}{mv} \quad (4)$$

in which h is Planck's constant, p is the momentum, m the mass and v the speed of the electron (when the electron is considered to be a particle). With the units of Planck's constant [J s] and the units of the momentum [kg m/s] we confirm the unit [m] for the wavelength. It must be emphasized that the wavelength in Eq. (4) is a wave property and the mass and the momentum are particle properties. Both are related to each other with Planck's constant.

Example 21.1
Determine de Broglie's wavelength for an electron with energy 1.5 eV.

Solution: We use the equation for the kinetic energy, rewritten for the momentum with p = mv:

$$E_{kin} = \frac{1}{2}mv^2 = \frac{p^2}{2m}$$
$$\Rightarrow p = \sqrt{2mE_{kin}} \quad (5)$$

Using de Broglie's equation in Eq. (4) we find:

$$\lambda = \frac{h}{\sqrt{2mE_{kin}}} = 1.0 \ nm \quad (6)$$

Note: a correction for possible relativistic properties, i.e., properties due to velocities close to the velocity of light, are needed for electrons of kinetic energies larger than 1 keV. For example, the wavelength calculated for an electron at 50 keV is off by 2.5 % if calculated with Eq. (6).

Substituting Eq. (4) in the standing wave condition of Eq. (3) yields:

$$2\pi r = n\frac{h}{mv} \Rightarrow mvr = \frac{nh}{2\pi} \equiv n\hbar \quad (7)$$

in which $\hbar = h/2\pi$ is a commonly used abbreviation. Eq. (7) indicates that the product of the speed and the radius of the orbit is constant for the electron because the mass of an electron is a constant value.

Bohr himself derived Eq. (7) in a different fashion. He did not rely on the intuitive wave idea for the electron introduced later by de Broglie, but instead worked with an argument from classical mechanics, expanding on our discussion of circular motion which we started in section 20.2. In spite of the need for a slightly longer discussion, it is worthwhile to follow this argument because we define a new quantity with unique properties in the process, called the *angular momentum*.

This second approach leading to Eq. (7) goes back to the year 1609 when Johannes Kepler, holding the post of imperial court astronomer to the Holy Roman emperor, published his first two laws of planetary motion. The second law is called the *area rule* and states that the hypothetical line drawn from the sun to the planet sweeps out equal areas during equal intervals of time. This law was generalized 56 years later when Sir Isaac Newton quantified the gravitational force.

When we wrote Newton's equation for circular motion in Eq. (20.17) we allowed a number of forces to combine to provide the centripetal acceleration. If we assume that the centripetal acceleration is due entirely to interaction with a single object then we call the force exerted by that object a *central force*. Central forces are of particular interest in physics as both gravity and the electric force are central forces. We saw this in Chapter 20 in which we studied the gravitational force. The electric force and gravity act in a radial direction (away from the center or towards the center) and their magnitudes are the same at a fixed distance in any direction.

If we consider a system with a central force, Kepler's law applies and can be shown to be a specific expression of a more general law: the conservation of the angular momentum.

Quantities which are conserved in nature command special interest in physics. Indeed we have found so far very few quantities which are conserved: momentum in the appendix of Chapter 3, energy in an isolated system in Chapter 5 and the net charge of a system in Chapter 9. Thus, we want to understand the concept of angular momentum.

As the name implies, the angular momentum is a concept closely related to the momentum. The key equation in characterizing the conservation of momentum is:

$$F_{net} = 0 = \lim_{\Delta t \to 0} \frac{\Delta(m \cdot v)}{\Delta t} \quad (8)$$

in which we used Newton's second law to establish that

the change of the momentum with time is zero when no external forces act on the system. We can proceed in an analogous fashion when studying the circular motion of an object on which a central force acts. For the circular motion it is more appropriate to consider the torque than the force as circular motion represents a rotation about the center. The magnitude of the torque (we again neglect the vector properties of torque in the current context) is defined in Eq. (4.20):

$$\tau = r F \sin\phi \qquad (9)$$

Motivated by the approach we took in the appendix of Chapter 3 to derive Eq. (8), we study Eq. (9) with respect to changes with time. The force on the right hand side of Eq. (9) is rewritten in the form $F = \Delta p/\Delta t$, which is the change of the momentum with time:

$$\tau = r \frac{\Delta p}{\Delta t} \sin\phi = r \frac{\Delta(mv)}{\Delta t} \sin\phi \qquad (10)$$

The radius does not vary with time for circular motion. The $\sin\phi$ term serves the purpose of selecting the force component perpendicular to the radius vector because the force component parallel to the radius vector does not contribute to the torque. Since both $\sin\phi$ and the radius do not change with time, Eq. (10) does not change when we move these terms into the bracket:

$$\tau = \frac{\Delta(r\, p\, \sin\phi)}{\Delta t} = \frac{\Delta(r\, mv\, \sin\phi)}{\Delta t} \qquad (11)$$

From Eq. (11) we establish a new conservation law with the same argument we used for the momentum before. Let's consider an isolated system, that is a system in which no external forces, and therefore, no net torque act on the system. For such a system, both sides of Eq. (11) are zero:

$$0 = \frac{\Delta(r\, mv\, \sin\phi)}{\Delta t} \qquad (12)$$

$$\Rightarrow r\, m\, v\, \sin\phi \equiv L = const$$

Thus, for a system without external forces the quantity L (angular momentum) is conserved. We note that angular momentum has the following properties:
(I) The unit of angular momentum is [kg m²/s], which is the same as [J s].
(II) Like the torque, the angular momentum is a vector quantity, resulting from the product of two other vectors, the momentum and the radius vector. Therefore, Eq. (12) can be written in vector product notation. As throughout the textbook, the vector properties of the angular momentum will not be considered; the magnitude of the angular momentum in Eq. (12) is sufficient for our discussion.

21.2.2. The radius of the hydrogen atom

Bohr used Eq. (12) to derive his model of the atom. Since the atom is a system with a central force and no other force acts on the electrons externally, the angular momentum for the atom must be conserved. Bohr chose the constant term on the right hand side of Eq. (12) such that only discrete values for L are possible because of his first postulate: $L = n\hbar = nh/2\pi$ where n is a positive integer. This statement is equivalent to Eq. (7) and is called *Bohr's quantum condition*. The choice of Max Planck's constant, h, is motivated by its association with discrete transitions in Planck's theory of the black body radiation. The term 2π is included as a conversion factor between linear and spherical coordinates of the system since the electron orbits are circles.

Next we show how Bohr's quantum condition leads to discrete allowed energy levels for the electron in an atom, as Bohr's first postulate requires.

Newton's second law for the circular motion of an electron in a hydrogen atom is based on Eq. (20.17). The force causing the centripetal acceleration is Coulomb's force. The magnitude of Coulomb's force is:

$$F = \frac{1}{4\pi\epsilon_0} \frac{q_1 q_2}{r_{12}^2} \qquad (13)$$

We apply Eq. (13) specifically to the interaction of the positive elementary charge of the nucleus ($q_1 = +e$) and the negative elementary charge of the orbiting electron ($q_2 = -e$). This force attracts the electron toward the nucleus, i.e., the Coulomb force is a central force and is sufficient to provide the necessary centripetal acceleration:

$$F_{net} = \frac{e^2}{4\pi\epsilon_0 r^2} = m\frac{v^2}{r} \qquad (14)$$

Multiplying both sides of Eq. (14) with mr² leads to:

$$\frac{me^2}{4\pi\epsilon_0} = \frac{m^2 v^2 r^2}{r} \qquad (15)$$

The numerator on the right hand side is then replaced by Bohr's quantum condition, which reads in quadratic form $(mvr)^2 = (nh/2\pi)^2$:

$$\frac{me^2}{4\pi\epsilon_0} = \frac{n^2 h^2}{4\pi^2 r} \quad \Rightarrow \quad r = n^2 \frac{\epsilon_0 h^2}{me^2 \pi} \quad (16)$$

Since the right hand side of Eq. (16) contains only the integer number n as a variable, it describes discrete radii. We call n therefore the *quantum number*. The smallest radius, for which the quantum number n is n = 1, is called the *Bohr radius*:

$$r_{Bohr} = \frac{\epsilon_0 h^2}{me^2 \pi} = 5.29 \times 10^{-11} \, m \quad (17)$$

21.2.3. The energy of the hydrogen atom

With this radius calculated, we can now determine the energy of the electron in the hydrogen atom. We start with the electric potential energy between electron and nucleus as defined in Eq. (9.53):

$$E_{el} = -\frac{e^2}{4\pi\epsilon_0 r} \quad (18)$$

Now we use Eq. (16) to substitute the radius r in Eq. (18):

$$E_{el} = -\frac{me^4}{4\epsilon_0^2 h^2} \frac{1}{n^2} \quad (19)$$

Since the electron is in motion, its total energy is larger than the electric potential energy in Eq. (19). The kinetic energy is obtained from multiplying both sides of Eq. (14) by r:

$$\frac{e^2}{4\pi\epsilon_0 r} = -E_{el} = mv^2 = 2E_{kin} \quad (20)$$

This leads to the total energy of the electron in the hydrogen atom, written as a function of the quantum number n of the orbit:

$$E_{total} = E_{el} + E_{kin} = \frac{1}{2} E_{el}$$

$$\Rightarrow \quad E_{total} = -\frac{me^4}{8\epsilon_0^2 h^2} \frac{1}{n^2} \quad (21)$$

21.2.4. The hydrogen spectrum

Eq. (21) is very important as it provides us with a direct experimental approach for testing Bohr's model: the radiation frequency in Bohr's second postulate is calculated from Eq. (21) in the form:

$$hf = \Delta E_{total} = \frac{me^4}{8\epsilon_0^2 h^2} \left(\frac{1}{n_{initial}^2} - \frac{1}{n_{final}^2} \right) \quad (22)$$

Eq. (22) is rewritten for the frequency of the emitted or absorbed light by dividing the equation by Planck's constant:

$$f = R_H \left| \left(\frac{1}{n_{initial}^2} - \frac{1}{n_{final}^2} \right) \right| \quad (23)$$

Eq. (23) defines the *Rydberg constant* R_H with:

$$R_H = \frac{me^4}{8\epsilon_0^2 h^3} = 3.29 \times 10^{15} \frac{1}{s} \quad (24)$$

There are two ways to test Bohr's model experimentally. The first approach is called *absorption spectroscopy*. Light is sent through a transparent hydrogen-filled gas cylinder. The frequency of the incident light is scanned across a range which includes the frequencies which are solutions to Eq. (23). The intensity of the transmitted light beam is detected. When the frequency of the incident light is an f-value consistent with Eq. (23), hydrogen atoms absorb the radiation as energy hf. Electrons are transferred from an initial to a final orbit, where $n_{initial} < n_{final}$. The energy difference in Eq. (22) is positive in this case because the total energy of the system is increased by the energy absorbed from the incident light ray. The energy lost by the light ray to the system corresponds to a loss of light intensity as recorded by a light detector.

The second way to verify Bohr's model is called *emission spectroscopy*. In this case, light with a wide range of frequencies is passed through a hydrogen–filled gas cell. A detector that measures the intensity of light as a function of frequency is placed at an angle off the straight direction of the incident beam. Thus, the detector records no light when the gas cell is empty. However, when hydrogen atoms absorb energy from the incident light beam, the electrons which have moved into orbits with higher energy (leading to an *excited atom*) will quickly drop back to the lowest energy state n = 1. When the electrons return to the lower orbit, Eq. (22) leads to a negative energy, which is the energy lost by the system. This energy leaves the atom as a photon in a random direction, including the direction to the detector.

Absorption spectra show a constant intensity across the observed frequency range with intensity gaps at certain frequencies. Sun light reaching the Earth has such a spectrum. Light from deeper, hotter zones of the sun's surface is radiated in the direction of the Earth. It passes through the outer, cooler zones of the sun where atoms absorb some of the light at frequencies determined by Eq. (23). Note that the sun's outer zones do not consist of atomic hydrogen alone. Therefore the missing lines in the sun's spectrum reveal the chemical composition of that zone. The element helium was discovered this way. Its name indicates that it was initially believed to be a metallic element present exclusively in the sun. The spectra shown in Fig. 21.1 for the amniotic fluid are a second example, however, with the absorbed intensity plotted instead of the transmitted intensity.

Emission spectra in turn consist of the complementary information, i.e., single intensity lines at characteristic frequencies. These correspond to the transitions shown in Fig. 21.6. The figure shows the transitions of electrons from higher energy orbits (excited states) to lower energy orbits. The transitions are grouped in so–called *spectroscopic series*, with (a) the *Lyman–series* with transitions in the lowest orbit, (b) the *Balmer–series* with transitions in the orbit with n = 2, (c) the *Paschen–series* with n = 3 and (d) the *Brackett–series*. Some of these series of emission lines had been observed before Bohr's model was proposed. The excellent agreement between measurements and the model helped Bohr's non–classical postulates to be accepted quickly.

In principle, the quantum number n can take any value between 1 and ∞. From a practical point of view, however, only the smaller values are of interest as the energy difference between higher n values becomes smaller and smaller due to Eq. (21). This is indicated in Fig. 21.6 by the dashed line labelled ∞ which we inter-

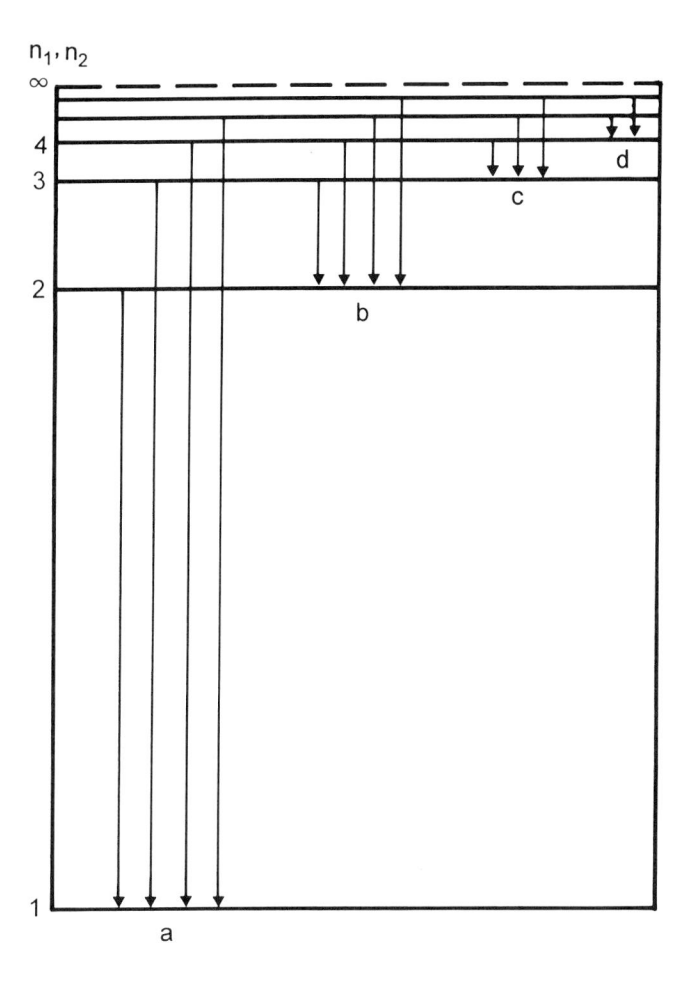

Fig. 21.6: The allowed electronic states in Bohr's atomic model. The ground state has quantum number n = 1, the excited states have quantum numbers n > 1. The frequency of emitted electromagnetic radiation (photon energy) is related to the energy difference of various levels in this term scheme. (a) Lyman series, (b) Balmer series, (c) Paschen series, (d) Brackett series.

pret as the ionization energy level, i.e., the energy level beyond which the electron leaves the atom. When an electron leaves, the atom becomes a positive ion. The energy values calculated in Eq. (21) are, therefore, energies relative to the ionization energy of the atom (with E = 0 eV at n = ∞). For the hydrogen atom we find:

$$\begin{aligned} E_{total}(n=1) &= -13.6 \ eV \\ E_{total}(n=2) &= -3.4 \ eV \\ E_{total}(n=3) &= -1.51 \ eV \\ E_{total}(n=4) &= -0.85 \ eV \\ E_{total}(n=5) &= -0.54 \ eV \end{aligned} \quad (25)$$

Example 21.2
What are the wavelength and the frequency of the light emitted by a hydrogen atom in which the electron makes a transition from the orbit n = 2 to the orbit n = 1 (called the *ground state*)?

Solution: For the frequency emitted as a result of this transition we use Eq. (23):

$$f = R_H \left| \left(\frac{1}{2^2} - \frac{1}{1^2} \right) \right| = \frac{3}{4} R_H \quad (26)$$

$$\Rightarrow f = 2.47 \times 10^{15} \, Hz$$

The corresponding wavelength is calculated from $c = \lambda f$ since the speed of light is known:

$$\lambda = \frac{c}{f} = \frac{3 \times 10^8 \, [m/s]}{2.47 \times 10^{15} \, [Hz]} \quad (27)$$

$$\Rightarrow \lambda = 1.21 \times 10^{-7} \, m = 121 \, nm$$

Thus, the lowest Lyman–series transition in hydrogen is not visible; the emitted light is in the UV part of the electromagnetic spectrum. This transition is seen in the spectrum of Fig. 20.12, just to the left of the broad main peak, indicating strong excitation of atomic hydrogen near the sun's surface.

Example 21.3
Does the hydrogen atom have transitions in the visible range of the electromagnetic spectrum?

Solution: The visible range of the electromagnetic spectrum is defined in Fig. 19.27 as the wavelength interval from 380 nm to 750 nm. Several lines of the Balmer series, which are transitions to the second lowest state in the hydrogen atom with n = 2, fall within this interval. These Balmer series lines are listed in Table 21.1.

Example 21.4
How much energy is required to ionize hydrogen atoms when they are
(a) in the ground state, and
(b) when they are in an excited state with quantum number n = 3?

Table 21.1: Wavelengths of the lowest four transitions in the Balmer series of the hydrogen atom.

$n_{initial} \rightarrow n_{final}$	wavelength
3 → 2	λ = 655 nm
4 → 2	λ = 485 nm
5 → 2	λ = 433 nm
6 → 2	λ = 409 nm

Solution: Ionizing an atom means to remove an electron. This is achieved when the atom absorbs at least an amount of energy such that the electron is lifted into the state with $n_{final} = \infty$.

Solution part (a): We insert $n_{initial} = 1$ and $n_{final} = \infty$ in Eq. (22):

$$\Delta E_{n=1} = h R_H \left(\frac{1}{n_{initial}^2} - \frac{1}{n_{final}^2} \right) = \quad (28)$$

$$= h R_H = 2.17 \times 10^{-18} \, J = 13.6 \, eV$$

Solution part (b): We insert $n_{initial} = 3$ and $n_{final} = \infty$ in Eq. (22):

$$\Delta E_{n=1} = h R_H \left(\frac{1}{n_{initial}^2} - \frac{1}{n_{final}^2} \right) = \quad (29)$$

$$= \frac{h R_H}{9} = 2.4 \times 10^{-19} \, J = 1.5 \, eV$$

21.3. Toward a quantum mechanical model

When Bohr's model for the hydrogen atom was proposed, it was immediately clear that it would require modifications or extensions to be suitable for atoms of other elements which have many more spectral lines than varying Bohr's quantum number n can explain.

There is only one group of atomic particles for which Bohr's model has been shown to apply beyond hydrogen: single–electron ions such as He^+ and Li^{2+}. In that case, the elementary charge e for the nucleus is replaced by Ze where Z is the atomic number taken from the periodic table.

Example 21.5
Calculate with Bohr's model of the atom the five lowest energy orbitals for the He$^+$ ion.

Solution: We repeat the calculation which led from Eq. (14) to (21). The numerator of Eq. (14) becomes $Ze \cdot e$ which equals Ze^2. Note the additional factor Z in the denominator of the corrected Bohr radius in Eq. (17). A second factor Z occurs in the numerator of Eq. (18) for the electric potential energy. Thus, when we replace the radius in Eq. (18), a factor of Z^2 results. Consequently we find for the total energy of the single electron in heavier single electron ions:

$$E_{total}(Z) = Z^2 \, E_{total}(Z=1) \qquad (30)$$

This allows us for Z = 2 (He) to calculate the values corresponding to Eq. (25) for the helium ion with a single positive charge:

$$\begin{aligned}
E_{total}(n=1) &= -54.4 \; eV \\
E_{total}(n=2) &= -13.6 \; eV \\
E_{total}(n=3) &= -6.0 \; eV \\
E_{total}(n=4) &= -3.4 \; eV \\
E_{total}(n=5) &= -2.2 \; eV
\end{aligned} \qquad (31)$$

Niels Bohr himself, together with Arnold Sommerfeld, made the first attempt to extend Bohr's original model to include other types of atoms. They argued that an electron should have three independent quantum numbers (instead of only one) since it moves in three dimensions and its motion in each of the three dimensions of space is independent. Continuing to hold on to classical physics to justify this set of quantum numbers, Bohr and Sommerfeld identified them as:

(I) the principal quantum number n, which is due to a quantization of the orbits with certain total energy values for the electron. This quantum number has already been discussed above in the context of Bohr's original model.
(II) The orbital quantum number *l*, which is due to the quantization of the angular momentum of the electron. This means that different electrons move on circular or elliptical orbits with different eccentricity around the nucleus, very much like the planets around the sun. Possible circular and elliptic orbits are illustrated in Fig. 21.7. Quantization means that only certain ellipses describe allowed orbits for the electron.
(III) The magnetic quantum number m_l, which is due to a quantization of the orientation of the orbit of the electron in an external magnetic field. This quantum number is called the magnetic quantum number because a non–uniform magnetic field allows us to split an atomic beam into as many components as there are allowed values for the magnetic quantum number.

Later a fourth quantum number was added to make the Bohr–Sommerfeld model consistent with the periodic system of elements. This quantum number is called *spin* and allows for two values (up or down). The classical concept behind the spin is the rotation of the electron about its own axis. This is another possible motion of the electron, similar to the rotation of the Earth about its own axis while it revolves around the sun. Two possible values of the spin correspond in this classical picture to the possible East–West or West–East rotation of a planet.

These semi–classical explanations for the quantum numbers are useful as long as they are used cautiously. The classical picture of planet–like electrons moving on ellipses of various eccentricity and orientation around the sun–like nucleus cannot explain many of the properties of atoms. In particular, the possible locations of a given electron (which we call *orbitals*) differ significantly from the planetary model. This is a significant deficiency as it is often the actual location of the electrons in atoms or molecules which we associate with the chemical properties, such as crystal formation or chemical reactions. We will, therefore, briefly review the quantum mechanical concepts which allow us to define the actual orbitals for electrons in atoms and mo-

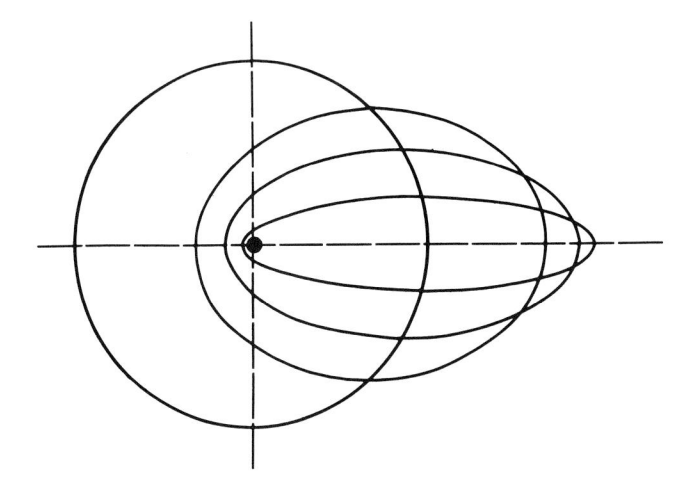

Fig. 21.7: Examples of circular and elliptic orbits of varying eccentricity.

lecules. With both the semi–classical and the quantum mechanical interpretation introduced, we can then construct atoms and molecules.

Quantum mechanics was developed in the 1920s by a new generation of physicists who were more willing to abandon classical concepts. Following Louis de Broglie's idea that an electron may act as either a particle or a wave, Erwin Schrödinger developed a wave equation model for the electron in an atom in 1926. What is very different from the planetary model which considers the electron as a particle is the interpretation of the solutions of Schrödinger's wave equation. The solutions, called *wave functions*, are not given any direct meaning but lead after further mathematical operations to *probability functions* which describe the probability to find an electron at a given time at a given position. Of particular interest are the solutions to Schrödinger's equation which are time independent, i.e., associated with standing waves, since these lead to time–independent probability functions, i.e., functions which describe the probability to find an electron at a given position relative to the nucleus at any time. Schrödinger identified these solutions as *stationary orbitals*.

The fact that we can only provide a probability for an electron to be at a certain point is an inherent feature of the wave–particle dualism. When you consider an electron to be a wave, for example as illustrated in a simplified fashion in Fig. 21.5, assigning the electron a specific position is not possible. On the other hand, when you consider an electron to be a particle, as illustrated in Fig. 21.4, locating the electron should be possible. Describing the location of an electron in an atom in the form of probabilities is, therefore, a compromise between both wave and particle properties of the electron.

Mathematically, the solutions to Schrödinger's equation for the atom are rather complex since they are three–dimensional waves. In analogy to the solutions to the wave equation in a confined tube discussed in Chapter 16, which allowed only certain frequency values, Schrödinger's equation also permits only certain values of the total energy of the electron for stationary solutions. These values of the total energy are called *eigenvalues*. The energy eigenvalues predicted by Schrödinger's equation are consistent with the values predicted by Bohr's model for the hydrogen atom.

However, the stationary solutions to Schrödinger's equation contain much more information than Bohr's model. They provide a justification of the three quantum numbers which Bohr and Sommerfeld proposed arbitrarily: Schrödinger's solutions for the orbitals of an electron are not all spherically symmetric. Consequently the three independent quantum numbers are needed to characterize all the solutions (the fourth quantum number, spin, was integrated into these formulas later).

It is not particularly instructive to study the various solutions to Schrödinger's wave equation in their explicit mathematical form. Instead, we will examine illustrations of the resulting orbitals. The orbitals differ when the values of the quantum numbers are different. To distinguish the many possibilities, the orbitals have been given names, which resulted from earlier spectroscopic observations of electron transitions between different orbitals. Table 21.2 summarizes the possible combinations of quantum numbers, which are based on the following selection rules:

$$(I) \quad 0 \leq l \leq n-1$$
$$(II) \quad -l \leq m_l \leq +l \quad (32)$$

Each set of quantum number values listed in Table 21.2 represents a different orbital. These orbitals can be illustrated in various ways:
(I) Two–dimensional plots of the radial probability show the probability of finding the electron as a function of distance r from the nucleus. Radial probability plots for six of the orbitals in Table 21.2 are shown in Fig. 21.8.
(II) Two–dimensional plots of the angular probability

Table 21.2: Quantum numbers and orbitals. The quantum numbers are: n, the principal quantum number; l, the orbital quantum number; m_l, the magnetic quantum number. The name of an orbital combines the number of the principal quantum number and a letter representing the orbital quantum number: s = sharp, p = principal, d = diffuse, f = fundamental. The magnetic quantum number is identified as an index (see examples in the text).

n	l	m_l	name
1	0	0	1s
2	0	0	2s
2	1	−1, 0, +1	2p
3	0	0	3s
3	1	−1, 0, +1	3p
3	2	−2, −1, 0, +1, +2	3d
4	0	0	4s
4	1	−1, 0, +1	4p
4	2	−2, −1, 0, +1, +2	4d
4	3	−3, −2, −1, 0, +1, +2, +3	4f

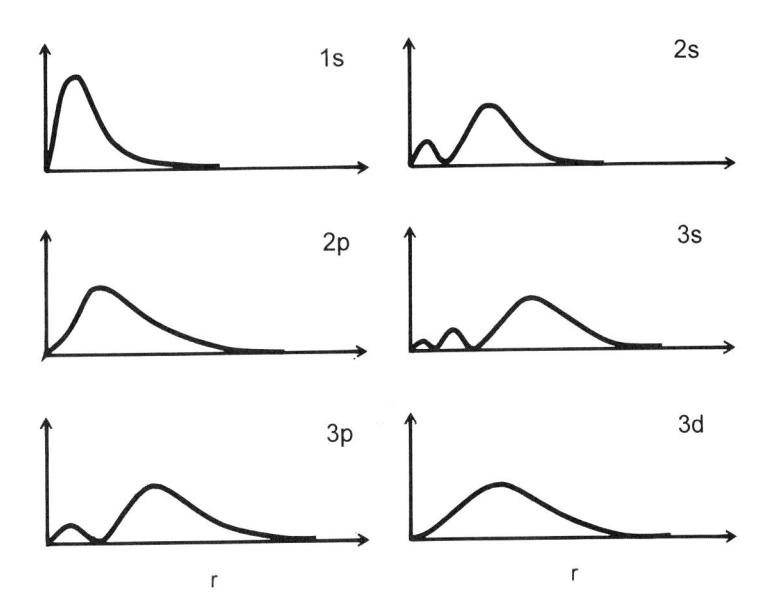

Fig. 21.8: The probability to find an electron as a function of distance r from the nucleus in various orbitals of an atom. Note that only the s–orbitals are spherically symmetric.

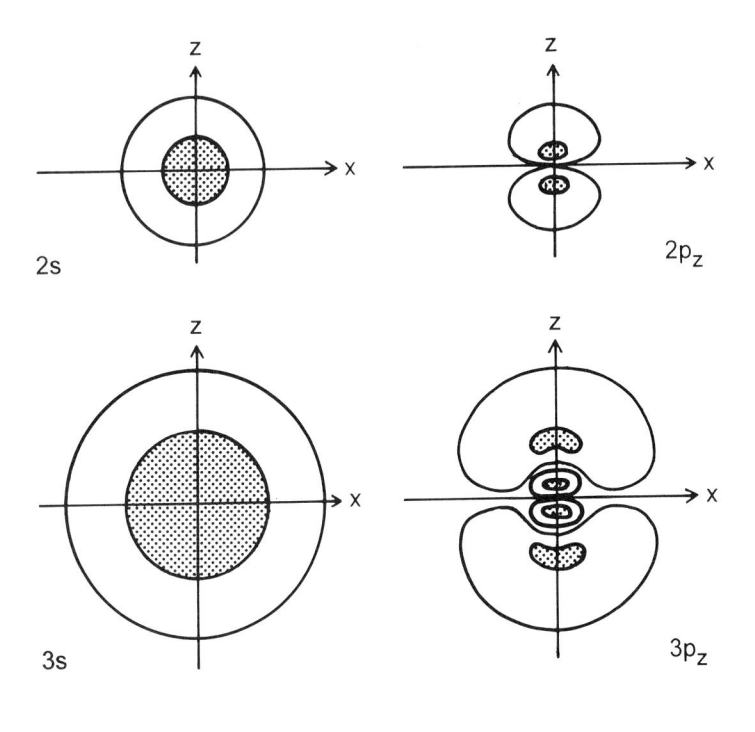

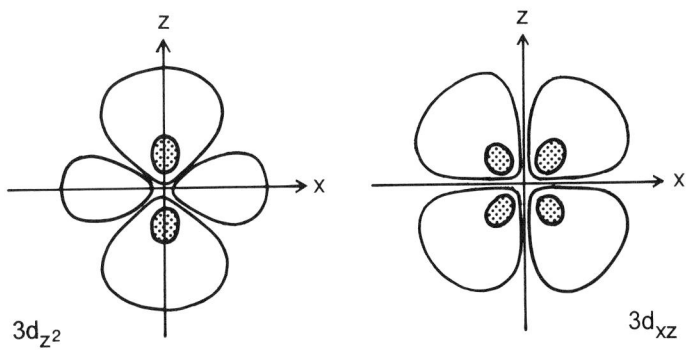

Fig. 21.9: Cross–section through a three–dimensional representation of the probability to find an electron in an atom as a function of position relative to the nucleus. The dotted areas indicate the volume within which the electron is found 50 % of the time, and the open areas indicate the volume within which the electron is found 99 % of the time. The notation of the orbitals is defined in Table 21.2.

show the probability of finding the electron as a function of the angle.

(III) The combination of radial and angular probability plots produces three–dimensional images. In these, the surfaces shown enclose the region in which the electron is to be found with a certain probability. Fig. 21.9 shows cross–sections of such plots representing the areas with a 50 % (dotted area) and a 99 % (open area) probability of finding the electron inside. In turn, Fig. 21.10 is an artist's sketch of the 99 % surfaces in three dimensions. The latter are very useful when trying to envisage processes in stereo–chemistry.

Once the orbitals of the atom are defined, quantum theory allows us to predict the order in which these orbitals are filled with electrons. This procedure is based on two principles:

(I) the *minimum energy principle* states that any electron added to an atom will occupy the next free orbital with the least total energy.

(II) The *Pauli principle* (named for Wolfgang Pauli) states that no two electrons in the same atom may have the same four quantum numbers (including spin).

Due to the Pauli principle, each atomic orbital can accommodate two electrons (due to the existence of two possible values for the spin quantum number). Thus, up to two electrons can be placed in each s–orbital, up to 6 electrons in the p–orbitals with a given quantum number n, up to 10 electrons in the d–orbitals with a given quantum number n, and up to 14 electrons in corresponding f–orbitals.

This explains the structure of the periodic table. Hydrogen has one electron in its 1s–orbital. Helium has two electrons in its 1s–orbital, therefore, this orbital is full. A single electron in an orbital is reactive, therefore, hydrogen is not found in isolated atomic form. In contrast, an electron pair in an orbital is chemically inert; therefore, helium does not undergo chemical reactions and is called a noble gas.

The third element in the periodic table accepts the third electron into the 2s–orbital since the 1s–orbital is already filled by the first two electrons. Thus, lithium behaves chemically similarly to hydrogen; it likes to form chemical bonds by releasing its single 2s–electron (valence electron). When a lithium atom releases its va-

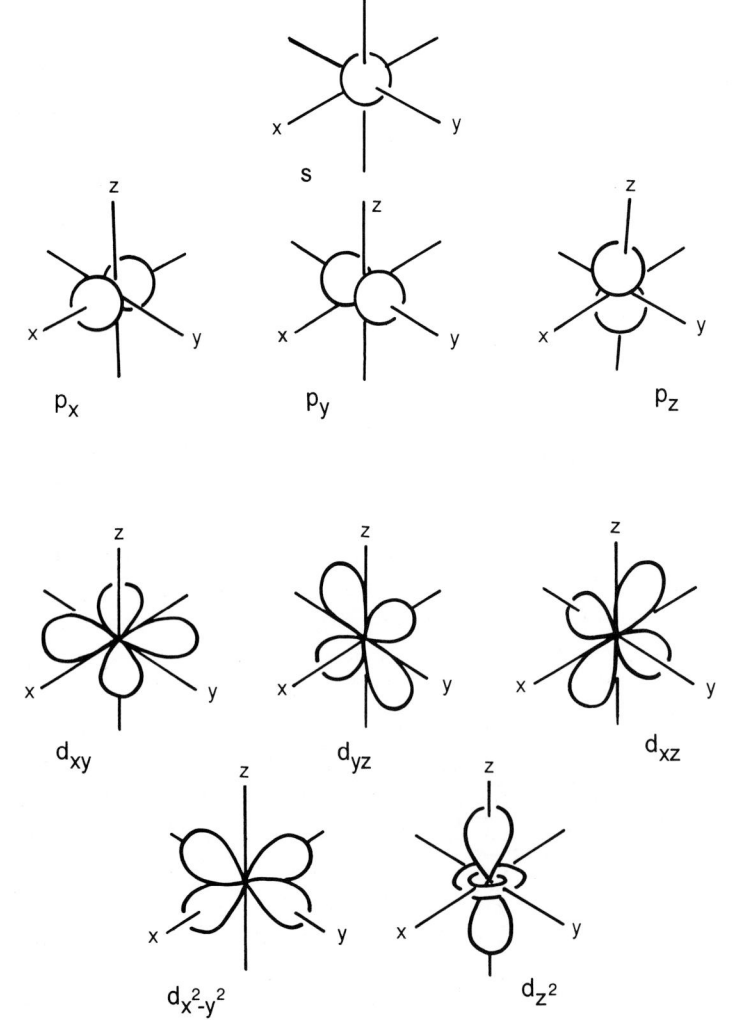

Fig. 21.10: Artist's sketch of the three–dimensional orbitals of an atom, representing the surfaces within which the electron is found 99 % of the time.

lence electron, it becomes a positive ion with a noble gas electronic configuration, which is characterized as an atom or ion for which all orbitals of a given quantum number n are filled with electrons.

The propensity of lithium to release an electron to obtain a noble gas electronic configuration is called *electropositive behavior*. Fig. 9.8 illustrates a second reason why the lithium atom tends to release its valence electron: the valence electron orbits much farther out than the 1s–electrons, increasing the radius from Li$^+$ to Li by a factor of more than 2.5.

The fourth element, beryllium, accepts the next electron also into the 2s–orbit. Different from helium, however, beryllium is extremely reactive. It is actually among the most dangerous elementary metals handled in the laboratory (highly flammable, poisonous). This indicates that a filled 2s–orbital is not sufficient to complete the second period in the periodic table, which would lead to an inert noble gas as the last element in the period. The second period is only completed when another 6 electrons are added, i.e., when we reach the element neon. We can predict this from Table 21.2. Beryllium has still three 2p–orbitals without electrons. These p–orbitals correspond to electron states with slightly higher energy; however, the energy difference is minimal and the two 2s–electrons can easily mix with the empty p–orbitals to form hybrid orbitals. This is not observed in isolated atoms, however is a critical property when forming molecules, as discussed below.

The fifth element, boron, is the first element with an electron in a p–orbital. The sixth element, carbon, has a distinguished position in the periodic system. With two 2s and two 2p electrons it has exactly half as many electrons as the second period can accommodate. This allows carbon to form chemical bonds with elements to both sides in the periodic table, e.g. CO_2 with oxygen and CH_4 with hydrogen. As the example of the methane molecule indicates, carbon can form up to four bonds, the maximum possible for an element in the second period. This enables carbon to form a wide range of different and complex compounds, an ability which is unparalleled in the periodic table. Thus, it is not surprising that life, which depends on such flexibility for the many biochemical tasks necessary for survival, is based on carbon compounds (organic chemistry).

21.4. Molecules

21.4.1. Molecular structure

Studying isolated atoms is of limited value as the materials around us and in our body are very rarely found in atomic form. Atoms form three types of chemical bonds. We already discussed some properties of the first two types in Chapter 9, (i) ionic systems in which an electronegative element receives an electron from a more electropositive atom, and (ii) metallic systems in which many electropositive atoms release their valence electrons into a common, loosely bound electron sea.

The third type of chemical bond is the covalent bond. We can only discuss covalent bonds now because we need to know the atomic orbital structure of the elements to develop the structure of the molecules. The approach is based on a *linear combination of atomic orbitals*, which is, therefore, called the LCAO–method. We discuss the LCAO–method using the simplest possible example: the formation of a hydrogen molecule from two hydrogen atoms:

$$2\,H \rightarrow H_2 \quad (33)$$

When applying the LCAO–method, we follow the same two steps we used for the atom above: (i) we determine the orbitals and their order with increasing energy, and (ii) then we use the available electrons to fill the orbitals from lowest to highest energy.

The orbitals of the hydrogen molecule result from the overlapping of the atomic orbitals as illustrated in Fig. 21.11. The figure shows the probability distribution to find an electron at distance r from each nucleus for the 1s–orbitals of the hydrogen atoms (dashed lines). When the two hydrogen atoms come close, a significant overlap of the two atomic probability distributions occurs. In this state the atomic orbitals are no longer consistent with stationary solutions to the Schrödinger equation, and the Pauli principle disallows two equivalent electrons to occupy an overlapping space. Instead, new molecular orbitals form.

We identify the chemical bond as the line where the greatest overlap of the two atomic orbitals occurs. A molecular orbital with the greatest overlap between the atomic orbitals along the line between the two nuclei, is called a sigma–bond (σ–orbital), i.e., a σ–bond is co-axial with the bond direction. This is the case in the hydrogen molecule, as Fig. 21.11(a) shows.

Like in atomic orbitals, two electrons can be accommodated in each molecular orbital due to the Pauli exclusion principle (since the two electrons have different spins). A simple arithmetic argument demonstrates that we have not yet completed the discussion of the formation of molecular orbitals when we have considered only the formation of a σ–orbital. Two atomic 1s–orbitals can accommodate a total of four electrons, two for each atom. The newly formed σ–orbital can only accommodate two electrons. Thus, a second orbital has

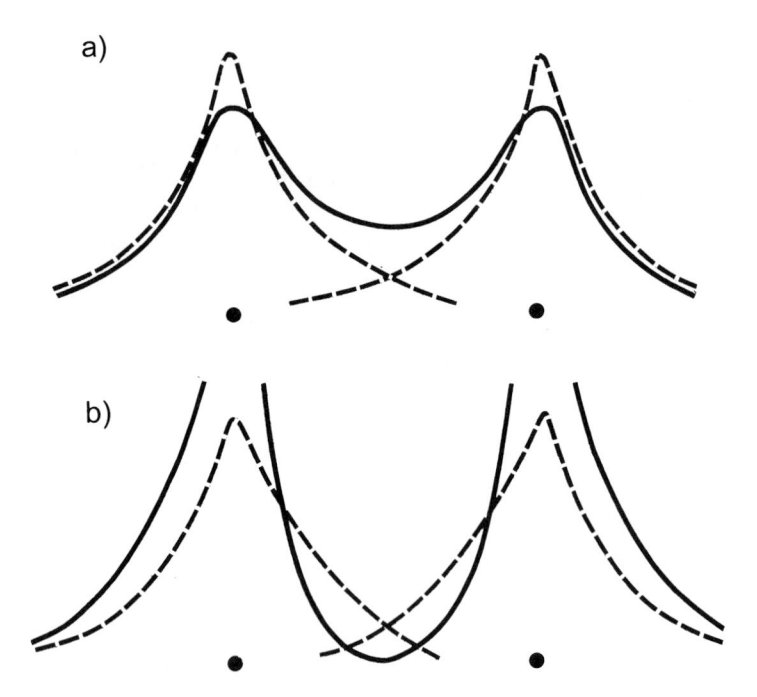

Fig. 21.11: Formation of (a) a binding σ–orbital and (b) an anti–binding σ*–orbital from two s–orbitals, e.g., in the formation of H_2 molecules. The two dots indicate the position of the two nuclei. The dashed lines represent the radial probability distribution for the electron in the separate atom. The solid lines represent the combined molecular orbitals.

to be formed from the two atomic 1s–orbitals. This is illustrated in part (b) of Fig. 21.11. The second molecular orbital is an anti–binding orbital, i.e., an orbital which minimizes the overlap between the two original atomic orbitals. This orbital is labelled a σ*–orbital, where the superscript * indicates the anti–binding character of the bond. Since the σ*–orbital can also accommodate up to two electrons, we have provided as many molecular orbital places for electrons as the combined atomic orbitals allowed. Thus, our model of the hydrogen molecule is complete.

Fig. 21.12 shows the same orbitals, however, it assigns to each orbital an energy level relative to the energy of the atomic orbital. Such a display is called a *term scheme*. The energies of the two molecular orbitals are different and both are also different from the energies of the atomic orbitals. How can we justify the term scheme shown in Fig. 21.12? For this we need to introduce a new quantum mechanical principle, called *Heisenberg's uncertainty relation*, discovered by Werner Heisenberg in 1927. The uncertainty relation states that it is impossible to know precisely both the position and the momentum of a particle at any given time instant.

Studying the following attempt to measure both as precisely as possible leads to a mathematical expression of the principle. We consider a particle placed under a microscope. By looking through the microscope we try to pin down the position of the particle to within an uncertainty of a small distance Δx. To do this, we must interfere with the particle. To be sure that it is within a distance interval Δx we need to use light of wavelength $\lambda \leq \Delta x$ for the observation. If the wavelength of the light is greater, then we cannot observe the particle, as discussed in Chapter 18. Based on de Broglie's arguments, light of wavelength λ carries a momentum p since $\lambda = h/p$, where h is Planck's constant. Thus, the momentum the light carries into the system during observation is at least $p = h/\lambda$. Since we cannot know what fraction of this momentum is transferred to the particle we observe, we find that the product of uncertainty of the position of the particle after the observa-

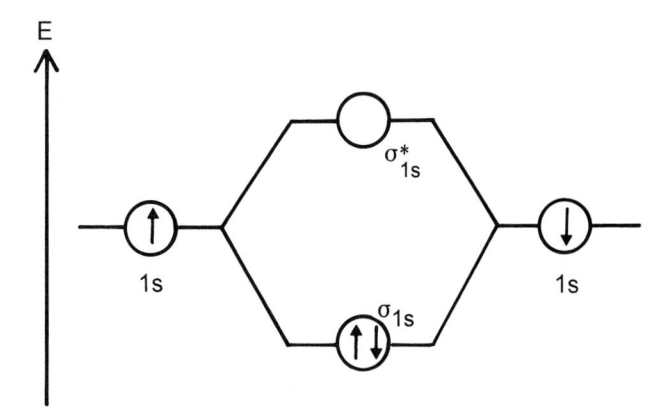

Fig. 21.12: The term scheme for the formation of a hydrogen molecule. Shown at left and right are the 1s–orbital energies of the two hydrogen atoms. The two molecular orbitals differ in energy with the binding orbital having a lower energy and the anti–binding orbital having a higher energy than the respective atomic orbitals. The arrows in the open circles indicate the electrons which fill the orbitals. Each orbital can accept two electrons due to the two possibilities of the spin quantum number; this is indicated by the up and down direction of the arrows.

tion, Δx, and the uncertainty of the momentum after the observation, Δp, is given by:

$$\Delta p \, \Delta x \geq \frac{h}{\lambda} \cdot \lambda = h \qquad (34)$$

Uncertainty of this kind does not exist in the realm of classical physics because in classical physics it is implicitly assumed that h = 0. We used the classical view when we assumed that the phenomena that we discussed in the first seventeen chapters are *deterministic*, which means they are fully predictable. In reality, Planck's constant is very small, but not zero. Therefore, we have to accept that we cannot know precisely both the momentum (from which we can calculate the energy when knowing the mass of the particle) and the position of a particle; the better we know the position, the greater is the uncertainty in momentum and energy, and vice versa, since the uncertainties in Eq. (34) are related by multiplication.

> *The uncertainty principle states that position and momentum of a particle cannot be measured precisely at the same time.*

We can apply Heisenberg's uncertainty principle to the orbitals that we developed for the hydrogen molecule. In comparison to the atomic orbital, the binding σ–orbital in Fig. 21.11 provides more space (larger Δx) to the electrons in this orbital. The uncertainty principle implies that the uncertainty in the energy of this orbital is less than that for the atomic orbital, i.e., the orbital can have a lower potential energy. The σ*–orbital, in turn, restricts the space in which electrons can be found more than the atomic orbital. This requires a larger uncertainty in energy, and thus, a higher energy level for the orbital.

The term scheme shown in Fig. 21.12 explains why H_2 molecules form and why He_2 molecules do not exist. In agreement with the minimum energy principle and Pauli's principle, the hydrogen molecule has two electrons in the σ–orbital while the σ*–orbital is empty. Thus, the formation of the hydrogen molecule is energetically favorable because the hydrogen molecule has a lower total energy than the system of two separate hydrogen atoms. The energy difference is released during the formation of the molecule. In turn, to break a hydrogen molecule into two hydrogen atoms, the energy difference must be added to the molecule from the environment. On the other hand, when two helium atoms try to form a molecule, both the σ–orbital and the σ*–orbital are occupied by two electrons. Thus, the helium molecule is energetically not favored over two separate helium atoms. Taking entropy considerations from Fig. 8.8(d) into account, it becomes clear that dissociation of a possible helium molecule is a spontaneous process.

Orbitals other than s–orbitals can overlap and contribute to chemical bonds, too. For this we have to consider molecules with partially filled p–orbitals. The molecular orbitals for the elements in the second period are shown in Fig. 21.13, and the energy term scheme for oxygen is shown in Fig. 21.14. The orbitals in Fig. 21.13 are derived in the same fashion as for the hydrogen molecule (LCAO–method). Note that each overlapping orbital that forms co–axially with the chemical bond between the two nuclei is called a σ–orbital and is accompanied by a non–overlapping σ*–orbital. Some atomic p–orbitals can overlap as well, leading to orbitals which are not rotationally symmetric to the bond. Such orbitals

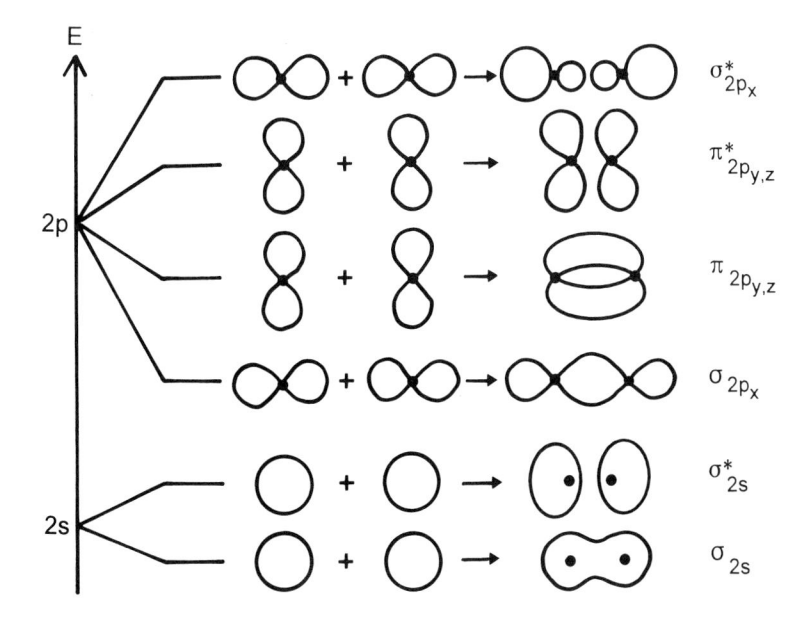

Fig. 21.13: The molecular orbitals formed by linear combination of equivalent orbitals in the first and second period of the periodic system.

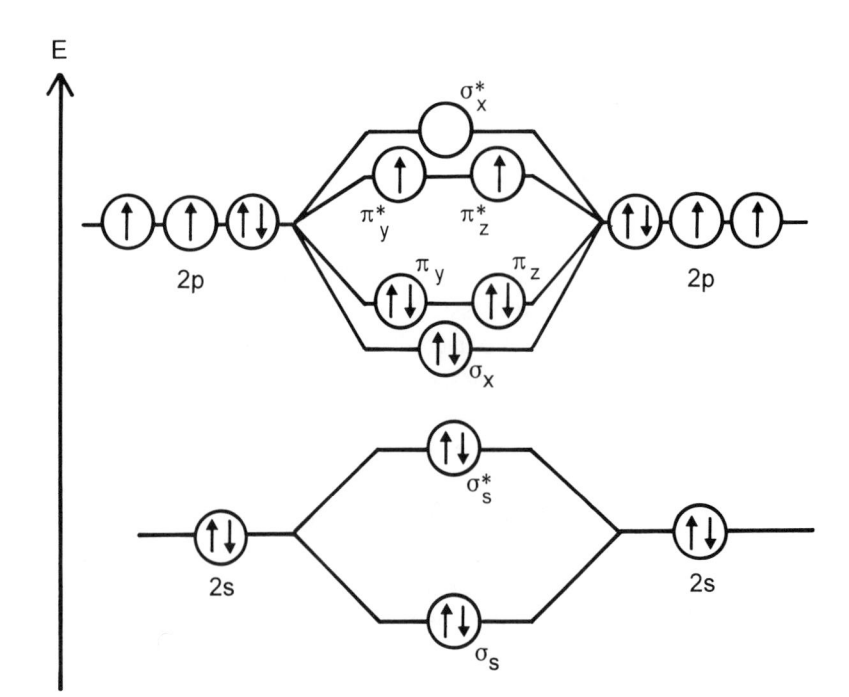

Fig. 21.14: Term scheme of the oxygen molecule. The comparison of the energies of the filled and empty states indicates the stability of the molecule relative to the two separated atoms. Unpaired electrons participate in chemical reactions; all orbitals of equal energy are occupied by a single electron before a second electron is added to the orbital.

are called π–orbitals. As before, each binding π–orbital must be accompanied by a non–binding π^*–orbital in order to accommodate the same number of electrons as the separate p–orbitals.

The term scheme in Fig. 21.13 indicates that the overlap between two p–orbitals is less effective than that between two s–orbitals. Thus, the energy difference of a π–orbital to the p–orbital from which it formed is less than that of a σ–orbital to the respective s–orbital.

The next step is to study the formation of molecules with more than two atoms, e.g. CH_4, NH_3 and H_2O. In the formation of these molecules, we observe a new phenomenon: *hybridization*. Hybrid orbitals are orbitals which hypothetically form in a single atom by mixing the various solutions of the Schrödinger equation, e.g., the s–orbital and all or some of the p–orbitals in the elements of the second period. This does not occur in isolated atoms because the atomic orbitals that we discussed earlier achieve the lowest energies for the respective atoms. However, when atoms or molecules approach each other, the mutual overlapping of orbitals can lead to hybridization when this produces a term scheme which allows for a lower energy of the final molecule.

Hybridization is illustrated in Fig. 21.15 for the case in which all three p–orbitals participate, e.g. in the case of the formation of a CH_4 molecule. We see that the four resulting sp^3–orbitals are directed toward the corners of a tetrahedron which leads to a bond angle $\theta = 109.47^0$. The angles between the chemical bonds of CH_4, NH_3 and H_2O are compared to this value in Fig. 21.16. All three molecules are sp^3 hybridized; the minor variation in the bond angle is due to the electrostatic repulsion between orbitals occupied by two electrons.

Note that hybridization may sometimes involve only one or two p–orbitals. For example, the carbon–carbon bond in organic molecules can either be based on sp^3–orbitals (single bond, e.g. in ethane (C_2H_6)), on sp^2–orbitals (leading to a double bond, e.g. in ethylene (C_2H_4)), or on sp–orbitals (leading to a triple bond, e.g. in acetylene (C_2H_2)).

21.4.2. How is light emitted?

For both atoms and molecules, we return to Bohr's postulates in section 21.2 to describe in more detail how light is emitted. The first postulate states that electrons do not radiate while they are in the allowed orbitals we discussed in the previous sections. However, as stated in the second postulate, electrons lose or gain energy when they transfer between two allowed orbitals. Since energy conservation applies, the energy difference between the initial and final orbital of the transition must be accounted for after the transition has occurred. If the transition is associated with an increase in the total energy of the electron, the energy must be provided to the atom or molecule, and if the transition is associated with a decrease in the total energy of the electron, the energy must be emitted from the atom or molecule.

As we discussed in Chapter 8, there are essentially two ways for a system to change its total energy: either it is a closed system that exchanges only heat with the environment, or it is an open system that exchanges both heat and matter with the environment. At the microscopic scale of atoms and molecules, both of these forms of exchange are possible, although they must be interpreted in a new way. An atom or a molecule acts as

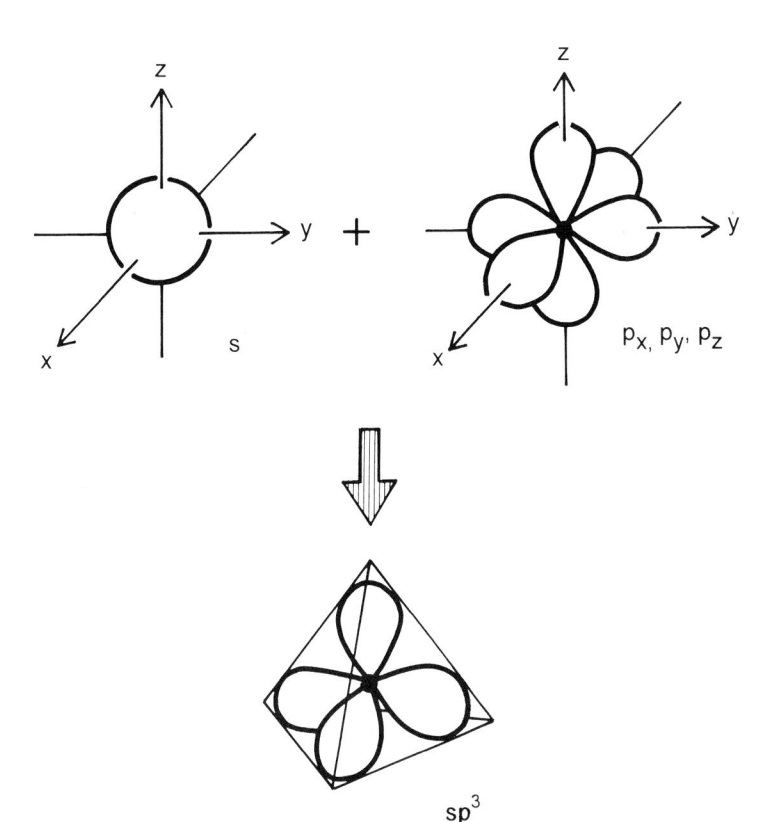

Fig. 21.15: Geometric sketch illustrating the formation of a hybrid sp^3–orbital which is formed by combining one atomic s–orbital and three p–orbitals.

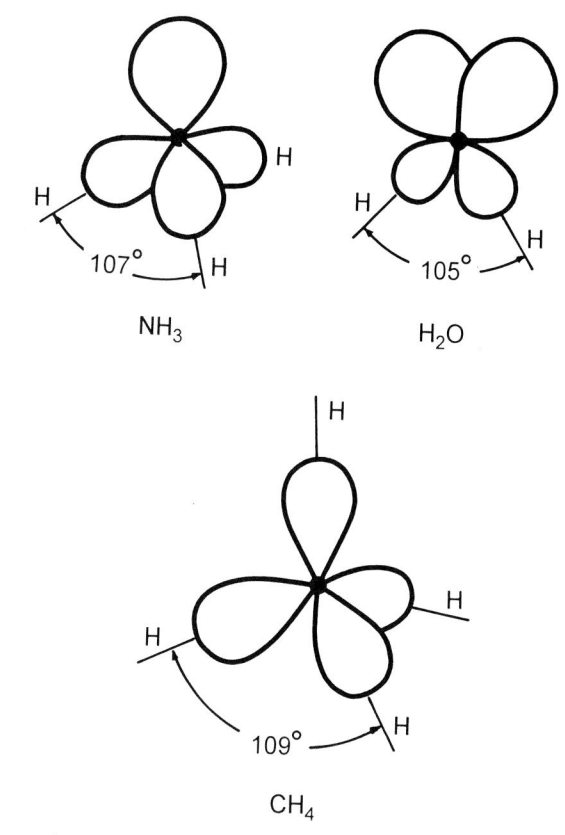

Fig. 21.16: Comparison of the bond angles in three sp^3–hybridized molecules. Only methane displays the theoretical angle of $\theta = 109.47°$. Asymmetric occupation of orbitals and the electrostatic repulsion between electrons lead to slightly lower angles in the ammonia and water molecules.

a closed system when the total energy is changed by absorbing or emitting electromagnetic radiation (photons). The emission may be in the form of visible light, but it may also be in the form of other types of electromagnetic radiation, ranging from microwave frequencies (this type of radiation excites the rotation of molecules, e.g. the rotation of water molecules in a microwave oven) to X–rays, which we discuss in the next chapter.

Atoms and molecules can also be open systems. In most cases this involves the addition or removal of an electron. In the next chapter we will also discuss cases in which other particles leave an atom, such as alpha–particles. These originate from the nucleus.

In the present section we focus on the atom or molecule as a closed system, i.e., the number and type of particles constituting the atom or molecule do not change. These are indeed the cases to which Bohr's second postulate applies. As mentioned earlier, Bohr attempted to provide a classical picture for his postulates as far as was possible. In the case of the second postulate the following explanation was given: we allow an electron in an atom to be briefly in two orbitals at the same time, which it must do during a transition from one orbital to the other since it cannot be anywhere between the two orbitals. If we consider the electron to oscillate between the two orbitals during the transition, then this corresponds to the classical case of electrons oscillating in an antenna, which we discussed in section 19.1. From that discussion we know that such an oscillating charge emits electromagnetic radiation. The radiation represents a loss of energy, and thus, the total energy of the electron is reduced. This occurs only if there is an unoccupied allowed orbital of lower energy. If not, the atom cannot lose energy as it is in the lowest energy state (ground state). However, the inverse process can happen, where we provide electromagnetic radiation externally and allow the electron to pick some of it up (absorption) to move to an allowed higher energy orbital.

The absorption and emission processes of electromagnetic radiation were early tools for analyzing atoms and molecules. Depending on the type of electromagnetic radiation, different experimental analytical methods (spectroscopy) are required, including infrared spectroscopy (IR) which samples vibrational excitations of molecules, and ultraviolet spectroscopy (UV) for electronic excitations.

A typical spectroscopic experiment for sodium will be described. Sodium is a metal. Solids are less accessible to spectroscopy as they allow many intermolecular processes which make the spectrum that is obtained harder to interpret. The preferred state of matter for spectroscopy is either a gas or a dilute solution in an inert matrix (e.g., an organic powder embedded in a potassium chloride (KCl) matrix for infrared spectroscopy). In the case of Na, a piece of the metal is placed in a vacuum chamber and heated to 100^0C at 10^{-7} torr. Sodium has an unusually high vapor pressure and, thus, an appreciable sodium vapor density develops in the chamber. The chamber has several windows which are transparent to visible light. We now shine light through the sodium vapor and analyze the intensity as a function of frequency for (i) light passing straight through the chamber, and (ii) light emerging from the vapor in other directions.

When shining white light (which is light with equal intensities across the visible range) through the chamber, we notice a loss of intensity at $\lambda = 589$ nm in the beam of light passing straight through the chamber. The wavelength $\lambda = 589$ nm corresponds to the absorption of energy for a transition between two allowed orbitals in the sodium atom. Electromagnetic radiation is also detected in directions other than parallel to the incident light beam. This electromagnetic radiation is yellow light, again with a wavelength of 589 nm. Thus, the atomic absorption and instantaneous re–emission processes allow for a selective scattering of light with well–defined frequencies. This process is called *fluorescence*. The scattered light is isotropic, i.e., it is observed with same intensity in any direction. We also refer to this process more specifically as resonant fluorescence: the external light interacts with the electron in the atom by forcing its oscillation between the two orbitals involved in the transition. Since external light does this only with exactly the right transition frequency, the term *resonant*, as defined in Chapter 16, applies.

George Gabriel Stokes noted that resonant fluorescence is not the only type of fluorescence that occurs in the experiment described above. Particularly for molecules, we also observe fluorescence when shining light through the vapor or solution which has a wavelength shorter than the wavelength corresponding to the light required to excite the atomic or molecular transition, i.e., fluorescence occurs also when the incoming light has higher energy than the atomic transition. The spectrum in Fig. 21.17 illustrates this for an eosine solution (eosine is an organic sodium–containing dye, used to enhance contrast in bacteriological studies). The primary beam in this experiment is monochromatic, which means that we do not shine white light through the solution, but shine only light of a particular wavelength through. The wavelength of the incident light is scanned. We use two intensity detectors, one placed in the path of the beam passing straight through the chamber to detect the absorption process and one at a large angle with the incident beam to analyze the re–emission process. Both detectors are tuned to a given wavelength which corresponds to an allowed electron transition in the eosine molecule.

We note from Fig. 21.17 that eosine molecules absorb energy most effectively at shorter wavelengths than the wavelengths at which they re–emit light. The difference in energy represents energy lost by the molecule during a collision with another molecule, i.e., the energy is either redistributed as kinetic energy (thermal energy) or is used to excite the collision partner. This fluorescence phenomenon is called *non–resonant fluorescence*. But how is it possible that an excited eosine molecule collides with another molecule if re–emission is instantaneous? Most excited atomic states have a lifetime of less than 10^{-8} s. This time is, however, sufficient for molecular interactions to take place, particularly at higher temperatures, and in solutions which are denser than gases.

In some cases, re–emission occurs after much longer times, as long as milliseconds. This is called *phosphorescence*, rather than fluorescence. This phenomenon is associated with a forbidden transition which traps the electron in the higher energy orbital despite the

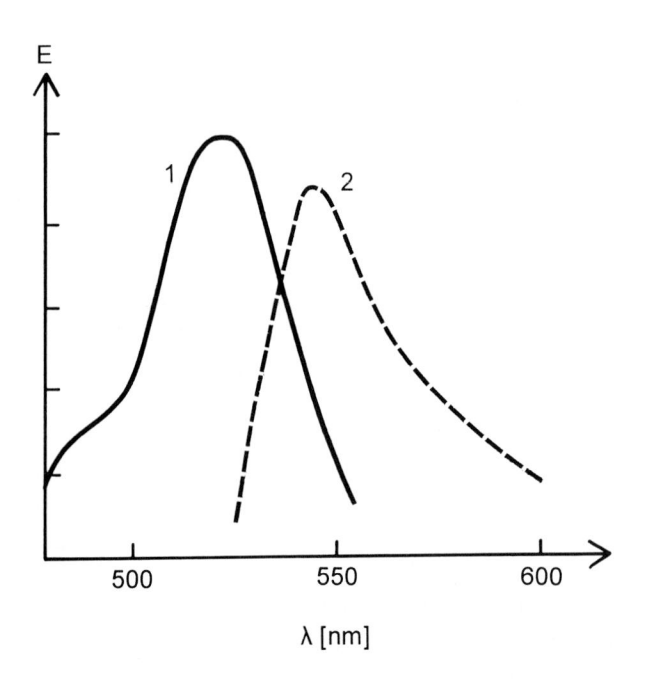

Fig. 21.17: Non–resonant fluorescence of eosine molecules. A monochromatic light beam scans from 450 nm to 600 nm. Both absorption (1) and re–emission (2) intensities of light corresponding to an allowed transition of the eosine molecule in the solution are recorded.

existence of an empty orbital at lower energy. The reason why a transition may be forbidden lies in the four quantum numbers which characterize each orbital. Transitions require an adjustment for the electron to the new set of quantum numbers; some of these adjustments are not possible. The same transition is then forbidden for absorption as well. This does not render the trapping impossible since the initial absorption may have occurred into a higher energy orbital because the re–emission can involve several transition steps of the electron. Examples of phosphorescence include the radiation emitted by zinc sulfide (ZnS) layers of a TV screen and the luminous dial of some clocks. *Luminescence* is a summary term which includes fluorescence and phosphorescence.

Excitation may occur chemically rather than electromagnetically. Chemiluminescence or bioluminescence occur in both some plants and some animals like the lightning bug (firefly).

21.5. Problems

P–21.1
Calculate for Bohr's atomic model the speed of the orbiting electron in the ground state.

P–21.2
In the spectrum of helium ions, a series of absorption lines exists (Pickering series) for which every other line coincides with a Balmer series line of the hydrogen atom (the remaining lines fall in between the Balmer series lines). Which transitions in the helium ion are responsible for the Pickering series?

P–21.3
A hydrogen is in its first excited state (n = 2). Using Bohr's atomic model calculate
(a) the radius of the electron's orbit,
(b) the potential energy of the electron, and
(c) the total energy of the electron.

P–21.4
Calculate the electric force on the electron in the ground state of the hydrogen atom.

P–21.5
What is the wavelength of light that can cause a transition of an electron in the hydrogen atom from the orbit with n = 3 to n = 5?

P–21.6
A hydrogen atom emits a photon with wavelength λ = 656 nm. Which transition did the hydrogen atom undergo to emit this photon?

P–21.7
Calculate the wavelength of an electron in a hydrogen atom which is in the orbit with n = 3.

P–21.8
Identify the molecule for which Fig. 21.18 shows the term scheme of the linear combination of the atomic orbitals.

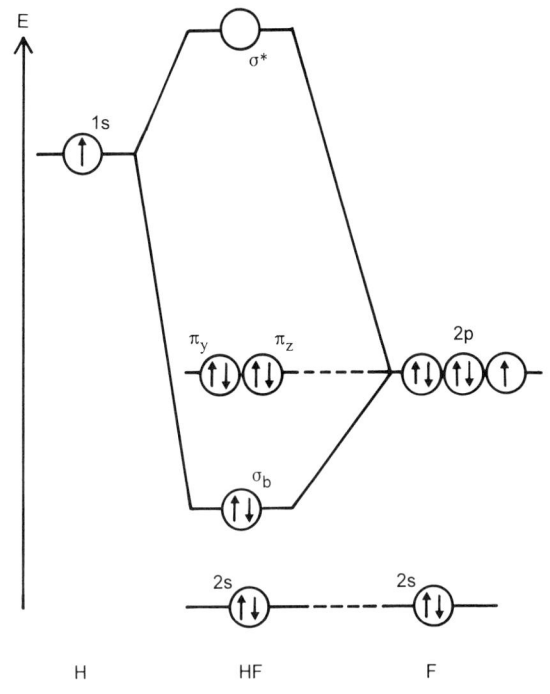

Fig. 21.18 for problem P–21.8

Summary

Definitions:
● Bohr radius of the hydrogen atom:

$$r_{Bohr} = \frac{\epsilon_0 h^2}{me^2\pi} = 5.29 \times 10^{-11} \, m$$

● Rydberg constant:

$$R_H = \frac{me^4}{8\epsilon_0^2 h^3} = 3.29 \times 10^{15} \, \frac{1}{s}$$

e is elementary charge, m mass of electron.

Laws:
● Bohr's postulates
(i) Electrons do not lose energy while they are in certain orbits.
(ii) Electrons lose or gain energy when they transfers be-

tween two allowed orbits:

$$\Delta E = E_{final} - E_{initial} = hf$$

h is Planck's constant, f is frequency of photon absorbed or emitted.
- Bohr's quantum condition for the atom:

$$mvr = \frac{nh}{2\pi} = n\hbar$$

with $\hbar = h/2\pi$ and n the quantum number (integer).
- De Broglie's wavelength of a particle:

$$\lambda = \frac{h}{p} = \frac{h}{mv}$$

p is momentum, m mass, v speed of the particle.
- Energy levels of the hydrogen atom (ionization energy level is at E = 0):

$$E_{total} = -\frac{me^4}{8\epsilon_0^2 h^2} \frac{1}{n^2}$$

- Electronic transitions in the hydrogen atom:
(i) written as an energy:

$$hf = \Delta E_{total} = \frac{me^4}{8\epsilon_0^2 h^2} \left(\frac{1}{n_{initial}^2} - \frac{1}{n_{final}^2} \right)$$

(ii) written as a frequency

$$f = R_H \left| \left(\frac{1}{n_{initial}^2} - \frac{1}{n_{final}^2} \right) \right|$$

with R_H the Rydberg constant.
- Selection rules for atomic orbitals:

(I) $0 \leq l \leq n-1$
(II) $-l \leq m_l \leq +l$

n is principal quantum number, l, is orbital quantum number, m_l, is magnetic quantum number. The spin quantum number m_s can take two values: $+\frac{1}{2}$, $-\frac{1}{2}$.
- Order of occupying atomic orbitals:
(i) minimum energy principle: an electron added to an atom occupies a free orbital with the least total energy.
(ii) Pauli principle: no two electrons in the same atom may have the same four quantum numbers.

Chapter XXII

Radiation

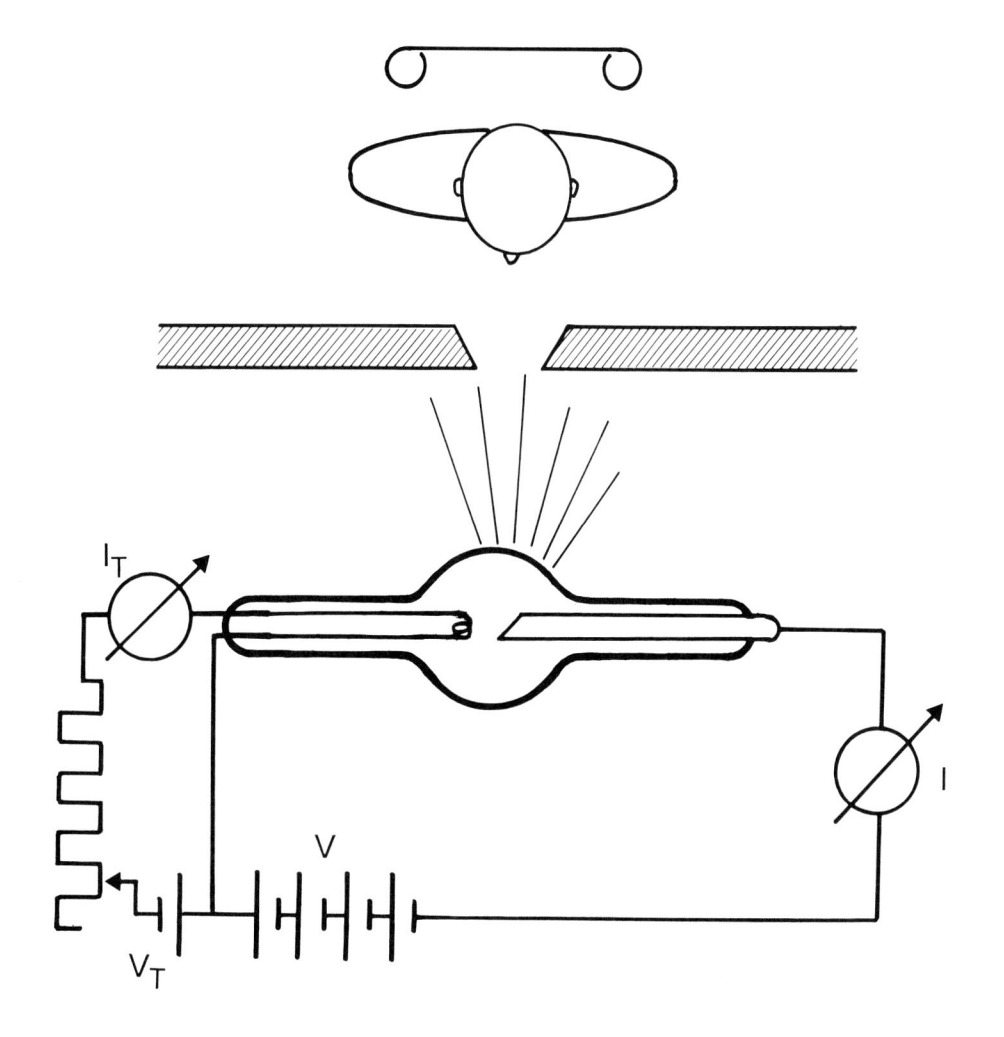

X–rays and nuclear physics

RADIATION
X–RAYS AND NUCLEAR PHYSICS

The atomic nucleus is five orders of magnitude smaller than the atom, but carries most of its mass. The nucleus contains neutrons and protons and is held together by the nuclear force, which is stronger than the electrostatic repulsion between the protons. This force has a very short range of only about 1×10^{-15} m.

Stable nuclei are characterized by certain ratios of protons and neutrons; other isotopes are radioactive and decay with a characteristic half–life. Four decay mechanisms are most frequently observed, which are associated with the loss of α–, β^-–, β^+– and γ–particles. The specific energy of these emitted particles allows for the use of the isotopes in chemistry and medicine as radio–tracers. Natural radioactivity is used for dating purposes, e.g., the radio–carbon method allows us to date organic material up to 50,000 years old.

The γ–particle is a high energy photon. Its energy exceeds that of X–rays which are emitted if a core electron of a heavy atom is removed and electrons from higher shells transfer to the lower orbital.

22.1. Origin of X–rays

X–rays are a type of electromagnetic radiation with high frequencies and high photon energies. The maximum range in medical applications lies between 30 keV (mammography) and 150 keV (high kilovoltage technique). These energies correspond to wavelengths in the range from 10^{-10} m to 10^{-12} m, as noted in Fig. 22.1. This radiation was discovered by Wilhelm Konrad Röntgen in 1895. X–rays are generated when high energy electrons interact with matter. For medical applications, X–rays are generated in X–ray tubes, as shown in Fig. 22.2. The X–ray tube consists of an evacuated glass tube and two electrodes. The vacuum is needed because the technique is based on accelerating free electrons toward a solid target electrode. In air, an electron would not be able to travel more than 1 millimeter. To generate the free electrons, a current I_T is sent through a thin metallic electrode, causing thermal evaporation of electrons based on the Richardson effect, which we discussed for the electron microscope in section 18.4. The electrons are then accelerated through a large potential difference ΔV toward a metallic anode. When the electrons strike the metal of the anode, X–rays are generated, which are

Fig. 22.1: Electromagnetic spectrum showing the relation between the frequency f, the wavelength λ and the photon energy $E = hf$.

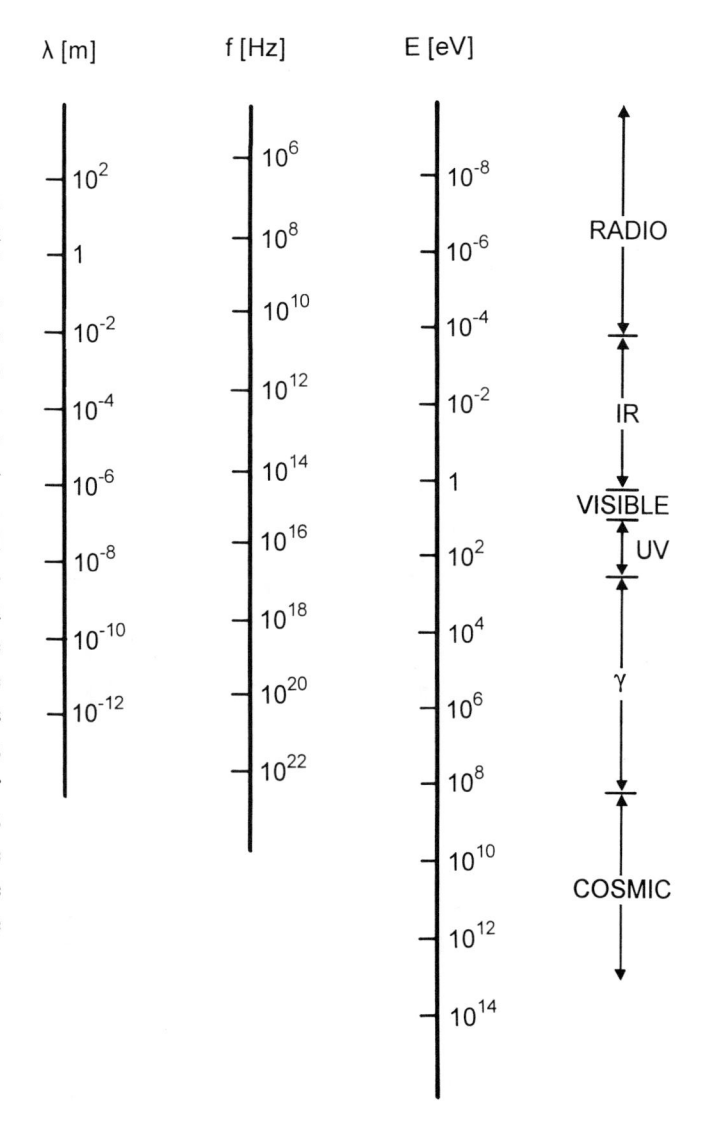

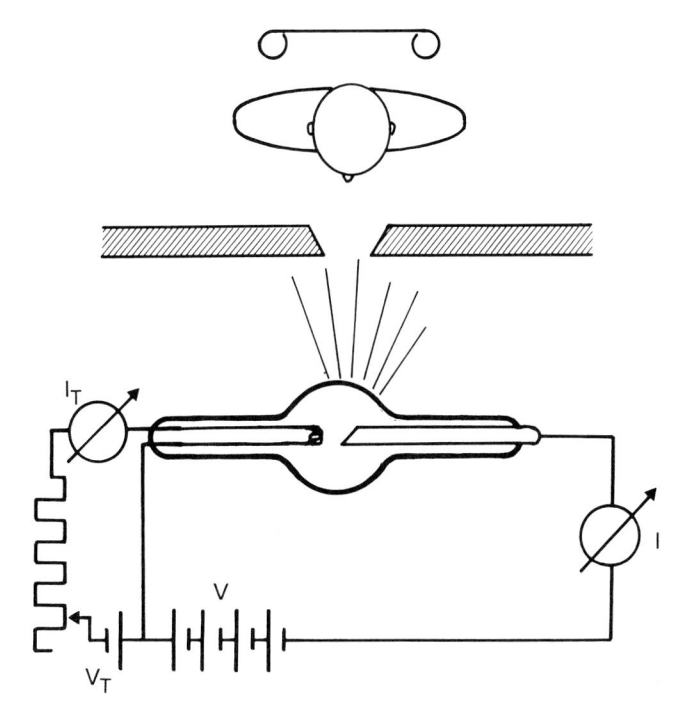

Fig. 22.2: X–ray tube and sketch of its standard use in medicine. Electrons are evaporated from a hot negative electrode in a vacuum tube. The free electrons are then accelerated by a high potential difference to strike the positive electrode. The generated X–rays leave the tube, are confined by a collimator, pass through the body of the patient and reach a photographic film.

called cathode rays for historic reasons. The glass tube is transparent for these rays (in the same fashion as it is transparent for visible light). The X–rays then travel through a collimator toward the patient. After penetrating the tissue they expose a film behind the patient. The film is developed and used by physicians for their diagnosis.

This process can be used to generate X–rays with a wide range of energies, as illustrated in Fig. 22.3. The figure shows the result of using a tungsten anode and an X–ray tube potential difference of $\Delta V = 100$ kV between cathode and anode. We need to discuss several features of the spectrum in Fig. 22.3 to understand the processes by which X–rays are generated:

(I) The figure shows that there is a maximum energy of X–rays with the cut–off energy at $E = 100$ keV;

(II) there is a broad peak which tails off toward larger energies. This radiation is called *bremsstrahlung*, and

(III) there are several sharp peaks around 55 and 70 keV. These peaks are due to *characteristic X–rays*.

The observation of a sharp cut–off energy is the result of the conservation of energy: even if an electron quickly slows down in the metal, it cannot radiate more than its total kinetic energy.

The interpretation of the second observation, the broad bremsstrahlung spectrum, expands on the explanation of the first observation. An electron with high energy penetrating a piece of solid matter may slow down more slowly, losing its kinetic energy in several steps. Fig. 22.4 illustrates a typical process in which an electron loses some of its energy. When the electron comes in close proximity to a nucleus within the anode, the direction of its motion changes due to the electrostatic attraction to the positive nucleus. Deviation from a straight path constitutes an acceleration, as discussed in

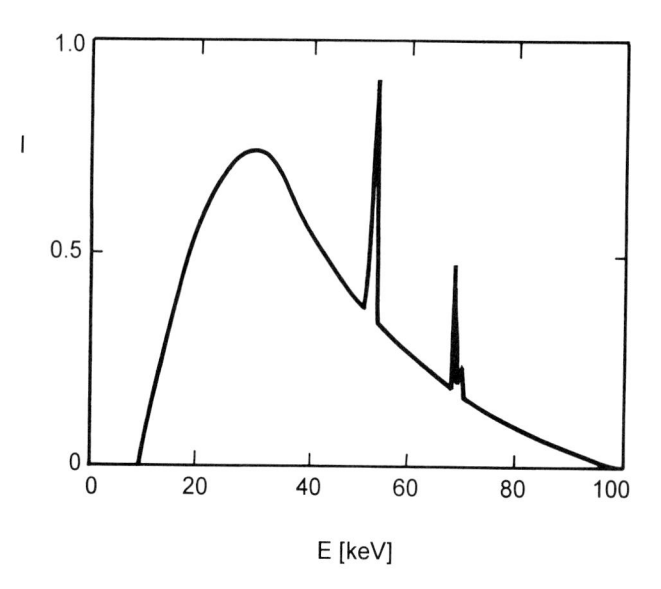

Fig. 22.3: The intensity spectrum of the electromagnetic radiation emitted by a tungsten electrode bombarded by 100 keV electrons. Note the cut-off at an X–ray energy of 100 keV. Two main features characterize the spectrum, a broad peak which is called bremsstrahlung, and several sharp peaks labelled characteristic X–rays.

601

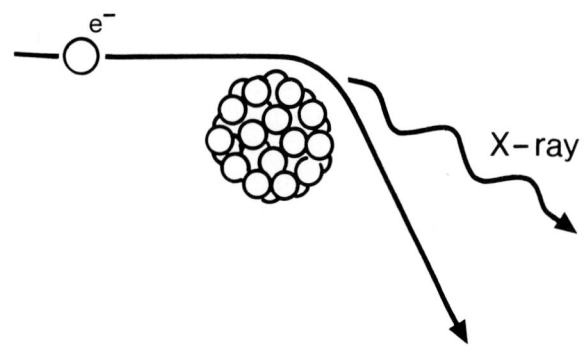

Fig. 22.4: Sketch of the process causing bremsstrahlung. An electron passes by a nucleus at close proximity and is attracted by the positive nuclear charge. The deflection occurs with a large angle. The electron emits X-rays while accelerating along a curved trajectory.

Chapter 20. An accelerating electron behaves like the electrons accelerating during the oscillation in an antenna: it emits electromagnetic radiation. In the case of the strong acceleration near a nucleus, that radiation has short wavelengths, lying in the X-ray part of the electromagnetic spectrum. The term bremsstrahlung was adopted as only electrons with a significant negative acceleration contribute to the X-ray intensity. Most other interaction processes, like the interaction with valence electrons in the anode atoms, lead to loss of energy in small amounts, which is converted into heat rather than radiation.

The explanation of the third observation in Fig. 22.3, the sharp peaks in the X-ray spectrum, requires the atomic model. This can experimentally be illustrated by changing the material in the anode; while the bremsstrahlung part of the X-ray spectrum varies little, the sharp peaks shift to new wavelengths. This is the reason why this part of the spectrum is called characteristic X-rays: the peaks are characteristic of the anodic material.

We saw already in the discussion of Bohr's model for elements heavier than hydrogen that the same transitions require more energy; the transition from n = 2 to n = 1 releases 10.2 eV in hydrogen, but 40.8 eV in He$^+$. However, these values apply only to atoms and ions which carry a single electron. To remove a valence electron from heavier atoms requires usually little energy. The situation during the bombardment with energetic electrons is different. The energetic electrons act like particles and can kick electrons out from one of the inner orbitals of the anode atoms. Once an inner electron

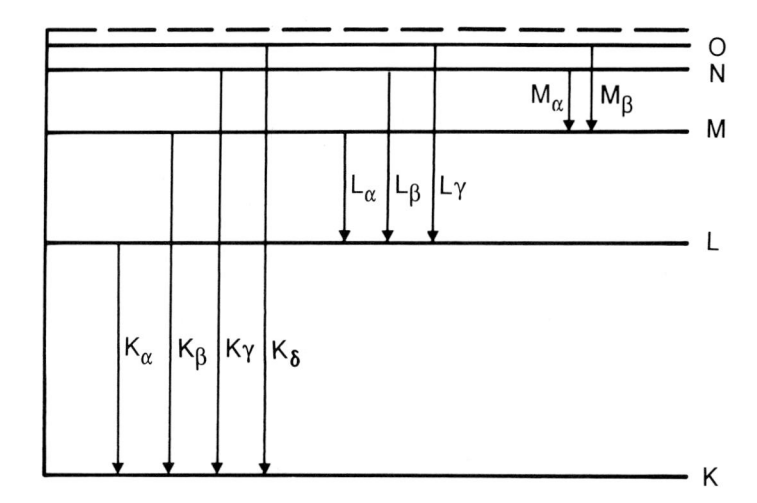

Fig. 22.5: Electron transitions in an atom in which an electron has been removed from an energetically lower orbital. Electrons from energetically higher orbitals make transitions to the vacancy, either in one or several steps. This corresponds to a range of possible transitions in heavier atoms, with several of the transitions in the X-ray part of the electromagnetic spectrum (characteristic X-rays). The figure indicates the standard notation used for these transitions, with the capital letter indicating the principal quantum number of the orbital with the vacancy (K-shell corresponds to n = 1). The index indicates the difference in the principal quantum numbers of the initial and final orbital of the electron which makes the transition (α corresponds to $\Delta n = 1$).

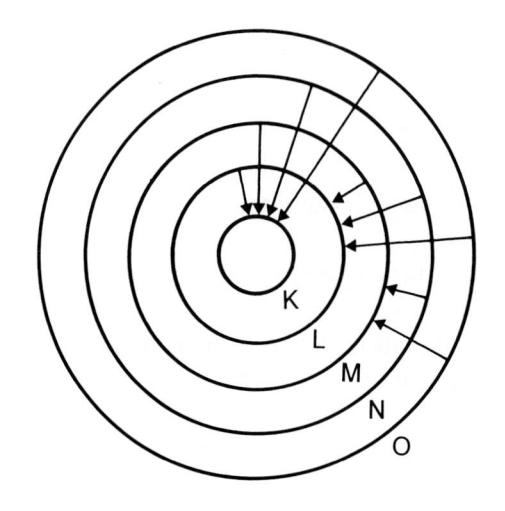

is removed, electrons in higher orbitals will fill the vacancy. The energy difference for the electrons involved in such transitions is large due to the large positive charge in the nucleus and due to the large energy difference between the lower lying orbitals.

There are several possible transitions of electrons into a lower orbital vacancy, as illustrated in Fig. 22.5. For an electron removed from the innermost orbital (the orbitals with quantum number n = 1 are called the K–shell), four possible transitions are shown, labelled with Greek letter indices. Other transitions leading to X–ray emission involve the initial removal of an electron from the L–shell (i.e., orbitals with n = 2) or from the M–shell (i.e., orbitals with n = 3).

Example 22.1
(a) Estimate the photon energy of the characteristic X–rays emitted from a tungsten anode when an electron from the M–shell (n = 3) drops into a vacancy created in the K–shell (n = 1).
(b) What is the wavelength of the X–rays?

Solution part (a): The best way to calculate this energy is to start from Eq. (21.30). We cannot simply substitute Z = 74, which is the number of positive charges in the tungsten nucleus, since the electrostatic force between an electron and the positive charge in the nucleus is partially screened by other electrons in the atom. In 1914, Henry Moseley showed that the effective value for Z is given by the number of protons in the nucleus, diminished by the number of electrons in shells at lower energy as the electron we allow to make the transition. In the K–shell we use Eq. (21.30), modified in the form $E_K = (Z-1)^2 E_1$, where E_1 is the ionization energy for the hydrogen atom. In the M–shell, we use $E_M = (Z-9)^2 E_3$ since there are 8 electrons in the L–shell and one electron in the K–shell (the other one has been kicked out), shielding the M–shell electron before the transition. Further, we know from Eq. (21.21) that $E_3 = E_1/3^2$. Thus, using $E_1 = -13.6$ eV from Eq. (21.25), we find:

$$\Delta E = E_K - E_M = \qquad (1)$$
$$= -72.5[keV] - (-6.4[keV]) = -66.1 \ keV$$

This transition contributes the second peak in Fig. 22.3.

Solution part (b): We get the wavelength from $\Delta E = hf$, i.e., $\Delta E = hc/\lambda$. This leads to $\lambda = 0.019$ nm.

22.2. The biological effects of X–rays

What effect do X–rays have on the human body? With this question we also return to the impact of electromagnetic radiation on human space exploration. Are there parts of the electromagnetic spectrum we have to fear, and reach the intensities of radiation in these parts of the spectrum dangerous levels anywhere, either in a hospital X–ray machine or in outer space?

It is important to answer these questions, of course, and we will do it in this section. However, before we start it may be useful to note that it is not appropriate to see the interaction of X–rays with tissue as something destructive and dangerous. If handled appropriately, X–rays are an invaluable tool in diagnosis and therapy, e.g. when used to obtain CAT (computed axial tomography) scans. It might be interesting to note further that X–rays are often used for unrelated scientific purposes. As an example, two pivotal contributions to the development of modern genetics are listed in which X–rays played a key role: Hermann Joe Muller's 1927 experiment which proved that genes are (artificially) mutable, and Francis Crick's and James Watson's 1953 proposal for the DNA structure.

Once Gregor Mendel's experiments had been rediscovered in the early years of the 20th century, an apparent discrepancy between Mendelism and Darwinism was noted in that the latter needs a steady change for evolutionary progress while the former is based on the stability of the genetic code. To test the apparent immutability of genes, Muller bombarded fruit flies with X–rays and linked new deformities in the offspring to the radiation, proving that he had artificially altered genes in the insects. George Beadle and Edward Tatum used in 1940 the same X–ray technique on a species of bread mould (neurospora) to prove the correlation between genes and enzymes: the mutation of certain genes led to the lack of certain enzymes in the offspring.

Crick and Watson discovered the double–helix structure of DNA from an X–ray crystallographic analysis. In this technique, usually applied in solid state physics to characterize crystal structures, patterns in X–rays scattered off the sample are used to determine bond lengths and bond angles. Crick's and Watson's collaboration was characterized by one science historian with the words: "the young, ambitious, supple minded American who knew some biology (Watson) and the effortlessly brilliant but unfocussed older Briton who knew some physics (Crick)."

We know from the medical use of X–rays that this type of electromagnetic radiation penetrates biological matter much more easily than light. Thus, whatever adverse effect radiation has on living biological material, the effect of light is limited to the surface (e.g., skin cancer due to UV radiation) while the damage done by X–rays may reach much deeper.

The ability to penetrate various materials depends on the actual energy of the X–rays and the consistency of the penetrated matter. For this discussion it is beneficial to consider the X–ray beam as a stream of particles (photons). If such a beam of X–rays has an energy of less than 1 MeV it loses intensity in matter by three processes: (i) scattering, which changes only the direction but not the energy of the X–ray photon, (ii) through photo–electrons, which are electrons that absorb an X–ray photon entirely by picking up the photon's energy as kinetic energy, and (iii) the *Compton effect*, which is an elastic collision between the photon and an electron.

The total attenuation follows the following relation:

$$I(x) = I_0\, e^{-\mu x} \qquad (2)$$

in which I_0 is the incident intensity and $I(x)$ is the intensity at the depth x. μ is the *attenuation coefficient* in unit [m^{-1}]. That means that the X–ray intensity decreases with the same exponential law (Beer's law) which we found in Chapter 16 for sound.

Table 22.1 illustrates how the attenuation varies with energy of the X–ray beam. X–ray attenuation is usually quantified in the form of a *mass attenuation coefficient* μ/ρ, which is the attenuation coefficient per unit density of the material penetrated by the radiation, in unit [m²/kg]. This definition allows us to exclude variations due to density changes for the same material, which is useful particularly for biological materials. Table 22.1 reports values of μ/ρ for aluminium and copper for three different X–ray wavelengths. We see that the higher the X–ray energy (i.e., the shorter their wavelengths), the farther the X–rays penetrate.

To obtain an impression of what the X–ray attenuation effect means for biological materials, we consider a typical X–ray set–up used in medical applications. The medical X–ray facility consists of a tungsten anode in a vacuum tube with an electron acceleration potential of 100 kV. This leads to X–rays emitted from the tungsten electrode as shown in Fig. 22.3. Fig. 22.6 shows in logarithmic representation the intensity fraction of 100 keV (solid line) and 50 keV (dashed line) X–rays reaching various depth d in bone material (1), and in muscle tissue or water (2). The x–axis is given as the product of path–lengths and density as only the combination of both factors are physiologically important in this context. For muscle tissues, the transmitted intensity is reduced to 10 % at a tissue thickness of $d = \rho/\mu \approx 8 - 10$ g/cm², which corresponds to an actual thickness of about 9 cm. The same intensity reduction is reached for bone material at thicknesses $d = \rho/\mu \approx 4 - 5$ g/cm², which correspond to a bone thickness of about 2 to 3 cm.

Note that the lost X–ray intensity in Fig. 22.6 is not reflected, but either scattered (Compton effect) or absorbed by the bone and the tissue. The absorbed fraction causes the adverse biological impact. It is measured and reported in two ways:

(I) as the amount of ionization occurring in the material due to the radiation (*exposure dose*), and
(II) as the energy deposited by the radiation in the material (*absorbed dose*).

Table 22.1: Mass attenuation coefficient μ/ρ [m²/kg] as a function of X–ray wavelength.

λ [nm]	μ/ρ(Al)	μ/ρ(Cu)
0.01	0.016	0.033
0.1	1.5	13.1
0.2	10.2	18.8

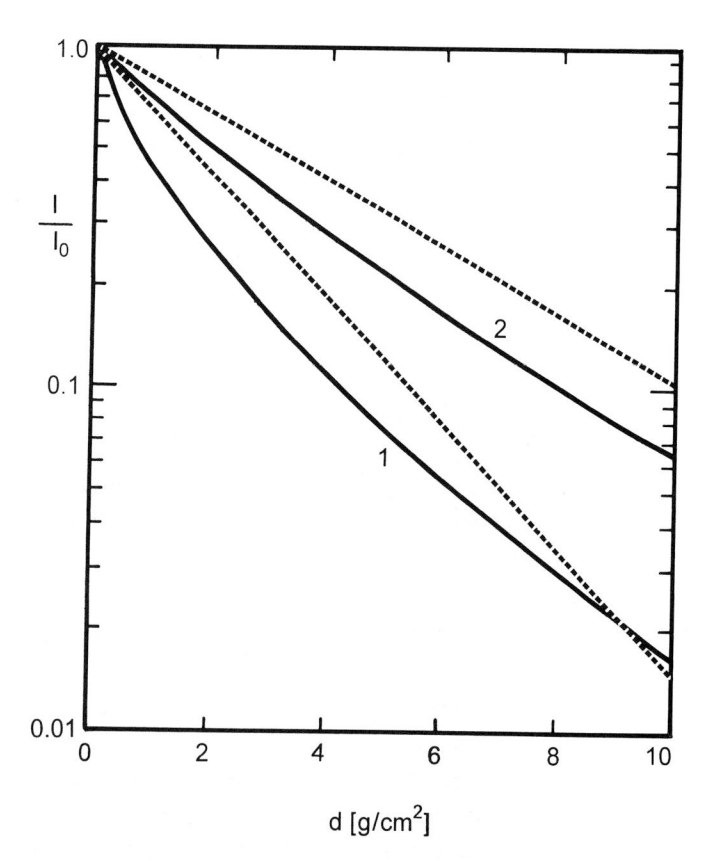

Fig. 22.6: Intensity attenuation of X–ray beams of 100 keV (solid lines) and 50 keV (dashed lines) in human bones (curves 1) and muscle tissue (curves 2). The depth is given in unit [g/cm²], which represents the density multiplied with the path length in the tissue.

Before we can quantify the biological impact of X–rays, we must define the unit systems used to measure the respective dose or dose rate. The *dose* is the total amount of ionization or energy deposited in a given amount of material and the *dose rate* is the amount of ionization or energy deposited in a given amount of material per time unit (often reported per hour [h]).

The first dose we define was also the first system used historically: the *exposure dose* is defined as the total charge generated by the ionizing radiation per kilogram of air (unit [Cb/kg]). The reference to air at standard conditions (sea level pressure) stems from the original observations of cosmic radiation. Cosmic radiation at sea level generates about 1 ion/cm³s. As a result, there is a steady state concentration of ions present; this concentration is about 1×10^3 ions/cm³. Another, non–standard unit often used for the exposure dose is the unit Röntgen [R]. It is defined in the form:

$$1 \, [R] = 2.08 \times 10^9 \, \frac{ion \; pairs}{cm^3}$$

$$1 \, [R] = 2.58 \times 10^{-4} \, \frac{Cb}{kg} \tag{3}$$

Therefore, cosmic rays cause an ionization dose rate of 1.7×10^{-6} R/h, which is about 10 % of the total ionization dose rate on the surface of the Earth, with the rest due to natural radioactive elements in the environment. The ionization dose rate in the van Allen belt is as high as 50 R/h and strong samples in therapeutic nuclear medicine (cobalt source) have ionization dose rates as high as 10^4 R/h at a distance of 100 cm from the source.

The quantity that is now more commonly used is the energy dose. The energy dose is the amount of energy deposited per kilogram of air in [J/kg]. The unit *Gray* is introduced as a derived standard unit for the energy dose, 1 [Gy] = 1 [J/kg]. This unit has replaced an older, non–standard unit that you may still find in the literature (and which should not be mixed up with the unit radians), the unit [rad] with the conversion 1 Gy = 100 rad. Note that for most biological materials both doses are roughly equivalent with 1 R ≅ 1 rad = 0.01 Gy.

Penetrating radiation, such as X–rays, are capable of destroying live tissue either through the ionization effect, which leads to the breaking of chemical bonds, or though energy deposition. Energy deposition is damaging because a large amount of localized heat can break chemical bonds, particularly in large molecules such as DNA. The consequences for the surviving fraction of affected cells is illustrated in Fig. 20.13. Note the logarithmic scale used in that figure to illustrate the fraction of cells surviving a given energy dose in unit [Gy]. Curve 1 represents thyroid cells, curve 2 represents mammary cells, and curve 3 represents bone marrow. While there is an interval of minor sensitivity at low doses, all three curves have the same steep slope at larger energy doses. The initial non–exponential behavior is due to DNA–repair mechanisms operating in live cells. Even intensive UV radiation does not destroy tissue with the same efficiency, primarily due to the limited penetration depth of UV radiation, which does not allow it to reach many body cells, such as thyroid cells.

As dangerous as X–rays are for biological tissue, we usually don't have to worry about them, thanks to the low environmental X–ray doses we are exposed to. Inspecting Fig. 20.12, we note that the X–ray portion of the solar spectrum is not too intensive. This is partially due to the fact that the sun mainly consists of very light elements, and partially due to the outer gas layers of the sun which absorb most of the more intense radiation generated in the nuclear fusion processes which fuel the sun's core. The remaining radiation is absorbed by the upper layers of Earth's atmosphere.

However, for an astronaut, the danger of exposure to X–rays is significantly higher due to indirect processes. Particularly in the radiation belts, where intensive streams of energetic particles, mostly electrons, are coupled with an extremely low concentration of gas molecules, any such particle that strikes the spaceship or, even worse, the astronaut's suit during an extra–vehicular activity (EVA), generates X–rays in the form of bremsstrahlung. Fig. 22.7 illustrates that this is a serious issue in the radiation belts around the Earth. The figure shows a double–logarithmic plot of the electron density as a function of altitude. The high density of energetic electrons in the radiation belts and their ability to generate penetrating X–rays is the main reason why orbiting missions remain at altitudes below 1000 km above the Earth's surface, as shown in Fig. 20.1. On the other hand, as soon as a mission has passed beyond 25,000 km above the Earth's surface, the density of energetic electrons is reduced. However, radiation remains dangerous because the absorbing atmosphere no longer protects the astronauts against more intensive high–energy electromagnetic radiation, e.g. during sun flares.

But we cannot evaluate the risk for a Mars mission on the basis of electromagnetic radiation alone. X–rays are only one part of the emission during sun flares, as X–rays are only one part of the environmental radiation exposure on the Earth. We must take other forms of radiation into account before a final judgement of radiation risks can be made.

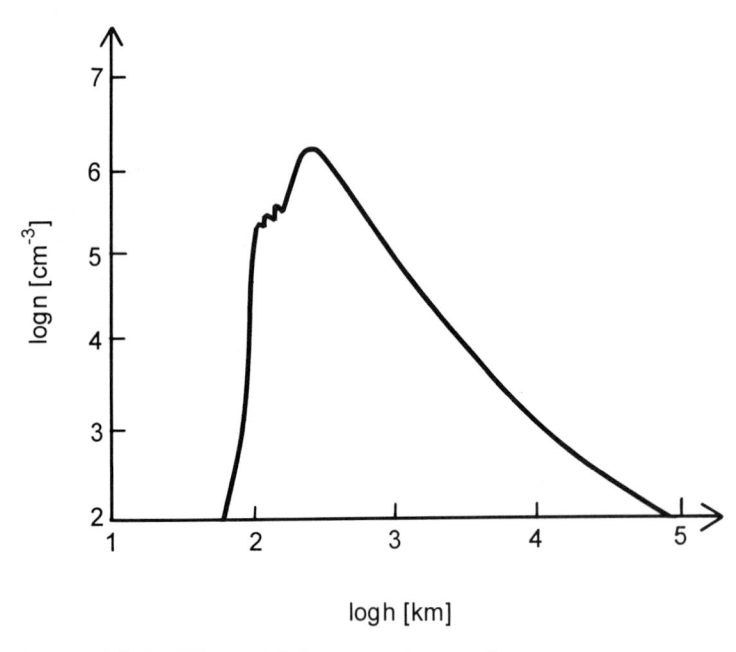

Fig. 22.7: Double–logarithmic plot of the density of free electrons as a function of altitude. The interaction of these energetic electrons with atmospheric molecules are the primary origin of X–rays in the upper part of the atmosphere.

22.3. The stable atomic nucleus

Once the atomic hypothesis had been accepted, questions arose about the composition and structure of the atom. This question was split into two separate parts early in the discussion: Heinrich Hertz (1891) and Philipp Lenard (1900) had shown that atoms consist of a tiny nucleus, which contains essentially all the mass of the atom, and a large space around the nucleus which they said is "as empty as the outer space in the universe".

In Chapter 21 we established the structure and composition of the atom excluding the nucleus: the electron is the elementary particle present in the atomic shell and, by the 1930s, quantum mechanics properly described the structure of the orbitals.

The nucleus remained more elusive, primarily due to its small size in comparison to the atom as a whole. The first indication of its composition came from studying cosmic rays and instable, i.e., *radioactive*, elements. Since the primary cosmic rays, protons and α–particles, travel vast distances in outer space before reaching the Earth, they must be stable. The interaction of the primary cosmic rays with molecules of the atmosphere at altitudes of 20 to 30 km causes the secondary cosmic rays which reach the surface of the Earth. Due to the short period of time that it takes for the secondary cosmic rays to penetrate the Earth's atmosphere, they can include unstable particles, e.g neutrons and muons, and anti–matter particles, e.g. positrons (which are identical to electrons but carry a positive charge).

As more and more of these particles were discovered, it became clear that there is a large number of additional phenomena in which they are involved and which are not explained by the atomic model.

In the 1930s the first conclusive discoveries and theoretical models for the nucleus emerged. The field was defined as nuclear physics, a discipline that investigates the stable nuclei in the atoms of regular matter, and the limits of stability that are evident in radioactivity. In more recent decades, the field has evolved into a discipline called high–energy physics or subatomic physics, which is focussed on the systematic study of the large number of particles which are smaller than the atom.

In this section we focus on two aspects of nuclear physics: the composition of stable nuclei and the radioactive decay processes, which we study to link to modern subfields in medicine, such as radiology and nuclear medicine.

From the onset of atomic research it was clear that the nucleus must contain as many positive charges as there are electrons in its shell because atoms are electrically neutral. Let us assume that we want to built a nucleus from fundamental particles, which we call *nucleons*. If there were only one type of nucleon carrying a positive charge, the nucleus of the hydrogen atom would contain just one of these nucleons. We run immediately into a problem with this approach, though, because the nucleus of a helium atom has two positive charges but four times the mass of a hydrogen nucleus.

Since a single positive nucleon is, therefore, not sufficient to explain the mass and charge properties of all nuclei, the question was whether two different nucleons would do. There were two possibilities considered in the 1920s, either a combination of positive and negative particles, or positive and electrically neutral particles. The first proposals were based on combining protons and electrons to make up the nucleus. Both particles were known to exist, the electron (e⁻) had been discovered in 1897 by Thomson and the proton (p$^+$) had been observed in the primary cosmic rays. In turn, no neutral particles had at that time been found.

With the development of quantum mechanical concepts in the mid 1920s it became clear that the helium nucleus cannot contain four protons and two captured electrons, because this would require a violation of Heisenberg's uncertainty relation: if we confine an electron to a space as small as the nucleus (i.e., accept a very small uncertainty in the position of the electron), the energy of the electron must significantly exceed the energy needed for the electron to escape from the nucleus. The same problem does not apply to the protons in the nucleus due to their much larger mass.

Thus, it was theoretically postulated that the atomic nuclei must contain protons and an electrically neutral nucleon, called the *neutron*. The neutron (n^0), however, remained elusive until 1932, when James Chadwick discovered it indirectly (by observing protons set free from hydrogen atoms in collisions with neutrons). There are two reasons why the neutron is hard to observe experimentally:

(I) a neutral particle interacts with matter much less than a charged particle. Most interactions we observe are based on the electrostatic force because it is the only strong and far–reaching fundamental force; gravity is too weak, and the nuclear and weak force act only across distances of the size of the atomic nucleus.

(II) Free neutrons are not stable, they are only stable as part of a nucleus. We quantify stability later with the concept of the half–life. This is the time by which 50 % of an initial amount of unstable particles have decayed. Protons and electrons are stable since their half–life at least exceeds the age of the universe. This also applies to a neutron in a nucleus. However, when the neutron is separated from a nucleus, its half–life is only 12.5 min, i.e., after this short period half of the isolated neutrons no longer exist. What happens when a neutron decays is written in the following form:

$$n^0 \rightarrow p^+ + e^- + \bar{\nu} + \Delta E \quad (4)$$

The neutron decays into a proton, an electron and an anti–neutrino (which is the anti–matter particle to the neutrino. Neutrinos are not discussed in this textbook). The ΔE term in Eq. (4) indicates that there is also energy released, in this particular case $\Delta E = 0.77$ MeV.

The fact that the neutron decays rather quickly when isolated, but is stable when it is part of a nucleus indicates that nucleons act different as part of nuclear matter.

Example 22.2
Calculate the binding energy of the helium nucleus.

Solution: We establish the uniqueness of the intra–nuclear environment by calculating first the change in mass when 2 protons and 2 neutrons form a helium nucleus (α–particle):

$$\Delta m = m_\alpha - \left(2m_{p^+} + 2m_{n^0}\right) =$$
$$= (4.002604 - 2 \cdot 1.007825 - ... \quad (5)$$
$$... - 2 \cdot 1.008665) \, u$$

which yields:

$$\Delta m = -0.03076 \, u \quad (6)$$

i.e., the helium nucleus is lighter than the four particles it is made of. This is a surprising result we cannot understand with the classical concepts we studied so far: mass was conserved in all the experiments that we have considered so far. However, Albert Einstein showed in 1905 that mass can be interpreted as a form of energy with the conversion formula:

$$E = mc^2 \quad (7)$$

in which c is the speed of light in vacuum. Thus, even a small amount of mass corresponds to a tremendous amount of energy. When the helium nucleus formed, the mass difference in Eq. (6) has been converted into binding energy that holds the four nuclei together:

$$E_{binding}(He) = (0.03076 \, u)\left(3 \times 10^8 \left[\frac{m}{s}\right]\right)^2 \quad (8)$$
$$\Rightarrow E_{binding} = 28.3 \, MeV$$

Calculating binding energies for all stable elements allows us to compare the contribution of each nucleon to the total binding energy. In the case of the helium nucleus this energy is 7.1 MeV, i.e., 28.3 MeV divided by 4 nucleons. Fig. 22.8 shows that this value roughly holds constant across the periodic table; the binding energy per nucleon, E_n, varies between 5.5 MeV and 8.5 MeV

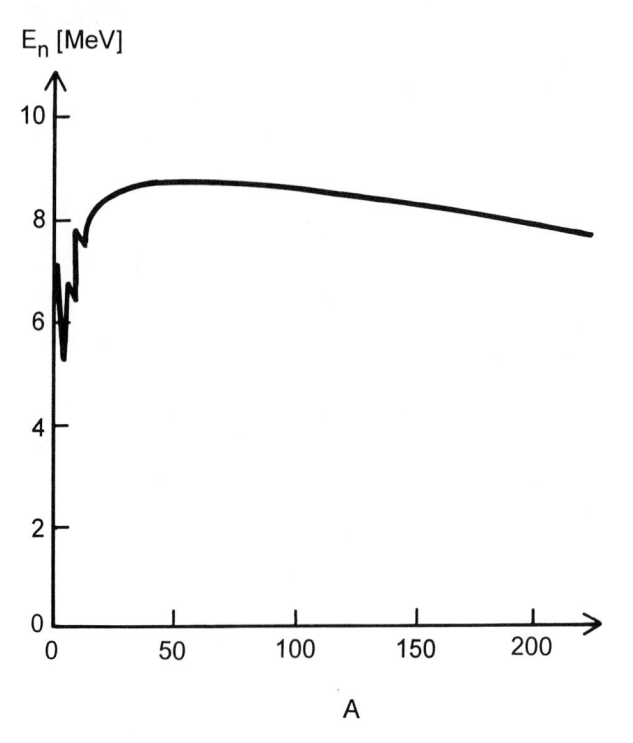

Fig. 22.8: Binding energy per nucleon in nuclear matter as a function of the mass of the nucleus. The binding energy per nucleon varies only slightly with an average value of about 8 MeV.

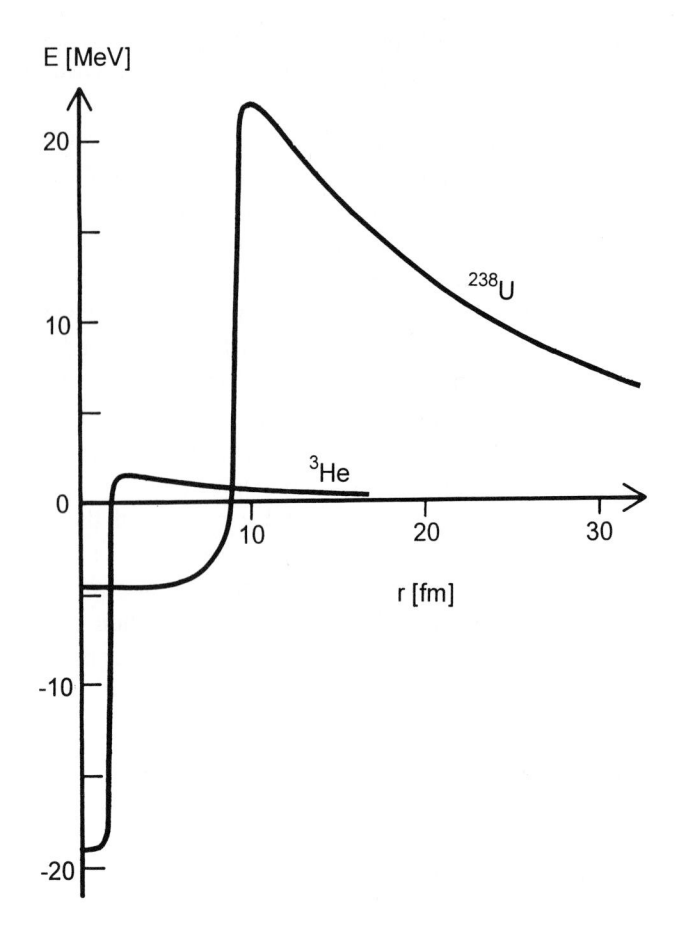

Fig. 22.9: Potential energy profile for an approaching proton as a function of distance from the center of a ^{3}He and a ^{238}U nucleus. The high energy barrier is due to electrostatic repulsion; the low energy within the nucleus is due to the attractive nuclear force. The length scale of the abscissa is given in femtometers.

from deuterium to uranium.

That we need such extremely large binding energies to form stable nuclei (in comparison, typical chemical energies are of the order of 1 eV) was already anticipated when Hertz, Lenard and Rutherford had illustrated how small atomic nuclei indeed are: there is a factor of 10^5 difference between the size of an atom and the size of a nucleus. To obtain a stable nucleus, a nuclear force must exist which exceeds the repulsive Coulomb force acting between any two protons in the nucleus, i.e., at a distance of about 10^{-14} m. Hideki Yukawa developed a potential energy model for the nuclear force, taking into account its very short range. Fig. 22.9 shows the potential energy for a proton approaching one of the lightest nuclei, a ^{3}He nucleus (which is a light helium isotope), or one of the heaviest nuclei, an uranium (^{238}U) nucleus. Note the unit of the distance axis: a femtometer is 10^{-15} m. An approaching proton at first encounters the repulsive Coulomb force, like we observed in Rutherford's experiment. However, when the proton penetrates the nuclear matter, it suddenly feels an attractive force, which is essentially constant across the nucleus.

With variations in both the number of protons and number of neutrons in the nucleus, a wide range of different nuclei can be formed. There are more than 1700 known nuclei, of which 271 are stable. We must always report two of three numbers to unequivocally identify a nucleus: (i) the mass number A, which corresponds to the number of nucleons in the nucleus, (ii) the atomic number Z, which corresponds to the number of protons in the nucleus, and (iii) the number of neutrons, N. These numbers are related by:

$$A = Z + N \qquad (9)$$

It is common practice to identify the atomic number Z and the mass number A, and to connect them with the familiar chemical symbol X (although the atomic number and the chemical symbol are synonymous terms). The general notation and two common examples (carbon and oxygen) are given in the following form:

$${}^A_Z X \quad e.g.: \quad {}^{12}_{6}C \,, \; {}^{16}_{8}O \qquad (10)$$

Various terms have been introduced to identify relations between different nuclei. The most frequently used terms are:

(I) *isobaric nuclei*, which refers to nuclei with the same mass number, A = const. An example are the three nuclei:

$$\substack{96\\38}Sr \quad \substack{96\\39}Y \quad \substack{96\\40}Zr \tag{11}$$

(II) isotopic nuclei (*isotopes*), which refers to nuclei with the same atomic number, Z = const. Two examples are:

$$\substack{1\\1}H \quad \substack{2\\1}H \quad \substack{3\\1}H$$
$$\substack{11\\6}C \quad \substack{12\\6}C \quad \substack{13\\6}C \quad \substack{14\\6}C \tag{12}$$

where the names of the isotopes in the first line are hydrogen, deuterium and tritium. 81 elements in the periodic table have stable isotopes. When referring to isotopes, the atomic number is often omitted, since the information is already contained in the chemical symbol. For example, we later discuss a carbon–dating method for determining the age of biological systems based on the carbon isotope with A = 14. Instead of referring to this isotope in the form shown in Eq. (12) you find often the abbreviated notation ^{14}C.

(III) *Isomers*, which refers to identical nucleus composition, A = const and Z = const, but different energy states of the nucleus. Nuclei, which result from radioactive decay, or are the result of a nuclear reaction, are often not in the ground state (labelled g) but in an excited state (labelled m for metastable). Several such isomers are important for nuclear medicine. An example is scandium:

$$^{46m}Sc \quad ^{46g}Sc \tag{13}$$

22.4. Radioactive decay

Of the 1700 nuclei which have been studied, more than 1400 are not stable. Many of these occur naturally: some decay so slowly that they are still around from the time the solar system formed, e.g. uranium; others are formed in nuclear reactions of stable isotopes with particles of the cosmic rays, e.g. ^{14}C. The first radioactive decay was observed in 1896 by Henri Becquerel, when he noticed that an uranium salt emits invisible radiation that darkens a photographic plate. Systematic studies by Marie and Pierre Curie led to the discovery of several radioactive isotopes by the beginning of the twentieth century.

An isotope is radioactive if there is a non–zero probability that the nuclei of this isotope decays after a finite time. For each radioactive isotope, we know its type of decay. There are three types of particles which are emitted by all but the heaviest radioactive nuclei (which may undergo fission): emission of a helium nucleus (α–decay), emission of an electron (β$^-$–decay) or emission of a positron (β$^+$–decay). Many of the decay processes are accompanied by the emission of X–rays, which are called γ–rays when they originate in a nuclear process. Using the notation of Eq. (10) we can indicate which new nucleus results from a decay process:

$$\alpha\text{--}decay: \quad {}^{A}_{Z}X \rightarrow {}^{A-4}_{Z-2}Y + {}^{4}_{2}He$$

$$\beta^{+}\text{--}decay: \quad {}^{A}_{Z}X \rightarrow {}^{A}_{Z-1}Y + e^{+} \tag{14}$$

$$\beta^{-}\text{--}decay: \quad {}^{A}_{Z}X \rightarrow {}^{A}_{Z+1}Y + e^{-}$$

The isotope X is called the parent nucleus and Y is called the daughter nucleus.

When an individual radioactive nucleus decays cannot be predicted. Radioactive decay is a statistical process, which means that each nucleus decays randomly and independently of the others. As in other statistical processes, we can only make quantitative statements about a large number of radioactive nuclei.

Assuming that we start with a sufficiently large amount of one unstable isotope, e.g. N nuclei, then we define a rate of radioactive decay, $-\Delta N/\Delta t$, where the negative sign indicates that the number of nuclei is decreasing. For any type of radioactive decay the decay rate is observed to be proportional to the number of radioactive nuclei at time t:

$$-\frac{\Delta N}{\Delta t} = \lambda N \tag{15}$$

λ is the decay constant and has the unit [1/s]. We have discussed equations like Eq. (15) several times before in this textbook. The linear proportionality between decay rate and absolute amount of a quantity leads to an exponential law describing, in the case of Eq. (15), the time dependence of the number of radioactive nuclei present in a sample if we start with N_0 radioactive nuclei at time t = 0:

$$N(t) = N_0 \, e^{-\lambda t} \tag{16}$$

Instead of reporting the decay constant λ, or the mean lifetime $T_{mean} = \lambda^{-1}$, in the literature the half–life $T_{1/2}$ is usually given. This time represents the time after which 50 % of the initial number of radioactive nuclei in the sample have decayed. We can relate the half–life to the decay constant λ, and then rewrite Eq. (16) using $T_{1/2}$. To develop this relation we substitute $t = T_{1/2}$ in Eq. (16) with $N(t) = N_0/2$:

$$\frac{N_0}{2} = N_0 \, e^{-\lambda T_{1/2}} \qquad (17)$$

After dividing both sides by N_0 and taking the natural logarithm of each side, we find:

$$\ln \frac{1}{2} = -\lambda \, T_{1/2} \qquad (18)$$

which is equivalent to:

$$\ln 2 = \lambda \, T_{1/2} \qquad (19)$$

Solving Eq. (19) for the half–life yields:

$$T_{1/2} = \frac{\ln 2}{\lambda} \qquad (20)$$

The radioactive decay law, Eq. (16), is illustrated in Fig. 22.10, highlighting the half–life. Note that the decay of 3/4 of the initial amount of radioactive nuclei requires a time of $2T_{1/2}$. We can relate the mean lifetime and the half–life using Eq. (20):

$$T_{mean} = \frac{1}{\lambda} = 1.44 \, T_{1/2} \qquad (21)$$

At this point we define one more term. The number of decays per time unit of a radioactive sample, $\Delta N/\Delta t$, is defined as activity A, i.e., $\Delta N/\Delta t = A$. The standard unit for the activity is the unit [Bq] (Becquerel) with the definition that 1 Bq = 1 decay/s.

Example 22.3

We consider a sample which contains 3×10^{16} nuclei of ^{226}Ra, which has a half–life of 1600 years. What is the activity of the sample at $t = T_{1/2}$?

Solution: This is not a laboratory experiment since the two reference times are 1600 years apart. In the first step we determine the decay constant λ. For this we express the half–life in standard unit [s]: $T_{1/2} = 5 \times 10^{10}$ s. Thus:

$$\lambda = \frac{\ln 2}{T_{1/2}} = 1.4 \times 10^{-11} \, s^{-1} \qquad (22)$$

We substitute this value into Eq. (15) to determine the activity at $t = 0$ (initially):

$$A = \lambda N_0 = 1.4 \times 10^{-11} [s^{-1}] \, 3 \times 10^{16}$$
$$\Rightarrow \quad A = 4.1 \times 10^5 \, Bq \qquad (23)$$

We use the same formula to calculate the activity at the half–life of the sample:

$$A = \lambda \frac{N_0}{2} = 2.05 \times 10^5 \, Bq \qquad (24)$$

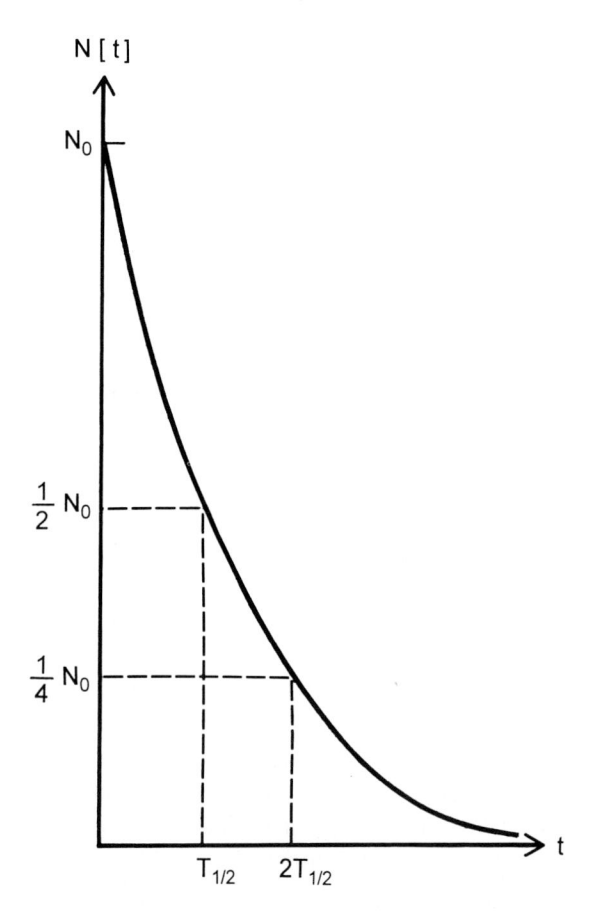

Fig. 22.10: Sketch of the number of nuclei of a given radioactive isotope in a sample as a function of time. The dashed lines indicate the reduction after one half–life at $t = T_{1/2}$ and two half–lifes at $2 \, T_{1/2}$.

22.5. Biological impact of particle radiation

Having defined several new types of energetic radiation in this section, we return to the question of their impact on a biological sample. In principle, the same issues are relevant as in the case of X–rays. Due to the high energy of the particles emitted in nuclear processes, they can penetrate into biological tissues, even though not to the same depth as X–rays, as illustrated qualitatively in Fig. 22.11 and quantified in Table 22.2

The biological impact of high energy particles is due to the deposition of their kinetic energy in the tissue sample and due to the ionization close to the trajectory of the penetrating particle. Thus, the same dose units defined for X–rays above are useful, the unit Röntgen [R] for the exposure dose and the unit Gray [Gy] for the energy dose. The range values in Table 22.2 allow us further to calculate the affected tissue volume.

When comparing the effect of same amounts of radiation on the same biological sample (e.g. human tissue), different types of radiation have different degrees of adverse impacts. This led to the definition of a new variable, the *equivalent dose* with the unit Sievert [Sv]. The equivalent dose is defined such that the same equivalent dose of any type of radiation has the same degree of impact on tissue. This is achieved by introducing a *quality factor* W_R to convert the energy dose:

$$Equiv.Dose\ [Sv] = W_R \cdot Ener.Dose\ [Gy] \quad (25)$$

Typical values of the quality factor are given in Table 22.3 for the different types of radiation discussed in this chapter. The list also includes neutrons which are generated in nuclear reactors. The table illustrates as a rule of thumb that the heavier the emitted particle in a nuclear process, the higher the adverse biological impact.

The equivalent dose is used when various types of radiation occur, e.g., in the cases compared in Fig. 20.14. Table 22.4 lists some typical pathological consequences of whole–body exposures to various equivalent doses. Note that the biological effect is dependent on whether the dose is received over a long period or within a short time. Protracted exposure is better tolerated due to the damage repair mechanisms operating in living cells. These repair mechanisms were noted as the initial plateau in Fig. 20.13. However, alterations in the cells may lead to long–term effects, which are often only diagnosed years after the dose has been received. These effects usually include degenerative changes or organ malfunctions due to the damage to blood vessels. For leukemia, the risk factor for whole body exposure is given as 10^{-4} [1/Sv], i.e., 0.01 [%/Sv].

Table 22.2: Range of various forms of radiation in biological tissue or water.

Radiation type	Energy	Range
α–particles	5 MeV	40 μm
β–radiation	20 keV	10 μm
β–radiation	1 MeV	7 mm
γ–radiation	20 keV	6.4 cm
γ–radiation	1 MeV	65 cm
neutrons	1 MeV	20 cm

Table 22.3: Quality factors W_R for the biological impact of radiation. These values are rough data, they are used in radiation protection.

Radiation type	W_R
X–ray and γ–radiation	1
$β^+$, $β^-$	1
n^0	5 – 10
α	10

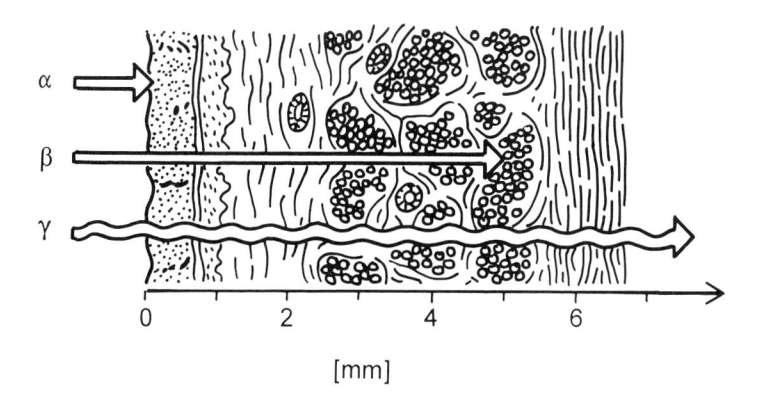

Fig. 22.11: Sketch illustrating the range of different types of radiation at 1 MeV incident energy. α–particles cannot penetrate even the outmost layer of the skin, β–particles reach several millimeters deep into the skin, and γ–rays pass through the entire body.

Table 22.4: Medical impact of various whole body equivalent doses.

Equiv. Dose [Sv]	Pathological diagnosis
1 – 5	Serious temporary alterations of the blood count
4 – 5	50% death rate in 30 days
10 – 50	Vomiting and nausea
50 – 100	Brain and nerve damage, death in 1 week

At this point we should review for a final time the question whether we should embark on a mission to Mars. Certainly, mankind's history proves that we are adventurous enough to do things of this sort. The Spanish–Portuguese explorer Ferdinand Magellan left Spain with 250 men on September 20, 1519, to sail around the Earth for the first time. On September 6, 1522, the surviving crew of 18 returned. Magellan himself was killed more than a year earlier in the Philippines. Thus, the first voyage around the Earth took more than a 100 days longer than the round trip to Mars would take!

Weightlessness and its effect on the bone density requires intensive exercise during space travel. This requires some discipline, particularly when considering travelling to Mars where a continuous radio contact with mission control is not possible; a signal delay of up to ten minutes between Earth and Mars prohibits conversations. However, space tourism to Mars is not anticipated in the near future, and a professional astronaut can be expected to stick to a daily exercise routine.

X–ray and particle radiation are the most serious issue. Even when allowing only a short total time of the mission to be spent on EVAs, electrically neutral radiation, such as neutrons and γ–rays can harm astronauts also within the spacecraft. During the moon–landing missions in the 1960s NASA simply gambled that no rise in the sun's activity would occur during the short missions. That is not a sufficient approach for a multi–year mission to Mars. The spacecraft design must include additional protection for the astronauts during a peak activity period of the sun.

But, like in all other endeavors of mankind, we have to keep in mind that it is not the elements which are our greatest enemy, it is man himself. In the words of the Russian cosmonaut Valery Ryumin, the main challenge in long–distance space travel is that "all the conditions necessary for murder are met if you shut any two men in a cabin and leave them together for two months."

22.6. Applications of radioactivity

Nuclear processes have widespread applications in chemistry, biology and medicine. We conclude the chapter by studying three representative examples.

22.6.1. Radioactive markers in chemistry

Mass spectrometers (see section 20.4) are capable of separating identical fragments of organic molecules when they are marked with isotopes, e.g. a fragment in which a ^{12}C atom is replaced by a ^{14}C isotope is heavier by two mass units. Carbon is usually introduced into the molecules through synthesis from $Ba\,^{14}CO_3$. A well–established example is the determination of the mechanism of the *Claisen reaction* in Fig. 22.12, where isotope marking showed where a particular carbon atom moved in an aromatic rearrangement. Note that the isotope marked carbon is not at the end of the ligand chain after the reaction took place.

22.6.2. Diagnostic nuclear medicine with tracers

A wide range of radioactive isotopes is used in medical diagnosis. An example is shown in Fig. 22.13. The top of the figure shows a thyroid gland ultrasound diagnosed as enlarged on the patient's left side. A normal thyroid gland weighs 20 g. It produces two hormones, an amount of 100 μg/day of thyroxine (tetraiodothyronine T_4) and 10 μg/day triiodothyronine T_3. Various organs are able to transform T_4 into T_3, which increases the metabolic rate.

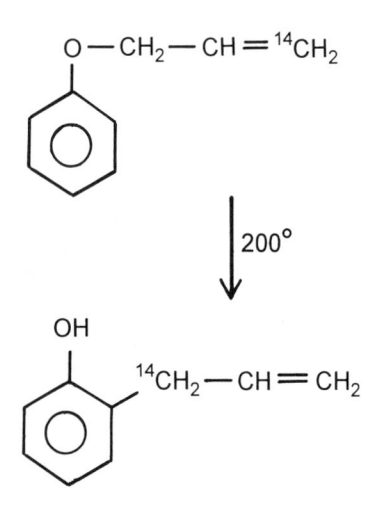

Fig. 22.12: Claisen reaction with the terminal carbon atom radioactively marked.

decay with a half–life of $T_{1/2}$ = 8.04 days.

If the radiological image resembles frame (a) in Fig. 22.13, a thyroid overproduction in the enlarged part of the thyroid is diagnosed; if the image resembles frame (b) a reduced absorption of iodine in the enlarged part of the thyroid is diagnosed which hints toward the possibility of thyroid cancer.

===

Example 22.4

In an accident a person ingests an amount of 0.05 MBq of a radioactive isotope which releases 1.5 MeV per decay. Assume that the radioactive element distributes uniformly throughout the person's body, with the person's mass m = 75 kg. The half–life of the radioactive element is 30 years. Calculate
(a) the energy dose rate in unit [Gy/s] of the initially ingested radioactive element, and
(b) the whole body energy dose in unit [Gy] after a period of 30 years.

Solution part (a): The energy released by the ingested amount of the radioactive isotope per second is calculated from the number of decays (given in MBq) and the energy released per decay event:

$$\frac{\Delta E}{\Delta t} = 5 \times 10^4 \left[\frac{decays}{s}\right] 1.5 \times 10^6 \left[\frac{eV}{decay}\right] \quad (26)$$
$$= 7.5 \times 10^{10} \frac{eV}{s} = 1.2 \times 10^{-8} \frac{J}{s}$$

in which we converted the energy 1.0 eV = 1.6×10^{-19} J. With the result in Eq. (26) we calculate the initial dose rate by dividing through the mass of the person:

$$\frac{1}{m}\frac{\Delta E}{\Delta t} = \frac{1.2 \times 10^{-8}\left[\frac{J}{s}\right]}{75[kg]} = 1.6 \times 10^{-10} \frac{Gy}{s} \quad (27)$$

Solution part (b): We use the same approach as in Example 22.3. The decay constant λ is obtained from Eq. (20):

$$\lambda = \frac{\ln 2}{T_{1/2}} = \frac{0.693}{9.46 \times 10^8 \, s} = 7.3 \times 10^{-10} \, Hz \quad (28)$$

With the decay constant, we calculate the initial number

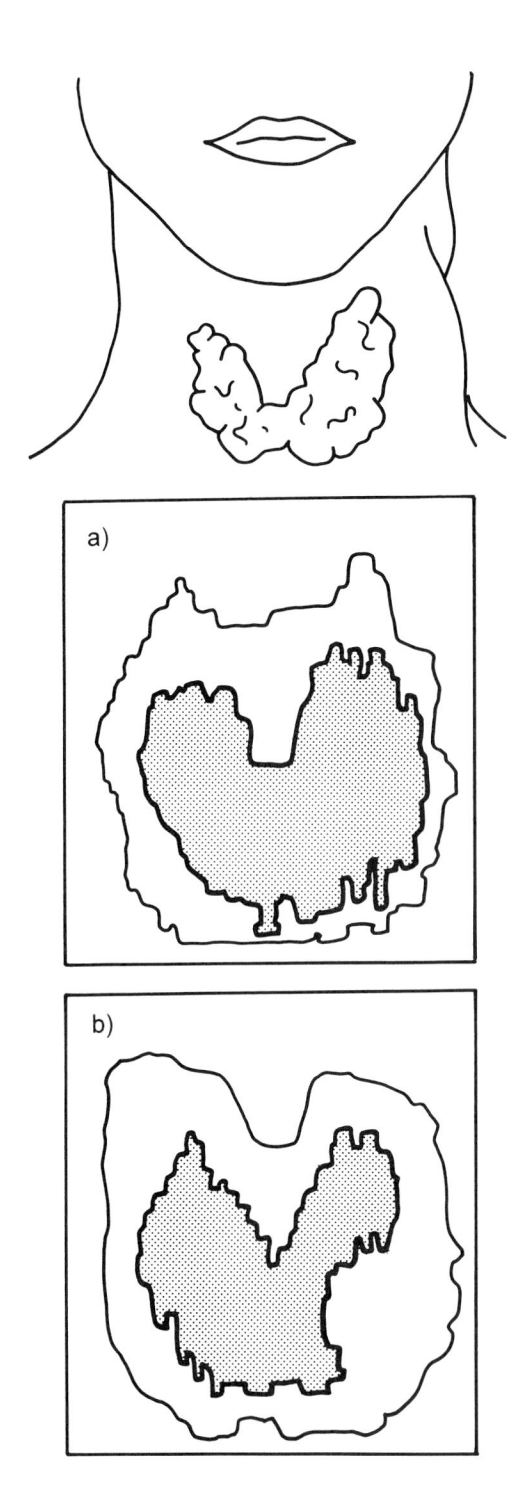

Fig. 22.13: A patient with an enlarged thyroid is given an oral dose of a ^{131}I containing drug. (a) and (b) show two possible outcomes of the radio–tracer diagnosis: in (a), the increased radiation from the enlarged part of the thyroid indicates an overproduction, and in (b), the lack of iodine absorption may indicate cancer.

Frames (a) and (b) of Fig. 22.13 show two possible results of a tracer study in nuclear medicine. This technique is based on the selective absorption of iodine in the thyroid gland. The patient is given orally a radioactive iodine sample containing ^{131}I. ^{131}I undergoes a β^-–

of radioactive nuclei in the ingested sample, using the initial activity A_0 in Eq. (15):

$$N_0 = \frac{A_0}{\lambda} = \frac{5 \times 10^4 [Bq]}{7.3 \times 10^{-10} [Hz]} \quad (29)$$

$$\Rightarrow N_0 = 6.85 \times 10^{13} \text{ particles}$$

After 30 years, which is the half–life of the radioactive particles in the sample, 50 % of the isotope material found in Eq. (29) have decayed. The total energy released into the person's body is obtained by multiplying this number with the energy released in every decay event (the same energy conversion is used as above):

$$E_{total} = \frac{1}{2} \cdot 6.85 \times 10^{13} [decays] \cdot \ldots$$

$$\ldots \cdot 1.5 \times 10^6 \left[\frac{eV}{decay}\right] 1.6 \cdot 10^{-19} \left[\frac{J}{eV}\right] \quad (30)$$

which yields:

$$E_{total} = 8.2 \, J \quad (31)$$

The whole body energy dose is obtained by dividing the result in Eq. (31) by the mass of the person, resulting in a whole body energy dose of 0.11 Gy. This corresponds to 0.1 – 1.0 Sv, depending on the type of radiation emitted. Based on Table 22.4, we would judge the accident as serious, but not severe.

22.6.3. Carbon–dating with ^{14}C

When a radioactive isotope has been decaying up to ten times its half–life, it is reasonably easy for us to determine the time interval over which it has been decaying if we have an indication of its initial activity. A short half–life (hours to months) makes a radioisotope useful in nuclear medicine or for marking of chemical compounds. A half–life of the order of millions of years enables us to measure the age of geological events.

^{14}C with $T_{1/2}$ = 5370 years is used to analyze the age of biological tissues up to 50,000 years old. This is a rather accurate method for determining the time of death of the organism which contained the tissue due to the way ^{14}C is produced and stored in the biosphere.

The primary cosmic rays continuously interact with the upper layers of the atmosphere and create a secondary shower of particles, which include short–lived neutrons. These neutrons can undergo a nuclear reaction with the most abundant nitrogen isotope in the atmosphere, ^{14}N. If a ^{14}N nucleus captures a neutron it becomes unstable and decays into a proton and a ^{14}C nucleus. The production rate of ^{14}C due to cosmic rays varies little, and is given as 2.4 ^{14}C/cm²s.

The nuclear reaction process with the secondary cosmic neutron releases enough energy to break the chemical bond of the atmospheric nitrogen molecule. The newly formed ^{14}C atom is highly reactive and forms carbon–dioxide with oxygen in the air:

$$^{14}C + O_2 \rightarrow \, ^{14}CO_2 \quad (32)$$

All living organisms participate in a continuous exchange of carbon–containing molecules within the biosphere and with the carbon–dioxide in the atmosphere through their metabolism. This leads to a steady–state amount of ^{14}C in a living body, characterized by a decay rate of 16.1 decays per minute and gram of carbon in the organism.

When an organism dies, its metabolism ceases. Thereafter no more ^{14}C is incorporated in the organism's remains, but the ^{14}C present at the time of death decays. This allows us to determine the age of biological samples, including wood, skin, hair, linen and parchment, by using Eqs. (15) to (20). Famous examples include carbon–dating of wood from the Death ship of the Egyptian king Sesostris III, who died about 3800 years ago, the scrolls at Qumram near the Dead Sea which are more than 1900 years old, and the Shroud of Turin (said to be the burial shroud of Jesus), which was made in AD 1320 (± 60 years).

The ^{14}C dating method is slightly less reliable than a simple half–life measurement. The main question is to what extent the cosmic ray intensity, and thus, ^{14}C production may have varied in the past 50,000 years. A method of calibrating the ^{14}C–measured age of wood by independently counting the rings in old trees is illustrated in Fig. 22.14. The averaged data (solid line) show variations as large as 900 years, which is attributed to changes in the geomagnetic field over the past 8000 years. Using ^{14}C methods for very recent samples is only possible to a limited extent due to two significant effects of human interference: the intensive burning of fossil fuels (lowering the ^{14}C concentration in the active biosphere) and the frequent test detonations of atomic and hydrogen bombs in the atmosphere in the 1950s and 1960s, which increased the ^{14}C concentration in the biosphere.

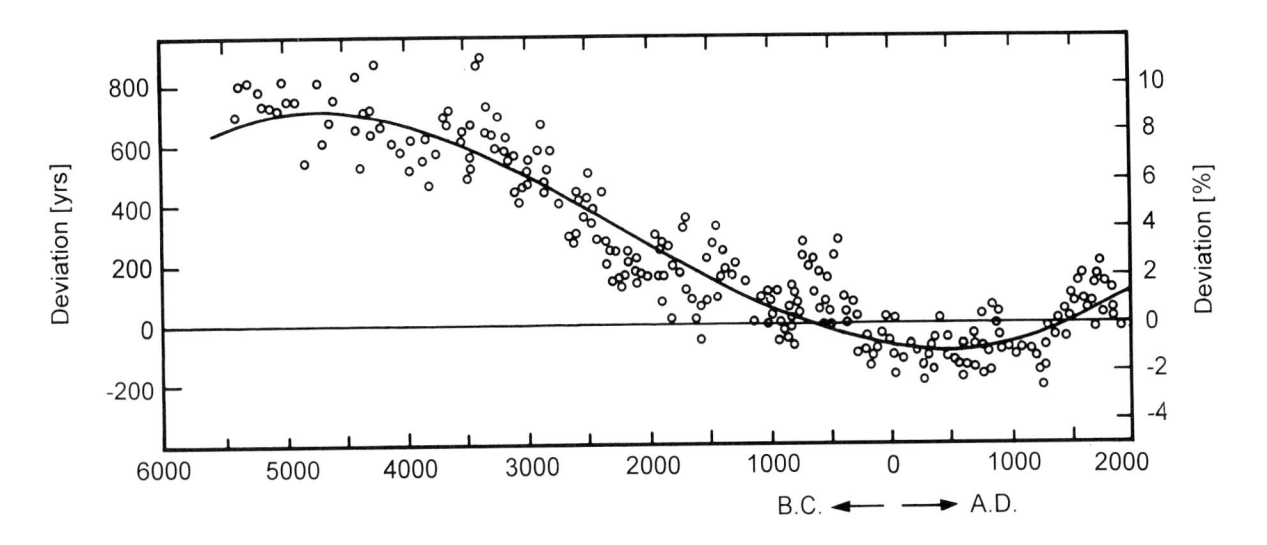

Fig. 22.14: Calibration of the carbon–dating technique. Each open circle corresponds to a wood sample which has been dated by the ^{14}C method and by counting tree rings. The deviations, shown on the ordinate, are caused by variations of the environmental production of ^{14}C due to nuclear reactions between neutrons from the secondary cosmic rays and atmospheric nitrogen nuclei. The calibrated curve allows dating of biological samples as old as 50,000 years.

22.7. Problems

P–22.1
Using the approach taken in Example 22.1, estimate the energy of K_α X–rays emitted from a gold anode.

P–22.2
The K–shell ionization energy of Cu is 8980 eV and the L–shell ionization energy is 950 eV. Determine the wavelength of the K_α X–rays emission of Cu.

P–22.3
The nucleus of the deuterium atom consists of one proton and one neutron. What is the binding energy of this nucleus if the mass of the deuterium nucleus is given as 2.014102 u?

P–22.4
A living organism has 16.1 ± 0.1 ^{14}C decays per minute and per gram carbon. The wood found in the Egyptian king Sneferu's grave measured 8.5 ± 0.2 decays/(min g). When was the tree cut from which this wood came?

P–22.5
Nuclear waste from power plants may contain ^{239}Pu, a plutonium isotope with a half–life of 24,000 years. How long does it take for the stored waste to decay to 10 % of its current activity level?

P–22.6
A small radioactive ^{210}Po source of 0.05 MBq is placed on a biological sample. This polonium isotope emits α–particles of 5.4 MeV. The range of the α–particles in the sample is 20 μm. What is the energy dose rate (per hour) absorbed by the biological sample?
Hint: Treat the source as a point source and use the density of water for the density of the sample.

P–22.7
A tracer study drug contains 11 kBq of a technetium isotope, ^{99}Tc, which has a half–life of 363 minutes. Technetium can be used as a substitute for ^{131}I in tracer studies of the thyroid gland. What is the activity of the drug when it is used after 3 hours?

Summary

Definitions:
● Notation of nuclei:
(i) mass number A: number of nucleons in nucleus,
(ii) atomic number Z: number of protons in nucleus,
(iii) number of neutrons, N with A = Z + N

$$^{A}_{Z}X \quad e.g.: \quad ^{12}_{6}C, \quad ^{16}_{8}O$$

- Decay processes:

$$\alpha\text{--decay}: \quad {}^{A}_{Z}X \rightarrow {}^{A-4}_{Z-2}Y + {}^{4}_{2}He$$
$$\beta^{+}\text{--decay}: \quad {}^{A}_{Z}X \rightarrow {}^{A}_{Z-1}Y + e^{+}$$
$$\beta^{-}\text{--decay}: \quad {}^{A}_{Z}X \rightarrow {}^{A}_{Z+1}Y + e^{-}$$

Units:
- Exposure dose: [R] (Röntgen) with

$$1\ [R] = 2.08 \times 10^{9}\ \frac{ion\ pairs}{cm^{3}}$$

$$1\ [R] = 2.58 \times 10^{-4}\ \frac{Cb}{kg}$$

- Energy dose: [Gy] (Gray) with 1Gy = 1 J/kg.
Non–standard unit [rad]: 1 rad = 0.01 Gy
- Equivalent dose: [Sv] (Sievert).

$$Equiv.Dose\ [Sv] = W_{R} \cdot Ener.Dose\ [Gy]$$

W_{R} is the quality factor.
- Activity: [Bq] (Becquerel) with 1 Bq = 1 decay/s.

Laws:
- Radioactive decay law:
(i) for activity A:

$$A = -\frac{\Delta N}{\Delta t} = \lambda\ N$$

λ [1/s] is decay constant.
(ii) for number of radioactive nuclei in sample, N:

$$N(t) = N_{0}\ e^{-\lambda t}$$

N_{0} is number of radioactive nuclei at time t = 0.
- Mean life–time: $T_{mean} = \lambda^{-1}$
- Half–life $T_{1/2}$: time after which 50 % of initial radioactive nuclei have decayed.

$$T_{1/2} = \frac{\ln 2}{\lambda}$$

$$T_{mean} = \frac{1}{\lambda} = 1.44\ T_{1/2}$$

Chapter XXIII

Magnetic Resonance Imaging

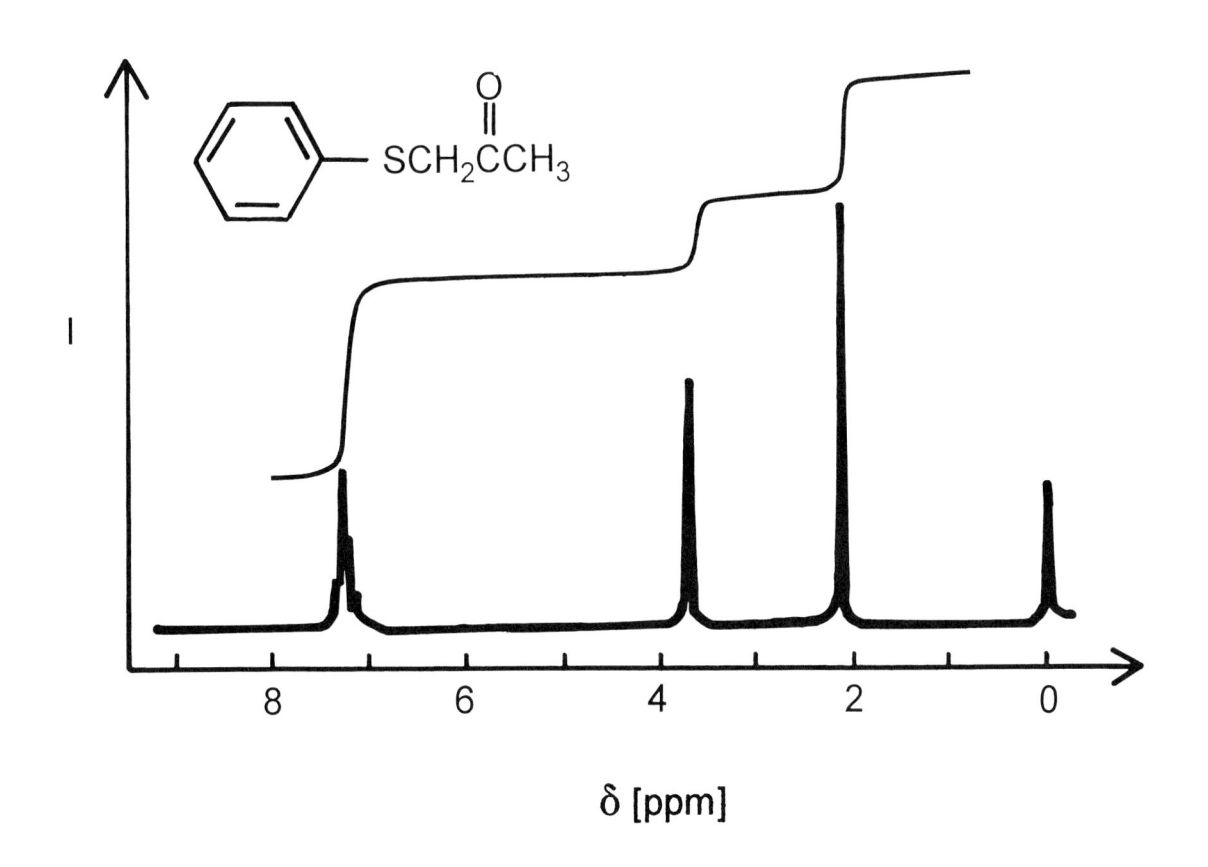

Nuclear spin and magnetic resonance

MAGNETIC RESONANCE IMAGING
NUCLEAR SPIN AND MAGNETIC RESONANCE

Many state–of–the–art medical diagnosis methods rely heavily on physical principles. This is particularly evident for Magnetic Resonance Imaging where atomic and nuclear physics concepts, such as spins and spin coupling, are paired with classical concepts from electromagnetism and thermodynamics.

The previous twenty–two chapters presented the concepts of physics as a cornerstone of physiology and biology. With the basic physical principles developed, we are now able to study all physiological phenomena in a healthy living organism and we are able to understand the impact of environmental conditions on individuals as well as entire species during their evolution.

Physics concepts play an equally pivotal role in human and veterinarian medicine in two ways:
(I) Physics allows us to establish sickness– and accident–related alterations in human and animal physiology. We referred to such examples several times, e.g. when describing edemas in Chapter 12.
(II) Physics allows us to understand the principles and applications of equipment and techniques used in the medical field, ranging from research tools, such as electrophoresis used to separate proteins in biochemistry laboratories, to advanced diagnostic and therapeutic methods, such as computer tomography used to obtain spatially resolved X–ray maps of a patient.

The current chapter presents an example of the latter role of physics in medicine: magnetic resonance imaging (MRI) is used to illustrate how a combination of several fundamental physics concepts is required to take advantage of an advanced medical technique.

Our approach can be divided in two steps. First, we establish *nuclear magnetic resonance* (NMR). As the technical term implies, the observation is based (i) on the properties of atomic nuclei, (ii) the use of magnetic fields and (iii) a resonance phenomenon. These three concepts combine topics we discussed in Chapter 16 (resonance), Chapter 19 (magnetism), Chapter 20 (magnetism and angular momentum), and Chapter 22 (nuclear properties). From the NMR principle, it is a small step to its use in an imaging mode, although the actual performance of the imaging and the interpretation of the images is quite challenging in its own right.

A second issue we must address is the question of medically relevant information contained in an NMR signal. The most frequent use of the technique is to detect and locate tumors in the body of a patient. Thus, the NMR signal from a tumorous cell must differ from the NMR signal from a healthy cell. This discussion will allow us to distinguish the medical use of NMR.

The ultimate purpose of this last chapter is, however, to stimulate readers to apply the same physics–based analytical approach to the wide range of medical research, diagnosis and therapeutic techniques they will encounter during their further course of study or professional career.

23.1. The spin

23.1.1. Classical concept of spin

We studied physical phenomena associated with the rotational motion of objects in section 20.2. The discussion in that section focussed primarily on the orbiting of a satellite in a gravitational force field, e.g., the orbiting of the moon or the International Space Station about the Earth, or the rotation of an electron about the nucleus in the electric field of a hydrogen atom. For the circular motion, we introduced a new quantity in Eq. (21.12), called the angular momentum L:

$$L = p\, r\, \sin\phi = m v\, r\, \sin\phi \quad (1)$$

in which p = mv is the linear momentum of the object, r is the distance from the axis of the circular motion and ϕ is the angle between the momentum vector and the radius vector, $\phi = \sphericalangle(\mathbf{p}, \mathbf{r})$. The angular momentum of a system is conserved when no external net torque acts on it.

We want to investigate the system Earth/moon a little bit further with respect to the conservation of angular momentum. In this system, we find two contributions to the total angular momentum. The first is due to the orbiting of the moon about the Earth. The distance from the Earth to the moon is given as r = 384,000 km (a distance which light travels in about 1 second). The speed of the moon along its orbit is obtained from the radius of the orbit and the time for a complete revolution; the circumference given as $2\pi r$ and the period given as 28 days (which we therefore call a month). Treating the moon as a point mass, which in this context is a reasonable approximation, provides us with the moon's contribution to the total angular momentum of the Earth/moon system:

$$L_{moon} = m_{moon} \frac{2\pi r}{T} r = m_{moon} \frac{2\pi r^2}{T} \quad (2)$$

$$= 7.3 \times 10^{22} [kg] \frac{2\pi (3.84 \times 10^8 [m])^2}{2.42 \times 10^6 [s]}$$

which yields:

$$L_{moon} = 2.8 \times 10^{34} \frac{kg\ m^2}{s} \quad (3)$$

A second contribution to the angular momentum is due to the rotation of the Earth itself. Since the Earth rotates about its own axis, this does not lead to a motion of the Earth along an orbit. To distinguish this rotation from the rotation of the moon about the Earth, we call a rotation of a body about its own axis a *spin*. Quantitatively, the term spin stands for the angular momentum of this motion, with the same unit as the angular momentum, i.e., [kg m²/s] = [Js]. The spin of the Earth would not contribute to the angular momentum if we could neglect the Earth's radius and treat the Earth as a point mass. Remember that we established in Chapters 2 and 3 that point masses do not rotate, or that their rotation can be neglected for all other considerations. However, we know that the Earth is not a point, but is an extended (nearly spherical) body with a radius of 6370 km. Thus, would an assumption that the Earth is a point mass be justified? The way to answer this question is to determine the contribution of the Earth's spin to the total angular momentum of the Earth/moon system and see whether we can indeed neglect this contribution.

But how do we calculate the contribution of a spin to the angular momentum? The best approach is to imagine the Earth cut into a very large number of small segments, of which we can treat each as if it were a point mass. The angular momentum of the Earth is then the sum of the contributions of all segments:

$$L_{Earth} = \sum_i m_i v_i r_i \quad (4)$$

in which m_i is the mass, v_i is the velocity and r_i is the distance from the axis of the *i*-th segment. Since the velocity and the position vectors are perpendicular to each other for each segment, $\sin\phi_i = 1$ for all values of index i. This equation can be simplified by replacing the velocity by the angular frequency (compare Eqs. (20.10) and (20.12)):

$$\omega = \frac{v_i}{r_i} \quad (5)$$

This is a simplification since various segments have different speeds, but all have the same angular frequency with $\omega = 2\pi/T$ and the period T equal to 24 hours for planet Earth. Thus, ω has no index i in Eq. (5), and Eq. (4) can be rewritten in the form:

$$L_{Earth} = \omega \sum_i m_i r_i^2 \equiv \omega \Theta \quad (6)$$

in which the sum has been replaced by Θ, which is called the *moment of inertia*.

The formula for the moment of inertia is similar to Eq. (4.25) for the center–of–mass: a rigid body is divided into a very large number of segments leading to a sum over the product of the mass and some geometrical properties of the segment. In the case of the center–of–mass, the geometrical term is the distance to a reference point on the rigid body, and in the case of the moment of inertia the geometrical term is the square of the distance to the axis of the rigid body. Like in the case of the center–of–mass, evaluating Θ leads to simple expressions for highly symmetric bodies. If a body is irregular in shape or density, the effort to analyze the sum in Eq. (6) might become extensive. An example of a highly symmetric body for which the sum in Eq. (6) resumes a simple form is a sphere with a uniform density. $\Theta = 0.4MR^2$ follows in this case, with M the total mass of the sphere and R the radius of the sphere. Using this formula for the Earth is only approximately justified as the mass distribution of the Earth is not uniform with a very massive iron core, as shown in Table 20.1.

Assuming a spherical Earth of uniform density, we rewrite Eq. (6) in the form:

$$L_{Earth} = \omega \Theta = \frac{2\pi}{T} \frac{2}{5} m_{Earth} r_{Earth}^2 \quad (7)$$

which leads to:

$$L_{Earth} = \frac{4\pi}{5} \frac{5.98 \times 10^{24}[kg] \, (6.37 \times 10^{6}[m])^2}{8.64 \times 10^{4}[s]} \quad (8)$$

$$\Rightarrow L_{Earth} = 7 \times 10^{33} \frac{kg \, m^2}{s}$$

Comparing Eqs. (3) and (8), we find that the major contribution to the total angular momentum of the Earth/moon system arises from the rotation of the moon, however, 20 % of the total value is attributed to the Earth's spin.

The fact that the Earth's contribution is a non–negligible contribution becomes evident when we study how the length of a day changes in the course of time. Such a change occurs due to a slowing process of the spin of the Earth. The gravitational attraction of the moon on the water of the Earth's oceans causes two tidal domes, one stationary beneath the moon and one on the opposite side. Due to the rotation of the Earth, the two tidal domes move as tidal waves continuously around the planet with a high tide every 6 hours and 12 minutes at any point along the seashore. Every time the tidal waves crash into a continent the Earth's rotation is slowed by a tiny fraction.

The tidal slowing of the Earth's rotation is about 20 ± 5 μs/year. Nevertheless, this effect was already proposed in 1700 by Immanuel Kant, who interpreted data from Edmund Halley (famous for Halley's comet), who in turn had noticed a discrepancy in the historic records of a total eclipse in the year 484 AD. The historic record showed that the total eclipse was seen along the line from the Greek island of Rhodes to Lebanon, but Halley's precise calculations showed that it should have been observed along the line from Lisbon in Portugal to Cyprus. Thus, there had been a small but indisputable slowing of the Earth's spin over the 1200 years from the eclipse to Kant's and Halley's days.

Modern scientific research has revealed direct proof for the tidal slowing of the Earth's spin, in particular in form of annual and daily variations in the deposits of chalk in 300 million year old Devonian coral reefs which indicate that a year then was 400 ± 10 days. Note that there is a discrepancy between the current rate of 0.05 μs/day and the average rate since the Devonian period with 0.07 μs/day. This indicates that the effect depends on the location of the continents, which varies over long periods due to continental drift.

Even though very slowly, the tidal slowing will eventually reduce the contribution of the Earth's spin to the total angular momentum to a negligible amount. To conserve the angular momentum of the Earth/moon system, the moon must pick up the difference. The moon can do this in two ways as seen from Eq. (1): it can increase its distance from the Earth and it can change is orbiting speed. These two developments are not independent, however, but are governed by Johannes Kepler's third law. This law states that the ratio of the cube of a satellite's mean distance, r, to the square of its orbiting period, T, is constant: r^3/T^2 = const. This allows us to determine the final state of motion of the Earth/moon system: its final angular frequency value will be $\omega = 1.33 \times 10^{-6}$ s^{-1}, which corresponds to the length of a day as well as a month, each lasting 56 of our current days; the distance from the Earth to the moon will have increased to 1.56 times the current distance.

A last comment on the issue of spin in the Earth/moon system. You notice that we did not discuss a contribution due to the moon's spin. This is due to the fact that the moon spins very slowly. It takes exactly one month to spin once, which leads to the well–known effect that it is always the same side of the moon which faces Earth. This is not accidentally; the moon's mass is not evenly distributed and, therefore, the heavier end points toward Earth while the lighter end points away from the source of the gravitational attraction.

23.1.2. Nuclear spin

The discussion in the previous section of the concept of spin in the Earth/moon system serves the purpose to establish this concept before applying it to less visible systems, in particular the next system we want to study: the spin of an atomic nucleus. Like the moon in the Earth/moon system, the electrons can be pictured in Bohr's model (see section 21.2) to orbit the nucleus. An angular momentum can be attributed to their motion. At the center of the atom, the nucleus can also be considered to rotate about its own axis. This is again a classical picture, but a useful one as we see below. The rotation of the nucleus leads to a nuclear spin contribution to the total angular momentum of the atom.

At that point, however, the similarities to the Earth/moon system end:

(I) Different from the moon, the orbiting electrons each carry a spin of their own. We already used this fact in Chapter 21 implicitly when we allowed two electrons (differing only in their spin–quantum number) to fill each of the orbitals identified in Table 21.2 to describe all elements in the periodic table. For this reason, the Pauli principle was written in section 21.3 such that any two electrons in the same atom must differ in at least one of four quantum numbers; either one of the three listed in Table 21.2 or the spin–quantum number. Helium, as an example, has two electrons which have the same three quantum numbers as found in Table 21.2, i.e., $n = 1$, $l = 0$, $m_l = 0$, but they do not violate Pauli's principle since they differ in their spin value m_s. This can be pictured in a classical model: one electron spins in the direction East to West, the other West to East. Since we want to develop the basic physical principles for MRI in this section, the electron spin is not discussed further. Note, however, that there are interesting experimental methods based on the measurement of effects due to the electron spin. In particular, electron spin resonance (ESR) is used to identify unpaired electrons, e.g. in electrically neutral molecules called *radicals*.

(II) No tidal waves or any other mechanism exists to allow the electrons to interfere with the spin of the nucleus. With no mechanism in place to exert a torque on the nucleus, its spin is constant. Therefore, the nuclear spin allows us to identify a particular nucleus in the same fashion as the mass and the charge of the nucleus.

(III) The underlying forces for the Earth/moon and atomic system are different. While gravity causes the moon and Earth to constantly fall toward each other, it is the electric force which holds an atom together. This leads to additional effects which we discuss in this section, such as a magnetic dipole moment of the nucleus.

(IV) Electrons and nuclei are much smaller than the moon and the Earth. In Chapter 21 we found that we must ultimately use quantum–mechanical models to describe physical properties at the atomic level properly. This remains true in the current discussion: nuclear spins have features which classical spin systems do not have. Of these we have to consider the quantization of the spin.

The spins of a nucleus can only be zero or an integer multiple of the value $h/4\pi = \hbar/2$ in which h is Planck's constant with unit [Js]. The values for various important nuclei are shown in Table 23.1. Nuclei with a zero spin cannot be used for nuclear magnetic resonance techniques such as MRI. Therefore, of the most common elements in bio–organic molecules, only hydrogen is sensitive to the process discussed in this section.

Table 23.1: Nuclear spin S for selected elementary particles and atomic nuclei.

Nucleus	Spin	Nucleus	Spin
neutron	½ℏ	proton (^{1}H)	½ℏ
deuteron (^{2}H)	ℏ	α (^{4}He)	0
^{12}C	0	^{13}C	½ℏ
^{14}N	ℏ	^{16}O	0
^{19}F	½ℏ	^{31}P	½ℏ

23.2. Spins in a magnetic field

23.2.1. Magnetic dipole moment of nuclei

The spin is not observed directly, but indirectly due to a magnetic dipole moment of the nucleus which is a consequence of the presence of the spin.

A spin leads to a magnetic dipole because the nucleus is not electrically neutral. We saw in Chapter 21 that the nucleus contains neutrons and protons, while the electrical neutrality of an atom follows from the presence of a number of electrons in the shell, matching the number of protons in the nucleus. When a charged particle spins about its axis, the individual charges describe a circular motion, i.e., they form an electric current loop. How this current loop causes a magnetic dipole moment is shown in analogy to the electric case we discussed in Chapter 9.

In electricity we started with the concept of a separate charge. The electric force was defined as the product of the charge and the electric field present at the position of the charge. In turn, this allowed us to define the electric field as the electric force per unit charge:

$$F_{Coulomb} = qE \quad \Rightarrow \quad E = \frac{F_{Coulomb}}{q} \qquad (9)$$

The same approach cannot be taken to define a magnetic field, because there are no separate magnetic charges (magnetic monopoles).

Thus, to develop an analogy to electricity, we need to look at the next simplest case, which is the electric dipole which has two equal but opposite charges with a separation distance d. The electric dipole was introduced in section 9.4, where we found that the combination of charge q and distance d characterized the dipole in the form given in Eq. (9.30):

$$\mu_{el} = q\, d \quad [Cb\ m] \qquad (10)$$

in which μ_{el} is called the *electric dipole moment*. The electric dipole moment can be interpreted as a vector pointing in the direction of the line connecting the two charges, in which case d is written as a position vector: $\mu_{el} = q\, \mathbf{d}$. For such an electric dipole the electric field can be calculated by extending calculations such as those which led to Eq. (9.29). This results in the electric field of an electric dipole shown in Fig. 23.1: the field vector points at each position toward the negative charge (as defined in Fig. 9.12) and the lines of the electric field form the unique structure of the field shown in the right sketch of the figure. Thus, the electric field of a dipole

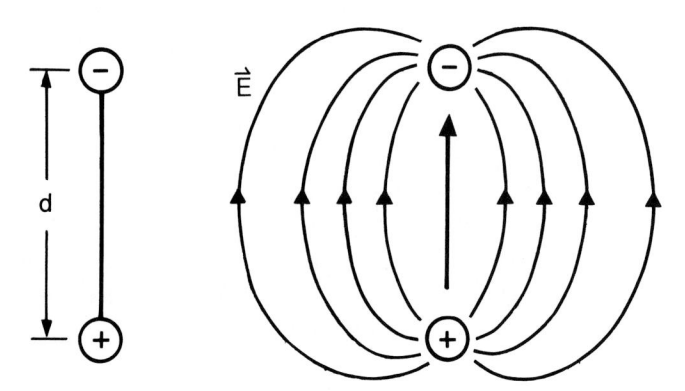

Fig. 23.1: Electric field of an electric dipole.

Fig. 23.2: Magnetic field (a) of a bar magnet and (b) of a circular current loop.

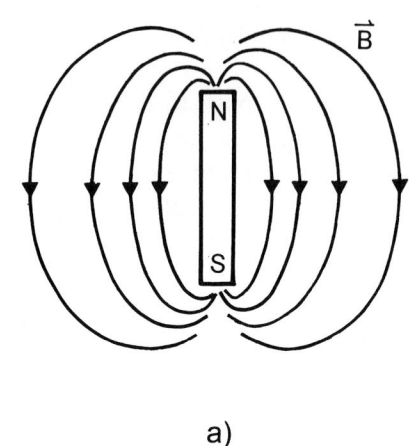

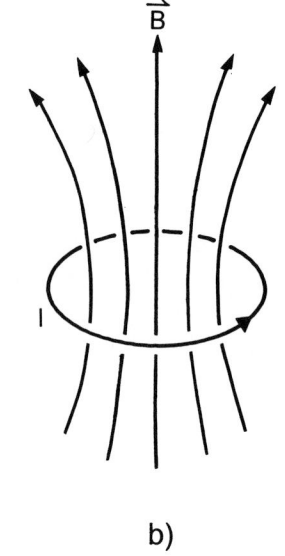

is anisotropic, i.e., not varying in the same fashion in each possible direction away from the dipole. Perpendicular to the dipole, a larger value of the electric field is measured at a given distance than in any other direction.

We have seen similarly shaped magnetic fields in Chapters 19 and 20. In Fig. 20.19, the magnetic field of planet Earth is illustrated. The similarity of the field to the electric field lines in Fig. 23.1 led to the (oversimplifying) model of the Earth to be a bar magnet. The magnetic field of a bar magnet is shown in Fig. 23.2(a). The sketch illustrates why the magnetic field in this case is equivalent to the electric field of a dipole: a bar magnet consists of a north pole and a south pole at a fixed distance d from each other, i.e., a structure very similar to the two separated charges of an electric dipole.

A second magnetic field of the same shape is found in Fig. 19.12, showing a solenoid arrangement. Allowing a circular current to flow in a fixed loop resembles the solenoid closely. This is illustrated in Fig. 23.2(b) where the magnetic field of a single, circular current is shown.

The similarities of the magnetic field with the electric field of an electric dipole allows us to identify the bar magnet or the circular current as a magnetic dipole. In analogy to the electric case, a *magnetic dipole moment* is identified. For the current loop, the current I replaces the charges of the electric case, and the area A (including the normal vector for orientation) replaces the distance vector:

$$\mu_{mag} = I\,A\,n^0 \qquad (11)$$

The area A is defined as the area enclosed by the current loop. A current loop is a good model for the spinning nucleus in which protons describe circular paths around the axis of the spin. The current for a spinning nucleus is calculated from the charge and the speed of the charge along its orbiting path.

With the electric and magnetic dipoles defined, we can establish what interaction we obtain between a dipole and an external field. We develop this concept again for the electric and magnetic cases in analogy.

A dipole represents an extended body and not a point mass. An external field causes a force acting on the dipole. We learned in Chapter 4 that a force can act in two different ways on an extended body, either causing a linear acceleration or causing a rotation. The latter case occurs when the external force does not act in the direction of the axis of the extended body, causing a torque.

The electric and magnetic cases allow us, therefore, to establish a torque on the dipole when the external field and the axis of the dipole are not parallel. This is illustrated in Fig. 23.3. In part (a) of the figure an electric dipole is shown with an external electric field acting

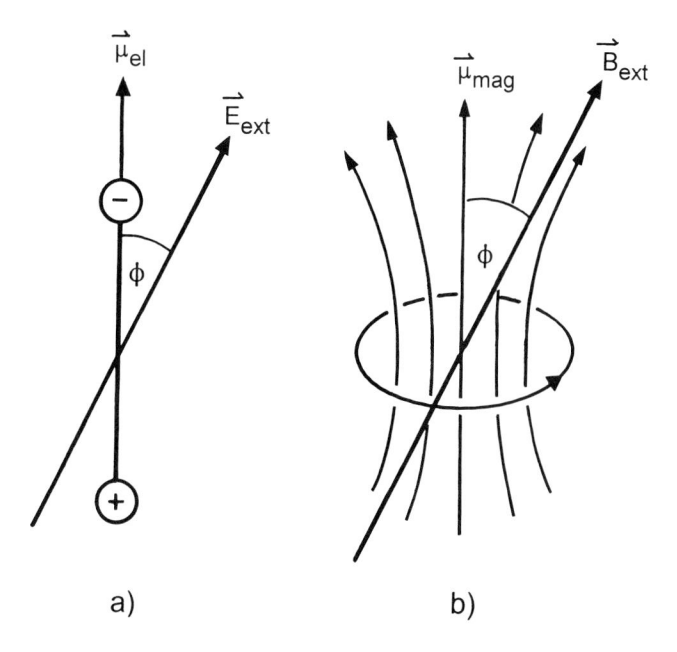

Fig. 23.3: (a) Electric dipole moment, oriented with an angle φ relative to an external electric field. (b) Magnetic dipole moment of a current loop, oriented with an angle φ relative to an external magnetic field.

on the dipole such that the dipole vector and the electric field vector form an angle φ. With the torque, the dipole moment and the electric field all representing vectors, a proper formulation of the relation of these three quantities is again based on the vector product concept we do not introduce in this textbook. We can write the magnitude of the torque in analogy to the discussion of the mechanical case in section 4.2:

$$\tau = \mu_{el} E_{ext} \sin\phi = q\, d\, E_{ext} \sin\phi \quad (12)$$

Thus, the torque is zero when $\phi = 0^0$, i.e., when the dipole is fully aligned with the external electric field. For any other orientation of the dipole, the net torque causes a rotation of the dipole until it is aligned with the external field. This effect for example led to the very large capacitance values for polar molecules in Table 13.3, such as water.

The magnetic case is analogously discussed in Fig. 23.3(b). A current loop is shown which causes a magnetic dipole moment as quantified in Eq. (11). An external magnetic field (for example caused by a horse–shoe magnet) acts under an angle φ on the magnetic dipole. The torque is again a vector quantity, for which we quantify its magnitude only:

$$\tau = \mu_{mag} B_{ext} \sin\phi = I\, A\, B_{ext} \sin\phi \quad (13)$$

The torque disappears when the external magnetic field and the normal vector, representing the area enclosed by the loop, are parallel, i.e., $\phi = 0^0$. Thus, like we saw for water molecules which align themselves with the external electric field, we expect magnetic dipoles (be it small iron pieces like in a compass or be it small circular current loops like atomic nuclei) to align with the external magnetic field.

Small bar magnets succeed in aligning with the external field when they are mobile. This effect is observed in volcanic lava, where small crystallites with a magnetic dipole moment are frozen in alignment with the Earth's magnetic field. Since the Earth's magnetic field changes its North–South polarity once in a while, associating volcanic ash layers with fossil finds allows a rough dating of the latter. This method was used to independently confirm radioisotope dating of the Australophithecus afarensis (Lucy) fossil, which we discussed in section 4.5.

The magnetic dipole moments of atomic nuclei with a spin also align in external magnetic fields. This is illustrated in Fig. 23.4 for hydrogen atoms. Note that part (b) of the figure shows, however, that two orientations occur: one with parallel and one with anti–parallel alignment. The sketch of Fig. 23.4 oversimplifies the situation. The actual orientations of the magnetic dipole

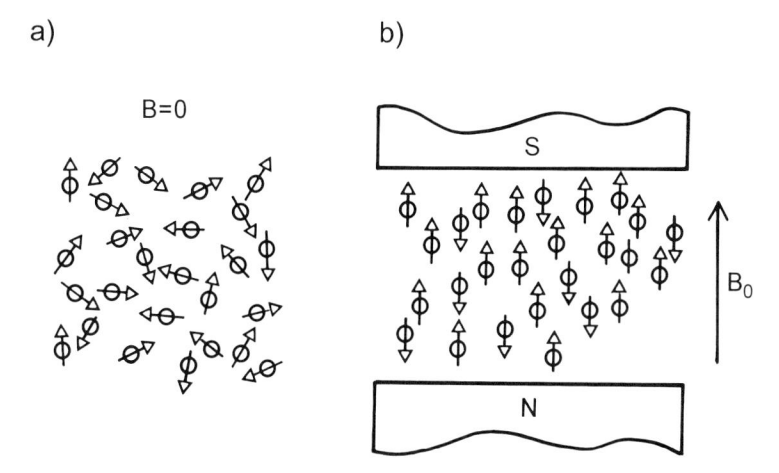

Fig. 23.4: Sketch of the alignment of the magnetic dipole moments of a sample in an external magnetic field.

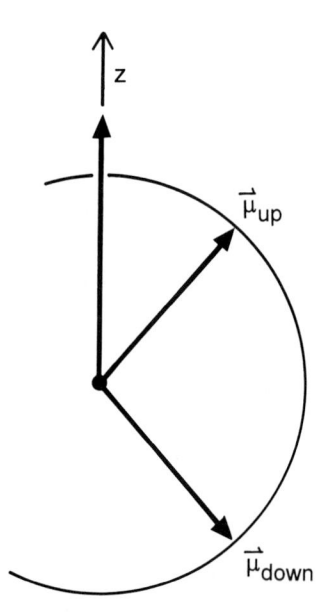

Fig. 23.5: Quantum–mechanically allowed orientations of a spin ½ ℏ nucleus with an external magnetic field, which is oriented in the positive z–direction.

moment for a nucleus with spin of ½ℏ with respect to an external magnetic field along the z–axis are shown in Fig. 23.5; one orientation has a z–component parallel to the magnetic field and the other orientation has a z–component anti–parallel to the magnetic field.

Thus, the orientation of an atomic nucleus differs from the orientation of the magnetic crystallites in the volcanic ash. For the atomic nuclei, the orientation is a quantum–mechanical effect. That means, for a nucleus with spin of ½ ℏ there are only two orientations possible, as shown in Fig. 23.5; any other orientation is not allowed, and therefore, can not be observed!

23.2.2. Experiment by Stern and Gerlach

In 1922, Otto Stern and Walther Gerlach proved experimentally that the orientation of the spin is quantized in a magnetic field. Different from our discussion above, however, the experiment established the atomic spin, not the nuclear spin. The experiment is shown in Fig. 23.6. It consists of a non–uniform horse–shoe magnet and a vacuum chamber. Silver metal is evaporated thermally from a crucible in the vacuum system. An atomic silver beam is selected with collimators in the direction of the gap of the magnet. In this set–up the atomic beam passes through the magnetic poles perpendicularly to the magnetic field lines. Since silver atoms have a spin of ½ ℏ due to an unpaired electron in the outer shell, two orientations are possible in the external magnetic field, one parallel and one anti–parallel to the field. A force is exerted on the atom due to the interaction between the magnetic dipole moment and the magnetic field, with the two orientations leading to a splitting of the beam.

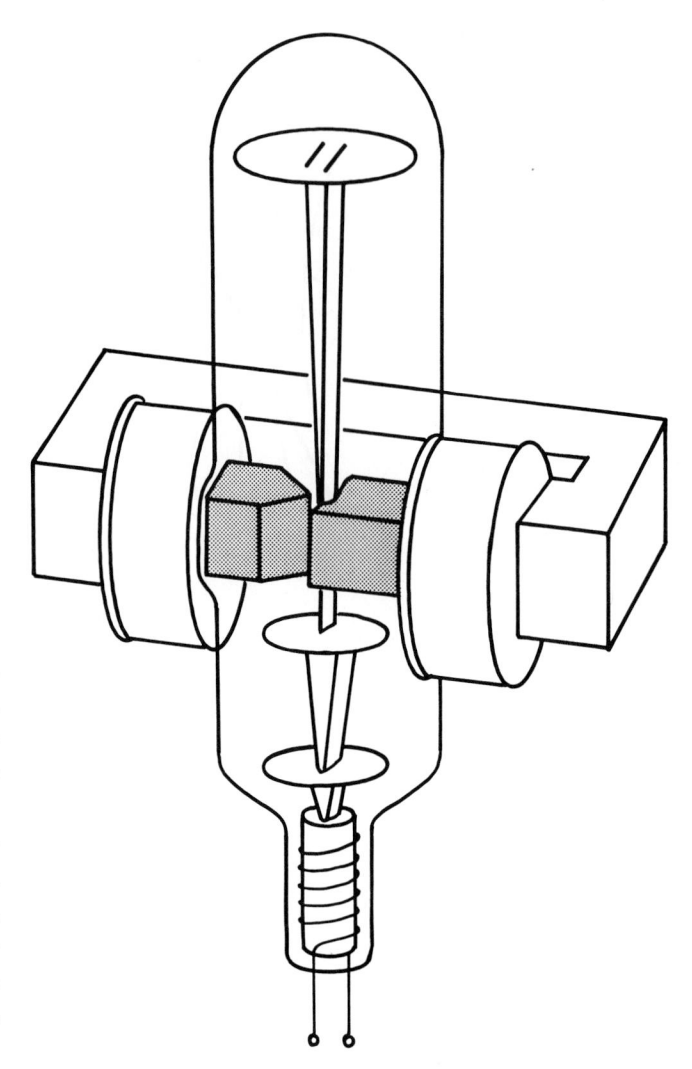

Fig. 23.6: Set–up of the experiment by Stern and Gerlach. An atomic silver beam travels in vacuum. After passing a non–uniform magnetic field the beam is split due to the atomic spin.

The result of the measured intensity of the silver atomic beam as a function of position on the screen is shown in Fig. 23.7, with the solid line representing the result with the magnetic field and the dashed line representing the result without the magnetic field. The two peaks of the solid line are not perfectly separated. This is due to the thermal energy of the evaporated silver atoms which have a broad Maxwell–Boltzmann velocity distribution (see Fig. 6.16).

On closer inspection, it is possible to illustrate that each of the two peaks in Fig. 23.7 splits again, although to a much lesser degree than the split due to the spin of the valence–electrons. This secondary split is due to the nuclear spin of the silver atoms. For atoms where no effect is expected due to the electrons in the atomic shell (so–called *diamagnetic atoms*) only a splitting due

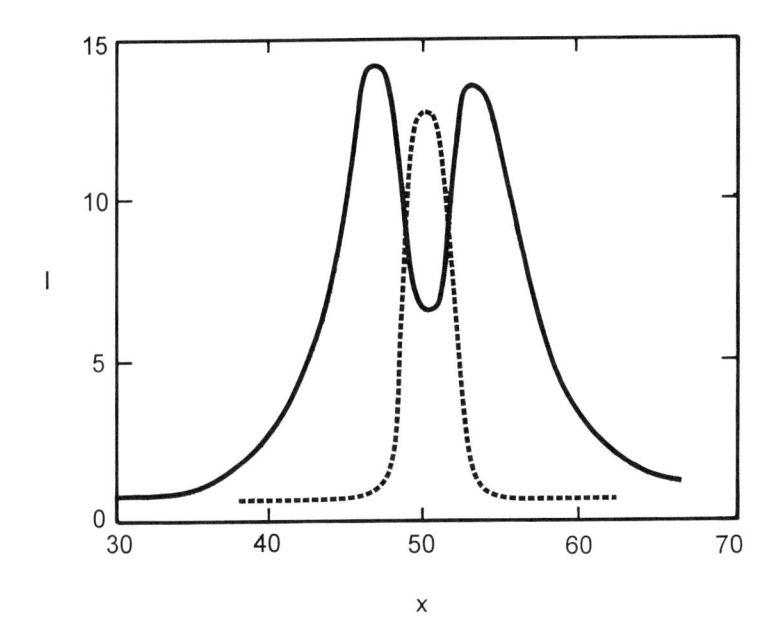

Fig. 23.7: Result of the experiment by Stern and Gerlach, showing the intensity of the measured atomic beam as a function of position on the observation screen. Without a magnetic field, a single peak (dashed line) is observed with a width representing the Maxwell–Boltzmann velocity distribution of the atoms coming from the source. With the magnetic field, the beam splits in two components, one associated with the z–component of the spin directed in the direction of the magnetic field and one with the z–component of the spin directed anti–parallel to the magnetic field.

to the nuclear spin is observed. The number of the observed peaks in measurements like Fig. 23.7 reveals in these cases the spin, and the distance between the peaks allows us to calculate the nuclear magnetic dipole moment.

23.2.3. Energy of a spin in a magnetic field

As we did several times before, we establish the energy for a particle with a magnetic dipole moment in a magnetic field in analogy to an electric dipole which is brought into an electric field. For simplicity, we confine both discussions to uniform fields, i.e., avoiding the more complicated case we referred to with the magnet used in the Stern–Gerlach experiment.

The energy of an electric dipole in a uniform electric field is established in Fig. 23.8. The electric field lines are horizontal, with the electric field directed towards the right. The direction of the electric dipole forms an angle α with the direction of the field lines. Using the definition of the electric energy for a point charge for each of the two charges forming the dipole we find:

$$E_{el} = q_+ V_+ + q_- V_- = q(V_+ - V_-) \quad (14)$$

in which V_+ and V_- are the electric potential at the positions of the positive and negative charge, respectively. We know from Chapter 9 that the electric energy, and thus, the electric potential, vary linearly in a uniform electric field. Therefore, we need to find the difference in the position along the direction of the external field for the two charges forming the dipole in Fig. 23.8. As the figure illustrates, the difference in position is d cosα. With this distance we can rewrite Eq. (14) in the form:

$$E_{el} = q(|E| \, d \cos\alpha) = \mu_{el} \cdot E \quad (15)$$

in which the charge q and the distance between the charges, d, are combined to the electric dipole moment, and in which the cos α term is recognized as a mathematical term due to the dot–product between two vectors, i.e., the electric field and the electric dipole moment.

The energy of a magnetic dipole in a uniform magnetic field can be derived in analogy, leading to:

$$E_{mag} = \mu_{mag} \cdot B = I A B \cos\alpha \quad (16)$$

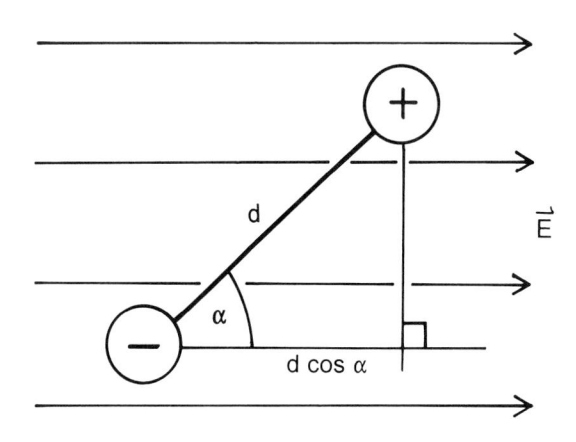

Fig. 23.8: An electric dipole in a uniform external electric field. This sketch allows us to calculate the electric energy of the dipole as a function of its orientation relative to the field.

625

In this case, α is the angle between the direction of the magnetic field **B** and the unit vector **n⁰**, which is normal to the area of the current loop.

Using Eq. (16), we can now calculate the difference in energy for two nuclei which display the two allowed orientations of the spin in a magnetic field, as shown in Fig. 23.5. For a nuclei with spin ½ℏ, which we focus on in the present discussion and for which Fig. 23.5 applies, the two orientations are directed such that the difference of the two dot–products in Eq. (16) for the spin parallel and anti–parallel to the magnetic field leads to:

$$\Delta E_{mag} = \mu_{mag} B_0 \quad (17)$$

in which B_0 is the applied magnetic field.

Eq. (17) is illustrated in Fig. 23.9. The figure shows the magnetic energy of a nucleus with a spin of ½ℏ as a function of the external magnetic field for both the parallel and anti–parallel orientations. The two orientations are labelled with the respective spin quantum–numbers. The energy difference for a particular external field of magnitude B_0 is highlighted. Note that the energy difference increases linearly with the magnitude of the external magnetic field.

In the same fashion as we discussed this for electrons in atomic shells in Chapter 21, a system which occupies a state of higher energy can relax by emitting a photon while transferring into the state of lower energy. Equally, external photons can be absorbed to excite a system from the lower state to the higher state. This is a resonance effect. Fig. 23.10 indicates how a resonant transition occurs for nuclei in the lower of the two spin states in a uniform magnetic field. If photons with the right amount of energy are used, a nucleus in the parallel state can be brought into the anti–parallel state. The energy of the photon absorbed in this process, hf, is determined by the energy difference between the two states, as quantified in Eq. (17): $hf = \mu_{mag} B_0$.

23.3. Experiments with the nuclear spin

23.3.1. Resonance measurements

The transition energy between the two states of a ½ℏ–spin nucleus in an external magnetic field is unusually small in comparison to transitions between electronic states in atoms that we discussed in Chapter 21. Even for strong fields, such as |**B**| = 10 T, the frequency of the photon causing the resonance is only 500 MHz, and for a typical magnetic field of |**B**| = 1 T the transition occurs at 50 MHz. Such very small energies lead to an important thermodynamic consideration, which we have to pursue before we can establish the resonance measurement technique used in MRI.

Whether a transition energy is small or large is decided by a comparison between the thermal energy available to the system and the energy needed to observe a resonance transition between two states of the system, $\Delta E_{excitation}$. We distinguish two cases:

$$(I) \quad \Delta E_{excitation} \ll kT$$
$$(II) \quad \Delta E_{excitation} \gg kT \quad (18)$$

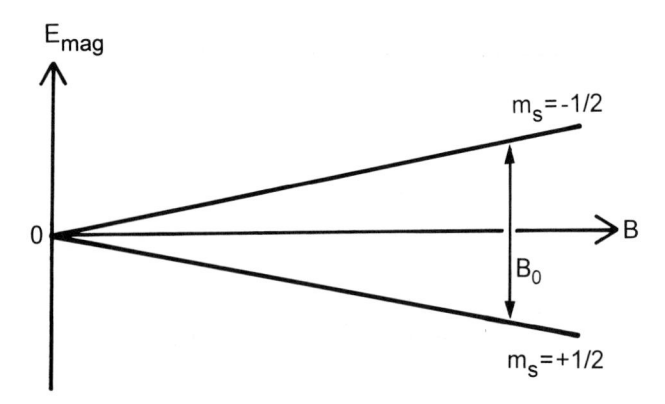

Fig. 23.9: The magnetic energy of a magnetic dipole splits into two energy levels for a nucleus with spin ½ℏ when brought into a uniform external magnetic field. The energy difference is proportional to the magnitude of the magnetic field.

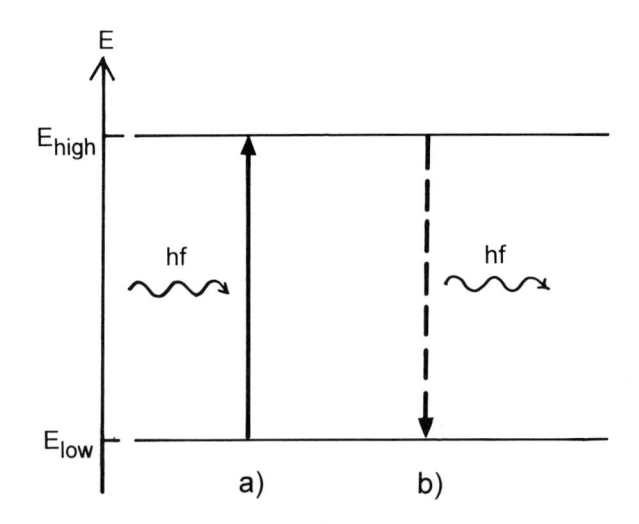

Fig. 23.10: Transition processes for a nuclear spin in an external magnetic field: absorption of radiation allows us to excite the nucleus (spin flips into anti–parallel orientation) and emission of radiation allows the nucleus to return to the lower energy state (spin flips into parallel orientation).

in which kT, the product of the Boltzmann constant and the temperature, is a measure of the thermal energy available per atom or molecule, based on the discussion in Chapter 6 for the kinetic gas model.

In case (I) enough thermal energy is present that every atom or molecule can undergo a transition from a lower to a higher energy state without the need of externally provided photons. Thus, the system is fully excited with an (almost) equal number of atoms or molecules in the excited and the lower state in Fig. 23.10.

In case (II) of Eq. (18) the thermal energy of the system is insufficient to allow atoms or molecules to obtain the energy to undergo an excitation. Consequently, essentially all atoms or molecules are in the lower state.

We found in earlier chapters examples for both cases: rotational excitation states for gas molecules are separated from the ground state of rotation by very small energies, laying in the microwave energy range. Thus, most molecules occupy higher rotation states at room temperature. On the other hand, electronic excitation states, as discussed in Chapter 21, are separated by larger energy gaps from the ground state (in the visible to UV energy range), and thus, atoms and molecules are exclusively occupying the ground state (lowest energy state) in respect to electronic excitations.

We want to decide what type of case we are dealing with for the spin orientations of a nucleus in an external magnetic field by evaluating Eq. (18). For this we assume a large magnetic field of up to 10 T, which then is associated with an excitation frequency of up to 500 MHz. We further assume that the probe is at room temperature during the experiment. This assumption is particularly justified for MRI measurements as cooling of human patients is not possible without causing damage to the tissue. This leads to (i) for the energy of the transition:

$$hf \leq 500 \, [MHz] \, 6.63 \times 10^{-34} \, [Js]$$
$$\Rightarrow \quad hf \leq 3.3 \times 10^{-25} \, J \quad (19)$$

and (ii) for the thermal energy of the system:

$$kT = 1.38 \times 10^{-23} \left[\frac{J}{K}\right] 298 [K]$$
$$\Rightarrow \quad kT = 4.1 \times 10^{-21} \, J \quad (20)$$

Thus, the thermal energy exceeds the energy needed for the transition between the two states of a spin in an external magnetic field by more than a factor of 10^4. As a consequence, both states in Fig. 23.10 are almost equally occupied in the probe with a difference in favor of the lower level of the order of only 1×10^{-4} %!

This means that a resonance technique using the transition between orientations of spins in an external magnetic field differs greatly from other well-established resonance techniques such as infrared (IR) or ultra-violet (UV) spectroscopy. In the latter techniques, externally provided photons of the resonance energy lead to intensive absorption as practically all molecules are in the ground state and half of them could be excited at any time. In the nuclear spin resonance case, we expect much weaker signals as almost all spins which could be excited are excited already.

23.3.2. Nuclear magnetic resonance (NMR)

Fig. 23.11 illustrates the experimental set-up with which

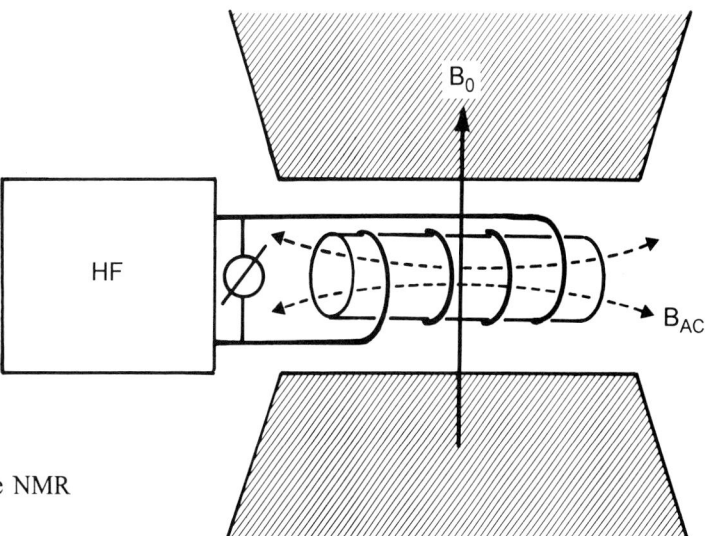

Fig. 23.11: Experimental set-up of the NMR experiment.

we can excite resonant transitions in the orientation of nuclear spins in an external magnetic field.

A large magnet is needed, indicated by the shaded areas and the magnetic field B_0, to provide a constant and uniform external magnetic field which causes the two orientations of the spin to split into two separate energy levels. For resonance experiments of hydrogen nuclei in molecules, a magnetic field of 2.349 T is used in a standard set–up. This magnetic field leads to a resonance frequency of 100 MHz, which is typically used in NMR and for MRI in medicine.

The resonance radiation of about 100 MHz is provided by an external high–frequency generator. The frequency can be scanned across a range of ± 500 Hz, which is a minor variation of 1×10^{-3} %. The ability to sweep the frequency through this range is needed to adjust to the actual external magnetic field, but also plays an important role in allowing a chemical composition analysis in NMR as discussed briefly below.

Note that Fig. 23.11 indicates that the high–frequency signal provided through an electric solenoid arrangement can also be interpreted as causing an alternating magnetic field. This relates to a classical interpretation of the resonance effect, in which the nuclear spins are considered to be tops which undergo a precession motion about the magnetic axis. With the external push due to the alternating magnetic field, which wiggles on the top, it is possible to cause the top to flip to an inverted precession motion.

The recording technique of nuclear magnetic resonance experiments has significantly changed when more powerful computers became available. When Edward Purcell and Felix Bloch initially developed the technique, the experiment was done in the so–called cw–mode (continuous wave–mode) where the external high–frequency (HF) is swept through a ± 500 Hz range around the 100 MHz signal. It is easy to imagine how a spectrum results in this case: whenever the external frequency sweeps across an actual resonance frequency, nuclear spins absorb energy from the high–frequency field and change their orientation to the higher state. The energy absorption in the probe leads to the need of a higher power input of the high–frequency generator, and a separate instrument (indicated as a circle with an arrow in Fig. 23.11) records the power input of the HF unit as a function of the frequency.

However, this technique has significant drawbacks. With individual resonances as narrow as 1Hz, most of the sweep passes through frequency intervals without resonances, not leading to useful data. Even worse, the small difference in occupation between the lower energy and higher energy levels requires many sweeps to be overlapped before a statistically significant signal is obtained.

To improve and accelerate the recording technique, E. L. Hahn developed a different approach, which is based on a short pulse in real time sent through the solenoid. In analogy to Fig. 16.21, we know that such a pulse represents a wide range of frequencies sent through the system at once. The resulting signal requires a Fourier transformation to reveal the single frequencies which were absorbed. Fourier transformations require extensive computing capacity. Typical operational conditions for a pulsed Fourier–transform NMR are pulse lengths of about 50 µs, followed by a data acquisition period of 1 second. Then the next pulse is sent through the system.

A ^{1}H–NMR example for a chemical compound is discussed from organic chemistry. A chemically pure sample, here 1–thiophenylpropanone–(2), is dissolved in an NMR–inert solvent, i.e., a solvent which does not contain hydrogen. Typically, we use CCl_4 as a non–polar solvent (in the present case) or D_2O as a polar solvent. The sample is then brought into the magnet of the NMR apparatus and a resonance measurement is obtained. Fig. 23.12 shows the resulting spectrum. Several features can be noticed:

(I) The abscissa is not shown as a frequency but is given in unit [ppm] (parts per million) with a peak at a zero–reference point. The reference point is the result of a calibration with an additional sample of tetramethyl–silane, $(CH_3)_4Si$, which has 12 equivalent hydrogen atoms. This compound is used as a reference point such that any peak at a resonance frequency different from the resonance frequency of tetramethylsilane, f_{TMS}, is considered as chemically shifted. The chemical shift δ is quantified in the form:

$$\delta \ [ppm] = \frac{f_{sample} - f_{TMS}}{f_0} \cdot 10^6 \quad (21)$$

The basic frequency f_0 for the spectrum shown in Fig. 23.12 is 100 MHz. The factor 10^6 causes the chemical shift to be given in the ppm–unit.

(II) Two curves are shown in Fig. 23.12, a step function and a spectrum of discrete peaks at various resonance frequencies. The step function is the result of integrating the area under each of the peaks. This measurement is provided since the step height is proportional to the number of equivalent hydrogen atoms in each molecule.

(III) The hydrogen atoms in the thiophenylpropanone molecule give rise to three peaks at different chemical shifts. This is the most important aspect of the application of the NMR technique in structural analysis studies in chemistry. The external magnetic field B_0 determines only to first order the magnetic field at the position of a

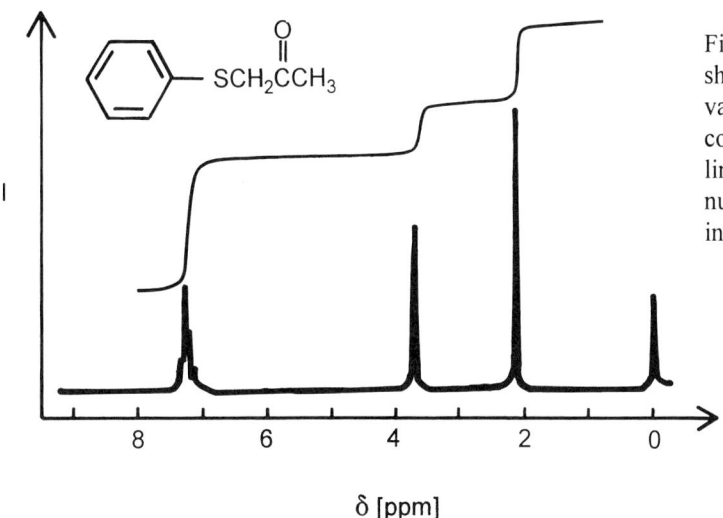

Fig. 23.12: A typical NMR spectrum, showing peaks which correspond to various resonances (thick line) and the corresponding integrated signal (thin line) which is used to quantify the number of equivalent hydrogen atoms involved in the respective transition.

hydrogen nucleus within the molecule. The actual magnetic field varies slightly from this magnitude due to minor magnetic field contributions at the position of the hydrogen nucleus caused by atomic electrons which move within the molecule. This contribution varies with the relative location of functional groups in chemical compounds. For example, in the thiophenylpropanone molecule shown as an inset in Fig. 23.12, three types of hydrogen atoms with variable environments can be identified, (a) five hydrogen atoms attached to the benzene ring at $\delta = 7.25$ ppm, (b) two hydrogen in the double–substituted methyl–group ($-CH_2-$) at the center of the molecule at $\delta = 3.73$ ppm, and (c) 3 hydrogen atoms in the methyl–group at the end ($-CH_3$) with $\delta = 2.16$ ppm. The step height of the integral measurement identifies the ratio 5:2:3 in this order from lower to higher resonance frequency in the spectrum.

Chemical shifts, and signal splitting, as can be seen for the 5 hydrogen atoms of the benzene group in Fig. 23.12, are important tools to identify unknown chemical compounds based on their NMR spectra. At the same time, these fingerprint–type of details are only useful when a single chemical compound has been isolated for the NMR measurement. We do not discuss the chemical shift or signal splitting further since these details cannot be used in MRI where a separation of chemical compounds in the human body is not possible.

23.4. The NMR technique in medicine: MRI

Magnetic Resonance Imaging (MRI) combines the material sensitive information of NMR with modern computer–based imaging techniques.

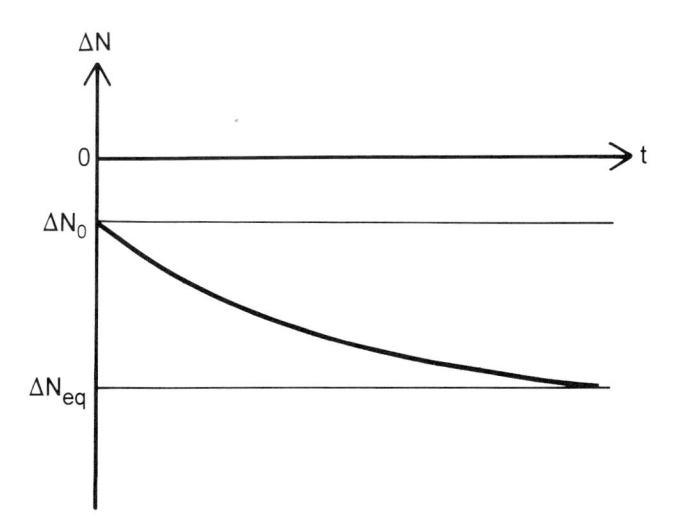

Fig. 23.13: Decay of the population change of a spin system in a magnetic field after a high–frequency pulse has been sent through the sample. An exponential decay law determines the curve. The characteristic decay time constant is calculated from the curve.

At first glance one may expect little useful information from an NMR signal obtained from a random sample of human tissue. The range of complex molecules and the multitude of hydrogen atoms in widely varying local magnetic environments should lead to an indifferent signal. Indeed, no chemical shift information is collected. However, it was experimentally established that the relaxation times associated with the relaxation process in Fig. 23.10 vary with the tissue material.

The time dependence of the relaxation process following a high–frequency pulse is illustrated in Fig. 23.13. The figure shows the difference in occupation of the upper and the lower energy state for the nuclear spins in a probe as a function of time after the pulse. The occupation difference in thermal equilibrium is discussed in section 23.3, where we showed that the lower level is slightly more occupied: $N_{upper} - N_{lower} = \Delta N_{eq} < 0$.

The high–frequency pulse increases the number of nuclei occupying the upper energy level, but does not lead to an inversion of the occupation. Inversion of the occupation cannot be achieved for a two–level system; either a third level feeding the upper energy level or a decay mechanism of the lower energy level (towards another, even lower level) would be needed. Thus, the figure shows the case in which at time t = 0 (instance of the pulse) the occupation difference is $N_{upper} - N_{lower} = \Delta N_0 < 0$. Then the decay of the occupation difference toward the equilibrium value, $\Delta N(t)$, can be written in the form:

$$\Delta N = \Delta N_{eq} + \left(\Delta N_0 - \Delta N_{eq}\right) e^{\left\{-\frac{t}{T_{relax}}\right\}} \quad (22)$$

This formula is consistent with Fig. 23.13 as is easily confirmed by substituting t = 0 and t = ∞. For t = 0 we note that $e^0 = 1$, i.e., we obtain $\Delta N(t=0) = \Delta N_0$ as shown in the figure. For t = ∞ we note that $e^{-\infty} = 0$, i.e., we obtain $\Delta N(t=\infty) = \Delta N_{eq}$, again in agreement with the figure.

The experimental set–up by E. L. Hahn provides for short HF–pulses. The data analysis in the MRI mode is simplified as the time dependent relaxation is directly recorded and no Fourier transformation is needed. But is such a measurement for a human tissue useful? This is answered experimentally by comparing the relaxation times for various forms of tissues in their healthy states

Table 23.2: Relaxation time of hydrogen nuclear spins in an external magnetic field as a function of tissue with and without tumors.

Tissue	Relaxation time T_{relax} [s] healthy	with tumor
Breast	0.37	1.08
Skin	0.62	1.05
Muscle	1.02	1.41
Liver	0.57	0.83
Stomach	0.77	1.24
Lung	0.79	1.10
Bone	0.55	1.03
Water	3.6	—

and when diseased by a tumor. Table 23.2 shows for a wide range of tissues that significant changes of the relaxation time take place when tumors are present.

Note that the data in Table 23.2 are empiric data. The physiological origin of the variations in relaxation times are not discussed in this textbook.

Different from NMR measurements, however, a spatial resolution is needed in MRI. We do not want to disect the patient to analyze a particular tissue, we rather want to do the analysis non–intrusively with the tissue embedded in the patient. This requires that the entire patient (or at least the part of the patient we want to survey for tumors) is placed in the magnet and within the solenoid. To obtain a signal only from a given sampling depth within the patient (relative to a fixed reference plane, not relative to the patient's skin), a constant gradient magnetic field is overlapped with the constant magnetic field B_0. As this gradient field is varied, the fixed high–frequency is the proper resonance frequency only in a thin layer at any given time. Alternatively, the gradient field can be held fixed and the high–frequency can be varied, as Figs. 23.9 and 23.10 suggest.

When we use multiple projections and analyze the data appropriately with a computer, overlapping planes produce stripes and overlapping stripes produce single segments of information. This information is processed such that relaxation times are usually shown in false–color codes.

Chapter XXIV

General Appendix

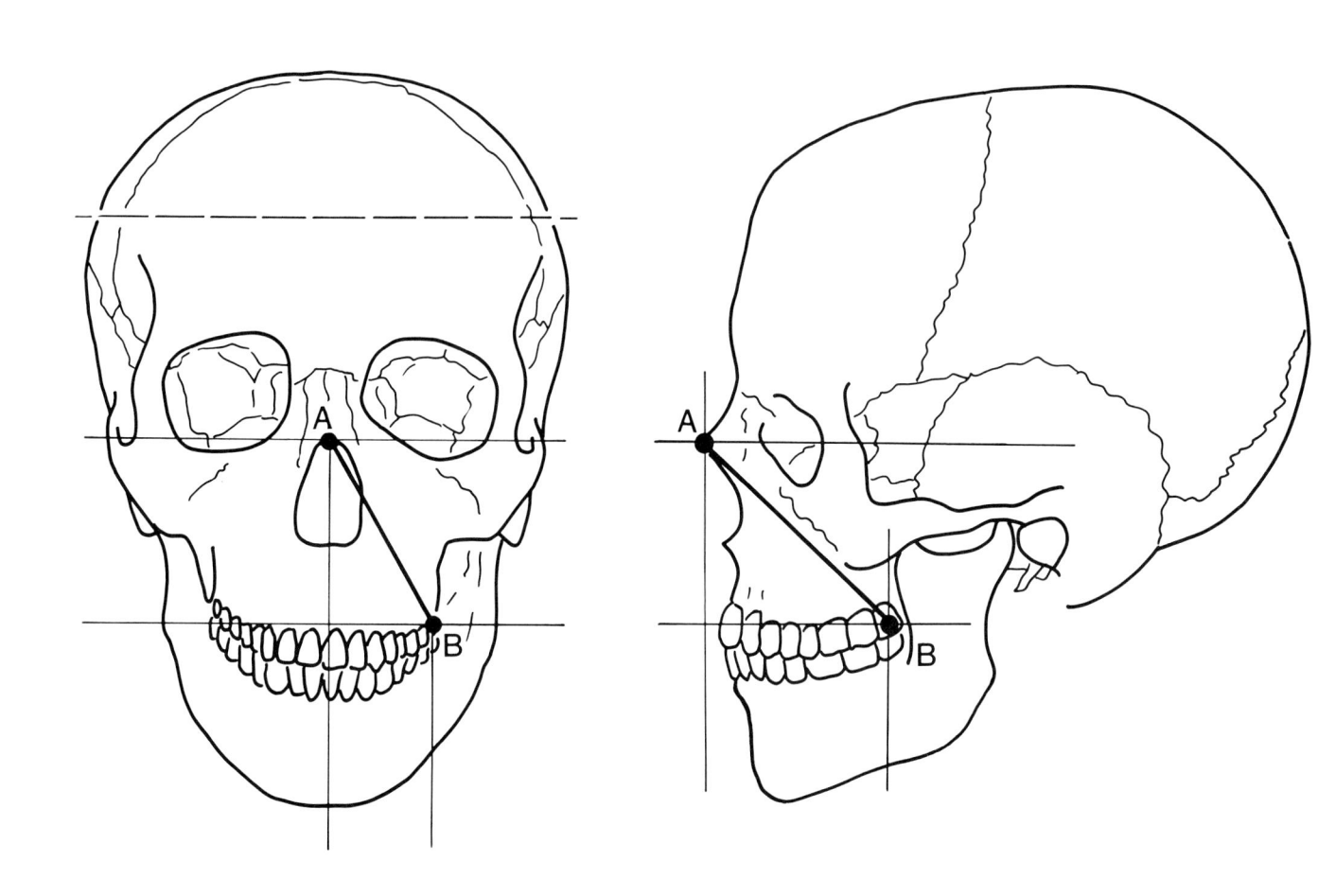

GENERAL APPENDIX

24.1. Mathematical concepts

24.1.1. Geometry

Often you will evaluate angles from the sketch of a problem. To do this, it is necessary to know which angles in a given situation are equal, and which angles add up to 90^0 or 180^0. Inspecting Figs. 24.1 and 24.2, confirm that
$\alpha = \gamma$
$\alpha + \beta = 180^0$
$\epsilon = \phi$, $\epsilon = \theta$, and
$\delta + \theta = 180^0$.

We use three trigonometric functions in the text, the sine function ($\sin\theta$), the cosine function ($\cos\theta$) and the tangent function ($\tan\theta$). It is important to know how they are connected for a right triangle. Defining one angle in the triangle as θ, the trigonometric functions are given as follows:

$$\sin\theta \equiv \frac{length\ of\ side\ opposite\ to\ \theta}{length\ of\ hypotenuse}$$

$$\cos\theta \equiv \frac{length\ of\ side\ adjacent\ to\ \theta}{length\ of\ hypotenuse} \quad (1)$$

$$\tan\theta \equiv \frac{length\ of\ side\ opposite\ to\ \theta}{length\ of\ side\ adjacent\ to\ \theta}$$

The following relations apply for negative angles:

$$\sin(-\theta) = -\sin\theta$$
$$\cos(-\theta) = \cos\theta \quad (2)$$
$$\tan(-\theta) = -\tan\theta$$

Relations between the sine and cosine functions follow from Eq. (1):

$$\sin(90^0 - \theta) = \cos\theta$$
$$\cos(90^0 - \theta) = \sin\theta \quad (3)$$

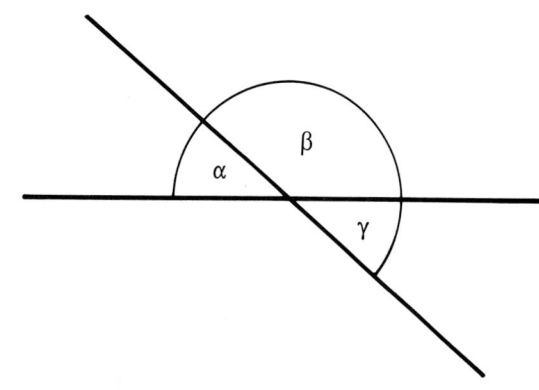

Fig. 24.1: The three angles adjacent to an intersection of two straight lines are related in the form $\alpha = \gamma$, $\alpha + \beta = 180^0$ and $\beta + \gamma = 180^0$.

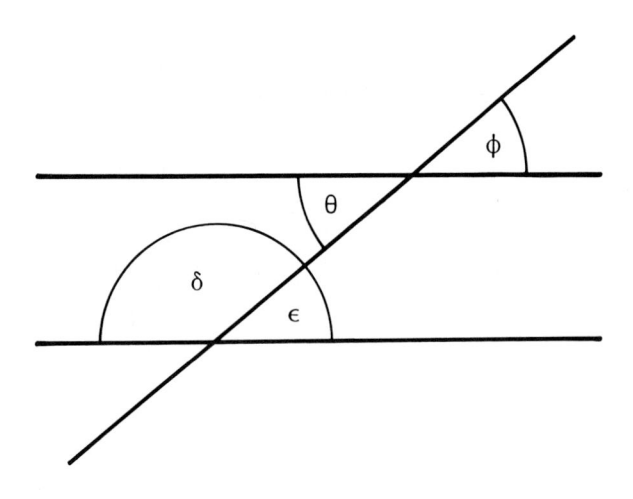

Fig. 24.2: The four angles δ, ϵ, θ and ϕ, which are adjacent to a straight line which intersects with two parallel straight lines are related in the form $\epsilon = \phi$, $\epsilon = \theta$, and $\delta + \theta = 180^0$.

Example 24.1
Identify in the triangle given in Fig. 24.3 the trigonometric functions for angles ψ and ϕ.

Solution: The following relations hold:

$$\sin\psi = \frac{a}{c}\ ;\ \cos\psi = \frac{b}{c}\ ;\ \tan\psi = \frac{a}{b}$$
$$\sin\phi = \frac{b}{c}\ ;\ \cos\phi = \frac{a}{c}\ ;\ \tan\phi = \frac{b}{a} \quad (4)$$

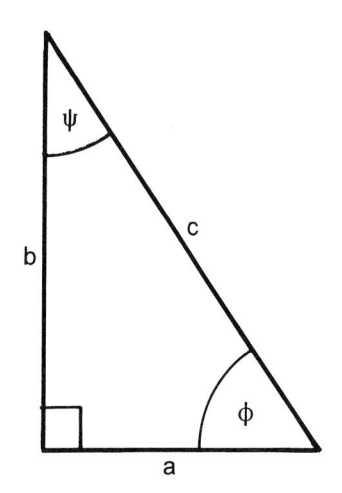

Fig. 24.3: A right triangle with all three sides and angles labelled.

The Pythagorean theorem states for a right triangle in which c is the length of the hypotenuse, and a and b are the lengths of the legs opposite and adjacent to the angle θ, that:

$$c^2 = a^2 + b^2 \qquad (5)$$

This is illustrated in the left sketch of Fig. 24.4. The two sketches on the right side of the figure demonstrate how simple the Pythagorean theorem is proven: the four triangles in the left box are arranged to leave open the area c². They are then rearranged in the same box at right to leave open two areas, a² and b².

Example 24.2
(a) Confirm that the corners of the area labelled c² in the middle panel of Fig. 24.4 are right angles.
(b) Use the Pythagorean theorem to prove the following formula:

$$\sin^2\phi + \cos^2\phi = 1 \qquad (6)$$

(c) Use Eq. (4) to prove the following formula, which applies as long as $\cos\phi \neq 0$:

$$\tan\phi = \frac{\sin\phi}{\cos\phi} \qquad (7)$$

Solution part (a): The sum of the three angles in a triangle is 180°. Choosing the lower corner of the tilted area in the middle panel, the angles between the side of the larger box and the sides of the inner box are equal to the sum of the two angles (excluding the right angle) in each of the four identical triangles. Thus, the angle at the corner is 90° since this sum equals 90° and the larger box describes an angle of 180° at the corner point.

Solution part (b): We calculate $\sin^2\phi$ and $\cos^2\phi$ from Eq. (4). Using the Pythagorean theorem we get:

$$\sin^2\phi + \cos^2\phi = \frac{b^2}{c^2} + \frac{a^2}{c^2} = \frac{a^2+b^2}{c^2}$$

$$\Rightarrow \quad \sin^2\phi + \cos^2\phi = \frac{c^2}{c^2} = 1 \qquad (8)$$

Solution part (c): The proof is based on Eq. (4):

$$\frac{\sin\phi}{\cos\phi} = \frac{b/c}{a/c} = \frac{b}{a} = \tan\phi \qquad (9)$$

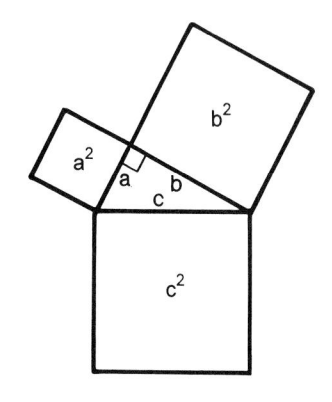

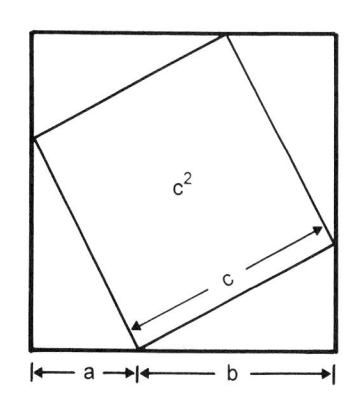

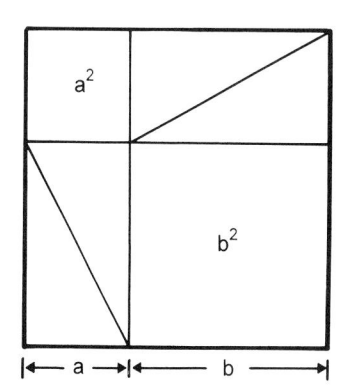

Fig. 24.4: Left panel: Illustration of the Pythagorean theorem for a right triangle with hypotenuse c. Middle and right panel: Simple geometric proof of the Pythagorean theorem. Each box has the total area (a+b)². Inserting four right triangles, with sides a and b meeting at the right angle, an area c² is left open in the middle panel and, after rearranging the four triangles in the right panel, the areas a² and b² are left open.

The following theorems for the sine function apply:

$$\sin(\alpha + \beta) = \sin\alpha \cos\beta + \cos\alpha \sin\beta$$
$$\sin(\alpha - \beta) = \sin\alpha \cos\beta - \cos\alpha \sin\beta \qquad (10)$$

For the cosine function we find:

$$\cos(\alpha + \beta) = \cos\alpha \cos\beta - \sin\alpha \sin\beta$$
$$\cos(\alpha - \beta) = \cos\alpha \cos\beta + \sin\alpha \sin\beta \qquad (11)$$

And for the tangent function we use:

$$\tan(\alpha + \beta) = \frac{\tan\alpha + \tan\beta}{1 - \tan\alpha \tan\beta}$$
$$\tan(\alpha - \beta) = \frac{\tan\alpha - \tan\beta}{1 + \tan\alpha \tan\beta} \qquad (12)$$

Further we note for the sum or difference of two sine function:

$$\sin\alpha + \sin\beta = 2\sin\left(\frac{\alpha+\beta}{2}\right)\cos\left(\frac{\alpha-\beta}{2}\right)$$
$$\sin\alpha - \sin\beta = 2\cos\left(\frac{\alpha+\beta}{2}\right)\sin\left(\frac{\alpha-\beta}{2}\right) \qquad (13)$$

and for the sum or difference of two cosine functions:

$$\cos\alpha + \cos\beta = 2\cos\left(\frac{\alpha+\beta}{2}\right)\cos\left(\frac{\alpha-\beta}{2}\right)$$
$$\cos\alpha - \cos\beta = 2\sin\left(\frac{\alpha+\beta}{2}\right)\sin\left(\frac{\alpha-\beta}{2}\right) \qquad (14)$$

For symmetric objects we require:

(I) *Circle*. Defining C as the circumference and A as the area for a two–dimensional circle of radius r, we get:

$$C = 2\pi r$$
$$A = \pi r^2 \qquad (15)$$

(II) *Triangle*. For a triangle with base a and height h, the area A is given as:

$$A = \frac{1}{2} a h \qquad (16)$$

(III) *Sphere*. Defining A as the surface area and V as the volume for a three–dimensional sphere of radius r, we get:

$$A = 4\pi r^2$$
$$V = \frac{4}{3}\pi r^3 \qquad (17)$$

(IV) *Cylinder*. Defining A as the mantle surface area and V as the volume for a right circular cylinder of radius r and height h, we get:

$$A = 2\pi r h$$
$$V = \pi r^2 h \qquad (18)$$

24.1.2. Algebra

Binomials and related terms
We use:

$$(a + b)^2 = a^2 + 2ab + b^2$$
$$(a - b)^2 = a^2 - 2ab + b^2$$
$$a^2 - b^2 = (a + b)(a - b) \qquad (19)$$
$$a^3 - b^3 = (a - b)(a^2 + ab + b^2)$$

Powers
Definitions:

$$a^1 = a$$
$$a^0 = 1 \qquad (20)$$
$$a^{-n} = \frac{1}{a^n}$$

Calculation rules with powers:

$$a^x \cdot a^y = a^{x+y}$$

$$a^x \cdot b^x = (a \cdot b)^x$$

$$\frac{a^x}{a^y} = a^{x-y} \tag{21}$$

$$\frac{a^x}{b^x} = \left(\frac{a}{b}\right)^x$$

$$(a^x)^y = a^{x \cdot y}$$

Logarithms

Logarithms were introduced by John Napier in 1614 to simplify mathematical operations. As you see below, when using logarithms we can use instead of powers multiplications, and instead of multiplications additions. The use of logarithms proves also useful when we analyze data graphically, as discussed in the next section.

Definitions: the term $c = \log_b a$ represents the number c which satisfies the equation $b^c = a$, i.e., the logarithm is the inverse operation to the power operation.

In the textbook, only two types of logarithm functions are used, the logarithms with base b = 10 (usually labelled log without a subscript) and the natural logarithm with base b = e = 2.71828..., in which e is Euler's number. This logarithm function is labelled "ln." Thus:

$$\log_{10} a = \log a = c \;\;\leftrightarrow\;\; a = 10^c$$
$$\log_e a = \ln a = c \;\;\leftrightarrow\;\; a = e^c = \exp(c) \tag{22}$$

The following rules apply to logarithms with any base; here we write them specifically for the case of base b = 10:

$$\log(x \cdot y) = \log x + \log y$$

$$\log\left(\frac{x}{y}\right) = \log x - \log y \tag{23}$$

$$\log x^y = y \cdot \log x$$

and for the case of base b = e:

$$\ln(x \cdot y) = \ln x + \ln y$$

$$\ln\left(\frac{x}{y}\right) = \ln x - \ln y \tag{24}$$

$$\ln x^y = y \cdot \ln x$$

For the same variable, both logarithm functions are related by a factor of ln(10):

$$\ln x = \ln 10 \cdot \log x$$
$$\Rightarrow \;\; \ln x = 2.3026 \log x \tag{25}$$

Non–linear equations

Quadratic equations occur frequently during algebraic calculations. For a quadratic equation, written in the form $ax^2 + bx + c = 0$, there are a maximum of two real solutions, labelled x_1 and x_2:

$$x_{1,2} = \frac{-b \pm \sqrt{b^2 - 4ac}}{2a} \tag{26}$$

24.1.3. Graphical analysis methods

Scientific progress is based on experimental data. These data are often plotted and presented without a (yet) conclusive model which would provide a mathematical formula for the relation between the shown parameters. The three most frequently used methods of representing such data are the linear plot, the logarithmic plot and the double–logarithmic plot.

Linear plots

In this most frequently used graph, the variation of a dependent variable (y) is illustrated as a function of an independent variable (x) by plotting y versus x, as shown in Fig. 24.5. We say that "y is linear in x" in the x-interval $[x_1, x_2]$ if the data in that interval can be fitted with a straight line, as shown in the figure. Mathematically, this linear behavior is described by the equation:

$$y = ax + b \tag{27}$$

in which a and b do not depend on the variables x and y. a is called the *slope* of the curve and is determined from:

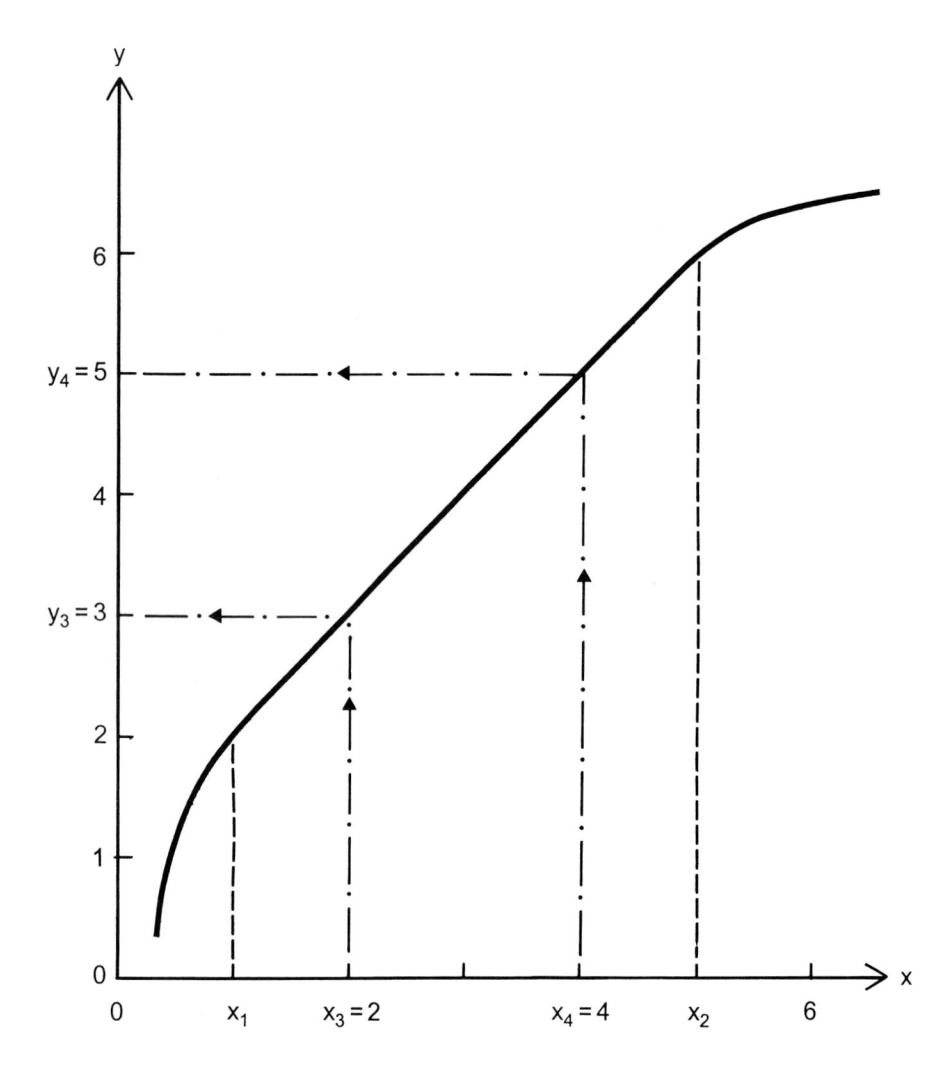

Fig. 24.5: Linear plot of a function y = f(x) with a linear dependence of y on x in the interval $[x_1, x_2]$.

$$a = \frac{y_4 - y_3}{x_4 - x_3} \quad (28)$$

where the values x_3 and x_4 must lie within the interval $[x_1, x_2]$. b is called the *intercept of the y–axis* and is the value of y at $x = 0$. The value of b is read from the plot directly if the point $x = 0$ lies within the interval $[x_1, x_2]$. If this is not the case, like in Fig. 24.5, then we choose a particular data point and substitute it together with the result of Eq. (28) in Eq. (27).

Example 24.3
Determine the slope and the intercept with the y–axis for the data shown in interval $[x_1, x_2]$ of Fig. 24.5.

Solution: We choose $x_3 = 2$ and $x_4 = 4$. The corresponding y–values are read from the graph (using the dash–dotted lines) as $y_3 = 3$ and $y_4 = 5$. Thus, from Eq. (28), we find $a = (5-3)/(4-2) = +1$.

For b, we choose the data point with $x_3 = 2$ and $y_3 = 3$. These data are then substituted in Eq. (27), leading to $3 = 1 \cdot 2 + b$. Thus, $b = +1$.

Logarithmic plots
Graphs other than linear plots are usually used for two purposes. Either a large variation of the data leads to an undesirable appearance of the plot or the data are tested for an exponential or power law dependence (see for example Figs. 13.25 to 13.27 for the impulse speed in nerves).

We study a possible exponential dependence first. In this case, the assumption is that the independent variable x and the dependent variable y are connected in the form:

$$y = a\, e^{b\, x} = a\, \exp(b\, x) \quad (29)$$

How can you convince yourself that Eq. (29) indeed de-

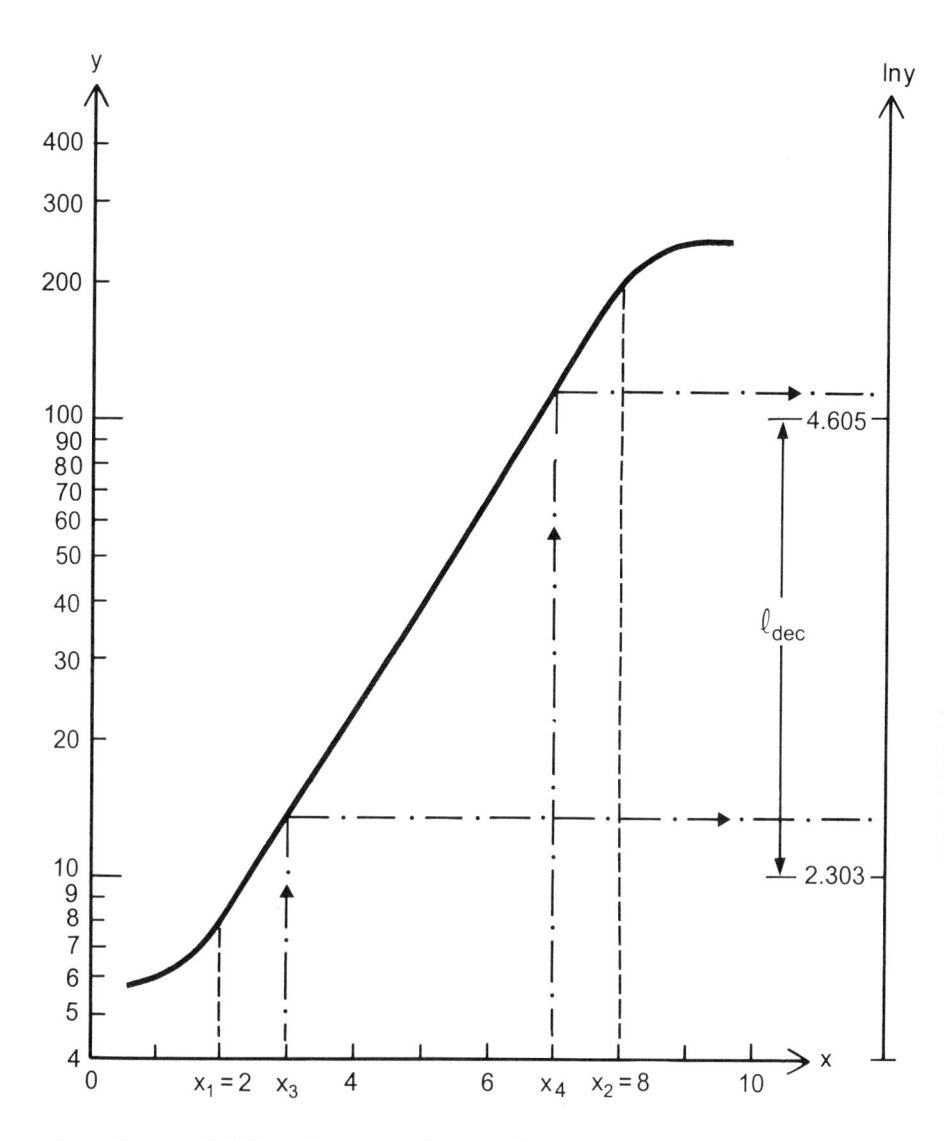

Fig. 24.6: A logarithmic plot of the function y = f(x) with an exponential dependence of y on x in $[x_1, x_2]$.

scribes a given data set? Often data sets show an increasing upward trend if plotted in a coordinate system with a y– and an x–axis. From such a trend one cannot determine whether Eq. (29) is appropriate to fit the data as other functions may lead to similar slopes of the data.

At this point we have two options. If you have logarithmic paper available or your graphics software allows you to use logarithmic axes, you show the data in the form y versus x using a logarithmic scale for the y–axis (ordinate). An example is shown in Fig. 24.6; another example is Fig. 22.6. Alternatively, we can plot ln(y) versus x where the natural logarithm of the y–data has been calculated first. An example is Fig. 16.34 where the ordinate is calculated in Eq. (16.26) as the logarithm of the pressure variation in a sound wave.

If the data points form a straight line segment in a logarithmic plot, e.g. in the interval $[x_1, x_2]$ in Fig. 24.6, then we know that the function in Eq. (29) applies to the data in that interval. From the logarithmic plot we determine the coefficients a and b, since the logarithmic plot corresponds mathematically to (see discussion of the logarithm function in section 24.1.2):

$$\ln(y) = \ln(a) + b\,x \qquad (30)$$

i.e., the slope of the straight line segment in Fig. 24.6 gives the prefactor in the exponent, b, and the intercept with the y–axis gives the logarithm of the prefactor of the exponential term, ln(a).

Example 24.4

For the data in Fig. 24.6, determine the parameters a and b in the data interval where Eq. (29) applies.

Solution: We need two data points from within the interval $[x_1, x_2]$ since there are two unknown parameters a and b. For these we choose $x_3 = 3$ and $x_4 = 7$. Notice that the values listed on the y–axis are y–values, not ln(y)–values. You can tell this first because the axis is labelled y and not ln(y) and also because the scale is not linear, i.e., the distance between the y = 0 and y = 100 tick–marks is not equal to the distance between the y = 100 and y = 200 tick–marks. In other plots it might be the case that the y–data are given as ln(y) with a linear scale. In that case we would read the corresponding ln(y) values directly off the y–axis of the graph, in the same fashion as we did to analyze Fig. 24.5.

However, in the present case an intermediate step in the data analysis is needed. In this step, we add a new ordinate, done in Fig. 24.6 at the right side, where the y–data are converted into ln(y)–data with a linear scale. Notice that on the new axis the distance between the y = 0 and y = 2.303 tick–marks is the same as that between the y = 2.303 and y = 4.606 tick–marks. With the new support scale established we read the ln(y)–values from this new axis and list them in Table 24.1.

As an example, it is illustrated how we arrive at the value $\ln(y_3) = 2.600$. Each decade on a ln–grid corresponds to an increment of ln(10) = 2.303. This increment corresponds to the length l_{dec} (expressed in unit [cm] as measured off Fig. 24.6). The value of $\ln(y_3)$ is a distance of $0.129 l_{dec}$ above the next lower full decade (here y = 10): $\ln(y_3) = 0.129 \cdot 2.303 + 2.303 = 2.600$.

With the data in Table 24.1, we determine in the next step the coefficient b in Eq. (30):

$$b = \frac{\ln(y_4) - \ln(y_3)}{x_4 - x_3} \qquad (31)$$

Substituting the data from the table leads for the coefficient b to b = (4.74 – 2.6)/(7.0 – 3.0) = 0.54.

In the last step we substitute the data pair x_3 and $\ln(y_3)$ in Eq. (30): $2.6 = \ln(a) + 0.54 \cdot 3.0 = 0.98$, which yields a = 2.66.

Double–logarithmic plots

If logarithmic plots do not lead to straight line segments, a double–logarithmic plot can be used to reveal whether the y–data depend on the x–variable in the form of a power law. Even if the real dependence is more complicated, a double–logarithmic plot often leads to straight line segments as that shown for the interval $[x_1, x_2]$, in Fig. 24.7: power laws are often good approximations to the actual physical or biological law.

Table 24.1: Data points from Fig. 24.6.

i	x_i	$\ln(y_i)$
3	3.0	2.600
4	7.0	4.740

Again, there are two equivalent forms which a double–logarithmic plot can take: either the x and y data are plotted directly on paper with logarithmic grids for the abscissa and ordinate. Examples are shown in Figs. 24.7 and 3.5(b). Alternatively, ln(x) and ln(y) can be plotted with a linear grid, like in Fig. 22.7 where both axes are converted to log data with the base 10.

For the straight line segment in Fig. 24.7 the dependence of y on the independent variable x is then given in the form of a power law with a and b constant:

$$y = a x^b \qquad (32)$$

When we rewrite both sides of Eq. (32) as the respective logarithmic value, Eq. (32) converts to:

$$\ln(y) = \ln(a) + b \ln(x) \qquad (33)$$

i.e., the slope of the straight line segment corresponds to b and the intercept of the ordinate equals ln(a). Analyze Fig. 24.7 for the purpose of practice yourself. You follow the same approach we took for the logarithmic axis in Fig. 24.6, except that the procedure must be applied to both axes in Fig. 24.7, as shown at the right side and at the top of the figure. You should find for the two coefficients values close to b = 0.68 and a = 5.07.

Example 24.5
The molecular mass (M) and radius (R) of various molecules are given in Table 24.2. Plot the data in double–logarithmic form and develop an empirical relationship between the two quantities, R = f(M).

Table 24.2: Molecular mass and radius of various molecules

Substance	M [g/mol]	R [10^{-10} m]
Water	18	1.5
Oxygen	32	2.0
Glucose	180	3.9
Mannitol	180	3.6
Sucrose	390	4.8
Raffinose	580	5.6
Inulin	5000	12.5
Ribonuclease	13500	18
β–Iactoglobulin	35000	27
Hemoglobin	68000	31
Albumin	68000	37
Catalase	250000	52

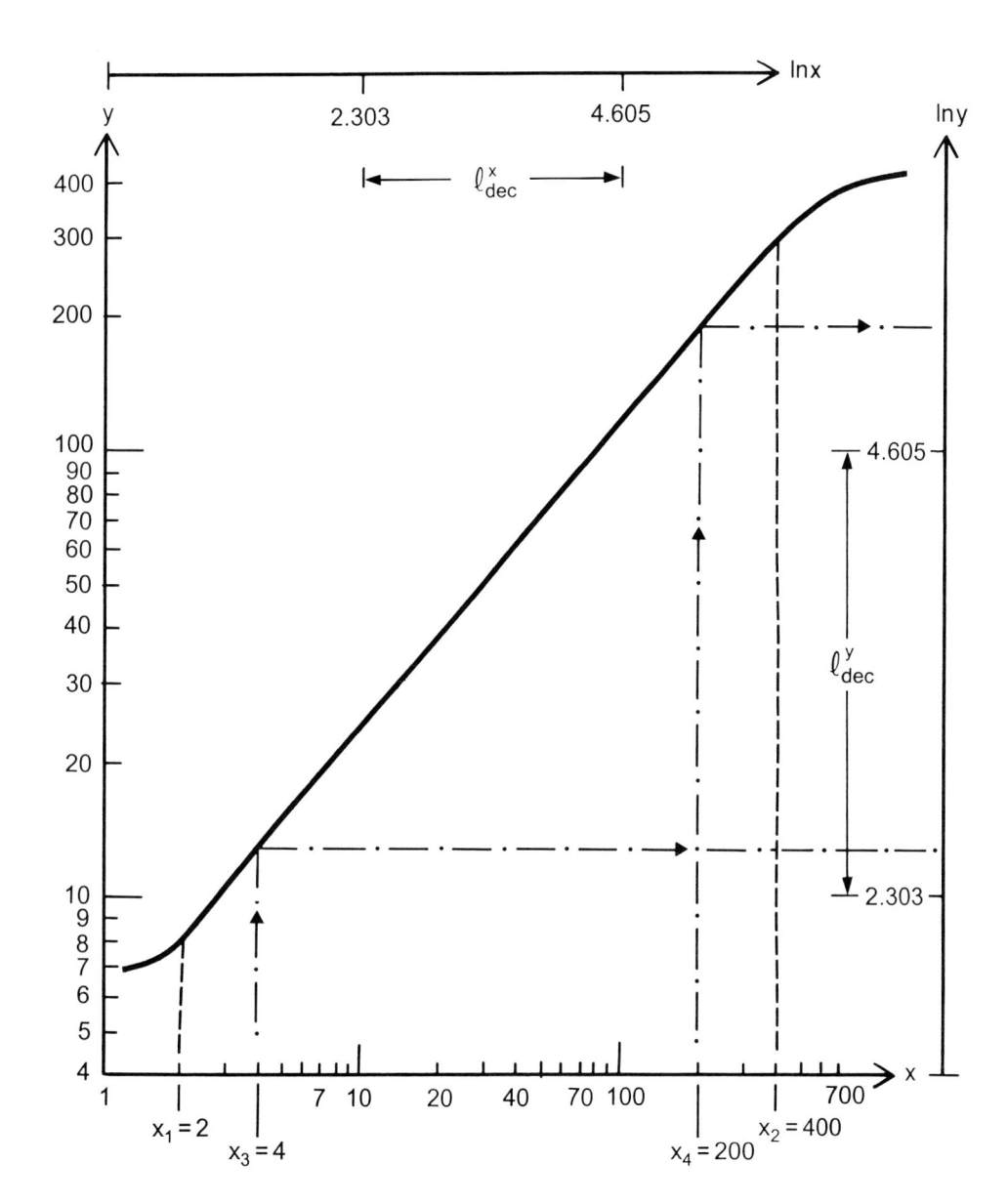

Fig. 24.7: Double–logarithmic plot of a function y = f(x) with a power law dependence of y on x in the interval [x₁,x₂].

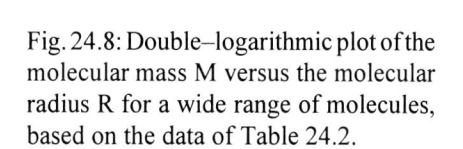

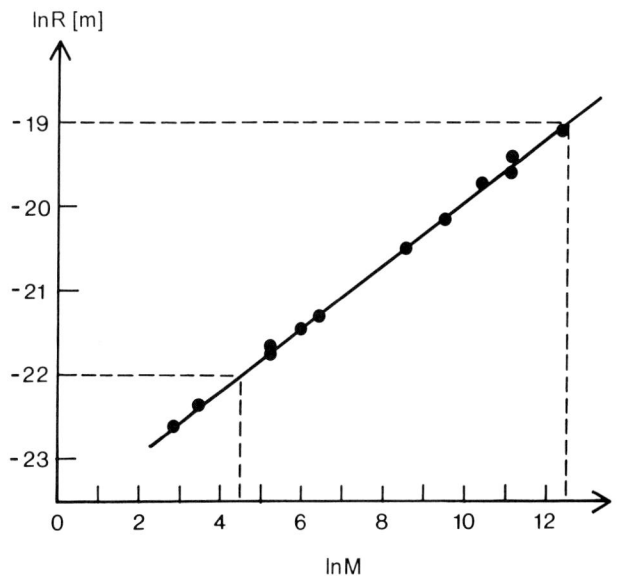

Fig. 24.8: Double–logarithmic plot of the molecular mass M versus the molecular radius R for a wide range of molecules, based on the data of Table 24.2.

Solution: The double–logarithmic plot of the data in Table 24.2 is shown in Fig. 24.8, where the abscissa values are taken from the first column of Table 24.2 in unit [g/mol] and where the ordinate values are taken from the second column of Table 24.2 in unit [m]. Note that the single data points deviate slightly from a straight line. It is possible, however, to draw a reasonable straight line (mathematically this is called the *best fit*) through the points. Using this straight line for the analysis of the constants a and b, instead of any particular data points, reduces the statistical error in the result.

To determine the constants a and b in the power law $R = a M^b$, we again analyze the problem in the form $\ln R = \ln a + b \ln M$ as described above. From Fig. 24.8 we read two data pairs (dashed lines), lnR and lnM, as listed in Table 24.3.

Table 24.3 allows us to write two linear formulas analogous to Eq. (33):

(I)	$-22.0 = b\, 4.5 + \ln a$
(II)	$-19.0 = b\, 12.5 + \ln a$
(II) − (I)	$+3.0 = b\,(12.5 - 4.5)$

Thus, $b = 0.375$ and $\ln a = -23.69$. The value for lna is obtained by substituting the result for b in one of the two formulas. From lna we calculate the parameter a as $a = 5.2 \times 10^{-11}$ m.

24.1.4. Vector algebra

The Cartesian coordinate system (named after René Descartes, "La Géométrie", 1637) is suitable for describing a three–dimensional mathematical space (Fig. 24.9). It is based on three orthogonal axes, which are labelled in order x–axis, y–axis and z–axis. The *right hand rule* was developed to confirm that a coordinate system is labelled properly: take your right hand and stretch the thumb and the index finger. They are automatically forming a right angle between them. Use your middle finger to point in a direction perpendicular to the thumb and the index finger. There is only one direction in which you can do this. Now point the thumb in the direction of the x–axis.

Table 24.3: Data sets from Fig. 24.8.

Data set	ln(M [g/mol])	ln(R [m])
#1	4.5	−22.0
#2	12.5	−19.0

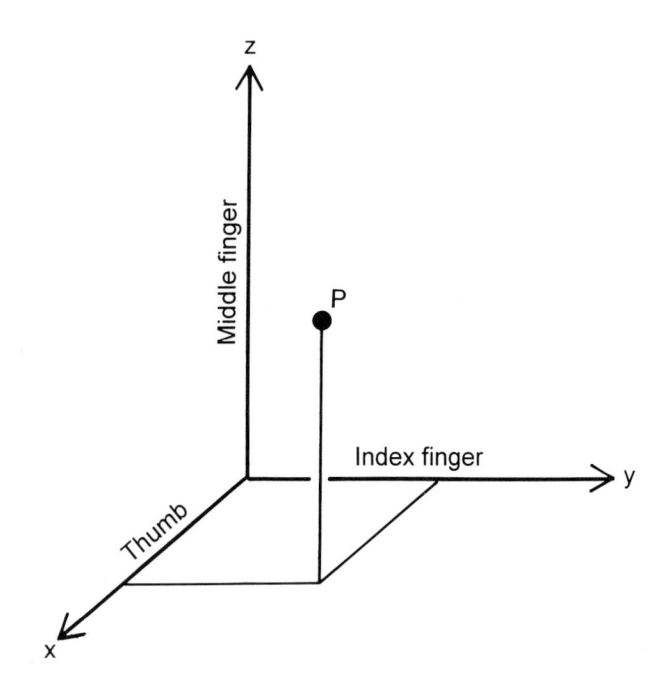

Fig. 24.9: Three–dimensional, perpendicular coordinates (Cartesian coordinate system). The order of the axes is determined by the right hand rule described in the text.

Then turn your hand such that the index finger points in the y–direction. At this point your middle finger points automatically in the z–direction.

The axes intersect at the *origin*. Three numbers are assigned to any point P which are proportional to the distances from the origin along each axis. These numbers are called the coordinates and are labelled using indices to identify the axis: p_x, p_y and p_z. This is illustrated in Fig. 24.10, where, for clarity, only a two–dimensional space is shown.

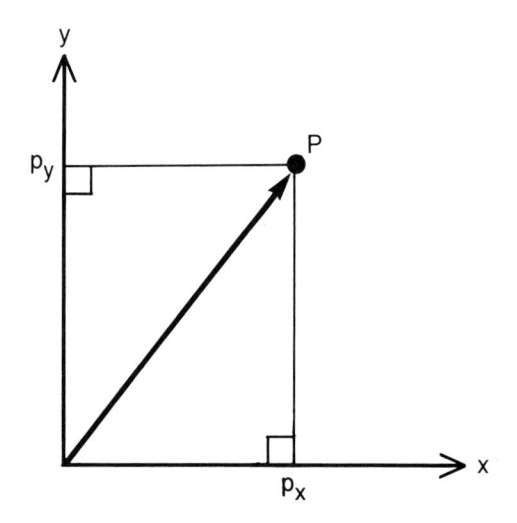

Fig. 24.10: Coordinates of point P in a two–dimensional Cartesian coordinate system. The coordinates are proportional to the lengths of the axes from the origin to the points of perpendicular projection of P onto the axes.

Associated with point P is an arrow reaching from the origin to point P, called *vector* **p**. A vector is represented by 2 or 3 numbers (the number of coordinates depending on the dimensionality of the given space), **p** = (p_x, p_y, p_z) or, as in Fig. 24.10, **p** = (p_x, p_y).

Vectors have to be distinguished from scalars, which are just numbers. In contrast, vectors have both magnitude and direction. The physical quantities discussed in this book are either described by a scalar (e.g. temperature) or by a vector (e.g. force). Even if a problem is one–dimensional, vector quantities retain their directional information, then carrying a + or – sign.

================

Example 24.6
We use the methane molecule as an example of the vector algebra concepts explained in this section. The methane molecule, CH_4, is shown in Fig. 24.11. In the figure the methane molecule is placed in a cube of side length l. Express the positions of the four hydrogen atoms and the carbon atom in the methane molecule in Cartesian coordinates.

Solution: The positions of the five atoms are
C: ($0.5l$, $0.5l$, $0.5l$), H_A: (0, 0, 0), H_B: (l, l, 0),
H_C: (0, l, l), and H_D: (l, 0, l).

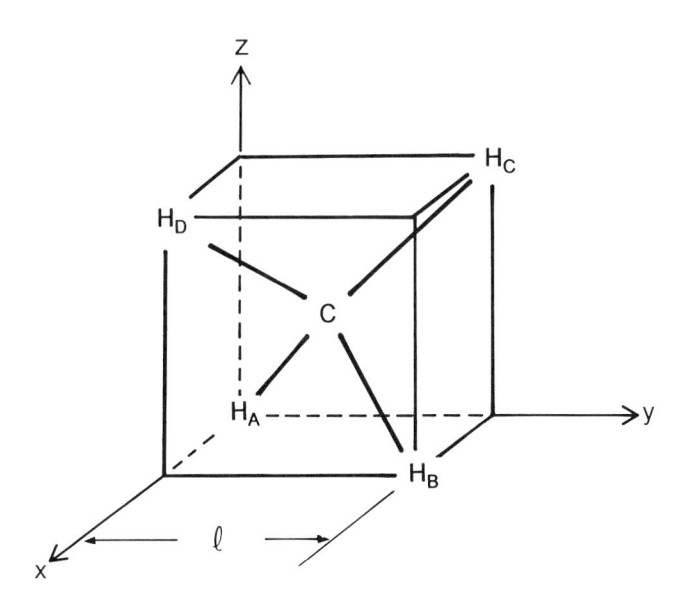

================

Fig. 24.11: The geometry of the tetrahedral methane molecule CH_4 is best described by placing the molecule in a cube of side length l in a Cartesian coordinate system. The four hydrogen atoms form four corners of the cube as shown. They are indistinguishable in a real molecule but have been labelled in the sketch with different indices for calculation purpose.

An alternative way to describe vectors is to use polar coordinates. We only apply these in this textbook for two–dimensional systems. The length $|\mathbf{p}|$ and the angle θ between the vector and the positive x–axis replace the two Cartesian coordinates, p_x and p_y, as shown in the top sketch of Fig. 24.12. The bottom sketch of Fig. 24.12 illustrates how the polar coordinates and the Cartesian coordinates are related to each other:

$$\sin\theta = \frac{p_y}{|\mathbf{p}|} \quad (34)$$

and

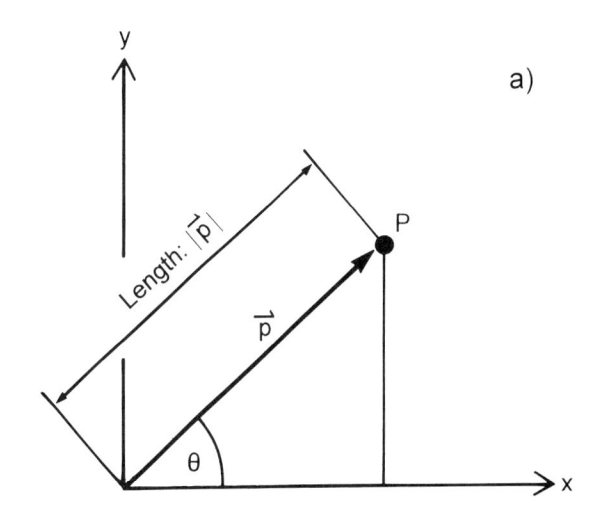

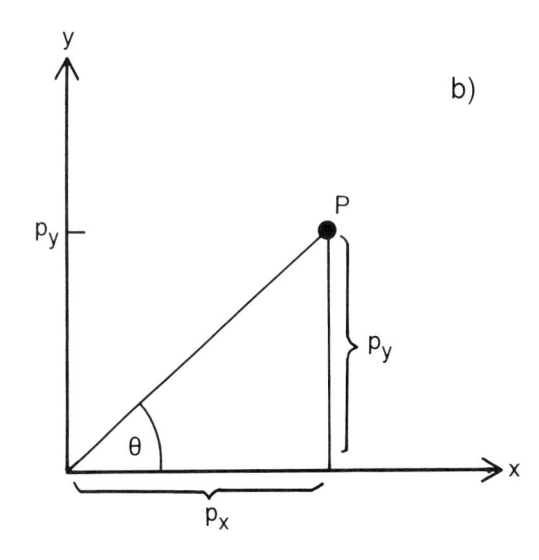

Fig. 24.12: Representation of the position of a point P using polar coordinates. (a) Definition of angle θ and length of vector, $|\mathbf{p}|$. (b) Sketch highlighting the trigonometric relations between the polar coordinates and the Cartesian coordinates.

$$\cos\theta = \frac{p_x}{|\boldsymbol{p}|} \quad (35)$$

With the basic vector definitions established, the fundamental vector operations can be introduced.

Magnitude or length of a vector
With the Pythagorean theorem, we find for the triangle in the bottom sketch of Fig. 24.12:

$$|\boldsymbol{p}| = \sqrt{p_x^2 + p_y^2} \quad (36)$$

For example, the length of the two-dimensional vector **p** = (3, 4) is |**p**| = 5.

Vector addition **a** + **b** = **r**
The vector addition is sketched in Fig. 24.13. For practical applications, each component of a Cartesian coordinate system is added separately:

$$\begin{aligned}
x\text{-component}: & \quad a_x + b_x = r_x \\
y\text{-component}: & \quad a_y + b_y = r_y \\
z\text{-component}: & \quad a_z + b_z = r_z
\end{aligned} \quad (37)$$

Thus, all algebra rules apply, e.g. the commutative law in the form **a** + **b** = **b** + **a**.

Multiplication of a vector with a scalar n**a** = **r**
Again, the operation is done for each component separately:

$$\begin{aligned}
x\text{-component}: & \quad n\, a_x = r_x \\
y\text{-component}: & \quad n\, a_y = r_y \\
z\text{-component}: & \quad n\, a_z = r_z
\end{aligned} \quad (38)$$

Combining the multiplication and addition of vectors, we introduce the subtraction of vectors in the form: **a** − **b** = **a** + (−1)**b**.

Vector multiplication
There are two ways to multiply two vectors with each other. The scalar product or dot product leads to a scalar (**a** • **b** = r) and the vector product or cross product leads to a vector (**a** x **b** = **r**). In this textbook, we use only the scalar product. Fig. 24.14 illustrates that the scalar product of two vectors is related to the product of the lengths of the two vectors once one vector has been projected onto the direction of the other vector:

$$\boldsymbol{a} \bullet \boldsymbol{b} = |\boldsymbol{a}|\,|\boldsymbol{b}|\,\cos\phi \quad (39)$$

Special cases are $\phi = 90^0$ with **a** • **b** = 0, $\phi = 0^0$ with **a** • **b** = |**a**| |**b**|, and **a** • **a** = |**a**|^2.
The scalar product is again calculated using the components of the vectors:

$$\boldsymbol{a} \bullet \boldsymbol{b} = a_x b_x + a_y b_y\ (+\ a_z b_z) \quad (40)$$

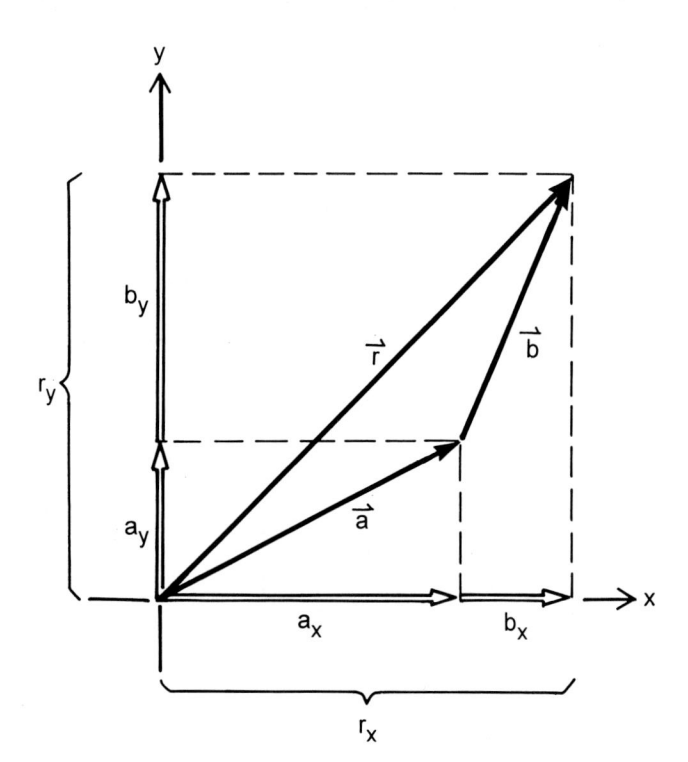

Fig. 24.13: Vector addition of vectors **a** and **b** and the relation of the components of the resulting vector **r** to the components of **a** and **b**, i.e., $a_x + b_x = r_x$ and $a_y + b_y = r_y$.

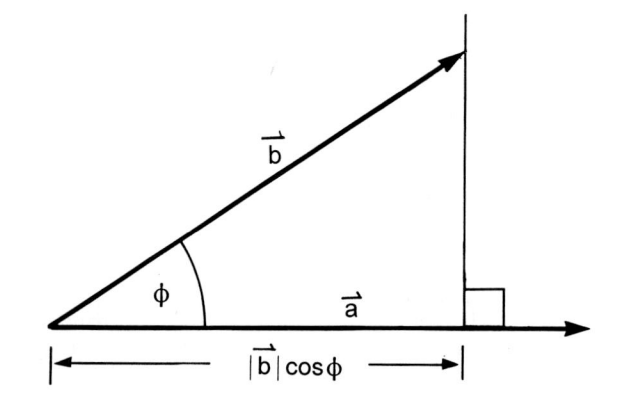

Fig. 24.14: Illustration of the origin of the factor $\cos\phi$ in the scalar product of vectors **a** and **b**.

For the Cartesian coordinate system with its orthogonal x–, y– and z–axes the components do not mix up in Eq. (40). Thus, vector algebra (with the exclusion of the vector product we do not discuss) is rather simple, as any operation is equivalent to the same algebraic operation for numbers, except that the operation is repeated for each component separately.

Example 24.7

(a) Calculate the angle between any two CH bonds in the methane molecule, shown in Fig. 24.11. This angle is called the tetrahedral angle for the sp^3–hybridization of carbon atoms in organic molecules. Hybridization is discussed in section 21.4.
(b) Using the length of 0.11 nm for a CH bond, determine the side length of the cube, l, and
(c) the distance between any two hydrogen atoms.

Solution part (a): We determine the vectors connecting the C atom with the hydrogen atoms H_A and H_B:

$$CH_A = -C + H_A =$$
$$(-\frac{l}{2}, -\frac{l}{2}, -\frac{l}{2}) + (0,0,0) = (-\frac{l}{2}, -\frac{l}{2}, -\frac{l}{2}) \quad (41)$$

$$CH_B = -C + H_B =$$
$$(-\frac{l}{2}, -\frac{l}{2}, -\frac{l}{2}) + (l,l,0) = (+\frac{l}{2}, +\frac{l}{2}, -\frac{l}{2}) \quad (42)$$

i.e., to get from the carbon atom to the hydrogen atom H_A, you have first to travel the vector **C** backwards to the origin, and then from the origin to the H atom forward along the vector $\mathbf{H_A}$. The angle θ, lying between the vectors, follows from the dot product:

$$CH_A \cdot CH_B = |CH_A| \cdot |CH_B| \cdot \cos\theta \quad (43)$$

The vector magnitudes on the right hand side are:

$$|CH_A| = |CH_B| = \sqrt{\left(\frac{l}{2}\right)^2 + \left(\frac{l}{2}\right)^2 + \left(\frac{l}{2}\right)^2}$$
$$|CH_A| = |CH_B| = \frac{\sqrt{3}}{2} l \quad (44)$$

and the dot product on the left hand side of Eq. (43) is calculated using Eq. (40):

$$CH_A \cdot CH_B =$$
$$(-0.5l, -0.5l, -0.5l) \cdot (0.5l, 0.5l, -0.5l) = \quad (45)$$
$$= -\frac{l^2}{4} - \frac{l^2}{4} + \frac{l^2}{4} = -\frac{l^2}{4}$$

thus, $\cos\theta = (-l^2/4)/(3l^2/4) = -\frac{1}{3}$ and $\theta = 109.47^0$.

Solution part (b): From Eq. (44), we know that $|CH_B| = \frac{1}{2}l\sqrt{3}$. With this length given as 0.11 nm we find from Fig. 24.11 that $l = 2|CH_B|/\sqrt{3} = 0.127$ nm.

Solution part (c): Since the distance between any two hydrogen atoms is equal to the magnitude of the vector connecting the two H atoms, we find for the example of the hydrogen atoms labelled A and B that the distance $|H_A H_B| = |-H_A + H_B| = (l^2 + l^2)^{1/2} = \sqrt{2} \cdot l = 0.180$ nm.

24.1.5. Summations

When adding more than two terms, it is convenient to use a condensed notation for the summation (sigma notation):

$$\sum_{i=1}^{N} F_i = F_1 + F_2 + F_3 + \ldots + F_N \quad (46)$$

in which i is an index that runs from 1 to N so that N terms of the quantity F are added. As an example, let us add the square–numbers from 1 to 5. This can be written in two ways:

$$1^2 + 2^2 + 3^2 + 4^2 + 5^2 = 55$$
$$\text{or} \quad \sum_{i=1}^{5} i^2 = 55 \quad (47)$$

24.2. Tables

24.2.1. Standard units

Mathematical and physical variables differ in that the latter carry a unit. 3.5 meters and 3.5 seconds are different quantities in physics, distinguished not by their numerical value (3.5) but by their unit. Many different units will be introduced in this textbook, however, all can be derived from just 7 basic units. These were internationally adopted in 1969 and are called the *Système International*. The SI units are listed in Table 24.4.

Table 24.4: SI–units

Length	[m]	meter
Time	[s]	second
Mass	[kg]	kilogram
Temperature	[K]	Kelvin
Amount of material	[mol]	mole
Electric current	[A]	Ampère
Luminous intensity	[Cd]	Candela

24.2.2. Standard prefixes

Some physical quantities take on very large or very small values, e.g., a chlorine ion (Cl$^-$) has a diameter of 1.81×10^{-10} meters and the Earth has a radius of about 6,370,000 meters. It is cumbersome to write numbers in either of these two forms. To avoid it, abbreviations have been introduced to express different multiples of ten (10^n) as shown in Table 24.5.

Table 24.5: Standard prefixes for terms of form 10^n

$n = 9$: G for "giga–"	$n = 6$: M for "mega–"
$n = 3$: k for "kilo–"	$n = -1$: d for "deci–"
$n = -2$: c for "centi–"	$n = -3$: m for "milli–"
$n = -6$: μ for "micro–"	$n = -9$: n for "nano–"
$n = -12$: p for "pico–"	$n = -15$: f for "femto–"

Examples:
$1.0 \ \mu m = 1.0 \times 10^{-6}$ m
$6.5 \text{ cm}^2 = 6.5 \cdot (10^{-2} \text{ m})^2 = 6.5 \times 10^{-4} \text{ m}^2$
$1.0 \ l$ (liter) $= 1.0 \text{ dm}^3 = 1 \cdot (10^{-1} \text{ m})^3 = 1 \times 10^{-3} \text{ m}^3$
The radius of the Earth is written as 6370 km and the diameter of the chlorine ion is 0.181 nm.

24.2.3. Typographic conventions

Brackets ([ ]) are used to indicate units when it is necessary to distinguish units and variables in formulas. An example is the letter m which may mean several different things in the same context, e.g. mass, then written as m, or the unit meter, then written as [m].

Scalars and vectors are defined in section 24.1.4. Scalars are printed in normal or in italic typeface, e.g. m or *m* for mass; vectors are printed in bold typeface, e.g. **p** for a position vector. In the figures, vectors are shown with an arrow above the parameter. The magnitude of a vector is then often written as |**p**|.

24.2.4. The Greek alphabet

Table 24.6: Greek capital and lower case letters

Alpha	A, α	Beta	B, β	Gamma	Γ, γ
Delta	Δ, δ	Epsilon	E, ϵ	Zeta	Z, ζ
Eta	H, η	Theta	Θ, θ	Iota	I, ι
Kappa	K, κ	Lambda	Λ, λ	Mu	M, μ
Nu	N, ν	Xi	Ξ, ξ	Omicron	O, o
Pi	Π, π	Rho	P, ρ	Sigma	Σ, σ
Tau	T, τ	Upsilon	Υ, υ	Phi	Φ, ϕ or φ
Chi	X, χ	Psi	Ψ, ψ	Omega	Ω, ω

24.2.5. Physical constants

The fundamental physical constants used throughout this text are summarized in Table 24.7. The table contains the name and symbol for each constant, a generally accepted value, and the value you will use for your work.

Materials constants occur often besides the fundamental physical constants. Materials constants take on various values depending on the choice of material while fundamental constants have one fixed value. An example is the density. We will use in many examples and discussions water since water is the biologically most important liquid. We use for the value of the density of water $1.0 \text{ g/cm}^3 = 1.0 \times 10^3 \text{ kg/m}^3$ at room temperature. However, the density variable cannot be replaced by this value automatically as other liquids or solids may also be considered.

A third type of constants are standard reference points. These are special values of a variable which may, however, resume other values in specific cases. An example is the air pressure. Under standard conditions (room temperature on the surface of the Earth) we use the value 1.0 atm.

Table 24.7: Fundamental physical constants (Sy = symbol).

Name	Sy	Value ± Uncertainty	Value used	Unit
Gravitational constant	G^*	$(6.6733 \pm 0.0031) \times 10^{-11}$	—	Nm^2/kg^2
Gravitational acceleration on surface of Earth	g	9.80665	9.8	m/s^2
Avogadro's constant	N_A	$(6.022169 \pm 0.000040) \times 10^{23}$	6×10^{23}	1/mol
Universal gas constant	R	8.31434 ± 0.00035	8.314	J/(mol K)
Boltzmann's constant	k	$(1.380622 \pm 0.000059) \times 10^{-23}$	1.38×10^{-23}	J/K
Molar volume of ideal gas		22.4136 ± 0.0006	22.4	litre
Electric force constant	k	—	9×10^9	Nm^2/Cb^2
Permeability of vacuum	μ_0	$4\pi \times 10^{-7}$	$4\pi \times 10^{-7}$	Tm/A
Permittivity of vacuum	ϵ_0	$(8.854185 \pm 0.00002) \times 10^{-12}$	8.85×10^{-12}	Cb^2/Nm^2
Elementary charge	e	$(1.6021917 \pm 0.0000070) \times 10^{-19}$	1.6×10^{-19}	Cb
Mass of electron	m_e	$(9.109558 \pm 0.000055) \times 10^{-31}$	9.1×10^{-31}	kg
Mass of proton	m_p	$(1.672614 \pm 0.000011) \times 10^{-27}$	1.67×10^{-27}	kg
Vacuum speed of light	c	$2.9977924562 \times 10^8 \pm 0.0037$ ppm	3×10^8	m/s
Planck's constant	h	$(6.626196 \pm 0.000050) \times 10^{-34}$	6.6×10^{-34}	J s
Stefan–Boltzmann constant	σ	$(5.66961 \pm 0.00096) \times 10^{-8}$	5.67×10^{-8}	$J/(sm^2K^4)$

24.2.6. Frequently used conversion factors

Pressure and energy are introduced in Chapter 5. From that point on, both concepts are used frequently. The conversion factors in Table 24.8 are based on the unit Pa (Pascal) as the SI–unit for pressure and the unit J (Joule) as the SI–unit for energy.

Table 24.8: Frequently used conversion factors

Pressure:
  1 atm = 1.013×10^5 Pa
  1 atm = 760 mmHg = 760 torr
  1 atm = 1.013 bar

Energy:
  1 cal = 4.184 J
  1 cal = 41.2929 cm^3 atm
  1 eV = 23.053 kcal/mol
  1 eV = 1.6×10^{-19} J

24.2.7. Periodic system of elements

A wide range of chemical elements and compounds play an important role in the issues discussed in this textbook. The periodic table (Table 24.9, see next page) provides a systematic overview of the chemical elements. The first value under the chemical symbol is the atomic number (corresponding to the number of positive charges in the nucleus and negative charges in the shell of a neutral atom); the last number is the atomic mass in atomic units (u), with an atomic unit (1 u) equal to 1/12th of the mass of a ^{12}C atom: 1 u = $1.6605677 \times 10^{-27}$ kg. A proton has a mass of 1.007276 u and an electron 5.49×10^{-4} u.

For some properties of matter, the periodic table is deceiving when not read carefully. For example, one wrong conclusion often drawn is to assume that atom sizes increase with atomic number. Fig. 9.8 shows the size of the atoms and the most frequent ions for a wide range of elements, indicating that heavier atoms may sometimes have smaller atomic or ionic sizes.

24.3. Problems

P–24.1
For the two solutions of a quadratic equation, Vieta showed:

$$(I) \quad x_1 + x_2 = -\frac{b}{a}$$

$$(II) \quad x_1 \cdot x_2 = \frac{c}{a}$$

(48)

in which we used the notations from Eq. (26). Show that both of Vieta's rules are correct.

Table 24.9: Periodic table. For each element, the symbol, atomic number and atomic mass (in unit [u]) are given.

Ia	IIa	IIIa	IVa	Va	VIa	VIIa	VIII			Ib	IIb	IIIb	IVb	Vb	VIb	VIIb	0
H 1 1.008																	He 2 4.003
Li 3 6.941	Be 4 9.012		⇐ Symbol ⇐ Atomic Number ⇐ Atomic Mass									B 5 10.81	C 6 12.01	N 7 14.01	O 8 16.00	F 9 19.00	Ne 10 20.18
Na 11 22.99	Mg 12 24.31											Al 13 26.98	Si 14 28.09	P 15 30.97	S 16 32.06	Cl 17 35.45	Ar 18 39.95
K 19 39.10	Ca 20 40.08	Sc 21 44.96	Ti 22 47.90	V 23 50.94	Cr 24 52.00	Mn 25 54.84	Fe 26 55.85	Co 27 58.93	Ni 28 58.70	Cu 29 63.55	Zn 30 65.38	Ga 31 69.72	Ge 32 72.59	As 33 74.92	Se 34 78.96	Br 35 79.90	Kr 36 83.80
Rb 37 85.47	Sr 38 87.62	Y 39 88.91	Zr 40 91.22	Nb 41 92.91	Mo 42 95.94	Tc 43 —	Ru 44 101.1	Rh 45 102.9	Pd 46 106.4	Ag 47 107.9	Cd 48 112.4	In 49 114.8	Sn 50 118.7	Sb 51 121.8	Te 52 127.6	J 53 126.9	Xe 54 131.3
Cs 55 132.9	Ba 56 137.3	La† 57 138.9	Hf 72 178.5	Ta 73 180.9	W 74 183.9	Re 75 186.2	Os 76 190.2	Ir 77 192.2	Pt 78 195.1	Au 79 197.0	Hg 80 200.6	Tl 81 204.4	Pb 82 207.2	Bi 83 209.0	Po 84 —	At 85 —	Rn 86 —
Fr 87 —	Ra 88 —	Ac‡ 89 —															

† Lanthanides: Ce, Pr, Nd, Pm, Sm, Eu, Gd, Tb, Dy, Ho, Er, Tm, Yb, Lu
‡ Actinides: Th, Pa, U, Np, Pu, Am, Cm, Bk, Cf, Es, Fm, Md, No, Lr

P–24.2
(a) Plot in double–logarithmic representation the two functions (I) $y = 4x^2$ and (II) $y = 4x^2 + 1$ in the interval $0.1 \leq x \leq 10.0$.
(b) What draw–back of double–logarithmic plots can you identify?

P–24.3
For the function $y = 2e^{3x}$
(a) plot y versus x for $0 \leq x \leq 2$,
(b) plot lny versus x for $0 \leq x \leq 2$,
(c) show that the slope of the logarithmic plot is 3, and
(d) show that the intercept of the logarithmic plot is ln 2.

P–24.4
For the function $y = 4x^3$
(a) plot y versus x for $0 \leq x \leq 4$,
(b) plot lny versus lnx for $0 \leq x \leq 4$,
(c) show that the slope of the double–logarithmic plot is 3, and
(d) show that the intercept of the double–logarithmic plot is ln 4.

P–24.5
We develop an empirical formula connecting the wing span and the mass of some species able to fly. Then we evaluate a few interesting consequences. (The first to make these considerations was Leonardo da Vinci).
(a) Use the data in Table 24.10 to draw a double–logarithmic plot lnW versus lnM where W is the wing span and M is the mass. Determine the constants a and b in a power–law relation $W = a M^b$.
(b) The largest animal believed ever to fly was a pterosaur species found in Texas and named Quetzalcoatlus northropi. This animal lived in the late Cretaceous 138 to 65 million years ago. It had an 11 m wing span. What is the maximum mass of this pterosaur? Note: the largest wing span of a living species is 3.6 m for the Wandering Albatross.
(c) Assume that man wishes to fly like a bird. What minimum wing span would be needed for a person of 70 kg to take off?

Table 24.10: Mass and wing span of various birds.

Bird	Wing span [cm]	Mass [g]
Hummingbird	7	10
Sparrow	15	50
Dove	50	400
Andean Condor	320	11500
Californian Condor	290	12000

P–24.6
(a) What is the sum of the two vectors **a** = (5, 5) and **b** = (–14, 5)?
(b) What are the magnitude and direction of **a** + **b**?
(c) What is the angle between **a** and **b**?

P–24.7
If vector **a** is added to vector **b**, the result is the vector **c** = (6, 2). If **b** is subtracted from **a**, the result is the vector **d** = (–5, 8).
(a) What is the magnitude of vector **a**?
(b) What is the magnitude of vector **b**?
(c) What is the angle between **a** and **b**?

P–24.8
Fig. 24.15(a) shows a shear fracture of the neck of the femur. In a shear fracture opposite fracture faces have slid past each other. Fig. 24.15(b) shows a sketch of a fracture with the net displacement AB along the fracture plane.
(a) What is the net displacement AB for a horizontal slip of 4.0 mm and a vertical slip of 3.0 mm?
(b) If the fracture plane is tilted by $\theta = 20°$ to the plane perpendicular to the bone, by how much have the two bones moved relative to each other along the bone's axis?

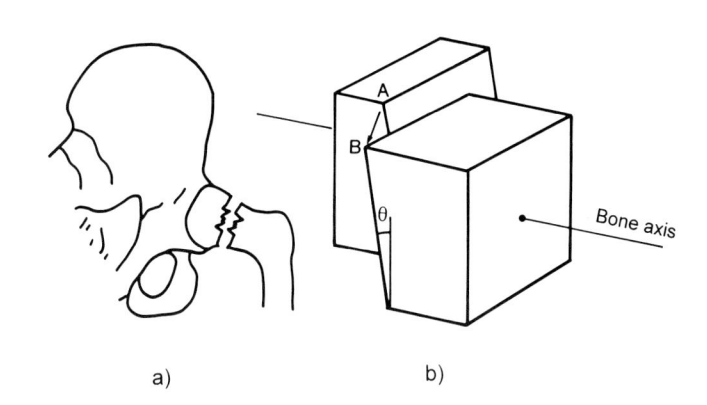

Fig. 24.15 for problem P–24.8

P–24.9
Fig. 24.16 shows a back view of an adult male and female human body (accompanied by two children).
(a) For a typical male, the vertical distance from the bottom of the feet to the neck is $d_1 = 150$ cm and the distance from the neck to the hand is $d_2 = 80$ cm. Find the vector describing the position of the hand relative to the bottom of the feet if the angle at which the arm is held is $\theta = 35°$ to the vertical.
(b) Repeat the calculation for a typical female with $d_1 = 130$ cm, $d_2 = 65$ cm and the same angle θ.

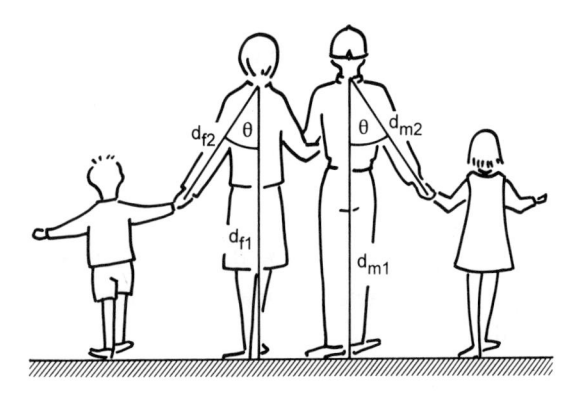

Fig. 24.16 for problem P–24.9

P–24.10
Fig. 24.17 shows (top) a front view and (bottom) a side view of a human skull. Two perpendicular projections such as these are often used to determine distances and angles in three–dimensional bodies, e.g. for focussed radiation therapy with high energy beams.
(a) Assuming that the diameter of the skull at the dashed line shown with the top skull in Fig. 24.17 is 16 cm, determine the distance from the tip of the nasal bone (point A) to the center of the last molar in the upper jaw (point B).
(b) Determine the angle between two lines connecting the point halfway between the two central maxilla incisor teeth and the last maxilla molars on either side.
(c) Compare the result in (b) with the result obtained from Fig. 24.18, which shows a top view of the permanent dentition.

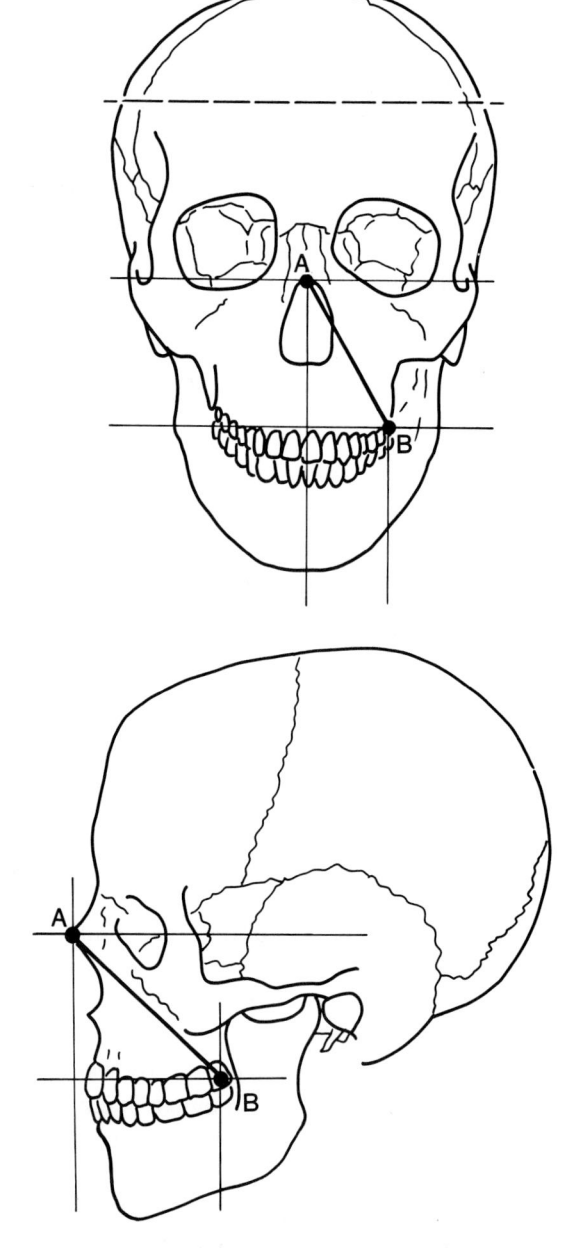

Fig. 24.17 for problem P–24.10(a,b)

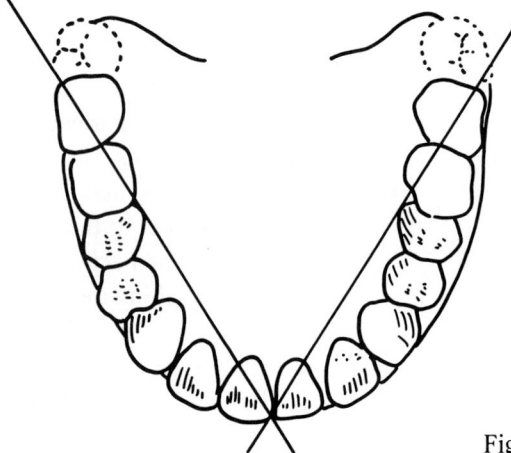

Fig. 24.18 for problem P–24.10(c)

Index

[A] 376
Abdominal muscle 147
Abductor muscle 85, 88
Aberration 488
Absorbed dose 604
Absorption 452, 541
Absorption coefficient 452
Absorption length 453
Absorption spectroscopy 584
Acceleration 18, 36, 554
Acceleration, average 19
Acceleration, centrifugal 556
Acceleration, centripetal 555
Acceleration, gravitational 17, 552
Acceleration, instantaneous 19, 36
Accommodation 501
Acetabulum 86
Acetone 351
Acetylene 594
Achilles tendon 15, 16, 26, 79
Acoustic environment 441
Acoustic lens 2
Acoustic reflex threshold 471
Actin filament 12, 410
Action potential, heart muscle 400
Action/reaction forces 26
Activation energy 211
Active ion transport 205
Active muscle force 412
Activity (radiation) 610
Adenine 221
Adenosine diphosphate 103
Adenosine triphosphate 103, 369
Adiabatic coefficient 176
Adiabatic process 175
ADP 103
Aerobic reactions 104
Aerospace medicine 552
Age, Earth 201
Age, sun 203
Air 340, 341
Air flow resistance 149, 185
Air pressure 291, 550
Air travel 348
Algal bloom 215
Alpha–decay 609
Alpha–particle 282, 564, 580, 611
Altitude 292, 348
Alveolar pressure 148
Alveolus 212, 215, 304, 344
Amino acid 222
Ammonia 94
Amniocentesis 578
Amniotic fluid 578
Amoeba 10
Ampère, André Marie 376, 529
Amphipathic 195

Amplitude 427, 448
Anabolic reaction 104, 234
Anaerobic reactions 104
Analyzer 536
Anaphylactic shock 341
Aneurysm 338, 418
Angle of incidence 486
Angle of reflection 486
Angle of refraction 492
Angular frequency 428, 619
Angular magnification 515
Angular momentum 582, 618
Anion 261
Ankle joint 66
Annelid 10
Annihilation factor 245
Anoxia 347
Antenna 533
Anterior chamber 482
Anti–binding orbital 592
Anti–node 457
Anvil 465
Aorta 319, 327, 330, 335, 398, 418
Apex 468
Apollo missions 552
Aqueous solution 259
Archimedes' principle 295
Area rule (Kepler's laws) 582
Areal charge density 270
Argonauts 297
Arrhenius, Svante 209
Arrhenius plot 210
Arterialize 315
Arteriole 330
Arteriosclerosis 337, 418
Artery 316, 337, 398
Artificial hip replacement 65
Artificial lens (eye) 505
Asexual reproduction 247
Aspen leaf 322
Astigmatism 502
Aston, Francis 570
Astronaut 552, 565
Atlas (bone) 66
[atm] 645
Atmosphere 342, 551
Atmospheric pressure 291
Atom 580
Atomic model 579
Atomic nucleus 284, 606
Atomic number 608
Atomic shell 585, 602
Atomic spectrum 585
Atomic spin 624
ATP 102, 369
ATPS 147
Atrio ventricular node 400

Atrium 398
Attenuation coefficient 604
Audiology 5
Auditory canal 453, 464
Auditory hair cell 468
Australopithecus afarensis 87
Australopithecus robustus 85
AV–bundle 400
Average acceleration 19
Average velocity 18
Aviation medicine 552
AV–node 400
Avogadro, Amedeo 158
Avogadro's number 159
Axis, optical 487, 498
Axis, rotation 62, 72
Axis (bone) 66
Axon 361, 386
Axoplasm 361

Back muscle 97
Back synapse, lower 360
Bacteria 105, 195, 216, 528
Balance 48
Ball and socket joint 62
Balloon 297
Balmer series 585
[bar] 645
Basement membrane 332
Basilar membrane 468
Bat 443, 477
Bathysphere 419
Battery 365
Beadle, George 603
Beat 473
Becquerel, Henri 609
Bee 528
Beebe, Charles 419
Beer's law 452, 604
Belousov–Zhabotinskii reaction 245
Benard cells 243
Bent lever arm 82
Benzene 351
Bernoulli, Daniel 320
Bernoulli's equation 320
Beta–decay 609
Biceps muscle 68, 95, 96
Biceps tendon 98
Bilirubin 579
Binding energy 607
Biological membrane model 194
Bioluminescence 597
Biosphere 550
Biot, Jean 537
Bipedal 87
Birch 307
Bird 28, 128, 334

650

Birth canal 90
Black body radiation 541
Black sea 297
Blimp 297, 309
Blind spot 484
Bloch, Felix 628
Blood 312, 340, 342, 354
Blood cell 212, 342, 395, 475
Blood flow 313
Blood pressure 293, 337
Blood volume 315
Bloom, algal 215
Blubber (whale) 200
Bohr, Niels 580
Bohr radius 584
Bohr's model of hydrogen atom 580
Bohr's postulates 580
Bohr's quantum condition 583
Boiling 348
Boltzmann, Ludwig 162, 230
Boltzmann's constant 166
Bone (material) 416, 436
Bone conduction 5
Bone density 563
Born, Max 430
Bowman's capsule 332
Boyle, Robert 151
Boyle's law 151
[Bq] 610
Brace 96
Brachial artery 337
Brackett series 585
Brain 298
Brain size, mammals 8
Brain size, primates 87, 90
Bremsstrahlung 601
Bronchial tree 212
BTPS 147
Bubble 300
Bulk modulus 415
Buoyancy 295
Buoyant force 52, 296

c (speed of light) 493, 535, 539
c (speed of sound) 443, 446, 447
[^{0}C] 130
^{14}C dating 614
^{14}C decay 614
Ca ion 400
CaCO$_3$ 536
Caisson disease 347
[cal] 132, 645
Calcaneus 16, 26, 80
Calcium ion 400
Calf muscle 16, 26
Calorie 132
Calorimeter 231, 232

Capacitance 371
Capacitor 371
Capillarity 305
Capillary 212, 215, 306, 319, 330
Carbohydrate 234
Carbon dating 614
Carbon–dioxide 159, 215, 341
Cardiac muscle 11, 400
Cardiac pacemaker cell 399
Cardiovascular system 312
Carnot, Sadi 179
Carnot process 179, 225, 249
Carpometacarpal joint 66
Cartilage 11
Casimir, H. B. 238
Cast 98
Catabolic reaction 104, 234
Cataract 602
Cation 261
[Cb] 254
Cell, eukaryotic 195, 221
Cell, muscle 12
Cell membrane (human) 194
Cell nucleus 221
Celsius, Anders 130
Celsius' thermometer 130
Center–of–mass 75, 91
Central force 582
Centrifugal acceleration 556
Centrifuge 557, 575
Centripetal acceleration 555
Cerebrospinal fluid 298
Cervical vertebra 66
Cetacea 2
Chadwick, James 607
Characteristic X–rays 601
Charge, electric 253
Charge, elementary 255
Charge density 270
Charles, Jacques 151
Charles' law 153
Chemical bond 430
Chemical equilibrium 237
Chemical potential 352, 364
Chemical shift 628
Chemiluminescence 597
Cherry 354
Chimpanzee 8, 87
Chlorine ion 261, 277, 387
Chloroform 351
Chromosome 221
Ciliary muscle 482, 501
Circular motion 553
Cl ion 387
Claisen reaction 612
Clausius, Rudolf 162, 225
Closed system 111

Closed tube 454
Close–grip lat pulldown 27
Clothes 198, 215
Cnidarian 10
CO$_2$ 159, 215, 341
Cochlea 468
Cochlear duct 468
Codon 222
Coefficient, absorption 452
Coefficient, adiabatic 176
Coefficient, attenuation 604
Coefficient, diffusion 206
Coefficient, efficiency 180, 225
Coefficient, linear expansion 130
Coefficient, Onsager's 240, 248
Coefficient, thermal conductivity 196
Coefficient, viscosity 323, 324
Coefficient of kinetic friction 55
Coefficient of static friction 54
Cohesion 289
Collagen 416, 418
Collapsed lung 304
Collision 163, 185
Color 526
Color receptors 543
Color triangle 543
Color vision 526
Common descent 222
Compact bone 416
Complexity 6
Compound microscope 518
Compressibility 415
Compression 117, 414
Compton effect 604
Concave mirror 487
Concentration curls 23
Concentration gradient 207, 238
Conduction, electric 376
Conduction, heat 196
Conductivity, electric 379
Conductivity, thermal 196, 248
Conductor 376
Cones 526
Confined medium 453
Conical pendulum 557
Coniferous trees 94
Conservation, angular momentum 582, 620
Conservation of energy 110, 128, 135, 281, 426
Conservation of momentum 53
Constant gradient (MRI) 630
Contact angle 306
Contact force 16, 34
Continuity, Equation of 318
Convection 198, 243
Converging lens 497

651

Conversation 472
Convex mirror 487
Copper 377, 379
Cornea 482, 501
Corrective lens 503
Corti, Alfonso de 468
Cosmic ray 540, 564, 605
Coulomb, Charles de 254
Coulomb force 254
Coulomb's law 254
Countercurrent flow 203, 207
Cousteau, Jacques 358
Covalent bond 260, 591
Creationism 246
Cretaceous 139, 246
Crick, Francis 221, 603
Crow 128
Crutches 57
Cuff (blood pressure measurement) 337
Curie, Marie and Pierre 609
Current, electric 376
Current density 377
Current loop 621
Cyclic motion 427
Cyclic process 177, 226
Cyclotron frequency 569
Cytosine 221

da Vinci, Leonardo 647
Dalton, John 344
Dalton's law 344
Damping 460
Dandelion 354
Darwin, Charles 201, 222
Dating 14C 614
[dB] 451, 471
de Broglie, Louis 520, 581
de Broglie wavelength 581
Debye–Hueckel theory 261
Decay, alpha 609
Decay, beta 609
Decay, radioactive 609
Decay, ^{14}C 614
Decay constant 609
Decay length (nerve) 385
Decay time (nerve) 380
Decibel 451, 471
Defibrillator 374
Deformation 290, 413
Dehydration 354, 358
Deltoid muscle 95
Dendrite 361
Density 48, 159, 290, 308, 563
Density variation 445
Dentist's mirror 491
Deoxyribonucleic acid 221, 268
Depolarization 363, 400

Depolarization vector 404
Descartes, René 192, 485
Deuterium 615
Diaphragm 147
Diastolic pressure 293, 337
Dielectric 372
Dielectric constant 372
Dielectric strength 395
Diffusion 205
Diffusion, facilitated 205
Diffusion, interstitial 211
Diffusion, substitutional 211
Diffusion coefficient 206
Diffusion length 212
Dinosaur 104, 140, 434
Diopter 495, 500
Dipole, electric 264
Dipole moment 266
Disorder 231
Disperse system 343
Dispersion, light 539
Displacement 112, 446
Distance, image 489, 498
Distance, object 489, 498
Diverging lens 497
Diver's paralysis 347
Diving 308, 331, 344, 477, 508
Diving board 79
DNA 221, 268
Dobzhansky, Theodosius 223
Dolphin 2, 443
Doppler, Christian 475
Doppler effect 4, 474
Doppler shift 476
Doppler ultrasound 475
Dose 565, 604
Dose, equivalent 565, 611
Dose rate 605
Double–logarithmic plot 638
[dpt] 495, 500
Drift velocity 376
Driving force 238, 240
Droplet 300
Dufour effect 248, 249
Dynamic equilibrium 366
Dynamo theory (Earth) 573
e (elementary charge) 255
E. coli 105
Ear 2, 32, 464
Eardrum 428, 465, 478
Earth, age 201
Earth, composition 573
Earth magnetic field 574
ECG 403
Echo–location 4, 443, 477
Ecosystem 7, 108
Ectotherm 106

Eddy current 534
Edema 354
Efficiency coefficient 180, 225
Egg 414
Egg shell 6, 194
Eigen, Manfred 245
Eigenvalue 588
Einstein, Albert 212, 485, 607
Einthoven, Willem 398, 405
El Greco 502
Elastic collision 163, 186
Elastic force 423
Elastic potential energy 425
Elasticity 412
Elastin 416, 418
Elbow joint 66, 68
Electric charge 253
Electric conduction 376
Electric conductivity 379
Electric current 376
Electric dipole 264
Electric dipole moment 266
Electric drift 368
Electric energy 271
Electric field 262, 370
Electric force 254
Electric potential 278
Electric potential energy 271
Electric shock 395
Electric work 271
Electrocardiogram 403
Electrochemical equilibrium 364
Electrochemical half–cell 365
Electrochemical process 362
Electromagnet 533
Electromagnetic radiation 570, 581
Electromagnetic spectrum 540
Electromagnetic wave 533
Electromotive force 366
Electron 255, 277, 366
Electron, wavelength 520
Electron lens 520
Electron microscope 520
Electron spin resonance 621
Electron volt [eV] 645
Electrophoresis 273
Electropositive behavior 591
Electrotonus spread 382
Elementary charge 255
Elementary particles 255
Elephant 8
Ellipsoid joint 62
Embolism 347
emf 366
Emission spectroscopy 585
Emulsion 341, 343
Enantiomer 538

Endolymph 46, 468
Endoskeleton 10
Endotherm 106, 131
Energy, activation 211
Energy, binding 607
Energy, elastic 425
Energy, electric 271
Energy, food 141, 234
Energy, ground state 586
Energy, internal 110, 165
Energy, ionization 585
Energy, kinetic 122
Energy, mechanical 122
Energy, nuclear 608
Energy, photon 541
Energy, potential 127, 425
Energy, sound wave 450
Energy, thermal 132
Energy, total 110
Energy, transition 626
Energy (definition) 121
Energy barrier 324, 608
Energy conservation 110, 128, 135, 281, 426
Energy conversion 109
Energy density (sound) 450
Energy flow 109
Energy stored in capacitor 372
Enthalpy 174, 231
Enthalpy of formation 233
Entropy 225, 234, 238
Entropy production 239, 243
Envelope (wave) 453
Environment 20, 110
Enzyme 222
Eocene 6
Eosine 596
Epidermis 34
Equation, Bernoulli's 320
Equation, Laplace's 447
Equation, lens maker 507
Equation, mirror 489
Equation, Nernst's 364
Equation, Onsager 240
Equation, Poisson's 176
Equation, Schrödinger 588
Equation, van der Waals 169
Equation of continuity 318
Equation of motion 24
Equations, Maxwell's 533
Equilibrium 109
Equilibrium, chemical 237
Equilibrium, dynamic 366
Equilibrium, electrochemical 364
Equilibrium, mechanical 20, 75, 290
Equilibrium, rotational 75
Equilibrium, thermal 131, 168

Equilibrium state 111
Equipotential line 281, 405
Equivalent dose 565, 611
Erect gait 109
Ergometer 135, 136
Erythroblastosis 578
Erythrocyte 212, 395, 475
Escherichia coli 105
ESR 621
Ethane 594
Ethylene 594
Eucalyptus tree 307
Eukaryotic cell 195, 221
[eV] 645
EVA 605
Evolution 222, 245
Evolutionary reversal 6, 90
Excitation 585
Exhalation 149, 183
Exoskeleton 10
Expansion, gas 117
Expansion coefficient, linear 130
Expiratory reserve volume 145
Exposure dose 604
Extended rigid body 71
External force 37
Extinction 246
Extracellular fluid 342, 362
Extra–vehicular activity 605
Eye 482, 501
Eye, color vision 526
Eye defects 502
Eye disease 502
Eyepiece 518

[F] 371
Facilitated diffusion 205
Farad 371
Faraday, Michael 371, 534
Faraday cage 571
Faraday's constant 364
Farsightedness 503
Fat 234
Fatigue 102
Fechner, Gustav 440
Femur 200, 416
Fermat, Pierre de 492
Fermat's principle 491
Ferris wheel 559
Fetal erythroblastosis 578
Fibrillation 408
Fibula 80
Fick, Adolf 206
Fick's law 206
Field, electric 262, 370
Field, magnetic 529, 567
Field emission microscope 520

Field force 16, 560
Field of vision 484
Filtration 331
Fire fly 597
Fission 609
Fixed axis 72
Flat interface 492
Flat mirror 486
Floating 296
Flow, blood 313
Flow, laminar 317
Flow, non–viscous 317
Flow, turbulent 332
Flow, viscous 322
Flow line 317
Flow rate 313, 318
Flow resistance 315, 326, 330
Flow tube 317
Fluid 312
Fluid mosaic model 194
Fluke 6, 200
Fluorescence 596
Flute 461
Flux, generalized 238, 240
Foam 343
Focal length 488, 497
Focal point 488, 497
Fog 343
Food 141, 234
Food consumption 108
Foot 79
Force, action/reaction pair 26
Force, buoyant 52, 296
Force, central 582
Force, contact 16, 34
Force, Coulomb 254
Force, elastic 423
Force, electric 254
Force, electromotive 366
Force, external 37
Force, field 16, 560
Force, generalized 238, 240
Force, gravitational 17, 552
Force, Lorentz 568
Force, magnetic 529
Force, muscle 411
Force, net 20
Force, normal 17
Force, nuclear 608
Force, restoring 422
Force (definition) 16
Force amplification (ear) 467
Forensic science 273
Formation factor 245
Formula, thin lens 499
Fosbury flop 91
Fourier, Jean Baptiste 196, 461

653

Fourier analysis 462
Fourier's law 196, 248
Fovea centralis 482
Free energy 236, 352, 364
Free–body–diagram 20
French flag 539
Frequency 428, 443
Frequency, angular 428
Frequency spectrum 458
Friction 53
Frog muscle 396
Fulcrum 79
Full body dose 566
Fusion 203
Future 229

g (gravitational acceleration) 17, 552
[G] 530
Gagarin, Yuri 552
Galen 360
Galvani, Luigi 360
Gamma ray 540
Gas 114, 151
Gas, ideal 158
Gas, kinetic theory 162
Gas constant 159
Gas pressure 115
Gas volume 115
Gauge pressure 292
Gauss, Carl 530
Generalized flux 238, 240
Generalized force 238, 240
Geometrical optics 485
Geostationary orbit 561
Geothermal effect 201, 214
Gerlach, Walther 624
Ghost 545
Gibbs, Josiah 236
Gibbs free energy 236, 352, 364
Gills (fish) 208
Ginglymoid joint 62
Glansdorff, P. 238
Glare 538
Glasses, prescription 503, 504
Glaucoma 502
Gliding joint 64
Glomerulus 332
Glucose 537
Gluteal muscle 88
Glycerine 215
Golgi, Camillo 222
Golgi apparatus 222
Gortex 307
Gradient 207, 238
Gradualism 222
Graphical analysis 635
Graves' disease 502

Gravitational acceleration 17, 552
Gravitational constant 17
Gravitational force 17, 552
Gravitational potential energy 127
Gravity 17, 32, 552
Gray 565, 605
Great trochanter 86
Greater cardiovascular system 313
Greenhouse effect 543
Ground state 586
Guanine 221
Guericke, Otto von 115
[Gy] 565, 605

Hahn, E. 628
Hair 126
Half–cell (electrochemistry) 365
Half–life 610
Halley, Edmund 620
Hammer (ear) 465
Harmonic motion 427
Harmonic oscillator 428
Harmonic waves 448
Harmonics 456
Harvey, William 398
HCl molecule 91, 269, 430
Hearing 2, 450, 470
Heart 177, 188, 398
Heart, muscle 401
Heart failure 356
Heat (definition) 132
Heat capacity 132, 172, 232, 289
Heat conduction 196
Heat convection 198, 243
Heat current 196
Heat death 229
Heat flow 196
Heat reservoir 170
Heat transfer rate 198
Heat–exchanger 203
Heel bone 16, 26, 80
Heisenberg, Werner 592
Heisenberg's uncertainty relation 592
Helicotrema 468
Helium 585
Helmholtz, Hermann von 135, 461, 470
Helox 358
Hematokrit 340
Hertz, Heinrich 428, 606
Hess, Viktor 474
Hindenburg (zeppelin) 297
Hinge joint 62
Hip bone 88
Hip joint 64, 85
Hodgkin, Alan 382
Hodgkin–Huxley model 386
Homeostasis 354

Homer 544
Hominid 87
homogeneous solution 343
Hooke, Robert 220, 420
Hooke's law 420
Hot air balloon 297
Human cell 195
Human voice 458
Humerus 72
Humid air 285
Humidify 342
Huxley, Andrew 382
Huygens, Christiaan 485
Hybridization 594
Hydration shell 261
Hydraulic stress 414, 421
Hydrogen atom 580
Hydrogen bond 267, 288
Hydrogen molecule 591
Hydrophilic 195
Hydrophobic 195
Hydrostatic skeleton 10
Hyperopia 502
Hyperoxia 347
Hypertonic 354
Hyperventilation 346
Hypodermic syringe 338
Hypoproteinemia 356
Hypothalamus 131
Hypothermia 334
Hypotonic 354
Hypovolemic shock 354
Hypoxia 313, 349
[Hz] 14, 428

^{131}I 613
Ice 289
Ideal dynamic fluid 317
Ideal gas 158
Ideal gas law 158
Ideal solution 350
Ideal stationary fluid 290
IL 451
Image 486, 498
Image distance 489, 498
Impermeable 193
Impulse, nerve 15, 363, 381
Incidence angle 486
Incompressible 290
Index of refraction 492, 539
Induction 534
Inelastic collision 187
Inelastic deformation 415
Inertia 20
Inflamation 356
Inflation, lung 304
Infrared 540

Infrared spectroscopy 595
Infusion 309
Inhalation 149, 183
Inner ear 2, 468
Insect 437
Inspiratory reserve volume 145
Instantaneous acceleration 19, 36
Instantaneous velocity 18, 36
Insulator 378
Intensity, sound 450
Intensity, spectrum 601
Intensity, X–ray 601
Intensity attenuation 604
Intensity level (IL) 451
Intercostal muscle 97, 148
Interface, flat 492
Interface, spherical 495, 506
Internal energy 110, 165
International Space Station 550, 561
Interstitial diffusion 211
Interstitium 342, 364
Inuit 493
Ion 260
Ionic bond 260
Ionic character 269
Ionic solution 259, 364
Ionization 585, 604
IR spectroscopy 595
Iris 482
Irradiance, solar 543, 565
Irreversible process 223, 236
Isentropic process 231
Isobaric nuclei 609
Isobaric process 173
Isochoric process 171, 224
Isolated superstructure 111
Isolated system 52, 110
Isomer 609
Isothermal process 172, 224
Isotonic 354
Isotope 609
ISS 550, 561

[J] 113, 132, 645
Jaw, lower 81
Joint 62
Joint, ankle 66
Joint, ball–and–socket 62
Joint, carpometacarpal 66
Joint, elbow 66, 68
Joint, ellipsoid 62, 64
Joint, ginglymoid 62
Joint, gliding 64
Joint, hinge 62, 66
Joint, hip 64, 85
Joint, knee 66
Joint, pivot 62, 66

Joint, saddle 62, 66
Joint, shoulder 64
Joint, spheroid 62, 64
Joint, synovial 64
Joule, James Prescott 132
Jurin's law 306

K ion 279, 386, 400
[K] 154
Kant, Immanuel 620
Kelvin, Lord 154, 201, 225
Kelvin's temperature scale 154
Kepler, Johannes 582
Kepler's laws 582, 620
Keratin–phosphate 104
[kg] 16
Kidney 313, 331
Kilogram 16
Kinematic equations 123, 138
Kinetic energy 122
Kinetic friction 54
Kinetic gas theory 162
Kirchhoff, Gustav 327
Kirchhoff's laws 327
Knee 56, 66
Knee cap 56
K–shell 603

[*l*] (liter) 644
Lamarck, Jean de 222
Laminar flow 317
Laplace's equation 447
Laplace's law 301
Larynx 463
Latency time 472
Latent heat 122, 131, 289
Latissimus dorsi muscle 97
Lavoisier, Antoine de 254, 341
Law, Beer's 452, 604
Law, Boyle's 151
Law, Charles' 153
Law, Coulomb's 254
Law, Dalton's 344
Law, Fick's 206
Law, Fourier's 196, 248
Law, gravity (Newton) 17
Law, Hooke's 420
Law, ideal gas 158
Law, Jurin's 306
Law, Kirchhoff's 327
Law, Laplace's 301
Law, Ohm's 326, 378
Law, Pascal's 290
Law, Poiseuille's 325
Law, Raoult's 350, 364
Law, Snell's 492
Law, Stefan's 542

Law, van't Hoff's 353, 356
Law of inertia 20
Law of reflection 486
Law of refraction 493
Laws, Kepler's 582, 620
Laws, Newton's 17, 36, 556
Laws, thermodynamics 111, 130, 225, 235
LCAO–method 591
Le Châtelier principle 243
Lead (ECG) 405
Leeuwenhoek, Antoni van 514
Lemon peel 296
Lenard, Philipp 606
Lens 497, 501
Lens, converging 497
Lens, corrective 503
Lens, diverging 497
Lens, electron 520
Lens, eye 482, 501
Lens, objective 518
Lens, ocular 518
Lens, thick 497
Lens, thin 497
Lens maker's equation 507
Lenz's rule 534
Lesser cardiovascular system 313
Lever arm 79
Life 10
Life–time (state) 610
Ligament 66
Light 485
Light, polarized 535
Light, speed of 493, 535, 539
Light absorption 541
Light dispersion 539
Light emission 594
Light microscope 516
Light ray 485
Light source 486
Lightning bug 597
Liley's method 579
Linear combination of atomic orbitals 591
Linear expansion coefficient 130
Linear plot 635
Linear polarized light 535
Lip 463
Liquid 288
Liter 644
Locomotion 10
Logarithmic plot 636
Longitudinal wave 445
Lorentz, Hendrik 568
Lorentz force 568
Lower back synapse 360
Lower jaw bone 81

L–shell 603
Lucy 87
Luminescence 597
Lung, collapsed 148, 304
Lungs 147, 160, 181, 304, 313, 463
Lyman series 585
Lysosome 222

[m] 644
Macromolecule 216, 357
Macula 33, 46
Magellan, Ferdinand 612
Magnet 527, 534
Magnetic break 534
Magnetic dipole moment 621
Magnetic field 529, 567
Magnetic force 529
Magnetic material 528
Magnetic quantum number 587
Magnetic resonance imaging 629
Magnetism 528, 567
Magnetite 528
Magnetotactic bacteria 528
Magnification 490, 499
Magnification, angular 515
Magnifier glass 516
Mandible 81
Mantis shrimp 28
Mars 268, 550, 562, 612
Mass 24
Mass attenuation coefficient 604
Mass extinction 246
Mass flow rate 318
Mass number 608
Mass spectrometer 570, 575
Masseter 81
Maxwell, James 162, 485, 533
Maxwell–Boltzmann velocity distribution 168, 230
Maxwell's equations 533
Mayer, Julius von 132
Mayow, John 341
Mayr, Ernst 223
Mean life–time 610
Mechanical energy 122
Mechanical equilibrium 20, 75, 290
Mediterranean Sea 297, 544
Meissner's corpuscle 124, 139
Melon 2
Melville, Herman 200
Membrane 192, 279, 332, 364
Merkel's corpuscle 34
Metabolic rate 106, 139, 141
Metabolism 102
Metallic bond 259
Meter 644
Methane 91, 641, 643

Microscope, compound 518
Microscope, electron 520
Microscope, field emission 520
Microscope, light 516
Microwave 540, 570
Middle ear 465
Migration 140
Millikan, Robert 255
Millikan's experiment 255, 271, 285
Mirror 486
Mirror, concave 487
Mirror, convex 487
Mirror, dentist 491
Mirror, flat 486
Mirror, sign convention 491
Mirror, spherical 487
Mirror equation 489
Mitochondrion 103, 104
Mixed phases 343
[mmHg] 292
[mol] 158
Molar heat capacity 133, 172
Molar mass 158
Mole fraction 344
Molecular orbital 591
Molecule 591
Mollusk, eye 483
Moment of inertia 619
Momentum, angular 582, 619
Momentum (definition) 52
Momentum conservation 53
Monet, Claude 524
Montgolfier, Joseph 552
Moseley, Henry 603
Motion, cyclic 427
Motion, rotational 62
Motion, simple harmonic 427
Motion, uniform circular 553
Mount Everest 292
MRI 629
M–shell 603
Muller, Hermann 603
Murein 195
Muscle 10
Muscle, cardiac 11, 400
Muscle, skeletal 11, 62
Muscle, smooth 11
Muscle cell 12
Muscle force 411
Mutation, neutral 247
Mutation, random 223, 247
Myelin sheath 361
Myelinated nerve 361, 391, 393
Myofibril 12
Myopia 504
Myosin filament 12, 410

[N] 20
N_2 341, 347
Na ion 261, 277, 386, 400
Na/K pump 368, 369
NaCl 363, 430
Nansen, Fritjof 199
Natural selection 222
Near point 501
Nearsightedness 504
Nematode 10
Neonatal respiratory distress syndrome 304
Nephron 332
Nephrotic syndrome 356
Nernst, Walther 235, 364
Nernst's equation 364
Nerve 360
Nerve, myelinated 361, 391, 393
Nerve, resting 363, 380
Nerve, unmyelinated 361, 393
Nerve impulse 15, 363, 391
Nerve membrane 270, 363
Net force 20
Neuron 361
Neutral mutation 247
Neutron 255, 607
Neutron decay 607
Newton, Sir Isaac 17, 36, 192, 485, 582
Newtonian fluid 326, 330
Newton's first law 20, 36
Newton's second law 24, 40
Newton's third law 26, 43
Nirenberg, Marshall 221
Nitrogen 341, 347
NMR 627
Nocireceptor 132
Node 456
Nodes of Ranvier 361, 393
Non–binding orbital 592
Non–harmonic excitation 461
Non–Newtonian fluid 341
Non–resonant fluorescence 596
Non–viscous flow 317
Non–wetting 307
Normal force 17
Notochord 11
Nuclear energy 608
Nuclear force 608
Nuclear magnetic resonance 627
Nuclear medicine 612
Nuclear spin 620
Nuclear waste 615
Nucleon 606
Nucleus, atom 284, 606
Nucleus, cell 221
Nucleus, radioactive 609
Nummulation 341

O_2 91, 215, 341
Object 486, 498
Object distance 489, 498
Objective lens 518
Objective plane 521
Ocular lens 518
[Oe] 530
Oersted, Hans 529
Ohm, Georg 378, 470
Ohm's law 326, 378
Oil drop experiment, Millikan's 255, 271, 285
One-arm dumbbell rows 18
Onsager, Lars 238
Onsager equation 240
Onsager's coefficient 240, 248
Open system 111
Opera singer 460
Optic nerve 482
Optical activity 537
Optical axis 487, 498
Optical depth 492
Optical illusion 525
Optics, geometrical 485
Optometrist 509
Orbit, geostationary 561
Orbit (atom) 581
Orbital 587
Orbital quantum number 587
Order 230
Organ of Corti 468
Oscillation 428
[osm] 354
Osmolarity 354
Osmoreceptor 354
Osmosis 353
Osmotic pressure 353
Ossification 11
Osteoporosis 563
Outer ear 2, 464
Oval window 465
Oxygen 91, 215, 341
Oxygen deficiency breathing 349
Oxygen mask 349
Oxygen-breathing 349

[Pa] 115, 292, 645
Pacemaker cell 399
Pacini, Filipp 50
Pacinian corpuscle 50
Pain receptors 132
Pain threshold 472
Palate 463
Parallel plates, charged 269
Parietal layer 147
Partial pressure 344
Particle, alpha 282, 564, 580, 611

Particle/wave dualism 581
Particles, elementary 255
Pascal, Blaise 115, 290
Pascal's law 290
Paschen series 585
Passive spread 381
Passive stretching force 411, 412
Pathological vasoconstriction 337
Pauli, Wolfgang 590
Pauli's principle 590
Pelican 28
Pelvis 88
Pendulum 141, 423, 432, 557
Penguin 204
Peptide 222
Perfusion, skin 204
Perilymph 468
Period 428
Periodic table 260, 646
Periodicity 470
Peripheral vascular dilatation 341
Permeability 193
Permeability of vacuum 530
Permittivity of vacuum 254, 372
Perspiration 198
Perturbation 382
Phagocytosis 206
Pharynx 463
Phase, wave 446
Phase (chemical) 343
Phase angle 428
[phon] 472
Phosphorescence 596
Phosphorylation 104
Photon 539
Photon energy 541
Photosynthesis 542
Physical membrane model 193
Physical pendulum 432
Piano 461, 477
Pickering series 597
Pigeon 528
Pinocytosis 206, 222
Piston 114
Pitch 458
Pivot joint 62
Planar mirror 486
Planck, Max 542
Planck's constant 582
Plasma (blood) 342
Plastic deformation 413, 415
Plethysmograph 161
Pleura 147, 181
Pleural pressure 148
Plot, double-logarithmic 638
Plot, linear 635
Plot, logarithmic 636

Point charge 254
Point mass 16
Poiseuille, Jean 326
Poiseuille's law 325
Poisson's equation 176
Polarization (dielectric) 372
Polarization (light) 535
Polarizer 536
Polo, Marco 348
Polyakov, Valery 562
Polymer 231
Pore 206, 332
Porpoise 2, 8, 443
Posture 48
Potassium ion 279, 363, 386, 400
Potential, chemical 352, 364
Potential, electric 278
Potential, resting nerve 363
Potential difference 279, 369
Potential energy, elastic 425
Potential energy, electric 271
Potential energy, gravitational 127
Power 114
P-peak 406
PQ-interval 406
Predator/prey ratio 108
Pre-exponential factor 211
Pregnancy 578
Prescription glasses 503, 504
Pressure, alveolar 148
Pressure, blood 293, 337
Pressure, gas 115
Pressure, gauge 292
Pressure, node 456
Pressure, osmotic 353
Pressure, partial 344
Pressure, pleural 148
Pressure, transmural 302
Pressure, turgor 353
Pressure amplification (ear) 467
Pressure variation 445, 448
Pressure-volume diagram 120, 148
pressure-volume-temperature diagram 156
Pressurized suit 552
Priestley, Joseph 341
Prigogine, Ilya 238
Primate 87
Principal quantum number 587
Principle of moderation 243
Prism 527
Process, adiabatic 175
Process, Carnot 179, 225, 249
Process, cyclic 177, 226
Process, electrochemical 362
Process, irreversible 223, 236
Process, isentropic 231

Process, isobaric 173
Process, isochoric 171, 224
Process, isothermal 172, 224
Process, reversible 180, 236
Process, spontaneous 228, 236
Prokaryote 195
Pronation 50
Protein 220, 234
Proto–Earth 201
Proton 255
Psychophysics 443, 483
Pterosaurs 647
Pulmonary artery 398
Pulmonary surfactant 304
Pulmonary system 313, 398
Pulmonary vein 398
Pulmonary volume 145
Punctuated equilibrium 247
Purcell, Edward 628
Purkinje fiber 399, 400
Purkyně, Jan 400
Push–up 26, 94
p–V diagram 120, 148
p–V–T diagram 156
Pyruvic acid 104

Q–peak 406
QRS–peak 407
Quadriceps femoris muscle 66, 96
Quadriceps tendon 56
Quality factor 611
Quantized charge 255
Quantum mechanics 586
Quantum numbers 584, 587

R value (house insulation) 214
[R] 605
[rad] 605
Radians 436
Radiation, Black Body 541
Radiation, electromagnetic 570, 581, 600
Radiation, heat 198
Radiation belt 564, 567, 605
Radiation damage 565, 604, 611
Radiation exposure 564
Radiation frequency 584
Radical 621
Radioactive decay 609
Radioactive marker 612
Radioactive nucleus 606
Radioactive tracer 612
Radioactivity 203, 609
Rainbow 527
Random mutation 223, 247
Range (tissue) 611
Ranvier, Louis 362

Ranvier, nodes of 361, 393
Raoult, François 350
Raoult's law 350, 364
Rate equation 245
Ray, cosmic 600, 564
Ray, gamma 540, 606
Ray model, light 485, 609
Reaction, aerobic 104
Reaction, anabolic 234
Reaction, anaerobic 104
Reaction, catabolic 234
Real image 486
Receptor (color) 543
Reciprocity 241
Recovery (nerve) 363
Reflected wave 465
Reflection 486, 536
Reflection, total 493
Reflection law 486
Refracting surface, sign convention 495
Refraction 492
Refraction, index of 492, 539
Refraction law 493
Refractive power 495, 499
Reissner, Ernst 468
Reissner's membrane 468
Relaxation time 630
Repolarization 363
Reproduction 289
Reservoir, heat 170
Residual volume 145
Resistance, thermal 214
Resistance (electric) 379
Resistance (flow) 315, 326, 330
Resistivity 378
Resistor 380
Resonance 459
Resorption 356
Respiration 144, 181
Respiratory distress 304, 345
Respiratory system 341
Respiratory work 183
Resting nerve 363, 380
Resting potential 363
Restoring force 422
Restriction enzyme 273
Retina 482
Reverse curls 27
Reversibility 223, 228
Reversible process 180, 236
Reynolds number 334
Ribonucleic acid 221
Richardson, Sir Owen 520
Richardson effect 520
Rigid body 71
Rima glottidis 463
Rinne–test 5

RNA 221
Rock salt 277, 430
Rods 526
Röntgen, Wilhelm 600, 605
Root–mean–square speed 167
Rotation 62
Rotation axis 62, 72
Rotational equilibrium 75
Round window 469
R–peak 406, 468
Rumford, Count 132
Ruska, Ernst 514
Rutherford, Ernest 282, 580
Rydberg constant 584
Ryumin, Valery 612

[s] 644
Sacrum 88
Saddle joint 62
Salt 260
Saltatory conduction 393
SA–node 399
Sarcomere 12
Satellite 561
Saturation 350
Scattering 604
Schleiden, Matthias von 220
Schrödinger, Erwin 588
Schrödinger's wave equation 588
Schwann, Theodor 220, 361
Schwann's cell 361
Screening effect 261
Scuba diving 308
Sea of Azov 297
Seagull 334
Second (time) 644
Sedimentation 557
Selection rules 588
Selective permeability 193
Semicircular canal 33, 46
Semi–closed tube 454
Semipermeable membrane 193, 364
Septum 398
Sexual reproduction 247
Shark 271
Shear modulus 414
Shearing stress 413
Shell, atomic 585, 602
Shivering 234
Shock, anaphylactic 341
Shock, electric 395
Shock, hypovolemic 354
Shoulder joint 64
SI units 644
Sievert 565
Sigma orbital 591
Sign convention, mirror 491

Sign convention, refracting surface 495
Sign convention, thin lens 499
Signal splitting 629
Silicon 210
Simple harmonic motion 427
Simple pendulum 423, 432
Sino–atrial node 399
Skeletal muscle 11, 62
Skeleton 10
Skull 84
Sliding filament model 12
Smoke 343
Smooth muscle 11
Snell, Willebrord 492
Snellen test 509
Snells' law 492
Snorkel 308
Sodium chloride 277, 363, 430
Sodium ion 261, 277, 386, 400
Sodium–potassium pump 368, 369
Soft matter 410
Solar irradiance 543, 565
Solenoid 532
Solution 259, 350
Solvent 289
Sommerfeld, Arnold 587
Soret effect 248, 249
Sound 443
Sound absorption 452
Sound intensity 450
Sound pressure level (SPL) 451, 471
Sound speed 443, 446, 447
Sound wave 443
Sound wave, energy 450
sp–orbital 594
sp^2–orbital 594
sp^3–orbital 594
Space medicine 552
Sparrow 528
S–peak 407
Speciation 222
Specific heat capacity 132
Specific rotation (light) 537
Spectroscopy 578, 585, 595
Spectrum, atomic 585
Spectrum, electromagnetic 540
Spectrum, frequency 458
Spectrum, visible 541
Speech 463
Speed, root–mean–square 167
Speed, wave 443
Speed of light 493, 535, 539
Speed of sound 443, 446, 447
Spherical aberration 488
Spherical interface 495, 506
Spherical mirror 487
Spheroid joint 62

Sphygmomanometer 337
Spin 587, 618
Spinal cord 298
Spirometer 145
Spirula 299
SPL 451, 471
Sponge 10
Spongin 10
Spontaneous process 228, 236
Spring 422
Spring constant 423
Sprinter 43
Squid, giant axon 386, 396
St. Lawrence river 297
Stahl, Georg 253
Standard electrode potential 366
Standard enthalpy 233
Standard entropy 233
Standard hydrogen half–cell 367
Standard man 22, 23
Standard unit 644
Standing wave 454, 581
Stasis 341
Static friction 54
Stationary fluid 290
Stationary orbital 588
Statistical physics 230
Statolith 33, 47
Steady state 242, 325
Steel 416
Stefan, Josef 542
Stefan–Boltzmann constant 542
Stefan's law 542
Stenosis 476
Stereoscopic hearing 472
Stereovilli 468
Stern, Otto 624
Stethoscope 337
Stimulated impulse (nerve) 381
Stirrup 465
Stokes, George 596
STPD 147
Straddle technique 91
Strain 412
Stress 412
Stress, hydraulic 414, 421
Stress, shearing 413
Stress, tensile 412
Stretching 412
Stretching force, passive 411, 412
Substitutional diffusion 211
Sucrose 207
Sugar 234
Sun 203, 542, 564
Superposition 454, 473
Superstructure, isolated 111
Supination 50

Supine position 294
Surface 292
Surface energy 299
Surface tension 299
Surfactant 304
Suspension 341, 343
[Sv] 565
Swim bladder 299
Synapse 361
Synaptic cleft 361
Synchrotron 569
Synovial fluid 64
Synovial joint 64
Syringe 308, 338
System 20, 110
System, closed 111
System, isolated 52, 110
System, open 111
Systemic system 313, 398
Systolic pressure 293, 337

T. rex 434
[T] 530
Talus 80
Tatum, Edward 603
Tectorial membrane 468
Temperature 130, 550
Temperature, Celsius scale 130
Temperature, human body 131, 197
Temperature, Kelvin scale 154
Tendon 15, 62
Tensile stress 412
Tension 21, 27
Tension, surface 299
Term scheme 592
Terminal speed 53
Tesla, Nikola 530
Test charge 262
Test current 529
Tetramethylsilane 628
Thermal conductivity coefficient 196, 248
Thermal energy 132
Thermal equilibrium 131, 168
Thermal resistance 214
Thermodynamics, first law 111, 130
Thermodynamics, non–equilibrium 238
Thermodynamics, second law 225
Thermodynamics, third law 235
Thermography 200
Thermometer 130
Thermomolecular pressure difference 241
Thermoreceptor 132
Thermoregulation 203
Thick lens 497
Thin lens 497

Thin lens, sign convention 499
Thin lens formula 499
Thomson, Sir Joseph 579
Thorax 97, 147
Threshold, hearing 477
Thymine 221
Thyroid gland 612
Tibia 80
Tidal slowing 620
Tidal volume 145
Timbre 458
Time constant nerve 381
Time invariance 223
Tissue 410
Tobacco mosaic virus 216
Toluene 351
Tongue 463
Tooth 96
Torque 73
[torr] 645
Total energy 110
Total reflection 493
T–peak 407
Trachea 147, 335, 341, 350, 463
Traction device 29, 57
Transcription 221
Transducer 361, 475
Transition energy 626
Transition state 211
Translational motion 71
Transmitted wave 465
Transmural pressure 302
Transparent 492
Transport phenomena 196, 241
Transverse wave 444, 535
Travelling wave 469
Triceps muscle 68, 96
Trigger (nerve) 363
Tropomyosin 12
Troponin 12
Tumor 630
Tungsten anode 603
Turbulent flow 332
Turgor pressure 353
Twisting 413
Tympanic chamber 468
Tympanic membrane 428
Tyrannosaurus rex 106, 434

[u] 645
Ultimate strength point 415
Ultrasound 475
Ultraviolet light 540
Ultraviolet spectroscopy 595
Unconfined medium 442
Ungulates 6
Uniform circular motion 553

Unit, standard 644
Universal gas constant 159
Unmyelinated nerve 361, 393
Upright posture 87
Uracil 221
Urine 332, 354
UV spectroscopy 595

[V] 278
Vacuum pump 115
Valence electron 590
Van Allen belt 552, 605
van der Waals, Johannes 169
van der Waals equation 169
van't Hoff, Jacobus 353
van't Hoff's law 353, 356
Variable of state 135, 226
Vascular flutter 337
Vasoconstriction 337
Velocity 18, 36, 553
Velocity, average 18
Velocity, drift 376
Velocity, instantaneous 18, 36
Velocity node 456
Velocity selector 571
Vena cava 398
Ventricle 398
Venturi–meter 320, 337
Vernes, Jules 550
Vestibular chamber 468
Vestibular organ 33, 46
Vibration 211, 424
Virtual image 487
Visceral layer 147
Viscosity 323, 340
Viscosity coefficient 323, 324
Viscous flow 322
Visible spectrum 541
Vision, color 526
Vitreous body 482
Vocal cord 463
Voice 458, 463
Volt 278
Volta, Alessandro 278
Voltage–clamped measurement 386
Volume, blood 315
Volume, gas 115
Volume flow rate 313, 318
Vortex 332

[W] 114
Walking 87, 434
Water 253, 288, 348
Water, dipole moment 267, 269
Water molecule 253, 299
Water strider 309
Watson, James 221, 603

Watt, James 114
Wave 442
Wave, electromagnetic 533
Wave, harmonic 448
Wave, longitudinal 445
Wave, phase 446
Wave, radio 443
Wave, reflected 465
Wave, sound 443
Wave, speed 443
Wave, standing 454, 581
Wave, superposition 454
Wave, transmitted 465
Wave, transverse 444, 535
Wave, travelling 469
Wave amplitude 448
Wave equation 446
Wave function 446, 588
Wavelength 443
Wavelength, de Broglie 582
Wavelength, electron 520
Weber–test 5
Weight 17
Weightlessness 553, 562
Wells, H. G. 229, 438
Wetting 307
Whale 2, 8, 199, 458, 472
White light 527
Wien, Wilhelm 571
Wien filter 571
Windkessel effect 418, 560
Wing 334, 337, 437
Wing span 647
Wood anemone 307
Work 111, 227
Work, electric 271
Work function 520
Wrist joint 64

X–ray 565, 600
X–ray, characteristic 601
X–ray crystallography 603
X–ray tube 600
Xylem fiber 307, 309

Young, Thomas 413, 527
Young–Dupré relation 308
Young's modulus 413
Yukawa, Hideki 608

Z disc 12, 410
Zeppelin, Graf Ferdinand von 297

α–decay 609
α–particle 564, 580, 611
β–decay 609
γ–ray 540, 609

[Ω] 379
π*–orbital 594
π–orbital 594
σ*–orbital 592
σ–orbital 591